BIOLOGY
THE UNITY AND DIVERSITY OF LIFE

THIRD EDITION

CECIE STARR
Belmont, California

RALPH TAGGART
Michigan State University

James Bonner, General Advisor
Professor Emeritus, California Institute of Technology

John Alcock, Arizona State University
Author of the animal behavior chapter

· Cleon Ross, Colorado State University
Author of the plant physiology chapters

Wadsworth Publishing Company
Belmont, California
A Division of Wadsworth, Inc.

On the cover: Greater sandhill cranes at their wintering grounds in New Mexico. The flock migrates annually between southeastern Idaho and New Mexico. One of the birds in the foreground sports a banding collar—a marker that biologists have used in tracking the movements of the flock and thereby identifying its distribution range. (Photograph by Gary Zahm)

A study guide has been designed to help students master the concepts presented in this textbook. Order from your bookstore.

Biology Editor: Jack C. Carey

Production Editor: Gary Mcdonald

Designer: Detta Penna

Art Editor: Wendy Calmenson

Copy Editor: Joan C. Pendleton

Illustrators: Joan Carol, Darwen Hennings, Vally Hennings, Joel Ito, Victor Royer

Permissions: Marion Hansen

ISBN 0-534-02742-3

Printed in the United States of America

1 2 3 4 5 6 7 8 9 10—88 87 86 85 84

Library of Congress Cataloging in Publication Data

Starr, Cecie.
　Biology: the unity and diversity of life.

　Includes index.
　1. Biology.　I. Taggart, Ralph.　II. Title.　[DNLM:
1. Biology.　　QH 308.2 S796b]
QH308.2.K57　　1984　　　574　　　83-6769

PREFACE

Biology encompasses a tremendous and scattered array of subdisciplines, each with its squadrons of practitioners who are bent on discovery. Discover they do, and the amount of new information to be assimilated balloons monthly. How can a survey book accurately portray this current work in addition to the heritage of biological research of past centuries?

An encyclopedic approach means covering many or most of the topics but not in any depth. This might be called Platte River writing (a mile wide and an inch deep), in that students can get to the other side without even getting their feet wet. Of course, they might not end up with much experience in self-navigation through deeper waters. Platte River writing can indeed move them quickly past ecology and molecular biology, for example. But will they, at the end, be able to separate facts from flawed logic in accounts of acid deposition, including the so-called acid rain? Will they be equipped to assess opinions about genetic engineering that might lead to improved crop yields, to genotypic cures for terrible human disorders, or, inadvertently, to a bacterial species with enhanced resistance to antibiotics? These are not esoteric issues, confined to research journals. They are being discussed repeatedly, sometimes in naïve ways, in news articles, in trade magazines, and on television. It becomes a question of obligation. Students can be left to sink or taught to swim, but there is no way to pretend that they will not be encountering deep rivers, some of which may change the course of their lives.

Somewhere between the Platte River and the Amazon lies a good river for learning. With the encouragement and proddings of about three hundred instructors and research specialists over the past seven years, we may have located it. There is agreement, more or less, that we should do the following things in a survey book:

1. State the principles that apply to all fields of biological inquiry, the most pervasive being the principles of evolution and energy flow.

2. Use those principles as a framework for presenting the material, rather than simply paying lip service to them.

3. Distill the main concepts and outline the research trends in all major fields.

4. Give enough examples of problem solving and experiments to provide familiarity with a scientific approach to interpreting the world.

5. Include enough comparative biology to convey a sense of the unity and diversity among living things.

6. Include enough human biology to enhance understanding of our evolution, behavior, and ecology as well as our body structure and functioning.

7. Be selective in developing the vocabulary necessary to comprehend what is being talked about today in each field.

8. Present the material accurately but not at a high level.

9. Write clearly, in a style that is not boring or patronizing.

10. Keep the writing free of bias and soapboxing, thereby giving students the chance to form their own opinions about the material presented.

11. Excise teleological wording.

12. Create easy-to-follow line illustrations and select photographs that are beautiful but not superfluous.

13. Make the line illustrations and photographs larger than the size of postage stamps.

14. Make the book long enough to cover all important topics but short enough so that carrying it to class does not produce hernias.

Anyone in his or her right mind would walk away at once from such an impossible order; which says something about biology writers if not their books. It took three years of obsessively full-time literature review and conceptual synthesis, writing, original art development, and revising to attempt to meet these criteria for the third edition—and still there never was enough time. Fortunately, parallel with this focused authorship, our reviewers responded to the challenge of creating a good book.

A few examples of their commitment: Along with his exquisitely detailed professional advice, James Bonner's manuscript evaluations included a treasury of personal insights into the events that shaped modern biology. John Alcock, concerned that introductory books are not keeping up with current trends in animal behavior studies, wrote the chapter on it himself. This time Cleon Ross, author of the plant physiology chapters, reviewed in microscopic detail major sections of the book. Stephen Hedman wrote original genetics problems and detailed solutions. William Leonard and Vernon Tipton each wrote a Commentary; Professor Tipton also coordinated a major review program. Jane Taylor was her characteristically dedicated self in creating a study guide and instructor's manual for the book. Through extended conversations and correspondence, John Blamire, Leon Harris, William Harvey, Tyler Miller, Marian Reeve, and Robert Smith profoundly influenced the course of revision. And just when we thought it was safe to get out of the manuscript, David Brumagen, Thomas Hemmerly, Jean DeSaix, Philip Mathis, and John Rickett convinced us to go back in and revise a little more.

A list of third-edition reviewers concludes this preface. There never is enough space to acknowledge all those who help create a book. To reviewers of this and earlier efforts, thank you for your insights, your criticisms, your praise. You will know, in reading through the book, where you have left your imprint.

Some Important Content Changes

This is not a cosmetic revision; we reworked all chapters. We split many into shorter chapters that will be more manageable to study. (For example, photosynthesis and carbohydrate metabolism are now covered separately.) The splits also allow more flexibility in adapting the book to different course sequences.

In response to user requests, we made several shifts in unit organization. Evolutionary biology is treated in a separate, expanded unit before organismic diversity. A separate unit on ecology follows. All plant anatomy and physiology (including flowering plant reproduction) is now organized in one unit. This unit on plant systems now precedes that for animals.

We reorganized and rewrote all chapters to reflect current information and trends. Biology is growing so rapidly, in so many directions, that all of us working on the revision felt that we had to take the time to stand back and develop an accurate, simple picture of how the parts are fitting together.

Just a few examples of currency: Photosynthesis and aerobic respiration are not talked about in a vacuum; chemiosmotic events of ATP formation are described simply, in terms of the cell structures in which they occur. Also, we don't stop with thirty-year-old models of DNA replication and recombination, and we give a current picture of protein synthesis. By working intensively with specialists, we developed clear, accurate introductions to animal anatomy and physiology (see, for example, discussions of homeostasis, neural and endocrine functioning, and muscle functioning). We use current models in plant physiology (see the treatments of transpiration and translocation). The evolution unit has new sections on macroevolution and evolutionary trends; it includes an updated picture on research into the origin of life. In Figure 31.10, we integrate a flowchart of biological evolution with newly available paleogeographic maps. The diversity unit provides coverage of bacterial phylogeny (including the intriguing Archaebacteria). We have essentially a new ecology unit, complete with current models of population dynamics, ecosystems, nutrient cycling, and succession, to name a few.

We have three new chapters: two short, provocative chapters on human genetics and human origins, and one on animal behavior. John Alcock, author of a widely respected textbook on animal behavior, did admirably in describing current research trends with such lively, succinct prose.

We are pleased that our writing style has been well received. However, we worked at refining it further. Each sentence was evaluated for clarity and content. The outcome is greater strength and precision in the text.

A New Illustration Program

All line art is now full color to allow better tracking of information within an illustration. More outstanding micrographs have been added. Almost all other photographs are in full color, the better to convey the magnificent diversity of living organisms and their environments.

For each chapter, we developed text and art simultaneously. Where feasible, we combined visual and written summaries to make complex concepts easier to grasp. In many line illustrations, the topics are presented as a series of steps, which are less intimidating than one large, complicated illustration. For examples, see the art on carbohydrate metabolism (pages 127, 130, 131), mitosis and meiosis (pages 143, 145, 150, and 154), and protein synthesis (page 220).

Case Studies and Commentaries

Our Case Studies show how general concepts apply to specific situations. For example, after the discussion of immune systems, a case study shows students how their bodies would mount an immune response to a bacterial attack (page 396). The Commentaries are "outside readings" built into the text. They explore such thought-provoking topics as cancer, allergy, death, cardiovascular and lung disorders, in vitro fertilization, sexually transmitted diseases, and the current food production crisis.

Perspectives

These end-of-chapter sections encourage students to take a moment for conceptual synthesis. They are bridges between chapters and units. Many also bridge chapter topics and the student's world, inviting reflection on the past and possible futures. See, for example, pages 517 and 677.

Study Aids

We never have assumed that students taking introductory biology already know enough about biology to spot all key concepts in page after text page. Italic sentences call attention to points that lead, step by step, to important concepts. These concepts are boxed within the text column and printed in boldface for emphasis. Taken together, they provide an easy-to-identify, *in-context summary* for each chapter. Many are in simple list form (see, for example, pages 158, 163, 179, 325, 372, and 600).

End-of-chapter questions are keyed to italic and boldface sentences within the chapter as a way of reinforcing the main points. Chapters Ten, Eleven, and Fifteen have *genetics problems*; the *solutions* for these problems are given in Appendix II. The *glossary* brings together the text's main definitions. The *index* is comprehensive, simply because students may find a door to the text more quickly through finer divisions of topics.

In addition, *advance organizers* are built into the text. Chapters begin by stating what the chapter is about, how the topics will unfold, and often how students may find the topics related to their interests. Chapter One is an advance organizer in its entirety. It introduces the most basic of all biological concepts—ones that students will be using throughout the book.

A word for Wadsworth: This publishing company is extraordinary. With virtually a new manuscript and well over a thousand pieces of art, the production challenges on this new edition seemed altogether nightmarish. No other company could have been more supportive and tolerant. When old rules didn't work, Kathie Head, Harold Parnes, and

Steve Rutter were flexible enough to invent new ones, and how many managers can lay claim to that? Gary Mcdonald was never stingy with personal or professional support. If part of a production editor's task is to keep authors from collapsing too soon, then Gary has done very well; we would be fortunate to work with him again.

And what a pleasure it has been, working with Detta Penna—she with the panache to pull off being as strong-willed as a strong-willed author, the good grace to do her best for the book, and the wit to keep us moving with the schedule. She is a real pro. Wendy Calmenson, our art editor, had the strong aesthetic sense, compulsivity, and competence to help hold an intricate art project together. Cheryl Carrington put out brush fires with commendable calm. Alan Noyes and his fine group of production artists did not yell at us once. Joan Carol, Darwen Hennings, Vally Hennings, and Joel Ito created many beautiful illustrations for us. Victor Royer pluckily took on a major share of the art, including many illustrations that were among the most difficult to render. Marion Hansen foolishly forgot how complex our books are and took charge of all permissions and photo research. She has our undying gratitude for seeing it through after she, too late, remembered. Neither can we forget Allison and Al, colleagues of Marion. All of these people are more than professional acquaintances; they are friends.

Once in a while, groups like this come together and create something special. That it happened at all is the culmination of a professional relationship that began many years ago, when Jack Carey convinced us to write this book. Jack is exceptional in the breadth of his knowledge and interests; he is the creative force behind what we accomplish. Perhaps more than any other editor, he can identify the often subtle shifts in how biology is being taught, then persuade us to toss out what we have done and write in new directions. With eighteen years of publishing experience, Jack has contributed immeasurably to the quality of the book's production as well as to its content. He is one of the best.

THIRD-EDITION REVIEWERS

Barbara Abraham, Hampton Institute
John Alcock, Arizona State University
Lester Allen, Brigham Young University
Paul Anderson, Massachusetts Bay Community College
Fred Andoli, California Polytechnic State University,
    San Luis Obispo
June Aprille, Tufts University
Peter Armstrong, University of California, Davis
William Balamuth, University of California, Berkeley
Edwin Banks, University of Illinois
Mary Barkworth, Utah State University
Barry Batzing, State University of New York, Cortland
Lawrence Beaver, United States Air Force Academy
Charles Beck, University of Michigan
Wayne Becker, University of Wisconsin, Madison
Elinor Benes, California State University, Sacramento
Howard Bern, University of California, Berkeley
William Birky, Ohio State University
Hal Black, Brigham Young University
John Blamire, Brooklyn College
David Bohr, University of Michigan
James Bonner, California Institute of Technology
William Bradshaw, Brigham Young University
Jim Brammer, North Dakota State University
Mike Breed, University of Colorado
Alan Brockway, University of Colorado
Richard Brower, Borough of Manhattan Community College
Barbara Brownstein, Temple University
Teresa Bruggeman, University of Michigan
Gil Brum, California State Polytechnic University, Pomona
David Brumagen, Moorhead State University
Ruth Buskirk, University of Texas
Clyde Calvin, Portland State University
Raul Cano, California Polytechnic State University,
    San Luis Obispo
Ted Case, University of California, San Diego
Robert Catlett, University of Colorado
Arthur Champlin, Colby College
Terry Christenson, Tulane University
Corbett Coburn, Jr., Tennessee Technological University
James Collins, Arizona State University
David Cotter, Georgia College
Stuart Coward, University of Georgia
William Crumpton, Iowa State University

Jean De Saix, University of North Carolina, Chapel Hill
Alfred Diboll, Macon Junior College
Robert Dott, Jr., University of Wisconsin, Madison
Stanley Duke, University of Wisconsin, Madison
Gerald Eck, University of Washington
Larry Epstein, University of Pittsburgh
James Estes, University of Oklahoma
Wayne Faircloth, Valdosta State College
James Farmer, Brigham Young University
Lewis Feldman, University of California, Berkeley
Robert Ferl, University of Florida
Donald Fisher, Washington State University
Jerran Flinders, Brigham Young University
David Fox, University of Tennessee, Knoxville
Anne Funkhouser, University of the Pacific
Douglas Futuyma, State University of New York, Stony Brook
William Ganong, University of California, San Francisco
Michael Ghiselin, University of Utah
David Glenn-Lewin, Iowa State University
Jon Goerke, University of California, San Francisco
David Goldberg, Woodmere, New York
Ben Golden, Kennesaw College
Norman Goldstein, California State University, Hayward
Anne Good, University of California, Berkeley
Helen Greenwood, University of Southern Maine
Katherine Gregg, West Virginia Wesleyan College
Robert Grey, University of California, Davis
Harlow Hadow, Coe College
James Hageman, New Mexico State University
Mary Alice Hamilton, Colorado College
William Hargreaves, DuPont Experimental Station
Kimball Harper, Brigham Young University
C. Leon Harris, State University of New York, Plattsburgh
William Harvey, Temple University
William Healy, College of the Holy Cross
Stephen Hedman, University of Minnesota, Duluth
Thomas Hemmerly, Middle Tennessee State University
Richard Heninger, Brigham Young University
William Hess, Brigham Young University
S. Robert Hilfer, Temple University
Sally Holbrook, University of California, Santa Barbara
E. Bruce Holmes, Western Illinois University
August Jaussi, Brigham Young University
Duane Jeffery, Brigham Young University

F. Brent Johnson, Brigham Young University
Jeanette Jones, Alabama A & M University
Clive Jorgenson, Brigham Young University
Donald Keith, Tarleton State University
George Kelly, Youngstown University
Richard Kessel, University of Iowa
Jack Keyes, University of Oregon
Richard Knauel, Northern Illinois University
William Kodrich, Clarion State University
Allan Konopka, Purdue University
Kathy Koshelynk, University of Colorado
Charles Krebs, University of British Columbia
Thomas Kunz, Boston University
Deborah Langsam, University of North Carolina, Charlotte
Ronald Leavitt, Brigham Young University
George Lefevre, California State University, Northridge
William Leonard, University of Nebraska, Lincoln
John Lott, McMaster University
Dorothy Luciano, formerly of University of Michigan
David Lygre, Central Washington University
Robert McAlister, Southern Methodist University
Larry McKane, California State Polytechnic University, Pomona
David Malloch, University of Toronto
Maurice Margulies, Smithsonian Radiation Biology Laboratory
Philip Mathis, Middle Tennessee State University
G. Tyler Miller, Jr., St. Andrew's Presbyterian College
James Miller, Delaware Valley College
Wade Miller, Brigham Young University
Lawrence Mitchell, Iowa State University
J. Robert Moore, Clarion State College
August Mueller, State University of New York
Joseph Murphy, Brigham Young University
Terrance Murphy, University of California, Davis
Steven Murray, California State University, Fullerton
Marlene Palmer, formerly of Vassar College
Herbert Papenfuss, Boise State University
Dennis Parnell, California State University, Hayward
Martha Pavlovich, Nassau Community College
Robert Peet, University of North Carolina, Chapel Hill
James Perley, Wooster College
Kathyrn Podwall, Nassau Community College
Marian Reeve, Merritt College
Reuben Rhees, Brigham Young University
Pam Rhyne, Kennesaw College
Rosemary Richardson, Bellevue Community College
John Rickett, University of Arkansas
Robert Robbins, Michigan State University
Cleon Ross, Colorado State University
Sam Rushforth, Brigham Young University
Richard Sagers, Brigham Young University
Frank Salisbury, Utah State University

Daniel Schadler, Oglethorpe University
Rudolph Schmid, University of California, Berkeley
Thomas Schoener, University of California, Davis
Erik Scully, Towson State University
Dennis Searcy, University of Massachusetts
David Smith, San Antonio Community College
H. Duane Smith, Brigham Young University
Robert Smith, West Virginia University
Paul Spannbauer, Hudson Valley Community College
David Stetler, Virginia Polytechnic Institute
Nicholas Sturm, Youngstown State University
William Surver, Clemson University
Dennis Swanger, Eastern Oregon State College
Robert Tamarin, Boston University
Jane Taylor, Northern Virginia Community College
Jay Tepperman, State University of New York
     Upstate Medical Center
F. Donald Tibbits, University of Nevada
Paula Timiras, University of California, Berkeley
Vernon Tipton, Brigham Young University
Frank Toman, Western Kentucky University
James Trammell, Jr., Arapahoe Community College
Joseph Travis, Florida State University
Shirley Tucker, Louisiana State University
Ronald Tyrl, Oklahoma State University
Ray Umber, University of Wyoming
Jane Underwood, University of Arizona
Arthur Vander, University of Michigan
Karen Van Winkle-Swift, San Diego State University
Joseph Varner, Washington University
Warren Wagner, University of Michigan
Callie Waldrop, Gadsden State Junior College
Laurence Walker, Stephen F. Austin State University
Herman Wallace, Utah State University
Michael Walsh, Utah State University
Stuart Ware, Northern Kentucky University
George Welkie, Utah State University
Adrian Wenner, University of California, Berkeley
John West, University of California, San Diego
Clayton White, Brigham Young University
Raymond White, San Francisco City College
Armond Whitehead, Brigham Young University
Herman Wiebe, Utah State University
Henry Wilbur, Duke University
Edward Wiley, University of Kansas
Kelly Williams, University of Dayton
Fred Wilt, University of California, Berkeley
Mary Wise, Northern Virginia Community College
Donald Wright, Brigham Young University
Richard Wright, Valencia Community College
Francis Yow, Kenyon College

CONTENTS IN BRIEF

UNIT ONE   UNIFYING CONCEPTS IN BIOLOGY

1   On the Unity and Diversity of Life   2
2   Methods and Organizing Concepts in Biology   20

UNIT TWO   THE CELLULAR BASIS OF LIFE

3   Atoms, Molecules, and Cell Substances   38
4   Cell Structure and Function: An Overview   58
5   Water, Membranes, and Cell Functioning   85
6   Energy Transformations in the Cell   98
7   Energy-Acquiring Pathways   110
8   Energy-Releasing Pathways   122

UNIT THREE   THE ONGOING FLOW OF LIFE

9   Cell Reproduction   138
10   Observable Patterns of Inheritance   160
11   Emergence of the Chromosomal Theory of Inheritance   178
12   The Rise of Molecular Genetics   192
13   From DNA to Protein: How Genes Function   211
14   Controls Over Gene Expression   223
15   Human Genetics   237

UNIT FOUR   PLANT SYSTEMS AND THEIR CONTROL

16   Plant Cells, Tissues, and Systems   248
17   Water, Solutes, and Plant Functioning   264
18   Plant Reproduction and Embryonic Development   276
19   Plant Growth and Development   288

UNIT FIVE   ANIMAL SYSTEMS AND THEIR CONTROL

20   Systems of Cells and Homeostasis   306
21   Integration and Control: Nervous Systems   319
22   Integration and Control: Endocrine Systems   344
23   Reception and Motor Response   354
24   Circulation   374
25   Respiration   398
26   Digestion and Organic Metabolism   409
27   Regulation of Body Temperature and Body Fluids   428
28   Principles of Reproduction and Development   440
29   Human Reproduction and Development   459

UNIT SIX   EVOLUTION

30   Individuals, Populations, and Evolution   478
31   Origins and the Evolution of Life   500

UNIT SEVEN   DIVERSITY: EVOLUTIONARY FORCE, EVOLUTIONARY PRODUCT

32   Viruses, Bacteria, and Protistans   520
33   Fungi and Plants   539
34   Animal Diversity   561
35   Human Origins and Evolution   590

UNIT EIGHT   ECOLOGY AND BEHAVIOR

36   Population Ecology   598
37   Community Interactions   614
38   Ecosystems   629
39   The Biosphere   648
40   Human Impact on the Biosphere   669
41   Animal Behavior   679

DETAILED TABLE OF CONTENTS

UNIT ONE   UNIFYING CONCEPTS IN BIOLOGY

1   ON THE UNITY AND DIVERSITY OF LIFE   2

Origins and Organization   4
Unity in Basic Life Processes   6
    Metabolism   6
    Growth, Development, and Reproduction   6
    Homeostasis   8
    DNA: Storehouse of Constancy and Change   8
Diversity in Form and Function   9
    The Tropical Reef   9
    The Savanna   12
    A Definition of Diversity   12
Energy Flow and the Cycling of Material Resources   16
Perspective   18

2   METHODS AND ORGANIZING CONCEPTS
     IN BIOLOGY   20

What Do You Do with an Observation?   20
On the "Scientific Method"   21
    COMMENTARY: *Processes of Scientific Inquiry*   22
Emergence of Evolutionary Thought   25
    Linnean System of Classification   26
    Challenges to the Theory of Unchanging Life   27
    Lamarck's Theory of Evolution   29
Emergence of the Principle of Evolution   29
    Naturalist Inclinations of the Young Darwin   29
    Voyage of the *Beagle*   30
    Darwin and Wallace: The Theory Takes Form   31
An Evolutionary View of Diversity   33
Perspective   36

UNIT TWO   THE CELLULAR BASIS OF LIFE

3   ATOMS, MOLECULES, AND CELL SUBSTANCES   38

Organization of Matter   38
    The Nature of Atoms   39
    How Electrons Are Arranged in Atoms   40
    COMMENTARY: *Keeping Track of Electrons: Some Options*   41
    Electron Excitation   41
Interactions Among Atoms in the Cellular World   42
    Ionic Bonding   42
    Covalent Bonding   43
    Hydrogen Bonding   44
    Hydrophobic Interactions   45

    Bond Energies   45
Acids, Bases, and Salts   45
Making and Breaking Bonds in Biological Molecules   47
Carbohydrates   48
    Monosaccharides   48
    Disaccharides and Polysaccharides   49
Lipids   50
    True Fats and Waxes   50
    Steroids and Related Substances   52
    Phospholipids and Glycolipids   52
Proteins   52
    Primary Structure: A String of Amino Acids   53
    Spatial Patterns of Protein Structure   54
    Protein Denaturation   55
    Protein-Based Substances   55
Nucleic Acids and Other Nucleotides   56

4   CELL STRUCTURE AND FUNCTION:
     AN OVERVIEW   58

Generalized Picture of the Cell   58
    Emergence of the Cell Theory   58
    Basic Aspects of Cell Structure and Function   59
    Cell Size   60
Prokaryotic Cells   64
Eukaryotic Cells   64
The Nucleus   68
    Nuclear Envelope   68
    Chromosomes   68
    Nucleolus   69
Organelles of an Endomembrane System   69
    Endoplasmic Reticulum and Ribosomes   70
    Golgi Bodies   71
    Lysosomes   72
    Microbodies   73
Other Cytoplasmic Organelles   74
    Mitochondria   74
    Chloroplasts and Other Plastids   74
    Central Vacuoles in Plant Cells   75
Internal Framework of Eukaryotic Cells   76
    The Cytoplasmic Lattice   76
    Microfilaments and Microtubules   77
Structures at the Cell Surface   78
    Cell Walls and Other Surface Deposits   78
    Microvilli   79
    Cilia and Flagella   80

Cell-to-Cell Junctions   81
Summary of Major Cell Structures and Their Functions   82

5   **WATER, MEMBRANES, AND CELL FUNCTIONING**   85

On Cellular Environments   85
Water and Cell Functioning   85
    The Importance of Hydrogen Bonds   86
    Solvent Properties of Water   88
Cytoplasmic Organization of Water   88
Cell Membranes: Fluid Structures in a Largely Fluid World   89
Movement of Water and Solutes Across Membranes   91
    Overview of Membrane Transport Systems   91
    Diffusion   92
    Osmosis   93
    Active Transport   94
    Endocytosis and Exocytosis   95
Membrane Surface Receptors   95
Perspective   97

6   **ENERGY TRANSFORMATIONS IN THE CELL**   98

On the Availability of Useful Energy   98
    Two Energy Laws   98
    Metabolic Reactions: Energy Changes in Cells   100
    Equilibrium and the Cell   101
Enzyme Function   102
    Activation Energy and Enzymes   102
    Enzyme Structure and Functioning   103
    Cofactors   104
    Effects of pH and Temperature on Enzyme Activity   104
    Controls Over Enzymes   105
Types of Energy Transfers in Cells   106
    Formation and Use of ATP   106
    Electron-Transfer Reactions   108

7   **ENERGY-ACQUIRING PATHWAYS**   110

From Sunlight to Cellular Work: Preview of the Main Pathways   110
Photosynthesis   111
    Simplified Picture of the Two Stages of Photosynthesis   111
    Chloroplast Structure and Function   112
The Light-Dependent Reactions   113
    Light Absorption in Photosystems   113
    Two Pathways of Electron Transfer   115
    Mechanism of ATP Synthesis   117
    Summary of Light-Dependent Reactions   117
The Light-Independent Reactions   118
    Summary of Light-Independent Reactions   119
    How Autotrophs Use Intermediates and Products of Photosynthesis   119
    Environmental Effects on Rates of Photosynthesis   120
Chemosynthesis   121

8   **ENERGY-RELEASING PATHWAYS**   122

Overview of the Main Energy-Releasing Pathways   122
    Glycolysis: First Stage of Carbohydrate Metabolism   124
    Aerobic Respiration   124
    Anaerobic Respiration   126
    Fermentation Pathways   126
A Closer Look at Aerobic Respiration   126
    First Stage: Glycolysis   126
    Second Stage: The Krebs Cycle   128
    Third Stage: Electron Transport Phosphorylation   129
    Glucose Energy Yield: Summing Up   131
Fuels or Building Blocks? Controls over Energy Metabolism   132
Perspective   133

UNIT THREE   THE ONGOING FLOW OF LIFE

9   CELL REPRODUCTION   138

Some General Aspects of Cell Reproduction   138
    The Molecular Basis of Cell Reproduction   139
    Kinds of Division Mechanisms   140
Components of Eukaryotic Cell Division   142
    Chromosomes: Eukaryotic Packaging of DNA   142
    Microtubular Spindles   143
The Cell Cycle   144
Mitosis: Maintaining the Number of Chromosome Sets   144
    Prophase: Mitosis Begins   144
    Metaphase   146
    Anaphase   147
    Telophase   148
Cytokinesis: Dividing Up the Cytoplasm   148
Meiosis: Halving the Number of Chromosome Sets   149
    Prophase I Activities   152
    Separating the Homologues   153
    Separating the Sister Chromatids   153
Where Cell Divisions Occur in Plant and Animal Life Cycles   156
    Animal Life Cycles   156
    Plant Life Cycles   157
Perspective   158

10   OBSERVABLE PATTERNS OF INHERITANCE   160

Mendel and the First Formulation of the Principles of Inheritance   160
    Mendel's Experimental Approach   161
    The Concept of Segregation   162
    Testcrosses: Support for the Concept   163
    Current Terms for Mendelian Units of Inheritance   163
    Probability: Predicting the Outcome of Crosses   163
    The Concept of Independent Assortment   165
Variations on Mendel's Themes   168
    Dominance Relations and Multiple Alleles   168
    Variable Expression of Single Genes   170

Interactions Between Gene Pairs 171
Multiple Effects of Single Genes 172
Environmental Effects on Phenotype 172
Continuous and Discontinuous Variation 175
Perspective 175

11 EMERGENCE OF THE CHROMOSOMAL THEORY OF INHERITANCE 178

Return of the Pea Plant 178
The Chromosomal Theory 179
Clues from the Inheritance of Sex 179
Enter the Fruit Fly 179
Sex Determination 179
Sex-Linked Traits 180
Linkage Groups and the Number of Chromosomes 182
Recombination and Linkage Mapping of Chromosomes 183
Visualization of Chromosomes 184
Changes in Chromosome Structure 185
Changes in Chromosome Number 187
Missing or Extra Chromosomes 187
Three or More Chromosome Sets 187
Chromosome Fission and Fusion 188
COMMENTARY: *Cytogenetics, Mr. Sears, and a Lot More Bread* 189

12 THE RISE OF MOLECULAR GENETICS 192

The Search for the Hereditary Molecule 192
The Puzzle of Bacterial Transformation 193
Bacteriophage Studies 194
The Riddle of the Double Helix 194
Patterns of Base Pairing 198
Unwinding the Double Helix: The Secret of Self-Replication 199
DNA Replication 200
Meanwhile, Back at the Forks . . . 200
Enzymes of DNA Replication and Repair 202
Summary of DNA Replication 203
DNA Recombination 203
Molecular Basis of Recombination 203
Recombinant DNA Research 205
Change in the Hereditary Material 207
Mutation at the Molecular Level 207
Perspective 209

13 FROM DNA TO PROTEIN: HOW GENES FUNCTION 211

Preview of the Steps and Participants in Protein Assembly 211
Early Ideas About Gene Function 212
The Genetic Code 214
Transcription of DNA into RNA 216
Messenger RNA Translation 217
Summary of Protein Synthesis 220
Meanwhile, Back at the Mitochondrion . . . 222

14 CONTROLS OVER GENE EXPRESSION 223

Types of Gene Controls 223
Gene Regulation in Prokaryotes 224
The Operon: Coordinated Unit of Transcription 224
Induction-Repression 225
Corepression 225
Other Prokaryotic Control Mechanisms 226
Gene Regulation in Eukaryotes 227
Comparison of Prokaryotic and Eukaryotic DNA 227
Transcript Processing 227
Chromosome Organization and Gene Activity 229
Variable Gene Activity in Eukaryotic Development 230
CASE STUDY: *The Not-So-Simple Slime Molds* 231
CASE STUDY: *Acetabularia* 233
Observations of Variable Gene Activity 233
Cancer: When Controls Break Down 234
Perspective 236

15 HUMAN GENETICS 237

Autosomal Recessive Inheritance 238
Sex-Linked Recessive Inheritance 238
Hemophilia 238
Green Color Blindness 240
Changes in Chromosome Number 240
Down's Syndrome 240
Turner's Syndrome 240
Trisomy XXY and XYY 241
Prospects and Problems in Human Genetics 241
Treatments for Phenotypic Defects 242
Genetic Screening 242
Genetic Counseling and Prenatal Diagnosis 243
Gene Replacement 244
COMMENTARY: *A Holistic View of Human Genetic Disorders* 244

UNIT FOUR   PLANT SYSTEMS AND THEIR CONTROL

16 PLANT CELLS, TISSUES, AND SYSTEMS 248

The Plant Body: An Overview 248
On "Typical" Plants 248
How Plant Tissues Arise 249
Plant Tissues and Their Component Cells 251
Parenchyma: Photosynthesis, Food Storage 251
Collenchyma: Supporting Young Plant Parts 251
Sclerenchyma: Strengthening Mature Plant Parts 252
Xylem: Water Transport, Storage, and Support 252
Phloem: Food Transport, Storage, and Support 254
Epidermis and Periderm: Interfaces With the Environment 255
The Root System 256
Root Primary Structure 256
Secondary Growth in Roots 258

The Shoot System   258
    Stem Primary Structure   259
    Leaf Structure   260
    Secondary Growth in Stems   261

17   WATER, SOLUTES, AND PLANT FUNCTIONING   264

Essential Elements and Their Functions   265
    Oxygen, Carbon, and Hydrogen   265
    Mineral Elements   266
Water Uptake, Transport, and Loss   267
    Water Absorption by Roots   267
    Transpiration   268
    Cohesion Theory of Water Transport   270
    The Paradox in Water and Carbon Dioxide Movements   270
    Stomatal Action   270
Uptake and Accumulation of Minerals   272
    Active Transport of Mineral Ions   272
    Feedback Controls Over Ion Absorption   272
Transport of Organic Substances Through Phloem   273
    Translocation   273
    Pressure Flow Theory   274

**18   PLANT REPRODUCTION
AND EMBRYONIC DEVELOPMENT**   276

Sexual Reproduction of Flowering Plants   276
    Overview of Key Reproductive Events   276
    Floral Structure   277
Gamete Formation   278
    Microspores to Pollen Grains   278
    Megaspores to Eggs   279
Pollination and Fertilization   280
    Pollination and Pollen Tube Growth   280
    Fertilization and Endosperm Formation   280
    Coevolution of Flowering Plants and Their Pollinators   280
Embryonic Development   284
    From Zygote to Plant Embryo   284
    Seed and Fruit Formation   285
    Dispersal and Germination   286
Asexual Reproduction of Flowering Plants   286

19   PLANT GROWTH AND DEVELOPMENT   288

Plant Growth: Its Nature and Direction   288
    Genetic Controls Over Development   288
    Patterns of Cell Enlargement   289
Plant Hormones   291
    Types of Plant Hormones   291
    Examples of Hormonal Action   292
Hormones, the Environment, and Plant Development   293
    Effects of Temperature   293
    Effects of Sunlight   294
    The Many and Puzzling Tropisms   295

The Flowering Process   297
Senescence   299
Dormancy   300
Biological Clocks in Plants   301
    CASE STUDY: *From Embryogenesis to the Mature Oak*   302

UNIT FIVE   ANIMAL SYSTEMS AND THEIR CONTROL

20   SYSTEMS OF CELLS AND HOMEOSTASIS   306

Some Characteristics of Animal Cells and Tissues   306
Kinds of Animal Tissues   308
    Epithelial Tissues   308
    Connective Tissues   310
    Nerve Tissues   313
    Muscle Tissues   313
Overview of Organ Systems and Their Function   314
Homeostasis and Systems Control   316
    The Internal Environment   316
    Homeostatic Control Mechanisms   316

**21   INTEGRATION AND CONTROL:
NERVOUS SYSTEMS**   319

The Neuron   319
Message Conduction   320
    The Neuron "At Rest"   321
    Changes in Membrane Potential   322
    Action Potentials   322
    Summary of Message Conduction Mechanisms   324
Message Transfers   325
    Synaptic Transmission Between Neurons   325
    Junctional Transmission Between Neurons
    and Muscle Cells   326
The Reflex Arc: From Stimulus to Response   327
Nervous Systems: Increasing the Options for Response   328
    Evolution of Nervous Systems   328
    Central Nervous Systems   331
    Peripheral Nervous Systems   332
The Human Brain   335
    Regions of the Cortex   335
    Information Processing in the Cortex   337
    Conscious Experience   339
    Memory   340
    Sleeping and Dreaming   340
Drug Action on Integration and Control   341

**22   INTEGRATION AND CONTROL:
ENDOCRINE SYSTEMS**   344

Hormone Function   344
    Comparison of Neural and Endocrine Cell Secretions   344
    Mechanisms of Hormone Action   345

Factors Influencing Hormone Levels in the Bloodstream 346
Components of Endocrine Systems 346
Neuroendocrine Control Center 347
  On Neural and Endocrine Links 347
  Interactions Between the Hypothalamus and Pituitary 347
Other Endocrine Elements 352
  Adrenal Glands 352
  Thyroid and Parathyroid Glands 352
  Gonads 352
  Glandular Tissues of the Pancreas, Stomach, and Small Intestine 352
  Hormone Functions of Kidneys 352
  Pineal Gland and Thymus Gland 353
  Prostaglandins 353

23 RECEPTION AND MOTOR RESPONSE 354

Sensing Environmental Change 355
  Primary Receptors 355
  Chemical Reception 356
  Mechanical Reception 356
  Light Reception 359
Movement in Response to Change 366
  Motor Systems 366
  Muscle Contraction 368
  Summary of Muscle Contraction 372
  Types of Muscular Responses to Action Potentials 373
  Neuromotor Basis of Behavior 373

24 CIRCULATION 374

Internal Distribution Strategies 374
Components of Blood 375
  Blood Composition and Volume 375
  Types of Blood Cells and Their Function 375
Structure and Function of Blood Circulation Systems 377
  Systematic and Pulmonary Circulation 377
  The Human Heart 378
  Blood Vessels 381
  Blood Pressure and the Distribution of Flow 383
  Hemostasis 384
  COMMENTARY: *On Cardiovascular Disorders* 386
Lymphatic System 386
  Lymph Vascular System 388
  Lymphoid Organs 388
Nonspecific Defense Responses 389
  External Barriers to Invasion 389
  Inflammatory Response 389
Specific Defense Responses: The Immune System 390
  Evolution of Vertebrate Immune Systems 390
  Killer T-Cells and the B-Cell Ways of Chemical Warfare 390
  COMMENTARY: *Cancer, Allergy, and Attacks on Self* 392
  The Basis of Self-Recognition 395

CASE STUDY: *The Silent, Unseen Struggles* 396

25 RESPIRATION 398

Oxygen Acquisition: Some Environmental Considerations 398
Respiration: An Overview 400
Human Respiratory System 400
  Respiratory Organs 400
  Relation Between the Lungs and the Pleural Sac 401
Ventilation 402
  Inhalation and Exhalation 402
  Controls Over Breathing 403
Gas Exchange and Transport 404
  Gas Exchange in Alveoli 404
  Gas Transport Between Lungs and Tissues 404
Ciliary Action in Respiratory Tracts 406
  COMMENTARY: *When the Lungs Break Down* 407

26 DIGESTION AND ORGANIC METABOLISM 409

Feeding Strategies 409
Human Digestive System: An Overview 411
  Components of the Digestive System 411
  General Structure of the Gastrointestinal Tract 412
  Gastrointestinal Motility 412
Control of Gastrointestinal Movements and Secretions 412
Structure and Function of Gastrointestinal Organs 413
  Mouth and Salivary Glands 413
  Pharynx and Esophagus 414
  Stomach 414
  Small Intestine 415
  Large Intestine 417
  Enzymes of Digestion: A Summary 418
Human Nutritional Requirements 418
  Energy Needs 418
  Carbohydrates and Lipids 419
  Proteins 419
  COMMENTARY: *Human Nutrition and Gastrointestinal Disorders* 420
  Vitamins and Minerals 421
Organic Metabolism 421
  The Vertebrate Liver 421
  Absorptive and Post-Absorptive States 424
  CASE STUDY: *Feasting, Fasting, and Systems Integration* 425

27 REGULATION OF BODY TEMPERATURE AND BODY FLUIDS 428

Control of Body Temperature 428
  Temperature Range Suitable for Life 428
  Heat Production and Heat Loss 429
  Thermal Regulation in Ectotherms 429
  Thermal Regulation in Birds and Mammals 430

Control of Extracellular Fluid   431
Water and Solute Balance   431
COMMENTARY: *Falling Overboard and the Odds for Survival*   432
Mammalian Urinary System   432
Kidney Function   433
Controls Over Fluid Volume and Composition   435
COMMENTARY: *Kidney Failure, Bypass Measures, and Transplants*   437

28 PRINCIPLES OF REPRODUCTION AND DEVELOPMENT   440

The Beginning: Reproductive Modes   441
Asexual Reproduction   441
Sexual Reproduction   441
Some Strategic Problems in Having Separate Sexes   441
Stages of Early Embryonic Development   443
Egg Formation and the Onset of Gene Control   444
Visible Changes in Amphibian Eggs at Fertilization   448
Cleavage: Carving Up Cytoplasmic Controls   448
Gastrulation: When Embryonic Controls Take Over   449
Organ Formation   449
Morphogenesis and Growth   450
Growth Patterns   450
Cell Movements and Changes in Cell Shape   450
Pattern Formation   451
Controlled Cell Death   453
Metamorphosis   454
Cell Differentiation   454
Aging and Death   456
COMMENTARY: *Death in the Open*   457

29 HUMAN REPRODUCTION AND DEVELOPMENT   459

Definition of Primary Reproductive Organs   459
Male Reproductive System   459
Male Reproductive Tract   459
Spermatogenesis   460
Sperm Movement Through the Reproductive Tract   461
Hormonal Control in the Male   461
Female Reproductive System   462
Female Reproductive Tract   462
Menstrual Cycle: An Overview   462
Ovarian Function   464
Uterine Function   466
Sexual Union and Fertilization   467
From Fertilization to Birth   468
Early Embryonic Development   468
CASE STUDY: *Mother As Protector, Provider, Potential Threat*   470
COMMENTARY: *In Vitro Fertilization*   472
Control of Human Fertility   473
Some Ethical Considerations   473
Possible Means of Birth Control   474

UNIT SIX   EVOLUTION

30 INDIVIDUALS, POPULATIONS, AND EVOLUTION   478

Variation: What It Is, How It Arises   479
The Hardy-Weinberg Baseline for Measuring Change   481
Factors Bringing About Change   481
Effects of Mutation   482
Genetic Drift   482
Gene Flow   483
Natural Selection   484
Examples of Natural Selection   484
Stabilizing Selection   485
Directional Selection   486
Disruptive Selection   488
Sexual Selection   488
Selection and Balanced Polymorphism   489
Evolution of Species   490
Defining a Species   490
Reproductive Isolating Mechanisms   491
Modes of Speciation   492
Macroevolution   493
A Time Scale for Macroevolution   494
Rates and Patterns of Change   495
Evolutionary Trends   497
Phyletic Evolution   497
Quantum Evolution   497
Mosaic Evolution   498
Extinction   498

31 ORIGINS AND THE EVOLUTION OF LIFE   500

Origin of Life   501
The Early Earth and Its Atmosphere   501
Spontaneous Assembly of Organic Compounds   502
Speculations on the First Self-Replicating Systems   502
The Age of Prokaryotes   504
The Rise of Eukaryotes   506
Divergence Into Three Primordial Lineages   506
Symbiosis in the Evolution of Eukaryotes   506
Origin of the Nucleus   508
Eukaryotes of the Precambrian   508
Life During the Paleozoic   508
Mesozoic: Age of the Dinosaurs   514
Cenozoic: Threshold to the Present   516
Perspective   517

UNIT SEVEN   DIVERSITY: EVOLUTIONARY FORCE, EVOLUTIONARY PRODUCT

32 VIRUSES, BACTERIA, AND PROTISTANS   520

Bacteria   520
Characteristics of Bacteria   520

Archaebacteria	522
Eubacteria	523
Fifteen Thousand Species of Bacteria Can't Be All Bad	524
Viruses	526
Characteristics of Viruses	526
COMMENTARY: *Bacteria, Viruses, and Sexually Transmitted Diseases*	527
Viroids	529
Protistans	529
Euglenids	530
Chrysophytes and Diatoms	530
Dinoflagellates	531
Protozoa	532
On the Road to Multicellularity	537

33   FUNGI AND PLANTS   539

Part I. Kingdom of Fungi	539
On the Fungal Way of Life	539
Fungal Body Plans	539
Overview of Reproductive Modes	540
Major Groups of Fungi	540
Mycorrhizal Mats and the Lichens	544
Species of Unknown Affiliations	545
Part II. Kingdom of Plants	546
Evolutionary Trends Among Plants	546
Algae: Plants That Never Left the Water	548
The Bryophytes	551
Ferns and Their Allies: First of the Vascular Plants	552
Gymnosperms: The Conifers and Their Kin	556
Angiosperms: The Flowering Plants	558
Perspective	560

34   ANIMAL DIVERSITY   561

General Characteristics of Animals	562
Body Plans	562
Major Groups of Animals	563
Sponges	563
Cnidarians	567
Flatworms	569
Turbellarians	569
Trematodes	569
Cestodes	570
Flatworm Origins	571
Roundworms	571
Two Main Lines of Divergence: Protostomes and Deuterostomes	572
Mollusks	573
Gastropods	573
Bivalves	574
Cephalopods	575
Annelids	576

Arthropods	578
Arthropod Adaptations	578
Chelicerates	580
Crustaceans	580
Insects and Their Kin	580
Echinoderms	581
Chordates	582
From Notochords to Backbones	583
Evolutionary Potential of Bones and Jaws	585
Lungs and the Vertebrate Heart	585
On the Vertebrate Nervous System	588

35   HUMAN ORIGINS AND EVOLUTION   590

The Primate Family	590
Primate Origins	590
General Characteristics of Primates	592
Early Hominids (Perhaps) and Their Predecessors (Maybe)	592
Ancient Apelike Forms	592
Australopithecines	593
The First Humans	593
COMMENTARY: *A Biological Perspective on Human Origins*	595

UNIT EIGHT   ECOLOGY AND BEHAVIOR

36   POPULATION ECOLOGY   598

Ecology Defined	599
Population Density and Distribution	600
Ecological Density	600
Distribution in Space	600
Distribution Over Time	601
Population Dynamics	601
Parameters Affecting Population Size	601
Life Expectancy and Survivorship Curves	601
Population Growth	602
Biotic Potential	602
Exponential Growth	602
Environmental Resistance to Growth	604
Tolerance Limits	605
Carrying Capacity and Logistic Growth	605
Reproductive Responses to Growth Limits	606
Factors That Regulate Population Growth	608
Density-Dependent and Density-Independent Factors	608
Extrinsic Influences	608
Intrinsic Influences	609
Human Population Growth	609
Doubling Time for the Human Population	609
Where We Began Sidestepping Controls	610
Age Structure and Fertility Rates	611
Perspective	612

37 COMMUNITY INTERACTIONS — 614

Habitat and Niche — 614
Types of Community Interactions — 617
Interspecific Competition — 618
  The Concept of Competitive Exclusion — 618
  Field Evidence of Competitive Exclusion — 618
  Coexistence in Resource Categories — 619
Predation — 620
Coevolution — 622
  Warning Coloration and Mimicry — 624
  Camouflage — 624
  Moment-of-Truth Defenses — 624
  Chemical Defenses — 624
  Predation and Seed Dispersal — 624
  Energy Outlays for Predation — 626
  Mutualism — 626
  Parasitism — 627

38 ECOSYSTEMS — 629

Organization of Ecosystems — 630
  Trophic Levels — 630
  Food Webs — 630
  CASE STUDY: *Biological Concentration of DDT* — 631
Energy Flow Through Ecosystems — 632
  Primary Productivity and Energy Storage — 632
  Major Pathways of Energy Flow — 632
  Energy Budgets — 635
Nutrient Cycling — 635
  A Model of Nutrient Flow — 635
  CASE STUDY: *Nutrient Recovery in the Arctic Tundra* — 636
  Nitrogen Cycling in Ecosystems — 638
  COMMENTARY: *Resources and the Human Condition* — 640
Succession — 643
  Succession Defined — 643
  Opportunistic and Equilibrium Species — 643
  Disturbances in Succession — 643
Species Introductions — 646

39 THE BIOSPHERE — 648

Components of the Biosphere — 649
Global Patterns of Climate — 649
  Mediating Effects of the Atmosphere — 649
  Air Currents — 649
  Ocean Currents — 650
  Seasonal Variations in Climate — 651
  Regional Climates — 651
Biogeochemical Cycles — 652
  Hydrologic Cycle — 652
  Gaseous Cycles — 653
  Sedimentary Cycles — 654
Aquatic Ecosystems — 655
  Freshwater Ecosystems — 655

  Marine and Estuarine Ecosystems — 656
Terrestrial Ecosystems — 658
  Effect of Soils — 658
  The Concept of Biomes — 658
  Deserts — 660
  Shrublands — 661
  Grasslands — 662
  Forests — 663
  Tundra — 667
  The City As Ecosystem — 667

40 HUMAN IMPACT ON THE BIOSPHERE — 669

  CASE STUDY: *Solid Wastes* — 670
  CASE STUDY: *Water Pollution* — 670
  CASE STUDY: *Air Pollution* — 672
  Acid Deposition — 672
  Industrial and Photochemical Smog — 674
Some Energy Options — 674
  Fossil Fuels — 675
  Nuclear Energy — 675
  Wind Energy — 677
  Solar Energy — 677
Perspective — 677

41 ANIMAL BEHAVIOR — 679

The Diversity of Behavior — 679
  Innate Behavior — 680
  Categories of Learning — 680
An Evolutionary Approach to Behavior — 680
  Genes, Environment, and the Development of Behavior — 680
  Evolution of Behavior — 682
Ecological Aspects of Behavior — 683
  Biological Clocks, Compasses, and Maps — 683
  Predator and Prey Behavior — 685
Behavioral Adaptation: Who Benefits? — 686
  On Individual Selection — 686
  CASE STUDY: *Siblicide Among the Egrets* — 686
  CASE STUDY: *Courtship Behavior* — 686
  CASE STUDY: *Competition for Females* — 688
  CASE STUDY: *Tactics of Defeated Males* — 688
On "Selfish" Behavior and Social Life — 689
  Parenting as Genetically Selfish Behavior — 690
  Individual Advantages of Group Living — 690
  Cooperative Societies of Birds and Mammals — 690
  Suicide, Sterility, and Social Insects — 693
Selection Theory and the Evolution of Human Behavior — 696

Appendix I Brief Classification System
Appendix II Solutions to Genetics Problems
Glossary
Index

UNIT ONE

UNIFYING CONCEPTS IN BIOLOGY

1

ON THE UNITY AND DIVERSITY OF LIFE

Buried somewhere in that mass of nerve tissue just above and behind your eyes are memories of first encounters with the living world. Still in residence are sensations of discovering your own two hands and feet, your family, the change of seasons, the smell of rain-drenched earth and grass. In that brain are traces of early introductions to a great disorganized parade of beetles, flowers, frogs, and furred things, mostly living, sometimes dead. There, too, are memories of questions—*What is "life"?* and, inevitably, *What is "death"?* There are memories of answers, some satisfying, others less so.

Observing, asking questions, accumulating answers— in this manner you have acquired a store of approximate knowledge about the world of life. During the journey to maturity, experience and education have been refining your questions, and no doubt the answers have been more difficult to come by. What *is* life? What characterizes the living state? The answer you get may vary, depending, for example, on whether it comes from someone arguing for or against legalized abortion. When does life end? Again the answer may vary, depending on whether it comes from a physician, a clergyman, or a parent of a severely injured person who must be maintained by mechanical life support systems because the brain no longer functions at all. Yet despite the changing character of the questions, the world of living things remains as it was before. Leaves still unfurl during the spring rains. Animals are born, they grow, reproduce, and die even as new individuals of their kind are being born. *The most important difference is in the degree of insight you now bring to those observations, questions, and answers about such events.*

It is scarcely appropriate, then, for a book to proclaim that it is your introduction to biology—"the study of life"— when you have been studying life ever since awareness of the world began penetrating your brain. The subject is the same familiar world that you have already thought about to no small extent. That is why this book proclaims only to be biology *revisited,* in ways that may help carry your thoughts about life to deeper, more organized levels of understanding.

Let us return at the outset to the question, What is life? It happens that the answer has yet to be reduced to a simple definition. The word embodies a story that has been unfolding in myriad directions for several billion years! To biologists, "life" is what it is by virtue of its ancient molecular origins and its degree of organization. "Life" is a way of capturing and systematically using energy and materials. "Life" is a commitment to some specific program of growth and development; it is a capacity for reproduction. "Life" means individual adjustment to shifting conditions—it is *adaptive* to short-term environmental change. "Life" is also adaptive, through generations of individuals, to change over long spans of time. As you can see, a short list of definitions can do no more than hint at all that the word conveys. Deeper insight into its meaning comes only with systematic and wide-ranging investigation of its characteristics, *for life cannot be understood in isolation from its history and its adaptive potential.*

Throughout this book, you will encounter different examples of living things—how they are constructed, how they function, where they live, what they do. You will also be coming across statements that highlight certain aspects of these examples and the generalizations that can be drawn from them. Such statements are printed in darker type and separated by lines from the text. All of these statements, taken together, will give you a fairly good sense of what "life" is.

With this in mind, let us now turn to a few examples that illustrate the most general concepts of all. Although these concepts are explored in greater detail in later chapters, they are summarized here to provide perspective on things to come. You may also find it useful to return to them as a way of reinforcing your grasp of details later on.

Figure 1.1 A common egret on the wing, against a background of bald cypress and Spanish moss. These three kinds of organisms are diverse in appearance, yet they have much in common. They illustrate the unity and diversity inherent in *all* of life, which is the subject of this chapter.

ORIGINS AND ORGANIZATION

Suppose someone asks you to point out the difference between a frog and a rock. The frog, you might say, has a body of truly complex organization. Its hundreds of thousands of individual cells are organized into tissues. Its tissues are arranged into organs such as a heart and stomach. The frog can move about on its own. Sooner or later (given a receptive member of the opposite sex), it can reproduce. A rock shows no such ordered complexity; it cannot move by itself, and it certainly cannot reproduce either on its own or in the company of another rock. If you deduce from this that a living organism has complex organization, the capacity to move, and the capacity to reproduce, then the frog is alive and the rock is not.

Now suppose someone asks you to point out the difference between a bacterium and a rock. A bacterium is one of the simplest kinds of organisms, no more than a single cell, really. Yet microscopic examination shows that bacterial bodies are organized in far more regular, orderly patterns than are the insides of a rock. All but a few bacteria have an outer wall. All have a plasma membrane (a partially permeable, saclike structure that helps control the kinds of substances moving into and out of the cell). In all bacteria, the membrane encloses a semifluid substance in which specific structures are embedded (Figure 1.2). All bacteria can divide and reproduce. Some bacteria move on their own through their surroundings; others, however, cannot. The "movement" criterion is becoming a little fuzzy now. However, by the other two standards (complex organization, together with a capacity to reproduce), a bacterium is alive.

Suppose you are now asked to compare a virus with a rock. A virus is a peculiar particle in the shadowy world between the living and the nonliving. Viruses do have a distinct organization; some, for instance, have a "head" end, a sheathlike midsection, and a "tail" end. A virus has no means whatsoever of moving on its own. It cannot reproduce on its own. Yet all viruses contain instructions for producing copies of themselves. The instructions must become incorporated into a living host cell to be carried out. In effect, a virus takes over the cellular machinery to the extent that the host starts following *viral* instructions. The machinery starts churning out parts that cannot be used by the cell, but that can be used for building new viruses! By your initial criteria—complex organization, movement, reproduction—is a virus alive? In some respects yes, in others no.

Somewhere below that shadowed boundary to the living world are tiny spheres, called microspheres (Figure

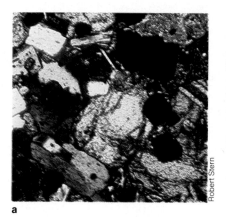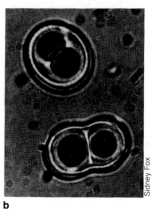

a   b

Figure 1.2 A hierarchy of structural organization between a frog and a rock. The sizes of the subjects in these photographs are not to the same scale relative to one another. (**a**) Basalt rock, thin-section, from Marianas Trench. (**b**) Microspheres, with their membranelike outer layer and their tendency to grow and fragment into new spheres. (**c**) Virus particles, with outer layers enclosing hereditary instructions. (**d**) Bacterial cell, sliced to show the inside. (**e**) Some of the complex structures within a single cell in a multicellular plant. (**f**) The many-celled frog body. (d from G. Cohen-Bazire)

1.2b). Under the right conditions, they assemble spontaneously from simple molecules. You can observe a similar kind of spontaneous assembly by pouring some oil into a glass of water. The oil molecules will not mix with water molecules; they cluster into droplets. Microspheres are something like these oil droplets. Each has an outer layer that acts like a simple membrane. The membrane structure passively controls the kinds of substances moving into and out of the sphere. This means that certain molecules can be isolated inside the sphere, away from random events in the surrounding environment. When concentrated inside, these molecules can become arranged in nonrandom ways relative to one another. Thus microspheres show at least some *potential* for organization. What about reproduction? When they accumulate some substances, microspheres can grow in size. They can even grow to the extent that parts break off and form new spheres, which grow in turn. However, the processes involved are not reproductive; they are only random chemical growth and fragmentation into (generally) nonidentical parts. So you are left to conclude that microspheres are not alive. Then again, you can sense that the degree of organization they do show is more intriguing than that of the rock.

And what about that rock? It does not seem any too remarkable when compared to a highly organized creature such as a bacterium. At the levels of viruses and micro-

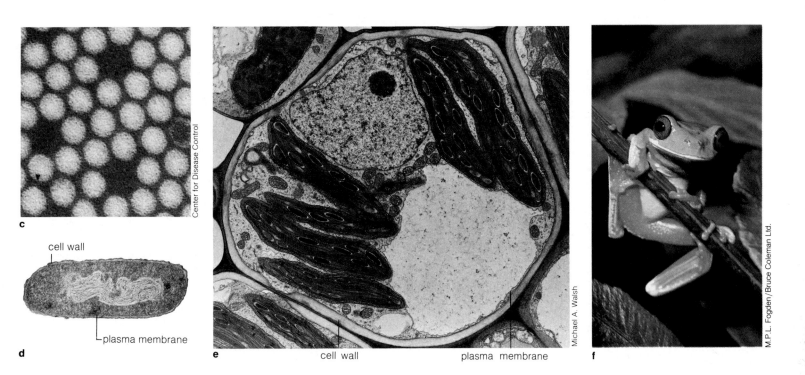

c
Center for Disease Control

cell wall
plasma membrane

d

e
cell wall
plasma membrane
Michael A. Walsh

f
M.P.L. Fogden/Bruce Coleman Ltd.

spheres, however, the difference begins to blur. At a still deeper level, the difference becomes nonexistent. Frog, bacterium, virus, microsphere, rock—all turn out to be composed of the same raw materials. These materials are particles called protons, electrons, and neutrons. They become organized relative to one another according to the same physical laws. At the heart of these laws is something called **energy**—a capacity for interaction between particles, a capacity to make things happen, to do work. Energetic interactions join these particles together, in predictable ways, and form atoms. They bind atom to atom in predictable patterns, thereby giving rise to the kinds of molecules that form (for example) all the frogs and rocks of our world. Energetic interactions hold a frog together and a rock together; the distribution of energy organizes and holds entire communities of organisms together. Thus we have a profound concept:

The structure and organization of the living as well as the nonliving world arise from the fundamental properties of matter and energy.

This concept has implications for questions about the origin of life. It now appears that living things probably originated as increasingly organized constellations of matter and energy. A later chapter will tell you more about the evidence supporting this idea. For now, take a careful look at Figure 1.3, which outlines the levels of organization in today's world. Then consider the idea that these levels echo successive stages in the history of life. According to this idea, interactions between atoms and molecules, under certain chemical conditions, led to the assembly of special large molecules that occur in all living things. Increasing molecular organization in some way led to structures possibly like microspheres. Along the way, molecules became organized relative to one another in ways that allowed them to duplicate themselves—and to lay the foundation for reproduction. This capacity led to the cell—the smallest unit of life still having the properties of life. Reproduction of cells and their interactions led to populations of single cells and of multicelled organisms, then to communities, ecosystems, and the biosphere.

What we are unfolding here is a picture of increasingly complex, interrelated patterns of order in the use of materials and energy. It accounts, as any speculation about the origin of life must do, for this apparent fact:

The "difference" between the living state and the nonliving state is one of <u>degree</u>, not of kind.

Biosphere
Entire zone of earth, water, atmosphere
in which life can exist on our planet's surface

⬆⬇

Ecosystem
All the energetic interactions and materials cycling
that link organisms in a community with one another
and with their environment

⬆⬇

Community
Two or more populations of different organisms that occupy
and are adapted to a given environment

⬆⬇

Population
Group of individuals of the same kind, occupying
a given area at a given time

⬆⬇

Multicellular Organism
Individual composed of specialized, interdependent cells
arrayed in tissues, organs, and often organ systems

⬆⬇

Organ System
Two or more organs whose separate functions
are integrated in the performance of a specific task

⬆⬇

Organ
One or more types of tissues
interacting as a structural, functional unit

⬆⬇

Tissue
One or more types of cells
interacting as a structural, functional unit

⬆⬇

Cell
Smallest *living* unit; may live independently
or may be part of multicellular organism

⬆⬇

Organelle
Structure inside a cell whose molecular
organization enhances specific cell activities

⬆⬇

Molecule
Two or more identical or different kinds of atoms bonded together

⬆⬇

Atom
Smallest unit of a pure substance that retains properties of that substance

⬆⬇

Subatomic Particle
Unit of energy and/or mass; electron, proton, neutron

Figure 1.3   Levels of organization in nature.

UNITY IN BASIC LIFE PROCESSES

Metabolism

So far, we have touched on the nature of life's organization—the bricks, so to speak, that are assembled in orderly ways to form each living thing. Underlying the assembly of the bricks themselves, and underlying all activities of the organisms in which they are found, are *energy transformations.* As you will read later, energy is stored in various substances. Stored energy can be released to do work, such as building cell parts. However, there is only so much energy available to living things. And there is no way an organism can create "new" energy from nothing. To stay alive, it must "borrow" energy from someplace else. The organism must tap an *existing* energy source in its surroundings, then transform the energy into forms appropriate for its requirements.

For example, plant cells use an energy-trapping process called photosynthesis. They absorb sunlight energy, which becomes conserved for a while in energy-rich molecules such as adenosine triphosphate (ATP). These molecules readily transfer some of their energy to molecular systems involved in cell construction, maintenance, and reproduction. As another example, energy stored in carbon-containing molecules present in cells can be released during programs that lead to the formation of more ATP. The most pervasive of these energy-releasing programs, and the one with the highest energy yield, is aerobic respiration.

All single-celled and multicelled organisms have a capacity for acquiring and using energy in stockpiling, tearing down, building up, and eliminating substances in controlled ways. This capacity, called **metabolism,** is a unique feature of living things.

All forms of life show metabolic activity: they extract and transform energy from their environment and use it for manipulating materials in ways that assure their own maintenance, growth, and reproduction.

Growth, Development, and Reproduction

Through the precision of metabolic events, living things come into the world, they grow and develop, they reproduce. Most then move on through decline and death according to a timetable for their kind. Even as individual organisms die, reproduction assures that the form and function of the living state are perpetuated along the axis of time.

Yet "an organism" is much more than a single organized form having a single set of functions during its lifetime. One example will make the point, even though actual details vary considerably from one kind of organism to the next.

A tiny egg deposited on a branch by a female moth (Figure 1.4) is a transitional form. It is a compact package that contains all of the instructions necessary for becoming an adult moth. It does not become transformed at once into a miniature winged moth that need only increase in size. Instead, developmental events going on inside the egg lead to an entirely different form: a wingless, many-legged larva called a caterpillar. The caterpillar hatches during a warm season when tender new leaves unfold. Not surprisingly, the caterpillar is a streamlined "eating machine" stage of this insect's life cycle. It has mouthparts capable of tearing and chewing leaves, and a metabolic capacity for extremely rapid growth. It eats and grows until some internal alarm clock goes off, setting in motion events that lead to profound changes in the living form. Some cells are disassembled, other cells multiply and are assembled in entirely different patterns. Tissues, too, are moved about during this stage of wholesale remodeling, the so-called pupal stage. From the pupa, the adult moth emerges. The moth is the "reproductive machine" stage, a form streamlined for reproduction and dispersal. Its head has a tubelike extension, a proboscis, which draws nectar from flowers. From the nectar comes energy that powers free-wheeling flights. For this insect, wings are emblazoned with colors and set to move at a frequency that can attract a potential mate. The moth is equipped with organs in which egg or sperm develop, and which enhance fertilization of an egg. With fertilization comes the beginning of a new life cycle.

None of these functional stages is "the insect." "The insect" is a series of stages in organization, with new adaptive properties emerging at each stage. It is possible to talk about the units of energy required to power insect flight, the food required for caterpillar growth, the chemical activities that trigger a transformation from caterpillar to pupa. All such metabolic events help describe the nature of life. Equally important is an understanding that metabolism itself proceeds within a framework of developmental events:

From the moment of its emergence, each living thing goes through a series of developmental stages—a continuum of changes in form and behavior. These developmental stages unfold at about the same rate and in the same way for all organisms of a given type.

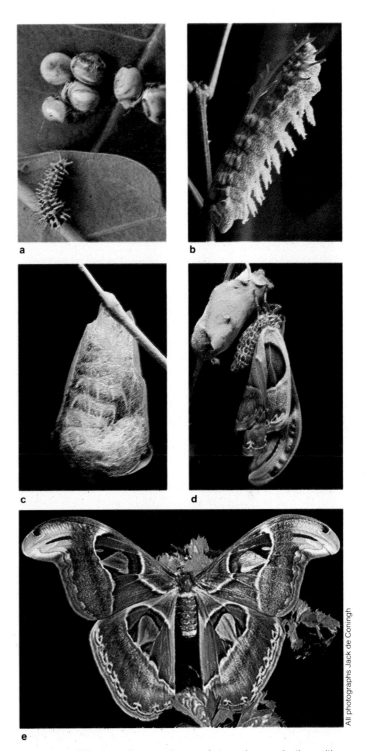

All photographs Jack de Coningh

Figure 1.4 "The insect"—a continuum of stages in organization, with new adaptive properties emerging at each stage. Shown here: the development of a giant moth, from egg (**a**) to larval stage (**b**), to pupal form (**c**), to emergence of the resplendent moth form (**d, e**).

Homeostasis

Any attempt to define the nature of life cannot focus exclusively on the organism, for the organism cannot exist apart from its surroundings. It most assuredly cannot exist without being able to respond to variations in those surroundings, whether random, cyclic, or self-induced. The living state happens to be maintained within rather narrow limits. Body concentrations of such substances as carbon dioxide and oxygen must not rise above or fall below certain levels. Toxic substances must be avoided or eliminated. Certain foods must be available and in certain amounts. Water, oxygen, carbon dioxide, ions and food of varied sorts, light, pressure, temperature—such environmental factors dictate the terms of survival. And such terms are subject to change.

How do living things respond to a changing environment? They respond in two ways. First, *all organisms have built-in means of maintaining the living state by making internal adjustments to changes in the surroundings.* The adjustments help maintain operating conditions within some tolerable range. This capacity for maintaining the "internal environment" is known as **homeostasis.** Individual cells have homeostatic controls. (For instance, cellular homeostasis depends in part on the plasma membrane. At various points in this membrane, substances in short supply can be moved into the cell, and other substances can be moved out.) Multicelled organisms also have homeostatic controls. (Birds, for instance, have sensors that signal the brain when outside temperatures drop. The brain may send signals to cells that control feather movements. Special movements lead to feather fluffing. Feather fluffing retains heat and thereby helps maintain body temperature.)

Homeostasis implies constancy, a sort of perpetual bouncing back to some limited set of operating conditions. In some respects, constancy is indeed vital. Your red blood cells will not function unless they are bathed in water that contains certain amounts of dissolved components. Your body works so that the bathwater, so to speak, is always much the same.

Yet living things also respond in a second way to changing conditions. *All organisms adjust to certain directional changes in the internal and external environments.* We might call this **dynamic homeostasis,** for the living state is maintained through adjustments that *shift* the organism's form and function over time.

A simple example will do here. In humans, irreversible chemical changes trigger puberty, the age at which sexual reproductive structures mature and become functional. At the time of puberty, the body steps up its secretions of such hormones as androgens (in males) and estrogens (in females). The increased secretions are necessary for sexual maturation. They call for entirely new events such as the menstrual cycle, which includes a rhythmic accumulation of substances that prepare the female body for pregnancy, followed by disposal of substances when pregnancy does not occur. It is not that homeostasis no longer operates. It is that developmental events now demand new kinds of adjustments in the internal state.

All forms of life depend on homeostatic controls, which maintain the living state as internal and external conditions change.

Some homeostatic controls keep certain conditions within some tolerable range throughout the life cycle.

Some homeostatic controls govern new kinds of adjustments in the internal state as the life cycle unfolds.

DNA: Storehouse of Constancy and Change

Upon thinking about the preceding examples, you might wonder what could be responsible for **inheritance**—the transmission, from parents to offspring, of structural and functional patterns characteristic of each kind of organism. How is it that a bacterium can divide and grow into two fairly exact copies of itself? How is it that corn seeds can germinate and grow into fairly exact replicas of parent corn plants? Within each individual, there must be a molecular storehouse of hereditary information. It must be a remarkable storehouse indeed, for it must contain all the details for a complete program of growth, development, maintenance, and reproduction.

There is another remarkable aspect of this storehouse of information. Although offspring generally resemble their parents in form and behavior, *variations* can exist on the basic plan. A newly produced bacterium might not be able to assemble (as it is supposed to) some molecule that is vital to its functioning. Sometimes humans are born with six digits on each hand instead of five. Even though the hereditary molecule must remain generally the same to assure overall fidelity in the transmission of traits, it somehow must be subject to change in some of its details!

As you have probably learned by now, the hereditary molecule has been identified. In all living cells it is deoxyribonucleic acid, or DNA. We now know that changes occasionally occur in the kind, structure, sequence, or number of its component parts. These changes are **mutations.** Most mutations are harmful, for the DNA of each kind of organism is a package of information that is finely tuned

Figure 1.5 Underwater tropical reef.

to a given environment. In addition, its separate bits of information are part of a coordinated whole. When one crucial part changes, the whole living system may be thrown off balance.

However, sometimes a mutation may prove to be harmless, even beneficial, under prevailing conditions. For example, a mutant form of a light-colored moth (*Biston betularia*) is dark-colored. When it rests on soot-covered trees, bird predators simply do not see it. In places where there happen to be lots of soot-covered trees (around industrial regions, for instance), the dark color can be advantageous: a mutant stands a better chance of reaching reproductive age than does its light-colored kin.

More will be said later about the twin features of constancy and change in the hereditary material. For present purposes, they can be summarized in the following way:

DNA is a storehouse of patterns for all heritable traits. Mutations introduce variations in the patterns. The environment—internal and external—is the testing ground for the combination of patterns that come to be expressed in each individual.

DIVERSITY IN FORM AND FUNCTION

Until now, we have focused on the unity of life. We have suggested that all living things are linked together, in origins and organization, through the properties of matter and energy; that they all rely on metabolic and homeostatic processes; and that they have the same molecular basis of inheritance. These are fairly recent ideas. Before refinements in microscopy and the emergence of molecular biology, there was no reason to suspect that all living things hold these characteristics in common. What *was* apparent, and difficult to explain, was the tremendous sweep of life's *diversity.* Why is almost every environment on earth host to an astonishing array of different organisms? Before offering a possible answer to this question, let's briefly consider some aspects of diversity in two entirely different settings.

The Tropical Reef

Imagine yourself exploring a tropical reef, of the sort shown in Figures 1.5 and 1.6. Long ago, small animals called corals began to grow and reproduce beneath the warm,

Figure 1.6 Who eats whom on the reef. (**a**) Crown-of-thorns, a sea star that feasts on tiny corals. (**b**) Sea anemone, an animal with weapon-studded tentacles, which ensnare tiny animals floating past. (**c**) Sponges, with pores opened toward the oncoming food-laden currents. (**d**) Clownfish, curiously at home above the mouth of a sea anemone—a mouth through which other kinds of edible fish quickly disappear. (**e**) Green algae, plants that are food for various reef organisms. (**f**) Red algae, food for various animals (but not for this chambered nautilus, a shelled animal that swims expertly after shrimp and other prey). (**g**) A school of goatfish, which feed on small,

spineless animals on the sea floor. Goatfish are tasty to humans, also to large fish. (**h**) Some fish are not on the general menu. Here, a blue wrasse safely picks off and dines on parasites that prey on this large predatory fish. (**i**) Stone crab. Depending on the species, crabs eat plants, animals, and organic remains. The moray (**l**) prefers meat. (**j**) Lion fish, with its fanned, poison-tipped spines warning away intruders. (**k**) Find the scorpion fish—a dangerous animal that lies camouflaged and motionless on the sea bottom, the better to surprise unsuspecting prey.

All photographs Douglas Faulkner

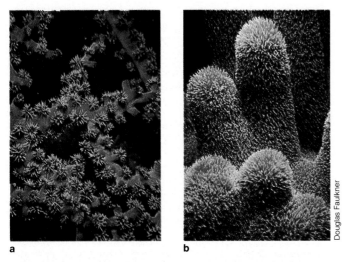

Douglas Faulkner

a   b

Figure 1.7 Two of the master builders of reefs: (**a**) green tube coral and (**b**) pillar coral, with individual animals sending out tentacles from their chambers.

clear nearshore waters (Figure 1.7). They left behind their skeletons as a foundation for more corals to build upon. As skeletons and residues accumulated, the reef grew. All the while, tides and currents carved ledges and caverns into it. Today, the reef's spine can be decked out with any number of *750 different kinds* of corals. Corals are colorful, soft or stonelike animals living together as colonies shaped like staghorns, domes, brains, flowers, mushrooms, cabbages, folded draperies, and fans. Plants called red algae typically encrust the coral foundation. In shallow waters behind the reef, red algae give way to blue-green forms. Many small transparent animals feed on algae and other plants. These animals in turn are food for still larger animals, including some of the world's *20,000 different kinds* of fishes. All about are predatory sea anemones, each having a mouth fringed with weapon-studded tentacles that capture smaller fish. Yet, hovering over the tentacles *is* a certain kind of fish! It is as edible as most others, but somehow it is not recognized as prey. The fish moves away, captures food, and returns to the anemone's tentacles—which give it protection from predators. The anemone eats food scraps that fall from the mouth of the fish. These two kinds of animals are, in effect, allies: one receives protection, the other receives food (Figure 1.6d).

The reef is also home for different kinds of sea stars. When feeding, a sea star extends its stomach outside its body, into coral chambers. Each chamber resident is digested in place before the stomach is pulled out. When sea stars reproduce, millions of larvae emerge and feed on microscopic algae. Then, as the larvae grow, they become food for the meat-eating corals! It is the corals that now grow and reproduce. In time they repopulate the reef regions that the earlier generation of sea stars had stripped clean. Sea star larvae that do escape grow to become diner instead of dinner, and thereby initiate a new cycle of death and life.

The Savanna

Clearly, reef organisms differ from one another in appearance and behavior. However, before speculating on what could account for the diversity, imagine yourself in another setting to see whether a comparison yields any similarities or differences that might provide added insight. In the shadow of Kilimanjaro, a volcanic peak rising high above the edge of the East African Rift Valley, grasslands sweep out to the northeast. This is the African savanna, a region of warm grasslands punctuated with scattered stands of shrubs and trees (Figure 1.8). More large ungulates (hoofed, plant-eating mammals) live here than anywhere else. One form, the giraffe, browses on leaves some five meters above the ground, far beyond the reach of other ungulates. Another form is the Cape buffalo (Figure 1.9). An adult male can weigh a ton, it has formidable horns, and its behavior is unpredictable. It is rarely troubled by predators. Other forms include zebra and impala—both smaller, more vulnerable, and more abundant than Cape buffalo. They are constantly troubled by such predators as lions and cheetahs. Their remains (as well as remains of lions and cheetahs) are picked over by scavengers—hyenas, jackals, vultures, and marabou storks (Figure 1.10).

Buffalo, zebra, impala, rhinoceros, giraffe—these and *eighty-five other kinds* of large, plant-eating animals live in the immense valley, as do different kinds of animals that feed on them. They exist side by side in time, moving westward, southward, and back again as dry seasons follow rains, as scorched earth gives way to new plant growth.

A Definition of Diversity

What tentative conclusions might be drawn from the preceding comparison of diversity in the reef and the savanna? One thing their diverse occupants have in common is specialization in "who eats whom," beginning with plants and proceeding through different forms of animals that eat the plants and one another. In fact, you could spend years observing organisms in any setting, at the microscopic as well as the macroscopic level, and you would find that they speak eloquently of the same challenge. *All organisms must*

Figure 1.8 The East African Rift Valley, some 6,400 kilometers (4,000 miles) long. The sparsely wooded grasslands in this valley are home for a diverse array of animal life and, as you will read in later chapters, were the probable birthplace of the human species.

be equipped to obtain a share of available resources. In large part, diversity in form, function, and behavior represents specialized ways to get and use resources—and to avoid becoming a resource for some other organism. In light of this observation, let us now address the question of how this diversity could have come about.

Since the time of origin, living things have required a constant supply of energy and materials. Think about the times when you yourself have encountered not abundance but shortages (of water, for instance, or gasoline, electricity, or lettuce). In the past, as today, resources were not necessarily abundant. More frequently than not, *members of every group of organisms must have been demanding a share of limited resources.* Imagine, next, that *variant* members occasionally appeared (perhaps through DNA mutations). Some variant forms might have been better equipped for getting a share of resources. Some might have been better equipped for

responding to predators, prey, or inadvertent allies around them. Accordingly, they would have tended to be the ones that survived and reproduced. Through reproduction, successful variations would have been perpetuated more than others. There would have been *natural selection,* within the group, of those individuals better adapted to prevailing conditions.

This line of thought amounts to one view of a main road to diversity. Other roads opened up also, as you will read in later chapters. Whatever the specific pathways taken, a strong argument can be made for the following:

Diversity is the sum total of variations in form, functioning, and behavior that have accumulated in different lines of organisms. These variations generally are adaptive to prevailing conditions or were once adaptive to conditions that existed in the past.

a

b

c

Figure 1.9 A sampling of the ninety kinds of large plant-eating animals that live in the savanna—a clear example of diversity in a single environment. (**a**) A herd of Cape buffalo. Imagine yourself a predator this close to the herd and you get an idea of one of the benefits of group living. (**b**) Zebra mother and offspring. (**c**) Male and female impala on the alert, ready to take cover in the nearby woods. (**d**) The rhinoceros, another formidably decked-out plant eater. (**e**) The giraffe, browsing on vegetation high up.

d

e

a

Norman Myers / Bruce Coleman Inc.

Figure 1.10 Predators and scavengers of the savanna. (**a**) An adult lioness standing over a fresh kill. These large cats stalk the herds at dusk or afterward, typically concealing themselves in dense or low-lying vegetation. (**b**) Vultures, together with marabou storks, feed on locusts, small birds, and small mammals—but they also clean up whatever carrion becomes available to them. In this dual predator-scavenger role, they are like other diverse animals of the savanna, including hyenas and jackals.

ENERGY FLOW AND THE CYCLING OF MATERIAL RESOURCES

The preceding summary statement is based on several assumptions about earth and life history. The geologic record does indeed suggest that there was a time, early in the history of life, when groups of simple organisms floated about independently of one another in shallow lakes or seas. They must have fed on substances already present in the environment (such as simple carbon-containing compounds that had accumulated through volcanic eruptions, erosion, and other geologic processes). Eventually, perhaps by chance when food supplies began to dwindle, they began relying more and more *on each other* as sources of materials and energy. Organisms, too, are stores of energy-rich molecules. Thus, by chance and by necessity, community interactions began and have continued in ever-richer diversity. Today, through these interactions, few energy sources are unex-

Timothy Ransom

ploited. One example will make the point, even though the cast of characters seems of a most improbable sort.

First we have the adult male elephant of the African savanna (Figure 1.11). It stands almost two stories high at the shoulder and weighs more than eight tons. This grazing animal eats quantities of plants, the remains of which leave its body as droppings of considerable size. Appearances to the contrary, locked in the droppings are substantial stores of unused nutrients. With resource availability being what it is, even waste products from one kind of organism are food for another. And so we next have little dung beetles rushing to the scene almost simultaneously with the uplifting of an elephant tail. With great precision they carve out fragments of the dung into round balls. The dung balls are rolled off and buried underground in burrows, where they serve as compact food supplies. In these balls the beetles lay eggs; hence the forthcoming offspring, too, will have a food supply. Also assured is an uncluttered environment. If the dung were to remain aboveground, it would dry out and pile up beneath the hot African sun. Instead, the surface of the land is tidied up, the beetle has its resource, and the remains of the dung are left to decay in burrows—there to enrich the soil that nourishes the plants that sustain (among others) the elephants.

Such interactions of organisms with their environment and with one another are the focus of **ecology.** Everywhere you look you will find different organisms locked into patterns of ecological interdependency. Some patterns may be simple and some complex, and some may seem to border on the outlandish. In almost all cases, the following is true:

Most existing forms of life depend directly or indirectly on one another for materials and energy.

At its most inclusive level, ecological interdependency encompasses the biosphere. With few exceptions, living organisms are linked together by a one-way flow of energy from the sun, and by a cycling of raw materials (such as carbon dioxide and oxygen) on a global scale. Only plants (and some photosynthetic microorganisms) can harness sunlight energy. They use this energy in constructing and maintaining the plant body. Other organisms feed, directly or indirectly, on energy stored in plant parts. Microscopic decomposers obtain energy by breaking apart molecules of plant and animal remains. Through their activity, they make available many vital raw materials for new generations of organisms (Figure 1.12).

Figure 1.11 An interdependency of a most improbable sort, beginning with the plants that feed the elephants (**a**), the dung that leaves the elephant (**b**), the beetles that roll dung balls away and bury them (**c**), ending with the beetle larva (**d**) that hatches in the dung—and the remains of the dung itself, enriching the soil in which plants grow, eventually to feed the elephants.

All photographs Roger K. Burnard

PERSPECTIVE

This chapter has touched on two fundamental characteristics of life: its unity and diversity. All organisms are *alike* in sharing common origins, in adhering to the same rules governing the organization of matter and energy, in relying on metabolic and homeostatic processes, in having the same molecular basis of inheritance. They are also dramatically *unalike* in appearance and behavior.

We have considered only a few representative examples of diversity. There are *several millions* of different kinds of living organisms. Only a fraction have been cataloged and studied. Many millions more once existed and became extinct. Explaining how such an immense amount of diversity arose, and at the same time accounting for its underlying unity, would be a significant accomplishment. In biology, the formulation of such an explanation was indeed accomplished. It is called the principle of evolution by means of natural selection. It is, in fact, the formal statement of the informal picture of natural selection presented earlier in the chapter. The principle was first formulated by Charles Darwin and Alfred Wallace, then later refined (especially during the past few decades). A principle, in essence, is an idea whose validity holds up even when many

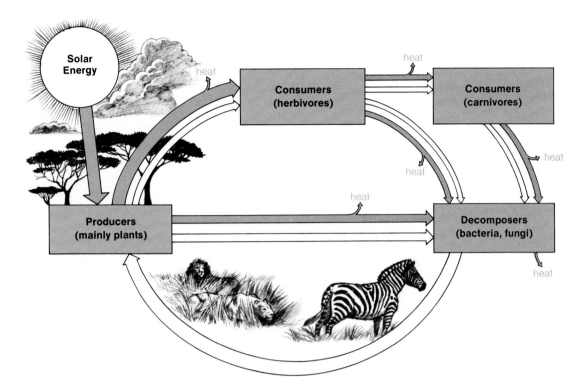

Figure 1.12 Energy flow and the cycling of materials through the biosphere. There is a one-way flow of energy from the sun (gold arrows), through producer organisms (mostly plants), and on through consumers (animals and some microorganisms) and decomposers (bacteria and fungi). The white arrows show the pathways by which raw materials are cycled.

different observations and experiments are used to test it. The Darwin-Wallace principle will be described in the next chapter, together with examples drawn from the extensive observations that led to its formulation. This powerful, integrative concept will provide you with a way of interpreting observations and experimental results described throughout this book. In turn, you will see how observations and experiments from many lines of inquiry—from the molecular level to the biosphere—lend support to the principle itself. It is because of this tremendous depth and range of substantiating investigations and tests that biologists in general consider the principle to be the most logical explanation for the apparent contradiction inherent in life: its unity *and* diversity.

Review Questions

1. For this and subsequent chapters, make a list of the **boldface** terms that occurred in the text. Write a definition next to each, then check it against the one in the text. (You will be using these terms later on.)

2. Why is it difficult to give a simple definition of life?

3. What is meant by "adaptive"? Give some examples of environmental conditions to which plants and animals must be adapted in order to stay alive.

4. If the structure and organization of all things arise from the basic nature of matter and energy, then what is the essential difference between living and nonliving things?

5. Study Figure 1.3. Then, on your own, arrange and define the levels of biological organization. What key concept ties this organization to the history of life, from the time of origin to the present?

6. What is metabolic activity? List some sources of energy that keep your own metabolic machinery operating.

7. What aspect of life is being overlooked when you talk about "the animal" called a frog? (Hint: What's a tadpole?)

8. What is DNA? What is a mutation? Why are most mutations likely to be harmful?

9. Outline the one-way flow of energy and the cycling of materials through the biosphere.

10. Define organismic diversity. Explain what is meant by "the unity and diversity of life." What theory is used in biology to reconcile the seeming paradox in this expression?

2

METHODS AND ORGANIZING
CONCEPTS IN BIOLOGY

Figure 2.1 Galápagos tortoises, one of many diverse species that Charles Darwin encountered on the Galápagos Islands. (The Bettmann Archive Inc.)

The preceding chapter claimed that the way this book is written might help carry your thinking about life to deeper, more organized levels of understanding. By itself, that is a somewhat presumptuous claim, for success depends partly on your willingness to consider using certain principles as a way of observing and interpreting the world of life. In biology, principles are not "laws" that demand your passive, unquestioning acceptance. Rather, you should expect this book to present evidence that supports these principles, then expect to make your *own* decision about whether the evidence seems plausible. All that is expected in return is for you to think with a critical, yet open, mind.

In one respect, this chapter introduces the most sweeping of all biological principles, the principle of evolution. It can be used to find meaning in a tremendous number of observations at all levels of biological organization, from molecules to the biosphere. This principle will be used as a way of explaining material in most of the chapters that follow. Details of the mechanisms by which evolution occurs can be postponed until later.

In another respect, this chapter is about the way that the biologist's mind works—how information is gathered, how it is interpreted, how interpretations are tested and tested again. As you will see, making sense of observations and interpretations is often a chancy thing. There is a saying in biology that *chance favors the prepared mind.* To this we might add, *chance also favors the open mind.* The same can be said of your own likelihood of success not only in your study of biology, but in all of your endeavors.

WHAT DO YOU DO WITH AN OBSERVATION?

Let's begin with the meaning of the word evolution. **Evolution** refers to change through time. In biology, it is said to encompass an ongoing series of environmentally tested changes in the form and function of living things. The process is said to have begun with the origin of life, some $3\frac{1}{2}$ billion years ago. The idea that evolution has been occurring through this nearly incomprehensible span of time is a fairly recent one. No one saw it happen, obviously. For that reason alone, one might just as well say that life has always existed in the forms we see today, that humans and petunias, Cape buffalo and crabs have always been precisely the same since the instant they were created. That is another idea, one that has been around for centuries. Yet the first is accepted as scientific, the other as not scientific, but rather an article of faith.

Why is the distinction made? Both ideas have roots in human abilities basic to all of us. Every human has the potential to make observations about some aspect of the world, then to summarize those observations in a broad statement, or generalization. For instance, you might observe that the sun rose today, just as it did yesterday, and just as it did all yesterdays past. You might therefore generalize that "The sun always rises." The term **inductive reasoning** refers to this process of generalizing from specific observations. Every human also has the potential for **deductive reasoning**—to start from what seems to be a valid generalization and, by reasoning from it, to arrive at a specific conclusion. This is sometimes called the "if-then" process. For instance, you might deduce that "*if* the sun always rises, *then* it will rise tomorrow." The next morning you see the sun rise, and you decide that your conclusion is correct. However, with training in the ways of science, it is more likely that you would not let things go at that. *For scientists go on to test ideas.* They test them under as many related conditions as might shed light on both the starting assumptions and the conclusions reached. Will observations made from different locations prove that the sun will indeed rise tomorrow? Will it "rise" for the Eskimo sledding across the frozen wastes during the time of near-perpetual darkness in the long arctic winter? What is "tomorrow" for an astronaut rapidly orbiting the earth or standing on the moon? Whether observations justify a belief that the sun will rise tomorrow depends on where one is standing—and on how one defines tomorrow.

Induction means generalizing from multiple specific observations. It is only as reliable as the sampling of observations that were made out of all those that could be made.

Deduction means drawing specific conclusions from existing generalizations. It is only as reliable as the starting assumptions on which it is based.

In science, explanations derived from inductive and deductive reasoning are tested. The tests are devised in such a way as to help confirm or disprove the starting assumptions and the conclusions reached.

ON THE "SCIENTIFIC METHOD"

With a scientific approach, an idea acquires credibility when it can be substantiated by investigation and test. There is no such thing as any one scientific method of doing this. But neither are the investigations and tests so loosely conceived that one person's evidence is another person's wishful thinking. Some examples of the rigorous investigative processes that give science its distinct character are described in the *Commentary* on page 22. The processes can be summarized in the following manner, although they are not necessarily employed in this exact order:

---

1. Review available observations. Be sure to note the exact range of conditions under which they have been made.

2. Use trained judgment in selecting and summarizing the relevant observations out of what could be nearly infinite observational trivia.

3. Work out a tentative explanation that seems in line with those observations. A tentative explanation is sometimes called a hypothesis (and sometimes an "educated guess").

4. Devise ways to test whether the explanation is valid. Think through how different but related conditions might affect the test outcome. Be sure the test you devise will address these so-called variables.

5. Carry out the tests. Repeat them as often as necessary to find out whether results consistently will be as predicted.

6. Report objectively on the tests and on the conclusions drawn from them.

There is considerable creativity within the boundaries of these investigative processes. Insights can result from accident, from sudden intuition, or from methodical search. Some individuals adhere to existing procedures, others may improvise as they go. Some tailor their work to reinforce an existing viewpoint, others deliberately take approaches that are likely to challenge prevailing views. No matter what the individual approach, however, the common element in all of science is the process of testing existing knowledge, *with the understanding that knowledge is an open system.*

It is a peculiar scientist who puts forward a closed book of truths, complete and perfect and demanding to be believed, no questions asked. In science, there are no absolute truths. There are only high probabilities that an idea is correct *within the framework of the observations and tests from which it is derived.* Instead of absolutes, there is the **suspended judgment**. This means a hypothesis is tentatively said to be valid in that it is consistent with observations at hand. You won't (or shouldn't) hear a scientist say, "There is no other explanation!" More likely you will hear, "Based on present knowledge, this is our best judgment at the moment."

COMMENTARY

Processes of Scientific Inquiry

William H. Leonard, University of Nebraska, Lincoln

How is it that scientists probe so skillfully into the monument of life and discover so much about its foundations? What is it about their manner of thinking that yields such precise results? Simply put, scientific inquiry routinely depends on a number of processes of gaining information in well-defined, orderly ways. These processes are not difficult to learn. They are not professional secrets. They can be used in searching for answers to questions encountered in everyday life as well as in methodical research.

Although the processes of scientific inquiry can be identified in a number of ways, six will be described:

    Making systematic observations
    Formulating a problem
    Hypothesizing
    Testing the hypothesis through experiments
    Collecting and organizing test results
    Generalizing from the results

Observing refers to ways that sensory systems detect information about the environment. Observations can be made directly, through systems of vision, hearing, taste, olfaction, and touch. They can be made indirectly, through use of special equipment (such as a microscope) that extends the range of perception. With practice, we can become skilled at *making systematic observations*. This means focusing one or more senses on a particular object or event in the environment, and screening out the "background noise" of information that probably has no bearing on our focus. The process of systematic observation helps us be selective about the volume of information our minds must process during the course of inquiry.

Formulating a problem means recognizing that some observations cannot be explained with existing knowledge or that the observation is open to question. Often

this recognition process is not as simple to carry out as it seems. For example, perhaps you've heard that the organic compound DDT is harmful. You might therefore ask, "What are the effects of DDT on living things?" The question is general in its focus, as initial research questions often are. It doesn't address what kinds of effects, how much DDT, or which kinds of organisms. Typically, the question evolves as an investigation unfolds. New observations can lead to recognition of related problems, perhaps very perplexing ones. Hence problem formulation is a process that can be repeated many times over. Such repetition helps sharpen the question being asked; it opens the mind to different aspects of a problem that may require a channeling of research in different directions.

Hypothesizing means putting together a tentative explanation to account for an observation. It is an educated guess—one that the mind puts together on the basis of prior information that it has filed away. This assimilated information comes from reading or discussing literature on studies or experiments dealing with the problem; it comes from firsthand knowledge of the phenomenon being observed.

When a hypothesis is scientific, it is *testable* through experiments. Experiments are devised to test whether predictions that can be derived from the hypothesis are correct. Thus the hypothesis must be constructed so that it provides a framework for stating the results of an experiment. Its content must be more specific than a problem statement, and often it is worded in the negative. Why is this so? Scientists tend to accept tentatively a plausible idea until it is shown to be false. It is difficult to prove experimentally that a hypothesis is true, because its validity would have to be demonstrated for all possible cases and under all possible conditions. That, obviously, is impossible. Scientists therefore continue to test hypotheses by devising experiments that might show them to be false. If they succeed, then the hypothesis must be modified or discarded. That is why hypotheses are expressed in the negative. For example, "DDT concentrations of 0.0001 percent by weight in the food of laboratory rats will not have harmful effects on the maintenance of the rat population over five years." If experiments reveal harmful effects at that dosage, then the hypothesis is not correct, and support is given to the idea that DDT is harmful.

Testing the hypothesis through experiments is at the heart of scientific inquiry. The goal is to control all variables except the one under study. Variables are events or conditions subject to change. For example, variables that are common to many biological experiments are the amount of light, temperature, and moisture. Others are concentrations of substances and numbers of organisms (population density) in a defined space. There are three general categories of variables:

independent variables	_the condition or event under study_
dependent variables	_ones that can possibly change because of the presence of, or change in, an independent variable_
controlled variables	_conditions that could affect the outcome of an experiment but that do not, because they are held constant_

An experimenter observes or manipulates one independent variable at a time, to identify any effects it has on dependent variables. If more than one independent variable were studied simultaneously, it would not be clear which one was responsible for the observed experimental results. For example, suppose you want to determine the relationship between the amount of water in the soil and the rate of growth for a particular plant. You would use several genetically identical specimens of the plant, each in a container of soil of different moisture. Here, the controlled variables would be conditions such as light, temperature, and soil composition. The dependent variable would be plant height as measured over a specified period of time. The one independent variable would be the amount of water in each container.

In one classic experimental design, a population of organisms is divided into two groups. The experimental group is the one subjected to the independent variable;

the control group is not. All other variables are held the same in both groups. Thus, any differences that show up in test results for the two groups can be attributed to the independent variable. The illustration shown below is an example of the use of experimental and control groups.

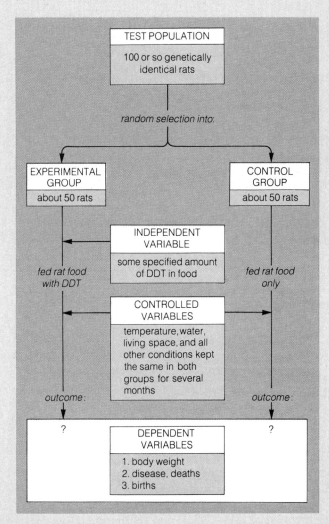

An example of a classic experimental design in biology. The experiment is designed to test the hypothesis that DDT ingested with food will not have harmful effects on laboratory rats over a period of time. With all other variables held constant, test results should refute or support the hypothesis.

This experiment has been used to test the hypothesis that laboratory rats ingesting DDT with normal food will lose weight, show less resistance to disease, and have a lower reproductive rate than rats not ingesting DDT. Notice that the rats were randomly assorted into either the experimental group or the control group. *Randomization* ensures that both groups are representative (or equivalent) samples of the original population. When any test group is not equivalent to a natural population, *sampling error* is introduced into the experiment. Then one could argue that any experimental results were due to differences in the composition of the different test groups, instead of a result of the independent variable.

Collecting and organizing test results is a necessary process in biological experiments. Data tables or graphs are used to organize and display information for analysis. Graphs are especially useful in illustrating trends or patterns. Data analysis is less mechanical and more conceptual than collecting and organizing the information. Often, statistical tests are used to determine if differences between experimental data and control data are *significant* (real) or are likely due only to chance. If it can be argued that the differences are due to chance only, then it can

also be argued that the independent variable had no effect. For example, say that at the end of an experiment on DDT effects, the average adult rat weight was 187.4 grams in the DDT-fed group, and 206.7 grams in the control group. Is this difference significant enough to suggest that there was an actual effect? The use of mathematical tools characteristic of statistical analysis could help in finding an answer.

Generalizing from test results requires careful and objective analysis of the data gathered. Usually, the hypothesis under test is accepted or rejected on the basis of conclusions drawn. A statement is written about what new insights (if any) have been gained into the original problem. Apparent trends are noted when the same data appear in test results gathered over a period of time. Often, further questions and hypotheses are posed in an attempt to guide additional studies of the problem.

Although the processes of inquiry have been described here with reference to biological research, they are applicable to many other endeavors. These processes represent a system of logically and systematically acquiring knowledge. They are eminently useful in any learning and decision-making activities.

Now, sometimes the weight of evidence in favor of a hypothesis is so convincing that the explanation is considered to be a **theory**: a coherent set of ideas that form a general frame of reference for further studies. In science, the word "theory" is not used lightly. It is bestowed only on those explanations that have a high probability of being valid, ones that can be relied upon with considerable confidence. Sometimes the evidence supporting a theory seems so overwhelming that the explanation is further elevated to the status of **principle**: a fundamental doctrine on which other concepts are based or from which they are drawn. Even so, a theory or principle is never entrenched. New observations and new test results may not fit with either one of them, and may call for replacement or modification. Far from being a disaster, such evidence stimulates the development of even more general, more adequate, yet always *revisable* explanations.

Obviously, individual scientists would rather come up with useful explanations than useless ones. However, they must always ask: "Is my explanation consistent with all existing observations and tests of what I hope to explain?" Knowing this, scientists must keep reminding themselves to be objective. This is not to say that all scientists are objective all of the time or even most of the time; no one can lay claim to that. It means only that scientists are expected as individuals to forsake pride and prejudice by testing their own beliefs, even in ways that might prove them wrong. Even if an individual scientist doesn't, or won't, *others will*—for science proceeds as a community that is both cooperative and competitive. There is a sharing of ideas, with the understanding that it is just as important to expose errors as it is to applaud insights.

This call for objectivity strengthens the theories and principles that do emerge from scientific investigations. Yet it also puts limits on the kinds of investigations that can be carried out. Beyond the realm of what can be analyzed with the technology available to us, certain events remain unexplained. Why do we exist, for what purpose? Why does any one of us have to die at one particular moment and not another? Why do we experience melancholy and joy? Why do we sense beauty in some things and recoil in horror from others? Answers to such questions are *subjective*; they come from within, as a consequence of all those variable factors shaping the consciousness of each individual. Because these factors can be infinitely variable, they do not readily lend themselves to scientific analysis.

This is not to say that subjective answers are without value. No human society can function without a shared commitment to standards for making judgments, however subjective they might be. Moral, aesthetic, economic, and philosophical standards vary considerably from one society to the next. But all help guide their members in deciding what is important and good, and what is not. All provide explanations that give meaning to what we observe and what we do.

Occasionally, science stirs up controversy when its investigations explain part of the world that was previously considered beyond natural explanation, or belonging to the supernatural. This is sometimes true when moral codes are interwoven with religious narratives, which grew out of observations by revered ancestors. Questioning some long-standing observation about the natural world may be misinterpreted as questioning morality, even though the two are not even remotely synonymous. Centuries ago, Nicolaus Copernicus analyzed planetary movements and concluded that the earth circles the sun. Today the statement seems obvious enough. Back then, it was heresy. The prevailing belief was that the Creator made the earth (and, by extension, humankind) the immovable center of the universe! Anybody could see the sun rise at one horizon, travel overhead, then set at the opposite horizon; the earth stayed put. Not long afterward a respected scientist, Galileo Galilei, studied the Copernican model of the solar system. He thought it was a good one, and said so. He was forced to retract his statement publicly, on his knees, and put the earth back as the fixed center of things. (Word has it that when he stood up he muttered almost inaudibly, "but it moves nevertheless.")

Today, as then, society has its sets of standards. Today, as then, science might call some aspects of those sets into question, as observations make a little more of the previously unknown explainable. Scientists as a group are no less moral, less lawful, less sensitive, less caring than any other group. They are not necessarily even less subjective. However, there is one additional standard that guides their individual and collective thinking when it comes to their investigations: *The external world, not internal conviction, must form the testing ground for scientific beliefs.*

Systematic observations, hypotheses, predictions, relentless tests—in all these ways, scientific beliefs differ from systems of belief that are based on faith, force, authority, or simple consensus. It is not any "law" that is the focus of biologists. Rather, the focus is on the observations that the "law" attempts to explain. A "law" can be invalidated by new evidence, gathered through ongoing tests and clarification of what those observations really mean.

There are, in the history of science, a few individuals who challenged the long-standing beliefs held not only by society at large but by the scientific community within it. In biology, Charles Darwin and Alfred Wallace are among them. It will be useful to trace their story and its antecedents. Doing so will give insight into why the principle of evolution is considered to be one of the most powerful integrative concepts of our time. Tracing their story will also show that the similarity between their separate journeys was not so much specific training as it was an underlying attitude. Both were willing to observe, gather evidence, and test their ideas—no matter how unsettling the outcome might be—with the reasoning that is the hallmark of the human species *and the discipline that is the hallmark of science.*

EMERGENCE OF EVOLUTIONARY THOUGHT

More than two thousand years ago, the seeds of biological inquiry were taking hold among the Hellenes, a people now known as the ancient Greeks. This was a time when popular belief held that supernatural beings intervened directly in human affairs. The gods, for example, were said to cause a common ailment known as the sacred disease. Yet from a physician of the school of Hippocrates, these thoughts come down to us:

It seems to me that the disease called sacred . . . has a natural cause, just as other diseases have. Men think it divine merely because they do not understand it. But if they called everything divine that they did not understand, there would be no end of divine things! . . . If you watch these fellows treating the disease, you see them use all kinds of incantations and magic—but they are also very careful in regulating diet. Now if food makes the disease better or worse, how can they say it is the gods who do this? . . . It does not really matter whether you call such things divine or not. In Nature, all things are alike in this, in that they can be traced to preceding causes. —On the Sacred Disease (400 B.C.)

Such was the spirit of the times; such was the commitment to finding natural explanations for observable events. Into this intellectual climate, Aristotle was born.

Aristotle was a naturalist who loved the world around him, and who described it in excellent detail. He had no reference books or instruments to guide him in formulating his descriptions, for the foundation of biological science in the Western world *began* with the great thinkers of this age. Yet here was a man who was no mere collector of random bits of information. *In his descriptions we have evidence of a mind perceiving connections between observations and constructing theories for explaining the order of things.* When Aristotle began his studies, he believed (as did others) that each kind of living thing was distinct from all others. Later he began to wonder about bizarre forms that could not be readily classified. In structure or function, they so resembled other forms that their place in nature seemed blurred. (For example, to Aristotle some sponges looked like plants, but they were animals in their feeding habits.) He came to view nature as proceeding ever so gradually from lifeless matter through ever more complex forms of animal life. This view is reflected in his model of biological organization (Figure 2.2), the first such theoretical framework to appear in the history of biology.

In the fourteenth century, this line of thought had become transformed into a rigid view of life. A great Chain of Being was seen to extend from the lowest forms, to humans, to spiritual beings. Each kind of being, or **species** as it was called, was seen to have a separate, fixed place in the divine order of things. Each had remained unchanged since the time of creation, a permanent link in the chain. Scholars believed they had only to discover, name, and describe all the links, and the meaning of life would be revealed to them. Contradictory views were not encouraged; scientific inquiry had become channeled into the encyclopedic assembly of facts.

As long as the world of living things meant mostly those forms existing in Europe, the task seemed manageable. With the global explorations of the sixteenth century, however, "the world" of life expanded enormously. Naturalists were soon overwhelmed by descriptions of thousands upon thousands of plants and animals discovered in Asia, Africa, the Pacific islands, and the New World. Some specimens appeared to be quite similar to common European forms, but some were clearly unique to different lands. How could these organisms be classified? The naturalist Thomas Moufet, in attempting to sort through the bewildering array, simply gave up and recorded such gems as this chaotic description of grasshoppers and locusts: "Some are green, some black, some blue. Some fly with one pair of wings; others with more; those that have no wings they leap; those that cannot fly or leap they walk; some have long shanks, some shorter. Some there are that sing, others are silent. . . ." It was not exactly a time of subtle distinctions.

Linnean System of Classification

The first widely accepted method of classification is attributed to Carl von Linné, now known by his latinized name, Linnaeus. This man was an eighteenth-century naturalist whose enthusiasm knew no bounds. He sent ill-prepared students around the world to gather specimens of plants and animals for him, and is said to have lost a third of his collectors to the rigors of their expeditions. Although perhaps not very commendable as a student advisor, Linnaeus did go on to develop the **binomial system of nomenclature**. With this system, each organism could be classified by assigning it a Latin name consisting of two parts.

For instance, *Ursus maritimus* is the scientific name for the polar bear. The first name refers to the genus (plural, genera), and the first letter of the name is capitalized. Distinct but obviously similar species are grouped in the same

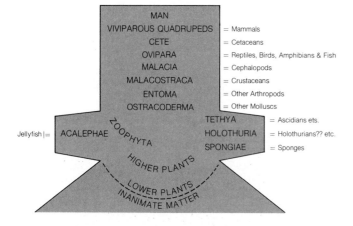

Figure 2.2 Scala Naturae—Aristotle's "ladder of life," the prototype of modern classification schemes. (From Singer, *A History of Biology*)

Table 2.1   Linnean System of Classification

Category	Includes:
Species	All organisms with distinct features that distinguish them from all other organisms
Genus	Collection of related species that share some features but are distinct from one another in some other features
Family	All closely related genera
Order	All closely related families
Class	All related orders
Phylum (or division, in botanical schemes)	All related classes
Kingdom	All related phyla; the most inclusive category of all

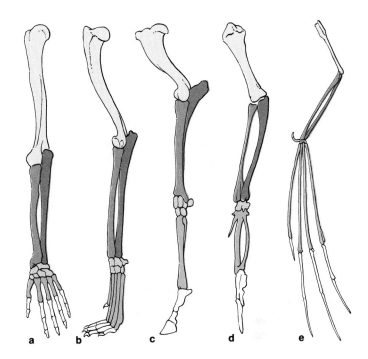

Figure 2.3 Homologous structures. Shown here, a forelimb from (**a**) a human, (**b**) a dog, (**c**) a horse, (**d**) a bird, and (**e**) a bat. The drawings are not to scale relative to one another. The homologous structures are shaded the same way from one animal to the next.

genus. For example, other bears are *Ursus arctos,* the Alaskan brown bear, and *Ursus americanus,* the black bear. The second, uncapitalized name is the species epithet. The species epithet is never used without the full or abbreviated generic name preceding it, for it can also be the second name of a species found in an entirely different genus. The Atlantic lobster, for instance, is called *Homarus americanus.* (Hence one would not order *americanus* for dinner unless one is willing to take what one gets.)

The binomial system was the heart of a scheme that was thought to mirror the patterns of links in the great Chain of Being. This classification scheme was based on perceived similarities or differences in physical features (coloration, number of legs, body size, and so forth). It eventually became structured in the manner shown in Table 2.1.

In retrospect, we can say that the Linnean system provided the basis for the first widely accepted, shared language for naming and classifying organisms. It came at a time when ordering was desperately needed. Yet we must also say that the Linnean system reinforced the prevailing view—that species were distinctly unique *and unchanging* kinds of organisms, each locked in place in the Chain of Being. To this day, the use of rigid categories for classifying organisms works in subtle ways on our perceptions of the diversity of living things.

Challenges to the Theory of Unchanging Life

By the late eighteenth and early nineteenth centuries, the somewhat passive cataloging of life was disrupted. Puzzling data were emerging from comparative anatomy (the dissection and comparison of body structure and patterning in major groups of organisms). For example, most mammals have two forelimbs. Whales have two flippers, humans have two arms, bats have two wings, and so forth. When early anatomists analyzed the forelimbs of different mammals, they found them to be **homologous structures**. Such structures develop in remarkably similar ways in embryos, they are constructed of the same kinds of materials, and they have the same general position in the body (Figure 2.3). At the same time, it was evident that there were variations in the size and shape of those structures, and in how they were put to use (as in flying versus swimming). What meaning could be assigned to the unmistakable homology? What could account for variations on the same body plan?

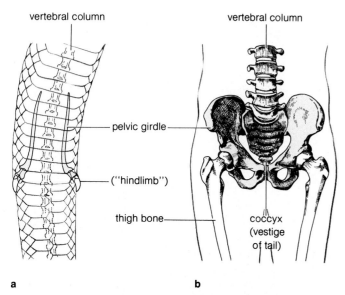

vertebral column

pelvic girdle

("hindlimb")

thigh bone

vertebral column

coccyx
(vestige
of tail)

a   b

Figure 2.4 Vestigial structures. (**a**) Vestiges of a pelvic girdle in a python. Small "hindlimbs" protrude through the skin on the underside, or ventral surface. (**b**) Pelvic girdle in humans.

One explanation was that, at the time of creation, there was no need to come up with completely new body patterns for all organisms when some patterns were so perfect and worked so well. If that were true, though, what could explain the discovery of **vestigial structures**—body parts that have no apparent function at all? For example, snakes and humans belong to the major group called vertebrates (animals with backbones). Unlike humans, snakes have no limbs. However, if snakes were created in a state of limbless perfection, why do some have what looks like remnants of a pelvic girdle? A pelvic girdle (Figure 2.4) is the set of bones to which hindlimbs attach! As another example, within the human body, at the tip of the backbone, anatomists discovered bony parts that looked exactly like those in an animal tail. What would the remnants of a tail be doing in a perfectly constructed human body? It was not a time of easy answers.

Also puzzling were data emerging from studies of the world distribution of plants and animals. For instance, naturalists found that marsupials (pouched mammals such as kangaroos) were rare in most places but abounded in Australia. Cactus plants were observed in North and South

American deserts, yet were nowhere to be seen in Australian and Asian deserts. If all species had been created at the same time in the same place, as most scholars then believed, *then how could so many be restricted to one part of the world or another?*

In the late eighteenth century, two hypotheses were advanced to explain these diverse observations. Both are credited to the zoologist Georges-Louis Leclerc de Buffon. If there had been only a single center of creation, thought Buffon, then species spreading out from it would have been stopped, sooner or later, by mountain barriers or oceans. What if there had been several "centers of creation"? *Perhaps the origin of species had been spread out in space.* In addition to this hypothesis, Buffon's work in zoology led him to suggest that species might not have been created in a perfect state. For instance, he saw the pig as "not formed on an original perfect plan, since it . . . has parts which can never come into action, as lateral toes, the bones of which are perfect, yet useless." *Perhaps species had become modified over time.*

Was there any evidence in support of these two hypotheses? Buffon thought there might be, with respect to fossils that occurred in different layers of the earth. Fossils had been known from antiquity, when they were considered mysteriously marked stones. Eventually they came to be accepted as the remains of once-living things. Also, fossils of different types were buried in what apparently was a progression of distinct layers under surface rocks and soil. In underlying, older rock layers, fossils of marine organisms were relatively simple in structure. In layers above them, fossils of similar structure showed more complexity. Finally, in the uppermost (most recently deposited) layers, they closely resembled living marine organisms. Some naturalists interpreted these patterns to be a record of a succession of changes in various forms of life. The time required for such changes and the reasons for change were not known— *but the very concept of change was at variance with the concept of the fixity of species.*

Many naturalists now tried to reconcile the new observations of changing fossil patterns with a traditional conceptual framework that did not allow for change. The nineteenth-century anatomist Georges Cuvier had spent twenty-five years comparing fossils with living organisms. He did not deny that there were changes in the fossil record and that the changes were somehow linked to earth history. However, his explanation was one of **catastrophism,** which can be summarized in the following way. There was only one time of creation, said Cuvier, which had populated the world with all species. Many had been destroyed in a global catastrophe. The few survivors repopulated the world. It was not that they were *new* species. Naturalists simply hadn't got around to discovering earlier fossils of them, fossils that *would* date to the time of creation. Another catastrophe wiped out more species and led to repopulation by the survivors, and so on until the most recent catastrophe—after which emerged the best of all possible survivors, Man. However, investigations never turned up the kinds of fossils needed to support Cuvier's explanation. Rather, they have turned up considerable fossil evidence against it (Chapter Thirty-One).

Lamarck's Theory of Evolution

One of Cuvier's contemporaries, Jean-Baptiste Lamarck, viewed the fossil record differently. Lamarck believed that life had been created in the past in a simple state. He believed further that it gradually improved and changed into the levels of organization we see today. The force for change was a built-in drive for perfection, up the Chain of Being. The drive was centered in nerve fibers, which directed "fluida" (vaguely defined substances) to body parts in need of change (in a manner unspecified). For instance, suppose the ancestor of the modern giraffe was a short-necked animal. Pressed by the need to find food, this animal constantly stretched its neck to browse on leaves beyond the reach of other animals. Stretching directed fluida to its neck, which made the neck permanently longer. The slightly stretched neck was bestowed on offspring, which stretched their necks also. Thus generations of animals desiring to reach higher leaves led to the modern giraffe. Conversely, a vestigial structure was an organ no longer being exercised enough. It was withering away from disuse, and each newly withered form was passed on to offspring. Such was the Lamarckian hypothesis of **inheritance of acquired characteristics**—the notion that changes acquired during an individual's life are brought about by environmental pressures and internal "desires," and that offspring inherit the changes.

Lamarck's contemporaries considered the hypothesis a wretched piece of science, largely because Lamarck habitually made sweeping assertions but saw no need to support them with observations and tests. In retrospect, perhaps we can find kinder words for the man. His work in zoology was respected. And he did indeed put together a foundation for an evolutionary theory: *All species are interrelated, they change through time, and the environment is a factor in that change.* It was his misfortune that he made some crucial observations but put them together in an explanation that was neither convincing in the way it was presented nor, in times to follow, supportable by tests.

Courtesy George P. Darwin

Figure 2.5 Charles Darwin, at about the time he accepted the position of ship's naturalist aboard H.M.S. *Beagle.*

EMERGENCE OF THE PRINCIPLE OF EVOLUTION

Naturalist Inclinations of the Young Darwin

Charles Darwin (Figure 2.5) was to develop an evolutionary theory that has had repercussions through the whole of Western civilization. Surely his early environment influenced that destiny. His grandfather, a physician and naturalist, was one of the first to propose that all organisms are related by descent. Darwin's family was wealthy, which meant he had the means for indulging his interests. When Darwin was eight years old, he was an enthusiastic but haphazard shell collector. At ten, he focused on the habits of insects and birds. At fifteen, he found schoolwork boring compared with the pursuit of solitude, hunting, fishing, and observing the natural world.

When the time came for college, Darwin attempted to study medicine. He abandoned the study upon realizing he never could practice surgery on his fellow humans, given the crude and painful procedures available. For a while he followed his own inclinations toward natural history. Then his father suggested that a career as a clergyman might be more to his liking, so Darwin packed for Cambridge. His

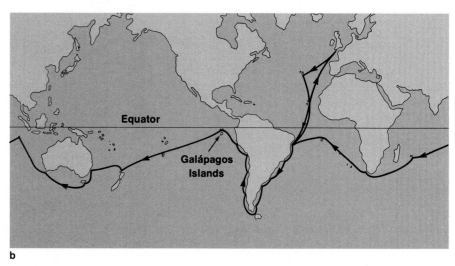

The Bettmann Archive Inc.

a

b

Figure 2.6 (**a**) The five-year voyage of the *Beagle,* shown as it appeared in the Straits of Magellan. (**b**) The Galápagos Islands, about 1,000 kilometers (600 miles) off the coast of Ecuador, support a number of unique plants and animals. The diversity of life on these isolated islands profoundly influenced Darwin's thinking.

grades were good enough to earn him a degree. But most of his time was spent with faculty members with leanings toward natural history. It was the botanist John Henslow who perceived and respected Darwin's real ambitions. It was Henslow who arranged for him to take part in a training expedition led by an eminent geologist. It was Henslow who, at the pivotal moment when Darwin had to decide on a career, arranged that he be offered the position of ship's naturalist aboard H.M.S. *Beagle.*

Voyage of the *Beagle*

The *Beagle* was about to sail to South America to complete earlier work on mapping the coastline. The prolonged stops at islands, near mountain ranges, and along rivers would present many opportunities to study diverse forms of life. Almost from the start of the voyage, the young man who had hated work suddenly began working with enthusiasm, despite lack of adequate training. Throughout the journey to South America, he collected and examined marine life. And he read—particularly Henslow's parting gift, the first volume of Charles Lyell's *Principles of Geology.*

Amplifying earlier ideas of the geologist James Hutton, Lyell argued that processes now molding the earth's surface—volcanic activity, the slow erosive force of wind and water, the gradual uplifting of mountain ranges—had also

been at work in the past. This concept is called **uniformitarianism.** It called into question prevailing ideas about the age of the earth. (For example, Jewish calendar-years were based on the concept that the earth was less than 6,000 years old.) Lyell's concept convincingly extended earth history back in time. Known geologic processes would require not a few thousand years but millions of years to reshape the landscape—*time enough, then, for species to evolve in ever richer diversity.*

Darwin began to see the implications of this concept on the Galápagos Islands, which arose long ago as volcanoes, devoid of life, from the seafloor (Figure 2.6). Many diverse organisms lived on those isolated islands. For example, different islands or island clusters were home to different finch species. Each species had a distinct beak that seemed related to particular kinds of food in the environment (Figure 2.7). Yet every species was similar to a single finch species that Darwin had observed back on the South American mainland. Later it would occur to him that the finches might have descended from a single ancestral species, which winds might have carried over to the Galápagos. If there had been time enough for various descendants of the original stock to evolve—and Lyell's work strongly suggested that there had been—then what *processes* brought about their evolution?

Certhidia olivacea
Probing bill, insect eater
Feeds in trees

Camarhynchus pallidus
Probing bill, insect eater
Uses twig or cactus spine
to probe insects from cactus

Camarhynchus heliobates
Grasping bill, insect eater
Feeds in trees

Camarhynchus crassirostris
Crushing bill, cactus seed eater

b

Figure 2.7 Examples of variation in beak shape among different species of Darwin's finches, as correlated with feeding habits.

Darwin and Wallace: The Theory Takes Form

The *Beagle* returned to England in 1836, after nearly five years at sea. In the years to follow, Darwin's writings established him as a respected figure in natural history. All the while, his consuming interest was the "species problem." *By what processes do species evolve?* In seeking an answer, Darwin patiently assembled his own data and examined other available research. Then he systematically analyzed the clues and difficulties they presented. *Whenever he developed an idea for explaining certain observations, he spent as much time trying to disprove it as he spent trying to support it.* Darwin wanted "to understand or explain whatever I have observed, to group all facts under some general laws. . . . I have steadily endeavored to keep my mind free so as to give up any hypothesis, however much beloved . . . as soon as facts are shown to be opposed to it." His attempt to be objective about his own work was admirable. The outcome would be impressive documentation for his concept of evolution.

Given a problem so complex, Darwin turned to a simpler question. Among domesticated animals, how do various **breeds** (varieties within a species) originate? Domesti-

cated pigeons proved illuminating. Darwin first determined that none of the flamboyant varieties was found in the wild, except for some that recently had escaped captivity. Then he observed that one pigeon species, the wild rock dove, shares certain features with all of these breeds (Figure 2.8). Darwin concluded that the wild rock dove might have been their common ancestor.

If the rock dove were the common ancestral species, how had humans molded it into diverse breeds? Darwin saw that the process was one of *selection* of the individual having certain traits, by promoting its reproduction more than others. To begin with, rarely are any two individuals exactly alike in an animal or plant population. (A population, recall, is a group of individuals of the same kind occupying a given area at a given time.) The members vary in such traits as size, form, coloration, and behavior. Animal or plant breeders selectively breed individuals having the traits they desire. For instance, in dairy-cattle farming, bulls that have sired excellent milk-producing daughters are favored. They are bred with cows that also have a high milk production rate. In this manner, selective breeding promotes the likelihood that each generation will have more good producers than poor ones.

Figure 2.8 A few examples of the more than 300 varieties of domesticated pigeons. Such forms are thought to have been derived, by selective breeding, from the wild rock dove.

Darwin reasoned that selection processes must also be at work in the natural world. He gained insight into what one process might be when he read *Essay on the Principle of Population* by Thomas Malthus, a clergyman and economist. Malthus had stated that, in the absence of controls, any population will outgrow its resources (Chapter Thirty-Six). When that happens, individuals must compete for what is available. This statement brought the meaning of Darwin's own observations into sharp focus. If there were a struggle for existence, then better-adapted individuals would have a competitive edge in surviving and reproducing. Differences in an ability to compete could lead to an accumulation of certain traits and elimination of others—a population could change. Darwin's view of how such adaptations came into being is known as the **theory of natural selection.** The theory is expressed here in modern form:

1. In any population, more offspring tend to be produced than can survive to reproductive age.

2. Members of the population vary in form and behavior. Much of the variation is heritable.

3. Some varieties of heritable traits are more *adaptive* than others: they improve chances of surviving and reproducing under prevailing environmental conditions.

4. Because bearers of adaptive traits have a greater chance of reproducing, their offspring tend to make up an increasingly greater proportion of the reproductive base for each new generation. This tendency is called *differential reproduction.*

5. *"Differential reproduction" is natural selection.* Adaptive forms of traits show up (are selected for) with increased frequency in a population, because their bearers contribute proportionally more offspring to succeeding generations.

Darwin proposed that the pace of this adaptive process was extremely slow. Even so, he stated that "I can see no limit to the amount of change, to the . . . coadaptations between all organic beings, one with another and with their physical conditions of life, which may have been effected in the long course of time through nature's power of selection." With enough time, the variations accumulated could so depart from the parent stock that at some point, descendants might even be considered a distinct new species. In Darwin's view, *natural selection could bring about evolution within species, as well as the origin of new species.*

Later chapters will go into examples of natural selection and other mechanisms of evolution. For now, we can limit ourselves to Darwin's conclusions: (1) evolution of species is gradual; (2) it proceeds through natural selection; and (3) selection does not *create* a new type of individual, but rather selective agents in the environment work on *existing* individuals that may vary in any number of traits.

After formulating his concept of evolution, Darwin continued his research. He gathered notes and sifted his data for flaws in his reasoning. Then, in 1858, his careful search was interrupted. He received a paper from Alfred Wallace outlining the very theory that he had been developing for two decades! Like Darwin, Wallace was a respected naturalist (Figure 2.9). He had thirteen years of research in South America and the Malay Archipelago to his credit. Like Darwin, he had been impressed with the writings of Malthus. Whereas Darwin had been working to document his ideas for more than twenty years, the concept of evolution by natural selection flashed into Wallace's mind and he wrote out his ideas in two days. This was the paper he sent to Darwin.

Despite the shock of seeing his theory presented by someone else, Darwin sent Wallace's paper at once to colleagues, suggesting that it be published. However, Darwin's colleagues would not let him set aside the years that had gone into his own development of the theory. They prevailed on him to gather his notes into a paper that could be presented simultaneously with Wallace's. In 1858, both papers were presented to the Linnean Society, along with a letter Darwin had written several years earlier outlining the main points of the theory. The next year, Darwin published his book *On the Origin of Species by Means of Natural Selection.*

Many versions of the Darwin-Wallace story emphasize the controversy the theory created in some quarters. However, Darwin's evidence was so detailed, and presented with such care, that the argument for evolving life was accepted almost at once by most naturalists and scholars from other disciplines. As the naturalist Thomas Huxley commented, the only rebuttal to the concept of evolution is a better explanation of the evidence—something which has yet to appear.

Ironically, even though the idea of evolution had at last gained respectability, almost seventy years would pass before most of the scientific community would agree with Darwin and Wallace's remarkable insight—that natural selection is a means by which evolution occurs. Not before then would it become clear that their explanation holds under many different tests, on many different levels of biological organization. In the meantime, their names would be associated mostly with the concept that life evolves—something that others had proposed before them.

American Museum of Natural History

Figure 2.9 Alfred Wallace. Although Darwin and Wallace had worked independently, they both arrived at the same concept of natural selection. Darwin tried to insist that Wallace be credited as originator of the theory, being the first to circulate a report of his work. Wallace refused; he would not ignore the decades of work Darwin had invested in accumulating supporting evidence.

AN EVOLUTIONARY VIEW OF DIVERSITY

With widespread acceptance of evolutionary thought, fresh winds began blowing through the rigid framework of classification systems. It was not that the systems themselves were swept away. Such schemes were and continue to be useful ways of storing and retrieving information about the diversity of life. The difference became one of identifying evolutionary links between past and present species. All those cataloged species were not necessarily exact copies of their ancestors; and their descendants might not be exact copies of the current species form. There was an ongoing history of life here—a history of change.

Ernst Haeckel was the first to apply the emergent evolutionary theory to classification schemes. He hypothesized that existing species could be used as models for

Table 2.2	Classification Scheme Used in This Book*
Kingdom	General Characteristics
Monera	Single cells. Some are autotrophs (able to build own food from simple raw materials, such as carbon dioxide and water, using sunlight or other environmental energy source). Some are heterotrophs (depend on tissues, remains, or wastes of other living things for food). Cell body is prokaryotic: it has no true nucleus or other membrane-bound internal compartment. *Representatives:* archaebacteria, eubacteria (including the cyanobacteria, or blue-green algae)
Protista	Single cells. Includes autotrophs and heterotrophs. Cell body is eukaryotic: it has a true nucleus and other membrane-bound internal compartments. *Representatives:* golden algae, diatoms, amoebas, sporozoans, ciliates
Fungi	Multicelled. Heterotrophs. Most rely on digestion outside the fungal body, then absorption (they first secrete substances that break down food, then breakdown products are absorbed across the fungal cell wall). All eukaryotic. *Representatives:* slime molds, true fungi
Plantae	Multicelled. Autotrophs. With few exceptions, plants build all of their own food through photosynthesis. All eukaryotic. *Representatives:* red algae, brown algae, green algae, mosses, horsetails, lycopods, ferns, seed plants (such as cycads, ginkgo, conifers, flowering plants)
Animalia	Multicelled. Heterotrophs of varied sorts, including plant eaters, meat eaters, parasites. All eukaryotic. *Representatives:* sponges, jellyfishes, flatworms, roundworms, segmented worms, mollusks, arthropods (such as insects and lobsters), echinoderms (such as sea stars), chordates (fishes, amphibians, reptiles, birds, mammals)

*This scheme is expanded upon in Unit Seven.

forms that lived long ago. From the simplest of these forms, there evolved more specialized branchings, much as a tree branches increasingly over time. From simple ancestral roots, evolutionary processes gave rise to different lineages specialized in form, function, and behavior. One "family tree" of life, which Haeckel presented in 1874, was typical of the models that were developed. In this tree, groups of organisms (phyla, classes, and some orders) were ranked hier-

archically according to observed similarities and differences among existing organisms, used as models for the past.

Today, classification schemes are still based on observed characteristics of existing organisms, but particular characteristics are now interpreted as being indicative of different lines of descent. A *genus* is now said to include only those species related by descent from a fairly recent, common ancestral form. A *family* includes all genera related by descent from a more remote common ancestor, and so on up to the highest (and most inclusive) levels of classification: *phylum* and *kingdom*. A scheme that takes into account the evolution of major lines of descent is known as a natural system, or **phylogenetic system of classification**.

Constructing phylogenetic systems of classification is not easy. Over time, environmental pressures and rates of evolution have not been the same from group to group. Also, the picture of interrelationships is not yet complete. Details must come from the fossil record, biochemistry, genetics, comparative anatomy, reproductive biology, behavior and ecology, geology, and geography. Some information, such as parts of the fossil record, is lost forever because of past upheavals in the earth's crust. Even so, now that we have a better idea of where to look, and of what we are looking for, many of the gaps are filling in fast.

Regardless of its strengths, no classification system should be viewed as *the* system. As long as there are observations to be made, different people will interpret relationships among organisms in different ways. Some group all forms of life into two kingdoms (plants and animals). Others group them into as many as twenty. In this book we use a modified version of Robert Whittaker's five-kingdom system. This version is summarized in Table 2.2 and sketched in Figure 2.10. Like other systems, it helps summarize current knowledge about life's diversity. It, too, is subject to modification as new evidence turns up.

In this model, organisms are assigned to kingdoms called the Monera, Protista, Fungi, Plantae, and Animalia. How did these kingdoms evolve? At least 3.5 billion years ago, the first cells were developing. They must have been much simpler than the one-celled bacteria found in the kingdom **Monera**. These bacteria have fairly complex systems for extracting energy from raw materials, and their body parts (such as cell walls) depend on systems for building some fairly complex molecules. Their ancestors were probably scavengers of simple compounds that natural geologic processes had produced. Existing bacterial lines are grouped as eubacteria and archaebacteria.

An entirely distinct bacterial line of descent (the urkaryotes) is now thought to have given rise to the king-

Labels in figure:

(proto-cells)

------- 3.5 billion years ago

archaebacteria   (urkaryote)   eubacteria
Monerans

amoeba   **Protistans**

sponges   protozoans   ciliates   yellow algae   red algae

green algae   **Plants**

brown algae

Animals   mosses

anemones   seed plants

flatworms   ribbon worms   slime molds   sac fungi   horsetails

snails   nematodes   water molds

octopuses   **Fungi**   lycopods   conifers   flowering plants

earthworms   club fungi   ferns

sea stars   fishes

lobsters   spiders   mammals

insects   reptiles   birds

doms **Protista**, **Plantae**, **Fungi**, and **Animalia**. Representatives of the ancestral stock have long since vanished. Today, most protistans are one-celled, like monerans. As you will read in Unit Seven, however, they differ from them in significant ways. Some protistans are like plants, others like animals, some like plants *and* animals, and still others like fungi! Protistans may be living examples of the kinds of organisms that existed at a main evolutionary crossroad in the distant past. At that point, one-celled forms began evolving in ways that gave rise to multicelled plants, fungi,

Figure 2.10 Simplified diagram of the five-kingdom model for classifying life forms. Only a few representative kinds of organisms are used to show the present scope of diversity. The general pattern suggests possible routes that may have led from the origin of life to this profusion of forms. Representatives of all kingdoms are still alive today.

and animals. Multicelled organisms are grouped into these three kingdoms on the basis of their energy-acquiring strategies. Plants assemble their own energy-rich food molecules. Fungi absorb nutrients from organic matter that they have already digested outside the fungal body. Animals eat (ingest) other organisms as food.

The separate pools of life in Figure 2.10 are not to be viewed as one flowing out of the other. *Representatives of all five kingdoms are alive today, side by side in time.* The generalized branching routes simply suggest how they might have arrived at where they are now. This is an evolutionary pattern of descent as many biologists now see it, as Darwin and Wallace might have envisioned it.

PERSPECTIVE

When Darwin disembarked from the *Beagle* with his observations and thoughts on life's diversity, he set in motion a chain of events that made the study of life simpler—and, at the same time, more complex. As you will discover in chapters to follow, the concept of evolving life provides a clear intellectual path through the seeming maze of species diversity. However, even though species are no longer generally regarded as unchanging, major questions have been raised concerning exactly *how* they change. *As in all of science, Darwin and Wallace's principle remains open to test, open to revision.* Is evolution always as extremely gradual as Darwin envisioned it? Or do some evolutionary changes occur rapidly (as some current investigators believe)? Is natural selection the only evolutionary process? What, exactly, causes the variation that selective agents act upon? Do species change only in directions corresponding to environmental pressures, or are there also built-in limits on which ways they *can* go? We will be returning to the more recent questions, hypotheses, and tests in later units of the book.

Readings

Darwin, C. 1957. *Voyage of the Beagle.* New York: Dutton. In his own words, what Darwin saw and thought about during his global voyage.

Dobzhansky, T. 1973. "Nothing in Biology Makes Sense Except in the Light of Evolution." *The American Biology Teacher* 35(3):125–129. Personal views of one of the world's leading geneticists, who argues that the principle of evolution does not clash with religious faith.

Futuyma, D. 1979. *Evolutionary Biology.* Sunderland, Massachusetts: Sinhauer Associates. Well-written synthesis of modern evolutionary thought. Includes one of the clearest synopses of evolutionary theories yet developed.

Gould, S. 1982. "The Importance of Trifles." *Natural History* 91(4): 16–23. Gould discusses the principles of reasoning that are evident in one of Darwin's last books (on worms). He argues persuasively that Darwin was indeed one of the great thinkers and not "a great assembler of facts and a poor joiner of ideas," as a detractor once wrote.

Mayr, E. 1976. *Evolution and the Diversity of Life.* Cambridge, Massachusetts: Belknap Press. Insights into a mind searching for ways to untangle the knot of biological diversity.

Moorhead, A. 1969. *Darwin and the Beagle.* New York: Harper and Row. Well-illustrated account of the places Darwin visited, what he observed, and the home to which he returned.

Singer, C. 1962. *A History of Biology to About the Year 1900.* New York: Abelard-Schuman. Out of date, but contains absorbing portrayals of the men and women who led the way in developing basic biological concepts.

Review Questions

1. Define inductive and deductive reasoning.

2. How do beliefs derived from a scientific approach differ from beliefs based on faith, force, authority, or simple consensus?

3. These terms are important in scientific testing: control group, experimental group, independent variables, dependent variables, controlled variables, randomization, sampling error. Can you define them?

4. Design a test to support or refute the following hypothesis: The body fat in rabbits appears yellow in certain mutant individuals—but only when those mutants also eat leafy plants containing a yellow pigment molecule called xanthophyll.

5. Witnesses in a court of law are asked to "swear to tell the truth, the whole truth, and nothing but the truth." What are some of the problems inherent in the question? Can you think of a better alternative?

6. Spend some time watching television (commercials, news broadcasts, documentaries), and write down examples of statements presented as facts. Also write down why you think each one might be plausible or nonsense. (For example, when "leading doctors" are said to recommend something, what kind of doctors are they, how many are they, are they doctors everywhere or in a village in Samoa, and what, exactly, are they leading in?)

7. List and define the main categories in the Linnean system of classification. How do you suppose this system influences our perceptions of the diversity of living things?

8. What is a phylogenetic system of classification? How are organisms grouped in the Whittaker system?

9. State the key points of the theory of natural selection. What is meant by differential reproduction?

UNIT TWO

THE CELLULAR BASIS OF LIFE

3

ATOMS, MOLECULES, AND CELL SUBSTANCES

Sunlight energy enters a photosynthetic cell in a blade of grass and sets up a commotion among some of its molecules. Because of the way those molecules are arranged relative to one another, the commotion is highly channeled: energy is absorbed, converted, transferred to energy carriers, and used in building food molecules. A bacterium in your gut depends on energy stored in the sugar present in milk. It can extract that energy because it has a set of enzymes, of specific shape and composition, whose sole function is to assure that milk-sugar molecules are dismantled with utmost speed. What happens if you stop drinking milk? If the bacterium doesn't have other enzymes able to handle other foods, that is the end of the bacterium. Your body resists viral attacks with the help of antibodies—protein molecules of specific shape and composition that can inactivate invaders or lead to their destruction. If your body cannot produce particular antibody molecules that respond to particular viruses, you may be in deep trouble.

No matter what example comes to mind, all events in the living world begin with the organization and behavior of atoms and molecules. It is here that all energy transfers and transformations within and between living things originate. It is here that the shape and function of cells, and the multicelled body, are determined. What is it about carbohydrates, lipids, and proteins that makes them such suitable building blocks in cell architecture? How can some molecules change shape or be zipped open with such precision, so that vital reactions can be played out on their surfaces? Why is it that some molecules can be broken apart more easily than others, so that their inherent energy is readily accessible? Answers to such questions are found in rules governing (1) the internal organization of atoms, and (2) how atoms and molecules behave relative to one another.

Table 3.1	Atomic Number and Mass Number of Elements Commonly Found in Living Things			
Element	Symbol	Atomic Number	Most Common Mass Number	Abundance in Human Body* (% Wet Weight)
Hydrogen	H	1	1	10.0 ⎫
Carbon	C	6	12	18.0 ⎬ 96%
Nitrogen	N	7	14	3.0 ⎪
Oxygen	O	8	16	65.0 ⎭
Sodium	Na	11	23	0.15
Magnesium	Mg	12	24	0.05
Phosphorus	P	15	31	1.1
Sulfur	S	16	32	0.25
Chlorine	Cl	17	35	0.15
Potassium	K	19	39	0.35
Calcium	Ca	20	40	2.0
Iron	Fe	26	56	0.004
Iodine	I	53	127	0.0004

*Approximate values.

ORGANIZATION OF MATTER

All the substances of our everyday world are alike in two respects: they occupy space and have mass. The pure substances are **elements**. Probably fewer than ninety different elements occur naturally, with no help from nuclear physics laboratories. Table 3.1 lists the ones that commonly occur in living things, along with abbreviations that can be used for their names. Two or more elements can combine and thereby form a **compound**. For example, hydrogen (H) and chlorine (Cl) can combine to form hydrochloric acid (HCl). All compounds, however, can be broken down into elements.

A chunk of an element such as carbon is composed of a gigantic number of atoms. An **atom** is the smallest divisible unit that still retains the properties of an element. (You can subdivide or cut some amount of an element into smaller and smaller bits. Each bit would still be "the element"— until you divided an atom of that element, whereupon you'd end up with something else.)

The atoms of all elements are composed of the same major kinds of building blocks, called **protons, neutrons,** and **electrons.** Yet each element displays unique properties. Why is this so? We can approach the question through a simple generalization:

The atoms of a given element differ from atoms of all other elements in the number and arrangement of their protons, neutrons, and electrons.

The number and arrangement of subatomic parts dictate how atoms can combine to form **molecules** (units of two or more atoms of the same or different elements bonded together). They dictate what the properties of different molecules will be and how (if at all) different molecules will interact. Thus a brief look at what goes on inside atoms will help explain why substances of life behave as they do.

The Nature of Atoms

Some amount of energy is inherent in every atom. The kind of energy we will consider here results from interactions called **electric charge.** When something is electrically charged, it has energy that allows it to push away or to attract something else that has a charge, even without touching it. Electric charges are positive or negative. Two identical charges (+ + or − −) tend to repel each other; two opposite charges (+ −) tend to attract each other.

Every atom has one or more protons, which have a positive charge. Every atom (except a form of hydrogen) also has one or more neutrons, which are electrically neutral. Protons and neutrons make up practically all the mass of an atom. They are both found in the atomic **nucleus**— the atom's central region. Electrons are negatively charged. They move rapidly about the nucleus and occupy most of the atom's volume.

Because no two elements have the same number of protons in their atoms, each element can be assigned a unique **atomic number**, equal to the number of protons in the nucleus. (For instance, a carbon atom has six protons; its atomic number is 6.) Atoms can also be assigned a **mass number**, which is the total number of protons *and* neutrons

in the nucleus. (For example, the most common kind of carbon atom has six protons and six neutrons; its mass number is 12.) Table 3.1 lists the atomic number and mass number for the most abundant elements in living things, and gives their relative abundances in the human body.

Even though all atoms of the same element have the same number of protons, individual atoms can vary slightly in the number of *neutrons*. This means they can have different mass numbers. For instance, "a carbon atom" might be carbon 12 (containing six protons, six neutrons), carbon 13 (six protons, seven neutrons), or carbon 14 (six protons, eight neutrons). Most elements have such different atomic forms, which are called **isotopes.** Some isotopes are used in biological research, in ways to be described later.

In any neutral atom you consider, the number of positively charged protons is exactly balanced by the *same* number of negatively charged electrons. In other words, an atom as a whole has a *net* charge of zero. However, atoms can be disturbed, and the balance between protons and electrons can be upset. The number of *protons* remains fixed, but one or more *electrons* can be knocked out of the atom, pulled away from it, or added to it. An atom that loses or gains one or more electrons is known as an **ion.**

For example, a sodium (Na) atom has eleven protons and eleven electrons. It can lose an electron, thereby becoming a positively charged sodium ion (Na+):

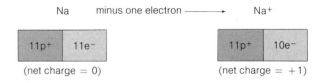

Similarly, a chlorine (Cl) atom has seventeen protons and seventeen electrons. It can gain another electron, thereby becoming a negatively charged chloride ion (Cl−):

Unlike the neutral atom, then, an ion has an overall positive or negative charge.

An atom as a whole has a net electric charge of zero.

An ion has an overall positive or negative charge.

How Electrons Are Arranged in Atoms

As Table 3.1 indicates, hydrogen is a main element in living things. Its most common form has only one proton and one electron, so it's the simplest kind of atom to think about. Its electron moves almost as fast as the speed of light in an **orbital** (a specific region of space around the nucleus, where you will find that electron most of the time). On the average, the electron is as close to the nucleus as it can get. For hydrogen, this orbital is like a spherical cloud (Figure 3.1).

A carbon atom has six electrons, nitrogen has seven, and oxygen has eight. How are all of the electrons arranged in these and other atoms? No matter how many electrons there are, each one is attracted to the positively charged protons in the nucleus. At the same time, each one is repelled by the other electrons present. *All the electrons must get as close as possible to the nucleus and as far away as possible from each other.* They do this by occupying different orbitals. Depending on the number of electrons in an atom, they occupy orbitals shaped like balls and dumbbells, teardrops and flabby inner tubes. In each case, though, *there are never more than two electrons in a given orbital.*

On the average, electrons in some orbitals have to spend more time farther away from the nucleus than others. The term **electron energy level** essentially means the same thing as "most probable distance from the nucleus." The lowest energy level is occupied by a spherical orbital closest to the nucleus. Four different orbitals can be squeezed into a second (higher) energy level, nine in the third (next highest), and so on. Figure 3.2 shows the arrangement of electrons in orbitals for a few elements.

It happens that electrons occupying the orbitals in the outermost energy level of an atom are the ones that interact with other atoms to form a molecule. In addition, most molecules form through interactions between outer orbitals that contain only *one* electron. If each of the highest occupied orbitals is filled with two electrons, an atom shows little tendency to combine with other atoms.

Elements composed of atoms that have two electrons in each occupied orbital tend to be chemically nonreactive substances.

Elements composed of atoms that have one or more orbitals containing only one electron tend to be chemically reactive substances.

The shapes of orbitals and the number of electrons present in the highest occupied energy level dictate how atoms combine in forming a molecule. Atoms don't just combine any which way (see *Commentary*). They combine only in certain positions, and these positions give rise to

Figure 3.1 Model of a key building block for the substances of life—hydrogen, with a lone electron zipping about the nucleus. (The dots don't represent electrons. They represent the probability distribution of the electron: the greater the density of dots, the more likely the electron will be in that region at any instant.)

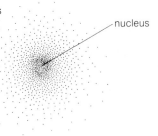

nucleus

		Number of Electrons in Each Orbital								
		First Energy Level (one orbital)	Second Energy Level (four possible orbitals)				Third Energy Level (nine possible orbitals)			
Element	Atomic Number									
Hydrogen	1	1								
Helium	2	2								
Carbon	6	2	2	1	1					
Nitrogen	7	2	2	1	1	1				
Oxygen	8	2	2	2	1	1				
Neon	10	2	2	2	2	2				
Sodium	11	2	2	2	2	2	1			
Chlorine	17	2	2	2	2	2	2	2	2	1

Figure 3.2 Distribution of electrons in atomic orbitals for a few elements.

COMMENTARY

Keeping Track of Electrons: Some Options

Atomic structure is most accurately represented by the orbital model, in which one or more rapidly moving electrons occupy some volume of space around the nucleus. Here, electron orbitals of different shapes occupy different energy levels (Figure 3.2). This model is useful because it gives insight into why atoms combine with one another only in specific positions rather than any which way. Hence the orbital model gives insight into the molecular basis for the organization characteristic of living systems. However, it is not necessarily the most convenient model to use when tracking interactions between atoms, especially those with many electrons.

A simplified (if not quite accurate) version of the orbital model is often used. In the shell model, energy levels that electrons occupy are represented by circles (shells) around the nucleus. Electrons in each level are drawn as dots somewhere on the circles. For example, shell models for hydrogen, sodium, and chlorine would look like the ones illustrated below.

An even more stripped-down convention uses the electron "dots" of the outermost energy level (or shell) with the chemical symbol for the atom. For example, hydrogen and sodium both have only one electron in the outermost shell; chlorine has seven. They would be represented as

$$\text{H} \cdot \quad \text{Na} \cdot \quad \text{and} \quad \overset{\cdot\cdot}{\underset{\cdot\cdot}{:\text{Cl}}} \cdot$$

The placement of the dots has no meaning whatsoever in terms of *how* electrons are actually arranged. Again, the use of such conventions is a matter of convenience.

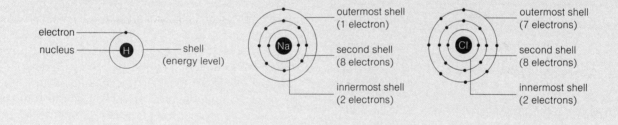

electron — nucleus — H — shell (energy level)

Na — outermost shell (1 electron) — second shell (8 electrons) — innermost shell (2 electrons)

Cl — outermost shell (7 electrons) — second shell (8 electrons) — innermost shell (2 electrons)

specific shapes of molecules. In turn, the shapes of different molecules give rise to the shapes and structures of cells. Molecules and cell structures must be assembled according to specific patterns. If they are not, cells don't function properly—or they don't function at all.

Electron Excitation

The electron arrangements shown in Figure 3.2 are for atoms that are being left alone, more or less. But sometimes electrons are hit with incoming light or heat energy. And electrons can *absorb* some of the additional energy. When an electron absorbs extra energy, it might move briefly to a higher energy level, farther from the nucleus. Within a fraction of a second, the excited electron returns to the lowest available energy level. As it does, the extra energy is *released*. Many metabolic events, including photosynthesis and visual perception, begin with the extra energy released from excited electrons.

Only specific energy levels are available to an electron. An electron can move to one level, or the next level, or the next, but never in between. It's something like standing on

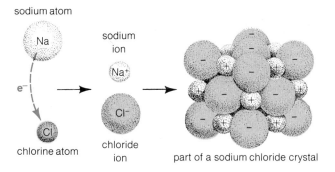

sodium atom

sodium
ion

chlorine atom

chloride
ion

part of a sodium chloride crystal

Figure 3.3 Ionic bonding in sodium chloride. Notice the orderly repeating pattern of the oppositely charged ions in the crystal lattice. (For simplicity, each atom and ion is drawn as a space-filling sphere.)

a ladder. You can stand on any of the rungs, and you can move your feet from rung to rung. But you certainly can't stand between rungs. All electrons gain or lose energy like that: in steps of certain sizes. Living things respond to this property. For instance, electrons in special molecules found in photosynthetic cells can be excited to higher energy levels by absorbing specific wavelengths (colors) of sunlight energy. These wavelength energies correspond exactly to specific "steps" on the energy ladder for electrons.

Electrons can gain and lose energy in increments.

INTERACTIONS AMONG ATOMS IN THE CELLULAR WORLD

In a **chemical bond,** the electron structure of one atom becomes linked with the electron structure of another atom (or atoms). Many such links depend on an atom giving up, gaining, or sharing one or more electrons. Others occur when an atom already bound in a molecule comes under the influence of neighboring molecules. *Hence a chemical bond is not an object; it is an* energy relationship.

Under the ranges of temperature, pressure, and moisture typically present inside and outside the cell, certain kinds of bonds predominate. Strong bonds commonly occur *within* molecules. Weak attractions typically occur *between* two or more molecules, or between different parts of the same molecule. Thousands of such interactions help stabilize the shape of many biological molecules. They influence the organization of molecules relative to one another in the

cell. Even so, it does not take much energy to disrupt the weak interactions and thereby disassemble or rearrange the molecules they helped hold together. Life processes depend as much on weak attractions as they do on stronger ones. In reading through the next sections, the following point will become evident:

Under cellular conditions of temperature, pressure, and moisture, the compounds of life are held together by strong bonds that involve a sharing of electrons, and by weaker interactions.

Ionic Bonding

Recall that it is possible for an atom to completely lose or gain one or more electrons and thereby become an ion. Such an event does not occur in isolation. Another atom of the right kind must be around to accept or donate the electrons.

Atoms tend to donate or accept electrons when their outermost orbitals are not completely filled. Filled orbitals normally represent more stable energy states than do partially filled ones. For instance, sodium tends to donate an electron to chlorine. Sodium, with eleven protons, has eleven electrons distributed in three energy levels (Figure 3.2). Only one of those electrons is present in the third. Chlorine, with seventeen protons, already has seventeen electrons in three energy levels—but one more will fill the orbitals in the third. When these two atoms encounter each other, an electron is transferred from sodium to chlorine. Both atoms thereby become oppositely charged ions, Na^+ and Cl^-, and both are now in a more stable state (Figure 3.3).

Depending on the environment in which the transfer is made, the two ions can remain together as a result of the attraction between them. This association is an **ionic bond:** an electron is fully transferred from one atom to another, but the resulting positive and negative ions remain together because of the mutual attraction of opposite charge. Thus Na^+ and Cl^- might remain in association as NaCl, or sodium chloride. Strictly speaking, there is no such thing as "a molecule" of NaCl in table salt, for the attraction is not restricted to a single pair of ions. The attraction can organize many NaCl units into an *ionic crystal,* a structure in which ions are repeated over and over in a regular, latticelike pattern. Figure 3.3 shows the crystalline structure of table salt. Molecules also can form crystalline structures.

In an ionic bond, a positive and a negative ion are linked by the mutual attraction of opposite charge.

Covalent Bonding

Types of Covalent Bonds. In some interactions, atoms do not give up electrons completely. In a **covalent bond**, one or more electrons is *shared* between atoms. Almost always, a pair of electrons is shared. For instance, hydrogen atoms (each with a lone electron) rarely exist by themselves. Often two are joined as a molecule. In this molecule, each atom's orbital overlaps the other, and both electrons move about both nuclei:

The single covalent bond of the hydrogen molecule can also be written as H—H. The single line means that an electron pair is shared by the two atoms. (Such representations, in which lines signify bonds, are called structural formulas.) More than one pair of electrons can be shared in covalent bonds. In a double covalent bond, two atoms share two electron pairs. This often occurs between carbon atoms and can be represented as C=C. In a triple covalent bond (such as C≡C), two atoms share three electron pairs.

When there is *equal sharing* of electrons, as there is in an H_2 molecule, atoms are joined in a **nonpolar covalent bond**. The word nonpolar implies symmetry in electric charge between both "ends" (poles) of the bonded atoms. The negatively charged electrons are likely to be as close to one atom as another. Because electron sharing fills the highest occupied energy level for both atoms, the molecule shows no net charge.

Atoms may also be joined by a **polar covalent bond**, in which there is *unequal sharing* of electrons. The word polar implies asymmetry in electric charge between the two ends of the bond. This happens when atoms of two different elements share electrons. No two elements have the same number of protons in the nucleus, so the attraction that they hold for electrons is not the same. Thus, shared electrons in a polar covalent bond are attracted more to one atom than to the other.

Consider what happens in a water molecule, which has one oxygen and two hydrogen atoms joined in this way:

H_2O molecule

The three atoms share electrons, so that all their highest occupied orbitals are filled. This means that *overall*, the water molecule shows no net charge. But oxygen has more protons in its nucleus than hydrogen does. Hence the electrons average more time at the oxygen end than they do at the hydrogen end of the water molecule. The unequal sharing of electrons means the charge within the bonds is asymmetrical, or polar. In any polar covalent bond, the atom that exerts the greater pull on shared electrons is said to be more *electronegative;* it behaves as if it carries a slight negative charge. The other atoms behave as if they carry a slight positive charge, so the molecule is still neutral, overall.

In a nonpolar covalent bond, one or more electrons are shared equally between atoms.

In a polar covalent bond, one or more electrons are shared unequally between atoms. The atom with the greatest share behaves as if it carries a negative charge (it is electronegative).

Covalent Bonds in Organic Compounds. The importance of covalent bonds is evident in the great variety of carbon-based compounds. Carbon is so essential to life that for more than a century, nearly all molecules containing carbon have been called organic ("organism-related") to distinguish them from inorganic ("lifeless") molecules. Carbon's versatility can be traced to its electron arrangement and its strong tendency to form as many as four covalent bonds.

When carbon combines with four other atoms, two of its six electrons reside in the lowest energy level. Each of its other four electrons zips about alone in a new, *hybrid* orbital that is shaped like a teardrop. The bulging end of each teardrop points at one of the four corners of a tetrahedron (a four-sided pyramid):

Other atoms can bond covalently to the same carbon at all four corners. The four atoms might be all the same, or they might differ from one another. For example, carbon bonded with four hydrogen atoms forms the compound methane (CH_4), a gas you often use in laboratory burners. Methane is called a *hydrocarbon,* because it's composed only of hydrogen and carbon atoms.

Functional Group	Structural Formula	Derivative Formed	Occurs In
hydroxyl (—OH)	⊐—OH	alcohol	sugars, fats, alcohols
carbonyl (—C=O)	⊐—C—H with =O	aldehyde	sugars
carbonyl (=O)	⊐—C—⊏ with =O	ketone	sugars
carboxyl (—COOH)	⊐—C—OH with =O	carboxylic acid	fats, amino acids
amino (—NH$_2$)	⊐—N—H with H above	amine	amino acids
phosphate (—PO$_4^{-3}$)	⊐—O—P—O$^-$ with =O and O$^-$	ortho-phosphate	nucleotides, phospholipids, phosphorylated sugars

Rosemary Richardson

Figure 3.4 Some biologically important functional groups. Here, the open-ended squares represent the carbon backbone of the organic molecule to which the functional group is covalently bonded.

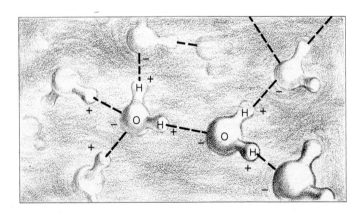

Figure 3.5 Hydrogen bonds between water molecules in liquid water.

The four-cornered pattern of carbon bonding typified by methane is the basis for a diverse array of covalently bonded molecules. Sometimes the basic structure is a chain (or skeleton) of carbon atoms; sometimes it is branched:

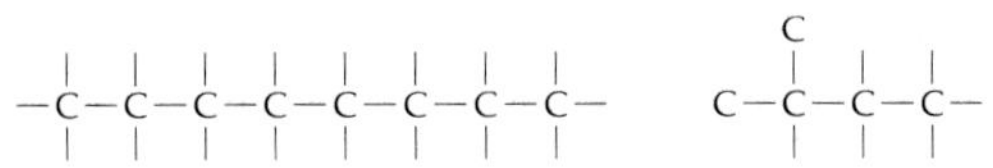

$$-C-C-C-C-C-C-C-C- \qquad C-C-C-C-$$

Often, covalently bonded carbon atoms form a ring structure:

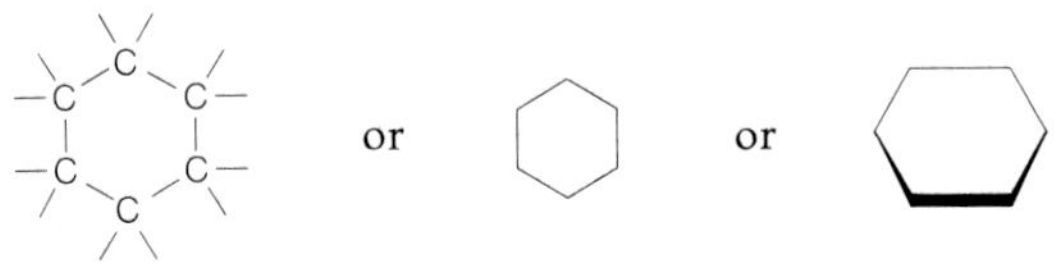

A ring structure can be shown with or without a carbon atom at each corner. When the stripped-down version is used, it is understood that a carbon atom still occurs at each corner, with enough hydrogen atoms attached to give each carbon atom four covalent bonds.

Functional Groups. Atoms (or groups of atoms) that can bond covalently to the carbon backbone of organic molecules are **functional groups**. They define the structure of a given family of organic compounds and determine their properties. For example, hydroxyl groups (—OH) impart high solubility to the sugars and alcohols in which they occur. Figure 3.4 lists some of the biologically important functional groups.

Hydrogen Bonding

Atoms participating in a polar covalent bond can interact at the same time with other molecules. For example, when hydrogen is covalently bonded to a highly electronegative atom, it acts as if it carries a slight positive charge. This means it can be weakly attracted to still another highly electronegative atom that might be in the vicinity. Neighboring oxygen, nitrogen, or fluorine atoms taking part in a polar covalent bond are electronegative enough to attract hydrogen in this way. The weak attraction between hydrogen and a highly electronegative atom in a different polar covalent molecule (or different part of the same molecule) is called a **hydrogen bond**.

Hydrogen bonding, as you will see, is extremely important to the stability of many large biological molecules. It also imparts some structure to liquid water (Figure 3.5). A hydrogen atom in one water molecule can form a weak hydrogen bond with the oxygen atom of a neighboring water molecule. The oppositely charged parts of every two neighbors tend to orient toward each other; and parts of like charge tend to orient away from each other. Such hydrogen bonds form throughout a body of water and account for some of water's remarkable properties. As you will read in Chapter Five, water's unusual temperature-stabilizing properties and cohesive properties arise from hydrogen bonding among its individual molecules.

In a hydrogen bond, an electronegative atom weakly attracts a hydrogen atom that is covalently bonded to a different atom.

Hydrophobic Interactions

Because its individual molecules show polarity, water interacts electrically with other polar substances that are placed in it. Polar molecules become dispersed among and form weak bonds with the polar water molecules. In other words, they *dissolve.* Substances that dissolve readily in water are said to be **hydrophilic**, or "water-loving." In contrast, substances that are wholly (or largely) uncharged on their surfaces are **hydrophobic**, or "water-dreading." They do not dissolve in water.

Consider what happens when oil is mixed with water. The oil shows no tendency to form weak attractions with the surrounding water molecules. In fact, as water molecules are slowly reunited by the hydrogen bonds that were broken during the mixing, they actually push out the oil. Molecules of oil are thus forced to cluster together, as they do in droplets or in a film on the water's surface. When they are clustered, less total surface area of the oil is directly exposed to water. Therefore, the oil interferes less with the energetically favorable attraction of water molecules for each other; the clustering represents a more stable arrangement.

In themselves, hydrophobic interactions of this sort are not bonds. But the clustering effect does influence the shapes of many complex molecules, such as proteins and lipid-based molecules. As such, it also influences the architecture of cell structures such as membranes, in ways that will be described in Chapter Five.

In a hydrophobic interaction, nonpolar groups cluster together in water. It is not a true bond; the surrounding water molecules simply hydrogen-bond with one another and thereby push out the nonpolar groups.

Bond Energies

Just how much energy is involved in the different kinds of bonds being described here? The values have actually been determined through measurements of the amount of energy needed to break the bonds apart.

Bond energy is measured in terms of kilocalories per mole. A **kilocalorie** is the same thing as a thousand calories—the amount of energy needed to heat 1,000 grams of water from 14.5°C to 15.5°C at standard pressure. (Because energy can be converted from one form to another, bond energies can be expressed in kilocalories even though the energy is used for something other than heating water.) A **mole** is a certain number (6.023×10^{23}) of atoms or molecules of any substance at all, just as "a dozen" can refer to any twelve doughnuts, roses, or any other objects. It signifies an amount whose weight, in grams, is numerically equal to the atomic weight (approximately the mass number) of the atoms composing the substance. For example, by referring to Table 3.1, you know that carbon has mass number 12; hence a mole of carbon weighs twelve grams. A mole of oxygen atoms (with mass number 16) weighs sixteen grams. (What would be the molecular weight of carbon dioxide, or CO_2?)

For covalent bonds between atoms of carbon, nitrogen, oxygen, and hydrogen, the bond energies typically are between 80 and 110 kilocalories per mole. Under cellular conditions, ionic bonds are much, much weaker. Typically the bond energy is about 5 kilocalories per mole. Bond energies typically average only 4 to 6 kilocalories per mole for hydrogen bonds.

ACIDS, BASES, AND SALTS

Acids and Bases. From time to time, with predictable frequency, water molecules also dissociate, or separate, into two charged parts:

 becomes

The departing hydrogen has no electron whatsoever (because the oxygen atom in the water molecule exerted greater pull on the electron being shared). This fleetingly naked proton is called a **hydrogen ion** (H^+). The —OH group left behind momentarily has one more electron than

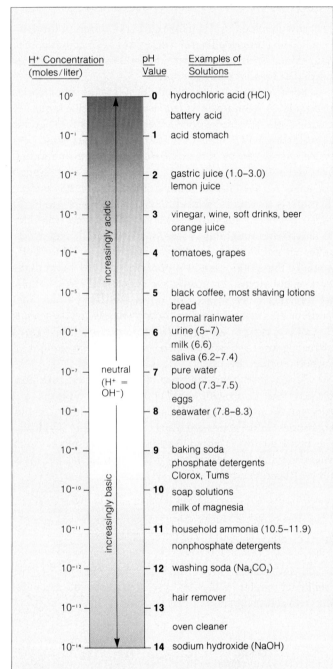

H⁺ Concentration (moles/liter)	pH Value	Examples of Solutions

10^0 — **0** hydrochloric acid (HCl)

battery acid

10^{-1} — **1** acid stomach

10^{-2} — **2** gastric juice (1.0–3.0)
lemon juice

10^{-3} — **3** vinegar, wine, soft drinks, beer
orange juice

10^{-4} — **4** tomatoes, grapes

10^{-5} — **5** black coffee, most shaving lotions
bread
normal rainwater

10^{-6} — **6** urine (5–7)
milk (6.6)
saliva (6.2–7.4)

10^{-7} — **7** pure water
blood (7.3–7.5)
eggs

10^{-8} — **8** seawater (7.8–8.3)

10^{-9} — **9** baking soda
phosphate detergents
Clorox, Tums

10^{-10} — **10** soap solutions
milk of magnesia

10^{-11} — **11** household ammonia (10.5–11.9)
nonphosphate detergents

10^{-12} — **12** washing soda (Na₂CO₃)

hair remover

10^{-13} — **13**

oven cleaner

10^{-14} — **14** sodium hydroxide (NaOH)

increasingly acidic

neutral (H⁺ = OH⁻)

increasingly basic

Figure 3.6 The pH scale, in which a fluid is assigned a number according to the number of hydrogen ions present in a liter of that fluid. The scale ranges from 0 (most acidic) to 14 (most basic), with 7 representing the point of neutrality.

A change of only 1 on the pH scale means a tenfold change in hydrogen ion concentration. Thus, for example, the gastric juice in your stomach is ten times more acidic than vinegar, and vinegar is ten times more acidic than tomatoes.

it has protons; it, too, has become ionized. This ionized remnant of a whole water molecule is a **hydroxide ion** (OH⁻).

Ionization of hydrogen isn't limited to water molecules. Other substances also undergo dissociation when they are placed in water. The dissociation results in a hydrogen ion and some kind of negatively charged ion. Carbonic acid is one such substance:

$$H_2CO_3 \rightleftharpoons HCO_3^- + H^+$$

carbonic acid   bicarbonate

Notice the double arrows in this reaction. They indicate that the events represented can run in two directions; the reaction is *reversible.* Carbonic acid can break apart into bicarbonate and hydrogen ions; but bicarbonate and hydrogen ions can join together to form carbonic acid. This example illustrates that some substances release hydrogen ions in solution and that others can combine with them. These substances are called acids and bases.

1. A substance whose molecules *release* hydrogen ions in solution is an <u>acid</u>.

2. A substance that *combines* with hydrogen ions in solution is a <u>base</u>.

In a glass of pure water, the amounts of H⁺ and OH⁻ are always the same. Hence pure water is said to be neutral. But suppose you pour some hydrochloric acid (HCL) into the water. This substance separates into Cl⁻ and H⁺ ions. With more H⁺ in the glass, the OH⁻ ions are more likely to bump into and combine with them, thereby forming water molecules. The outcome is that the hydroxide ion concentration decreases by as much as the hydrogen ion concentration increases.

Such changes in hydrogen ion concentration occur all the time in the cell environment. It is often useful to be able to define the extent of change taking place. The trouble is, it would be cumbersome to work with numbers at the molecular level. (For instance, that glass of pure water has 15,000,000,000,000,000 hydrogen ions in it!) That is why fluids are assigned a **pH value**: a number that is a shorthand way of referring to the number of hydrogen ions present in a liter of the fluid. Pure water, which is neutral, has a pH of 7. This is the midpoint of a scale ranging from 0 to 14 (Figure 3.6). A solution having a pH of less than 7 is *acidic.* If its pH is greater than 7, the solution is *basic.*

All living cells are sensitive to pH. Usually, the interior of a cell will not range far from neutrality. However, the outside *environment* may differ greatly in pH value. For instance, cells of sphagnum mosses growing in peat bogs function best in a highly acid range (3.2 to 4.6). Some nematodes thrive in places where pH is 3.4. For plants and animals living in river water, the pH ranges between 6.8 and 8.6. The fungus *Penicillium* tolerates extremely alkaline conditions (pH 11.1 in one case). Fluids bathing most cells of your body range between 6.9 and 7.5. (Exceptions include the highly acidic gastric juices bathing cells that line your stomach.)

Although the cell interior usually does not range far from neutrality, each cell is adapted to an environmental pH range that varies considerably among different kinds of organisms.

Normally, the cell interior does not show drastic shifts in pH. Yet how can this be? Consider that hydrogen ions are required for or leased during many reactions inside the cell. How are internal pH values maintained if hydrogen ions are being produced or utilized? Most cells have several mechanisms for adjusting to changes in internal pH. As you will read later, cells also have mechanisms for adjusting their pH values in response to pH changes in the external environment. Maintaining *internal* pH is partly accomplished with **buffers**: substances that combine with and/or release hydrogen ions as a function of pH.

When metabolic reactions produce an excess of H^+, buffers can accept the excess. When metabolic reactions deplete H^+, buffers act like hydrogen ion banks that are able to dole out reserves. Carbonic acid is one of the major buffers in cells. This acid, again, dissociates into bicarbonate and hydrogen ions in water. When extra hydrogen ions are added to the water, the excess quickly combines with the bicarbonate, forming carbonic acid. Similarly, when excess hydroxide ions are present, they quickly combine with the hydrogen ions, forming water. Phosphoric acid (H_3PO_4) is another major buffer in cells. To a lesser extent, some atomic groups present on the surface of proteins, fatty acids, and other molecules play buffering roles.

Cells depend on buffer molecules that help maintain internal pH within some tolerance range by combining with or releasing hydrogen ions as a function of pH.

Dissolved Salts. Next to water, salts are the main inorganic compounds present in the cell. A **salt** is a compound that has been formed by the reaction between an acid and a base. For example, sodium chloride (NaCl) is a salt:

$$HCl \quad + \quad NaOH \quad \longrightarrow \quad NaCl + H_2O$$

hydrochloric acid   sodium hydroxide, a base   salt

When placed in water, most salts dissociate into positively and negatively charged ions. In cells, the ions formed from salts include positively charged ions of potassium (K^+), sodium (Na^+), calcium (Ca^{++}), and magnesium (Mg^{++}). They also include the negatively charged chloride ions (Cl^-).

What functions do these ions serve? To give a few examples, potassium ions are used in activating many enzymes in complex land plants. They also seem to be involved in transporting nitrates and phosphates through the plant body. In most animals, nerve messages cannot travel without sodium and potassium ions. When bound with a protein called calmodulin, calcium ions take part in plasma membrane activities, cell movements, cell division, nerve function, even blood clotting. In the human body, about ninety percent of all ions dissolved in extracellular fluid are those of sodium and chlorine.

Cell functioning depends on salts: compounds that form by the reaction between an acid and a base, and that usually dissociate into positively and negatively charged ions in water.

MAKING AND BREAKING BONDS IN BIOLOGICAL MOLECULES

So far, the substances we have considered are fairly simple. At most they contain no more than a few dozen atoms. How do we get from such substances to the macromolecules of life, some of which contain thousands, even millions, of atoms? Many bonding processes are involved, but two can be outlined here to give you an idea of what goes on. The two are called condensation (or dehydration) and hydrolysis.

In **condensation**, small molecules (such as short carbon-based chains and rings) are covalently linked in a reaction that can also involve the formation of water. In effect, one molecule is stripped of an H atom and another is stripped of an —OH group; then the two molecules become covalently bonded. At the same time, the H and —OH released in the process can combine to form a water molecule (Figure 3.7a). By linking small molecule after small molecule in this manner, it is possible to assemble polymers. A *polymer* is a molecule composed of anywhere from three to millions of subunits of relatively low molecular weight that may or may not be identical.

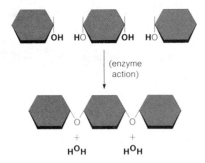

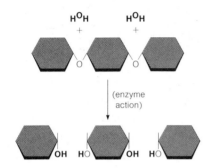

a *Condensation of three molecular subunits leads to a larger molecule. Water can be formed during the process.*

b *Hydrolysis of a molecule into three subunits.*

Figure 3.7 Examples of condensation (**a**) and hydrolysis (**b**).

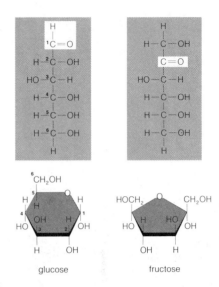

glucose   fructose

Figure 3.8 Straight-chain and ring forms of two monosaccharides: glucose and fructose. For reference purposes, the carbon atoms of glucose are numbered as shown. Notice that both glucose and fructose have the same formula ($C_6H_{12}O_6$), but that some of the atoms are arranged differently. The white areas show that some atoms form an aldehyde group in glucose, and that some form a ketone group in fructose.

Life depends on more than building up large molecules. It also depends on tearing them down. A molecule can be torn apart so that its subunits can be picked up and used in assembling other kinds of molecules. It can be torn apart for its energy or for easy disposal. **Hydrolysis** is a cornerstone of such activities. The process is something like condensation in reverse. When bonds between certain parts of molecules are broken, an H atom and an —OH group derived from water become attached to the fragments (Figure 3.7b).

In cells, both condensation and hydrolysis depend on the action of a class of proteins called enzymes, to be described later. Both processes are important in the ways that cells constantly cycle the atoms and molecules of life.

Condensation is the covalent linkage of small molecules in an enzyme-mediated reaction that can also involve formation of water.

Hydrolysis is the enzyme-mediated cleavage of a molecule into two or more parts by reaction with water.

CARBOHYDRATES

Trees, grasses, fruits and vegetables, cotton plants—all such plants and plant parts have carbohydrates as their main structural material. So do bacteria and fungi. Almost all protistans, fungi, and animals—as well as the plants themselves—depend directly or indirectly on carbohydrates for energy. A simple **carbohydrate** is made only of three elements: carbon, hydrogen, and oxygen. These elements are combined in about a 1:2:1 ratio. This means that for every carbon atom in a carbohydrate, there typically are two hydrogen atoms and one oxygen atom, or $[C(H_2O)]_n$. The "n" represents whatever number of carbon units are linked in the molecule.

Monosaccharides

The simplest type of carbohydrate is the **monosaccharide**: a sugar that typically has a skeleton of three, five, six, or seven carbon atoms. (The "saccharide" part of the name comes from a Greek word meaning sugar.) Monosaccha-

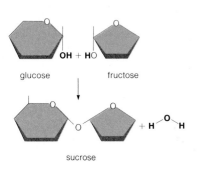

glucose   fructose

sucrose

Figure 3.9 Condensation of two monosaccharides (glucose and fructose) into a disaccharide (sucrose).

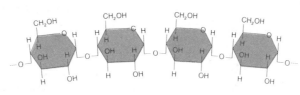

a

b

Figure 3.10 (**a**) Oxygen bridges between the glucose units of amylose, a form of starch. (**b**) The helical coiling of an amylose molecule, which is stabilized by hydrogen bonds.

rides that have five or more carbon atoms tend to form ring structures when they are dissolved in the fluid component of living cells. Among the most prevalent are the six-carbon sugars *glucose, fructose,* and *galactose;* and the five-carbon sugars *ribose* and *deoxyribose.*

Notice, in Figure 3.8, that both glucose and fructose have the same molecular formula ($C_6H_{12}O_6$). Yet they are different molecules, having slightly different properties. Why is this so? The atoms are arranged in slightly different ways in the two kinds of molecules. Glucose and fructose are **structural isomers**: they have the same number of each kind of atom, which are differently arranged. Several other six-carbon sugars have the same molecular formula; all are structural isomers of each other.

Disaccharides and Polysaccharides

When two simple sugar molecules become covalently bonded through condensation, the result is a **disaccharide** (Figure 3.9). For instance, the disaccharide *sucrose* is composed of one glucose and one fructose unit. Sucrose is the most abundant of all sugars. It is the form in which sugar is transported through leafy plants. Table sugar is sucrose that has been extracted and crystallized from such plants as sugarcane. Another disaccharide, *lactose* (or milk sugar) has a glucose and a galactose unit. Still another is *maltose* (two glucose units). Maltose occurs in germinating seeds. It is a main ingredient in brewing-industry products.

When more than two simple sugar molecules are bonded covalently through dehydration synthesis, the result is a **polysaccharide**. One, two, three, or four different

kinds of simple sugar units may be present in a polysaccharide. Some polysaccharides, such as *starch* and *glycogen,* are sugar storage forms. Starch is abundant in complex plants. Glycogen is the storage form in animals and fungi. Other polysaccharides, such as *cellulose,* are structural materials in the cell walls of complex plants.

Starch and cellulose are both assembled from glucose units, yet they have different properties. In cells, starch molecules can be clustered together in large granules (starch grains), which can be quickly hydrolyzed when glucose units must be made available. Cellulose, however, is tough, fibrous, and water-insoluble. Such differences can be traced to differences in the alignment of the links between glucose units in the two kinds of molecules. In starch, the alignment permits the glucose chain to twist into a coiled structure that favors the formation of granules (Figure 3.10). In contrast, the alignment in cellulose permits the molecule to have an extended structure. Different cellulose chains lie side by side, and hydrogen bonds form between —OH groups on *different* chains. The hydrogen bonds stabilize the cellulose chains in tight bundles (Figure 3.11). This bonding arrangement can be attacked only by specific enzymes present in termites, wood-rot fungi, and certain bacteria (Chapter Twenty-Six).

In glycogen, glucose units are bonded together in a highly branched structure (Figure 3.12). Glycogen is the form in which carbohydrates are stored in such animal tissues as liver and muscle.

Chitin, another polysaccharide, is secreted by cells in the outer tissue layer of many animals. This carbohydrate is modified, in that it contains nitrogen atoms. For many insects and crustaceans (such as crabs), chitin is the main

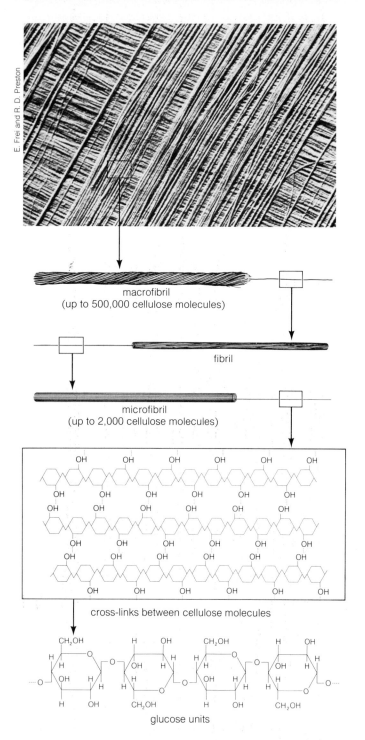

Figure 3.11 Structure of cellulose. Individual cellulose molecules are assembled from glucose units. Crosslinks form between —OH groups of the glucose units in neighboring chains. As many as 2,000 cellulose molecules can be aligned in a fine strand called a microfibril. Microfibrils in turn can be twisted together into a threadlike fibril. In some cells, fibrils are coiled, like a cable, into a macrofibril. A macrofibril may contain 500,000 cellulose molecules. It is as strong as a steel thread of equivalent thickness. The micrograph shows microfibrils in a cell wall of the alga *Chaetomorpha*.

macrofibril
(up to 500,000 cellulose molecules)

fibril

microfibril
(up to 2,000 cellulose molecules)

cross-links between cellulose molecules

glucose units

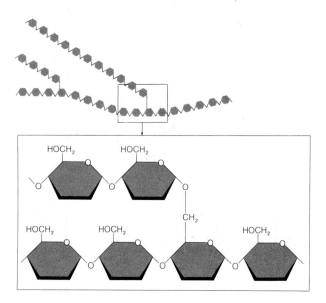

Figure 3.12 Branched structure of glycogen, a storage polysaccharide in some animal tissues. Abundant glycogen stores are especially characteristic of liver and skeletal muscle cells.

structural material in external skeletons, biting mouthparts, and other specialized structures such as eye lenses and copulatory organs. For most fungi, chitin imparts a degree of firmness to cell walls.

LIPIDS

Lipids are a diverse assortment of oily or waxy substances. They include true fats, waxes, steroids (such as cholesterol), terpenes, phospholipids, and glycolipids. Compared with a carbohydrate, a lipid molecule has fewer oxygen atoms relative to the number of carbon and hydrogen atoms. For the most part, its atoms are linked in nonpolar covalent bonds (C—C and C—H), which means that most regions of a lipid are hydrophobic (insoluble in water).

True Fats and Waxes

The so-called **true fats** are lipids composed only of carbon, hydrogen, and oxygen atoms. These atoms are arranged in two kinds of subunits: glycerol and fatty acid. *Glycerol* is an alcohol. It has a carbon skeleton to which three hydroxyl

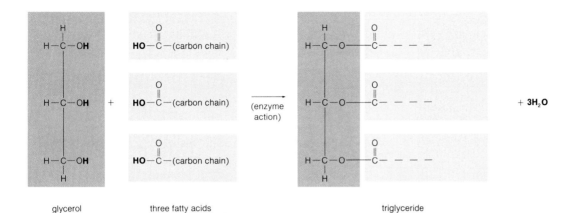

glodrol   three fatty acids   triglyceride
                 (acid group shaded tan)

Figure 3.13 Condensation of a fat molecule known as a triglyceride.

groups (—OH) as well as hydrogen atoms are attached. A glycerol molecule may be represented in this manner:

$$
\begin{array}{c}
\text{H} \\
\text{H—C—OH} \\
\text{H—C—OH} \\
\text{H—C—OH} \\
\text{H}
\end{array}
$$

A *fatty acid* has an unbranched carbon skeleton to which a carboxyl group (—COOH) as well as hydrogen atoms are attached. One kind looks like this:

Up to three fatty acid chains of this sort can be attached by condensation to a glpcerol molecule (Figure 3.13). The terms monoglyceride, diglyceride, and triglyceride refer to whether one, two, or three chains are attached.

Butter, bacon fat, and other animal fats are called *saturated fats,* because some maximum possible number of hydrogen atoms is covalently bonded to the carbon skeleton of their fatty acid "tails." The molecules of fully saturated fats are chains that pack tightly together. That is why these fats are usually solid or semisolid at room temperature. Figure 3.14 shows an example of a saturated fat.

Vegetable oils (such as soybean, corn, safflower, and linseed) are called *unsaturated fats.* Their fatty acid tails contain one or more double covalent bonds between carbon atoms. At each double bond, the molecule bends in

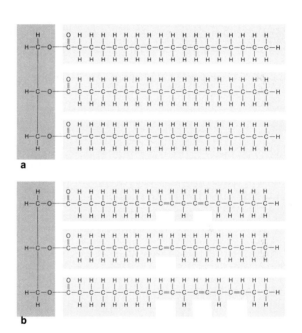

Figure 3.14 (**a**) Structural formula for glycerol tristearate, a fully saturated fat. (**b**) Linseed oil, an unsaturated fat.

space. This bending prevents a snug fit between chains. That's why unsaturated fats are usually fluid (oils) at room temperature.

In the lipids called **waxes,** long-chain alcohols are combined with long-chain fatty acids. In some plants, waxes of various types are secreted to the outer surface of cells or cell walls. The secretions help prevent water loss and impart some resistance to disease-causing organisms (Figure 3.15). Such waxes are important materials in *cutin,* a plant cell secretion that covers and waterproofs stem, leaf,

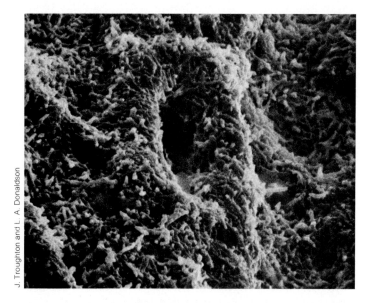

Figure 3.15 Extensive wax deposits on the leaf surface of a carnation (*Dianthus*).

J. Troughton and L. A. Donaldson

and fruit surfaces. Some waxes are included in *suberin*, a water-resistant substance found in cork cell walls of bark. Waxes are important in animals, also. Beeswax, a structural material secreted by honeybees, is used in constructing honeycomb. Modified sweat glands in your ears secrete a wax that helps keep relatively large objects (such as insects) from entering the ear canal.

Steroids and Related Substances

The lipids known as **steroids** have four carbon rings to which a variety of atoms may be attached. The steroid *cholesterol* has this structure:

Cholesterol itself is a component of most cell membranes. It may also undergo rearrangements that lead to formation of such substances as male and female sex hormones, and bile acids (which function in digestion). Cholesterol molecules are hydrophobic and thus are insoluble in fluids such as blood. They must be bound to other substances before they can be transported to their destination (Chapter Twenty-Four).

Terpenes are a diverse group of lipids assembled from five-carbon units. Often the units are strung together in long, water-insoluble chains:

This kind of chain is part of *chlorophyll* and *carotenoid* pigment molecules, which function in trapping light energy. The terpene chains help anchor the pigments to internal cell membranes of autotrophic microorganisms and plants. Terpenes also include natural rubber, turpentine, and many naturally occurring fragrances. Vitamins A, E, and K are all important terpene derivatives.

Phospholipids and Glycolipids

The **phospholipids** are among the most universally important substances in living things. These lipids are assembled from glycerol, fatty acids, a phosphorus-containing group, and usually a nitrogen-containing alcohol. Together with proteins, they are the most common substances in cell membranes.

The fatty acid region of a phospholipid is insoluble in water. That is one of the reasons why a cell membrane doesn't dissolve even though water is present on both sides. In contrast, the phospholipid region containing the phosphate and nitrogen is soluble in water. Also important are the **glycolipids**, which have water-soluble carbohydrate groups attached. These groups are one kind of site for chemical recognition between cells and substances present in the cellular environment (Chapter Five).

PROTEINS

Of all biological molecules, **proteins** are the most diverse in both structure and function. No matter what the process, proteins are sure to be involved. In this class of molecules are more than a thousand different *enzymes:* agents that make some particular metabolic reaction proceed much faster than it otherwise would. Also in this class of molecules are the main substances involved in movements of subcellular structures and movements of cells. These cells range from sperm to amoebas to those making up every muscle in your body. Here, too, are storage molecules, and transport molecules such as hemoglobin (which carries oxygen in blood). Here are structural materials of the first rank, the stuff of cell walls and membranes, bone and car-

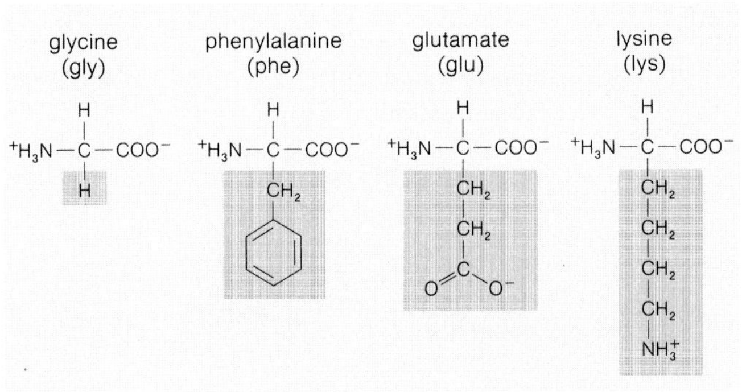

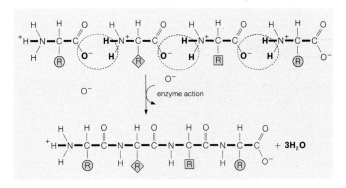

Figure 3.16 Structural formulas for four of the twenty common amino acids, with the R groups shaded in green. Glycine has a polar (but uncharged) R group. Phenylalanine has a nonpolar R group. In glutamate, the R group is negatively charged; in lysine, it is positively charged.

Figure 3.17 Condensation of a polypeptide chain from four amino acid units.

tilage, hoof and claw. Here are molecules serving as some kinds of hormones (chemical messengers) and others that help protect the vertebrate body against disease.

Primary Structure: A String of Amino Acids

For all their diversity, proteins typically contain some combination of only about twenty different kinds of amino acids. This is true of proteins in all living cells, from bacteria to those of plants and animals. An **amino acid** has four parts, all bonded covalently to the same central carbon atom. The parts are an amino group ($-NH_2$), a carboxyl group ($-COOH$), a hydrogen atom, and some distinct atom or cluster of atoms designated the R group (Figure 3.16). In most cellular environments, the amino and the carboxyl parts are ionized in this way:

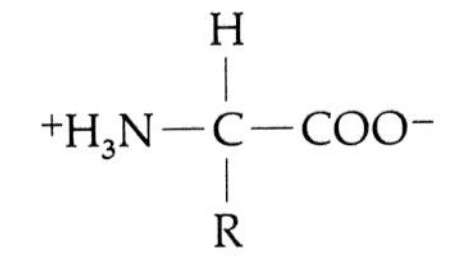

$$^+H_3N-\overset{\overset{\displaystyle H}{|}}{\underset{\underset{\displaystyle R}{|}}{C}}-COO^-$$

As you can see, the amino group has an extra hydrogen atom (without its associated electron), and the carboxyl group has lost a hydrogen atom but kept its electron.

How do amino acid units become assembled into proteins? Through condensation reactions, a covalent bond may form between the amino group of one amino acid and the carboxyl group of another. This covalent linkage is a **peptide bond**, and the molecule formed is a dipeptide. When three or more amino acids are strung together, the molecule is a *polypeptide chain.* Figure 3.17 depicts peptide bond formation.

Theoretically, any type of amino acid could follow any other in a polypeptide chain. But the actual sequence is always the same for all normal proteins of a given type. Figure 3.18 is an example of the characteristic sequence for one kind of protein. The specific sequence of amino acids in a polypeptide chain constitutes the **primary structure** of a protein. This sequence has major implications for the functional shape that a protein will assume within the cell environment.

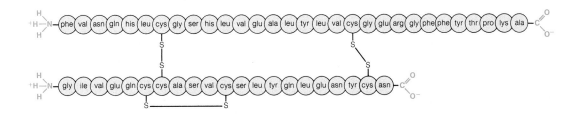

Figure 3.18 Linear sequence of amino acids in bovine (cattle) insulin, as determined by Frederick Sanger in 1953. This protein is composed of two polypeptide chains, linked together by disulfide bridges ($-S-S-$).

Spatial Patterns of Protein Structure

The primary structure of a protein influences its three-dimensional shape in two ways. The first has to do with regular bonding patterns along the polypeptide backbone. Notice the double bond in each gray-shaded square in Figure 3.17. Orbitals of electrons associated with this bond actually spread from the oxygen, around the carbon, and over to the nitrogen atom. Because of electron sharing, all atoms around the peptide bond tend to be positioned rigidly in the same plane (the gray square). Atoms can rotate only around the single covalent bonds on either side of the peptide linkage.

The rigid positioning of atoms in the peptide groups imposes some limits on the protein structures possible. Most often, the backbone becomes tightly coiled into a rodlike structure, with R groups pointing outward. Hydrogen bonds form between every fourth amino acid in the chain, and tend to hold the chain in a helical coil about its own axis (Figure 3.19). In other cases, the chain is almost fully extended, and hydrogen bonds form between *different* chains (Figure 3.19). These bonds can hold many chains side by side, in sheetlike array. The term **secondary structure** refers to a helical or extended pattern, brought about by hydrogen bonds at regular intervals along the polypeptide chain.

Figure 3.20 Three-dimensional structure of one of the four polypeptide chains of hemoglobin. Notice the irregular bends that disrupt the helical coiling of the polypeptide chain. Four such disruptions are caused by the presence of four proline molecules at different points in the primary sequence. The disk-shaped structure represents an iron-containing component called a heme group, to which one oxygen molecule may bind. (After R. Dickerson and I. Geis, 1969, *The Structure and Action of Proteins*, Benjamin)

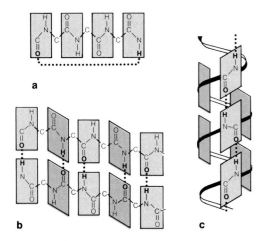

Figure 3.19 (**a**) Hydrogen bonding (dotted line) that forms between every fourth amino acid in a protein chain, which leads to an alpha pattern of protein structure. (**b**) The pleated, beta pattern in proteins. Dotted lines are hydrogen bonds that form between two chains. (**c**) The coiled alpha pattern of protein structure.

The second way in which primary structure influences a protein's final three-dimensional structure has to do with the R groups projecting from the backbone. Most helically coiled proteins also assume **tertiary structure**: they become further distorted into some permanent shape whenever an R group interacts with another R group some distance away, with the backbone itself, or with other substances present in the cell. For example, the amino acid proline has a bulky ring structure. Wherever it occurs in the amino acid sequence, the chain can't make a regular helical twist. Figure 3.20 shows one of the diverse shapes achieved through these and other interactions.

Quaternary structure, the fourth level of protein architecture, requires interactions between two or more polypeptide chains to form a functional protein. For instance, four polypeptide chains, each with an iron-containing heme group, interact spontaneously and form the globular structure of the *hemoglobin* molecule (Figure 3.21). Or consider the fibrous structure of *collagen*, the most common animal protein. Skin, bone, tendons, cartilage, blood vessels, heart valves, kidney membranes, corneas—all depend on the strength inherent in this protein. Each collagen molecule is a triple helix, composed of three coiled polypeptide chains. Three interacting chains form the quaternary struc-

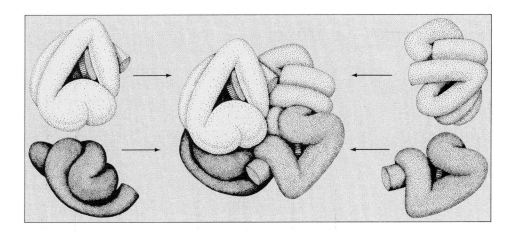

Figure 3.21 Quaternary structure of the protein hemoglobin, a red pigment circulating in blood of complex animals and carrying vital oxygen to tissues. Hemoglobin consists of four polypeptide chains, held tightly together by numerous weak bonds. Each polypeptide chain has a heme group, such as that shown in Figure 3.20. In different animals, there are slight variations in the amino acid sequence of hemoglobin's polypeptide chains. Thus the chains bend in slightly different ways in each case, which gives rise to variations in the way the molecules function to pick up and release oxygen. Such variations are adaptations to different oxygen levels in different environments. (Redrawn from R. W. McGilvery, 1970, *Biochemistry: A Functional Approach,* Saunders)

ture of the collagen molecule. Many molecules clustered together form fibrils of collagen (Figure 3.22).

Protein Denaturation

Many experiments support the idea that primary structure dictates the final shape of a protein under normal conditions. Among these are studies of proteins that have undergone **denaturation**: interactions holding the molecule in its three-dimensional form are disrupted, and the polypeptide chain unwinds or changes in some way. Denaturation can be brought about by exposure to high temperatures (typically, above 60°C) or by the presence of chemical agents that disrupt the weak bonds on which secondary, tertiary, and quaternary structure are based. Following the drastic structural changes brought about by denaturation, the protein can no longer perform its biological function.

For example, the white portion of an uncooked chicken egg is the protein albumin. When you fry or boil an egg, the heat does not affect the strong covalent bonds of its primary structure. But it destroys the protein's secondary and tertiary structure. Although denaturation can be reversed for some kinds of proteins when normal conditions

are restored, albumin isn't one of them. There is no way to uncook a cooked egg.

What is the important point to remember about protein structure? It can be summarized in this way:

In itself, a stretched-out polypeptide chain plays no functional role in a cell. However, its amino acid sequence dictates the final, three-dimensional structure of a protein—and this structure dictates how the protein will interact with other cell substances.

Protein-Based Substances

As Figure 3.20 implies, proteins may be linked with other substances. Iron-containing proteins include not only the hemoglobins but also the **cytochromes**, which transport electrons in most kinds of cells. Sugar-containing proteins are called **glycoproteins**. They include hormones involved in female reproductive cycles. In human blood, the glycoprotein gamma globulin helps protect the body against invaders. Glycoproteins embedded in cell membranes are sites of chemical communication.

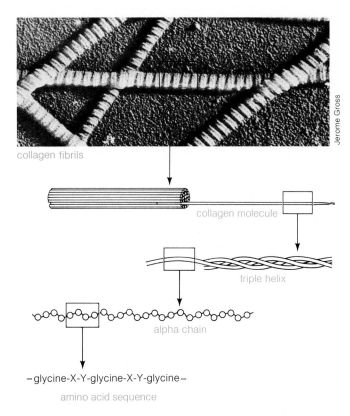

collagen fibrils

Jerome Gross

collagen molecule

triple helix

alpha chain

−glycine-X-Y-glycine-X-Y-glycine−

amino acid sequence

Figure 3.22 Structure of collagen, from fibrils (made visible through electron microscopy) down to its amino acid sequence. In this sequence, the X and Y designate proline and a modified amino acid called hydroxyproline (which is a proline with a hydroxyl group attached). (After D. Eyre, "Collagen: Molecular Diversity in the Body's Protein Scaffold," *Science* 207, 21 March 1980. Copyright 1980 AAAS)

Lipoproteins contain both lipids and proteins. Of recent interest are those to which cholesterol is bound as it is transported through the bloodstream. The proportion of lipid to protein in these molecules seems to vary among individuals. The variation is implicated in susceptibility to heart and circulatory disorders. Other protein-based substances include the **nucleoproteins**: compounds of proteins and nucleic acids. One such nucleoprotein is the DNA of all organisms except monerans. Many different proteins are bonded to the DNA along its entire length. These nucleoprotein fibers become coiled and folded in ways that enhance the shipment of hereditary instructions into new cells during cellular reproduction.

NUCLEIC ACIDS AND OTHER NUCLEOTIDES

Among the most important of all molecules of life are the nucleotides. Each **nucleotide** contains at least a five-carbon sugar (ribose or deoxyribose), a nitrogen-containing base (either a single-ringed pyrimidine or a double-ringed purine), and a phosphate group. For example, one nucleotide has a sugar, base, and phosphate group hooked together in this way:

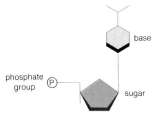

base

phosphate group

P

sugar

Three kinds of nucleotides or nucleotide-based molecules are the adenosine phosphates, the nucleotide coenzymes, and the nucleic acids. Later chapters will explore the structure and function of these molecules. Here, we can simply summarize their functions. The **adenosine phosphates** are relatively small molecules that function as chemical messengers within and between cells, and as energy carriers. Cyclic adenosine monophosphate (cAMP) is a chemical messenger. Adenosine triphosphate (ATP) is a nucleotide energy carrier. The **nucleotide coenzymes** transport hydrogen ions and their associated electrons, which are necessary in cell metabolism. Nicotinamide adenine dinucleotide (NAD^+) and flavin adenine dinucleotide (FAD) are two of these coenzymes.

The nucleotide-based molecules called **nucleic acids** are long single- or double-stranded molecules. They consist of nucleotide units strung into long chains, with a phosphate bridge connecting sugars and with bases sticking out to the side:

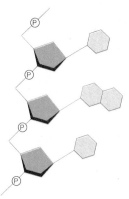

Deoxyribonucleic acid (DNA) and the ribonucleic acids (RNAs) are built according to this plan. DNA is usually a double-stranded molecule that twists helically about its own axis. The bases of one strand are connected by hydrogen bonds to bases of the other strand. You will be reading more about these molecules in chapters to come. For now, it is enough to know that genetic instructions are encoded in the sequence of bases strung together in DNA, and that RNA molecules function in the processes by which those instructions are used in building the proteins on which all forms of life are based.

Readings

Davis, B. 1980. "Frontiers of the Biological Sciences." *Science* 209: 78–83.

Dickerson, R., and I. Geis. 1969. *The Structure and Action of Proteins.* Menlo Park, California: Benjamin. A classic in the literature.

Eyre, D. 1980. "Collagen: Molecular Diversity in the Body's Protein Scaffold." *Science* 207: 1315–1322.

Frieden, E. 1972. "The Chemical Elements of Life." *Scientific American* 227(1):52–64. Good summary of the biological roles of different elements.

Lehninger, A. 1981. *Biochemistry.* Third edition. New York: Worth. Advanced reading, but a standard reference for the serious student.

Miller, G. 1981. *Chemistry: A Basic Introduction.* Second edition. Belmont, California: Wadsworth. Interesting, accessible introduction to chemical principles.

Morris, H. 1980. "Biomolecular Structure Determination by Mass Spectrometry." *Nature* 286:447–452.

Watson, J. 1976. *Molecular Biology of the Gene.* Third edition. Menlo Park, California: Benjamin. More than genes; this classic includes a concise survey of chemical bonding and the structure of large biological molecules.

Review Questions

1. What is an atom? An element? Each atom in a given chemical element is unique because of the _____ and _____ of its subatomic parts.

2. Define proton and electron. What happens when many negatively charged electrons jockey for position around positively charged protons in a nucleus? Why are the resulting, predictable arrangements important for life?

3. Explain how an ion differs from a neutral atom.

4. Electrons can absorb certain amounts of incoming energy that puts them into orbitals at higher energy levels. How many electrons can be squeezed into each orbital?

5. Atoms of chemically nonreactive elements have _____ electrons in each occupied orbital. Atoms of chemically reactive elements have _____ electrons in one or more orbitals.

6. Cell substances are held together largely by strong bonds that involve shared electrons, and by weaker interactions between atoms or ions of opposite charge. Name these kinds of bonds, and give examples of molecules in which they are found.

7. Is a film of oil on water an outcome of bonding between the molecules making up the oil?

8. Define the difference between an acid and a base. On the pH scale from 0 to 14, what is the acid range?

9. The environments in which cells occur typically shift in pH. Does the inside of the cell normally shift in a direction corresponding to the change?

10. Identify which of the following is the carbohydrate, fatty acid, amino acid, and polypeptide:
    a. $^+NH_3$—CHR—COO$^-$
    b. $C_6H_{12}O_6$
    c. $(glycine)_{20}$
    d. $CH_3(CH_2)_{16}COO^-$

11. Why do carbon atoms tend to combine so readily with other atoms? Explain the difference between saturated and unsaturated fats in terms of the carbon skeletons of their fatty acid tails.

12. Is this statement true or false? Not all proteins are enzymes, but all enzymes are proteins.

13. How do its side groups dictate how a protein molecule will interact with other cell substances? (Hint: Describe the four levels of protein structure.) What consequences do these interactions have for cell functioning?

14. Distinguish between the following:
    a. monosaccharide, polysaccharide
    b. phospholipid, glycolipid
    c. peptide, polypeptide

15. Describe the difference between a condensation reaction and hydrolysis.

16. Define the general structure and function of the three kinds of nucleotides or nucleotide-based molecules so important to cell functioning and reproduction.

4

CELL STRUCTURE AND FUNCTION: AN OVERVIEW

GENERALIZED PICTURE OF THE CELL

Emergence of the Cell Theory

Early in the seventeenth century, Galileo arranged two glass lenses in a cylinder. With this instrument he happened to look at an insect, and thereby came to describe the stunning geometric patterns of its tiny compound eyes. Thus Galileo, who was not a biologist, was the first to record a biological observation made through a microscope. The systematic study of the cellular basis of life was about to begin. First in Italy, then in France and England, biologists began to explore architectural details of a world whose existence had not even been suspected.

At mid-century Robert Hooke, "Curator of Instruments" for the Royal Society of England, was at the forefront of these studies. When Hooke first turned one of his microscopes to a thinly sliced piece of cork from a mature tree, he observed tiny, empty compartments. These he likened to the structure of honeycomb. He gave them the Latin name *cellulae* (meaning small rooms); hence the origin of the biological term "cell." They were actually dead cells, which is what cork is made of, although Hooke did not think of them as being dead because he did not know that cells could be alive. He also noted that cells in other plant

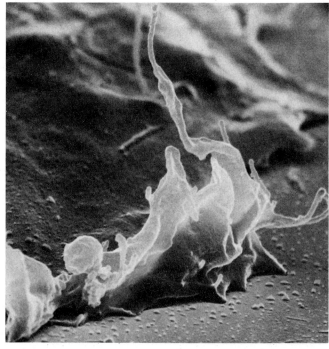

Jean-Paul Revel

Figure 4.1 A "cell"—a vaguely dreary name more suggestive of carton boxes than of things seething with life. Shown here, a scanning electron micrograph of the dynamic ruffling edge of a hamster kidney cell, caught on the move.

materials contained "juices." He did not speculate on what the juice-filled structures might represent.

Given the simplicity of their instruments, it is amazing that these pioneers saw all that they did. Antony van Leeuwenhoek, a shopkeeper, had the greatest skill in glassworking and possibly the keenest vision of all. He devoted all of his spare time to constructing lenses and to observing everything he could get hold of, including samples of sperm cells. He even observed a single bacterium—a type of organism so small it would not be seen again for another two centuries! However, this was primarily an age of exploration, not of interpretation. Once the limits of those simple instruments had been reached, biologists gave up interest in cell structure without ever having been able to explain what it was they had seen.

Then, in the 1820s, improvements in lens design tempted biologists to look once more into the cell. It now became clear that small structures were suspended within those cellular "juices." The botanist Robert Brown, for instance, reported the presence of a spherelike structure inside every plant cell he examined. He called the structure a "nucleus." By 1839, the zoologist Theodor Schwann reported the presence of cells in animal tissues. About this time, he began working with Matthias Schleiden, a botanist who had concluded that cells are present in all plant tissues and that the nucleus is somehow paramount in the reproduction of cells. Both investigators proposed that each living cell has the potential for independent existence. The term implies that a cell has the ability to continue living in the absence of other cells. It was Schwann who distilled the meaning of these new observations in what came to be known as the first two principles of the **cell theory**:

All organisms are composed of one or more cells.

The cell is the basic living unit of organization for all organisms.

Another decade passed before the physiologist Rudolf Virchow finished exhaustive studies into cell reproduction. He completed the basic theory with this principle:

All cells arise from preexisting cells.

Not only was a cell viewed as the smallest living unit, the continuity of life was now seen to be arising directly from the division and growth of single cells. Within each tiny cell, events were going on that had profound implications for all levels of biological organization!

Basic Aspects of Cell Structure and Function

What is it about individual cells that gives them the ability to harbor the quality we call "life"? At first glance, this question might seem difficult to answer, for cells and their contents are tremendously diverse. They vary in size, shape, and degree of elaboration—and they do so to a degree that is as notable as the variety that exists among large, multicelled organisms. On closer examination, however, we find that three structural features are essential for maintaining the living state in all cell types:

1. An enveloping **plasma membrane**, which is a physical boundary between internal cell events and the outside world. At the surface of this boundary membrane are regions that detect changing environmental conditions. Spanning the membrane are passageways through which substances move into and out of the cell, in highly controlled ways (Chapter Five).

2. A region of DNA, which contains instructions necessary for synthesizing all the organic substances a cell requires in growth, development, and reproduction. This region is called a **nucleoid** in monerans. It is called a **nucleus** in protistans, fungi, plants, and animals.

3. Internal membranes and particles that function in metabolism and biosynthesis. These elements are part of the **cytoplasm**, which includes everything *except* the plasma membrane and the region of DNA. They are bathed in a semifluid substance (the cytosol). With these cytoplasmic elements, a cell captures and converts energy into forms appropriate to drive its life processes. These elements work in interrelated ways to assure that cell parts can be built, operated, replaced, and reproduced.

The overall structural organization of all cells can be depicted in the following way. In this chapter and the next, we will be interpreting the functions of cells and cell parts in terms of their relationship to this basic structural plan:

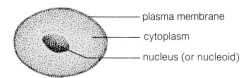

- plasma membrane
- cytoplasm
- nucleus (or nucleoid)

Table 4.1   Units of Measure Used in Microscopy

Unit	Equivalence in Millimeters	Equivalence in Micrometers	Equivalence in Nanometers	Equivalence in Angstroms
Millimeter (mm)	1	1,000	1,000,000	10,000,000
Micrometer (μm)	0.001	1	1,000	10,000
Nanometer (nm)	0.000001	0.001	1	10
Angstrom (Å)	0.0000001	0.0001	0.1	1

The micrometer is used in describing whole cells or large cell structures, such as the nucleus.

The nanometer is used in describing cell ultrastructures (those ranging from, say, mitochondria downward), even of macromolecules. Lipid molecules, for example, may be about 2 nanometers long; cell membranes may be 7 to 10 nanometers thick; ribosomes are about 25 nanometers across.

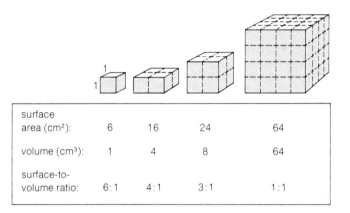

surface area (cm²):	6	16	24	64
volume (cm³):	1	4	8	64
surface-to-volume ratio:	6 : 1	4 : 1	3 : 1	1 : 1

Figure 4.2 Simple portrayal of the relationship between surface area and volume when a cube is enlarged. The cube to the left measures one centimeter on a side. As its linear dimensions increase, its surface area does not increase at the same rate as its volume. This relationship puts constraints on the nature of cell enlargement. Past a certain point, a volume of cytoplasm enlarging in all directions would outstrip the amount of plasma membrane surface available to service it.

Cell Size

Bird eggs are exceptionally large single cells, which you can observe with the unaided eye. So are individual cells in a watermelon. Some nerve cells running through a giraffe leg can be three meters long and are certainly what you would call enormous. Most whole cells, however, cannot be seen without the aid of a microscope. Usually their dimensions are on the order of micrometers. (As Table 4.1 indicates, a micrometer is only a millionth of a meter.) The

smallest bacterial cells are measured in *billionths* of a meter (nanometers); so are many internal cell structures.

The size of a cell is governed largely by how efficiently materials can move across the plasma membrane and become distributed through the cytoplasm. A cell survives only as long as it takes in nutrients, transports them through its entire volume of cytoplasm, then gets rid of wastes. For a small single cell, the plasma membrane provides enough surface area to take up required materials from the environment and to dispose of wastes. Materials are readily distributed through the interior by diffusion (the random motion of molecules).

What happens when a cell enlarges? It eventually encounters restraints imposed by the **surface-to-volume ratio**: as a cell's linear dimensions grow, its surface area does not increase at the same rate as its volume. Volume increases with the cube of the diameter, but surface area increases only with the square (Figure 4.2). If a round cell were to enlarge four times in diameter, with no other changes, its volume would increase sixty-four times ($4 \times 4 \times 4$). To sustain the expanded volume of cytoplasm, the cell would have to take in sixty-four times as many nutrients and dispose of sixty-four times as many wastes. However, a four-fold increase in diameter (with no other changes) would increase the cell surface area by only sixteen times. Thus each unit area of plasma membrane would be called upon to serve four times as much cytoplasm as it did before! Clearly, enlargement alone is not feasible. Past a certain point, a cell simply would die.

Constraints of the surface-to-volume ratio can be partly overcome by structural modifications to the cell body itself. In some photosynthetic bacterial and algal cells, the plasma membrane is folded repeatedly back on itself, and the folds are tucked inside the cytoplasm. Some intes-

Photo credits (vertical, along image edges): Kim Taylor/Bruce Coleman Ltd. · Hervé Chaumerton/Agence Nature · McCutcheon/ZEFA

a

b

c

Figure 4.3 Multicellular strategies for getting around the constraints of the surface-to-volume ratio. (**a**) One-dimensional growth in a cyanobacterium (cylindrospermum). (**b**) Two-dimensional growth in a red alga (Callible-pharis). (**c**) Three-dimensional growth in a whale. Here, internal transport systems assure even the internal cells of efficient materials exchange.

tinal cells have multiple projections on one side, each like the finger region of a glove. Such cell specializations work well in some fairly large single cells. In a *multicelled* body, the problem is compounded; for *all* living cells must be able to exchange materials with the environment.

Threadlike multicelled organisms are one response that permits greater mass and a suitable cell surface-to-volume ratio. Here, each cell is kept at the body surface, where it makes direct environmental contact (Figure 4.3). In many algae, strings of small cells are also highly branched into extensive—but still threadlike—bodies. Similarly, there are sheetlike multicelled organisms with each cell at or near the surface and with greater body mass. Examples include some protistans, a few algae, and (to some extent) the animals called flatworms. Photosynthetic cells in flat plant leaves are near the body surface, where they are better exposed to sunlight.

Massive multicelled bodies, such as your own, have internal systems of specialized cells and tissues for transporting materials between the environment and all living body cells. Many land plants have vascular tissues that transport fluids to and from cells; many animals have blood and lymph vessels that do the same thing. Such are the diverse adaptations that have been made to the constraints imposed by the surface-to-volume ratio.

Thus, even for massive multicelled bodies, we are still talking about cells that are microscopically small, for the most part. Red blood cells in your body are only about 6 to 8 micrometers in diameter; a string of about 2,000 of them would only be as long as your thumbnail is wide. Most of your other cells are only between 5 and 20 micrometers in diameter. The finest detail that the modern light microscope can resolve is about 200 nanometers across. However, in the past few decades, biochemical studies and electron microscopy have enabled us to penetrate more deeply into the world of cell structure and function. Figure 4.4 describes how light microscopes and the more advanced electron microscopes work. Figure 4.5 shows some examples of the kinds of images that can be formed with these instruments. It will give you an idea of the range of magnifications that you will be encountering for micrographs used throughout this book.

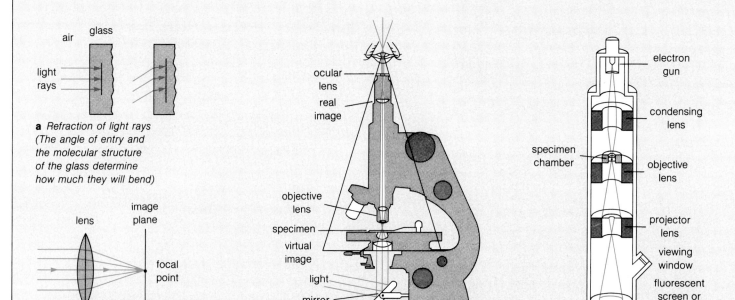

a *Refraction of light rays (The angle of entry and the molecular structure of the glass determine how much they will bend)*

b *Focusing light rays*

c *Compound light microscope*

d *Transmission electron microscope*

Figure 4.4 Microscopes—gateways to the cell.

Light Microscopes (a) Light microscopy relies on the bending, or refraction, of light rays. Light rays pass straight through the center of a curved lens. The farther they are from the center, the more they bend. (b,c) The *compound light microscope* is a two-lens system. All rays coming from the object being viewed are channeled to a single place behind the curved lens system.

A problem with this microscope is *spherical aberration:* when small objects are brought close to the objective lens, they can blur. Another problem is *chromatic aberration* (color distortion). Light comes in different wavelengths, or colors. For instance, red is a long wavelength, blue is a short one. Blue and red light rays are bent differently as they pass through the same piece of glass, so they don't end up at the same place. If you sharply focus the red part of an image, the blue part may be out of focus, and vice versa. The distortion often causes color halos around images of small objects.

If you wish to observe a *living* cell, it must be small or thin enough for light to pass through. Also, structures inside cells can be seen only if they differ in color and density from their surroundings—but most are almost colorless and optically uniform in density. Specimens can be stained (exposed to dyes that react with some cell structures but not others), but staining usually alters the structures and kills the cells. Finally, dead cells begin to break down at once, so they must be pickled or preserved before staining. Most observations have been made of dead, pickled, or stained cells. Largely transparent living cells can be observed through the *phase contrast microscope*. Here, small differences in the way different structures refract light are converted to larger variations in brightness.

No matter how good a lens system may be, when magnification exceeds 2,000× (when the image diameter is 2,000 times as large as the object's diameter), cell structures appear larger but are not clearer. By analogy, when you hold a magnifying glass close to a newspaper photograph, you see only black dots. You cannot see a detail as small as or smaller than a dot; the dot would cover it up. In microscopy, something like dot size intervenes to limit *resolution* (the property that dictates whether small objects close together can be seen as separate things). That limiting factor is the physical size of wavelengths of visible light. Red wavelengths are about 750 nanometers and violet wavelengths about 400 nanometers; all other colors fall in between. If an object is smaller than about one-half the wavelength, light rays passing by it will overlap so much that the object won't be visible. The best light microscopes resolve detail only to about 200 nanometers.

Transmission Electron Microscopes Electrons are usually thought of as particles, but they also behave like waves. Electron wavelengths are much smaller than the smallest visible light wavelengths. The more energy an electron has, the shorter its wavelength. It takes very little energy to excite an electron to wavelengths of about 0.005 nanometer—about 100,000 times shorter than those of visible light! Ordinary lenses cannot be used to focus such accelerated streams of electrons, because glass scatters them. But each electron carries an electric charge, which responds to magnetic force. A magnetic field can divert electrons along defined paths and channel them to a focal point. Magnetic lenses are used in *transmission electron microscopes* (d).

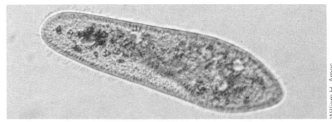

a

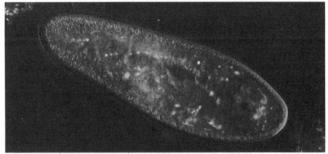

b

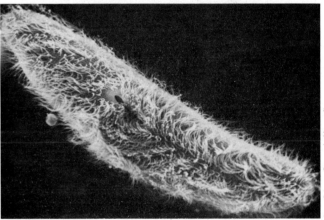

c

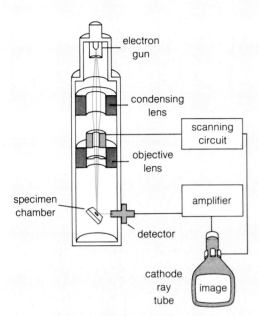

electron
gun

condensing
lens

scanning
circuit

objective
lens

amplifier

specimen
chamber

detector

cathode
ray
tube

image

e *Scanning electron microscope*

Resolution of existing transmission electron microscopes is limited to between 0.2 and 1.0 nanometer, because there is an electrical equivalent to spherical aberration. Also, electrons must travel in a vacuum, otherwise they would be randomly scattered by molecules in the air. Cells can't live in a vacuum, so living cells cannot be observed at this higher magnification. In addition, specimens must be sliced extremely thin so that electron scattering corresponds to the density of different structures. (The more dense the structure, the greater the scattering and the darker the area in the final image formed.) Specimen fixation is crucial. Fine cell structures are the first to fall apart when cells die, and artifacts (structures that do not really exist in cells) may result. Because most cell materials are somewhat transparent to electrons, they must be stained with heavy metal "dyes," which can create more artifacts.

With *high-voltage electron microscopes*, electrons can be made ten times more energetic than with the standard electron microscope. With the energy boost, intact cells several micrometers thick can be penetrated. The image produced is something like an x-ray plate and reveals the three-dimensional internal organization of cells (see, for example, Figure 4.20b).

Scanning Electron Microscopes (**e**) With a *scanning electron microscope*, a narrow electron beam is played back and forth across a specimen's surface, which has been coated with a thin metal layer. Electron energy triggers the emission of secondary electrons in the metal. Equipment similar to a television camera detects the emission patterns, and an image is formed. Scanning electron microscopy is limited to surface views, and it does not approach the high resolution of transmission instruments. However, its images have fantastic depth.

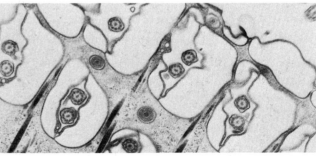

d

Figure 4.5 Comparison of image-forming abilities of microscopes. The specimen is *Paramecium*. (**a**) Conventional light microscope, bright-field, 2900×. (**b**) Phase contrast microscope, 1100×. (**c**) Scanning electron microscope, 500×. Notice hairlike cilia (motile structures) on surface. (**d**) Transmission electron micrograph, glancing section through body surface, 17,800×. The cilia (circles) have been cut, like whiskers with a razor.

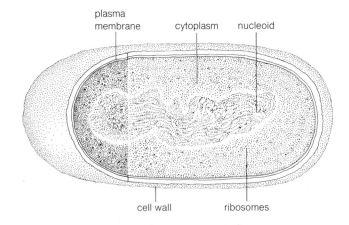

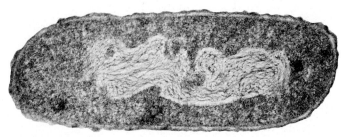

Figure 4.6 Body plan of the bacterium *E. coli*, a prokaryotic cell. The transmission electron micrograph shows a specimen in longitudinal section, 28,000×. (G. Cohen-Bazire)

PROKARYOTIC CELLS

In terms of cellular organization, there are two distinct kinds of cells: prokaryotic and eukaryotic. Prokaryotic cells are structurally the simpler of the two and are thought to have the most ancient lineage. They are all bacterial cells, including the cyanobacteria (formerly called blue-green algae).

The term **prokaryotic** means "before the nucleus." Prokaryotic cells have no membrane-bound nucleus (as eukaryotic cells do) nor any other well-developed membrane-bound compartments in the cytoplasm, for that matter. What they all have is a plasma membrane, cytoplasm, and a nucleoid, an irregularly shaped region in which DNA is concentrated (Figure 4.6). They all have **ribosomes**, which are RNA-protein structures that participate in protein synthesis in the cytoplasm. Ribosomes are only about fifteen to twenty-five nanometers in diameter. Each is composed of two subunits. One of these subunits serves as a platform on which amino acids are linked into protein chains; the other subunit contains enzymes that speed the linkages.

Most prokaryotic cells also have a rigid or semirigid *cell wall* outside the plasma membrane. A cell wall supports and provides shape for the cell. The prokaryotic cell wall

is composed of substances that the cell itself secretes. Sometimes it has a coating that serves a protective function.

Internal membrane specializations are limited. In cyanobacteria and purple sulfur bacteria, the plasma membrane folds inward into the cytoplasm. These membrane regions are sites of energy conversions of photosynthesis. In a few bacterial species, the cytoplasm also contains a few photosynthetic membrane sacs. Such infoldings and sacs do increase the membrane surface, hence the number of reaction sites available. Even so, they do not begin to approach the internal membrane complexity of eukaryotic cells.

EUKARYOTIC CELLS

Protistan, fungal, plant, and animal cells show tremendous diversity. Yet they are clearly alike in one feature: a reliance on many specialized membrane-bound compartments, or **organelles**, of the cytoplasm. Eukaryotic cells generally contain some number of these organelles at some stage:

nucleus	*hereditary instructions for synthesis, cell operation*
endoplasmic reticulum	*synthesis, modification, distribution of materials*
Golgi bodies	*modification, distribution of materials*
lysosomes	*digestion, disposal*
microbodies	*material conversions, disposal*
mitochondria	*energy extraction, conversion*

The most conspicuous of these organelles is the nucleus, which never is present in prokaryotes. Hence protistan, fungal, plant, and animal cells are called **eukaryotic**, a term that means "true nucleus."

Other organelles are found in some eukaryotic cells but not others. For example, photosynthetic protistans and plants all have one or more *plastids*, which serve varied functions. Some, such as the chloroplast, are compartments for sunlight energy conversions, food assembly, and food storage. Cells of true fungi and land plants also have one or more *central vacuoles*. The main function of central vacuoles is to help increase cell surface area during growth.

Aside from these organelles, other structural features are characteristic of eukaryotic cells. Current research suggests that eukaryotic cells may rely on some kind of *cytoplasmic lattice* during at least some stages of their development. This lattice is an internal framework that supports ribosomes, fibers, and organelles, and organizes them rela-

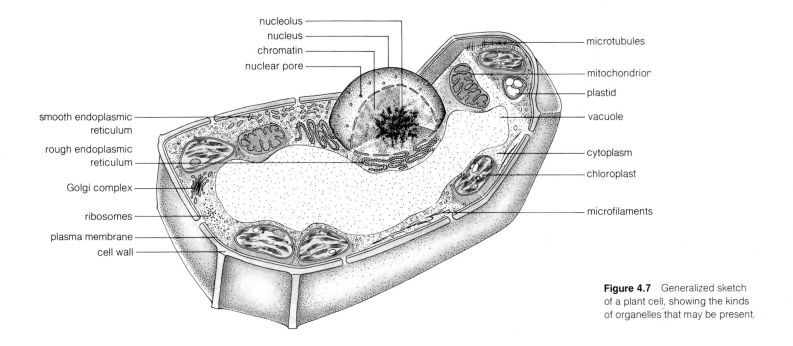

nucleolus
nucleus
chromatin
nuclear pore

microtubules
mitochondrion
plastid
vacuole

smooth endoplasmic reticulum
rough endoplasmic reticulum
Golgi complex
ribosomes
plasma membrane
cell wall

cytoplasm
chloroplast
microfilaments

Figure 4.7 Generalized sketch of a plant cell, showing the kinds of organelles that may be present.

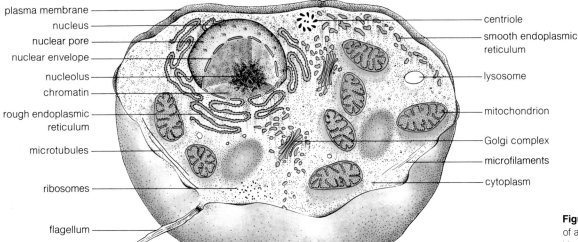

plasma membrane
nucleus
nuclear pore
nuclear envelope
nucleolus
chromatin
rough endoplasmic reticulum
microtubules
ribosomes
flagellum

centriole
smooth endoplasmic reticulum
lysosome
mitochondrion
Golgi complex
microfilaments
cytoplasm

Figure 4.8 Generalized sketch of an animal cell, showing the kinds of organelles that may be present.

tive to one another. Many protistans, true fungi, and land plant cells have a *cell wall* surrounding the plasma membrane. If you were asked to identify the main structural feature that distinguishes plant cells from those of animals, it would be their cellulose-containing walls.

Figures 4.7 and 4.8 are three-dimensional sketches that show how these various structures and organelles might be arranged in a typical plant and animal cell. Keep in mind that calling them "typical" is like calling a squid or a watermelon plant a "typical" animal or plant; tremendous variation exists on the basic structural plan. Figures 4.9 and 4.10 show how some of these structures and organelles actually appear in thin sections of cells examined with the transmission electron microscope.

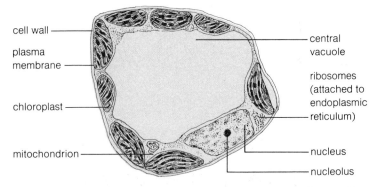

cell wall
plasma membrane
chloroplast
mitochondrion

central vacuole

ribosomes (attached to endoplasmic reticulum)

nucleus

nucleolus

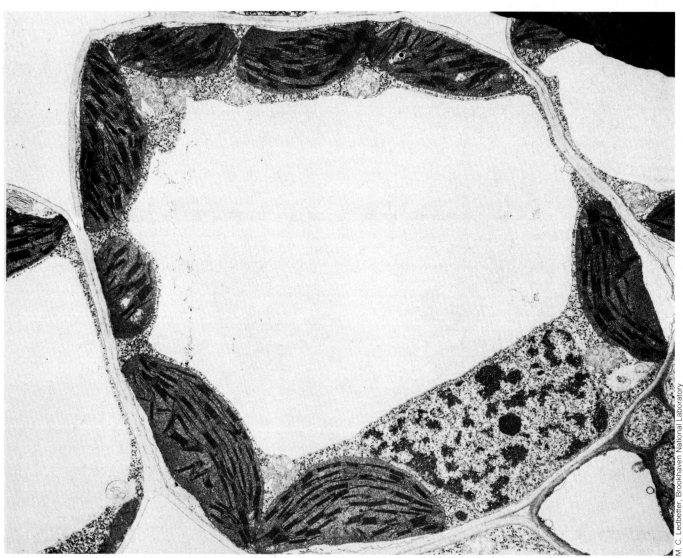

M. C. Ledbetter, Brookhaven National Laboratory

Figure 4.9 Transmission electron micrograph of a plant cell from a blade of timothy grass, cross-section, 11,300×.

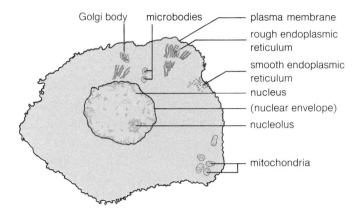

Golgi body   microbodies   plasma membrane

rough endoplasmic
reticulum

smooth endoplasmic
reticulum

nucleus

(nuclear envelope)

nucleolus

mitochondria

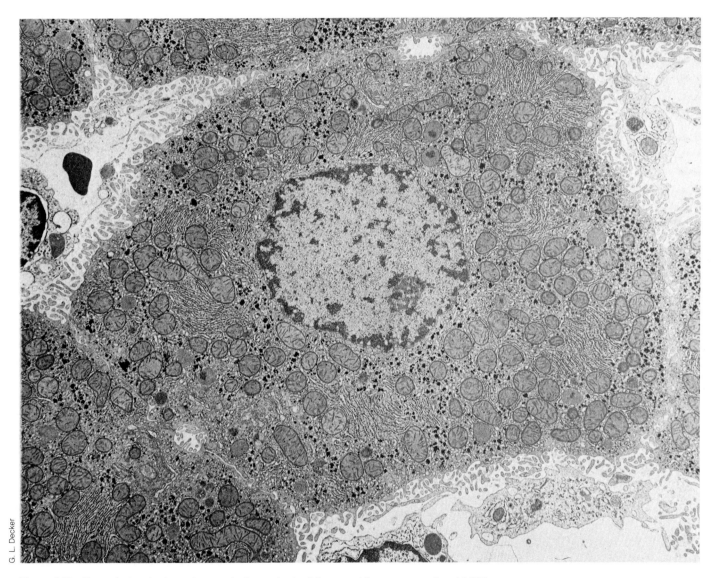

G. L. Decker

Figure 4.10   Transmission electron micrograph of an animal cell from a rat liver, cross-section, 15,000×.

Figure 4.11 Electron micrograph of the nucleus (in cross-section) from a bat pancreatic cell, 12,600×. Arrows point to pores in the nuclear envelope.

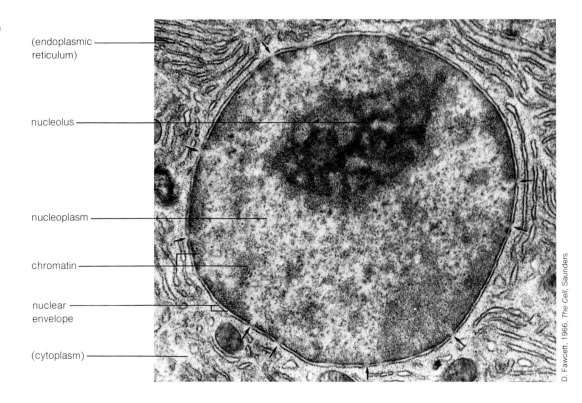

(endoplasmic reticulum)

nucleolus

nucleoplasm

chromatin

nuclear envelope

(cytoplasm)

D. Fawcett, 1966, *The Cell*, Saunders

THE NUCLEUS

The eukaryotic **nucleus** is the membrane-bound compartment in which hereditary instructions reside. These instructions govern synthesis of all organic molecules required in cell construction. They help control the cytoplasmic activities that keep a cell alive, and they govern growth and division. Messages sent out from the nucleus also help direct cellular responses to changes in the environment. The cellular events under nuclear control can be rapid, highly directional, and highly specific.

Nuclear Envelope

Separating the contents of a nucleus from the cytoplasm is a two-membrane system, the **nuclear envelope** (Figures 4.11 and 4.12). Inside the nucleus is the nucleoplasm, a complex suspension of particles and molecules. Some studies suggest that a latticelike framework exists in the nucleoplasm, giving shape to the nucleus itself and helping to position the hereditary material within it.

The outer surface of the nuclear envelope, which faces the cytoplasm, is richly peppered with ribosomes. In some places, this outer membrane is continuous with endoplasmic reticulum. Pores extend across both membranes of the envelope at regular intervals (Figure 4.12). A mass of material fills much of the pore and extends beyond its diameter. At the center of this material is a small opening. Although ions and small molecules (such as monosaccharides) move freely through the openings, the pore organization seems to exert extremely selective control over the movement of RNA molecules from the nucleus to the cytoplasm.

Chromosomes

From the appearance of the nucleus in Figure 4.11, you may have concluded that the nucleus is composed of tiny bits of grainy material. When microscopists of the 1800s stained such nuclei for observation, the "granules" soaked up most of the stain and became quite distinct. At that time the nuclear material was named **chromatin**. (The word means "colored material.") Sometimes, when the nuclei being ob-

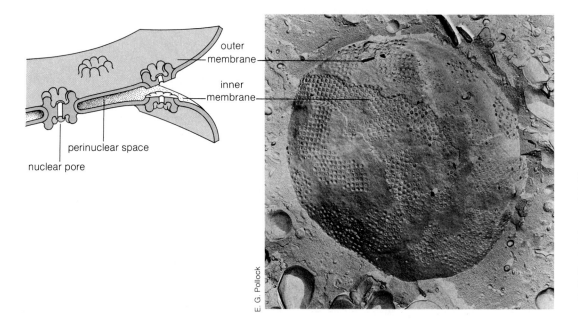

outer
membrane

inner
membrane

perinuclear space

nuclear pore

E. G. Pollock

Figure 4.12 Inner and outer membranes of a nuclear envelope. The micrograph shows both nuclear envelope membranes of a nucleus that has been freeze-fractured, a technique described in Chapter Five. Notice how pores span both membranes. They are sites where ions and molecules move into and from the nucleus, 25,000×.

served were undergoing division, the dark-staining substance looked threadlike rather than grainy. The distinct threadlike structures were called **chromosomes**, meaning "colored bodies." How were the observations explained? The tiny grains were thought to become joined together to form chromosomes when the nucleus was about to divide.

Refinements in microscopy have since changed the picture. Chromosomes are not assembled and disassembled each time the nucleus divides. Even in a nondividing nucleus, they are stretched out as long, thin threads that are all but indistinct when viewed with the light microscope. "Chromatin" and "chromosome," in short, are one and the same thing. The distinction has been retained simply to indicate the appearance of the dark-staining material of the nondividing and dividing nucleus.

Nucleolus

As cells go through a prescribed course of growth and development, one or more dense masses of irregular size and shape form in the nucleus. The mass is a **nucleolus** (plural, nucleoli). It consists of densely packed chromosome regions and the proteins and precursor RNA strands from which the two subunits of a ribosome are assembled. A complete, fully functional ribosome (with its two subunits joined to-

gether) is found only in the cytoplasm. However, ribosomal subunits are assembled separately in the nucleolar region of the nucleus, then shipped to cytoplasmic destinations.

A nucleolus is shown in Figure 4.11. Such nucleoli retain their distinct appearance only between nuclear divisions.

ORGANELLES OF AN ENDOMEMBRANE SYSTEM

Within the nucleus, molecules of RNA are produced on particular stretches of DNA that contain hereditary instructions for building particular proteins. The RNA molecules move from the nucleus to the cytoplasm, where their messages are used in assembling proteins. In eukaryotic cells, as in prokaryotic, protein synthesis takes place at intact ribosomes. However, in eukaryotic cells alone, protein synthesis, modification, and transport also require an interconnected system of membrane structures and organelles. This system, which functions in the processing and transport of proteins and other substances, is called the **endomembrane system** of eukaryotic cells. It includes the nuclear envelope and the plasma membrane. Its additional components are the endoplasmic reticulum, Golgi bodies, lysosomes, and microbodies.

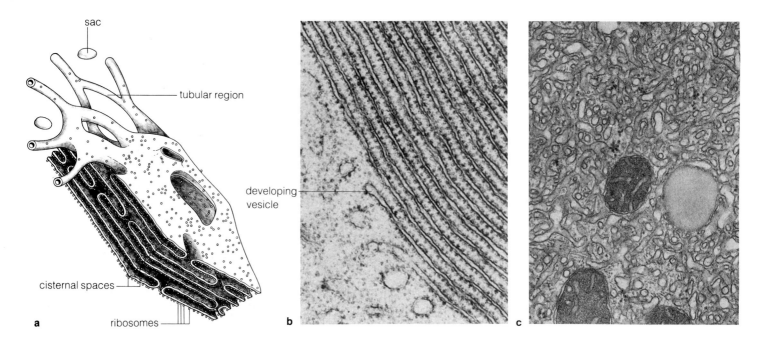

a — sac, tubular region, developing vesicle, cisternal spaces, ribosomes

b

c

Figure 4.13 (**a,b**) Rough endoplasmic reticulum, showing how the membrane surface facing the cytoplasm is studded with ribosomes. 25,000×. (**c**) Smooth endoplasmic reticulum, in cross-section. 35,000×. (a, Bloom and Fawcett, *A Textbook of Histology*; b,c, Daniel S. Friend, M.D.)

Endoplasmic Reticulum and Ribosomes

The organelle called **endoplasmic reticulum**, or ER, is a system of membranous tubes, sacs, and flattened channels (cisternae) that forms a distinct compartment within the cytoplasm. The area that the system encloses is known as the cisternal space (Figure 4.13). In terms of appearance and function, there are two main types of ER. The difference corresponds largely to whether ribosomes are present on the ER membrane on the side facing the cytoplasm. Rough ER has ribosomes attached, which gives the membranes a grainy, or rough, appearance in electron micrographs. Smooth ER has no ribosomes attached to it. Most cells contain both types of ER, although the relative proportions vary considerably among different cells.

Rough ER is concerned with protein synthesis and transport. It is most highly developed in protein-exporting cells, such as liver and pancreatic cells. Polypeptide chains are assembled on its attached ribosomes. Some of the chains are used in assembling new membrane; they become in-

corporated into the rough ER membrane itself. Others cross the membrane and move into the cisternal space. There, the chains undergo modifications by having carbohydrate, lipid, and other groups added to them. Once they are inside the cisternal space, the chains become folded into the final protein shape, and they cannot move out again. Eventually, ER channels enclosing them become pinched off, forming membranous sacs. The sacs have varied destinations. Some are secretory: they transport their protein cargo to the plasma membrane, fuse with it, and thereby release their contents to the outside. Other sacs function as storage vessels in the cytoplasm. Still others merge with smooth ER and, in some cases, enter the Golgi membrane system. There, the proteins undergo further modification.

Smooth ER, which is free of ribosomes, usually has the form of narrow pipes. (Often this membrane system looks like clustered sacs in micrographs because the "pipes" have been sliced crosswise during specimen preparation, as they have been in Figure 4.13.) Different enzymes are housed in different smooth ER systems. Depending on the kinds of enzymes present, smooth ER varies in function. Some smooth ER accepts, modifies, and transports proteins from rough ER. Some smooth ER functions in the breakdown of energy-rich glycogen or fat molecules. Smooth ER is also associated with lipid production. It is most abundant in lipid-synthesizing cells. These include cells in developing plant seeds, some intestinal cells (which make triglycerides from lipid subunits), and cells of the adrenal cortex (which make some kinds of steroid hormones).

Skeletal muscle cells have a highly specialized form of smooth ER. This system is known as the *sarcoplasmic reticulum*. It is arranged, collarlike, around the contractile units of muscle cells. Large amounts of calcium ions are stored in and released from cisternal spaces of these membranes. The calcium ions function in signal transmission between nerve and muscle cells.

Golgi Bodies

The term **Golgi bodies** refers collectively to sets of smooth membranes that are stacked into flattened, fluid-filled sacs (cisternae). Each stack of membranes is a Golgi body; in plants, it sometimes is called a *dictyosome* (Figure 4.14). In these stacks, proteins exported from the ER become modified, then they become enclosed in secretory or lysosomal vesicles that have pinched off from the Golgi membranes. Most often, a Golgi body resembles a stack of pancakes— usually eight or less, and usually curled at the edges. The topmost pancakes (the ones closest to the plasma membrane) bulge at the edges; these are the bulges that break away as membranous vesicles.

Depending on the cell type, there may be only a few or as many as 25,000 Golgi bodies in the cytoplasm. The difference corresponds to the secretory activity of a given cell type. At some stages of development, the cell may have none whatsoever. When present, Golgi bodies are distributed fairly uniformly in the cytoplasm of plant cells. They become concentrated near the endoplasmic reticulum or just outside the nuclear envelope in animal cells.

There is continuous variation in chemical composition and membrane structure from the nuclear envelope, endoplasmic reticulum, Golgi bodies, secretory vesicles, to the plasma membrane. The nuclear envelope resembles ER membranes and is probably derived from them. Transition vesicles of protein-secreting cells derived from the ER membranes fuse with Golgi membranes. The Golgi membranes accepting these vesicles resemble ER in structure and chem-

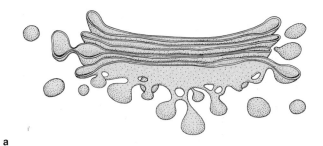

a

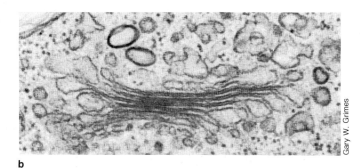

Gary W. Grimes

b

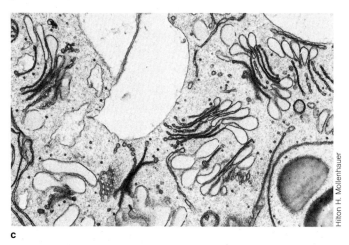

Hilton H. Mollenhauer

c

Figure 4.14 (**a**) Sketch of a Golgi body, with its stacked membranous sacs. (**b**) Golgi body from an animal cell, as it looks when sliced lengthwise, 53,300×. (**c**) Golgi body in a root cap cell of corn, 14,000×. Notice the swollen edges of the stacks, and the free vesicles just beyond them.

ical composition; indeed, proteins needed in building Golgi membranes are assembled in rough ER. Golgi membranes farthest away from the endoplasmic reticulum resemble the plasma membrane. This chemical and structural continuum is one of the reasons why the organelles being described are now considered to be parts of the same endo-

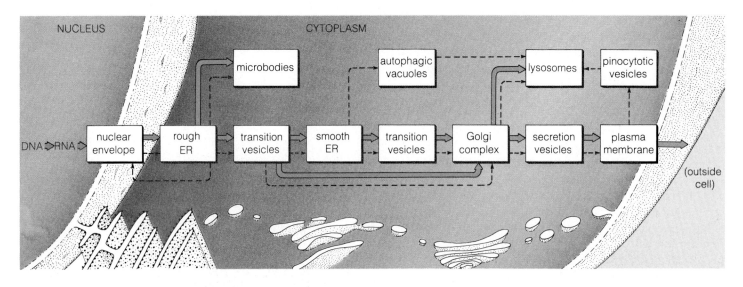

Figure 4.15 Summary of the endomembrane system of eukaryotic cells. The flow of membrane that interconnects the separate organelles of this system is indicated by dotted lines. The purple arrows indicate pathways of protein synthesis, transport, modification, storage, and secretion. Other substances besides proteins are processed and transported in organelles of this system.

membrane system. Figure 4.15 summarizes the main links between organelles in this pathway of materials assembly, modification, transport, and storage or secretion.

Lysosomes

One product of the endomembrane system is the cytoplasmic organelle called the **lysosome**. Lysosomes occur in protozoans (animal-like protistans), multicelled animals, some plants, and some fungi (especially yeasts). In all cases, lysosomes function in digestion and disposal. As part of normal maintenance activities, a cell routinely breaks down foreign particles, malfunctioning structures, and worn-out organelles into their component molecules. Lysosomes contain about forty different hydrolytic enzymes necessary for these tasks. The enzymes are able to break down virtually every large biological molecule, including polysaccharides, DNA, RNA, proteins, and certain lipids. Obviously, the enzymes able to do this could not be allowed to float about in the cytoplasm; they would destroy everything in sight. Instead, the lysosomal membranes keep them isolated from the cytoplasm.

Lysosomes act on substances that are already enclosed in two kinds of membranous containers, either *endocytotic*

vesicles or *autophagic vacuoles.* The first kind form when part of the plasma membrane infolds around dissolved particles and, in some cases, around bacterial cells that contact the outer membrane surface. The infolded membrane pinches off as a vesicle and moves into the cytoplasm. The membranes of autophagic vacuoles are possibly derived from ER. These vacuoles form around substances and structures already in the cytoplasm. Lysosomes fuse with each kind of membranous container. In this way, substances and structures such as the worn-out mitochondrion visible in Figure 4.16 become enclosed in the lysosome, where they are rapidly destroyed. The molecular leftovers of hydrolysis are small enough to be transported across the lysosomal membrane and picked up for use in various cellular building programs.

Perhaps you are wondering why the enzymes don't dismantle the lysosomal membranes along with everything else. Although the picture is far from clear, the cell apparently expends energy to maintain and replace the lysosomal membranes. This energy expenditure counters the constant enzyme attacks. A cell falls apart rapidly once it dies. Without energy outlays, lysosomal membranes begin to deteriorate. Once they do, the enzymes flood into the cytoplasm and rapidly destroy cell structures.

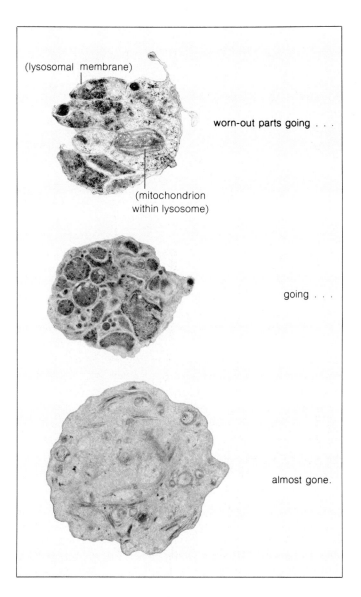

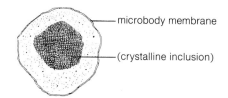

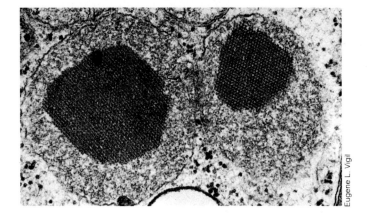

Figure 4.17 Glyoxysomes from a castor bean cell, in thin section. This kind of microbody is abundant in lipid-rich cells in germinating seeds.

(lysosomal membrane)

worn-out parts going . . .

(mitochondrion within lysosome)

going . . .

almost gone.

Figure 4.16 Digestion of organelles as seen in a lysosome. 12,000×. (Gary W. Grimes)

Microbodies

Seldom in the real world is the supply of substances precisely matched to cellular needs. A cell must be able to convert some substances to different kinds that are required but not available. **Microbodies** are membranous containers for different enzymes that take part in a range of conversion reactions.

Microbodies occur in at least some cells of all eukaryotic species. Apparently, they form as buds that break away from rough ER membranes, carrying with them enzymes that had already been synthesized and stockpiled in the ER cisternal spaces. Generally, microbodies are round or oval structures, about 0.2 to 1.5 micrometers in diameter. Figure 4.17 shows an example. In serial section, some microbodies are larger and more irregularly shaped. (Serial sections are repetitive specimen layers, like slices of a loaf of bread.)

Two kinds of microbodies are called peroxisomes and glyoxysomes. In *peroxisomes,* some enzymes take part in pathways by which amino acids and other substances are converted to fuel molecules. In plant leaf cells, peroxisomes figure in an alternative photosynthetic pathway, by which carbohydrates can still be assembled under unfavorable environmental conditions. In all cases, hydrogen peroxide forms as a by-product of the reactions. This substance is poisonous to cells. However, other enzymes in the peroxisome destroy the hydrogen peroxide as fast as it is produced. *Glyoxysomes* are found only in lipid-rich plant cells. They are particularly abundant in germinating peanut, watermelon, cucumber, and castor bean seeds. Some of the enzymes in glyoxysomes take part in converting storage fats and oils to the sugars necessary for rapid, early growth.

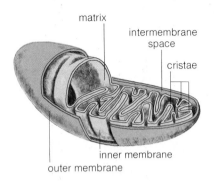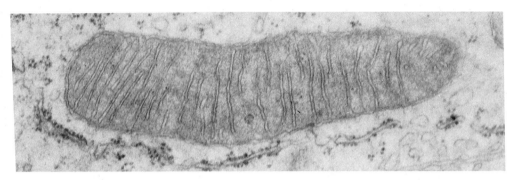

matrix
intermembrane space
cristae
inner membrane
outer membrane

Figure 4.18 Micrograph and generalized sketch of a mitochondrial membrane system. 49,600×. (Richard Kolberg)

OTHER CYTOPLASMIC ORGANELLES

Mitochondria

Eukaryotic cells typically thrive in *aerobic* conditions (in which oxygen is present). Oxygen is an abundant component of the present atmosphere. All eukaryotic cells have the capacity to use oxygen in metabolic reactions that release considerable energy stored in carbon-containing molecules. Some of the released energy is then conserved in high-energy bonds of ATP. These oxygen-dependent reactions are called aerobic respiration. They occur in an organelle called the **mitochondrion** (plural, mitochondria). All eukaryotic cells have at least one mitochondrion; some have many thousands.

Mitochondria commonly are about one to five micrometers long, or about the size of some bacterial cells. Their size places them near the limit of resolution in light microscopes. Some mitochondria are round, some tubelike or threadlike, and some have the shape of a potato (Figure 4.18). Their structures are not rigidly shaped. Depending on cellular conditions, mitochondria can grow and branch out, even fuse with one another and divide in two.

Like the nuclear envelope, the mitochondrial membrane is double. An outer membrane forms the boundary layer that faces the surrounding cytoplasm. The inner membrane folds back into the mitochondrion. Most commonly, the inner membrane takes the form of *cristae*, or deep infoldings, of the sort shown in Figure 4.18. The double membrane system creates two compartments within the organelle. One is an intermembrane space (between the two mitochondrial membranes); the other is the mitochondrial matrix. The controlled flow of hydrogen ions from one compartment to the other is central to ATP formation during aerobic respiration (Chapter Eight).

Eukaryotic cells typically contain anywhere from a dozen to a thousand mitochondria. Animal cells generally have more mitochondria than plant cells do. Some, such as amphibian eggs, contain more than a hundred thousand; they power the rapid, intense growth and development of the amphibian embryo. Mitochondria are also abundant near the surface of absorptive or secretory cells, which require considerable energy to move substances across the plasma membrane. Mitochondria are also abundant in muscle cells and in nerve cell regions that actively communicate with neighboring cells.

Chloroplasts and Other Plastids

Most plant cells contain plastids: organelles specialized in photosynthetic food production and in storage. There are three main kinds of plastids:

chloroplasts	*with photosynthetic pigments and starch-storing capacity*
chromoplasts	*with pigments that are not functioning in photosynthesis*
amyloplasts	*with starch-storing capacity, no pigments*

The **chloroplasts** are organelles specializing in photosynthesis. They are double-membraned containers that are commonly oval or disk-shaped (Figure 4.19). They average two to ten micrometers in length. In land plants, chloroplasts appear green. Among the algae they appear green, yellow-green, or golden brown. Their color depends on the

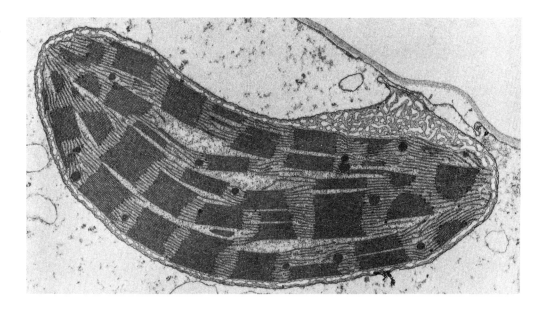

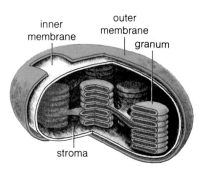

Figure 4.19 Micrograph and generalized sketch of a chloroplast membrane system. 20,200×. (L. K. Shumway)

kinds and relative numbers of light-absorbing pigment molecules embedded in their membranes. For instance, the pigment *chlorophyll* appears green because it absorbs all wavelengths (colors) of visible light except those corresponding to green light, which it transmits. Chlorophyll is found in all chloroplasts. Sometimes it is not immediately noticeable because other photosynthetic pigments mask its presence, as they do in brown algae.

In land plants, chloroplasts also serve as temporary storage sites for *starch grains*. During daylight, starch grains are assembled within them from photosynthetically produced sugars. At night (when there is no photosynthetic activity), starch grains are degraded and the products are moved out of the chloroplasts. The products are transported to longer-term storage sites or to actively growing regions of the plant body.

The most common types of chloroplasts have a complex internal structure. The inner chloroplast membrane gives rise to stacked membrane systems that become suspended in the *stroma* (a semifluid matrix). Each membrane stack is called a *granum* (plural, grana). Membranes of the granum are sites where sunlight energy is trapped and where ATP is formed. The molecules so produced are then transported to the stroma. There, they are used in building sucrose, starch, and protein molecules from carbon dioxide, water, and other raw materials. Chapter Seven describes the nature and sequence of these reactions.

The plastids called **chromoplasts** store pigments that are not functioning in photosynthesis. These pigments are red or brown. They give petals, fruits, and some roots (such as carrots) their characteristic color.

The plastids called **amyloplasts** are colorless. They occur in stems, roots, seeds, and other plant parts that are exposed to little (if any) sunlight. When starch assembled in the plant cell is not exported, it can be concentrated in amyloplasts, out of the way of metabolic activity. For instance, amyloplasts are abundant in potato cells and in many seeds, where they serve as storage sites for starch grains.

Central Vacuoles in Plant Cells

Mature and still-living plant cells have a large, fluid-filled **central vacuole**. This organelle forms through fusion of smaller, membrane-bound vesicles during cell growth and development. Usually a central vacuole takes up as much as fifty to ninety percent of the plant cell interior; the cytoplasm is confined to a narrow zone between the vacuolar membrane and the cell wall. (See, for example, Figure 4.9.) Sometimes the central vacuole serves as a storage area for ions, metabolic products such as amino acids and sugars, and toxic compounds. However, its main function seems to

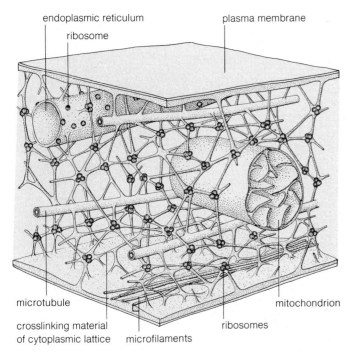

endoplasmic reticulum
ribosome
plasma membrane

microtubule
crosslinking material
of cytoplasmic lattice
microfilaments
ribosomes
mitochondrion

a

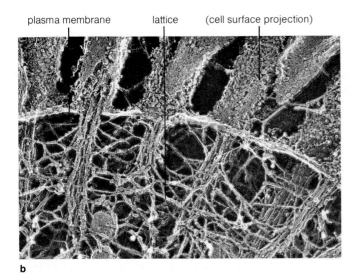

plasma membrane   lattice   (cell surface projection)

b

Figure 4.20 Model of a cytoplasmic lattice of an animal cell. (**a**) This lattice model shows how some of the microtubules, microfilaments, and crosslinking material are arranged relative to the plasma membrane and some cytoplasmic organelles. (**b**) The meshwork has been made visible by high-voltage electron microscopy. (a, after K. R. Porter and J. B. Tucker, "The Ground Substance of the Living Cell," *Scientific American*, March 1981. Copyright © 1981 by Scientific American, Inc. All rights reserved; b, N. Hirokawa, J. Heuser)

be one of increasing cell size and surface area. The resulting increase in surface area enhances absorption of essential minerals, which are present only in dilute amounts in watery environments or in moist soil. As fluid pressure builds up inside the vacuole during plant growth, it presses against the rigid plant cell wall. The cell becomes extended and enlarged permanently under this force, and mature cells become rigid.

INTERNAL FRAMEWORK OF EUKARYOTIC CELLS

The Cytoplasmic Lattice

The micrographs you have looked at so far give an idea of the kinds of organelles present in eukaryotic cells. However, they shouldn't be interpreted to mean that organelles remain located precisely this way relative to one another. *Few living cells are internally rigid.* If you were to look through a microscope at a living cell, you would likely be impressed with its constant internal motion. Cellular contents stream about. In plant cells, chloroplasts move in response to changes in the sun's overhead position. In most eukaryotic cells, sacs form at the plasma membrane, pinch off, and move to specific cytoplasmic regions. Other sacs bud from Golgi complexes, move toward and fuse with the plasma membrane, and thereby release their contents to the outside. Even animal cells from an organ that usually stays put (say, the liver) move actively when separated from the tissue and placed in a culture dish. Figure 4.1, which shows a hamster kidney cell, hints at the internal mechanisms by which a cell can move part of its body through the environment.

The fact that cells show internal movements does not necessarily mean their structures and organelles swim about or float freely through the cytoplasm. *Proper cell functioning requires nonrandom organization.* How do eukaryotic cells organize the internal movements and maintain diverse structural shapes? So far, several structural elements that contribute to the interior framework have been identified in animal cells, plant root tip cells, and diatoms (single-celled protistans). In animal cells, the elements are known to include microtubules, smaller microfilaments, and strands intermediate in size between the two. They are organized into an irregular, three-dimensional network that pervades the cytoplasm. This network is called the **cytoplasmic lattice**. One model of the lattice, as developed by Keith Porter, is shown in Figure 4.20.

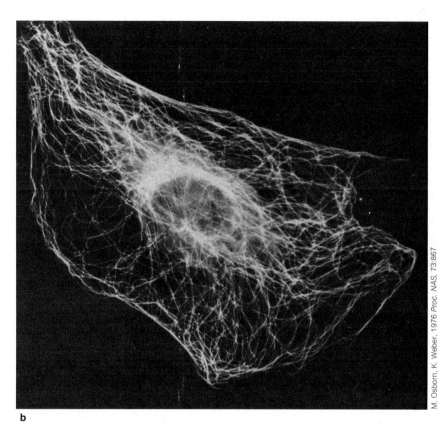

R. Pollack, Columbia University

M. Osborn, K. Weber, 1976 *Proc. NAS, 73:867*

a   b

Figure 4.21 Location of microfilaments and microtubules in the cytoplasm of eukaryotic cells. These images are the result of *indirect immunofluorescence*. With this method, the location of a given cell substance is revealed after the cell takes up molecules that have been "labeled" with fluorescent dyes. The molecules chosen combine preferentially with specific proteins. When the cell is illuminated with ultraviolet light, it is possible to see the glow from the bound molecules, hence the location of the protein in question. In (**a**), the protein so identified is actin. The actin-containing filaments in this cell, taken from mouse tissue, are moving the cell body from the lower left to the upper right. In (**b**), the protein is tubulin; it is seen as part of a microtubular network extending from the nucleus to the periphery of this animal cell.

Although the cytoplasmic lattice seems to have an irregular structure, its organization may turn out to be anything but random. Crosslinking material appears to hold microtubules and microfilaments in particular arrangements in local regions. Organelles and ribosomes are also regionally positioned. This positioning might be related to the organization of enzymes taking part in specific metabolic events. At least some enzymes involved in protein synthesis and in extracting energy from sugar molecules are embedded in the lattice. Also embedded in the lattice are the proteins *actin* and *myosin*. Both function in *contraction* (a shortening that may alternate with extension of certain filaments found in muscle and nonmuscle cells).

Microfilaments and Microtubules

The **microfilament** found in cytoplasmic lattices is a small, flexible strand, about five nanometers thick. Actin is one of its structural components (Figure 4.21). If an animal cell having microfilaments arranged in a ring around its midsection is made to contract, the cell pinches in two (as it does during cell division). If a cell having microfilaments attached to both the plasma membrane and organelles is made to contract, the organelles are drawn toward the cell surface. In a cell crawling across a culture dish, microfilaments running from the lower advancing edge to the upper midsurface help move the body forward. In plant cells especially, microfila-

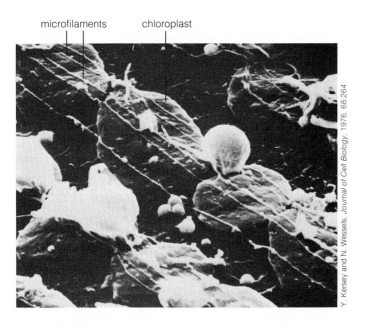

Figure 4.22 Scanning electron micrograph of a plant cell, showing some of its microfilaments. In many plant cells, cytoplasmic streaming of organelles such as the chloroplasts shown here seem to occur along well-defined tracks of microfilament bundles.

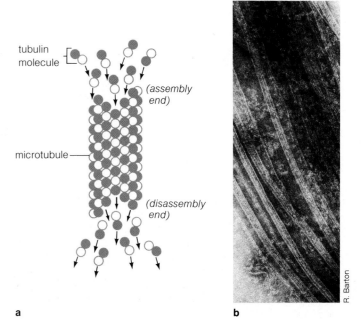

Figure 4.23 One model of microtubule assembly. Microtubules are constructed of two-part proteins called tubulins. Once constructed, microtubules become coated with proteins that stabilize the tubulin walls. (**a**) Microtubule assembly and disassembly occur in controlled ways at specific times, in the cell. (**b**) The orderly packing arrangement of the tubulins can be identified in this micrograph of several microtubules. (a, R. Sloboda, *Am. Scientist,* 1980, 68:290)

ments take part in *cytoplasmic streaming,* a constant directional motion of organelles (Figure 4.22).

The **microtubule** is a hollow cylinder assembled from protein subunits called tubulins (Figure 4.23). Typically, a microtubule is about twenty-five nanometers in diameter and of variable length. The list of events in which microtubules take part is impressive, and growing. Microtubules are involved in organelle movements. They help divide hereditary material during nuclear division. Microtubules just beneath the plasma membrane help dictate the shape of many cells and their surface extensions. In growing plant cells, they probably function in the oriented deposition of cellulose molecules during wall building. Microtubules are key components of cilia and flagella, two types of motile structures that will be described shortly.

In living cells, microtubules appear at different times, in different regions of the cytoplasm or nucleoplasm. They apparently arise from *microtubule organizing centers,* or MTOCs. These organizing centers have been identified with the use

of electron microscopes. They are masses of dense material that seem to be sites where tubulin subunits are polymerized into microtubules.

STRUCTURES AT THE CELL SURFACE

Cell Walls and Other Surface Deposits

One or more layers of surface deposits surround the plasma membrane of many cell types. The layers are called coats, capsules, sheaths, and walls. **Cell walls** provide support and resist mechanical pressure. They also confer tensile strength when cells expand with incoming water, as they do in growing plant cells. Cell walls provide mechanical support for many aboveground plant parts.

Even the most solid-looking walls are porous. If they were not, there would be no movement of substances to and from the plasma membrane, and a cell would quickly starve or poison itself with metabolic wastes. To varying degrees, water and solutes move through microscopic spaces that exist in the cell wall.

Cell walls occur among bacteria, protistans, fungi, and plants. Most walls have carbohydrate frameworks, but they are structurally quite diverse. Compounding the inherent diversity are variations in wall thickness, composition, and consistency brought about by variations in environmental conditions. Even cells of the same species can show such wall variations.

All plant cell walls have cellulose as the basic strengthening component. The cellulose fibers are synthesized at the plasma membrane as thin strands. The strands are bundled together and added to a developing *primary cell wall* (Figure 4.24). Primary walls with cellulose are highly porous. After the main growth phase, many types of plant cells also deposit an inner, rigid *secondary cell wall.* For example, lignin is an important component of secondary walls, including those in wood. As another example, cutin is a waterproofing substance that restricts water loss. In land plants ranging from mosses to redwoods and flowering plants, cutin with a wax coat is deposited on outer walls of cells that make up the surface layer of parts exposed to the air.

Animal cells don't produce walls, although some secrete products to the cell surface layer of tissues in which they are found. Generally, the animal way of life demands great flexibility and movement rather than rigid external support for cells. Animal cells that do assume a well-defined shape (for instance, the paramecium in Figure 4.5) usually rely on structural elements of the cytoplasmic lattice that are located just beneath the plasma membrane.

Microvilli

Among animal cells particularly, the plasma membrane often becomes specialized in ways that greatly increase the surface area exposed to the environment. The increase means that larger amounts of molecules can be transported to and from cells. A **microvillus** is a slender, cylindrical extension of the cell surface that functions in absorption or secretion of molecules (Figure 4.25). Microvilli are profuse on villi, which are dense outfoldings of epithelium in the small intestine. Here, most nutrients are absorbed into the body (Chapter Twenty-Six). Microvilli also occur on sensory cells concerned with absorbing light and with absorbing dissolved molecules in ways that lead to senses of taste and smell.

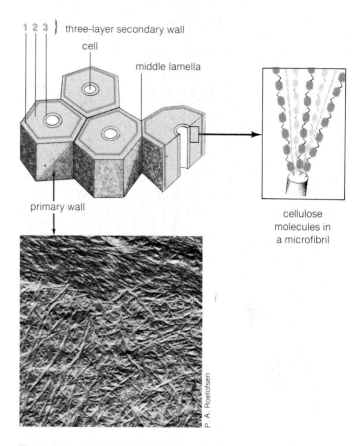

Figure 4.24 Primary and secondary cell walls in plants, as they would appear in partial cross-section. The boxed insets show progressively finer detail of secondary wall organization. The micrograph shows the primary wall of a plant cell. The microfilaments are largely of cellulose.

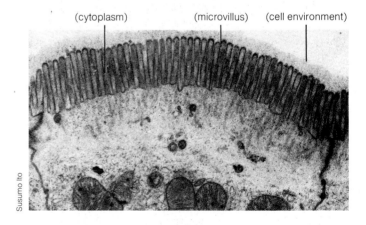

Figure 4.25 A slice through an epithelial cell with numerous microvilli projecting from its surface. 21,000×.

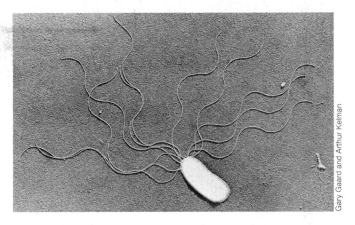

Figure 4.26 *Pseudomonas marginalis,* a bacterium that causes soft-rot diseases of vegetables including lettuce and potatoes. 12,800×.

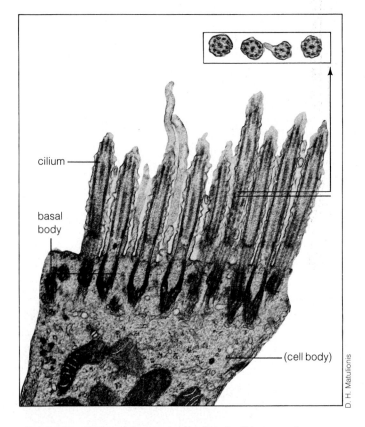

cilium

basal body

(cell body)

Figure 4.27 Electron micrograph of a ciliated cell from nasal epithelium, long-section. 68,000×. The boxed inset depicts four of the cilia as they would appear in cross-section at the same magnification. Notice the position of the basal body at the base of each motile structure.

Cilia and Flagella

Some cell surface extensions are much larger and more complex than microvilli. Single-celled organisms use these extensions as a means of moving rapidly through watery environments. Some extensions also occur on the surface layers of various animal organs, where their rapid movements propel fluids or mucus in one direction or another.

Many prokaryotic cells have motile extensions called **bacterial flagella** (singular, flagellum). Bacterial flagella occur at one end of the cell or at both ends, either singly or in tufts. Sometimes they are scattered over the cell surface. These motile structures are composed of the protein *flagellin*. Although a bacterial flagellum looks something like a whip (Figure 4.26), it functions more like a propeller. It rotates around the attachment point. The rotation can propel some bacteria a distance that corresponds to thirty-seven of their cell bodies, laid end to end, in a single second. For their size, bacteria move faster than you do.

Among eukaryotic cells, motile extensions are true **flagella** and **cilia** (singular, cilium). Cilia are shorter than flagella, and more numerous where they do occur. (See, for example, Figure 4.27.) Both structures are assembled from microtubules. Most commonly, nine pairs of microtubules are arranged radially about two central microtubules. This is called a *9 + 2 array* of microtubules. Figure 4.28b shows an example. Such microtubular arrays extend outward from the cell body, within a sheath that is continuous with the plasma membrane.

The microtubular array of cilia and flagella arises from short, barrel-shaped structures called **centrioles**. A centriole has nine radially arranged triplets of microtubules. After the cilium or flagellum has formed, the centriole remains attached at its base, just beneath the plasma membrane.

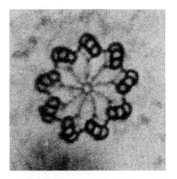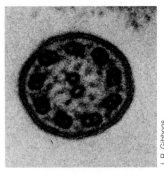

Figure 4.28 Basal body (**a**) and flagellum (**b**) from the protistan *Trichonympha,* cross-section. 127,500×.

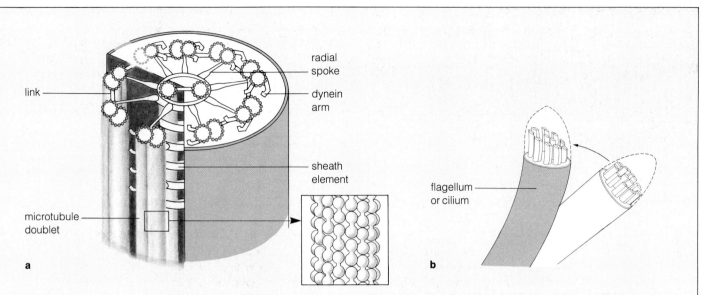

Figure 4.29 Movement of cilia and flagella. (**a**) All radial microtubules in the 9 + 2 array are anchored to the two central microtubules. (**b**) In an unbent cilium or flagellum, all doublets extend the same distance into the tip. With bending, the doublets on the outside of the arc are displaced farthest from the tip.

Numerous clawlike "arms" extend at regular intervals along the length of each microtubule doublet in the outer ring. The arms are composed of dynein, an ATP-hydrolyzing enzyme. All arms protrude in the same direction—toward the next doublet in the ring. When dynein binds and splits an ATP molecule, the angle of the arm changes with respect to the doublet in front of it. The arm bends and is strongly attracted to the doublet in front of it. On contact, the arm "unbends" with great force and causes its neighbor to move. The dynein releases its hold, whereupon it can grab another ATP molecule and attach to a new binding site on the doublet.

Thus dynein arms on one doublet swim back and forth like tiny oars, displacing the neighboring doublet with each oarlike arc. The flagellum or cilium bends toward the side where the displacement is greatest.

Henceforth it is called the **basal body** of the motile structure (Figure 4.27). Centrioles can be observed in the cytoplasm of many eukaryotic cells. Typically these cells belong to species that have motile structures during at least one stage of the life cycle. Like DNA molecules, centrioles are duplicated and passed on to the next generation through cell division (Chapter Nine).

Cilia and flagella are the source of movement for single-celled predators and prey that live in aquatic environments. Flagellated male reproductive cells occur among protistans, fungi, some plants, and most animals. Such cells must be able to move through a liquid medium to reach and fertilize female reproductive cells. Among many animal species, cilia carry out other roles. Cilia project in dense arrays from cells of organs such as nasal passages and tubelike bronchi of the respiratory system, where they help move fluids and dissolved particles. Many sensory organs depend on modified cilia (Chapter Twenty-Three).

Cell-to-Cell Junctions

When we turn to multicelled plants, fungi, and animals, we find that the cell environment is more complex. Each living cell must still interact with its physical surroundings; but it also must interact with its cellular neighbors. At the surface of tissues, cells must link tightly together, so that the interior of the organism (or organ) is not indiscriminately exposed to the outside world. In all tissues, cells must recognize one another and physically stick together. Finally, in tissues where cells must act in a coordinated way (as they do in heart muscle tissue), the cells must share channels for exchanging signals, nutrients, or both.

Cell Junctions in Animals. Three kinds of cell-to-cell junctions have been identified in animal tissues. **Tight junctions** occur between cells making up epithelial tissues (which line the body's outer surface, inner cavities, and

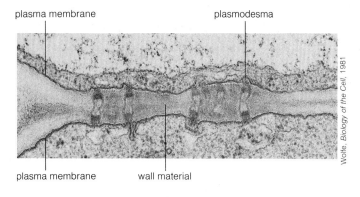

plasma membrane   plasmodesma

plasma membrane   wall material

Wolfe, Biology of the Cell, 1981

Figure 4.30 Electron micrograph of plasmodesmata crossing the wall material between two corn cells.

organs). At each tight junction, criss-crossed rows of proteins embedded in the plasma membrane of one cell are linked to matching protein rows in the plasma membrane of the adjacent cell (Figure 20.1). Each double row forms a tight sealing strand that helps bar the free passage of molecules across the epithelium. The criss-crossing imparts flexibility at tight junctions, and thereby helps hold cells together under mechanical stress.

Adhering junctions are not barriers; they are more like separate rivets or spot welds. These junctions span the plasma membranes of two cells and interlink their cytoplasmic lattices. Figure 20.2 shows a desmosome, an adhering junction that is profuse in epithelium subject to considerable stretching (such as that of the skin, heart, and stomach).

Gap junctions have small, open channels that directly link the cytoplasm of adjacent cells. Only small molecules and ions can pass through the channels. In heart muscle and smooth muscle, gap junctions function in extremely rapid communication between cells. In liver and other tissues, gap junctions allow ions, nutrients, and hormones to pass directly from one cell to the next.

Cell Junctions in Plants. The kinds of junctions found between animal cells are absent in plants. Here, cells are linked wall-to-wall, not membrane-to-membrane. However, junctions analogous to gap junctions are present (Figure 4.30). These structures are called **plasmodesmata** (singular, plasmodesma). They interconnect all living cells in multicelled plants. In a single cell, between 1,000 and

100,000 plasmodesmata can penetrate both the primary and secondary walls. The rate at which nutrients and other substances are transported between adjacent cells is related to the number of plasmodesmata linking them together.

We will be returning to details of such cell-to-cell interactions in later chapters. Here, the point to remember is this:

In multicelled organisms, coordinated functioning among individual cells depends on the linkage and communication provided by specialized zones in the plasma membranes of adjacent cells.

SUMMARY OF MAJOR CELL STRUCTURES AND THEIR FUNCTIONS

All living things are made of one or more cells; each cell is a basic living unit of structure and function; and a new cell arises only from cells that already exist. Beginning with this cell theory, we have looked at the internal structures of this fundamental living unit. We have seen that, at the minimum, all cells have a nucleus (or nucleoid), cytoplasm (with its enzymes and ribosomes), and a plasma membrane that acts as a boundary layer between the internal cell environment and the surroundings.

To this basic plan, eukaryotic cells have additional and diverse embellishments—membranous compartments of varied sorts, concerned with the acquisition and processing of materials and energy in highly controlled, specialized ways. These organelles are summarized in Table 4.2, along with the structures common to both prokaryotic and eukaryotic cells. Details of how they function will occupy our attention in chapters to follow.

Readings

Bloom, W., and D. Fawcett. 1975. *A Textbook of Histology.* Philadelphia: Saunders. Advanced reading, but an excellent reference book with beautiful electron micrographs.

Esau, K. 1977. *Anatomy of Seed Plants.* Second edition. New York: Wiley.

Fawcett, D. 1966. *The Cell: An Atlas of Fine Structure.* Philadelphia: Saunders. Outstanding collection of micrographs.

Geise, A. 1979. *Cell Physiology.* Fifth edition. Philadelphia: Saunders. Exceptional reference text on cell functioning related to structure and evolutionary antecedents.

Table 4.2 Structures Typically Found in Prokaryotic and Eukaryotic Cells

Cell Structure	Function	Prokaryotic	Eukaryotic			
		Moneran	Protistan	Fungi	Plant	Animal
Cell wall	Protection, structural support	✓*	✓*	✓*	✓	
Plasma membrane	Regulation of substances moving into, out of cell	✓	✓	✓	✓	✓
Nucleoid	Region of DNA (hereditary control)	✓				
Nucleus	Membrane-enclosed region of DNA		✓	✓	✓	✓
DNA molecule	Encoding of hereditary information	✓	✓	✓	✓	✓
RNA molecule	Transcription, translation of DNA messages into specific proteins	✓	✓	✓	✓	✓
Chromosome (DNA + protein)	Packaging of DNA during nuclear division; control of gene expression		✓	✓	✓	✓
Nucleolus	Assembly of ribosomal subunits		✓	✓	✓	✓
Ribosomes	Protein synthesis	✓	✓	✓	✓	✓
Endoplasmic reticulum	Isolation, modification, transport of proteins and other substances		✓	✓	✓	✓
Golgi body	Modification, assembly, packaging, secretion of substances		✓	✓	✓	✓
Lysosome	Isolation of digestive enzymes		✓	✓*	✓	✓
Microbodies	Isolation of enzymes used in energy and material conversions		✓	✓	✓	✓
Mitochondrion	Aerobic energy metabolism		✓	✓	✓	✓
Photosynthetic pigment	Light-energy conversion	✓*	✓*		✓	
Plastid: Chloroplast	Photosynthesis, some starch storage		✓*		✓	
Chromoplast	Pigment storage				✓	
Amyloplast	Starch storage				✓	
Central vacuole	Increasing cell surface area, storage				✓	
Cytoplasmic lattice	Cytoplasmic organization, support		✓*	✓*	✓*	✓
Microtubule, microfilament	Structural support, subcellular and cellular movement		✓	✓	✓	✓
Microtubular organizing center	Gives rise to microtubule systems (e.g., spindles, centrioles)		✓	✓	✓	✓
Complex flagellum, cilium	Movement through environment		✓*	✓*	✓*	✓
Centriole	Gives rise to cilia and flagella		✓*	✓*	✓*	✓

*Known to occur in at least some groups.

Kessel, R., and C. Shih. 1974. *Scanning Electron Microscopy in Biology: A Student's Atlas of Biological Organization.* New York: Springer-Verlag. Stunning micrographs of cell structures and products.

Lazarides, E., and J. Revel. 1979. "The Molecular Basis of Cell Movement." *Scientific American* 240(5):100–113. Fine summary article on research into cell movement.

Ledbetter, M., and K. Porter. 1970. *Introduction to the Fine Structure of Plant Cells.* New York: Springer-Verlag.

Means, A., and J. Dedman. "Calmodulin—An Intracellular Calcium Receptor." *Nature* 285:73–77.

Newcomb, E. 1980. "The General Cell." In *The Biochemistry of Plants,* vol. 1 (N. Tolbert, editor). New York: Academic Press. Current, authoritative survey of plant organelles and the terminology used to describe them.

Novikoff, A., and E. Holtzmann. 1976. *Cells and Organelles.* Second edition. New York: Holt, Rinehart and Winston. Nice introduction to cell structure and function. Paperback.

Porter, K., and J. Tucker. 1981. "The Ground Substance of the Living Cell." *Scientific American* 244(3):57–67. Excellent summary of studies on the internal scaffolding of cell cytoplasm.

Satir, B. 1975. "The Final Steps in Secretion." *Scientific American* 233(12):28–37.

Staehelin, L., and B. Hull. 1978. "Junctions Between Living Cells." *Scientific American* 238(5):140–152. Excellent article summarizing research into epithelial cell junctions in animals.

Weibe, H. 1978. "The Significance of Plant Vacuoles." *Bioscience* 28:327–331.

Review Questions

1. All cells share three structural features: a plasma membrane, a nucleus (or nucleoid), and cytoplasm. Can you describe the functions of each?

2. Why is it highly improbable that you will ever encounter a predatory two-ton living cell on the sidewalk?

3. Are all cells microscopic? Is the micrometer used in describing whole cells or extremely small cell structures? Is the nanometer used in describing whole cells or cell ultrastructure?

4. State the three principles of the cell theory.

5. Suppose you want to observe details of the surface of an insect's compound eye. Would you benefit most from a conventional light microscope, transmission electron microscope, or scanning electron microscope?

6. Eukaryotic cells generally contain these organelles: nucleus, endoplasmic reticulum, Golgi bodies, lysosomes, microbodies, and mitochondria. Can you describe the function of each?

7. Describe the structure and function of chloroplasts and mitochondria. Mention the ways in which they are similar.

8. Is this statement true or false? All chloroplasts are plastids, but not all plastids are chloroplasts.

9. What is a cytoplasmic lattice? How do you suppose it might aid in cell functioning?

10. What are the components of the endomembrane system? Sketch their general arrangement, from the nuclear envelope to the plasma membrane, and describe the role of each in the flow of materials between these two boundary layers.

11. What are the functions of the central vacuole in mature, living plant cells?

12. Lysosomes dismantle and dispose of malfunctioning organelles and foreign particles. Can you describe how?

13. Name some of the functions of microtubules and microfilaments.

14. Cell walls occur among which organisms: bacteria, protistans, plants, fungi, or animals? Are cell walls solid or porous?

15. In plants, is a secondary cell wall deposited inside or outside the surface of the primary cell wall? Do all plant cells have secondary walls?

16. Describe the difference between a bacterial flagellum, eukaryotic flagellum, and cilium.

17. What gives rise to the microtubular array of cilia and flagella? Distinguish between a centriole and a basal body.

18. In multicelled organisms, coordinated interactions depend on linkages and communication between adjacent cells. What types of junctions occur between adjacent animal cells? Plant cells?

19. With a sheet of paper, cover the Table 4.2 column entitled Function. Can you now name the primary functions of the cell structures listed in this table?

20. Having completed the exercise in item 19 above, can you now write a paragraph describing the difference between prokaryotic and eukaryotic cells?

ON CELLULAR ENVIRONMENTS

Describing cell structures as things unto themselves is like describing the human body without mentioning the environment in which it has come to exist. This approach just doesn't tell us much about the functional significance of some particular array of parts. For instance, why are human eyes forward-directed instead of one on each side of the head, newtlike? Why do humans have slender, grasping fingers and thumbs, yet relatively stubby, nongrasping toes? Why paired lungs, paired ears, and a four-chambered heart? The development of such structures began with environmental pressures long ago, as Chapter Thirty-Five will describe. Still, the same idea applies here, at the level of cells. Why do cells have plasma membranes instead of solid barriers to the outside? Why do some cells have porous walls, and "tails," and sticky coatings? The significance of *cell* structures becomes apparent by looking at the nature of the environments in which they function.

Consider, at the outset, that cellular life must be maintained within a narrow range of conditions. At all times, metabolic activity requires the presence of water, the availability of only so many ions of specific sorts, and exposure to only a limited range of temperature and pressure. For most cells in most places, such environmental factors are not constants. For example, ion concentrations change with the tides in estuaries, where seawater mixes with freshwater currents from rivers and streams. However, ion concentrations *inside* single-celled organisms that live in estuaries cannot change to the same extent. If they did, the cells would die, for reasons that will soon become apparent. The point is, *survival depends on adaptations that permit tolerance of variable conditions.* At the cellular level, one of the most fundamental of all adaptations is the plasma membrane—a largely fluid structure in a largely fluid world. This intriguing structure, and the environment in which it functions, is the subject of this chapter.

WATER AND CELL FUNCTIONING

On the average, about seventy-five to eighty-five percent of an active cell is water. Considerable water also bathes its outer surface. Many surface parts of multicelled plants, animals, and fungi are exposed to dry soil or air, but all of the living cells in these regions are still in contact with water present inside the body.

5

WATER, MEMBRANES, AND CELL FUNCTIONING

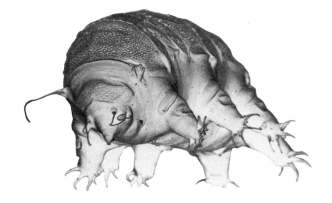

Figure 5.1 Without water there is no life—sort of. One of many organisms whose cells can adapt to extremely dried-out environments: a water bear on the prowl, magnified 300 times. (Robert D. Schuster)

It is not that life necessarily ends in the absence of water. Some plant spores can resume active growth after being dried out for centuries. Some worms called nematodes, when given enough time to prepare themselves for the occasion, can stay dried out for decades—only to resume activity upon being moistened again. Or consider the tardigrade, also known as the water bear (Figure 5.1). This tiny animal lives in ponds and damp soil. Its moist home may freeze over in winter or bake beneath the summer sun, yet the water bear survives. It dries out very carefully and enters a state of suspended animation. Certain body parts, through which water normally escapes, are withdrawn from exposure to air. The body contracts so tightly that it looks like a small barrel. As the body contracts, its cells produce a compound that replaces the water normally surrounding large biological molecules. The compound apparently holds these molecules in place and protects them from mechanical damage. Thus, through tight packing and controlled drying out, the structure of each cell is maintained during harsh times. When moist conditions return, the water bear revives and actively goes about the business of living.

Water bears, nematodes, rotifers, lichens, mosses, spores, and seeds—all are well matched to environments in which water periodically becomes scarce. Yet with their seeming independence of free-flowing water, the key word in all of this is *active* existence:

None of the activities associated with the term "living" can proceed without water.

What is it about water that makes it so central in cell functioning? Cells depend especially on three properties of water: its ability to stabilize temperature, its internal cohesion, and its outstanding capacity to dissolve many substances.

The Importance of Hydrogen Bonds

Temperature Stabilization. The temperature-stabilizing properties of water arise largely through the capacity of water molecules to form hydrogen bonds with one another, in the manner described in Chapter Three. These properties include high specific heat, high heat of vaporization, and high heat of fusion.

The term **specific heat** refers to how much heat energy is required to increase the temperature of a single gram of a substance by 1°C. As you probably know, temperature is a measure of the rate of molecular motion. Substances differ in how much energy it takes to make them reach equivalent states of molecular motion. In liquid water, the hydrogen bonds among individual molecules must *first* be broken and kept from forming again; only then can the molecules themselves undergo greater movement and thereby cause an increase in temperature. That is why water can absorb considerable heat without undergoing a significant increase in temperature.

The term **heat of vaporization** refers to the amount of heat energy that must be absorbed before a single gram of liquid will be converted to gaseous form. It takes 539 calories of heat energy to bring a gram of water past its boiling point of 100°C. (By comparison, the heat of vaporization for water is twice that for ethanol and almost five times that for chloroform.) This property, too, can be traced to hydrogen bonds. Because of these bonds, individual water molecules resist separating from each other in liquid water. When a water molecule absorbs enough heat energy from its surroundings, hydrogen bonds can be broken and it can escape from the water's surface. This liberating process is called *evaporation.* The molecules that escape have obtained most of the energy to do so from the surrounding liquid. Hence, with their departure, the surface temperature of the liquid is lowered. Oasis plants and many animals cool off through evaporative water loss.

Water also has a high **heat of fusion**, which means that it resists changing from liquid to solid form with decreases in temperature. Individually, the hydrogen bonds between water molecules are weak. At room temperature, water is fluid because these bonds are constantly breaking and rapidly forming again, thereby restraining as well as allowing some freedom of molecular movement. Only when the temperature drops below 0°C do things settle down enough for water molecules to become locked in the rigid bonding pattern characteristic of ice (Figure 5.2).

Other examples could be given of water's temperature-stabilizing properties. Here it is enough to summarize their importance this way:

Because of hydrogen bonds between its molecules, water serves as a stabilizing factor against local temperature extremes inside and outside the cell.

Cohesion. The term **cohesion** refers to molecular bonds that resist rupturing when placed under tension (in other words, when they are being stretched). It is a term that can

Roger K. Burnard

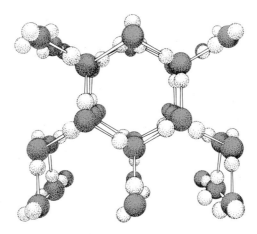

Figure 5.2 Crystal lattice structure of ice. The brown spheres represent oxygen; the white spheres, hydrogen. The "sticks" connecting them represent hydrogen bonds. Below 0°C, each water molecule becomes locked by four hydrogen bonds into a crystal lattice. In this bonding pattern, molecules are spaced farther apart than they would be in liquid water at room temperature (where constant molecular motion usually prevents the maximum number of hydrogen bonds from forming). Because of the extended bonding pattern, ice is less dense than liquid water and is able to float on it. During winter freezes, sheets of ice that form on surfaces of ponds, lakes, and streams act like a blanket that holds in the water's heat. (Molecular motion in ice is minimal, hence heat conduction through ice to the air is minimal.) As a result, the water below remains tolerable for many kinds of aquatic organisms through the winter months.

apply to attractions between the same or different kinds of molecules. In pure water, each molecule is attracted to and hydrogen-bonded with other molecules. The cumulative effect of so many hydrogen bonds is that liquid water has high cohesion. At air-water interfaces, hydrogen bonds exert a constant inward pull on molecules at the water's surface and impart a high surface tension to it. In order to break through the surface of a water layer, some hydrogen bonds must be broken. The cohesive forces of water resist this surface breakthrough. That is why beads of water form; that is why a pond surface resists penetration by small leaves and certain insects (Figure 5.3). Also, cohesive forces combined with other factors give water molecules the capacity to pull one another up through narrow, cellular pipelines to the tops of even the tallest trees.

Because of numerous hydrogen bonds between its molecules, liquid water shows cohesiveness: these bonds (which individually are weak) resist breaking even when some force puts them under tension.

William H. Amos

Figure 5.3 The water strider, an insect adapted to water's high surface tension (resulting from the tenacity with which water molecules cling to one another through hydrogen bonds).

Solvent Properties of Water

Water is an outstanding solvent because of the polar nature of its individual molecules. In a water molecule, recall, the oxygen atom has greater electronegativity than the hydrogen atoms. Thus the oxygen atom, which behaves *as if* it carries a slight negative charge, is weakly attracted to positively charged ions or molecules. Similarly, the hydrogen ions, which behave *as if* they carry a positive charge, are weakly attracted to negatively charged ions or molecules.

Consider the way that water becomes organized around ions. Crystals of table salt (NaCl) separate into Na^+ and Cl^- when they are placed in water. Water molecules tend to cluster around each positively charged ion, with their "negative" ends pointing toward it:

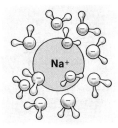

Similarly, water molecules tend to cluster around each negatively charged ion, with their "positive" ends pointing toward it:

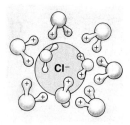

These so-called "spheres of hydration" shield charged ions and keep them from interacting. They also force ions to remain dispersed in the water. When spheres of hydration form around a charged substance, the substance is said to be *dissolved* in water. Water thus acts as a **solvent** (a fluid in which one or more substances can be dissolved). The dissolved substances are known as **solutes**. Most molecules held together by ionic bonds are soluble in water. So are polar molecules, which tend to form hydrogen bonds with water (Chapter Three).

Most substances that become dissolved in water remain unchanged by the association, because water is relatively inert: it doesn't chemically alter its solutes. This means that molecules essential for life can be transported in blood or sap (a sucrose-rich fluid), or can be stored in solution, without becoming changed into something non-essential or downright toxic.

Because of its solvent properties, water does not chemically alter the substances dissolved in it, but it does influence their positioning.

CYTOPLASMIC ORGANIZATION OF WATER, SOLUTES, AND LARGER PARTICLES

So far, we have been talking about small water molecules and the kinds of ions dissolved in cytoplasmic water. Cytoplasm also contains **colloidal particles**, which are too large to be dissolved but small enough to keep from settling out in response to gravity. Because of the constant molecular motion of individual water molecules, colloidal particles are constantly bombarded from random directions, and this bombardment keeps them dispersed in the fluid. (In contrast, particles in a true suspension are large enough to settle out.)

Even though colloids are small, they collectively present a large surface area to the surrounding water and solutes. Think about what this means in the case of protein molecules that are dispersed in cytoplasm. Proteins, recall, have ionizing groups on their surfaces. Depending on cellular pH, the protein surface can be positively or negatively charged, overall. For example, the excess hydroxide ions associated with increases in pH react with the protein, rendering its amino groups neutral and the carboxyl groups negatively charged. The negatively charged groups attract positive ions from the surroundings—which then attract negative ions. Both kinds of ions in turn attract water molecules. Thus an electrically charged "cushion" of ions and water can form around the protein surface:

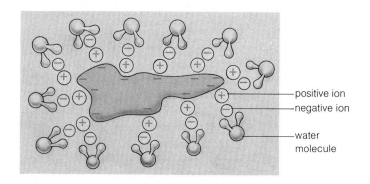

When ions and molecules surround colloidal particles in this manner, the colloids are said to be in the *sol state.* The sol state can change with shifts in such factors as pH, ion concentrations, and temperature. For example, under some cellular conditions, the surfaces of proteins become neutralized and begin adhering in a continuous, spongy network known as the *gel state.* Blood clotting is an example of this kind of transformation. During the clotting process, activated enzymes strip certain proteins of several negatively charged groups, and the proteins stick together in a sponge-like net.

The gel state is best typified by gelatin desserts, which are largely protein, sugar, and water. Although gelatin is solid (as opposed to liquid), solutes readily move through it. (Put some drops of food coloring on a cube of Jell-O and watch what happens.)

Lipids, carbohydrates, and nucleic acids also become organized in the fluid environment of the cytoplasm. Consider the behavior of phospholipids in water. These molecules contain fatty-acid tails (which are hydrophobic and therefore repel water). They also contain a polar "head," which is linked to the tails by a phosphate group. The polar head attracts water and therefore is hydrophilic. Phospholipid structure can be drawn in this generalized way:

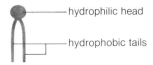

In fluids, phospholipids tend to become arranged into a two-layer film, since this is the configuration with the lowest energy level. In this **lipid bilayer**, hydrophobic tails point inward, tail-to-tail, and form a region that excludes water. The hydrophilic heads point toward the surrounding water molecules and are hydrogen-bonded with them:

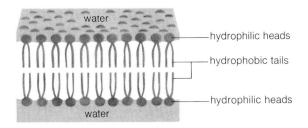

This arrangement is the framework of all cell membranes. Thus membrane organization arises partly in response to water molecules in the cellular environment.

Again, at least seventy-five percent of a living cell is water. As suggested by the examples given above, solutes and insoluble structures in cells organize water molecules in their vicinity. This organized water is bound to the solutes. There are so many solutes and hydrophilic structures within cells that most of the cytoplasmic water is organized, or bound. It is probable that in most cells, little (if any) free water is present.

The regional positioning and organization of biological molecules arises partly in response to interactions with cytoplasmic water.

CELL MEMBRANES: FLUID STRUCTURES IN A LARGELY FLUID WORLD

So far, we have looked at the chemical nature of both the internal and external environment of a cell. We are now ready to consider the **cell membrane**: a remarkable structure that can form sheets and closed compartments in the cytoplasm, as well as a surface boundary layer (the plasma membrane) that separates cytoplasm from the surrounding world.

Only in the past few decades have we begun to understand membrane structure and function. Long before this, there were hints that membranes are fluids rather than solid structures. For instance, it was known that cells punctured with fine needles did not lose cytoplasm when the needle was withdrawn. Instead, the cell surface seemed to flow over and seal the punctured region! Yet how could a *fluid* cell membrane remain functionally distinct from fluid surroundings?

For a time, researchers thought the membrane was composed only of lipids, possibly organized in the bilayer arrangement sketched earlier. By the late 1960s, however, the true nature of cell membranes started to become apparent, largely through electron micrograph studies. For example, freeze-fracturing and freeze-etching, two new methods of preparing specimens for study, yielded finer details of membrane structure (Figure 5.4). By 1972, S. Singer and G. Nicholson put together the first summarization of what has become known as the **fluid mosaic model** of membrane structure. In this model, *the lipid bilayer forms a sort of fluid sea, in which diverse proteins are suspended like icebergs or anchored at various points on its surface.*

The word "fluid" refers to the lipid bilayer's consistency, which is similar to light machine oil. The sources of

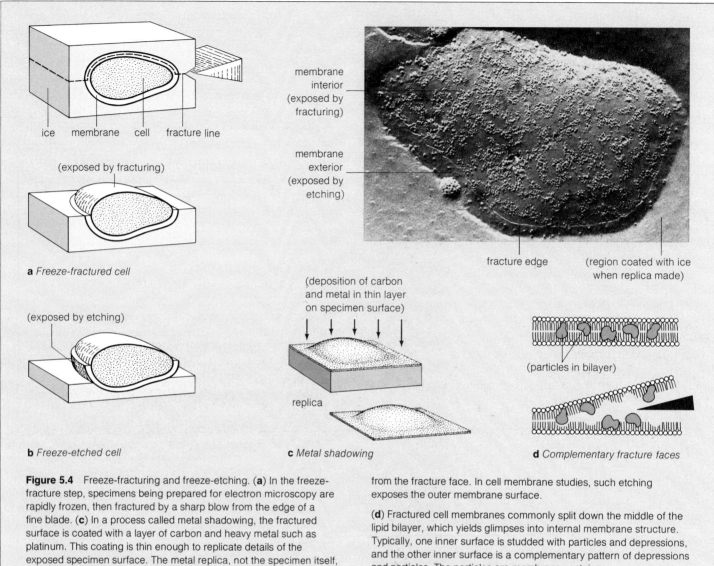

Figure 5.4 Freeze-fracturing and freeze-etching. (**a**) In the freeze-fracture step, specimens being prepared for electron microscopy are rapidly frozen, then fractured by a sharp blow from the edge of a fine blade. (**c**) In a process called metal shadowing, the fractured surface is coated with a layer of carbon and heavy metal such as platinum. This coating is thin enough to replicate details of the exposed specimen surface. The metal replica, not the specimen itself, is used for preparing electron micrographs.

(**b**) Sometimes before the metal replica is made, specimens are freeze-etched, which simply means that additional ice is evaporated from the fracture face. In cell membrane studies, such etching exposes the outer membrane surface.

(**d**) Fractured cell membranes commonly split down the middle of the lipid bilayer, which yields glimpses into internal membrane structure. Typically, one inner surface is studded with particles and depressions, and the other inner surface is a complementary pattern of depressions and particles. The particles are membrane proteins.

The micrograph shows a portion of a replica of a red blood cell, prepared by freeze-fracturing and freeze-etching. (P. Pinto da Silva and D. Branton, *J. Cell Biology,* 1970. 45:598)

this fluidity are certain types of lipids that have double bonds (unsaturated regions) in their tails. Double bonds introduce bends in hydrocarbon chains—and this creates kinky tails (Figure 5.5). Other lipids contributing to the fluidity have relatively short tails, which cannot interact with their neighbors as strongly as long-tailed lipids can do. Both types disrupt the rigid packing that is typical of long-chain fatty acids in the lipid bilayer.

The word "mosaic" refers to the intricate composite of proteins and lipids that make up the membrane. Diverse proteins are embedded within the fluid foundation of the bilayer or are weakly bonded to either surface. Some proteins are pumps and gates through which hydrophilic substances cross the membrane. Some are energy-transforming enzymes. Others intercept signals or serve as docks for specific substances, in ways that will be described later.

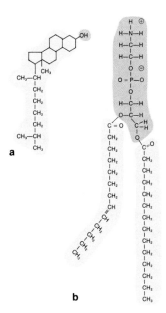

a

b

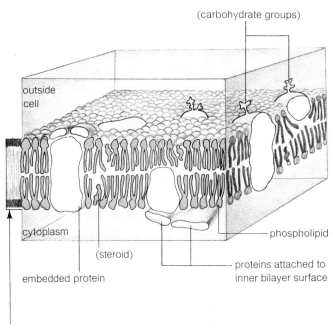

(carbohydrate groups)

outside
cell

cytoplasm

(steroid)

embedded protein

phospholipid

proteins attached to
inner bilayer surface

Figure 5.5 (**a**) Structural formula for cholesterol. (**b**) Structural formula for one of four main phospholipids in cell membranes. In both sketches, the brown area is the hydrophilic head, and the light gold areas are water-repelling tails. Notice the kink in the phospholipid's fatty-acid tail at the double bond and the relatively short cholesterol tail. Both disrupt the tight packing otherwise possible in clusters of straight hydrocarbon chains. The spaces created by such disruptions impart some fluidity to the cell membrane.

Lipid Bilayer

Figure 5.6 Fluid mosaic model of membrane structure, as described in the text. The micrograph shows a red blood cell membrane in thin section, at high magnification.

Figure 5.6 is a sketch of the mosaic model, keyed to a micrograph of the sort that shows the bilayer arrangement.

Throughout this book, we will be looking at different aspects of membrane structure and function. For now, the overall features that all cell membranes hold in common can be summarized this way:

1. Cell membranes are composed of lipids and proteins, both of which can have carbohydrate groups attached.

2. Membrane lipids have hydrophilic heads and hydrophobic tails. Two lipid sheets oriented tail-to-tail form a membrane bilayer. The hydrophobic zone tends to bar the transmembrane movement of most water-soluble substances.

3. Variations in the straightness and length of membrane lipids disrupt the rigid packing typical of long fatty-acid tails, hence much of the bilayer is fluid.

4. In general, membrane lipids function as a hydrophobic barrier between two fluid regions (either two cytoplasmic regions, or the extracellular environment and the cytoplasm).

5. Some membrane proteins regulate the transmembrane flow of water-soluble substances. Some are enzymes. Others are receptors for chemical signals or for specific molecules.

MOVEMENT OF WATER AND SOLUTES ACROSS MEMBRANES

Overview of Membrane Transport Systems

The fluid mosaic model of membrane structure gives insights into how substances move across membranes in controlled ways. All inherent membrane transport systems are proteins of one kind or another, built into the lipid bilayer. The action of these different proteins makes the cell membrane *differentially permeable*. This means that although some ions, water, and lipid-soluble molecules are free to travel across the membrane, protein transport systems govern how fast other molecules cross it, and whether they cross it at all.

Table 5.1 Summary of Membrane Transport Mechanisms
Passive Transport *Substance moves passively with the gradient; no direct energy outlay needed* 1. <u>Simple diffusion</u> through membrane by dissolving temporarily in phospholipid bilayer 2. <u>Facilitated diffusion</u> through protein channels across membrane 3. <u>Osmosis</u>, or diffusion of water through membrane by as-yet-unidentified transport mechanism in response to concentration gradient, pressure gradient, or both
Active Transport *Substance is moved against the gradient; requires energy outlay* 1. <u>Active transport</u> through protein channels in membrane; requires energy input to membrane-bound pumps (some with ATP-hydrolyzing enzymes) 2. <u>Exocytosis</u>, or expulsion of material enclosed in membrane vesicles that fuse with the plasma membrane 3. <u>Endocytosis</u>, or engulfment of large particles or bacterial cells through formation of vesicles derived from plasma membrane

Different kinds of transport systems exist, but they all work with or against one (or more) of the following kinds of transmembrane movements:

concentration gradient	*a difference in the concentration of some substance between two regions of a defined volume of space*
pressure gradient	*a difference in pressure between two regions*
temperature gradient	*a difference in temperature between two regions*
electric gradient	*a difference in electric charge between two regions*

Passive transport systems work *with* such gradients. They occur spontaneously, and they do not alter in any way the direction in which some substance happens to be moving on its own. Simple diffusion, facilitated diffusion, and osmosis are passive transport systems.

Active transport systems work *against* gradients. They require energy input to move some substance in a direction in which it shows little or no inclination to move on its own. They include active transport, exocytosis, and endocytosis.

Table 5.1 summarizes the main types of membrane transport mechanisms. Through a combination of these mechanisms, cells or organelles are supplied with raw materials and rid of wastes, at controlled rates. These mechanisms govern cell volume. They control secretions of cell products. They also help control pH within the cell or organelle within some functional range. Let's take a look at how these transport mechanisms work.

Diffusion

Simple Diffusion. When you first drop a sugar cube into a cup of water, the sugar molecules stay together in one region of the cup, and the water molecules are everywhere except in the spot that the sugar cube occupies. For each substance, you have created a concentration gradient. But soon the molecules of each kind of substance undergo **simple diffusion**: a random movement of like molecules from their region of greater concentration to the region where they are less concentrated. Gradually, sugar molecules tend to become dispersed through the cup, just as water molecules tend to become dispersed through the space that the sugar cube once occupied.

Diffusion of individual molecules occurs in fluids (either gases or liquids) and in solids to some extent. The unceasing motion inherent in all individual molecules drives diffusion. In cells, dissolved molecules are constantly moving and colliding millions of times each second. The collisions send molecules off in new, random directions. Eventually the random movements carry some of the molecules into different regions. As more molecules join them, collisions send molecules back and forth until at some point, there is no more *net* change in concentrations between the two regions. The molecules are uniformly dispersed.

The *rate of diffusion* depends on several things. Diffusion speeds up with increasing temperature, for heat energy causes molecules to move faster. Molecular size also affects diffusion rates, because small particles move faster than large ones do at the same temperature. Also, the greater the difference in concentrations between two regions, the faster the net movement. The reason is that with a greater *number* of molecules, there is a greater chance that a significant number will move into the neighboring regions.

Water, atmospheric gases such as oxygen and carbon dioxide, and a few other simple molecules diffuse readily across membranes. In fact, simple diffusion alone accounts for the greatest volume of substances moving across plasma membranes. Enclosed within a plasma membrane are millions of molecules of different substances. All jostle their neighbors and proceed along whatever concentration gradients exist for them. Over short distances (say, from one cytoplasmic region to another some fifty nanometers away), diffusion alone can distribute many substances within a fraction of a second. Simple diffusion is not effective over large distances, because of the time required for it to occur.

Simple diffusion accounts for the greatest volume of substances moved into and out of cells. It is also an important transport process within cells.

Facilitated Diffusion. In **facilitated diffusion**, lipid-insoluble ions and molecules still move in the same direction that gradients would take them, but they are passively assisted in a way that increases their *rate* of movements. Because the substances travel down a gradient, no direct energy outlay is necessary for facilitated diffusion. This transport mechanism is important in the movement of glucose, urea, and glycerol, to give a few examples.

It may be that facilitated diffusion occurs through permanently oriented channels or pores that span the membrane. This idea fits well with the fluid mosaic model. Experiments show that membrane proteins maintain a fixed orientation in the bilayer and may serve as the channels. Because membrane proteins have hydrophilic groups lining their interior, passive diffusion of water-soluble substances through them would be energetically favored over diffusion through the bilayer itself. Figure 5.7 depicts one idea of how such channel proteins might work.

Bulk Flow. In some cases, diffusion rates seem to be affected by **bulk flow**, whereby different ions and molecules in a fluid move together in the same direction in response to a pressure gradient. Bulk flow apparently occurs across the membranes of specialized plant cells that are concerned with the transport of organic molecules through the plant body. The idea is that a pressure gradient develops across the membranes of these cells, so that water flows across the membrane at very rapid diffusion rates.

Osmosis

Osmosis is the movement of water across any differentially permeable membrane in response to a solute concentration gradient, a pressure gradient, or both. In this book, we

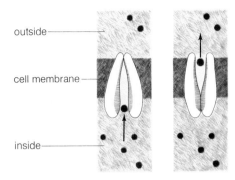

Figure 5.7 Simplified picture of one model of facilitated diffusion. The sketch shows a channel protein as if it were sliced down through its midsection. Different channel proteins have different hydrophilic groups along their interior surface (cross-hatched areas). Water-soluble ions and molecules could be attracted to and bind with these groups in a highly discriminatory way. The binding could trigger channel opening by bringing about changes in the protein's shape. As the substance moved through the channel, the protein shape would change again and close behind it.

will limit the use of the term to the movement of water molecules.

In response to solute concentration gradients and/or pressure gradients, water moves passively across cell membranes. Such water movement across differentially permeable membranes is called osmosis.

What are the effects of osmosis? Imagine that you have just made a plastic bag permeable to water molecules but impermeable to larger molecules. Suppose you fill the bag with water containing a two percent concentration of table sugar. Now put the bag in a container of distilled water (which has nearly all solutes removed from it). Water is less concentrated in the bag (where sugar molecules take up space) than it is on the outside. The net movement of water is inward—but sugar can't move out (the molecules are too large to pass through the holes in the "membrane"). Soon the bag swells with water (Figure 5.8). Because the bag can hold only so much, fluid pressure builds up and the bag might burst or spring a leak.

What happens when water is more concentrated inside the bag? Then the net water movement will be outward, and the bag will shrivel up (Figure 5.8). Only when water concentration is the same on both sides of the membrane will there be no net movement of water in either direction.

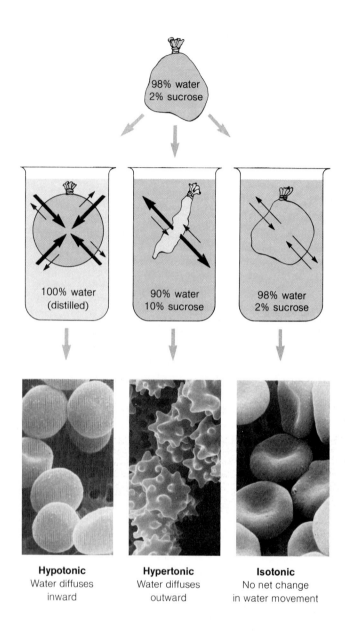

Hypotonic
Water diffuses
inward

Hypertonic
Water diffuses
outward

Isotonic
No net change
in water movement

Figure 5.8 Effects of osmosis in different environments. The sketches show why it is important for cells to be matched to solute levels in their environment. (In each sketched container, arrow width represents the relative amount of water movement.)

The micrographs correspond to the sketches. They show the kinds of shapes that might be seen in red blood cells placed in *hypotonic* solutions (influx of water into the cell), *hypertonic* solutions (outward flow of water from the cell), and *isotonic* solutions (internal and external solute concentrations are matched).

Red blood cells have no special mechanisms for actively taking in or expelling water molecules. Hence they swell up and burst, or shrivel up, if solute levels in their environment change. (Micrographs from M. Sheetz, R. Painter, and S. Singer, *J. Cell Biology*, 1976. 70:193)

The same kind of thing happens to living cells. When a red blood cell is immersed in distilled water, it swells and bursts. The cell contains many large organic molecules that can't move across its plasma membrane, so water concentration is higher outside. Internal pressure builds up as water moves in. Red blood cells have no mechanism for disposing of excess water, and eventually the plasma membrane bursts. When such a cell is immersed in a solution having a sugar concentration that is greater than the one inside, it loses water and shrivels up. Only when red blood cells are immersed in an environment where solute and water concentrations are the same as on the inside will there be no change in cell volume.

Land plant cells can survive in freshwater environments, which contain very little dissolved materials compared to the cytoplasm. They can do this because of mechanisms for controlling the inward or outward flow of water. When incoming water causes pressure to build up in the cell, the plasma membrane is prevented from bursting because it is surrounded by a plant cell wall strong enough to resist the pressure. The increasing internal pressure gradually forces water out through the membrane. When the outward flow equals the rate of inward diffusion, the internal pressure is constant.

Active Transport

Many ions (such as potassium and sodium ions) play important roles in cellular reactions. They must be moved into or out of the cell faster than diffusion alone can take them. Such substances can undergo **active transport**. At the molecular level, this means that they can be made to move in an energetically unfavorable direction (against some kind of gradient) when a membrane transport system receives an input of energy.

There is variation in how movements in an energetically unfavorable direction are accomplished. Basically, however, active transport occurs at the membrane proteins that maintain a fixed orientation in the bilayer. Here, active transport is triggered directly or indirectly by energy input. This energy becomes available to the systems through hydrolysis of energy-rich molecules, notably ATP (Chapter Six). Figure 5.9 is a simplified picture of what goes on. As much as seventy percent of the energy readily available in a cell may be devoted to active transport.

Four active transport systems have been studied intensively. The first, the *sodium-potassium pump*, is common to cells. In nerve cells, it primes membranes and makes them stand ready to receive messages from other cells. The second, the *calcium pump*, is vital in muscle function. Both of

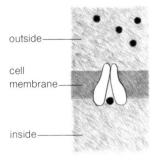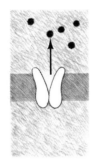

outside

cell
membrane

inside

ATP

a Molecule or ion binds to specific channel protein.

b Energy from ATP hydrolysis makes protein shape change.

c Channel opens, closes behind substance.

Figure 5.9 Simplified picture of active transport, in which a substance is moved in an energetically unfavorable direction (here, *against* a concentration gradient) when extra energy is supplied to the transport system. Facilitated diffusion as well as active transport occurs through channel proteins that span the lipid bilayer of cell membranes.

these active transport systems will be described in detail in later chapters. The other two kinds of systems are actually cotransporters, in which the passive transport of one substance is coupled with the active transport of another. In *sodium-linked cotransport*, sodium ions tag along passively during the active transport of sugars and amino acids. This system occurs in cell membranes of bacteria and animals. In *hydrogen-linked cotransport*, hydrogen ions tag along during the active transport of substances such as sugars. This system might be one of the most fundamental of all membrane mechanisms, for it occurs among organisms of all five kingdoms.

The features that all active transport systems at the molecular level hold in common can be summarized this way:

1. In active transport at the molecular level, substances are moved in an energetically unfavorable direction (against a concentration, pressure, temperature, or electric gradient).

2. Channel proteins spanning the membrane bilayer are the active transport systems. They are extremely selective in the kinds of ions and molecules that they will bind and transport.

3. The channel proteins act when specific ions or molecules are bound in place and when energy is directly or indirectly made available (often through ATP hydrolysis).

Endocytosis and Exocytosis

The active transport systems described so far can't carry more than one or two ions and molecules across the membrane at the same time. Yet some cells have the means to actively transport large particles across the plasma membrane, even to engulf other cells. Such transport requires energy outlays in order to form membrane-bound compartments that are necessary to accomplish these movements into and out of the cytoplasm.

Two examples may be given of **endocytosis**, whereby the plasma membrane infolds around foreign particles at or near the cell surface, then the enclosed space pinches off and enters the cytoplasm. The amoeba, a single-celled organism, relies on *phagocytosis*: the engulfment of solid particles or cells. For example, when an amoeba encounters an appetizing cell in its surroundings, one or two extensions of its membrane-enclosed cytoplasm move outward in the manner shown in Figure 5.10. The lobelike extensions curve back, toward the amoeba's body, and surround the particle. The membrane "pocket" so formed becomes an endocytotic vesicle, which moves into the cell interior. There it fuses with lysosomes (Chapter Four). Lysosomal enzymes digest the engulfed cell into small molecules, which diffuse across the vesicle membrane and are used by the cell. Phagocytosis is also the means by which certain white blood cells destroy harmful agents (such as bacteria) invading your body.

Another process for moving materials into animal cells is *pinocytosis*: the engulfment of liquid droplets. (The word means "cell-drinking.") In pinocytosis, a depression forms in the plasma membrane surface. As the membrane dimples inward, it surrounds some of the extracellular fluid. The vesicle pinches off and moves inside. There, it can dump its contents into the cytoplasm or fuse with other vesicles into large storage vacuoles.

Substances are also moved out of the cell by **exocytosis**. This process requires fusion of vesicles with the plasma membrane. For example, vesicles pinched off from Golgi membranes travel to and fuse with the plasma membrane, and their contents are secreted to the outside (Chapter Four). Figure 5.11 depicts this transport process.

MEMBRANE SURFACE RECEPTORS

Cell functioning depends on more than transport mechanisms across the membrane. It depends also on **membrane surface receptors**: diverse molecular sites at which cells chemically recognize and bind extracellular substances. The receptors often are carbohydrate groups attached to regions

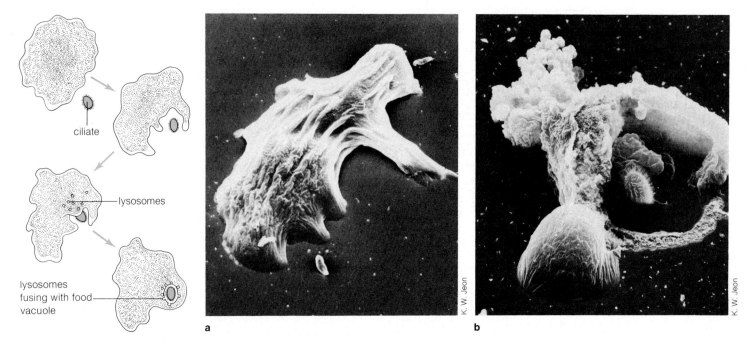

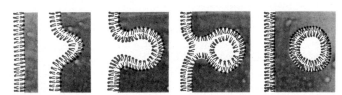

ciliate

lysosomes

lysosomes fusing with food vacuole

a

b

K. W. Jeon

K. W. Jeon

Figure 5.10 An example of endocytosis. Scanning electron micrographs show *Amoeba* with pseudopod extensions (**a**); then entrapping a ciliate by forming a vacuole around it (**b**). These micrographs correspond to the second and third sketches.

extracellular environment   dimpling   cytoplasm   vesicle

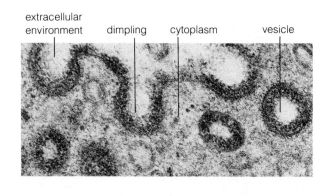

Figure 5.11 Pinocytosis in a red blood cell. The diagram (left to right) depicts vesicle formation. Exocytosis essentially occurs in reverse (in a sequence from right to left).

of membrane proteins and membrane lipids. These groups project into the cell environment (see, for example, Figure 5.6). Most of what is known about membrane surface receptors comes from studies of mammalian cells. When activated, some receptors lead to changes in cell metabolism or behavior. Others don't directly change cell activity. Rather, they provide the cell with some substance or remove a harmful substance from the environment.

In multicelled animals, membrane surface receptors function in cell-to-cell identity. Your own body cells, for instance, have surface markers that detect whether other cells they contact are like themselves or from another person (as they are in organ transplants). Such markers function in defense against tissue invaders. They also function in cell aggregation into tissues during the development of multicelled animals.

Among many eukaryotic cells, surface receptors are known to interact with cytoplasmic lattices (Chapter Four). The interactions are vital in determining how a cell responds to environmental conditions. Receptor signals transmitted to cytoplasmic elements seem to alter the distribution of microfilaments and microtubules. This distribution is a key factor in cell motion, shape, and growth. As we learn more about receptor signal mechanisms, basic biology and medical research will both benefit. These mechanisms are at the heart of cell functioning, cell division, and cellular responses to injury and attack.

Some membrane surface receptors function in altering cell metabolism or behavior. Others bind extracellular substances that the cell requires or harmful substances that must be inactivated.

In multicelled organisms, surface receptors also function in identifying cells of like type during tissue formation.

PERSPECTIVE

The main focus of this chapter has been the intriguing nature of the plasma membrane—a fluid structure that maintains its integrity in a largely fluid environment. With a consistency no greater than that of machine oil, this thin boundary layer around the cytoplasm controls which substances enter and leave cells, and how fast. Through interplays between passive and active transport mechanisms built into the membrane, this structure helps govern cell volume and cytoplasmic pH, vital ion concentrations and the stockpiling of nutrients, as well as the efficient release of harmful substances. Through surface receptors and structures of varied sorts, it senses and responds to events in the surrounding environment.

In chapters to follow, you will be reading about many events played out across not only the plasma membrane but cell membranes in general. For the membrane is also the physical stage for such diverse events as photosynthesis, cellular respiration, nerve message propagation, and communication between cells in the multicelled body. The cell membrane, in short, is central to our understanding of life processes.

Readings

Danielli, J. 1975. "The Bilayer Hypothesis of Membrane Structure." In *Cell Membranes* (G. Weissman and R. Claiborne, editors). New York: H. P. Publishing Company.

Giese, A. 1979. *Cell Physiology.* Fifth edition. Philadelphia: Saunders. Advanced reading, but excellent descriptions of the cellular environment. Good reference text for the serious student.

Lodish, H., and J. Rothman. 1979. "The Assembly of Cell Membranes." *Scientific American* 240(1):48–63.

Salisbury, F., and C. Ross. 1978. "The Water Milieu." In *Plant Physiology.* Second edition. Belmont, California: Wadsworth. One of the few clear introductions to the properties of water as they relate to plant cell functioning.

Singer, S., and G. Nicolson. 1972. "The Fluid Mosaic Model of the Structure of Cell Membranes." *Science* 175:720–731.

Stryer, L. 1981. *Biochemistry.* Second edition. San Francisco: Freeman. Excellent description of the molecular basis of cell membranes.

Wickner, W. "Assembly of Proteins into Membranes." *Science* 210: 861–868.

Wolfe, S. 1981. *Biology of the Cell.* Second edition. Belmont, California: Wadsworth. Contains an outstanding synthesis of current investigations into the structure and function of membranes.

Review Questions

1. Cell functioning depends on water's temperature-stabilizing properties and internal cohesion. What type of chemical bond represents the basis of these properties?

2. Describe how the polarity of the water molecule is the basis of the solvent properties of water. (As part of your answer, describe how spheres of hydration form around a positive or a negative ion.)

3. How do water molecules influence the regional organization of proteins and lipids in a cell?

4. Describe the fluid mosaic model of plasma membranes. What makes the membrane fluid? What parts constitute the mosaic?

5. List the six structural features that all cell membranes have in common.

6. What is meant by differentially permeable? What two general kinds of mechanisms associated with the plasma membrane regulate the movement of substances across a cell membrane.

7. List and define three kinds of passive transport systems, and three kinds of active transport systems.

8. Diffusion accounts for the greatest volume of substances moving into and out of cells. How does diffusion work?

9. What is osmosis, and what causes its occurrence?

10. Under what circumstances would active transport mechanisms come into play?

11. Describe some functions of membrane surface receptors.

6

ENERGY TRANSFORMATIONS
IN THE CELL

When you look at a single living cell beneath a microscope, you are watching a form seething with activity. Through its movements, it is identifying and taking in raw materials suspended in the water droplet on the slide. To power those tiny movements, the cell is extracting energy from food molecules it had stored away earlier. Even as you observe it, the cell is using materials and energy in building and maintaining its membranes and organelles, its stores of chemical compounds, its information-storage system, its pools of enzymes. It is alive; it is growing; it may reproduce itself. Multiply all of this activity by *75 trillion cells,* and you have an inkling of the activity going on in your own body as you are sitting quietly, doing nothing more than observing that single cell!

How cells trap, store, and use energy is a story of interest not only to biologists. It is also a story of how *you* trap and use energy—how you have the means to move, to think, to do all the things that go into being alive.

Soon enough, you will be following the main metabolic trails through cells. Before setting out, you may find it useful to get a general idea of how energy is transferred and transformed within cells, and of how enzymes and special energy-carrier molecules take part in what goes on. Often these topics are interwoven with presentations of the main metabolic pathways themselves. The premise here is that the pathways are easier to follow when they are kept as uncluttered as possible. If you study this chapter first, as you would study a map before traveling through some unfamiliar place, you will probably have a much smoother time on the cellular roads ahead.

ON THE AVAILABILITY OF USEFUL ENERGY

Two Energy Laws

All events large and small, from the birth of stars to the death of a microorganism, are governed by two laws of energy. Both laws concern the nature of energy in a given system (a "system" being the matter in some defined region) and its surroundings ("surroundings" being, if you carry it far enough, the rest of the universe).

The **first law of thermodynamics** deals with the *quantity* of energy available. It may be expressed this way:

The total amount of energy in the universe remains constant. More energy cannot be created. And existing energy cannot be destroyed; it can only undergo conversion from one form to another.

This first law tells us that you cannot increase the universal energy pool by making "new" energy out of nothing, and you cannot destroy any of it, either. *All you can do is hoard or let go of what's already there.*

All systems—the sun, whales, people, trees, candy, diamonds—have energy hoards. They have some energy that has the potential to be transferred or transformed but that is not, for the moment, doing either thing. Hence the name, **potential energy**. For instance, chemical bonds holding together sugar molecules in a candy bar are a form of chemical potential energy. When your cells break apart the molecules, they liberate some of the energy stored in these bonds. Some of this liberated energy eventually can be converted to other forms (for example, into the mechanical energy of muscle action). Each time a system lets go of some potential energy, there is a rise in **kinetic energy**—or energy associated with motion.

Notice the word "rise." All substances are already in motion, to varying degrees, depending on how fast their atoms are vibrating or interacting with one another. Electrons in chemical bonds constantly zip about nuclei, even in solid rocks. In a region of hot air, gaseous molecules randomly collide with one another faster than they otherwise would at lower temperature (Chapter Five). The point is, the difference between potential and kinetic energy isn't an either/or kind of thing. The difference has to do with the *degree* to which units of energy become spread out or organized in one region relative to another. When one system lets go of energy, the rise in motion puts the energy up for grabs. Depending on the direction of motion, this energy may be intercepted and hoarded temporarily in other systems, or it may simply diffuse throughout the surroundings.

This brings us to the second law of thermodynamics, which deals with the *quality* of energy available. Energy hoarded in some systems is high quality. Because it is organized in one place, it can be readily tapped to make things happen, to get work done. Energy spreading around as heat in the atmosphere is an example of low-quality energy. Because it is so dispersed and disorganized, it is not really accessible enough to be useful. Let's consider two examples of what this difference in quality means before formally stating the second law.

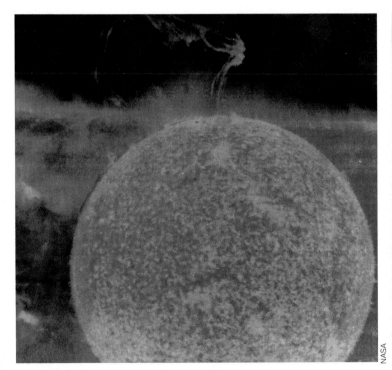
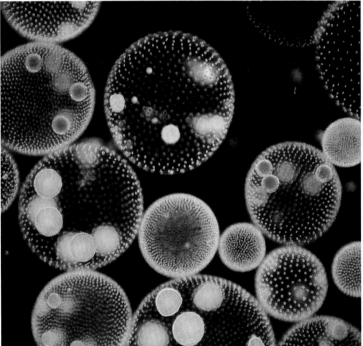

Figure 6.1 All events large and small, from the birth of stars to the death of a microorganism, are governed by laws of energy. Shown here, eruptions on the sun's surface and, to the right, *Volvox*—colonies of microscopically small single cells that capture sunlight energy necessary to drive their life processes.

Photons are units of light energy. They stream away from the sun and still contain high-quality energy when they reach the earth. Plants bombarded with the wave trains absorb some of the photon energy. They convert it to the chemical potential energy of sugar, then starch molecules. With each energy transfer and conversion, though, some energy is lost to the surroundings as heat. (The reason is that no system is efficient enough to hang onto all of the energy released during an energy change.) Even so, enough energy gets hoarded so that plant parts containing the starch molecules represent high-quality energy stores. When you eat plants, your body cells convert some of the energy to mechanical energy (such as muscle movements). Once again, some energy slips away as heat to the surroundings. In fact, your body steadily gives off metabolically generated heat about equal to that from a hundred-watt light bulb.

Whether you are talking about a fraction of a second or many billions of years, the spontaneous direction of energy flow is from high-quality to low-quality forms. (Here, "spontaneous" is used to mean the natural, or *most probable*, direction.) The **second law of thermodynamics** states it this way:

Left to itself, any system along with its surroundings spontaneously undergoes energy conversions to less organized forms. Each time that happens, some energy gets randomly dispersed in a form that is not as readily available to do work.

If the first law tells us that we can't get something from nothing, the second law tells us that we don't have a chance of breaking even. Although the total amount of energy in the universe stays the same, the amount available in high-quality forms that can be used to do work—to make things happen—is being frittered away. All energy tends to distribute itself *so uniformly* throughout a system that it cannot be converted back very easily to more organized forms. The term **entropy** refers to how much energy in a system has become so dispersed (often as evenly distributed, low-quality heat) that it is no longer available in organized forms that can be tapped to make things happen. The higher the value of entropy, the greater the degree of disorganization.

Entropy is constantly on the increase. As far as anybody can foresee, the universal rise in entropy will reach a maximum some billions of years hence. Then, the universe will be everywhere identical and at the same temperature, and nothing will ever change again. Yet life is one glorious pocket of resistance to this somewhat depressing flow toward oblivion. For the entropy of any local region can be lowered—*but only for as long as that region is resupplied with*

usable energy being lost from someplace else. The sun is steadily losing energy. Plants hoard some of the energy lost from the sun. Plants lose energy to other organisms that feed, directly or indirectly, on plants. Thus, only through energy transfusions from the sun does the world of life maintain a high degree of organization.

There is a steady flow of sunlight energy into the interconnected web of life, and this compensates for the steady flow of energy leaving it.

Metabolic Reactions: Energy Changes in Cells

Having looked at energy hoarding and dissipation on the grand scale, we can turn to how the tiny cell operates in the scheme of things.

As in all systems, a cell has some amount of internal energy. This amount is the sum of all the energetic interactions within atoms and between the atoms, ions, and molecules making up the cell body. What we call a **metabolic reaction** is some form of internal energy change.

Because a cell interacts with its environment, you can't really think of a cell as an isolated system. However, you *can* think about internal energy changes associated with life processes, because these changes are measurable. To measure a change in internal energy, you have to define certain properties. These include pressure, temperature, and the energy levels of substances present at the beginning of a reaction (the *reactants*) and at its conclusion (the *products*). Which particular reaction steps are followed, and how fast they are taken, have no effect on the *difference* between the initial energy state and what it is at the conclusion of some reaction. For example, most cells extract all of the energy that they can from a glucose molecule in about 140 steps. You can do the same thing all at once by igniting glucose over a hot flame. Glucose has only so much energy at the start of either process. If the same products are produced, then the same amount of energy must be released by the time the molecule is used up at the end of either process.

Let's assume that both temperature and pressure are constant in the cell body. How do we know whether the internal energy will increase or decrease during a given type of reaction? Combining the meaning of the first and second law of thermodynamics, we can say this:

A chemical reaction tends to proceed spontaneously toward a state of minimum energy and maximum disorder.

Under the conditions specified (constant temperature, pressure), reactions that release energy are known as **exergonic reactions**. (The phrase means "energy out.") Cells depend on many different exergonic reactions in which substances are combined, rearranged, or split apart. Of course, when atoms, ions, and molecules are moved around in these reactions, some energy slips away into the surroundings. Thus, the end products of exergonic reactions have *less* energy than do the starting substances. For example,

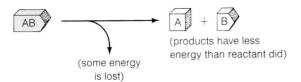

Cells also depend on endergonic reactions for combining, rearranging, and breaking apart substances. In **endergonic reactions** ("energy in"), extra energy must first be acquired from the surroundings, otherwise the reaction will not proceed on its own. In many reactions, this kind of energy input means that the end products have *more* energy than the starting substances:

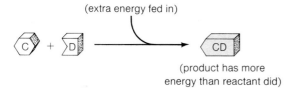

This kind of reaction does not violate the second law of thermodynamics; it occurs *only* when extra energy from some other system is fed into a reaction.

In living cells, breakdown or synthesis reactions commonly occur in sequential, stepwise fashion. These sequential conversions are called **metabolic pathways**. Some steps release energy, and others require energy input. The energy-releasing steps can be used to drive energy-requiring steps in the same metabolic pathway. For example,

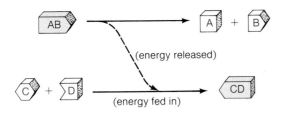

Such sequences are efficient ways to make the most out of energy hoards. To be sure, the total energy change from beginning to end is the same, regardless of the path taken. But stepwise reactions of this sort increase the number of opportunities for energy transfer.

Also, in metabolic pathways, the product of one reaction often is used as a starting substance for another reaction in the series. When used this way, it is called an *intermediate* product of the pathway.

Through reliance on metabolic pathways, cells make more efficient use of energy that might otherwise be lost to the surroundings during an energy change.

Materials as well as energy can link reactions in metabolic pathways. Products from one or more reactions can serve as intermediates for subsequent reactions in the series.

Equilibrium and the Cell

You might now be thinking that reactions proceed only one way in cells. Under certain conditions, though, they may also proceed in what seems to be an improbable direction. Products of *lower* energy can revert to reactant molecules having *higher* energy:

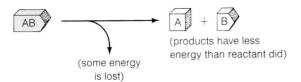

An increase in concentration, temperature, or pressure can drive a reaction in an improbable direction. How does the increase do this? To keep things simple, let's limit our concern to the effects of increased concentration.

When many reactant molecules are concentrated together, there is a greater probability that they will collide with each other, which they do. For instance, carbon dioxide and water molecules in your body react to form carbonic acid. The carbonic acid goes on to dissociate into bicarbonate and H^+ ions:

$$CO_2 + H_2O \longrightarrow H_2CO_3 \longrightarrow HCO_3^- + H^+$$
$$\text{carbonic} \qquad \text{bicarbonate}$$
$$\text{acid}$$

As time goes on, more and more product molecules form, so not as many reactant molecules are left. The reaction rate drops accordingly. All the while, however, *product* concentration has been increasing—which means that product molecules, too, start colliding more frequently! Some fraction will have enough collision energy to be driven in the reverse direction:

$$CO_2 + H_2O \longleftarrow H_2CO_3 \longleftarrow HCO_3^- + H^+$$

This overall reaction, in the forward and reverse direction, illustrates a general point. As long as both reactant and product molecules are not funneled somewhere else, almost any reaction proceeds in both directions. Eventually, if left to themselves, all reactions approach **equilibrium**: they run about as fast in the improbable (reverse) direction as in the more probable one. Then, there is no further *net* change in concentrations of reactants or products unless conditions change. (It's something like a room that has as many people entering as leaving. The total number of people in the room stays the same, even though the particular mix of individuals in the room is constantly changing.)

It is important to understand that equilibrium doesn't imply equal concentrations. Product concentration might be greater or lower than that of the reactants—*depending on how much energy is being fed into or released from the reaction at equilibrium.* For example, reactions that give off considerable energy are common in metabolic pathways. The point at which equilibrium is reached favors the products so much that the reverse (energy-requiring) reactions hardly occur, unless the product concentration is very high, or the reactant concentrations are very low, or both.

One final point should be made here. The hallmark of the cellular world is dynamic change. Availability of raw materials shifts. Requirements for different products vary over time. As long as a cell is alive and growing, its reactions are seldom at equilibrium. The concentrations of products and reactants can be changing continuously.

Cellular homeostasis is a dynamic state. It is assured through constant adjustments to internal and external change—through never-ending approaches toward and retreats from equilibrium, along many metabolic pathways.

ENZYME FUNCTION

Activation Energy and Enzymes

For any reaction to occur, molecules must collide with a certain minimum energy. This minimum energy is the **activation energy** for the reaction. Because molecules have a wide range of speeds, there are always a few collisions between very fast molecules in which the activation energy is exceeded. The occurrence of such collisions increases rapidly with increasing temperature, so that reactions that proceed at a negligible rate at room temperature can be made to occur at high temperature.

Consider what happens when you strike a match to start wood burning. The heat energy makes wood molecules

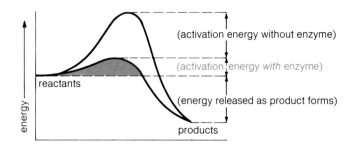

Figure 6.2 Enzymes and activation energy. Activation energy is like a small hill over which reactants must be pushed before a reaction will proceed. Enzyme action lowers the required activation energy in either direction.

jostle faster. They are more likely to collide with oxygen molecules in the air, and more will collide with enough energy to react. Bonds are broken, new bonds form, and light and heat energy are released. The released heat energy increases the collision rate between remaining molecules, so the reaction continues. Without that initial boost from the match, though, the average kinetic energy of the molecules isn't enough for wood to react with oxygen in the atmosphere.

As it happens, the starting substances for exergonic reactions that normally take place in cells tend to react slowly on their own. For life to continue, spontaneous reactions that would take years or decades to reach completion must be made to occur within a fraction of a second. Of course, if you've ever burned your fingers on a match, you know that boosting the temperature is not a good way of speeding up reactions in living things. Metabolic reactions must occur within a range of lower temperatures. Enzymes make this possible.

Enzymes are *catalysts*—substances that speed up chemical reactions. They do so not by supplying activation energy, but by *lowering* the activation energy needed for a reaction to occur. Because the activation energy is lowered, more collisions will have energies in excess of the activation energy, so the reaction proceeds faster than it otherwise would. Enzyme action affects only the rate of a reaction, not the reaction's inevitable outcome.

Enzymes speed up the rate at which a reaction approaches equilibrium by lowering the activation energy required.

Enzymes only affect the reaction rate. They do not change the proportions of reactants and products that will be present once equilibrium is reached.

Figure 6.2 is a generalized picture of enzyme effects on exergonic reactions. The effects are impressive. Because an enzyme is not permanently altered or used up by a reaction, it can act again and again with astonishing speed. A single molecule of the enzyme carbonic anhydrase can combine water and carbon dioxide to form 100,000 molecules of carbonic acid in one second. That's about a million times faster than the reaction proceeds on its own!

Enzyme Structure and Functioning

How are enzymes able to lower the activation energy required for a reaction? Enzyme structure provides us with some clues. Enzymes are proteins whose structure arises from the folding of one or more polypeptide chains into diverse, three-dimensional shapes. Somewhere in each enzyme, at least one small region is folded into a groove, or cleft, that serves as a catalytic site. Here, one (or more) reactants becomes temporarily bound to the enzyme. While the reactant is bound, it rapidly undergoes internal rearrangements, cleavage, or union with other reactants (Figure 6.3). Of course, the same atoms, ions, or molecules can be reactants for many different metabolic reactions. But each *enzyme* binds only a certain reactant or set of reactants. The ones that an enzyme does bind are referred to as its **substrates**. An enzyme cleft to which one or more specific substrates become bound is called an **active site**.

Enzymes are extremely selective about which substances they will temporarily bind. For enzyme action to occur, the shape and chemical group of an active site must be complementary to the shape and chemical groups of a reactant.

Notice the phrase "temporarily bound" in the preceding paragraph. Binding at an active site is a *reversible* event, because only weak bonds are involved. Hydrogen bonds, ionic bonds, and other weak attractions predominate in the microenvironment that an active site represents. Later on, in different parts of this book, you will be reading about various aspects of enzyme action. These aspects will probably make more sense if you keep this point in mind:

Substrates do not stay permanently attached to an active site, because the bonds they form with the enzyme are weak; hence the enzyme-substrate attachment reaction is easily reversible.

At one time, the active site was thought to be a rigid arrangement of charged, polar, and nonpolar groups precisely matched to some substrate, much like a lock is pre-

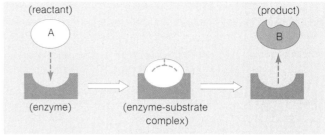

a Reactant undergoes internal rearrangements to form a different substance.

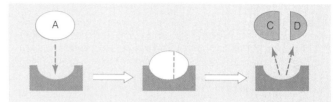

b Cleavage of reactant creates two (or more) products.

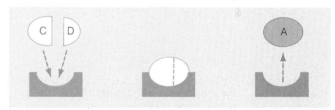

c Union of two (or more) reactants creates one (or more) product.

Figure 6.3 Simplified picture of the effects of enzyme action on a substrate or set of substrates.

cisely matched to its key. However, even though enzymes and substrates must be complementary, active sites are not rigid. They undergo changes during binding. This idea is the basis for the currently favored view of enzyme-substrate interaction, called the **induced-fit model**.

To understand the features of this model, consider that in any chemical reaction, internal bonds holding a reactant together are weakened or broken, and atomic or molecular parts become rearranged into the form of the product. For one brief moment, though, the parts being shuffled around assume an intermediate configuration known as the *transition state*. Now, suppose the active site almost but not quite matches up to its substrate. Then the initial binding between them would not be as strong as it could be. However, the interaction would be enough to induce a change in the

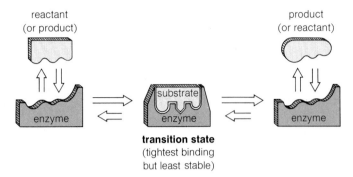

reactant
(or product)

product
(or reactant)

substrate
enzyme

enzyme

enzyme

transition state
(tightest binding
but least stable)

Figure 6.4 Induced-fit model of enzyme-substrate interactions. Only when the substrate is bound in place is the active site complementary to it. The most precise fit occurs during the transition state (see text). Because the active site can change shape, it can be complementary to both the reactant and the product. Thus enzymes can speed up a reaction in either direction, depending on cellular conditions. The longer arrows signify the spontaneous direction in this example.

shape of the active site (Figure 6.4). The active site assumes a shape that exactly matches that of the intermediate form. This pulls the binding reaction toward the optimum fit of the transition state. The intermediate form in any reaction is unstable. Given the right conditions, the reaction can be pulled readily in the favored direction. In this sequence of events, the substrate *induces* the optimum fit for the enzyme-substrate interaction.

What actually gets a substance into the transition state? At least three mechanisms, working alone or in combination, might be involved. All have the effect of reducing the activation energy required for a reaction to occur.

First, enzymes *orient* their substrates in positions that promote interaction. Reactant molecules, atoms, and ions collide on their own in the environment, but they do so from random directions. This means that their mutually attractive chemical groups often don't make contact, so reaction doesn't always occur. In contrast, extensive but weak bonding in the active site orients reactants in close and correct alignment. The alignment enhances the probability of reactants moving into the transition state. The effect is one of lowering the activation energy.

Second, when substrates are bound at an active site, their internal bonds become distorted and strained. Some parts of the reactant break apart under the strain, others may be "bent" at angles approaching those found in the transition state. In either case, the outcome is a lowering of the required activation energy.

Finally, an enzyme has amino acid side groups that can serve as hydrogen-ion donors or acceptors. Depending on the orientation of the substrate in the active site, some of these groups may acquire or give up the ions. When they do, they create shifts in pH in the microenvironment of the active site. Altered pH can send reactants into the transition state. This is what happens in hydrolytic enzymes, for example.

Cofactors

Enzymes, again, consist of polypeptide chains. However, many enzymes also require participation of chemical components, called **cofactors**, for proper enzyme function. Many inorganic ions (such as ferrous iron, or Fe^{++}) serve as cofactors. So do several nonprotein organic molecules called *coenzymes.* Coenzymes are carriers of atoms or functional groups during reactions. For example, coenzyme-A is a carrier of carbon-containing groups during the enzyme-mediated breakdown of pyruvate (a three-carbon compound) and fatty acids.

In some cases, metals and inorganic ions are tightly bound to the enzyme. In other cases, cofactors are bound only loosely and transiently to the enzyme during the reaction. Nicotinamide adenine dinucleotide (NAD^+) and flavin adenine dinucleotide (FAD) are examples of these transient carriers. Their particular cargo consists of hydrogen and associated electrons, which are necessary in enzyme-mediated electron transfers that will be described shortly.

The precursors of various coenzymes are known as vitamins. A vitamin is an organic nutrient that the body requires only in extremely small amounts. For example, pantothenic acid is an essential component of coenzyme-A. Riboflavin (vitamin B_2) is a component of FAD. Most water-soluble vitamins function as components of coenzymes. Even though you require only traces of these vitamins in your diet, your body would suffer serious consequences in their absence (Chapter Twenty-Six).

Effects of pH and Temperature on Enzyme Activity

Enzymes are adapted to specific conditions in the cellular environment. For instance, each kind of enzyme functions only within a certain pH range. The reason is that hydrogen bonds and other weak attractions holding the enzyme in its three-dimensional shape are extremely sensitive to pH changes in its surroundings. Most enzymes are effective at or near pH 7, which is generally optimum for most cell types.

Exceptions include pepsin, which functions in the extremely acid medium of the stomach. Trypsin, found in the small intestine, functions in a more basic medium (about pH 8.5).

With very few exceptions, enzymes can't tolerate high temperature, either. The rate of enzyme activity does increase as the environment heats up, until a maximum rate is reached. That rate is the optimum temperature for a given enzyme. When temperature increases further, the reaction rate plummets. Again, the reason is the sensitivity of hydrogen bonds. Increased temperature increases the kinetic energy of the enzyme's molecular framework; and molecules in the surroundings also collide more frequently with the enzyme itself. At some point, the disturbances are so great that denaturation occurs. Hydrogen bonds holding the protein in its coiled secondary structure break, hydrophobic interactions shift, and the protein chains unwind. With these structural changes, the enzyme stops working. Even brief exposure to temperatures above optimum will destroy enzymes. Without enzymes, metabolism grinds to a halt and cells die.

Enzymes work only on specific substrates, and they work only within some specific range of environmental conditions.

Controls Over Enzymes

Just about everything that happens to cells—their growth, maintenance, and reproduction—comes under the influence of enzymes. Hence control over enzyme activity is vital. These controls help govern which sets of substances will be formed in a cell, when they will be formed, and in what amounts. How do these controls work? It is important to understand that a cell doesn't depend on the activity of one single enzyme molecule of a given type. There can be many, many copies of the same kind of enzyme, all active at once. Control mechanisms work to decrease the number of enzyme copies that are available and functioning.

In one way or another, all controls over enzyme activities limit the number of molecules of a given enzyme that are active at any given time.

We will look at some control mechanisms in later chapters. Here, let's consider just one important control to get an idea of what goes on. **Allosteric enzymes** are control agents. The name allosteric implies that these enzymes can take on "other shapes." Such enzymes have an active site for substrate molecules—and another site that binds with inter-

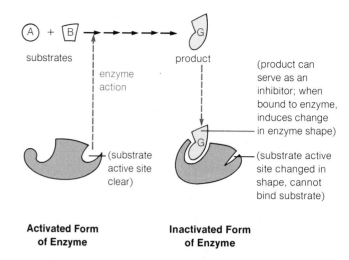

Figure 6.5 Feedback inhibition based on allosteric enzymes. In this example, the product itself acts as the inhibitor of enzyme activity. When the inhibitor is bound to the enzyme, the shape of the enzyme changes. The changes prevent substrates from binding to the active site.

mediate or end-product molecules. In some cases, when a molecule is bound at the "other" site, it so distorts the active site that the enzyme no longer matches up with its substrates. (See, for example, Figure 6.5.) Thus intermediate or end-product molecules act as regulators over the very enzyme that helps lead to their assembly. Only when such molecules are released from the "other" site does the enzyme resume normal activity. This kind of control, in which an increase in some substance (or activity) inhibits the very process leading to the increase, is called **feedback inhibition**.

Thus inhibition of enzyme activity is one kind of control mechanism. Others regulate when and where an enzyme becomes operational. (For example, many digestive enzymes exist first as *inactive precursor forms*. They don't become functional until the body requires them or until they are secreted into the proper body region.) Some controls also regulate the *synthesis* of enzymes or their precursor forms. Not all enzymes are needed all the time, and not all are even needed in the same cells.

Controls over enzyme activity include mechanisms that inhibit the activity of enzymes already formed; mechanisms that activate precursor forms of enzymes; and mechanisms that control synthesis of enzymes.

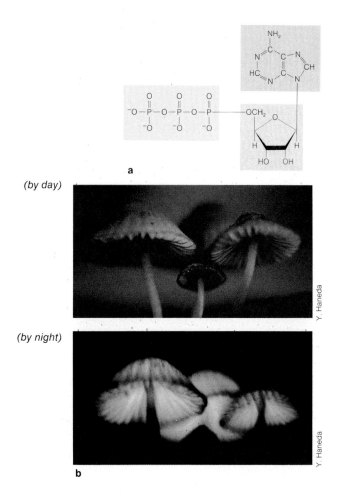

a

(by day)

(by night)

Y. Haneda

Y. Haneda

b

Figure 6.6 (**a**) Structural formula for ATP. The triphosphate group is shaded in gold, the sugar ribose is shaded in gray, and the adenine portion is shaded light brown.

Bioluminescence is the production of light energy during the reaction of ATP with specific compounds in various organisms, such as the fungus *Mycena lux-coeli* shown in (**b**). In bacterial bioluminescence, a special enzyme (luciferase), flavin mononucleotide, and oxygen are required for the reaction.

TYPES OF ENERGY TRANSFERS IN CELLS

By now, you have become acquainted with certain aspects of metabolism—with factors that dictate the direction in which a reaction will proceed, and with the way a reaction depends on enzymes for speedy completion. In passing, you have read that energy released in some reactions can be transferred to others. How, you might be wondering, are these transfers actually made? Two kinds of molecules are necessary: energy carriers and electron carriers. Let's consider some energy carriers first.

Formation and Use of ATP

In many reactions, some of the energy released is used in forming compounds with phosphate bonds. For reasons that will soon be apparent, the energy embodied in phosphate bonds is readily accessible for many different cellular activities.

A major energy-carrying phosphate compound in living things is the nucleotide **adenosine triphosphate**, or **ATP**. The energy that drives its formation can be obtained from sunlight energy conversions, or from reactions in which organic and inorganic compounds are degraded.

As Figure 6.6 shows, ATP is composed of adenine (a nitrogen-containing compound), ribose (a five-carbon sugar), and three linked phosphate groups (a triphosphate). The key parts of the molecule are the triphosphate's two $(P)—O—(P)$ linkages, otherwise known as *pyrophosphate bonds*. The (P) is a standard symbol for a phosphate group. The linkages shown are commonly called "high-energy" phosphate bonds. It isn't that the bonds themselves are remarkable. Rather, the term refers to the relatively large amount of useful energy that is readily released during hydrolysis of such bonds.

What is it about these bonds that makes them so ready to part with their energy? At pH 7, the triphosphate carries four negative charges, and these charges are much closer together than they would like to be. This means that ATP is highly charged and energetically somewhat unstable. In fact, the end phosphate group is attracted more to the surrounding water than it is to its partners, so hydrolysis is a favored reaction. ATP hydrolysis relieves the tension, so to speak, for the charge distribution in the detached phosphate group is more harmonious.

The products of ATP hydrolysis contain less chemical energy than the reactant molecule does. *And the greater the energy change during a reaction, the more energy becomes available for transfer to other substances in the cell.* Under standard conditions, the useful energy released during the reaction is about seven kilocalories per mole of ATP.

In most biological reactions, only one of the two phosphate bonds in ATP is split. The result is **adenosine diphosphate** (ADP) and inorganic phosphate (HPO_4^{--} or, more simply, P_i):

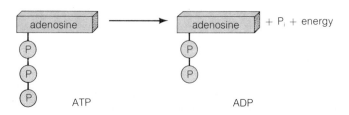

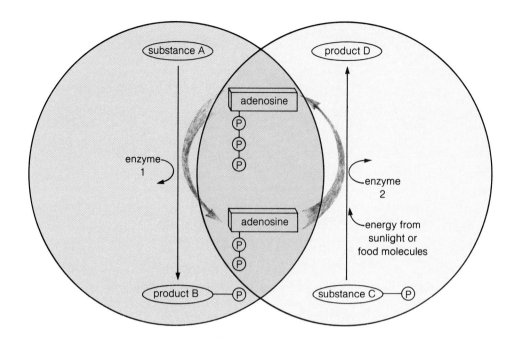

Figure 6.7 Coupled reactions in which ATP plays a role. Some of the energy captured in ATP when substance C is converted to D is used to drive the reaction in which substance A is converted to B. Here, the yellow circle represents the energy-releasing reaction; and the blue circle represents the energy-requiring reaction.

Under certain conditions a second hydrolysis occurs, from ADP to **adenosine monophosphate** (AMP) and inorganic phosphate:

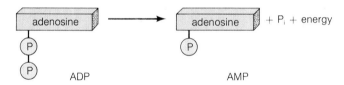

When ATP is hydrolyzed in these ways, the energy released would, by itself, do little more than heat the surroundings. It would be like turning on an electric motor without connecting it to anything. The motor would whir, the surrounding air would warm up, and electricity would be dissipated—and nothing would get done. However, when you take a pulley belt and couple that motor to, say, a sewing machine, that same energy can be harnessed for use. In cells, enzymes make such connections. In the process, they help conserve energy that would otherwise be lost.

Enzymes couple energy-yielding reactions such as ATP hydrolysis to the energy-requiring reactions involved in performing useful cellular work.

For example, a phosphate group detached from ATP can be transferred, through enzyme action, to another molecule in the cell. A molecule that has a phosphate group attached to it is said to have undergone **phosphorylation**. Thus phosphorylated, the molecule acquires some of the energy released from ATP. It thereby becomes more reactive:

Often, in this more reactive state, the molecule will take part in some reaction that might not otherwise proceed on its own. A good example is glucose, which in most organisms will not undergo any reaction until it receives a phosphate group from ATP in an enzyme-mediated reaction.

Energetically unfavorable reactions (ones that don't proceed spontaneously) can be driven indirectly by an input of energy released from a favorable reaction, such as the splitting of ATP.

Active transport mechanisms, too, depend on enzymes that couple ATP hydrolysis to specific tasks. In this case, changes in the shape of membrane-bound enzymes and other proteins are geared to thrusting some substances into or out of cells. ATP transfers are also vital in biosynthesis reactions and cell movements.

Figure 6.7 is a generalized picture of how enzymes and ATP interact in driving metabolic reactions. Although each

Table 6.1 Some Electron Carriers Important in Metabolic Reactions

Electron Carrier	Main Function	Acceptor Form (oxidized)	Donor Form (reduced)
Nicotinamide adenine dinucleotide	Accepts electrons, hydrogen at food breakdown sites; transfers and donates them to ATP production sites	NAD^+	NADH
Nicotinamide adenine dinucleotide phosphate	Accepts electrons, hydrogen at sunlight energy conversion sites; transfers and donates them to biosynthesis sites	$NADP^+$	NADPH
Flavin adenine dinucleotide	Accepts electrons, hydrogen at food breakdown sites; transfers and donates them to ATP production sites	FAD	$FADH_2$
Flavin mononucleotide	Acceptor-donor of electrons, hydrogen in many membrane-bound electron transport systems	FMN	$FMNH_2$
Cytochrome, with an iron-containing (Fe) ring	Acceptor-donor of electrons in many membrane-bound electron transport systems	Fe^{+++}	Fe^{++}
Oxygen	Final electron acceptor outside many membrane-bound transport systems	O	O^-

kind of enzyme works only for a specific reaction, ATP can be used in many different reactions as an intermediate energy source. That is why ATP is sometimes called the "universal energy currency" of cells.

ATP transfers usable energy to diverse reactions concerned with energy metabolism, biosynthesis, active transport, and cellular movement.

You may be wondering where all the ATP comes from. If ATP were used up like nonreturnable bottles, cells would be in trouble. For instance, the mass of ATP that your cells break down each day adds up to more than your total body weight! Obviously the leftover ADP or AMP molecules are not discarded. Instead, they are recharged with energy from some outside source (ingested or stored nutrients, for example) and prepared for reuse by phosphorylation. Thus a single molecule may be phosphorylated, broken down, and rephosphorylated thousands or even millions of times in a single day.

Electron-Transfer Reactions

Electron transfers are at the heart of reactions concerned with energy use. Electrons never float about randomly in cells. They are always transferred from one substance (the donor) to another (an acceptor). When an atom or molecule gives up one or more electrons, it is said to be *oxidized*. When an atom or molecule accepts one or more electrons, it is said to be *reduced*. You have probably come across the phrase **oxidation-reduction reaction**. It simply refers to an electron transfer. In many of these reactions, hydrogen is also removed from donor molecules and is transferred along with the electrons.

The molecules that take part in electron transfers can be free-moving, carrying electrons and hydrogen from one reaction site to a different reaction site in the cell. They also can be bound in cell membranes, such as those of chloroplasts and mitochondria. Table 6.1 lists some important examples of electron carriers.

Among the most important free-moving electron carriers are the molecules NAD^+ and $NADP^+$. Nicotinamide adenine dinucleotide, or NAD^+, accepts electrons and hydrogen from nutrient molecules that are being degraded. In its reduced form, it is abbreviated **NADH**. This form transfers the electrons and hydrogen to reaction sites where ATP is formed. As its name suggests, $NADP^+$ is a molecule of nicotinamide adenine dinucleotide with a phosphate group attached. This carrier molecule is important in photosynthesis. Its reduced form, **NADPH**, transfers electrons and hydrogen from sites of sunlight energy conversion to reaction sites where sugars and other carbon-containing molecules are synthesized.

Free-moving electron carriers such as NAD$^+$ and NADP$^+$ accept electrons and hydrogen at one reaction site in the cell, and transfer them to different reaction sites concerned with ATP production or biosynthesis.

Membrane-bound electron carriers take part in a series of oxidation-reduction reactions that lead to ATP formation. They are part of **electron transport systems**, which consist of several electron carriers and enzymes positioned in organized arrays in cell membranes. One membrane-bound carrier is flavin mononucleotide, or **FMN**. Other membrane-bound carriers are **cytochromes**, which have a molecular ring with an iron atom at its center. This ring is the site of electron acceptance and transfer.

In electron transport systems, oxidation-reduction reactions occur in enzyme-mediated steps, one after the other. For example, in some systems, the first molecule accepts electrons and hydrogen from NADH. Then the electrons are transferred, in stepwise reactions, to other membrane-bound carriers that include cytochromes. The last electron carrier in the series gives up the electron to some kind of external acceptor molecule (one that is not part of the electron transport system). Oxygen is one type of final acceptor molecule.

The point of such oxidation-reduction sequences is the generation of usable forms of energy. By analogy, think of an electron transport chain as a staircase. Electrons that have been "raised" (excited) to the top of the staircase have the most potential energy. The electrons drop down the staircase, one step at a time (they are transferred from one electron carrier to another). With each drop, some of their extra energy is released. Some of this energy is used to do work—to move H$^+$ in ways that establish pH and electric gradients across membranes, for example. Such gradients, you will discover, are essential in ATP formation.

Membrane-bound electron carriers form electron transport systems that function in ATP production.

This completes our introduction to the connections between energy, enzymes, energy carriers, and electron carriers. These connections are vital in the energy-trapping and energy-utilization pathways of the cell, two topics that will occupy our attention in the chapters that follow.

Readings

Ferdinand, W. 1976. *The Enzyme Molecule.* New York: Wiley.

Miller, G. 1978. *Chemistry: A Basic Introduction.* Belmont, California: Wadsworth. Outstanding introductory book.

Stryer, L. 1975. *Biochemistry.* San Francisco: Freeman.

Wolfe, S. 1981. *Biology of the Cell.* Second edition. Belmont, California: Wadsworth. Excellent discussion of enzyme structure and function.

Review Questions

1. State the first and second laws of thermodynamics. Which law deals with the *quality* of available energy, and which deals with the *quantity*? Can you give some examples of high-quality energy?

2. Does the living state violate the second law of thermodynamics? In other words, how does the world of living things maintain a high degree of organization, even though there is a universal trend toward disorganization?

3. In some cells, a large amount of the internal energy of a glucose molecule is released in a reaction that takes 140 steps. Imagine a supercell that can do the same thing in half the time by way of a different reaction. How will this different, faster route affect the difference between the initial energy state of the glucose molecule and what it will be at the end of the reaction?

4. In metabolic reactions, does equilibrium imply equal concentrations of reactants and products? Can you think of some cellular events that might keep a reaction from approaching equilibrium?

5. Describe an enzyme and its role in metabolic reactions. How do enzymes affect the proportions of reactants and products that will be present at equilibrium?

6. Define "substrate" and "active site." Why is binding at an active site a readily reversible event?

7. Can you give a reason why your diet should include trace amounts of vitamin B$_{12}$ (riboflavin)?

8. The high temperatures associated with severe fevers can impair cell functioning. Can you explain why?

9. Describe three forms of controls over enzyme activity. Do these controls inactivate all enzymes of a given type, or do they decrease the number of active enzymes of a given type?

10. Describe what is meant by a "high-energy bond." Name two molecules in which high-energy bonds occur, and describe the role they play in cells.

11. What is an oxidation-deduction reaction? What is its function in cells?

12. Name three electron carriers that function in oxidation-reduction reactions. Can you identify the abbreviations used for the oxidized and reduced forms of these carriers?

13. Some electron carriers are like free-moving trucks between reaction sites in the cell. Can you name one? Others are bound in cell membranes, as part of electron transport systems. Can you name two?

7

ENERGY-ACQUIRING PATHWAYS

Just before dawn in the Midwest the air is dry and motionless; the heat that has scorched the land for weeks still rises from the earth and hangs in the air of a new day. There are no clouds in sight. There is no promise of rain. For hundreds of miles in any direction you care to look, crops stretch out, withered or dead. All the sophisticated agricultural methods in the world can't save them now. In the absence of one vital resource—water—life in each cell of those many thousands of plants has ceased.

In Los Angeles, a student reading the morning newspaper complains to no one in particular about the hike in food prices that the Midwest drought will mean. In Washington, D.C., economists busily calculate the crop failures in terms of decreased tonnage available for domestic consumption and for export, and of what it means to the nation's balance of payments. In Africa, a child with bloated belly and spindly legs waits passively for death. Even if food from the vast agricultural plains of North America were to reach her now, it would be too late. Deprived too long of vital food resources, cells of her body will never grow normally again.

You are about to explore the ways that cells acquire and use energy. You will be considering cellular pathways that might at first seem to be far removed from the world of your interests. However, knowledge of these pathways is a key to understanding what it means to acquire food, why energy must be expended to get it, why food supplies cannot keep up with increasing demands, and what might be done to replenish the supplies. Directly or indirectly, these concerns will touch your life in decades to follow.

FROM SUNLIGHT TO CELLULAR WORK: PREVIEW OF THE MAIN PATHWAYS

No matter what the organism, all activities associated with the term "living" are fueled by the chemical bond energy of organic molecules. Growing, moving, staying alive, reproducing—all depend on energy stored and released through the coordinated assembly and disassembly of certain carbon-containing molecules. What sources of energy are available in the environment? How do cells trap and store some of this energy in organic forms? How do they tap the stores so that energy becomes available at particular times for cellular work? Many different metabolic pathways are employed in trapping, storing, releasing, and using energy. Which ones are employed depends on the kind of organism and on the energy sources available to it.

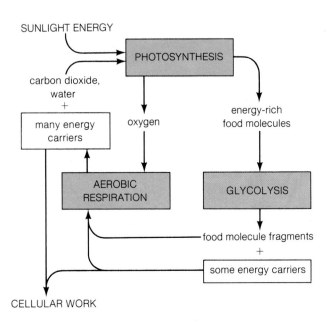

Figure 7.1 Links between three major energy-trapping and energy-releasing pathways, to be described in this chapter and the next.

An **autotrophic organism** can obtain all of the carbon it needs from carbon dioxide (CO_2), a gaseous substance that is present in the atmosphere and that dissolves readily in water. There are two major groups of autotrophs. *Photosynthetic autotrophs* obtain energy from sunlight. *Chemosynthetic autotrophs* obtain energy by oxidizing such inorganic substances as sulfur and ammonium. Both kinds of organisms use their environmentally derived energy in forming energy-rich food molecules from energy-poor carbon dioxide. They are, literally, "self-nourishing" organisms (which is what the word autotroph means). The photosynthetic autotrophs include all plants, some protistans, and some bacteria. The chemosynthetic autotrophs are limited to a few kinds of bacteria.

In contrast, a **heterotrophic organism** must obtain carbon and all metabolic energy from organic molecules that have already been assembled by autotrophs. Animals, fungi, many protistans, and most bacteria fall in this category. They are not self-nourishing; they feed on autotrophs, each other, and organic wastes.

It follows, from the above, that photosynthesis—the energy trapping and storing activities of the photosynthetic autotrophs—is the main source of energy that flows through the living world. How is energy that is stored in photosynthetic products released for cellular work? Almost all autotrophs and heterotrophs rely on the same kinds of pathways to do this. These energy-releasing pathways are called glycolysis and aerobic respiration.

Figure 7.1 summarizes the flow of energy through the pathways of photosynthesis, glycolysis, and respiration, and the cycling of materials through them. In this chapter, our main focus will be on photosynthesis, where the flow of energy begins. The energy-releasing pathways are topics reserved for the next chapter.

PHOTOSYNTHESIS

Simplified Picture of the Two Stages of Photosynthesis

In **photosynthesis**, sunlight is the source of energy that ultimately drives the formation of energy-rich organic molecules from carbon dioxide. Photosynthesis occurs in two stages. In the first stage, light energy is absorbed by chlorophyll and other pigment molecules embedded in photosynthetic membranes (such as those of chloroplasts). The absorbed energy undergoes conversion and is used in the formation of ATP and NADPH. In the second stage of

photosynthesis, ATP and NADPH are used in reactions by which carbon dioxide is converted into sugars and other carbon-containing products. The photosynthetic reactions can be summarized in this way:

$$\text{sunlight} + 2H_2O + CO_2 \longrightarrow O_2 + (CH_2O) + H_2O$$

Here, hydrogen is obtained when water molecules are split. The hydrogens are transferred, by way of oxidation-reduction reactions, to CO_2, forming compounds based on some number of (CH_2O) units. For instance, for the reactions leading to glucose formation, you'd have to multiply everything by six (to get the six carbons, twelve hydrogens, and six oxygens of the glucose molecule):

$$\text{sunlight} + 12H_2O + 6CO_2 \longrightarrow 6O_2 + C_6H_{12}O_6 + 6H_2O$$

The above equation summarizes the overall route by which energy from sunlight becomes converted to chemical potential energy in the bonds of glucose. However, it doesn't provide much insight into what actually goes on. For example, oxygen is shown as a by-product of photosynthesis. Where did it come from? As another example, why is water shown as a by-product as well as a reactant? Obviously, the summary equation must be expanded a bit. Such expansion will show us that photosynthesis takes place in two reaction stages, not one. The *light-dependent reactions* are concerned with ATP and NADPH formation. The *light-independent reactions* are concerned with actual production of sugars and other organic compounds:

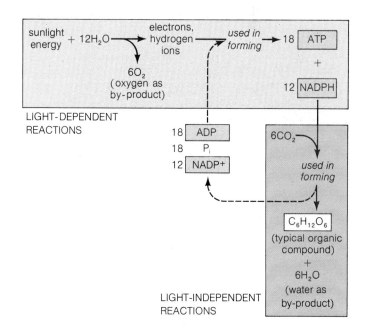

As you can see, oxygen is obtained when water molecules are split during the first reaction stage. Also, "new" water is produced during the synthesis reactions of the second stage. Notice how ATP (with its energy-rich phosphate bonds) and NADPH (with its electron and hydrogen cargo) bridge the two reaction stages. Keep this bridge in mind as you read through the following sections, for it is central to the events of photosynthesis.

Chloroplast Structure and Function

To keep things simple, let's focus on photosynthesis as it occurs in the kinds of chloroplasts found in most land plants. Figure 4.19 showed the general structure of the chloroplast, an organelle with a double outer membrane that surrounds a semifluid matrix called the **stroma**. Within the stroma, internal membranes form a continuous system of stacked disks and flattened channels. Each membranous stack is a **granum**. The individual disks of each stack are

Klaus Hackenberg / ZEFA

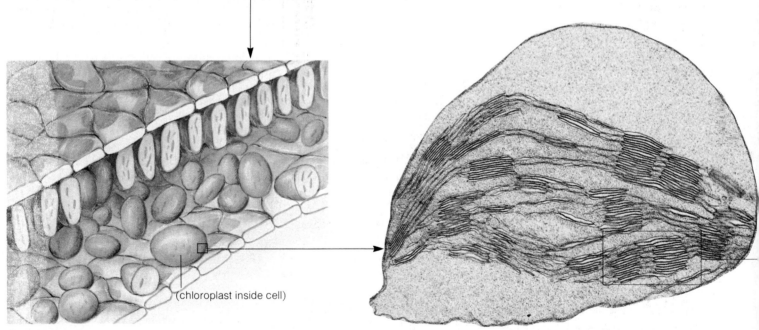

(chloroplast inside cell)

a

b Harry T. Horner

Figure 7.2 Functional zones of a chloroplast from the leaf of a sunflower plant (*Helianthus*). The light-dependent reactions of photosynthesis occur at thylakoid membranes, and they lead to ATP and NADPH formation. The light-independent reactions occur in stroma. They lead to production of sugars and other carbon-containing molecules. (**a**) Section through sunflower leaf, showing chloroplast-containing cells. (**b**) Chloroplast in cross-section, 25,000×. (**c**) Two of the grana, 93,000×. (**d**) Where photosynthetic reactions occur.

called **thylakoids** (Figure 7.2). The pigments and enzymes necessary for photosynthesis are embedded in these membrane structures.

No matter how simple or complex the arrangement of photosynthetic membranes may be, they all create a compartment that is functionally separated from the stroma. This compartment serves as a reservoir for hydrogen ions:

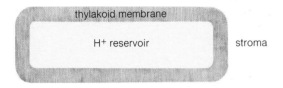

The first stage of photosynthesis is carried out on the thylakoid membranes, and it depends on this H^+ reservoir in ways that will be described shortly. The second stage is carried out on the thylakoid membrane side facing the stroma; this is the food production zone in the chloroplast.

THE LIGHT-DEPENDENT REACTIONS

The **light-dependent reactions**, the first stage of photosynthesis, consist of three kinds of events: light absorption, electron transfers that lead to ATP and NADPH formation, and replacement of electrons in the substance that originally gives them up. We will consider the mechanism of light absorption first.

Light Absorption in Photosystems

Sunlight reaches the earth as packets of energy called *photons.* The energies of photons vary, and they correspond to different wavelengths (colors) of light. The shorter the wavelength, the more energetic the photon. *Pigments* are molecules that can absorb photons of particular wavelengths. For instance, chlorophyll molecules are pigments that absorb light of blue and red wavelengths. They transmit rather than absorb green wavelengths; hence chloro-

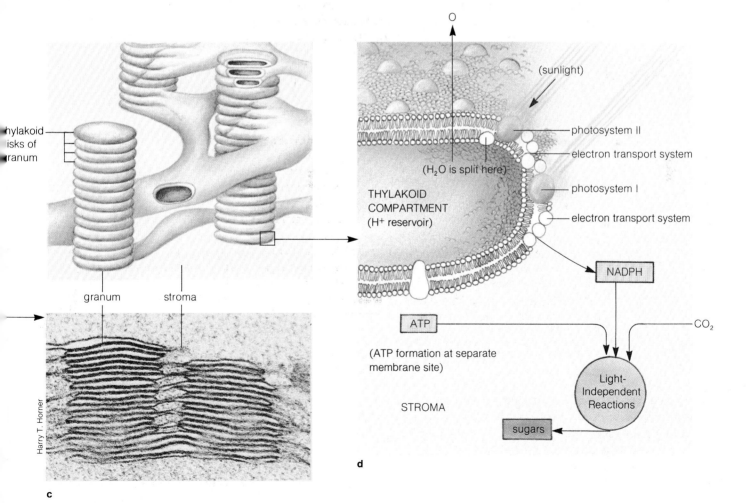

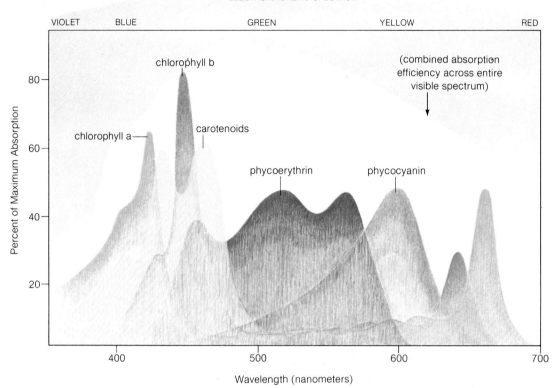

GAMMA RAYS   X–RAYS   ULTRAVIOLET   INFRARED   MICROWAVES   RADIO WAVES

VISIBLE LIGHT PORTION OF
ELECTROMAGNETIC SPECTRUM

VIOLET   BLUE   GREEN   YELLOW   RED

Figure 7.3 (Above) Where wavelengths of visible light occur in the electromagnetic spectrum. Light rays are streams of many different kinds of vibrating photons. The greater the frequency of their vibrations, the shorter the wavelength (and more energetic) the light rays. What we sense as "visible" light are wavelengths ranging from about 400 to 750 nanometers. This is about the range of sensitivity shown by photosynthetic organisms, also.

Why is photosensitivity limited mostly to this range? Shorter wavelengths (strong ultraviolet rays, x-rays, cosmic rays) scarcely warrant a welcome mat in cells. They are so energetic that they can break bonds holding organic molecules together—hence they can destroy living cells. Longer wavelengths (infrared and below) are not energetic enough to power the chemical changes in molecules necessary for the formation of NADPH, an extremely important energy carrier molecule.

(Below) Ranges of wavelength absorption for photosynthetic pigments. The absorption peaks correspond to the measured amount of energy that is actually absorbed and used in photosynthesis. The colors used here correspond to the colors that each kind of pigment transmits. (Thus, the chlorophylls show peak absorption of blue and red wavelengths, and transmit wavelengths in between.) Together, the different photosynthetic pigments have the potential to absorb most of the available energy in the spectrum of visible light.

phyll appears green. The yellow carotenoids absorb violet and blue wavelengths but transmit yellow. Figure 7.3 shows the degree to which these and other photosynthetic pigments absorb light of different wavelengths. Collectively, photosynthetic pigments have the potential to absorb most of the available energy in the spectrum of visible light.

In green plants, the main photosynthetic pigments are chlorophyll *a*, chlorophyll *b*, and the carotenoids. They are embedded in thylakoid membranes, in clusters of 200 to 300 molecules. The pigments of each cluster interact as a light-harvesting unit. There are two kinds of light-harvesting units, called **photosystems I and II**. The first kind responds

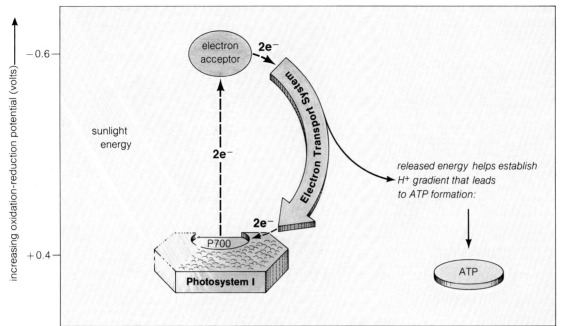

Figure 7.4 Cyclic photophosphorylation, which yields one energy-rich ATP molecule.

better than the second to wavelengths approaching 700 nanometers. This photosystem contains a specialized chlorophyll molecule that is named, appropriately, P700. By comparison, photosystem II responds better to light of slightly shorter wavelengths; it has a specialized chlorophyll molecule that is named P680.

In both photosystems, most of the pigments are like antennas: they transmit the energy they receive. Incoming light energy is transferred rapidly from one to another, and another—until the energy reaches a P700 or P680 molecule, which acts like an energy trap. When enough energy flows into the trap, an electron of this molecule is raised to a higher energy level (Chapter Three). In this excited state, the electron is readily transferred to a membrane-bound electron acceptor, of the sort described in the preceding chapter. Thus, *the first event of photosynthesis is the light-activated transfer of an electron from one substance to another.*

Two Pathways of Electron Transfer

Once excited electrons from P700 or P680 molecules are transferred to a membrane-bound transport system, they take part in a series of oxidation-reduction reactions. Some of the energy released in these reactions is used elsewhere, in the formation of ATP from ADP and inorganic phos-

phate. What is the ultimate destination of the electrons? That depends on the kind of final electron acceptor that will greet them at the end of the transport system.

In the simplest pathway of electron transfers, photosystem I operates alone. As Figure 7.4 suggests, electrons of increased energy are expelled from a P700 energy trap, and they eventually are returned to the same photosystem that gave them up. Because the electrons travel full circle, the operation of photosystem I alone is said to be cyclic. Because the electrons first gain energy from photons and then contribute that energy to phosphorylating ADP, the entire pathway is known as **cyclic photophosphorylation**. The important thing about it is this:

For every two electrons entering the cyclic photophosphorylation pathway, the energy yield is one ATP molecule.

Cyclic photophosphorylation probably represents the way that ancient bacteria first harnessed light energy for producing usable cellular energy (ATP). Now, the energy of ATP is enough to do a lot of things. But it is not enough to build complex carbohydrates except by roundabout and rather inefficient pathways. This probably wasn't too critical for those early photosynthesizers; they were microscopically small, and their cellular building programs could

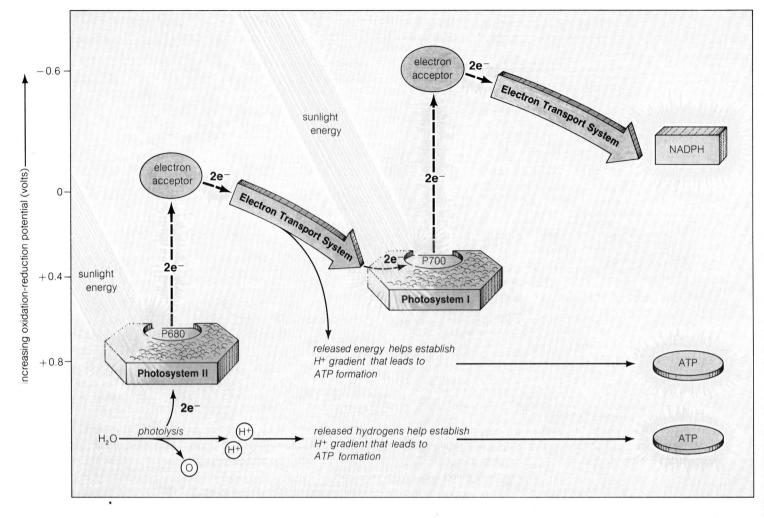

Figure 7.5 Noncyclic photophosphorylation, which yields one NADPH and two ATP molecules.

scarcely have been enormous. By comparison, existing land plants *are* enormous and much more complex. These plants have correspondingly greater energy demands, and it is doubtful that they could have evolved on the basis of the cyclic pathway alone.

Apparently, natural selection long ago went to work on the cyclic pathway, expanding it to include a second photosystem and a second transport chain. When the two photosystems function together, electrons don't flow in a cycle. Instead, they end up in a molecule of NADPH—a molecule that has about *seven times* as much energy as ATP, as well as reducing power that can be used directly in the synthesis of complex carbohydrates! This expanded pathway is known as **noncyclic photophosphorylation**. In existing land plants, it is the heart of photosynthesis.

In the noncyclic pathway, absorbed light energy causes the chlorophyll P680 of each photosystem II to give up an electron. This occurs over and over again. The excited electrons are transferred to an acceptor molecule, which in turn transfers them to an electron transport system. Energy released during the oxidation-reduction reactions in this system is used in other reactions that generate ATP. As Figure 7.5 shows, however, the electrons are not returned to photosystem II when they reach the end of the transport system. They are delivered instead to chlorophyll P700 of photosystem I.

When P700 absorbs enough light energy, electrons are boosted to a higher energy level. This boost is necessary for the operation of the noncyclic pathway. The electrons are transferred to an acceptor molecule, which passes them on to a second transport system. Here the final acceptor is NADP+—which combines with electrons and with hydrogen ions to form NADPH.

The one-way flow of electrons to NADPH means that something else has to replace the electrons that originally entered the noncyclic pathway. That something else is water. When P680 first absorbs light energy, it takes on a positive charge. It exerts a very strong pull on electrons in water molecules, so that H_2O is split into oxygen, hydrogen ions, and the associated electrons. Because photon energy indirectly drives the reaction, the process is called **photolysis**. The hydrogen ions released in photolysis play a role in separate reactions that lead to the formation of ATP.

The fact that the noncyclic pathway produces oxygen as an end product has had repercussions for the evolution of life. Oxygen has been accumulating since this pathway first emerged, about 1.4 billion years ago (Chapter Thirty-One). It has changed the entire character of the earth's atmosphere. And it has made possible the energy-yielding form of metabolism called aerobic respiration, to be described in the next chapter.

Overall, there are two key points to remember about noncyclic photophosphorylation:

For every two electrons entering the noncyclic photophosphorylation pathway, there is an energy yield of one NADPH and two ATP molecules.

Oxygen, an end product of the noncyclic pathway, has had profound influence on the character of the atmosphere and, as a result, on the evolution of energy-yielding forms of metabolism.

Mechanism of ATP Synthesis

Let's go back now to that H^+ reservoir inside the thylakoid disks of chloroplasts, and see how it functions in the formation of ATP during the light-dependent reactions. Hydrogen ions are added directly to this reservoir by photolysis, which occurs within the thylakoid compartment:

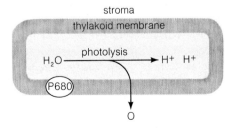

Also, some membrane-bound electron carriers of the transport system between photosystems I and II help build up the reservoir. They pick up H^+ from the stroma at the same time that they accept electrons. However, other electron acceptors that follow them in the series will take the electrons but *not* the hydrogens—which are expelled into the thylakoid interior:

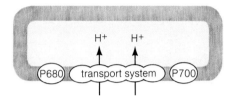

The H^+ concentration inside the thylakoid disk becomes much greater than on the outside. Thus some of the energy released during photolysis and electron transfers is stored briefly, as an H^+ concentration gradient (and an associated electric gradient).

ATP is generated by a reverse flow of hydrogen ions (down the gradients). The flow occurs through a channel protein system that spans the membrane. The combined force of the H^+ gradient and electric gradient across the membrane is enough to propel the hydrogens back to the stroma. In some way, the force is linked to enzymatic machinery that causes ADP and inorganic phosphate to combine into ATP:

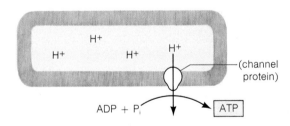

The idea that this kind of electrochemical gradient across a membrane drives ATP synthesis is known as the **chemiosmotic theory**. As you will see, it is also being used to explain ATP formation in mitochondria (Chapter Eight).

Summary of Light-Dependent Reactions

So far, we have described separately the events of the light-dependent reactions as they occur in chloroplasts of green plants. We can now summarize the events in an integrated picture of the first stage of photosynthesis:

Light Absorption

1. In chloroplasts, light is absorbed by photosystems (clusters of pigments, such as the chlorophylls, which are embedded in thylakoid membranes).

2. Light absorption activates the transfer of electrons from chlorophyll P700 or P680 to an electron carrier.

Cyclic Electron Transport

1. When photosystem I operates alone, the electrons flow through a transport system and are delivered back to P700 (the original electron donor of the photosystem).

2. Energy released in the transport system reactions promotes the transfer of hydrogen ions from the stroma to the H^+ reservoir inside the thylakoid.

3. The accumulation of hydrogen ions sets up an electrochemical gradient across the membrane. Hydrogen ions flow down the gradient through a channel protein system that spans the membrane.

4. Energy associated with the outward flow of hydrogen ions is coupled to the phosphorylation of ADP in the stroma.

5. This entire pathway is called cyclic photophosphorylation. It yields one ATP molecule for every two electrons entering the pathway.

Noncyclic Electron Transport

1. Photosystems I and II can operate together. When they do, there is a one-way flow of electrons from P680, through a transport system, to P700, and another transport system. The electrons are donated to $NADP^+$, which combines with H^+ in the stroma to form NADPH.

2. Photolysis (splitting H_2O into oxygen, hydrogen ions, and electrons) replaces the P680 electrons sent down the noncyclic pathway. The hydrogens released inside the thylakoid also increase the H^+ gradient across the membrane, hence promote the formation of ATP.

3. Operation of the transport system between P680 and P700 promotes formation of ATP.

4. This pathway is called noncyclic photophosphorylation. It yields one NADPH and two ATP molecules for every two electrons entering the pathway.

THE LIGHT-INDEPENDENT REACTIONS

Once the light-dependent reactions produce ATP and NADPH, a photosynthetic cell can build sugars and other carbon-containing molecules. The pathways now followed do not depend directly on sunlight; that is why they are called the **light-independent reactions**. (They can proceed as long as ATP and NADPH are available. Because ATP and NADPH normally are produced only during daylight, the light-independent reactions usually don't proceed for very long in the dark.) These reactions require the following substances:

1. ATP and NADPH from the light-dependent reactions
2. Carbon dioxide from the air around photosynthetic cells
3. Ribulose bisphosphate (RuBP), a five-carbon sugar
4. Enzymes that catalyze each reaction step

To see how the reactions work, we can follow the events whereby six carbon dioxide molecules are used in the formation of one glucose molecule. The reactions take place on the stromal surface of thylakoid membranes. First the enzyme RuBP-carboxylase hooks up carbon dioxide to a molecule of RuBP. The result is a highly unstable six-carbon intermediate, which is promptly hydrolyzed into two molecules of a three-carbon compound. This compound is phosphoglyceric acid (PGA). This initial reaction sequence, in which carbon dioxide is combined with organic molecules, is called **carbon dioxide fixation**. For every six carbon dioxide molecules fixed, twelve PGA molecules are produced.

Each molecule of PGA is now phosphorylated by ATP and reduced by hydrogen from NADPH. Thus energy becomes stored in covalent bonds of twelve three-carbon compounds called phosphoglyceraldehyde, or PGAL.

In a complex reaction series driven by energy from ATP, five of every six PGAL molecules are used in the formation of new RuBP molecules—which can be used in acquiring more carbon dioxide. One of every six PGAL molecules is combined and rearranged into intermediates that lead, eventually, to the six-carbon sugar glucose (Figure 7.6).

The entire reaction series is called the **Calvin-Benson cycle** in honor of its discoverers, Melvin Calvin and Andrew Benson. It yields enough RuBP to replace the six used up in carbon dioxide fixation. It also produces glucose. The ADP, phosphate, and $NADP^+$ leftovers from the cycle are returned to the sites of light-dependent reactions—where they can be converted once again to NADPH and ATP.

Glucose is not the only end product of the Calvin-Benson cycle. Every carbon atom in every molecule in photosynthetic cells has its origins in these reactions. Compared with other examples, however, it is easier to show how a summary equation of photosynthesis balances out when glucose is the example, as you saw at the start of the chapter.

Summary of Light-Independent Reactions

The steps in the light-independent reactions can be summarized in the following way:

---

1. Carbon dioxide is fixed to RuBP, making an unstable intermediate that is hydrolyzed into two three-carbon PGA molecules.

2. PGA is phosphorylated (made more reactive) by ATP, and reduced by NADPH. Thus chemical energy becomes stored in PGAL.

3. Through complex reactions, PGAL is rearranged into new RuBP molecules and into glucose.

4. Because only one of every six PGAL molecules is funneled into glucose production, it takes six turns of the Calvin-Benson cycle to produce one molecule of glucose.

Figure 7.7 relates the light-independent reactions to the overall events of photosynthesis.

How Autotrophs Use Intermediates and Products of Photosynthesis

Glucose is a readily usable molecule, and one that is in high demand. At any given moment, you will find little free glucose in photosynthetic cells. Much of it is used at once as building blocks for all compounds that make up the plant body or as fuel to provide energy for cellular work. Typically, the products of photosynthesis become converted to forms that can be readily transported through the plant body. Among land plants, sucrose is the most important of these transportable molecules. Other products end up in storage form, such as starch. In simple plants such as some kinds of algae, glucose becomes stored as starch within the chloroplast that produces it. Starch is the most common carbohydrate storage product in plant leaves, stems, and roots. In potato plants, sucrose produced in leaf cells moves down to specialized underground stem regions, called tubers (the "potatoes"). There, it is converted to and stored

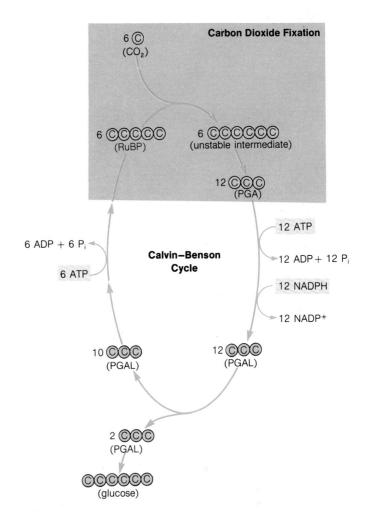

Figure 7.6 Summary of the light-independent reactions of photosynthesis. (Only the carbon atoms of the different molecules are depicted.)

as starch. In sugar beets, onions, and sugarcane, sucrose itself is the main storage form.

Photosynthetic autotrophs are able to synthesize lipids and amino acids with the intermediates and products of photosynthesis. PGA produced in carbon dioxide fixation can be used as a carbon source in amino acid synthesis. Amino acids are used in building all cell proteins. Lipids are required for the assembly of all cell membranes. Indeed, more than ninety percent of the carbon fixed by some green algae is used in constructing proteins and lipids. These plants have a brief life cycle, and they live in places where

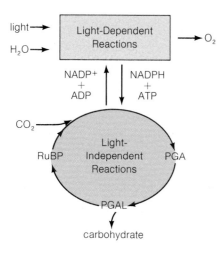

Figure 7.7 Summary of the main reactants, intermediates, and products of photosynthesis.

sunlight and water are plentiful. They are able to put most of their photosynthetic products into growth and reproduction, rather than diverting them to energetically expensive storage forms of the sort that other photosynthesizers use in prolonged periods of growth and in times of stress.

Environmental Effects on Rates of Photosynthesis

Photosynthetic organisms are found in almost all environments, ranging from glacier margins to ocean surface waters to searing deserts. But *rates* of photosynthesis are not the same from one setting to the next, even from one kind of plant species to the next in the same setting! How warm or cold is the air? How intense is the sunlight? How much water is available? These and other aspects of the physical environment profoundly affect photosynthesis in different plants.

For example, many tropical grasses seem well adapted to high light levels, high temperatures, and limited water. Here we are talking about important agricultural crops such as corn and sugarcane, as well as tenacious weeds such as crabgrass. Yet this same combination of environmental factors puts other kinds of plants (such as lettuce, conifers, and bluegrass) under severe stress.

The tropical grasses fare better as a result of a more complex leaf structure and a carbon fixation system that *precedes* the Calvin-Benson cycle. These plants have two types of photosynthetic leaf cells (called mesophyll and

bundle-sheath cells). In mesophyll cells, an enzyme known as PEP-carboxylase catalyzes a reaction between carbon dioxide and phosphoenol pyruvate (PEP), which is a three-carbon compound. The result is oxaloacetate, a compound with four carbon atoms. Plants that can do this are called *C4 plants*. (By comparison, "C3" plants rely solely on the Calvin-Benson cycle, in which the first compound formed by carbon dioxide fixation is the three-carbon PGA.)

Once oxaloacetate is formed, it is actively transported to an adjacent bundle-sheath cell. There, carbon dioxide is released and picked up in the Calvin-Benson cycle. The PEP is returned to the mesophyll cells—where it accepts more carbon dioxide. *In C4 plants, one leaf cell type specializes in preliminary carbon dioxide uptake and rapid, active transport of the fixed carbon dioxide to another leaf cell type, where the Calvin-Benson cycle operates.*

What is the advantage of this division of cellular labor? For the answer, we have to look at RuBP-carboxylase, the enzyme that catalyzes the formation of PGA in the Calvin-Benson cycle. It happens that oxygen and carbon dioxide compete for the active site of this enzyme. When light levels increase, so does photosynthesis—and so does the amount of oxygen given off during the light reactions (when water molecules are split). Above a certain level, the oxygen outcompetes carbon dioxide—which greatly slows the net rate of carbon dioxide fixation. The word *photorespiration* refers to the effect of light levels on the way that oxygen and carbon dioxide compete for the active site on RuBP-carboxylase. In C4 plants, photorespiration does not occur in the bundle-sheath cells because of the rapid, active transport of carbon dioxide into them. As a result, C4 plants fix more carbon dioxide per unit time than C3 plants do, because there is no oxygen interference (no photorespiration).

Because C4 plants have a mechanism for concentrating carbon dioxide inside the leaf, they can continue to photosynthesize even on hot, dry days, when sunlight is intense and when water must be conserved. Almost all land plants have leaf surface layers with a waxy covering, which helps retard moisture loss. Water escaping from the plant does so largely by way of tiny passages extending across the surface layers. (These passages, called stomata, are described in Unit Four.) On hot, dry days, almost all of the openings close, which does help conserve water. At the same time, not as much carbon dioxide can enter the leaf—and oxygen (an end product of photosynthesis) builds up. The combinations puts C3 plants at a disadvantage in terms of the rate at which carbon dioxide can be fixed. This is one of the reasons why lovers of bluegrass lawns in Southern California might have to extend their affection to crabgrass—less lush, perhaps, but certainly hardier in that part of the world.

CHEMOSYNTHESIS

Photosynthesis so dominates the energy-trapping pathways that it is sometimes easy to overlook other, less pervasive routes. Like photosynthesizers, chemosynthetic autotrophs can live completely on an inorganic diet. Unlike photosynthesizers, they harness energy not from sunlight but from the oxidation of such inorganic substances as ammonium ions and iron or sulfur compounds.

For example, sulfur-oxidizing bacteria can convert sulfur compounds to sulfuric acid (H_2SO_4), which is highly acidic. In agricultural regions where the soil is alkaline, farmers sometimes plow powdered sulfur into the soil. There, the action of sulfur-oxidizing bacteria reduces the soil pH to levels that will support crops.

As another example, some nitrifying bacteria present in soil use ammonia (NH_3) molecules as their energy source, stripping them of hydrogen ions and electrons. Nitrite ions (NO_2^-) and nitrate ions (NO_3^-) are the remnants of these energy-securing routes. Compared with ammonium ions, nitrite and nitrate ions are readily washed out of the soil, so the action of nitrifying bacteria can lower the soil fertility. (That is why chemical inhibitors of nitrifiers are sometimes added to soil.) We will return to the effects of nitrifying bacteria in the ecology unit of the book. Here, in this unit, we will turn next to the pathways by which the products of photosynthetic and chemosynthetic autotrophs can be used as energy sources for cellular work.

Readings

Becker, W. 1977. *Energy and the Living Cell.* New York: Lippincott. This small paperback is an excellent introduction to bioenergetics. It is highly recommended to the serious student who would like a more detailed understanding of topics covered in this chapter.

Bjorkman, O., and J. Berry. 1973. "High-Efficiency Photosynthesis." *Scientific American* 229(4):80–93. One of the first summarizations of research into photosynthesis in C4 plants.

Govindjee and R. Govindjee. 1974. "The Primary Events of Photosynthesis." *Scientific American* 231(6):68–82.

Hinkle, P., and R. McCarty. 1978. "How Cells Make ATP." *Scientific American* 238(3):104–125. Good summary of Mitchell's chemiosmotic theory of ATP formation.

Kok, B. 1976. "Photosynthesis: The Path of Energy." In *Plant Biochemistry*, vol. 3 (J. Bonner and J. Varner, editors). New York: Academic Press.

Miller, K. 1979. "The Photosynthetic Membrane." *Scientific American* 102–113.

Mitchell, P. 1979. "Keilin's Respiratory Chain Concept and Its Chemiosmotic Consequences." *Science* 206:1148–1159. Mitchell's own view of how the chemiosmotic theory was developed.

Park, R. 1976. "The Chloroplast." In *Plant Biochemistry*, vol. 3 (J. Bonner and J. Varner, editors). New York: Academic Press.

Review Questions

1. Define the difference between autotrophs and heterotrophs, and give examples of each. In what category do photosynthesizers fall?

2. Summarize the photosynthesis reactions in words, then as an expanded equation. Distinguish between the light-dependent and the light-independent stage of these reactions. Be sure to show the electron and hydrogen "bridges" between these two stages.

3. Oxygen is a product of photolysis. What *is* photolysis, and does it occur during the first or second stage of photosynthesis? Is water a by-product of the first or second stage?

4. Describe where the light-dependent reactions occur in the chloroplast, and name the molecules formed there. Do the same for the light-independent reactions.

5. A thylakoid compartment is a reservoir for which of the following substances: glucose, photosynthetic pigments, hydrogen ions, fatty acids?

6. Why might photosensitivity be limited mostly to the range between 400 and 750 nanometers?

7. Sketch the reaction steps of noncyclic photophosphorylation, showing where the excited electrons eventually end up. Do the same for the cyclic pathway. Which pathway has the greater energy yield?

8. Is oxygen an end product of cyclic or noncyclic photophosphorylation?

9. Describe the chemiosmotic theory of ATP formation in chloroplasts. Use sketches to show the proposed movements of hydrogen ions across thylakoid membranes.

10. Which of the following substances are *not* required for the light-independent reactions: ATP, NADH, RuBP, carotenoids, free oxygen, carbon dioxide, enzymes?

11. Suppose a plant carrying out photosynthesis were exposed to carbon dioxide molecules that contain radioactively labeled carbon atoms ($^{14}CO_2$). In which of the following compounds will the labeled carbon first appear?

    a. NADPH   c. PGAL
    b. pyruvate   d. PGA

12. How many turns of the Calvin-Benson cycle are necessary to produce one glucose molecule? Why?

13. Give examples of how different autotrophs use the intermediates and products of photosynthesis.

14. What aspects of the physical environment can affect the rate of photosynthesis? Why do some C4 plants function better than typical C3 plants under high light levels, high temperatures, and limited water?

15. Give an example of a chemosynthetic autotroph, mentioning the environment in which it might be found.

8

ENERGY-RELEASING PATHWAYS

It is one of the quirks of the human mind that plants just aren't thought about very often as living *organisms*. Even vegetarians who become nauseous at the thought of eating the flesh of an animal can relish the flesh of a peach. Perhaps it is understandable. Lacking autotrophic equipment of our own, we have to depend on something to produce energy for us; and if we carried a concern for the sanctity of life too far, we'd all starve to death.

Yet there is an undeniable unity among organisms that becomes evident at the biochemical level. All animals, plants, fungi, protistans, and most bacteria use autotrophically produced carbohydrates for fuel and structural materials in much the same way that you do. All depend on the release of chemical bond energy from carbohydrates to help produce ATP—the prime energy carrier for life in all of its forms. There is, in short, a remarkable similarity in responses to the ebb and flow of energy through the individual—hence through the biosphere. We will return to this idea at the conclusion of the chapter.

OVERVIEW OF THE MAIN ENERGY-RELEASING PATHWAYS

ATP is a molecule that readily gives up energy to a wide variety of cellular reactions. Its production is central to cellular building and maintenance programs. ATP can be produced by photosynthesis and by chemosynthesis, as described in Chapter Seven. It also can be produced by **carbohydrate metabolism**, which involves the release of chemical bond energy from various carbohydrates. Release of this energy requires two kinds of enzyme-mediated activities: phosphorylation and oxidation-reduction. Let's look first at the role played by phosphorylation.

Phosphorylation: You have probably heard the expression, "It takes money to make money." It means making an initial investment of some money that you already have in order to help support some activity that will produce more money in return. Cells do essentially the same thing in carbohydrate metabolism. For example, when cells break down a glucose molecule, they make an initial investment of two ATP molecules. ATP can transfer its terminal phosphate group to the carbon backbone of such molecules, thereby energizing them (making them more reactive). The energy input helps drive enzyme-mediated reactions in which covalent bonds (C—C and C—H) are rearranged or split. Chemical potential energy is released during these reactions, and some of this energy ultimately is transformed into the energy inherent in phosphate bonds of new ATP. For an original investment of two ATP molecules, the cell can get back between four and thirty-six or more new ATP molecules for each glucose molecule being degraded.

Oxidation-Reduction: Now, there is quite a bit of difference between four and thirty-six ATP molecules as the potential energy harvest from a single molecule of glucose. What determines the outcome? For the answer, we have to look at the way that ATP formation is coupled to electron transfer (oxidation-reduction reactions). The electrons are originally derived from the carbohydrate that has been made reactive. At specific reaction steps, enzymes strip away hydrogen atoms, then transfer them to coenzymes that function as transient carriers for the hydrogen and its associated electrons. NAD+ is one such coenzyme; in its reduced state, it is called NADH (Chapter Six).

If you liken electron energy levels to steps of a staircase, then NADH is at the top step for glucose metabolism. It carries high-energy electrons, and it can transfer them only to an acceptor molecule at a lower energy level. In turn, this molecule can transfer the electrons only to an acceptor at a still lower energy level. Obviously, there can be more energy transfers if the final acceptor is really low on the energy staircase than if it is higher up. This is important to think about, for the energy released at several steps of the energy staircase is coupled to the formation of new ATP. When "lower" steps are never reached, the chance to form more ATP is lost.

a   b   c

Figure 8.1 Living things have the means to strip electrons from different substances and transfer them about—and these electron transfers are coupled to ATP formation.

In *anaerobic respiration,* one of the most ancient metabolic pathways, the "spent" electrons end up being transferred to inorganic compounds in the environment. (**a**) For example, some bacterial residents of sulfur hot springs use sulfate as the final electron acceptor.

(**b**) Through photosynthesis, plants produce energy-rich food molecules, which accumulate in plant parts such as these grapes. The dustlike coats on the grapes are populations of yeasts, which use *fermentation* pathways. Here, electrons stripped from sugar molecules flow back to the sugar breakdown products themselves.

(**c**) Plants and animals can break down photosynthetically derived food molecules in *aerobic respiration,* which has the greatest ATP yield of all. In this pathway, the spent electrons flow to oxygen, an abundant component of the atmosphere.

As you can see, carbohydrate metabolism is not just the release of energy; *it is a series of energy transformations.* The pathways of carbohydrate metabolism differ in how far those transformations proceed. How far they proceed depends on the kind of final electron acceptor used. And the final electron acceptor that *can* be used depends on the type of cell and on environmental conditions.

Given these differences, we can group the pathways of carbohydrate metabolism into three main categories:

Aerobic respiration

Anaerobic respiration

Fermentation

Figure 8.2 is a simplified picture of pathways that fall in these categories, along with the ultimate destinations of the electrons (and hydrogen) used in the energy transformations. Aerobic respiration is the most pervasive pathway, and it will occupy our attention for most of this chapter. Before considering its details, however, let's look briefly at some general features of all the main pathways of energy metabolism.

Glycolysis: First Stage of Carbohydrate Metabolism

Aerobic respiration, anaerobic respiration, and fermentation all *begin* with the same preparatory reactions, known as **glycolysis.** The term "glycolysis" refers to the partial breakdown of sugars, although other organic compounds can also enter the reactions. For example, a glucose molecule (with its backbone of six carbon atoms) is phosphorylated and then degraded into two molecules of pyruvate, a three-carbon compound. Energy released in the reactions can be used to form four ATP molecules. However, because two ATP molecules have been invested to make glucose more reactive, the *net yield* from glycolysis is two ATP.

During glycolysis, hydrogen and electrons are transferred to NAD$^+$, forming the reduced carrier NADH. In some way, NADH must be stripped of these electrons after glycolysis. The reason is that there are only so many NAD$^+$ molecules available, and if they were all to become loaded down with hydrogen and electrons, glycolysis would grind to a halt. Following glycolysis, pyruvate is used in reactions that regenerate NAD$^+$. Whether additional ATP is generated in the process now depends on the particular pathway taken.

Glycolysis is the preparatory stage in three kinds of energy-releasing pathways (aerobic respiration, anaerobic respiration, and fermentation).

In glycolysis, glucose (or some other substrate) gives up electrons and hydrogen to two NAD$^+$, forming two reduced carriers (NADH).

In itself, glycolysis has a net energy yield of two ATP for each glucose molecule being degraded to pyruvate.

Aerobic Respiration

In **aerobic respiration**, oxygen is the final acceptor of electrons carried by NADH—and oxygen is low on the electron energy staircase. The reactions occur in an electron transport system that is bound in a mitochondrial membrane. (In aerobic bacteria, it is bound in the plasma membrane.) Electron acceptors of the transport system relieve the NADH of its electron and hydrogen cargo. By doing so, they regenerate the NAD$^+$ necessary for glycolysis to continue.

With this oxygen-dependent pathway, carbohydrates can be broken down completely to carbon dioxide and water. In mitochondria, much more of the usable energy stored in glucose can be released, and a good part of it can be used in the formation of many ATP molecules as the following summary equation indicates:

$$C_6H_{12}O_6 + 6O_2 \longrightarrow 6CO_2 + 6H_2O$$
carbon
dioxide

$$\boxed{\text{energy yield} = 36\ \text{ATP}}$$

No other energy-releasing pathway has so great a yield. Almost all eukaryotes depend on it.

Aerobic respiration requires the presence of oxygen as the final electron acceptor for the reactions.

From glycolysis (in the cytoplasm) to the final reactions (in the mitochondrion), this pathway commonly yields thirty-six ATP molecules for every glucose molecule oxidized.

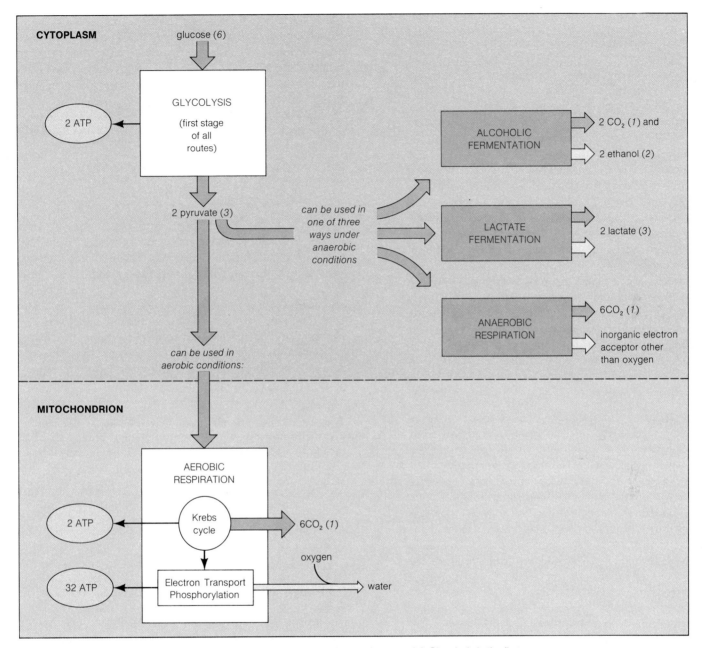

Figure 8.2 Overview of carbohydrate metabolism, using glucose as the starting material. Glycolysis is the first stage of all three of the main categories of carbohydrate metabolism (aerobic respiration, anaerobic respiration, and fermentation). Depending on the organism and on environmental conditions, one of the four routes shown can follow glycolysis.

Gold arrows indicate the ultimate destination of hydrogen and electrons used for the reactions. Blue arrows indicate the flow of carbon atoms from glucose to the carbon-containing products. (Italic numbers in parentheses refer to the number of carbon atoms in each molecule of the compound listed.)

A simple way to remember the net energy yield of the four routes shown is to add up the ATP from start (in all cases, glycolysis) to finish. The net yield is only two for anaerobic respiration; the same is true for the fermentation routes shown. Aerobic respiration commonly has a net yield of thirty-six ATP molecules for each glucose molecule being metabolized.

Anaerobic Respiration

In **anaerobic respiration**, an inorganic compound other than oxygen (nitrate, for example) is the final acceptor of electrons donated by NADH. This kind of pathway also requires a membrane-bound transport system. However, the energy yield is not as great as it is from the aerobic route, because the final electron acceptor is not as low as oxygen on the energy staircase. In fact, the oxidation-reduction reactions add no more ATP to the small yield from glycolysis. They do, however, allow electrons and hydrogen to flow away from NADH, and thereby regenerate NAD^+.

A number of prokaryotes thrive in anaerobic environments. (Many kinds die when they are exposed to oxygen.) They include denitrifying bacteria, which return fixed nitrogen to the atmosphere as N_2. They also include methanogenic bacteria, which thrive in such anaerobic settings as mud, the animal gut, and some sewage treatment facilities. *Escherichia coli*, a resident of your digestive tract, uses this pathway. So do sulfate-reducing bacteria, some of which live in soils, aquatic habitats, and the animal intestine.

Fermentation Pathways

In **fermentation**, an intermediate or product of carbohydrate metabolism is the final acceptor of electrons from NADH. An external acceptor is not used (as it is in the other two pathways). Instead, the electrons originally pulled away from some carbon atoms become attached to other carbon atoms of the substance being metabolized. Thus there are electron transfers, but no *net* change in oxidation. Extracting energy from a carbohydrate without oxidizing it is a characteristic of all fermentation routes. Two such routes are described here. The reactions for both take place in the cytoplasm, and no membrane-bound transport system is involved.

In *lactate fermentation*, pyruvate from glycolysis undergoes rearrangements into an intermediate form that serves as the final electron acceptor. Upon accepting electrons and hydrogen from NADH, the intermediate is converted into lactate, a three-carbon compound:

$$C_6H_{12}O_6 \longrightarrow 2C_3H_6O_3$$
lactate

energy yield = 2 ATP

Many bacteria rely on lactate fermentation. Milk or cream turned sour is a sign of their activity. The reactions also occur in animal cells that normally rely on aerobic respiration. For them, lactate fermentation is an alternative pathway that can be used when oxygen is in short supply (Chapter Twenty-Six).

In *alcoholic fermentation*, the intermediate acetaldehyde is the final electron acceptor and is converted into the product ethyl alcohol (or ethanol):

$$C_6H_{12}O_6 \longrightarrow 2CH_3CH_2OH + 2CO_2$$
ethanol

energy yield = 2 ATP

Yeasts, which are single-celled fungi, use this pathway. The gaseous product of the reactions (carbon dioxide) helps yeast dough to rise. The fermentation activities of some yeasts lead to the alcohol portion of beers, distilled spirits, and wines (Figure 8.1).

The carbohydrates entering an anaerobic pathway are not completely degraded, and considerable energy remains in the products. No additional ATP is generated. Both anaerobic respiration and fermentation serve only to regenerate NAD^+.

The second stage of both anaerobic respiration and fermentation yields no more ATP. Its function is to regenerate NAD^+, the electron acceptor essential for the ATP-producing stage of glycolysis.

A CLOSER LOOK AT AEROBIC RESPIRATION

From beginning to end, the aerobic pathway consists of three stages of reactions. The first, glycolysis, takes place in the cytoplasm. In eukaryotes, the other two stages occur in mitochondria. The second stage is the **Krebs cycle**. Here, pyruvate from glycolysis is completely degraded to carbon dioxide, and many reduced electron carriers are produced. The final stage is **electron transport phosphorylation**. These final oxidation-reduction reactions lead to the formation of considerable ATP.

First Stage: Glycolysis

Figure 8.3 lists the key reaction steps in glycolysis. The reactions begin when two ATP molecules make a substrate

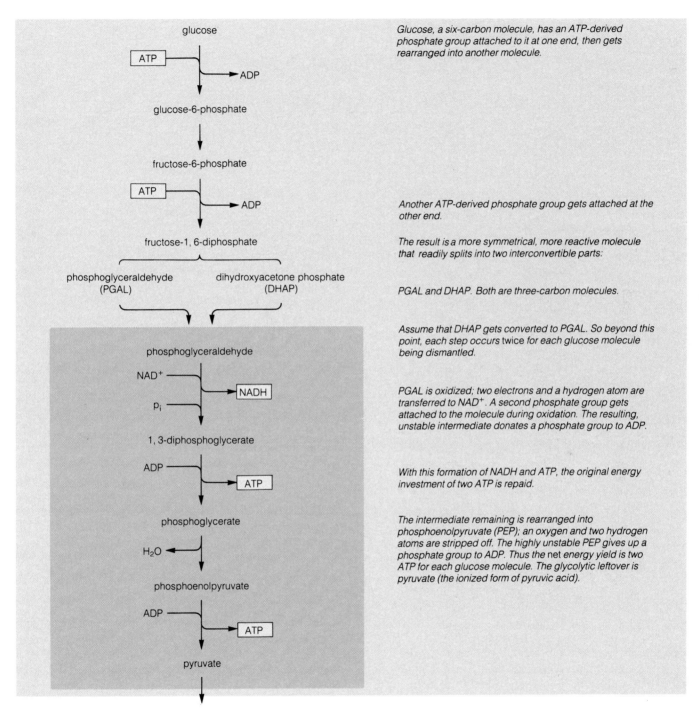

glucose

ATP ⟶ ADP

glucose-6-phosphate

fructose-6-phosphate

ATP ⟶ ADP

fructose-1, 6-diphosphate

phosphoglyceraldehyde (PGAL) dihydroxyacetone phosphate (DHAP)

phosphoglyceraldehyde

NAD^+ ⟶ NADH

p_i

1, 3-diphosphoglycerate

ADP ⟶ ATP

phosphoglycerate

H_2O

phosphoenolpyruvate

ADP ⟶ ATP

pyruvate

Glucose, a six-carbon molecule, has an ATP-derived phosphate group attached to it at one end, then gets rearranged into another molecule.

Another ATP-derived phosphate group gets attached at the other end.

The result is a more symmetrical, more reactive molecule that readily splits into two interconvertible parts:

PGAL and DHAP. Both are three-carbon molecules.

Assume that DHAP gets converted to PGAL. So beyond this point, each step occurs twice for each glucose molecule being dismantled.

PGAL is oxidized; two electrons and a hydrogen atom are transferred to NAD^+. A second phosphate group gets attached to the molecule during oxidation. The resulting, unstable intermediate donates a phosphate group to ADP.

With this formation of NADH and ATP, the original energy investment of two ATP is repaid.

The intermediate remaining is rearranged into phosphoenolpyruvate (PEP); an oxygen and two hydrogen atoms are stripped off. The highly unstable PEP gives up a phosphate group to ADP. Thus the net energy yield is two ATP for each glucose molecule. The glycolytic leftover is pyruvate (the ionized form of pyruvic acid).

(to oxidation-reduction stage of aerobic respiration, anaerobic respiration, or fermentation)

Figure 8.3 Glycolysis, with glucose as the example of how carbohydrates undergo initial degradation in this pathway. All the steps in the brown-shaded area occur *twice* for each glucose molecule. Glycolysis may be followed by aerobic respiration, anaerobic respiration, or fermentation.

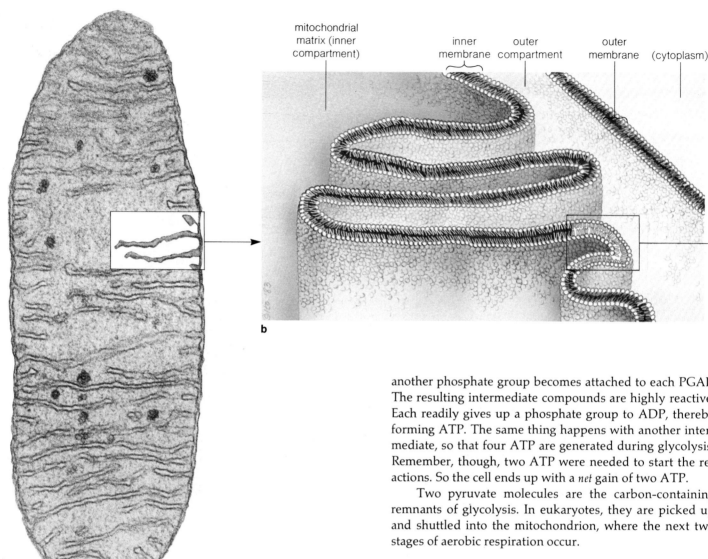

mitochondrial matrix (inner compartment)

inner membrane   outer compartment   outer membrane   (cytoplasm)

a

b

another phosphate group becomes attached to each PGAL. The resulting intermediate compounds are highly reactive. Each readily gives up a phosphate group to ADP, thereby forming ATP. The same thing happens with another intermediate, so that four ATP are generated during glycolysis. Remember, though, two ATP were needed to start the reactions. So the cell ends up with a *net* gain of two ATP.

Two pyruvate molecules are the carbon-containing remnants of glycolysis. In eukaryotes, they are picked up and shuttled into the mitochondrion, where the next two stages of aerobic respiration occur.

such as glucose more reactive by donating two phosphate groups to it. The resulting diphosphate compound is split into phosphoglyceraldehyde (PGAL) and dihydroxyacetone phosphate (DHAP). These two molecules are structural isomers, and the DHAP is readily converted to PGAL.

The two PGAL molecules now undergo oxidation: each transfers two electrons (and one of its hydrogen atoms) to NAD$^+$. In this way, two NADH are formed. Some of the energy lost by the electrons during the transfers is used to attract inorganic phosphate from the cytoplasm. In this way,

Second Stage: The Krebs Cycle

In the Krebs cycle, every two pyruvate molecules from glycolysis are completely oxidized to six carbon dioxide molecules (which have only one carbon atom each). Figure 8.4 shows the mitochondrial region where these reactions take place.

Before entering the Krebs cycle proper, both pyruvate molecules undergo conversion to acetyl-CoA (a two-carbon compound with coenzyme-A attached). The preparatory conversions result in the formation of two NADH, two acetyl-CoA, and two carbon dioxide molecules. After this, *two* turns of the Krebs cycle are needed to process the two acetyl-CoA molecules into four carbon dioxide molecules.

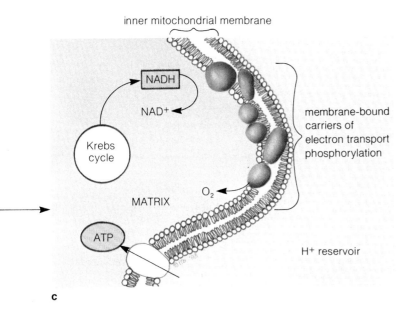

inner mitochondrial membrane

NADH

NAD+

Krebs cycle

membrane-bound carriers of electron transport phosphorylation

MATRIX

O_2

ATP

H+ reservoir

c

Figure 8.4 Functional zones of the mitochondrion. (**a**) Mitochondrion from a bat pancreatic cell, thin section. (Keith Porter)

(**b**) A closer look at the membrane-bound compartments within the mitochondrion. No matter how diverse they are in appearance, the inner membrane foldings create two compartments within the organelle. One compartment extends into all regions between the outer and inner membranes. The inner compartment is the one identified as the mitochondrial matrix. (**c**) The inner compartment is the site of Krebs cycle activities. Most Krebs cycle enzymes are in the matrix itself; some are bound in the matrix side of the inner membrane. The electron transport phosphorylation system is bound in the inner membrane. Its operation sets up a hydrogen ion gradient across this inner membrane, and this gradient is coupled to ATP formation.

These conversions produce two ATP molecules and eight more electron carriers (six NADH and two $FADH_2$). Figure 8.5 indicates the reaction steps necessary for these conversions.

The Krebs cycle (including the preparatory conversions leading to it) produces a total of two ATP, eight NADH, and two $FADH_2$ molecules for each glucose molecule being metabolized.

Third Stage: Electron Transport Phosphorylation

In the third stage of aerobic respiration, the electrons and hydrogen being carried by NADH and $FADH_2$ are sent down a membrane-bound transport system that promotes the formation of ATP from ADP and inorganic phosphate. At the end of the transport chain, oxygen accepts the electrons and combines them with hydrogen to form water.

Electron transport phosphorylation in mitochondria involves two events: (1) the transfer of electrons and hydrogen through a membrane-bound transport system, and (2) actual ATP formation.

Does this sound familiar? It should: the same kind of events take place in chloroplasts (Chapter Seven).

Figure 8.4 indicates the general arrangement of the electron transport system in the inner mitochondrial membrane. The inner membrane creates two functional compartments on either side of the transport system. According to the chemiosmotic theory (Chapter Seven), electron transport sets up a hydrogen ion gradient across the membrane by expelling hydrogen to the outer compartment:

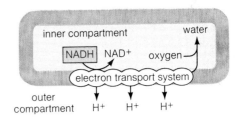

inner compartment
water
NADH NAD+ oxygen
electron transport system
outer compartment
H+ H+ H+

ATP formation depends on the reverse flow of hydrogen ions through a channel protein that spans the membrane. As in chloroplasts, the H+ movement drives the phosphorylation of ADP:

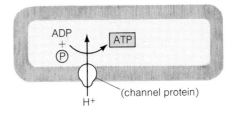

ADP + P
ATP
(channel protein)
H+

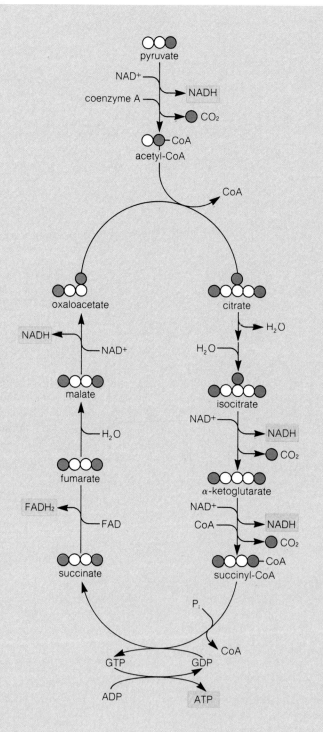

Step 1. As pyruvate enters the mitochondrion, a carbon atom is removed as CO_2. At the same time, two electrons and an H^+ ion are removed and transferred to NAD^+, producing NADH. The result is the conversion of one of the two remaining carbon atoms to an acid group. The two-carbon compound is linked to a molecule called coenzyme A, or CoA.

Step 2. The Krebs cycle proper begins when the two-carbon acid is coupled with a four-carbon compound having two acid groups (oxaloacetate). This produces citrate, a six-carbon compound having three acid groups. CoA is released for reuse.

Step 3. After two intermediate reactions, an acid group is split off the six-carbon compound and is released as CO_2. At the same time, two electrons and an H^+ ion are removed, forming a second molecule of NADH.

Step 7. And another NADH molecule is produced by the transfer of two more hydrogen atoms. The product of this last reaction is the same four-carbon compound that the cycle starts with. Thus, we are ready for another turn of the Krebs cycle.

Step 6. Two more hydrogen atoms are removed, but this time they are passed on to FAD, producing $FADH_2$.

Step 5. During the next conversions, the energy released when the CoA is split off is used to produce an ATP molecule. (Actually the related compound GTP is formed by addition of a phosphate group to GDP, but GDP then transfers its phosphate to ADP.)

Step 4. Now the third and last carbon atom is split off as another CO_2 molecule. Once again electrons and an H^+ ion are given off to produce NADH. In the process, a new acid group is linked to coenzyme A. The rest of the cycle works to convert this new four-carbon molecule with two acid groups to the related compound oxaloacetate, with which the cycle begins once again.

Figure 8.5 The Krebs cycle, second stage of aerobic respiration. Each brown circle signifies a carbon atom in the molecule, and each white circle signifies a carboxyl group (—COO⁻) or a carbon dioxide molecule produced when an acid group is split away. Remember that for each glucose molecule being metabolized, two pyruvate molecules have been formed. So two turns of the Krebs cycle must occur for each glucose molecule oxidized.

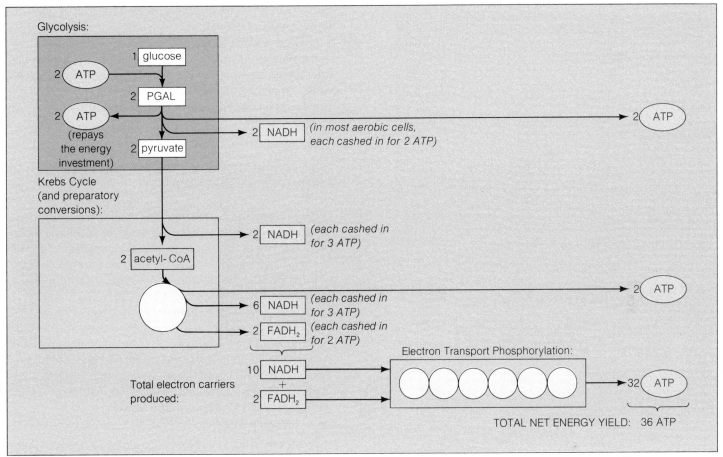

Figure 8.6 Summary of the energy harvest from one glucose molecule sent through the aerobic respiration pathway. Actual ATP yields vary, depending on cellular conditions and on the mechanism used to transfer energy from cytoplasmic NADH into the mitochondrion.

One NADH produced within the mitochondrion can yield three ATP. One cytoplasmic NADH (from glycolysis) may yield two or three ATP, depending on what kind of shuttle mechanism transfers its energy cargo to a membrane-bound transport system in the mitochondrion. In heart and liver cells, the cargo is shuttled right to the "top" of the transport chain. Thus three ATP molecules are generated—which means an overall energy harvest of thirty-eight ATP. In other cells, the energy cargo is delivered "lower" in the transport chain, so there is only enough energy to generate two ATP molecules. In this case, the overall energy harvest is thirty-six ATP.

Glucose Energy Yield: Summing Up

Now that we've looked at some of the details of the three stages of aerobic respiration, we can put together an integrated picture of the energy harvest from one glucose molecule. As Figure 8.6 and Table 8.1 suggest, the net ATP yield from glycolysis, through the Krebs cycle, and through electron transport phosphorylation, is thirty-six ATP. This total is common for most aerobic cells. The actual yield varies

according to how much energy is expended in transferring electrons to the mitochondrial transport system, and on where, exactly, electrons enter the transport chain. For example, in heart and liver cells, the yield can be thirty-eight ATP for the reasons indicated in Figure 8.6.

For every NADH molecule produced in the Krebs cycle, three ATP are produced. For every $FADH_2$ molecule, two ATP are produced. The two NADH from glycolysis can also be shuttled into the mitochondrion, where each can be used in producing two ATP, generally. Thus,

Table 8.1 Summary of the ATP Yield from the Complete Oxidation of One Glucose Molecule	
Energy-Extraction Pathways	Energy Yield
Glycolysis:	2 ATP
Krebs cycle:	2 ATP
Electron transport phosphorylation:	
2 NADH from glycolysis: 4 ATP* 8 NADH from Krebs cycle: 24 ATP 2 FADH₂ from Krebs cycle: 4 ATP	32 ATP
	A total of 36 ATP

*Can be 6 in heart and liver cells.

thirty-two ATP are typically produced during electron transport phosphorylation.

There are 263 kilocalories of energy stored in the terminal phosphate bonds of thirty-six ATP. Given that 686 kilocalories are stored in glucose, the energy-releasing efficiency of aerobic metabolism is (263/686), or thirty-eight percent, assuming the best of cellular conditions.

FUELS OR BUILDING BLOCKS? CONTROLS OVER ENERGY METABOLISM

Glycolysis and the Krebs cycle actually serve two functions in cellular metabolism. First, they can dismantle food molecules for energy that can drive ATP formation. Second, intermediates formed during the reactions can be diverted to **biosynthesis**: the assembly of all lipids, carbohydrates, proteins, and nucleic acids that make up a cell (Figure 8.7).

What determines whether a given molecule will be oxidized as an energy source for generating ATP? What determines whether it will be pulled out of energy-releasing pathways in intermediate forms that can be used as building blocks? The main controls are enzymes that catalyze steps in which the energy change is so great that the reactions are, for all practical purposes, irreversible.

Enzymes catalyzing key reactions in glycolysis and the Krebs cycle govern whether molecules are degraded as an ATP-generating energy source or are converted to intermediate forms that can be used in biosynthesis.

In glycolysis, for example, phosphofructokinase is such an enzyme. It adds a second phosphate group onto a glucose molecule before the glucose undergoes cleavage. However, when the cell has enough energy and/or raw materials, ATP concentrations increase. High concentration of ATP happens to be an inhibitor of phosphofructokinase; it puts the brakes on enzyme activity. Low ATP concentrations allow

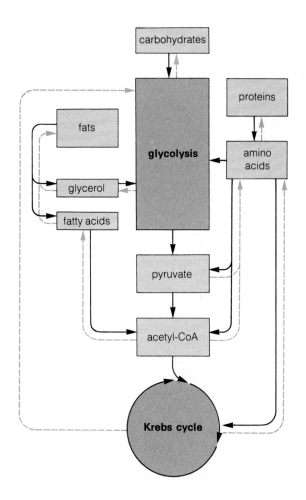

Figure 8.7 Where various substances flow into the glycolytic pathway and the Krebs cycle (black arrows). Different intermediates of glycolysis and the Krebs cycle can be pulled out of the energy-releasing pathways and used in biosynthesis (blue arrows).

rapid enzyme activity—which leads to increased rates of ATP production.

Through integration of enzyme activity, cells constantly adjust to resource supplies and demands. Enzymes can commit storage sugars or fats to energy-releasing pathways in times of stress or heightened activity. Cells do not require certain kinds of carbohydrates to be taken in as food, because enzymes can pull out intermediates of glycolysis and the Krebs cycle, and divert them to pathways for building all the carbohydrates necessary. Other enzymes can direct intermediates to the assembly of about twenty amino acids, which are building blocks for protein synthesis. This is true for autotrophic cells, at least. Many heterotrophic cells have lost the ability to build some of the different kinds of amino acids found in proteins. Our own cells are enzymatically equipped to assemble only twelve of the amino acids required; the remainder must be obtained from food (Chapter Twenty-Six).

PERSPECTIVE

In this unit, you have read about fundamental connections between matter, energy, and the cell. These connections exist in the pathways by which energy is trapped, stored in molecules, then released through controlled oxidations. Trapping environmental energy through photosynthesis, releasing energy from carbon-containing compounds through aerobic respiration—taken together, these are central events in the living world.

Later chapters will turn to the greater picture of the origin and evolution of life. However, the following overview of how these three kinds of pathways came to be linked may give you a sense of how important they are for the continuation of life on this planet.

It appears that when life originated, the environment contained simple molecules that contained mostly carbon, hydrogen, oxygen, and nitrogen. Such carbon-containing compounds would have been food for the first forms of life. Most likely, ATP was generated by pathways similar to glycolysis; and fermentation routes must have predominated because free oxygen was not present in the atmosphere at that time. From about $3\frac{1}{2}$ billion to 600 million years ago—the golden age of prokaryotes—mutations probably led to alterations in metabolic machinery. In at least some ancient mutants, enzyme systems for degrading carbon compounds were modified and extended. The systems were used in building energy-rich molecules from carbon dioxide and water. How were the reactions made to run in an energetically unfavorable direction? Sunlight energy was harnessed; photosynthesis had emerged.

It was a milestone in evolutionary time. Oxygen, the by-product of photosynthesis, now began to accumulate and eventually would change the entire character of the earth's atmosphere. In the beginning, at least some bacterial cells were opportunistic about the increasing oxygen concentrations. Oxygen is, after all, a willing electron acceptor for oxidation-reduction reactions. In some cells, aerobic oxidation of carbon-containing molecules did indeed develop. Once oxygen became abundant, the mutant cells could abandon photosynthetic mechanisms and survive with respiratory mechanisms alone.

With aerobic respiration, life became permanent and self-sustaining. For the final products of this pathway—carbon dioxide and water—are precisely the materials needed to build sugar molecules in photosynthesis! Thus the flow of carbon, hydrogen, and oxygen through the energy pathways of living organisms came full circle. Through this so-called **carbon cycle** (Figure 8.8), organisms are locked into interdependence. Many similar cycles have come to exist for other essential materials, such as nitrogen and phosphorus.

Perhaps one of the most difficult connections you are asked to perceive is the link between yourself—a living, intelligent being—and such remote-sounding things as energy, metabolic pathways, and the cycling of oxygen, hydrogen, nitrogen, and carbon. Is this really the stuff of humanity? Think back, for a moment, on the discussion of the water molecule. A pair of hydrogen atoms competing with an oxygen atom for a fair share of the electrons joining them doesn't exactly seem close to our daily lives. But from this simple inequality, the polarity of the water molecule arises. As a result of the polarity, hydrogen bonds form between water molecules. And that is a beginning for the organization of lifeless matter which leads, ultimately, to the organization of matter in all living things.

For now you can imagine new kinds of molecules interspersed through some aqueous environment. Many will be nonpolar and will resist interaction with water. Others will be polar and will respond by dissolving in it. Certain molecules, such as phospholipids, contain both water-soluble and water-insoluble regions. In swirling, agitated water (as in a primordial sea, perhaps, pounding against some ancient shore?), they form a two-layered film around a water droplet. Such phospholipid bilayers are the basis for all cell membranes, hence all cells. The cell has, from the beginning, been the fundamental *living* unit.

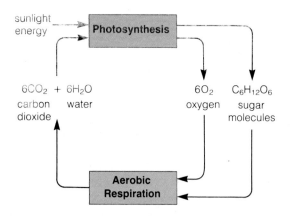

Figure 8.8 The carbon cycle, in which energy-rich molecules of carbon, hydrogen, and oxygen flow through all organisms on earth. In this recycling of matter through time, each birth is an affirmation of our ongoing capacity for organization, each death a renewal.

With membrane organization, the interior of the bilayer is separated from the environment. Through this isolation, chemical reactions can be contained and controlled. The essence of life *is* chemical control. This control is not brought about by some mysterious force. Instead, a class of protein molecules—enzymes—puts molecules into action in precisely regulated ways. It is not some mysterious force that tells enzymes when and what to build, and when and what to tear down. Instead it is a chemical responsiveness to the kinds of molecules present in the environment and to energy changes in the environment. And it is not some mysterious force that creates the enzymes themselves. DNA, the slender double strand of heredity, has the chemical structure—*the chemical message*—that allows molecule to faithfully reproduce molecule, one generation after the next. Those DNA strands "tell" the many billions of cells in your body how countless molecules must be built and torn apart for their energy.

Roger K. Burnard

So yes, oxygen, hydrogen, nitrogen, and carbon represent the stuff of you, and us, and all of life. But it takes more than molecules to complete the picture. It is because of the way these molecules are organized and maintained by a constant flow of energy that you are alive. It takes outside energy from sources such as the sun to drive the formation of new molecules. Once molecules are assembled into cells, it takes outside energy derived from food, water, and air to sustain their organization. Individual plants, animals, fungi, protistans, and bacteria are part of an interconnected web of energy use and materials cycling. That web threads through all levels of biological organization. Should energy fail to reach any part of any one of these levels, threads there will unravel; and life in that region will dwindle and cease.

For energy flows through time in only one direction—from forms rich in potential energy to forms having progressively less usable stores of it. Only as long as sunlight flows into the web of life—and only as long as there are molecules to recombine, rearrange, and recycle with the aid of that energy—does life have the potential to continue in all its rich diversity.

Life is, in short, no more *and no less* than a marvelously complex system of prolonging order. Sustained by energy transfusions, it continues because of a capacity for self-reproduction—the handing down of hereditary instructions. With these instructions, it has the means for organizing energy and materials generation after generation. Even with the death of the individual, life is prolonged. With death, molecules are released and can be recycled once more, providing raw materials for new generations. In this flow of matter and energy through time, each birth is affirmation of our ongoing capacity for organization, each death a renewal.

Readings

Brock, T. 1979. *Biology of Microorganisms.* Second edition. Englewood Cliffs, New Jersey: Prentice-Hall. Clear descriptions of the energy-releasing pathways of microorganisms. For students planning to continue their education in biology, this book will be a valuable addition to personal reference libraries.

Capaldi, R. 1977. "The Structure of Mitochondrial Membranes." In *Mammalian Cell Membranes* (G. Jamieson and D. Robinson, editors). Boston: Butterworth.

Lehninger, A. 1982. *Principles of Biochemistry.* Second edition. New York: Worth. A remarkably clear, accessible introduction to a topic that is sometimes approached with trepidation. Lehninger lets the elegance and excitement of his subject shine through.

Stanier, R., E. Adelberg, and J. Ingraham. 1976. *The Microbial World.* Fourth edition. Englewood Cliffs, New Jersey: Prentice-Hall.

Stryer, L. 1981. *Biochemistry.* Second edition. San Francisco: Freeman. Clearly written and authoritative; incorporates results and theories arising from current research into energy metabolism.

White, A., et al. 1978. *Principles of Biochemistry.* Sixth edition. New York: McGraw-Hill. A standard reference for the serious student. Good perspective on the evolution of metabolic pathways sprinkled throughout the text.

Wolfe, S. 1981. *Biology of the Cell.* Second edition. Belmont, California: Wadsworth. Up-to-date and comprehensive coverage of topics introduced in this chapter.

Review Questions

1. ATP can be produced by the release of chemical bond energy from carbohydrates. Phosphorylation and oxidation-reduction reactions are needed to do this. Can you describe the roles of these types of reactions in carbohydrate metabolism? (Refer to pages 122–124 before formulating your answer.)

2. There are four main pathways of carbohydrate metabolism: lactate fermentation, alcoholic fermentation, anaerobic respiration, and aerobic respiration.
    a. Each pathway starts with eletrons stripped from some carbohydrate. For each one, can you say where the "spent" electrons end up?
    b. Which of the pathways occur in the cytoplasm? In the mitochondrion?

3. Is the following statement true? Glycolysis can proceed only in the absence of oxygen.

4. Glycolysis is the first stage of all main pathways of carbohydrate metabolism. If you include the two ATP molecules formed during glycolysis, what is the *net* energy yield from one glucose molecule for each pathway?

5. Summarize the steps of aerobic respiration. Do this in words, then as a chemical equation.

6. Study Figure 8.6. Then, on your own, diagram the net energy yield from one glucose molecule sent down the aerobic pathway, from glycolysis through the Krebs cycle and oxidative phosphorylation.

7. Make a rough sketch of a mitochondrion, showing the arrangement of the inner and outer membranes. Using the chemiosmotic theory, can you describe how movements of hydrogen ions across these membranes might lead to ATP formation?

8. In anaerobic routes of glucose breakdown, further conversions of pyruvate do not yield any more usable energy. What, then, is the advantage of the conversion?

9. What happens to electron acceptors NAD^+ and FAD in glycolysis and in the Krebs cycle? How are the reaction products used?

10. What happens to NADH and $FADH_2$ in oxidative phosphorylation? Explain how electrons and hydrogen atoms stripped from them are used.

11. Why are oxygen atoms important in oxidative phosphorylation?

12. What are the main controls that determine whether a given molecule will be used in biosynthesis pathways or as an energy source for generating ATP?

13. Study Figure 8.8. Then, on your own, diagram the cycling of carbon through the biosphere.

UNIT THREE

THE ONGOING FLOW OF LIFE

At any given instant, a cell draws sustenance from its surroundings. At any instant, it is dismantling some molecules, diverting fragments from one pathway to another, and building new cell structures. In the preceding unit, we have observed these and other aspects of the cellular world. We have observed the cell frozen, as it were, at some random moment in order to chart the flow of energy and materials through it. With these observations behind us, we are ready to add another dimension to our concept of the cell: its reproduction, its continuity through time.

9

CELL REPRODUCTION

SOME GENERAL ASPECTS OF CELL REPRODUCTION

Reproduction, in its broadest sense, means making copies. The word often evokes images of identical copies as might emerge one after another from a printing press. Many living organisms, such as single-celled bacteria, can indeed produce identical copies of themselves by dividing and then growing as two new cells. Many other organisms produce "copies" that are not identical, that show some greater or lesser degree of dissimilarity to their parents. For example, you arose through reproduction, you are similar in many ways to both of your parents, but you are not an exact copy of either one. In the biological sense, **reproduction** means producing new cells or multicelled individuals that may (or may not) be exact replicas of their parents.

Biological reproduction takes place in a **life cycle**, a recurrent frame of events by which individuals are produced, grow, and develop according to the genetic program of the species. The simplest life cycles are those of single-celled organisms, in which reproduction through cell division alternates with cell growth. Grow, divide, grow, divide— this "cell cycle" *is* the life cycle. The picture becomes more complex for multicelled plants and animals. Hundreds, thousands, or many millions of cells may be growing and dividing as the plant or animal body changes progressively in form and function through time. At some point, however, one or more of those cells become specialized for reproduction. Here, also, it is the single cell that grows and divides— and starts the cycle over again.

It makes no difference whether the organism is a bacterium, mushroom, corn plant, pine tree, spider, fish, frog, or human. At some stage, a single, dividing cell represents the bridge to the next generation. Answers to three questions about this cellular bridge are central to an understanding of reproduction. *First,* what structures and substances are necessary for inheritance? *Second,* are they divided and distributed into daughter cells in particular ways? *Third,* what are the division mechanisms themselves?

Researchers in cytology, genetics, and molecular biology approach these questions in different ways, for they are working at different levels of biological organization. Because the questions are addressed from different perspectives, we will require more than one chapter to consider the answers (and best guesses) about the reproductive process. However, the next few summary paragraphs may be useful in keeping the overall picture in focus when reading through the chapters of this unit.

The Molecular Basis of Cell Reproduction

Each new cell must receive a complete set of hereditary instructions and a particular assortment of cytoplasmic elements. The reasons for this are as follows. The messages of inheritance are encoded in the molecular structure of DNA, which has four different kinds of nucleotides serving as the code words (Chapter Three). The linear order in which the four occur varies in a DNA strand, like beads of four different colors in a necklace. The information encoded in different nucleotide sequences can be used to build different structural products. Each product-specifying nucleotide sequence in DNA is a **gene**. Now, as Figure 9.1 suggests, a protein is a gene-specified product. Although some proteins serve as structural materials, others serve as enzymes that catalyze the assembly of lipids, carbohydrates, and other organic molecules into new cellular components. Thus, with a DNA-derived capacity to make sets of enzymes and other proteins, a new cell has the means to build all of the macromolecules and structures necessary to duplicate the parent cell.

As you can see, a daughter cell must receive a copy of all the product-specifying genes present in the parent cell. That is why the DNA of the parent cell is replicated prior to division. That is why special division mechanisms exist, for each daughter cell must receive a *complete* copy of hereditary instructions, not parts only of one or both copies. There must be *equality* in the division of DNA.

Also prior to division, certain types of enzymes, RNA molecules, and (in eukaryotes) organelles must become

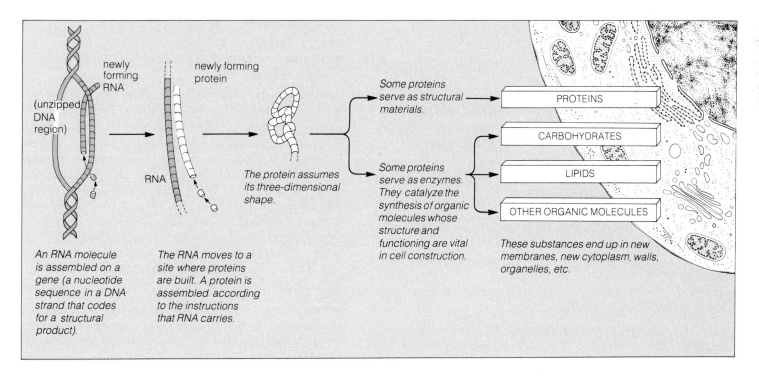

Figure 9.1 Simplified picture of how hereditary instructions contained in DNA lead to the construction of a new cell. With a DNA-derived capacity to make sets of enzymes as well as other proteins, all the organic materials necessary for specific aspects of cell structure and functioning can be synthesized.

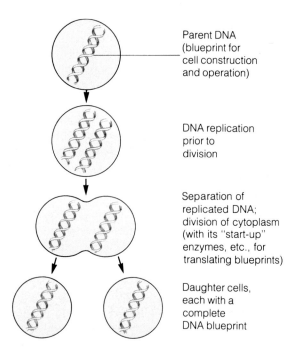

Parent DNA (blueprint for cell construction and operation)

DNA replication prior to division

Separation of replicated DNA; division of cytoplasm (with its "start-up" enzymes, etc., for translating blueprints)

Daughter cells, each with a complete DNA blueprint

Figure 9.2 Prerequisites for cell reproduction. DNA replication must precede cell division, and so must the accumulation and regional positioning of cytoplasmic elements. (For clarity, only a short segment of DNA is portrayed.)

Table 9.1	Overview of DNA and Cytoplasmic Division Mechanisms		
Mechanism	Outcome	Used by	Functions in
Prokaryotic fission	Concurrent DNA and cytoplasmic division	Bacteria	Reproduction
Mitosis	Nuclear DNA division only	Protistans, some fungi	Reproduction
		Plants, animals, some fungi	Multicellular growth (by cell divisions)
Meiosis	Nuclear DNA division only	Protistans, fungi, plants, animals	Reproduction (through gamete or meiospore formation)
Cytokinesis	Cytoplasmic division only, during late mitosis or meiosis (or after they are completed)		

stockpiled in the cytoplasm. They will function in the initial translation of DNA instructions in newly formed cells (Figure 9.2). In addition, this assortment of substances and organelles must become positioned in specific regions of the cytoplasm. Otherwise a new cell conceivably could receive too little of the required "start-up" machinery (or none at all) when the cytoplasm divides.

DNA replication, and the regional positioning of cytoplasmic substances and organelles, must precede cell division.

Kinds of Division Mechanisms

Table 9.1 summarizes the main division mechanisms that underlie cell reproduction. The most straightforward is **prokaryotic fission**. Here, the same process divides both the cytoplasm and replicated DNA into daughter cells. The process is one of membrane growth, and it can be illustrated by a simple example. Suppose that you place a bacterium

on a nutrient-rich medium in a culture dish. For the next twenty or thirty minutes, the bacterium feeds and grows. During this period, it also replicates its DNA. Prokaryotic DNA is not enclosed in a nuclear envelope, as it is in eukaryotes. It is attached to the plasma membrane. The replicated DNA also becomes attached nearby. Membrane growth occurs between the two attachment regions. As the membrane grows, the two DNA molecules are moved apart (Figure 9.3). Membrane and wall material now grow across the cell midsection, and the bacterium divides in two. This is a form of *binary* fission, for the cell body becomes partitioned into two equivalent parts (Figure 9.4).

In prokaryotic cell reproduction, an original DNA molecule and its replica are both attached to the plasma membrane; and membrane growth between their attachment sites separates them and allows distribution into daughter cells.

Eukaryotes rely on different DNA division mechanisms. Greater stores of DNA are required for their life cycles, which are more extended and more complex than those of prokaryotes. The eukaryotic DNA molecule itself has a much longer nucleotide sequence. And this molecule is complexed with many proteins into the structures called **chromosomes**. Also, with only one exception, the hereditary instructions are divided up among a set of anywhere from two to many hundreds of different chromosomes that vary in length and shape. As if this were not enough, a eukaryotic cell can have *more* than one set of chromosomes!

Most eukaryotic cells are **diploid**, a word meaning that they have two sets of chromosomes. For instance, your body cells are diploid. (They contain two complete sets of hereditary instructions, one from each of your parents.) Many eukaryotic cells are **polyploid**, with three or more sets.

In eukaryotes, hereditary instructions are divided up among a set of two or more different chromosomes, which vary in length and shape. Also, there can be two or more sets of these chromosomes in a cell.

Think about what a greater and more complex store of DNA means in terms of cell reproduction. The task of dividing and distributing hereditary instructions cannot be entrusted to the somewhat simple mechanism of prokaryotic fission, with its solitary membrane attachment point for each solitary DNA molecule. More sophisticated mechanisms must be employed to assure equality in the division of DNA for forthcoming daughter cells. Such division mechanisms do indeed exist. They are called mitosis and meiosis. Both are limited to division of the nucleus only. Cytoplasmic division, or *cytokinesis,* is a separate event. It usually occurs when nuclear division is nearing completion or at some stage after it is completed.

Mitosis maintains the number of chromosome sets in the nucleus from one cell generation to the next. Thus, if the nucleus of the parent cell is diploid, so will be the daughter nuclei. If a parent nucleus is polyploid, then polyploid daughter cells will follow. *With mitosis, the number of chromosome sets in the nucleus does not change.*

Meiosis changes the number of chromosome sets in the nucleus. It assures that daughter nuclei will be **haploid**. (The word means ''half'' the number of chromosome sets.) *With meiosis, the number of chromosome sets in each daughter nucleus is exactly half of what it was in the parent nucleus.* Meiosis occurs only in life cycles that include formation of special reproductive cells called gametes and meiospores.

Before looking at details of these two nuclear division mechanisms, let's begin with two features that are essential for their operation.

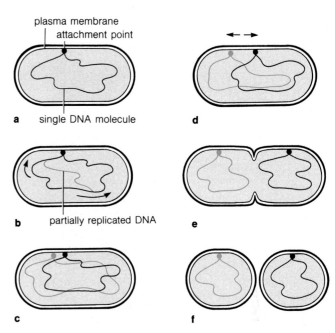

Figure 9.3 Prokaryotic cell division and reproduction through binary fission. (**a**) Generalized drawing of a bacterium before its single DNA molecule is replicated. The DNA appears to be attached to the plasma membrane at a single site. (**b**) Replication begins at some point on the DNA molecule and proceeds in two directions away from the initiation site. (**c**) The replicated DNA is attached at a site close to the attachment site of the parent molecule. (**d**) Membrane growth occurs between the two attachment sites and moves the two DNA molecules apart. (**e**) Once the DNA molecules are apart, membrane growth occurs through the cell midsection. (**f**) Depositions of plasma membrane and cell wall material at the cell midsection divide the cytoplasm in two.

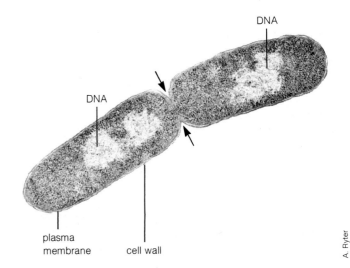

Figure 9.4 Binary fission in *Escherichia coli*, shown here in longitudinal section. Cytoplasmic division is not yet completed.

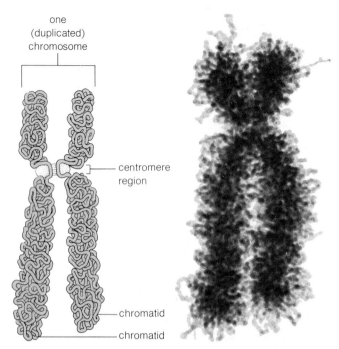

one
(duplicated)
chromosome

centromere
region

chromatid

chromatid

Figure 9.5 A human chromosome as it appears in the duplicated form just before nuclear division. The two chromatids remain attached at the centromere region. The corresponding sketch is drawn to suggest compactness and complexity. As you will read in Chapter Fourteen, chromosome structure is more highly organized. (E. J. Dupraw. *DNA and Chromosomes*, Holt, Rinehart and Winston, 1970)

COMPONENTS OF EUKARYOTIC CELL DIVISION

The capacity to handle increased amounts of DNA arose more than a billion years ago, among organisms that were ancestors of modern-day eukaryotes. This capacity was based on two developments: (1) the packaging of DNA and certain proteins into compact chromosome structures, and (2) a system of microtubules that can handle the separation of more than one chromosome at a time during division.

Chromosomes: Eukaryotic Packaging of DNA

A prokaryotic DNA molecule does not have other substances complexed with it along its entire length. In contrast, eukaryotic DNA and many different proteins are complexed together into a flexible, fiberlike molecule. The proteins are organized along the entire length of the molecule and they make up most of its weight. The DNA-protein fiber is one kind of *nucleoprotein*. One such nucleoprotein is the same thing as one chromosome.

Chromosome Appearance. During some stage of the life cycle, the chromosome is more or less extended, like a thin thread. When extended, the genes it carries are accessible to enzymes that take part in cell activities. At other stages, the proteins that are complexed with the DNA interact and cause the chromosome to coil up into a tightly condensed form. Regardless of its degree of extension or condensation, the chromosome remains a continuous nucleoprotein fiber.

When a eukaryotic nucleus is about to divide, each chromosome within it becomes duplicated by mechanisms to be described in Chapter Twelve. Suffice it to say here that each chromosome is now composed of two nucleoprotein fibers, with one being a copy of the other. The two remain attached at one spot, like Siamese twins. When joined this way, the two nucleoproteins are known as **sister chromatids**. Together they represent one (duplicated) chromosome. The spot where the nucleoproteins are held together is a local region where the chromosome narrows down; this region is the **centromere**. One such region is identified in Figure 9.5.

The terms that we have used here to describe chromosomes will be necessary in explaining the mechanisms of eukaryotic cell division. To reinforce their importance, the terms are summarized here:

1. Each molecule of eukaryotic DNA is complexed with many proteins into a flexible fiber (a nucleoprotein).

2. Between divisions, nucleoproteins are typically stretched out, so that the DNA instructions are available for cell growth and maintenance.

3. Prior to division, each nucleoprotein is replicated (copied). The original and the replica stay attached for a while as "sister chromatids."

4. Prior to and during early stages of division, sister chromatids become condensed into a highly compact structure.

5. The word "chromosome" can refer to a single (unduplicated) nucleoprotein or to duplicated nucleoproteins (sister chromatids).

Chromosome Number. The duplicated chromosome shown in Figure 9.5 is in a highly condensed form, just before actual division. This example is from a human somatic (body) cell. Such cells are diploid. They normally have two sets of twenty-three chromosomes, or forty-six total. Figure 9.6 shows what all forty-six look like after they have been duplicated and are in a highly condensed form.

Diploid cells of other eukaryotic organisms also have a characteristic number of chromosomes. Table 9.2 gives a

Table 9.2	Diploid Number of Chromosomes in the Somatic Cells of Some Eukaryotes*	
Nematode, *Ascaris megalocephala*		2
Fungus imperfecti, *Penicillium*		4
Mosquito, *Culex pipiens*		6
Fruit fly, *Drosophila melanogaster*		8
Garden pea, *Pisum sativum*		14
Corn, *Zea mays*		20
Lily, *Lilium*		24
Yellow pine, *Pinus ponderosa*		24
Frog, *Rana pipiens*		26
Earthworm, *Lumbricus terrestris*		36
Rhesus monkey, *Macaca mulatta*		42
Human, *Homo sapiens*		46
Orangutan, *Pongo pygmaeus*		48
Chimpanzee, *Pan troglodytes*		48
Gorilla, *Gorilla gorilla*		48
Potato, *Solanum tuberosum*		48
Amoeba, *Amoeba*		50
Horse, *Equus caballus*		64
Horsetail, *Equisetum*		216
Adder's tongue fern, *Ophioglossum reticulatum*		1,262

*These examples are a sampling only. Chromosome number for most species falls between ten and fifty.

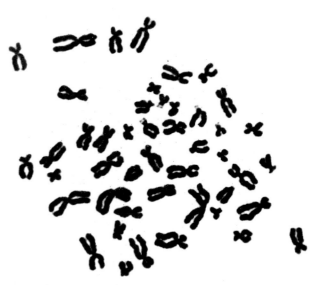

Figure 9.6 From a somatic cell of a human adult male, forty-six chromosomes as they appear in the duplicated and highly condensed state. (S. Brecher)

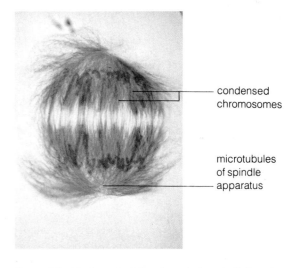

condensed chromosomes

microtubules of spindle apparatus

Figure 9.7 Micrograph of the microtubular spindle in a plant cell undergoing nuclear division. (Andrew S. Bajer)

few examples. A nematode (*Ascaris megalocephala*) has the lowest, with only two chromosomes per diploid cell. There are twenty chromosomes in the diploid cells of corn, water fleas, asparagus, and many other species. One fern species (*Ophioglossum reticulatum*) has one of the highest numbers known (1,262). In forthcoming illustrations on mitosis and meiosis, only a few chromosomes will be shown for the sake of clarity. Keep in mind that the number of chromosomes being used is only one example, and that the number is different for different species.

Microtubular Spindles

A membrane-growth mechanism assures equality in the division of prokaryotic DNA. When we turn to eukaryotes, we find that DNA division depends on a **microtubular spindle**. There are many varieties of spindles, but all are alike in basic structure and function. Each consists of a parallel array of thin, cylindrical structures called microtubules (Figure 9.7). Each spindle helps establish polarity in the nucleus: it forms two distinct poles to which sister chromatids of each chromosome can move, once they are separated from each other. In many species, the spindle also helps move apart the two sister chromatids.

In sections that follow, you will be reading about spindles used in plant and animal cells. No matter what the species, however, the following generalization is true:

In eukaryotic cells, nuclear division depends on (1) formation of distinct poles by a microtubular spindle, and (2) attachment of sister chromatids of each chromosome to opposite ends of that spindle.

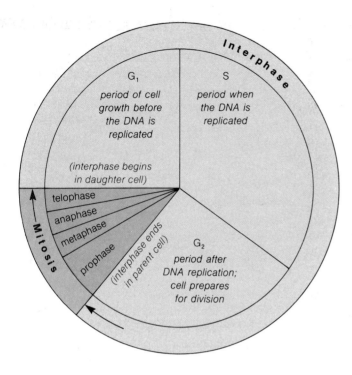

Figure 9.8 Eukaryotic cell cycle. This drawing has been generalized. There is great variation in the length of different stages from one cell to the next.

THE CELL CYCLE

In eukaryotic cells, mitosis is only a small part of a sequence of events known as the **cell cycle**. These events include mitosis proper, cytokinesis, then interphase (Figure 9.8). **Interphase** is the period of cell growth, maintenance, and differentiation. It is also the period in which DNA is replicated. Mitosis itself can last from a few minutes to an hour or more, depending on the cell type and on environmental conditions. Cells generally spend most of their time in interphase. There are three distinct stages to interphase:

G_1 *a "gap" (interval) before DNA replication*

S   *"synthesis" (replication) of DNA*

G_2 *a second "gap" in the cell cycle, before mitosis*

The duration of the S stage as well as mitosis does not vary much in most organisms. But the G_1 stage varies considerably. For instance, the G_1 stage cannot even be detected during the extremely rapid first divisions by which a fertilized sea urchin egg becomes transformed into a multicelled embryo. Except for the cells of growing root and shoot tips, a complex plant consists mostly of cells arrested in G_1.

Whole populations of single-celled protistans remain in G_1 when environmental conditions do not favor growth. Normally, skeletal muscle cells and nerve cells of your body never leave the G_1 stage. What you have of these cells is all that you ever will have.

So far, we have described the chromosome and microtubular spindle, which are the main participants in mitosis. We have also described where mitosis occurs in the cell cycle. With this information, we are ready to turn to the division events themselves.

MITOSIS: MAINTAINING THE NUMBER OF CHROMOSOME SETS

Mitosis is the nuclear division process underlying reproduction of single-celled eukaryotes and physical growth (through cell divisions) in multicelled eukaryotes. Figure 9.9 shows the mitotic division of a plant cell (*Haemanthus*). With the onset of mitosis, cell construction, growth, and maintenance activities idle. Profound changes now take place in the nucleus. The nuclear changes flow smoothly, one into the other. But it is simpler to consider them as occurring in four sequential stages: prophase, metaphase, anaphase, and telophase.

Prophase: Mitosis Begins

The first stage of mitosis, called **prophase**, is evident when chromosomes become visible in the light microscope as threadlike structures. The term mitosis refers to this emergence. (It comes from the Greek *mitos,* which means thread.) By late prophase, the threads become folded and condensed into thicker, rodlike chromosome structures of the sort shown in Figure 9.10.

While condensation is proceeding, a microtubular spindle begins to form in the cytoplasm. Most take on one of two shapes. In cells that contain centrioles (Chapter Four), the ends of the spindle microtubules converge at each pole. There, short microtubules radiate around the centrioles like starbursts:

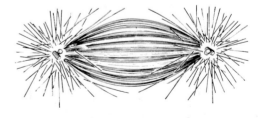

This is called an *astral* spindle (astral means starlike).

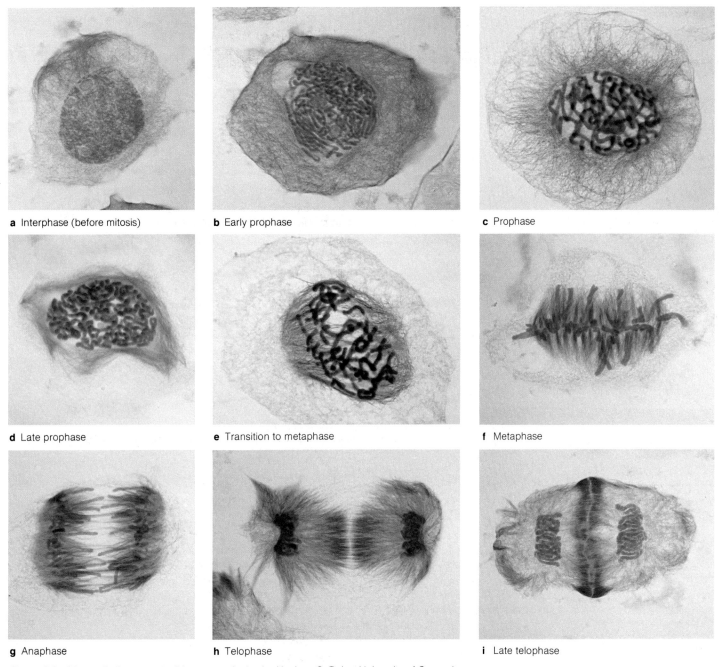

a Interphase (before mitosis)

b Early prophase

c Prophase

d Late prophase

e Transition to metaphase

f Metaphase

g Anaphase

h Telophase

i Late telophase

Figure 9.9 Plant cells (*Haemanthus*) in stages of mitosis. (Andrew S. Bajer, University of Oregon)

At one time, it was thought that spindles arose from centrioles. Yet spindles also form in dividing cells that do not have centrioles. This is especially evident in dividing cells of many land plants. Here, microtubules form a barrel-shaped *anastral* spindle (without "stars" at the poles).

All such spindles are produced from microtubular organizing centers: molecular systems that function in assembling microtubules (Chapter Four). In cells with centrioles, such systems have been identified around the centrioles themselves, where they are densely clustered.

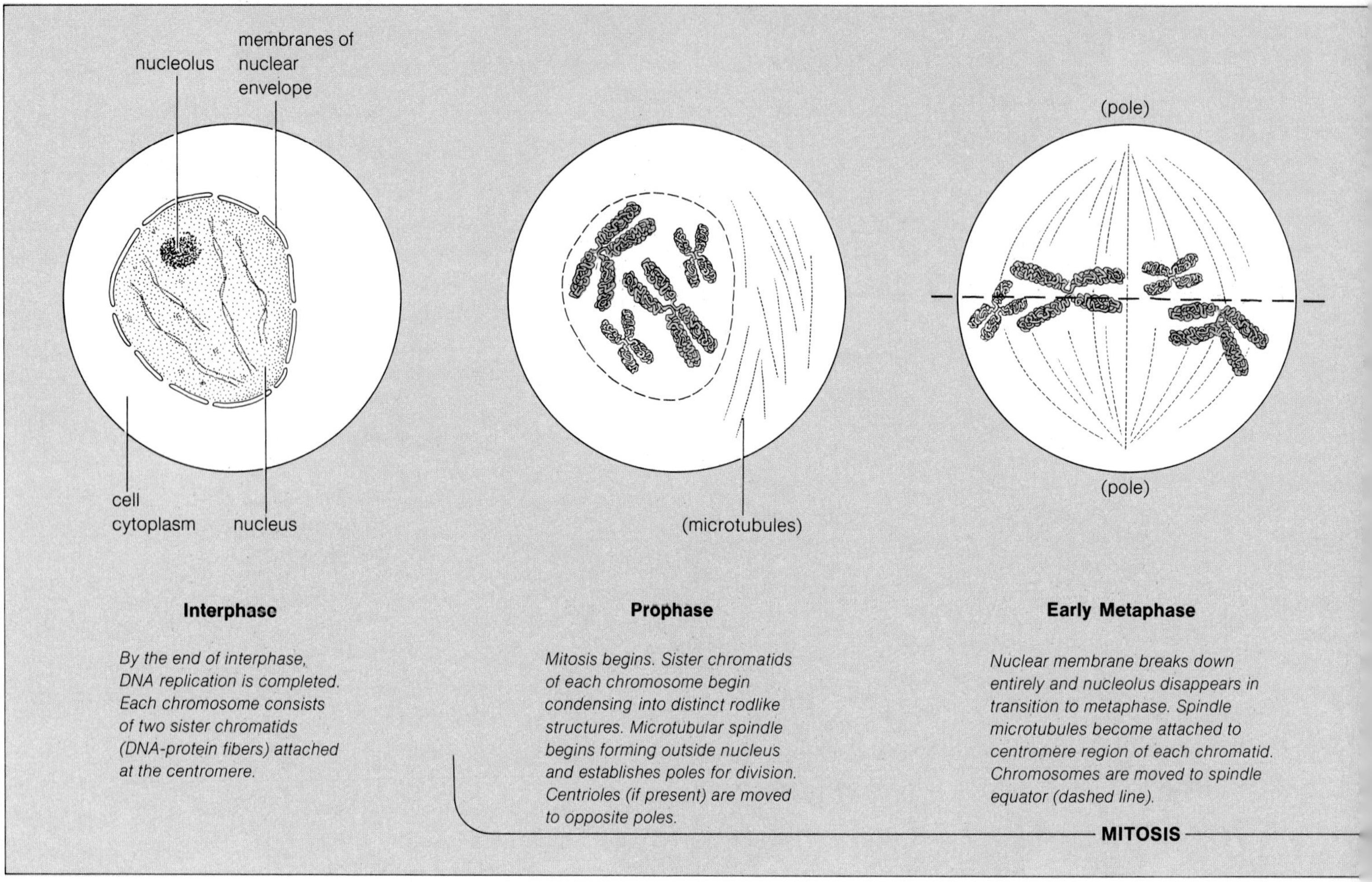
membranes of nuclear envelope
nucleolus
cell cytoplasm
nucleus
(microtubules)
(pole)
(pole)
Interphase
By the end of interphase, DNA replication is completed. Each chromosome consists of two sister chromatids (DNA-protein fibers) attached at the centromere.
Prophase
Mitosis begins. Sister chromatids of each chromosome begin condensing into distinct rodlike structures. Microtubular spindle begins forming outside nucleus and establishes poles for division. Centrioles (if present) are moved to opposite poles.
Early Metaphase
Nuclear membrane breaks down entirely and nucleolus disappears in transition to metaphase. Spindle microtubules become attached to centromere region of each chromatid. Chromosomes are moved to spindle equator (dashed line).
MITOSIS

Figure 9.10 Mitosis: the nuclear division mechanism by which the number of chromosome sets in a parent nucleus is maintained in daughter nuclei.

The drawing shows a generalized diploid cell, with two sets of chromosomes. (The blue-shaded chromosomes are a set derived from one parent; the gold-shaded chromosomes are a set derived from another parent during sexual reproduction, as described on page 150.) To help you in keeping track of the destination of each chromatid, the same kind of chromosome structure is shown through all stages of mitosis proper. But keep in mind that chromosome structure changes considerably through these stages.

Like chromosomes, centrioles are duplicated prior to division; new cells cannot build new centrioles from scratch. During interphase, an existing centriole pair becomes positioned just outside the nuclear envelope. The pair undergoes duplication. Then spindle microtubules separate the two centriole pairs (Figure 9.11).

Metaphase

The transition from prophase to **metaphase** is marked by fragmentation and disappearance of both the nuclear envelope and the nucleolus. As soon as this happens, the spindle moves into the space that the nucleus once filled. All the while, chromosomes continue to condense. They reach their most compact shape in early metaphase.

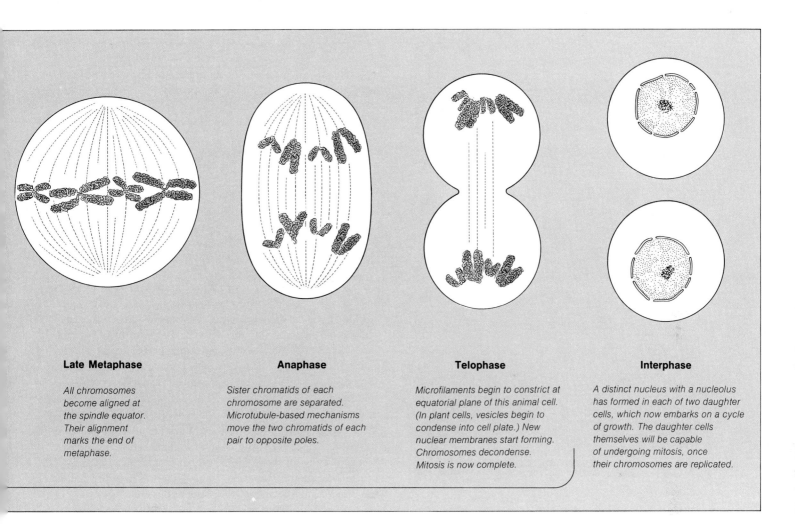

Late Metaphase

All chromosomes
become aligned at
the spindle equator.
Their alignment
marks the end of
metaphase.

Anaphase

Sister chromatids of each
chromosome are separated.
Microtubule-based mechanisms
move the two chromatids of each
pair to opposite poles.

Telophase

Microfilaments begin to constrict at
equatorial plane of this animal cell.
(In plant cells, vesicles begin to
condense into cell plate.) New
nuclear membranes start forming.
Chromosomes decondense.
Mitosis is now complete.

Interphase

A distinct nucleus with a nucleolus
has formed in each of two daughter
cells, which now embarks on a cycle
of growth. The daughter cells
themselves will be capable
of undergoing mitosis, once
their chromosomes are replicated.

During metaphase, the spindle apparatus becomes attached to each condensed chromosome at a **kinetochore**, a disk-shaped structure within the centromere region. The kinetochore of one chromatid of each chromosome connects with microtubules extending from one spindle pole. The kinetochore of its sister chromatid connects with microtubules extending from the opposite pole. As more and more microtubules attach to each kinetochore, chromosomes move toward one pole and then the other, almost as if being subject to a tug-of-war. Then all the chromosomes take up final positions halfway between the two poles at the spindle equator (Figure 9.10c). This alignment is extremely important for the precise separation and movement of sister chromatids to opposite poles. It is the dominant event of metaphase. Once alignment is complete, metaphase is over.

Anaphase

Two events characterize **anaphase**: the separation of sister chromatids of each chromosome and their movement to opposite poles. The mechanism underlying their physical separation is not understood, but they all separate at about the same time.

How do the separated sister chromatids actually reach their polar destinations? In most cells, the movement seems to be the combined result of at least two different mechanisms. Microtubules attached to the centromere regions shorten, which *pulls* each chromatid toward one pole. (See, for example, Figure 9.12.) Other microtubules that extend from pole to pole begin to elongate, which *pushes* the poles apart before division occurs.

Figure 9.11 Formation of a mitotic spindle in eukaryotic cells having a pair of centrioles in the cytoplasm. Centrioles, like chromosomes, are duplicated prior to division.

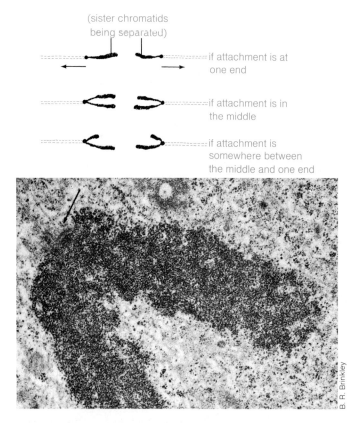

(sister chromatids being separated)

if attachment is at one end

if attachment is in the middle

if attachment is somewhere between the middle and one end

Figure 9.12 Micrograph of an anaphase chromatid being pulled to a spindle pole by microtubules (arrow). 24,000×. Depending on the location of the centromere region (which contains the attachment site for spindle microtubules), a chromatid can appear straight, U-shaped, or J-shaped as it is being moved.

Telophase

Telophase begins once the sister chromatids of each chromosome arrive at opposite spindle poles. Each "chromatid" is now a separate chromosome. During telophase, condensation is reversed, so that the chromosome now becomes extended in the threadlike form. Patches of nuclear envelope appear alongside them. Patch joins with patch, and eventually a new, continuous nuclear envelope separates the hereditary material from the cytoplasm. Once the nucleus is completed, telophase is completed—and so is mitosis.

CYTOKINESIS: DIVIDING UP THE CYTOPLASM

Cytoplasmic division, or **cytokinesis**, usually accompanies nuclear division. Exceptions do exist. For instance, cytoplasmic division does not follow mitosis in some protistans, such as ciliates. Each single-celled body has multiple nuclei. The same condition occurs in some insects, plants, and many fungi at certain stages of the life cycle. In most cases, though, cytokinesis extends from late anaphase through telophase.

In most animal cells, the onset of cytokinesis is marked by the appearance of scattered deposits of material around microtubules at the spindle equator. The deposits accumulate until they form a distinct layer across (typically) the cell midsection. Soon a shallow, ringlike depression appears at the plasma membrane in the plane above this layer (Figure 9.13). The depression is called a **cleavage furrow**. Here, the plasma membrane is being pulled inward by a ring of microfilaments that has become attached to the plasma membrane. The microfilaments contain contractile proteins (two of which are actin and myosin). When the microfilaments contract, they do so from the cell periphery to the interior. The inward movement cuts the cytoplasm in two.

As in animals, cytokinesis in most land plants begins with the formation of a layer of material at the spindle equator. However, these plant cells have fairly rigid cell walls, which do not lend themselves to the formation of cleavage furrows. Hence we find a different mechanism of cytokinesis in plant cells, one called **cell plate formation**. This mechanism is depicted in Figure 9.14.

At first, material deposited at the spindle equator is enclosed in membranous vesicles derived from Golgi complexes (Chapter Four). More and more vesicles accumulate, then fuse together, and gradually they form a continuous layer. This layer eventually extends from one side of the cell to the other. Within each membranous vesicle are pectin

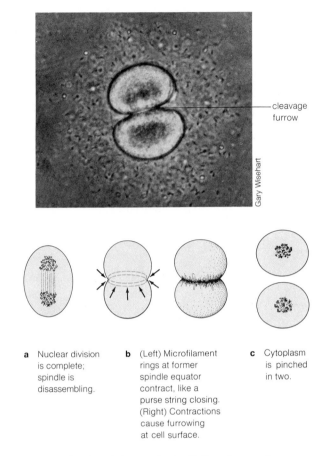

a Nuclear division is complete; spindle is disassembling.

b (Left) Microfilament rings at former spindle equator contract, like a purse string closing. (Right) Contractions cause furrowing at cell surface.

c Cytoplasm is pinched in two.

cleavage furrow

Gary Wisehart

Figure 9.13 Cytokinesis in an animal cell. The micrograph corresponds to the sketches in (**b**).

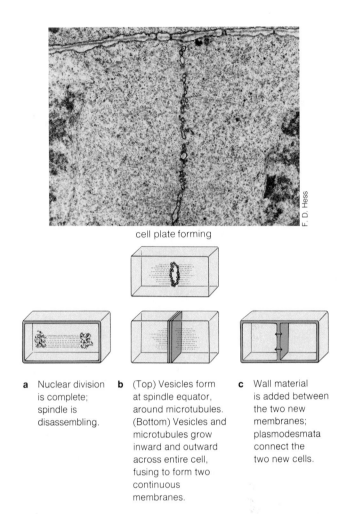

cell plate forming

F. D. Hess

a Nuclear division is complete; spindle is disassembling.

b (Top) Vesicles form at spindle equator, around microtubules. (Bottom) Vesicles and microtubules grow inward and outward across entire cell, fusing to form two continuous membranes.

c Wall material is added between the two new membranes; plasmodesmata connect the two new cells.

Figure 9.14 Cytokinesis in a plant cell. The micrograph shows vesicles fusing together at the spindle equator; they will form part of the new plasma membranes between the two daughter cells. Wall material will be added between the membranes formed here.

and various polysaccharides, which are major wall constituents. Thus the vesicle membranes give rise to plasma membranes, and their contents provide the raw materials for new walls. The developing membrane layers and wall material form a partition called the cell plate.

MEIOSIS: HALVING THE NUMBER OF CHROMOSOME SETS

As you have seen, mitosis maintains the number of chromosome sets in the nucleus from one cell generation to the next. In contrast, meiosis *changes* the number of chromosome sets to exactly half of what it was in the parent nucleus.

Take another look at Figure 9.5, which shows a chromosome from a diploid nucleus at metaphase. This chromosome is duplicated (it consists of two sister chromatids). Now take a look at Figure 9.6, which shows a complete set of such chromosomes. Clearly they are not all alike. Some are longer than others, and they have different shapes, depending on their centromere location. On close analysis, you would discover that for each chromosome of a given length and shape, there is another chromosome that has the *same* length and shape. Each pair of morphologically equivalent chromosomes in a nucleus are called **homologues**. (Some species have sex chromosomes, which differ morphologically in males and females. But sex chromosomes, too, function as a homologous pair in cells undergoing meiosis.)

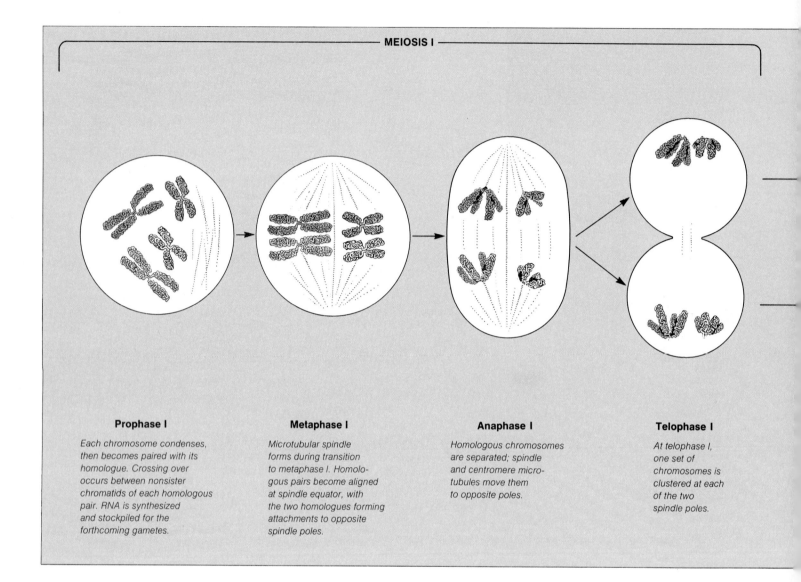

Prophase I

Each chromosome condenses, then becomes paired with its homologue. Crossing over occurs between nonsister chromatids of each homologous pair. RNA is synthesized and stockpiled for the forthcoming gametes.

Metaphase I

Microtubular spindle forms during transition to metaphase I. Homologous pairs become aligned at spindle equator, with the two homologues forming attachments to opposite spindle poles.

Anaphase I

Homologous chromosomes are separated; spindle and centromere microtubules move them to opposite poles.

Telophase I

At telophase I, one set of chromosomes is clustered at each of the two spindle poles.

Figure 9.15 Meiosis: a nuclear division mechanism by which the number of chromosome sets in a parent nucleus is reduced by half in each daughter nucleus. Only two kinds of homologous chromosomes are shown here. The blue-shaded chromosomes are derived from one parent; the gold-shaded ones are their equivalents from the other parent.

Homology in chromosome sets arises through **sexual reproduction**, a process that begins with meiosis and ends at fertilization. In this process, meiotic division precedes the formation of **gametes**, which are haploid sex cells. During meiosis, chromosomes pair with each other, homologue to homologue, then they are separated from one another. Each gamete ends up with one chromosome of each morphological type. At *fertilization*, the nuclei of two haploid gametes fuse, which restores the parental chromosome number in the new individual. (Usually, each gamete has been derived from a separate parent. There are exceptions, such as self-fertilizing plants.)

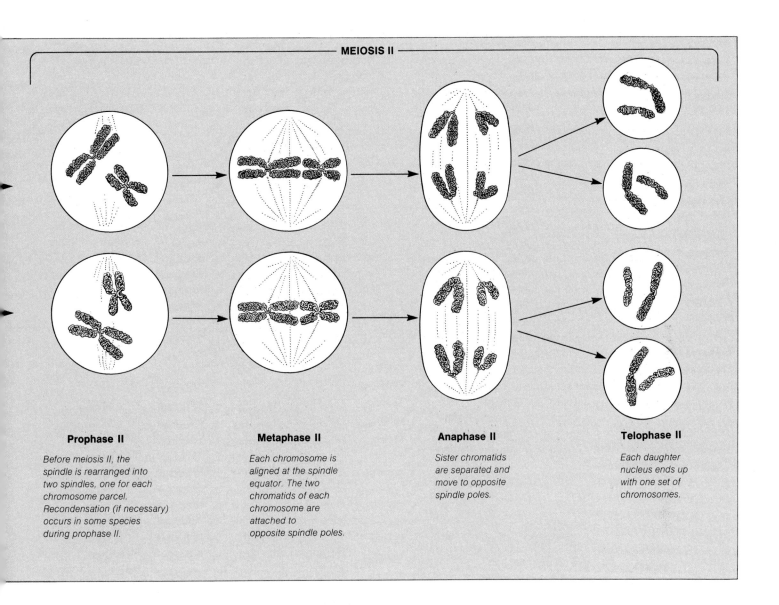

MEIOSIS II

Prophase II

Before meiosis II, the spindle is rearranged into two spindles, one for each chromosome parcel. Recondensation (if necessary) occurs in some species during prophase II.

Metaphase II

Each chromosome is aligned at the spindle equator. The two chromatids of each chromosome are attached to opposite spindle poles.

Anaphase II

Sister chromatids are separated and move to opposite spindle poles.

Telophase II

Each daughter nucleus ends up with one set of chromosomes.

If we refer to a diploid chromosome set as $2n$ and a haploid set as $1n$, then sexual reproduction can be seen to consist of chromosome reduction and chromosome doubling:

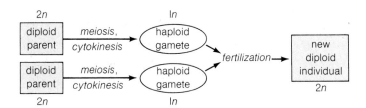

The meiotic divisions on which sexual reproduction are based are illustrated in Figure 9.15. In some ways, they resemble mitotic division. Each chromosome is already duplicated before the nucleus enters meiosis; microtubular spindles establish poles and move chromatids to them. In fact, meiosis probably evolved through modifications to mitotic systems that already existed.

Meiosis requires two divisions, which proceed through stages having the same names as mitosis. During interkinesis (the brief transition period between them), there is no DNA replication:

First Division		Second Division
prophase I		prophase II
metaphase I	interkinesis	metaphase II
anaphase I	*no DNA replication*	anaphase II
telophase I		telophase II

The following sections describe some of the key events associated with these stages.

Prophase I Activities

The first stage of meiosis, **prophase I**, consists of five kinds of activities: chromosome condensation, homologue pairing, recombination, gene transcription, and chromosome recondensation. During *condensation,* sister chromatids align tightly with each other. They draw so close together that they look like a single thread.

During *pairing* activities, each homologous chromosome becomes aligned with its partner. The homologues undergo **synapsis,** a process by which they are drawn together, zipperlike, and attached along their length. A "gap" of about 100 nanometers is all that separates them. Electron micrographs show that the gap actually contains highly organized bands of proteins that function in chemical recognition between the homologues. When two homologues are thus joined together, they form a **tetrad** (a structure consisting of four linked chromatids).

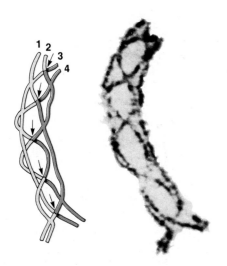

Figure 9.16 Paired homologous chromosomes (grasshopper cell) after crossing over. Sister chromatids of one are labeled 1 and 2; those of its homologue, 3 and 4. Arrows show chiasmata. (B. John)

The *recombination* events of prophase I usually begin once the same genes are matched up, in the same order, along the length of synapsed chromatids. First, two nonsister chromatids undergo breakage in corresponding regions. The breakage can be depicted in the following way:

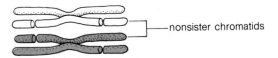

Only two breakage regions are shown here. There can be (and usually are) three or more such regions in tetrads. The two exposed ends of each break do not simply stick back together. Each joins, in a crosswise fashion, to the opposite end of the corresponding break in the nonsister chromatid:

crossing over at two sites

This event is called **crossing over:** two nonsister chromatids of synapsed chromosomes have exchanged corresponding segments at breakage points.

As recombination draws to a close, all four chromatids of each tetrad separate slightly from one another. Their separation marks the transition to the *gene transcription* events of prophase I. This is the stage when RNA is assembled and stockpiled for use by the new individual that eventually develops following fertilization (Chapter Fourteen).

Although homologous chromosomes were held close together before this, they now repel each other strongly. Even so, they remain joined together at a few sites. Microscopic examination has revealed that one chromatid extends across a nonsister chromatid of the tetrad at each of these sites. Such crossings between two nonsister chromatids are called **chiasmata** (singular, chiasma), which means "crosses." Figure 9.16 shows a tetrad with five chiasmata. Each one is visible evidence that breakage and exchange (a crossover) occurred earlier in prophase I. (It does not necessarily indicate exactly where the actual breaks occurred, for chiasmata can slip down toward the ends of chromatids as the homologues move apart.)

At the conclusion of prophase I, chromatids undergo *recondensation*. No more transcription is possible: the DNA instructions are no longer available to enzymes when chromatids coil tightly into short rods. At no other stage of meiosis do chromatids become so condensed. During re-condensation, chiasmata are physically forced toward the chromatid ends. Often, homologues end up being held together at their tips only.

The Importance of Crossing Over.   Crossing over is one of the most important events in meiosis. Why is it so important? Recall that genes are specific DNA regions containing instructions that can be used to build specific products. However, a gene for a given product can occur in alternative forms, known as **alleles**. Consider two equivalent genes in a pair of homologous chromosomes from (say) a daisy. One gene might specify an enzyme that controls synthesis of a pigment that makes daisy flowers appear yellow. Its equivalent gene in the homologue might specify a variant form of the enzyme, one that leads to production of white flowers. In other words, equivalent genes on homologous chromosomes can specify the same or different forms of the same kind of product. Suppose that different alleles on nonsister chromatids are aligned with each other at synapsis. If they are affected by a crossover, then the result can be **genetic recombination**: new combinations of alleles can end up in a chromosome, hence in a reproductive cell, and finally in a new individual. In the sketch below, each newly incorporated segment may contain one or more alleles that differ from the forms that were carried on the segment donated:

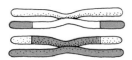

segments exchanged at corresponding sites

As you will read in later chapters, genetic recombination is a source of tremendous diversity among organisms.

Separating the Homologues

The transition to **metaphase I** is strongly reminiscent of events in mitosis. A microtubular spindle forms outside the nuclear envelope. Chromosomes are lined up at the spindle equator. But there is a major difference: in metaphase I, the lineup is *paired,* homologue with homologue. Both sister chromatids of one chromosome become attached to one spindle pole; and both sister chromatids of the homologue become attached to the opposite pole (Figure 9.15).

Which homologue of a pair ends up on one side of the spindle equator or the other is random. In other words, the entire chromosome set inherited from one parent is not necessarily lined up on one side with the other chromosome

set lined up on the opposite side. Assume that no more than three homologous pairs are involved. Any of these combinations can occur during alignment at metaphase:

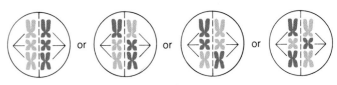

(Here, the brown chromosomes are derived from one parent, and the gold are derived from the other.) These four arrangements could occur with about equal likelihood. The random alignment of homologous chromosomes at metaphase I is a major source of genetic variation in sexually reproducing organisms (Chapter Eleven).

During **anaphase I**, the homologues of each pair separate from each other. By the time anaphase is over, one set of chromosomes is clustered at each of the two spindle poles (Figure 9.15). Each set contains one of each kind of chromosome characteristic of the parent cell. Each chromosome is still in the duplicated form, though; it consists of two sister chromatids.

Anaphase I gives way to telophase and interkinesis. Typically these stages are fleeting, no more than a pause in activity before the final meiotic division. In cells having centrioles, the two centrioles of a pair move to opposite poles. There is no DNA replication between divisions.

Separating the Sister Chromatids

As you have seen, the first meiotic division consists of many activities (pairing and crossing over between homologous chromosomes, gene transcription, separation of homologues). In contrast, the second meiotic division has one overriding function: the separation of sister chromatids of each chromosome. In this respect, meiosis II is just about the same as mitosis (Figure 9.17). Chromosome condensation (if any) proceeds during a brief prophase II. Chromosomes are moved to the spindle equator during metaphase II. And the two chromatids of each chromosome are moved apart, then delivered to opposite spindle poles. Each chromosome set at a spindle pole is haploid; it consists of only half the number of chromosomes that were present in the diploid parent nucleus. But that number consists of one chromosome of each type; it is a complete set of hereditary instructions. Now nuclear envelopes form around each chromosome parcel in telophase II, and chromosomes decondense. Meiosis is completed.

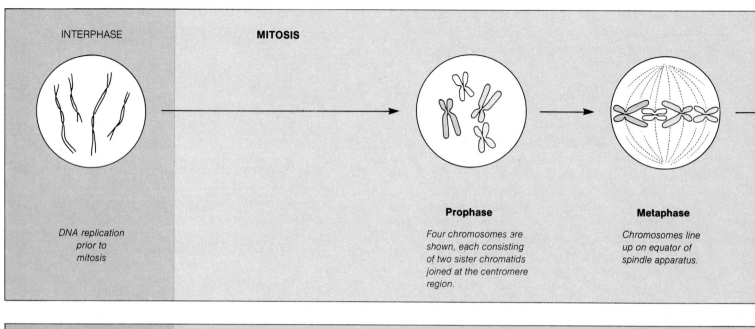

MITOSIS

Prophase

Four chromosomes are shown, each consisting of two sister chromatids joined at the centromere region.

Metaphase

Chromosomes line up on equator of spindle apparatus.

DNA replication prior to mitosis

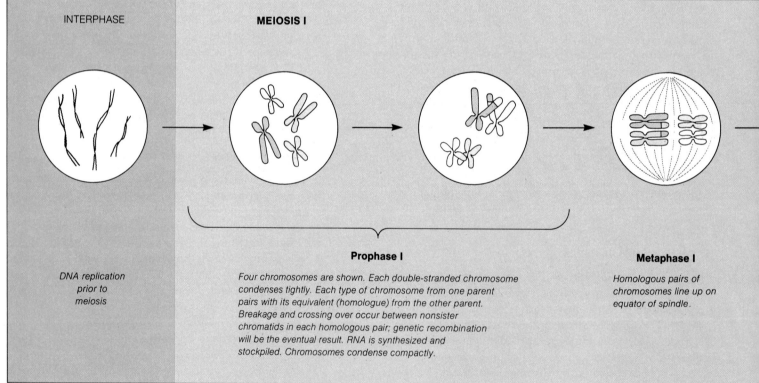

INTERPHASE

MEIOSIS I

Prophase I

Four chromosomes are shown. Each double-stranded chromosome condenses tightly. Each type of chromosome from one parent pairs with its equivalent (homologue) from the other parent. Breakage and crossing over occur between nonsister chromatids in each homologous pair; genetic recombination will be the eventual result. RNA is synthesized and stockpiled. Chromosomes condense compactly.

Metaphase I

Homologous pairs of chromosomes line up on equator of spindle.

DNA replication prior to meiosis

Figure 9.17 Summary of mitosis and meiosis. In these examples, the parent nucleus is diploid, with two chromosome sets (one gold-shaded, one blue-shaded).

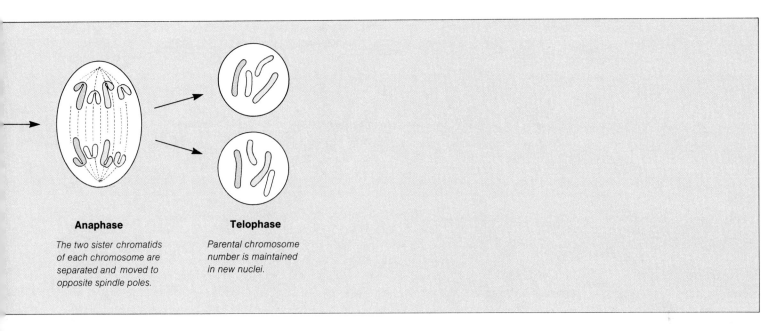

Anaphase

The two sister chromatids
of each chromosome are
separated and moved to
opposite spindle poles.

Telophase

Parental chromosome
number is maintained
in new nuclei.

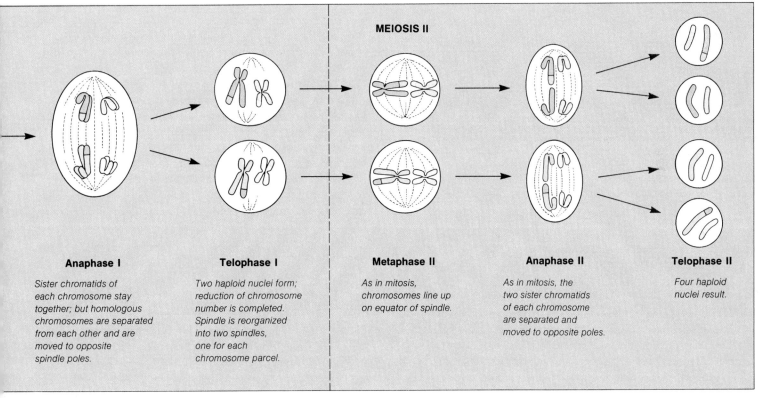

MEIOSIS II

Anaphase I

Sister chromatids of
each chromosome stay
together; but homologous
chromosomes are separated
from each other and are
moved to opposite
spindle poles.

Telophase I

Two haploid nuclei form;
reduction of chromosome
number is completed.
Spindle is reorganized
into two spindles,
one for each
chromosome parcel.

Metaphase II

As in mitosis,
chromosomes line up
on equator of spindle.

Anaphase II

As in mitosis, the
two sister chromatids
of each chromosome
are separated and
moved to opposite poles.

Telophase II

Four haploid
nuclei result.

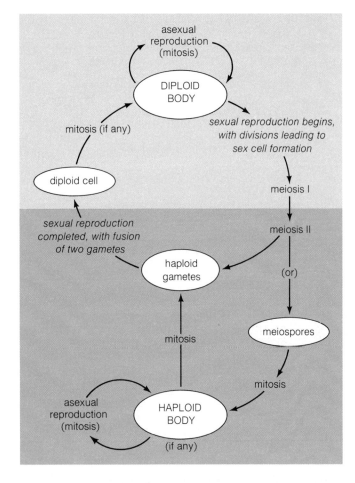

Figure 9.18 Where sexual reproduction and asexual reproduction may occur in life cycles. Dark green defines the haploid stage; light green shading depicts the diploid stage. (After Maurice Margulies)

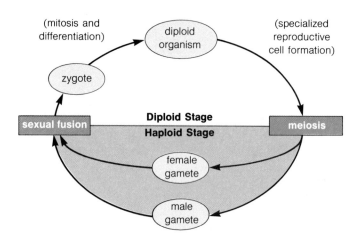

Figure 9.19 Generalized life cycle for animals.

WHERE CELL DIVISIONS OCCUR IN PLANT AND ANIMAL LIFE CYCLES

Prokaryotic fission, mitosis, meiosis—these division mechanisms are the basis of cell reproduction. Each one can also be the basis of reproducing the individual, in the case of single-celled organisms. Mitosis and meiosis can also lead to the formation of new multicelled individuals. Meiosis figures only in *sexual* reproduction. Recall that the two crucial events of sexual reproduction are meiosis (halving the number of chromosome sets for sex cells) and fertilization (doubling the number of chromosome sets in the new individual). In contrast, mitotic cell division (as well as

prokaryotic fission) is considered to be a form of *asexual* reproduction, because sex cells and fertilization are not involved.

Where do sexual and asexual reproduction occur in the life cycles? Figure 9.18 provides a generalized picture. Notice that diploid and haploid bodies can both occur in the same life cycle. This is by far the most common pattern among eukaryotes. Among animals, the diploid body is multicelled and more conspicuous than the haploid body (which is typically no more than a single-celled gamete of microscopic size). Among plants, mitotic cell divisions can intervene between meiosis and gamete formation, then between fertilization and meiosis. The term **alternation of generations** refers to any life cycle in which multicelled haploid bodies alternate with multicelled diploid bodies.

Animal Life Cycles

Figure 9.19 shows a generalized life cycle for animals. Typically, the cycle consists of the formation of haploid male and haploid female gametes, with their subsequent fusion. Gamete formation, or **gametogenesis**, occurs only in special reproductive cells in the male and female. These gametes take part in reproducing the whole diploid organism. Generally, a cell that undergoes meiosis produces four haploid cells. Some or all of these cells then undergo differentiation prior to sexual fusion.

In male animals, gamete formation is called **spermatogenesis** (Figure 9.20). A diploid reproductive cell (spermatogonium) grows in size and becomes a primary spermatocyte. It is a large, immature cell. It undergoes the first meiotic division, which leads to two secondary spermatocytes. Both of these cells undergo the second meiotic division. The result is four haploid spermatids. Each spermatid changes in form, develops a tail, and thereby becomes a **sperm**: the mature haploid male gamete.

Female gamete formation, or **oogenesis**, follows a similar sequence of events (Figure 9.21). However, a major difference is that considerable cytoplasmic substances accumulate in the female reproductive cell. Also, the cells formed during the meiotic divisions are not equal in size or function. A primary oocyte undergoes meiosis I, but one of the resulting cells ends up with nearly all of the cytoplasm. This cell is the secondary oocyte. Following meiosis II, it will become the mature **egg**, or **ovum** (plural, ova). The other cells produced during the meiotic division are called polar bodies. They are extremely small, compared with the ovum, and do not function as gametes.

After the nuclei of male and female gametes fuse, the first cell formed is called the **zygote**. Through mitosis and cytokinesis, the zygote grows and differentiates into a multicelled individual. (For single-celled eukaryotes, of course, the first cell formed *is* the new individual.) At some point, this organism will produce haploid gametes, and a life cycle may be repeated once more.

Plant Life Cycles

Like animal life cycles, plant life cycles include gamete formation and fertilization. This reliance on sexual reproduction probably originated with protistanlike ancestors that gave rise to both plants and animals. Since then, however, plants and animals have gone their separate ways. For most land plants, there is a conspicuous multicelled haploid body as well as a multicelled diploid body.

A pine tree, for example, is a multicelled diploid individual. At some point, some of its cells undergo meiosis. But the cells that form after meiosis are not gametes. They are **meiospores**: haploid cells that divide by mitosis and differentiate into multicelled haploid bodies. Because a pine tree gives rise to meiospores, it is called a **sporophyte** ("spore-producing plant"). In contrast, the haploid body produced by one of its meiospores is called a **gametophyte**: it will be the "gamete-producing plant." Sooner or later, some of *its* cells divide by mitosis and produce cells that do function as gametes.

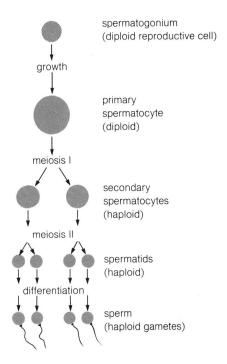

Figure 9.20 Generalized picture of spermatogenesis in male animals.

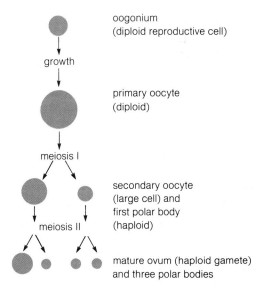

Figure 9.21 Generalized picture of oogenesis in female animals. This sketch is not drawn to the same scale as Figure 9.20. A primary oocyte is *much* larger than a primary spermatocyte.

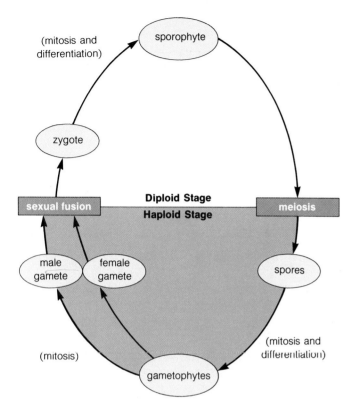

Figure 9.22 Generalized life cycle for complex land plants.

Sporophytes and gametophytes are usually quite different in appearance. Compared to the pine tree, for instance, the pine gametophytes are small. The immature male gametophytes are the *pollen grains* that drift like clouds of dust from tree branches at certain times of year. They house cells that will mature into haploid sperm. The female gametophytes are tiny structures perched on female pine cone scales. They house the cells that will mature into haploid ova. After fertilization, the diploid zygote formed will divide by mitosis and develop into an embryo which, with its protective layers, is called a seed. The seed will germinate and mature into the diploid sporophyte body called the pine tree (Figure 9.22).

The recurring haploid and diploid states in the pine are one example of alternation of generations in land plants. Chapter Thirty-Three will describe the evolutionary development of increasingly dominant sporophyte generations in land plant life cycles, as well as environmental changes that may have fostered them.

PERSPECTIVE

In this chapter, the focus has been on nuclear and cytoplasmic division mechanisms that form the basis of cell reproduction. You have seen that alternating periods of growth and division in individual cells are central to all life cycles, from the simplest to the most complex. In later chapters, the focus will be on cytological and molecular aspects of specific events in the life cycle. When reading through those details, you may find it useful to refer back to the following list of key concepts:

1. DNA has all the hereditary instructions necessary to construct a new cell of a given species. The instructions are encoded in genes: nucleotide sequences that specify particular products, which are used in cell maintenance and growth.

2. Before a cell divides, its DNA is duplicated. This is true of prokaryotes and eukaryotes.

3. When a cell divides, each new cell receives (1) a complete copy of all genes present in the parent cell, and (2) a particular array of cytoplasmic substances and organelles that serve as "start-up machinery" in carrying out hereditary instructions.

4. Prokaryotic cells reproduce asexually, through a form of binary fission. The single prokaryotic DNA molecule is replicated, and one whole molecule ends up in each daughter cell when the parent cell divides at its midsection.

5. Cell reproduction is more complex in eukaryotes. Mitosis and meiosis are two different nuclear division mechanisms. Actual cytoplasmic division (cytokinesis) proceeds at a late stage of these divisions or at some point afterward.

6. Mitosis and meiosis involve (1) the packaging of DNA and many proteins into structures called chromosomes; and (2) microtubular spindles that separate replicated chromosomes during nuclear division.

7. Mitosis is the basis of asexual reproduction of many single-celled eukaryotes, as well as growth in cell number in multicelled eukaryotes.

8. Mitosis *maintains* the parental number of chromosome sets in daughter cells.

9. Most eukaryotes reproduce sexually at some stage of the life cycle. Sexual reproduction requires the formation of gametes (sex cells) followed by fertilization (usually, the fusion of nuclei of two gametes from two different parents). Meiosis is necessary for gamete formation.

10. In a eukaryotic cell, hereditary instructions are divided up among anywhere from two to many hundreds of different chromosomes, which vary in length and shape. A chromosome "set" consists of one of each type of these different chromosomes.

11. A eukaryotic cell can have one or more sets of these various chromosomes. For example, a diploid cell has two sets of morphologically equivalent chromosomes, which are called homologues. (Each set has usually been contributed by a separate parent.)

12. Prior to gamete formation, meiosis *reduces* the parental number of chromosome sets by half in each daughter cell. Each daughter cell is haploid and may function as a gamete. Upon fertilization, the parental number of chromosome sets is restored.

13. Meiosis consists of two nuclear divisions. In the first division, homologous chromosomes (each consisting of two sister chromatids) synapse with their partner, then are separated. In the second division, the two sister chromatids of each chromosome are separated, and one chromatid of each type ends up in each daughter nucleus.

14. Nonsister chromatids can cross over during meiosis, the result being genetic recombination: new combinations of alleles in a chromosome (and, eventually, a new individual). Genetic recombination is a source of tremendous diversity in the form and function of organisms.

Readings

Berrill, N., and G. Karp. 1976. *Development.* New York: McGraw-Hill. Good coverage of gametogenesis and the events of fertilization.

Bonner, J. 1974. *On Development: The Biology of Form.* Cambridge, Massachusetts: Harvard University Press.

Daly, H., J. Doyen, and P. Erlich. 1978. *Introduction to Insect Biology and Diversity.* New York: McGraw-Hill.

Edmunds, L., Jr., and K. Adams. 1981. "Clocked Cell Cycle Clocks." *Science* 211:1002–1013. Major article summarizing research into the cell division cycle. Advanced reading, but the article conveys the excitement of new theories in the making.

Lewin, R. 1981. "Do Chromosomes Cross-Talk?" *Science* 214:1334–1335. Highlights current research and speculations on chromosome organization in the nucleus.

Wolfe, S. 1981. *Biology of the Cell.* Second edition. Belmont, California: Wadsworth. Comprehensive reference text. The chapters on mitosis and meiosis are outstanding in their synthesis and interpretations of myriad investigations into DNA division and cell division.

Review Questions

1. DNA directly or indirectly governs which organic substances occur in a cell. Refer to Figure 9.1, then explain in your own words how it does this.

2. Define three types of DNA division mechanisms. Which do prokaryotes use? Which do eukaryotes use?

3. Compared with prokaryotes, eukaryotes generally have more complex and larger amounts of DNA. Handling all this DNA during cell reproduction requires (1)_____ and (2)_____ .

4. What is a nucleoprotein? During cell construction and maintenance, what form does a nucleoprotein take? Before and during nuclear division, what hapens to it?

5. Does "chromosome" refer to a single (unduplicated) nucleoprotein, or to duplicated nucleoproteins (sister chromatids)?

6. What is the basic function of a mitotic spindle?

7. Name the four main phases of mitosis, and characterize each phase. When does mitosis take place in the cell cycle?

8. When, and in which cells, does meiosis occur? Name the main phases of meiosis.

9. In the nucleus of diploid cells, a pair of morphologically equivalent chromosomes are called _____ .

10. Does crossing over occur during mitosis or meiosis? At what stage does it occur, and what is its significance?

11. Define cytokinesis. Describe what happens when it occurs in an animal cell and in a plant cell.

12. Outline the steps involved in spermatogenesis, then in oogenesis.

13. Distinguish between the sporophyte and the gametophyte phases of some plant life cycles.

10

OBSERVABLE PATTERNS OF INHERITANCE

Figure 10.1 Gregor Mendel, founder of modern genetics. (The Granger Collection, New York)

MENDEL AND THE FIRST FORMULATION OF THE PRINCIPLES OF INHERITANCE

Biology toward the end of the nineteenth century was dominated by talk of Darwin and Wallace's theory of natural selection (Chapter Two). Many biologists were skeptical of whether natural selection of adaptive traits did indeed occur. Nurturing their skepticism was a prevailing notion about the transmission of traits between generations. Sperm from males, eggs from females—these were known to be bridges of inheritance. And in some way, hereditary material from both sperm and egg had to *combine* in order to produce a new individual. At the time, the widely accepted hypothesis was that hereditary material from two parents blended at fertilization, much like cream blending into coffee. This "blending" notion gave little insight into why a distinctive trait, such as freckled skin, can still turn up among generations of nonfreckled offspring. Instead it conjured up pictures of all offspring becoming the homogenized equivalent of *café au lait*.

For example, if blending were the rule, then a herd of white stallions and black mares would produce only gray horses, which thereafter would produce only gray horses. A field of red clover and white clover would give way to pink clover, which thereafter would produce more just like itself. Blending scarcely explained the observable fact that in such populations, not all horses are gray, nor all flowers pink. It was considered a rule anyway. And Darwin had problems on this account, because uniform populations would present no variation whatsoever for selective agents to act upon. That being the case, "evolution" simply could not occur.

But even before the theory of natural selection was made public, evidence concerning the physical basis of inheritance was accumulating in a monastery garden in Brünn, northeast of Vienna. Gregor Mendel, a scholarly, mathematically oriented monk, was beginning to identify rules governing inheritance.

The monastery of St. Thomas was somewhat removed from the European capitals, which were then the centers of scientific inquiry. Yet Mendel was not a man of parochial interests, who simply stumbled by chance onto principles of great import. Having been raised on a farm, he was well aware of agricultural principles and their application. He kept abreast of new breeding experiments and developments described in the available journals. Mendel was a founder of the regional agricultural society. He won several awards for developing improved varieties of fruits and vegetables. After entering the monastery, he spent two years at the University of Vienna, honing his skills in math-

Trait	Dominant Form of Trait in One Parent Plant	× Recessive Form of Trait in Another Parent Plant =	Number of Second-Generation Plants Showing Dominant Form	Number of Second-Generation Plants Showing Recessive Form
seed shape	round	wrinkled	5,474	1,850
seed color	yellow	green	6,022	2,001
pod shape	round, inflated	wrinkled, constricted	882	299
pod color	green	yellow	428	152
flower color	purple	white	705	224
flower position	axial (along stem)	terminal (at tip)	651	207
stem length	tall (6–7 feet)	dwarf (¾–1½ feet)	787	277
Average ratio for all of the traits tested:			3:1	

a

Jean M. Labat/Ardea, London

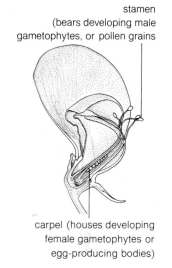

stamen
(bears developing male gametophytes, or pollen grains

carpel (houses developing female gametophytes or egg-producing bodies)

b

Figure 10.2 (**a**) Results from Mendel's series of seven monohybrid cross experiments with the garden pea. (**b**) Flower from a garden pea (*Pisum sativum*), sectioned to show the location of stamens (the male reproductive organs) and the carpel (the female reproductive organ).

ematics. During those years he was influenced by Franz Unger, a botany professor. Unger was of a mind that plant diversity had not always existed, but had come about gradually by natural processes. Shortly after his university training, Mendel began a series of experiments on the nature of plant diversity. Through his combined talents in plant breeding and mathematics (as yet not considered even remotely relevant to plant breeding), he perceived patterns in the emergence of traits from one generation to the next.

Mendel's Experimental Approach

For his experiments, Mendel chose different varieties of the garden pea plant (Figure 10.2). This sexually reproducing plant is self-fertilizing. Both male and female gametophytes (the gamete-producing bodies) develop in the same flower, so fertilization can occur between eggs and sperm from the same flower. But the garden pea also lends itself to **cross-fertilization**: gametes from one individual can undergo sexual fusion with gametes from another. To prevent a plant from self-fertilizing, Mendel opened flower buds and removed the structures bearing the male gametophytes (the pollen-bearing stamens shown in Figure 10.2). Then he brushed pollen from another plant on the "castrated" flower buds, and cross-fertilization followed.

Recall, from Chapter Two, that the scientific method depends on trained judgment in selecting what appears to be relevant from a potentially immense range of observations on a given subject. Mendel didn't try to track the inheritance patterns of all traits all at once. Initially he concentrated on one trait at a time, and—more telling—on crossing plants with clearly contrasting forms of the trait.

For the first two years of his studies, Mendel obtained plants that were distinctive in one or more traits. For example, some of these plants were white-flowering; others were purple-flowering. He allowed these plants to self-fertilize for several generations. In this way, he made sure that the plants to be used in the actual experiments were **true-breeding strains**: all self-fertilized offspring would display the same form of the trait as their parent. (Thus white-flowering plants would yield only white-flowering offspring, not purple, pink, or any other color.)

When parents that are true-breeding for different forms of one or more traits are crossed, the offspring are called hybrids. When one trait only is being studied, the cross is known as a **monohybrid cross**. When two traits at a time are studied, it is a **dihybrid cross**. Mendel performed both kinds of hybrid crosses among his carefully bred experimental groups. He tracked the course of inheritance through several generations, using contrasting traits as the observable—and quantifiable—results of hereditary mechanisms hidden from view. These contrasting traits are listed in Figure 10.2.

It will be useful to retrace a few of Mendel's experiments. The conclusions he drew from them have turned out to apply, with some modification, to all sexually reproducing organisms.

The Concept of Segregation

Mendel's first set of experiments were monohybrid crosses. In one cross, he transferred pollen from a true-breeding purple-flowered plant to a true-breeding white-flowered plant. The cross-fertilized parent produced seeds that were planted the following season. All of the seeds grew into plants bearing *only* purple flowers.

What had happened to the white-flower trait? Had it disappeared? Mendel allowed the purple-flowered plants of this first generation to undergo *self*-fertilization rather

than cross them with new plants. (Can you guess why?) Seeds from the self-fertilized plants were harvested, then planted the following season. When the second-generation plants matured, some had white flowers! The white-flower trait had not been lost. For some reason, it simply didn't get expressed in the first-generation offspring.

Here you might make note of a few symbols that have become entrenched in genetics. By convention, P stands for the parent generation. F_1 means first-generation offspring. F_2 means the offspring of F_1 individuals, and so on. (The F stands for the Latin *filius*, meaning son.)

For all of the monohybrid crosses Mendel conducted, results were much the same. One of the contrasting traits seemed to disappear in F_1 plants, only to show up again in some F_2 plants. Mendel called this form of the trait **recessive**, for in some way it was masked by the expression of the contrasting form. In these experiments, at least, the contrasting form of the trait was **dominant**, or fully expressed, in all hybrid F_1 plants.

Mendel arrived at an explanation for the results. First he assumed that a hybrid must have two "units" of hereditary material for each trait. One unit has been transmitted to it by the sperm, the other by the egg. Each unit can specify either the dominant or recessive form of the trait, but not both. Second, Mendel assumed that *units of heredity do not blend together, but remain distinct entities throughout an individual's life.* Then, during gamete formation, the two units of a pair are *separated* from each other and end up in different gametes. Let A stand generally for the dominant unit of a pair, and a stand for the recessive. Then true-breeding parents showing the dominant trait can be designated AA, and true-breeding parents showing the recessive trait, aa. Following Mendel's reasoning, the units are separated and end up in separate gametes:

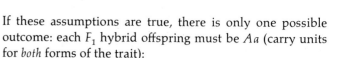

If these assumptions are true, there is only one possible outcome: each F_1 hybrid offspring must be Aa (carry units for *both* forms of the trait):

$$(\text{fertilization}) \quad \textcircled{A} \times \textcircled{a} = \boxed{Aa}$$

On the basis of this reasoning, Mendel formulated a basic principle. It is still considered a useful starting point for a discussion of the nature of inheritance:

Mendelian principle of segregation. In sexually reproducing organisms, each kind of hereditary unit comes in pairs. The two units of each pair segregate from each other and end up in separate gametes.

Testcrosses: Support for the Concept

Mendel gained support for his concept of segregation through a different kind of experimental cross. In a **testcross**, first-generation hybrids are crossed back to the parent known to be true-breeding for the recessive trait being studied. For example, purple-flowering F_1 individuals were backcrossed to the parental white-flowering plant. If Mendel's idea were not correct (if the recessive unit had somehow lost its identity when combined with the dominant unit), then only the dominant form of the trait would show up in the second-generation offspring:

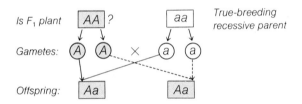

If Mendel's idea were correct, though, there would have to be about as many recessive as dominant individuals in the offspring from the testcross:

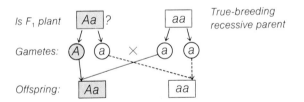

This is exactly what happened in the testcrosses. About half of the F_2 offspring were purple-flowering (Aa) and half were white-flowering (aa).

Current Terms for Mendelian Units of Inheritance

Since Mendel's time, the process by which segregation occurs has become better understood. Studies at the molecular and cellular levels have yielded insights into the mechanisms of meiosis (described in the preceding chap-

ter). As you might imagine, the terminology used to describe these events has also evolved, to the extent that Mendel's view of the physical units of inheritance would now be expressed the following way:

1. Distinct units of heredity—**genes**—are the physical basis for all traits of an individual.

2. Each gene has its own **locus**, a particular location on the chromosome.

3. A gene for any given trait may occur in one of two or more alternative forms, known as **alleles**.

4. Diploid body cells have two alleles for each trait, on two separate chromosomes (the homologues derived from two parents). The two alleles at a given locus constitute a **gene pair**.

5. A gene pair may consist of identical or different alleles. For instance, both alleles for flower color may specify white. Then again, they may specify alternative forms. (One may specify purple, the other white.)

6. If the two alleles of a gene pair are identical, the individual is a **homozygote** for the trait. If they are not identical, the individual is a **heterozygote** for the trait.

7. In heterozygotes, expression of one allele of a gene pair may mask expression of the other (it's the dominant form of the trait). Even so, *both* alleles retain their physical identity throughout the individual's life.

8. A **dominant trait** is one that is observable in heterozygotes.

9. A **recessive trait** is one that is observable *only* in homozygotes.

10. The term **genotype** refers to an individual's genetic makeup. It may mean a single gene pair or the sum total of genes in the individual.

11. The term **phenotype** refers to an individual's observable traits (its structure, physiology, and behavior).

Probability: Predicting the Outcome of Crosses

In his numerous monohybrid crosses, Mendel carefully *counted* and *recorded* how many offspring showed the dominant form of a trait and how many showed the recessive. Certain numerical ratios become apparent through this quantitative approach. And these ratios provided strong evidence for the discrete nature of hereditary units.

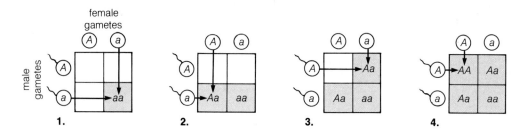

Figure 10.4 Punnett-square method of predicting the probable ratio of traits that will show up in offspring of self-fertilizing individuals known to be heterozygous (*Aa*) for a trait. The circles represent female gametes, or eggs; circles with "tails" represent male gametes, or sperm. The letters inside gametes represent the dominant or recessive form of the trait being tracked. Each square depicts the genotype of one kind of offspring.

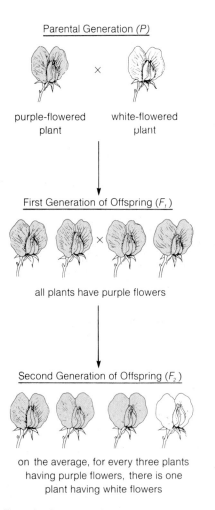

Figure 10.3 Example of a pattern that emerged regularly in Mendel's crosses between true-breeding parents differing only in one contrasting trait (here, flower color). All first-generation plants showed the dominant form of the trait. On the average, though, three of every four second-generation plants showed the dominant form—and one showed the recessive.

On the average, for every three F_2 plants showing the dominant form of the trait, there was one showing the recessive. Figure 10.3 gives an example of this pattern from the monohybrid crosses for flower color. How could this kind of 3:1 phenotypic ratio arise?

Given his knowledge of mathematics, Mendel was able to come up with an explanation. He began with the assumption that gametes (sperm and egg) combine at random—by chance—at fertilization. Hence *which* combinations of alleles will occur among the offspring can be predicted by certain rules of probability, which apply to chance events. **Probability** simply means the number of times that an outcome of some event *will* happen, divided by the number of times it *could* happen.

There are several ways of predicting the probable ratio of traits in second-generation offspring of monohybrid crosses. The easiest to understand is the **Punnett-square method**, which is shown in Figure 10.4. Assume, as Mendel did, that each F_1 plant carries one dominant (*A*) and one recessive (*a*) allele, and that those alleles end up in separate gametes. Then two kinds of gametes must be produced, in equal proportions: half will be *A*, and half will be *a*. This is true for both sperm and eggs. Given that any sperm is as likely to fertilize one egg as another, there are four combinations possible in a monohybrid cross:

Possible Event:	*Probable Outcome:*
sperm *A* meets egg *A*	$\frac{1}{4}AA$ offspring
sperm *A* meets egg *a*	$\frac{1}{4}Aa$
sperm *a* meets egg *A*	$\frac{1}{4}Aa$ or $\frac{1}{2}Aa$
sperm *a* meets egg *a*	$\frac{1}{4}aa$

As you can see, three outcomes are possible in the second-generation offspring of a monohybrid cross: $\frac{1}{4}AA$, $\frac{1}{2}Aa$, and $\frac{1}{4}aa$. By simple addition, it becomes clear that the dominant allele will probably end up in $\frac{3}{4}$ of the offspring

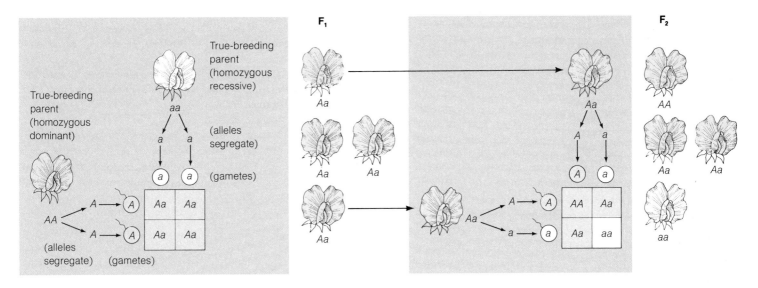

Figure 10.5 Results from one of Mendel's monohybrid crosses, with the Punnett-square diagrams showing the possible allelic combinations in first- and second-generation offspring.

$(\frac{1}{4}AA + \frac{1}{2}Aa)$; and that the recessive allele will end up in $\frac{1}{4}$ of them. That is a probable phenotypic ratio of 3:1.

Figure 10.5 shows the results of one of Mendel's crosses, using the Punnett-square method. Figure 10.6 shows how the same method can be used in predicting the outcome of testcrosses.

It's important to keep in mind that Mendel's ratios weren't *exactly* 3:1. (See, for example, the numerical results in Figure 10.2.) To understand why, flip a coin a few times. We all know that a coin is just as likely to end up heads as tails. But often it ends up heads, or tails, several times in a row. Only when you flip the coin many times can you be assured that the actual outcome will be close to that predicted. When only a few events are observed, the actual ratio may differ considerably from the predicted one.

Mendel succeeded largely because he crossed hundreds of plants and kept track of thousands of offspring, rather than restricting his experiments to a few plants as others had done. Almost certainly his understanding of probability kept him from being confused by minor deviations from his predicted results.

The Concept of Independent Assortment

By analyzing the ratios of phenotypes from his monohybrid crosses, Mendel made some remarkably astute observations about what must be occurring at the genotypic level.

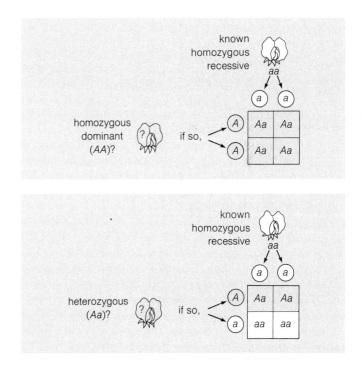

Figure 10.6 Punnett-square method of predicting the outcomes of a testcross between an individual known to be homozygous recessive for a trait (here, white flower color) and an individual that shows the dominant form of the trait. If the individual of unknown genotype is homozygous dominant, all offspring will show the dominant form of the trait. If the individual is heterozygous, about half the offspring will show the recessive form.

He was actually observing some results of homologous chromosome separation during meiosis, although he didn't know about chromosomes *or* meiosis. At that time nobody did. He guessed, correctly, that the two alleles of each gene pair are segregated from each other and distributed to separate gametes.

Mendel extended this concept to the dihybrid cross, in which the alleles of *two* gene pairs are tracked simultaneously. For instance, in one experiment he started with true-breeding purple-flowered *tall* plants and white-flowered *dwarf* plants. Like the purple-flower allele, the "tall" allele was dominant. Hence Mendel anticipated that all of the first-generation offspring would be purple-flowered and tall. In this he was correct. However, what would turn up in the second-generation hybrid offspring? Mendel speculated that the results would reflect one of two outcomes. They would show that the hereditary units derived from each parent either traveled together into gametes or segregated into gametes independently.

Let A and B represent the two dominant alleles for flower color and height. Let a and b represent their recessive alleles. Gametes from a homozygous dominant ($AABB$) parent would have to be AB; those from the homozygous recessive ($aabb$) would have to be ab. A cross between these plants would produce all $AaBb$ offspring. Now assume these first-generation plants produce gametes of their own. If genes travel together as a group, only *two* gene combinations would be possible in those gametes: AB (originally from one parent) and ab (originally from the other).

If, however, the two genes being donated by a parent segregated independently of each other, four gene combinations would be possible in sperm as well as in eggs:

$$\tfrac{1}{4}AB \quad \tfrac{1}{4}Ab \quad \tfrac{1}{4}aB \quad \tfrac{1}{4}ab$$

By simple multiplication (four kinds of sperm times four kinds of eggs), you can see that there are *sixteen possible combinations* in second-generation dihybrid plants!

Figure 10.7 shows the number of plants that could be homozygous dominant and heterozygous for one or both of the two genes being tracked. It also shows the number of plants that could be homozygous recessive for one or both of the genes. When we add up the combinations, we get $\tfrac{9}{16}$ tall purple-flowered, $\tfrac{3}{16}$ dwarf purple-flowered, $\tfrac{3}{16}$ tall white-flowered, and $\tfrac{1}{16}$ dwarf white-flowered plants. That is a phenotypic ratio of 9:3:3:1.

In all of Mendel's dihybrid crosses, results were close to this ratio. It is characteristic of dihybrid second-generation offspring in which two gene pairs exhibiting dominance are involved. On the basis of these results, Mendel proposed a second principle of inheritance:

Mendelian principle of independent assortment. Genes controlling different traits are segregated independently of one another into gametes.

When independent assortment does occur, the potential variety can be staggering. In a simple monohybrid cross, only three genotypes are possible (AA, Aa, and aa). In general, every additional gene locus involved in a cross between heterozygous parents multiplies the number of genotypic combinations by 3. Thus a dihybrid cross can yield nine genotypes; a trihybrid cross can yield twenty-seven. In crosses between parents differing in ten genes, there are almost 60,000 possible genotypic combinations. When the parents differ in fifteen genes, the possible combinations exceed 14 million!

It is important to keep in mind, though, that independent assortment does not always occur. Later studies with different kinds of organisms revealed that certain genes are inherited *as a group*, just as Mendel's alternative hypothesis partly suggested. You will read about this so-called gene linkage in the next chapter.

The results from Mendel's experiments clearly suggested that hereditary material comes in units that retain their physical identity throughout an individual's life. In 1865 Mendel reported the experimental results on which this conclusion was based before the Brünn Society for the Study of Natural Science. His report made no impact whatsoever. The following year his paper was published. Apparently it was read by few and understood by no one. Remember that Mendel was going up against the well-entrenched blending theory of inheritance. His mathematical analysis of traits probably would not have made sense to anybody but mathematicians—who probably would not have had the least bit of interest in pea plants.

Worse yet, Mendel later experimented with hawkweed. This plant repaid his interest by producing only the dominant form of certain traits in both the first and second generations! He did not know, as we do now, that hawkweed seeds can form without fertilization of gametes; diploid cells in the female reproductive organs can give rise directly to another plant having the exact same genetic makeup as its parent. Mendel must have been bitterly disappointed by this seeming refutation of his conceptual work. By 1871 he became an abbot of the monastery, and his experiments gave way to administrative tasks. He died in 1884, the founder of but not a participant in modern genetics.

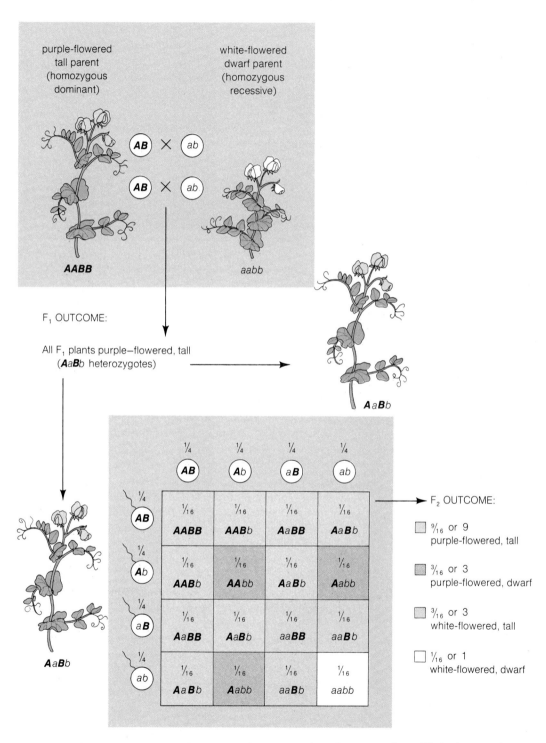

Figure 10.7 Results from Mendel's dihybrid cross between true-breeding parent plants differing in two traits (flower color and height). Here, *A* and *a* represent the dominant and recessive alleles for flower color. *B* and *b* represent the dominant and recessive alleles for height. On the average, the phenotypic combinations in the *F₂* generation occur in a 9:3:3:1 ratio.

Figure 10.8 Incomplete dominance at one gene locus. Red-flowering and white-flowering homozygous snapdragons produce pink-flowering plants in the first generation. The red allele (shown here as *R* for dominant and *r* for recessive) is only partially dominant in the heterozygous state.

VARIATIONS ON MENDEL'S THEMES

Dominance Relations and Multiple Alleles

The second-generation phenotypic ratios that Mendel obtained from his monohybrid crosses (3:1) and dihybrid crosses (9:3:3:1) were fairly clear-cut. The reason is that the dominance pattern *for the traits he happened to study* arises through segregation of a fully dominant allele from a fully recessive allele in heterozygotes. Since Mendel's time, studies have shown that the possibilities are much more interesting than these cases of "all-or-nothing" dominance would suggest.

For instance, when homozygous red-flowered and white-flowered snapdragons are crossed, the first-generation plants all have *pink* flowers. Without further tests, this outcome might seem to imply a blending of hereditary material in offspring. However, cross-fertilization between first-generation individuals will yield these phenotypes: $\frac{1}{4}$ red, $\frac{1}{2}$ pink, and $\frac{1}{4}$ white (Figure 10.8). This is an example of **incomplete dominance**, in which the activity of a so-called dominant allele is not completely able to mask the expression of a recessive partner. Apparently one "red" allele is not enough to form sufficient pigment to make the flowers appear red, as two red alleles can do in homozygous dominants.

Incomplete dominance doesn't refute the concept of segregation. Rather, it shows that phenotypic variations can arise within the framework of Mendelian inheritance patterns.

As another example, the blue Andalusian chicken is a phenotypic outcome of a cross between homozygous white-feathered and homozygous black-feathered parent birds. Neither the black nor the white allele is dominant. Both alleles are expressed in a mosaic color pattern that appears blue because of the way it refracts light (Figure 10.9). The pattern is an example of **codominance**, in which the characteristics of *both* phenotypes appear.

Dominance relations can also exist in a **multiple allele system**. The term refers to all the alternatives possible at a given gene locus for a population of organisms. For instance, a multiple allele system exists for the *ABO blood group locus* on a human chromosome. This system has several alleles, with three being the most common: I^A, I^B, and i. Alleles I^A and I^B are codominant when paired with each other. Allele i is recessive when paired with I^A or I^B. This means that four phenotypes are possible based on these six genotypic combinations:

A (either $I^A I^A$ or $I^A i$)   AB ($I^A I^B$)

B (either $I^B I^B$ or $I^B i$)   O (*ii*)

Alleles I^A and I^B at the ABO locus code for enzymes that attach certain substances to human red blood cells. The substances act as *antigens* (they elicit a defense response when they enter the bloodstream of another individual of unlike blood type). Their invasion triggers the production or mobilization of molecules called *antibodies,* which chemically combine with specific antigens and thereby inactivate them (Chapter Twenty-Four). The body's ability to recognize and reject incompatible substances has been used to identify blood types in humans. Such identification is vital for individuals requiring blood transfusions. Blood of the wrong type can cause clumping as well as bursting of red blood cells. The outcome can be fever, jaundice, and tissue damage.

It happens that type A persons always have antibodies that act against type B antigens (Figure 10.10). Hence a sample of their blood will cause clumping (agglutination)

Figure 10.9 Codominance at one gene locus. A white-feathered and a black-feathered homozygous parent can produce blue Andalusian offspring. Some feather areas are fine mosaics of black and white, which appear to be blue because of the way they refract light. Neither allele is dominant; both phenotypes are expressed.

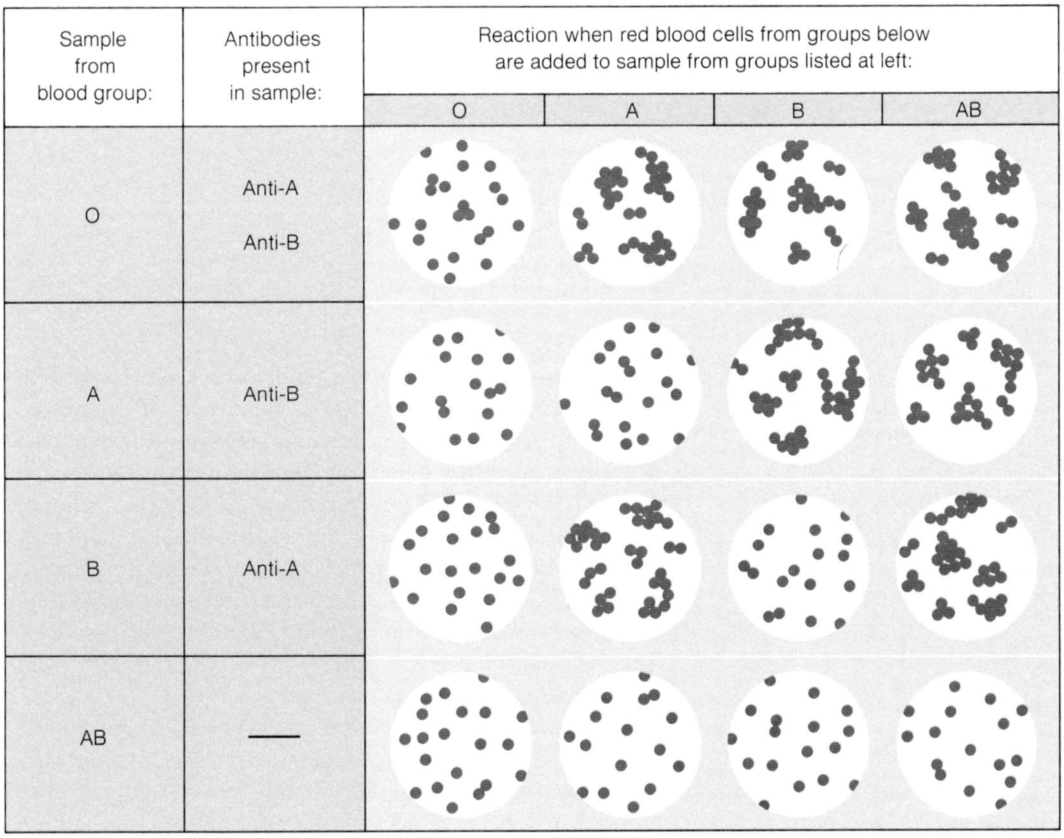

Sample from blood group:	Antibodies present in sample:	Reaction when red blood cells from groups below are added to sample from groups listed at left:			
		O	A	B	AB
O	Anti-A Anti-B				
A	Anti-B				
B	Anti-A				
AB	—				

Figure 10.10 Agglutination responses in drops of blood of type O, A, B, and AB, when mixed with blood samples arising from the same and different genotypes. (F. Ayala and J. Kiger, *Modern Genetics,* © 1980 Benjamin / Cummings)

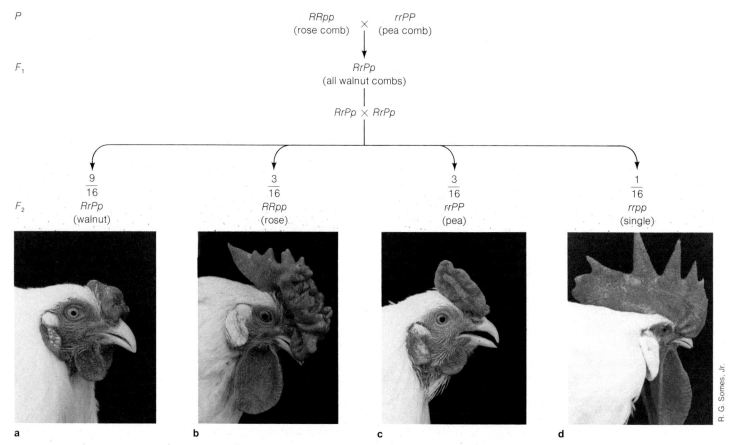

P   RRpp   ×   rrPP
      (rose comb)   (pea comb)

F_1 RrPp
      (all walnut combs)

      RrPp × RrPp

$\frac{9}{16}$ $\frac{3}{16}$ $\frac{3}{16}$ $\frac{1}{16}$

F_2 RrPp   RRpp   rrPP   rrpp
    (walnut)   (rose)   (pea)   (single)

a   b   c   d

Figure 10.11 Interaction between two gene pairs affecting the same trait in domestic breeds of chickens. The initial cross is between a Wyandotte (with a rose comb on the crest of its head) and a brahma (with a pea comb). With complete dominance at the gene locus for pea comb and at the gene locus for rose comb, the products of these two nonallelic genes interact and give walnut combs (**a**). With complete recessiveness at both loci, the products interact and give rise to single combs (**d**).

of type B and type AB blood cells. Similarly, a type B person has antibodies that react against type A antigens; and this leads to clumping of type A and type AB blood cells. A type AB person has neither antibody. Thus type AB individuals can receive blood from any donor. Type O red blood cells have low amounts of A and B antibodies and can be given in small volumes to anyone without adverse effects. However, the type O individual can receive only type O blood.

Variable Expression of Single Genes

It was Mendel's genius to limit his studies to dominant and recessive traits that were always the same in offspring—purple *or* white flowers, round *or* wrinkled peas, tall *or* short

stems. However, some genes are not always expressed with such fidelity in the individual's phenotype. "Penetrance" means the proportion of individuals who show the expected phenotype. A fully penetrant gene is always expressed. An incompletely penetrant gene may be expressed phenotypically in some individuals but not in others. A gene may also vary in the *degree* to which it is expressed in different individuals, or even different parts of the same individual. This aspect of gene action is called "variable expressivity." The resulting phenotype differs, to varying degrees, from one individual to the next.

For example, *Huntington's chorea* is a fatal human genetic disorder. Afflicted persons first start to twitch involuntarily in different body regions. The nervous system becomes affected in ways that destroy physical and mental ability;

Figure 10.12 A rare albino rattlesnake. Albinos show an absence of or marked reduction in melanin pigment formation. There are several different forms of albinism, which arise from different gene interactions. Normal coloration depends on the conversion of protein and the amino acid tyrosine to small, melanin-containing particles. Several enzyme-mediated steps are needed for the conversion. In *true albinos*, epistatic genes block expression of the gene coding for tyrosinase, the first enzyme needed. Without tyrosinase, no pigment whatsoever can form. At least six other epistatic blocks can occur along the conversion route. If they occur at later steps, slight amounts of pigment still form and impart some color to the individual.

death follows. The mutant gene responsible for Huntington's chorea is dominant but shows variable expressivity, in that the phenotypic disorders can begin at any age. The mutant gene is incompletely penetrant, because the disease does not show up in all afflicted persons, who may die of old age or other causes before its onset.

Penetrance and variable expressivity are dictated by genetic factors, environmental factors, or both. They are also influenced by interactions between gene pairs, in ways that will now be described.

Interactions Between Gene Pairs

Until now, we have been concerned primarily with phenotypic expression of the single gene pair. You might be left with the impression that phenotype is a fine mosaic of non-overlapping traits, arising individually from nonoverlapping gene pairs. However, even though a single gene pair may have a key effect on some trait, it doesn't have exclu-sive dominion over any trait. Most genes act in concert with others to produce some effect on phenotype.

Two kinds of interactions can be traced to modifier genes and epistatic genes. A **modifier gene** modifies the phenotypic expression of other genes. An **epistatic gene** interferes with or prevents the expression of others. For example, W. Bateson and R. Punnett discovered that comb shapes in poultry are produced by different allelic combinations of two pairs of genes. In a cross between a rose-comb Wyandotte chicken and a pea-comb brahma chicken, the combs of the first-generation offspring were neither rose-shaped nor pea-shaped. All showed an entirely new phenotype, dubbed walnut comb (Figure 10.11). Crosses between first-generation individuals produced second-generation phenotypes in a 9:3:3:1 ratio, as Mendelian genetics would predict. But in some of the second-generation individuals, an entirely different phenotype—the single comb—emerged! In this case, each gene pair acts as a modifier of the expression of the other.

Modifier genes and epistatic genes are known to influence coat color in mice and other mammals. Four of the genes identified so far help control the type, distribution, and amount of *melanin* (a brown-black pigment molecule) in a given hair or body region. The combination of alleles at the first two gene loci is the basis for coat color. However, the allelic combinations at the other two can modify the *degree* to which the first two are expressed. They give rise to variations in how much pigment is actually produced. This leads to variations in coat-color intensity, which can range from light to dark.

The third gene is epistatic to both of the first two coat-color genes. The homozygous recessive condition gives rise to one form of *albinism*, a phenotype arising from an absence or near-absence of melanin. True albino mammals have white hair, light skin, and red or pink eyes. (With absorptive pigment absent from the retina, red light is reflected from blood vessels in the eye.) Albinism also occurs among birds, amphibians, fishes, and reptiles. Figure 10.12 shows an albino rattlesnake.

Multiple Effects of Single Genes

Since Mendel's time, studies have also shown that a single gene can exert several effects on seemingly unrelated aspects of an individual's phenotype. This aspect of gene expression is known as **pleiotropy**.

Sickle-cell anemia is an example of pleiotropic effects. The red oxygen-carrying pigment in the blood of most adult humans is hemoglobin A, or HbA. Some individuals carry a variant form known as HbS. It results from a single substitution of one amino acid (valine) for another one (glutamate) in the hemoglobin molecule. The variant form can still carry oxygen. But when HbS molecules give up their oxygen cargo to other cells in the body, they interlock chemically with one another. They actually stack up like long, rigid poles. This causes the red blood cells to become distorted into "sickle" shapes (Figure 10.13). Deformed cells clump together in capillaries (blood vessels having tiny diameters). They block oxygen movement into the fluid-filled spaces between cells that the capillaries are supposed to service and they block carbon dioxide removal from the cells. The impaired gas transfers cause severe damage to many internal organs and tissues. The one normal allele of heterozygotes (HbA/HbS) is fully functional, so heterozygotes show few disease symptoms even though a portion of their blood cells are sickled. It is the homozygous recessive who shows serious phenotypic consequences.

Environmental Effects on Phenotype

We have looked at some of the ways in which phenotype can be altered through interactions between alleles and between genes at different loci. One more factor has profound effects on phenotype, and that is the environment. Genes provide the chemical messages for growth and development. But neither growth nor development can proceed without environmental contributions to the living form.

Earlier chapters pointed out the kinds of external environmental factors—water, ions, food, suitable temperature—that affect the functioning of organisms. Here we can give examples of variations in the phenotype of individuals confronted with variations in the environment.

Consider the effect of external temperature on the coat color in Siamese cats (Figure 10.14). In these animals, the main pigment molecule is a brown-black form of melanin. Melanin formation begins when the amino acid tyrosine undergoes successive modifications into a large molecule that contains repeating units of the pigment. Each step along the way must be catalyzed by a specific enzyme. One of these enzymes is tyrosinase. One allele of the gene locus coding for tyrosinase produces a heat-sensitive form of the enzyme. In cats homozygous for the mutant allele, dark fur occurs in the relatively cool extremities (paws, ears, tail, nose). But light fur is present on warmer body parts, where the enzyme is less active.

The water buttercup (*Ranunculus aquatilis*) provides another example of environmental effects on phenotype. This plant grows in shallow ponds. Some of its leaves develop underwater. The submerged leaves are finely divided, compared with the leaves growing in air. When a leaf-bearing stem is half in and half out of the water, its leaves display both phenotypes (Figure 10.15). Thus the genes responsible for leaf shape produce very different phenotypes when external conditions are different.

The internal environment also gives rise to variations in gene expression. For example, some humans show *polydactyly* (the presence of extra digits in sets of fingers, toes, or both). As the human embryo develops, a dominant allele controls how many bone sets will form within the paddlelike appendages destined to become hands and feet. Expression of this allele can vary, depending on physical conditions in the embryo's internal environment. Some carriers of the dominant allele end up with five-fingered hands but six-toed feet; others have five-toed feet but six-

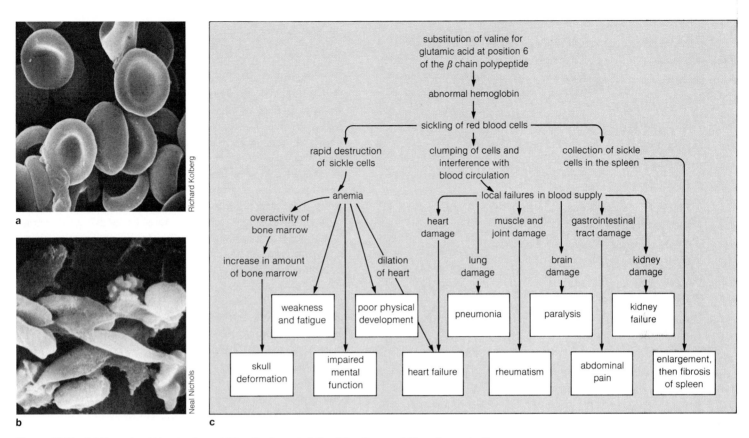

a

b

c

Figure 10.13 (**a**) Normal red blood cells and (**b**) cells characteristic of the disease sickle-cell anemia. Because of their abnormal, asymmetrical shape, sickle cells do not flow smoothly through fine blood vessels. They pile up in clumps that block blood flow. The tissues served by the blood vessels become starved for oxygen and nutrients even as they become saturated with waste products. (**c**) Possible pleiotropic effects in sickle-cell homozygotes. (After Neel and Schull, in *Genetics,* Second edition. Copyright © 1976, Monroe W. Strickberger, Macmillan Publishing Co., Inc.)

Figure 10.14 Environmental effect on phenotype in the Siamese cat. In these animals, fur on the paws, ears, and nose is darker than on the rest of the body. These regions normally are cooler than the main body. Some cats are homozygous recessive for a key gene involved in the formation of the dark pigment melanin. The enzyme produced by this recessive allele is heat-sensitive: it is less active at warmer temperatures. Hence the lighter fur color on warmer body parts.

Figure 10.15 Variable expressivity resulting from variation in the external environment. Leaves of the water buttercup (*Ranunculus aquatilis*) show dramatic phenotypic variation, depending on whether they grow underwater or above it. This variation occurs even in the same leaf if it develops half in and half out of water. (Reprinted with permission of Macmillan Publishing Co. from *Development in Flowering Plants* by John G. Torrey. Copyright © 1967 by John G. Torrey)

fingered hands. For others, the number of fingers is different on their two hands, and/or the number of toes is different on their two feet (Figure 10.16).

Examples of this sort should not lead you to believe that interactions between genes and the environment are always clear-cut. Most often, environmental effects are pervasive in ways that deny analysis. Even in the case of identical twins (which arise from division of a single fertilized egg), the intrauterine environment introduces variable effects. At the very least, twin embryos occupy different positions in space, and their bodies are oriented differently. Also, their attachment sites to the mother and the nature of their connections to the maternal bloodstream cannot be identical. These and a multitude of individually small environmental effects no doubt influence their phenotypic potential in different ways even before birth.

Finally, gene expression shifts with changes in the organism itself. Think about how paddlelike buds of some animal embryos are transformed into sets of fingers and sets of toes. Some of the cells making up tissues over the bone sets in each "paddle" seem to die on cue, so that the bone sets become separated from one another as individual fingers and toes. For all such specialized cells of multicelled organisms, what we call *aging* is really a final developmental stage in gene expression. Profound cellular changes are known to be occurring through alterations in enzyme ac-

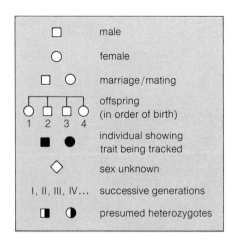

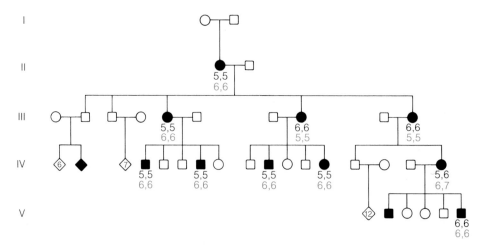

Figure 10.16 Pedigree of polydactyly, showing variable expressivity of the dominant allele for the trait. The phenotype of female I is uncertain; but she probably was polydactylous. The number of digits on each hand is shown in black numerals, the number on each foot is shown in blue. (The boxed inset explains some of the symbols used in constructing pedigree diagrams.)

tivities. These alterations in turn are probably occurring through changes in the activities of genes coding for the enzymes themselves. What transpires in the internal environment to set the pace of development and aging? That we do not know, although Chapter Twenty-Eight looks at some interesting possibilities. For now, the general point to keep in mind is this:

Throughout an individual's life, gene expression is influenced by varying conditions in the internal and external environments.

Continuous and Discontinuous Variation

The traits Mendel studied would now be called examples of **discontinuous variation**: phenotypes fell into one or another of a few clearly distinguishable classes. By observing the results of simple genetic crosses, it was possible to distinguish even heterozygotes as being of one genotype or another. Such differences in phenotype were important in Mendel's work, for they were the only markers he could use in identifying and tracking genotypes. You might say that his studies were *qualitative* in focus, because differences could be established by simple observation, without precise measurements.

However, most of the phenotypic differences in any population are not qualitative. For example, not all humans can be readily classed as tall *or* short, fat *or* thin, and so forth. In most traits, humans and other organisms show **continuous variation**: small degrees of phenotypic variation occur over a more or less continuous range. Measurements of such small differences must be *quantitative,* requiring precise measurements of individuals of the population. The term **quantitative inheritance** refers to the transmission of traits showing continuous variation.

H. Nilsson-Ehle, R. Emerson, and E. East were among the first to develop the idea that quantitative inheritance arises through the additive influence of three or more gene pairs affecting the same trait. For instance, human skin color ranges through hues of blacks, browns, and whites. Human skin color is known to be influenced by a number of similarly acting genes at different loci. These genes control the type, distribution, and amount of melanin pigment in the skin. Their effect is roughly additive, with the intensity of skin pigmentation being determined by the total number of alleles active at all the different loci. Together they act as **polygenes**, with the small effects of each producing quantitative variations in some trait (Figure 10.17).

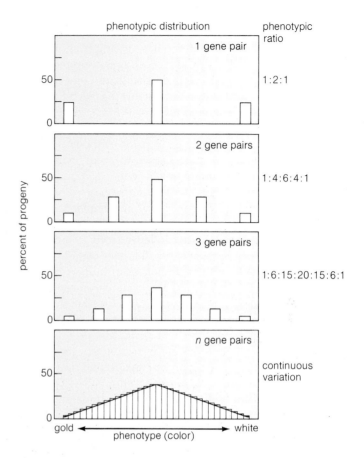

Figure 10.17 Distribution of phenotypes in a range of color differences between two extremes (darkest gold to white). The distribution reflects the number of gene pairs contributing to phenotypic expression. As the number of governing genes increases, so does the number of phenotypes. With polygenes, the phenotypic classes merge to form a continuous spectrum between gold and white.

It is important to understand that polygenic expressions are not a result of "blending," a term that suggests loss of the original identity of hereditary traits. Rather, *all genes retain their physical identity, regardless of the phenotype produced by their combined positive and negative effects.*

PERSPECTIVE

With his experimental observations and interpretations, Mendel established the foundations for genetic analysis—the study of inheritance patterns. Although his interpretations have since been extended, we still rely on them as a baseline for analyzing differences arising from monohybrid, dihybrid, and trihybrid crosses. A phenotypic ratio of 3 dominant to 1 recessive in second-generation hybrid offspring does indeed reflect inheritance based on a single gene pair. A phenotypic ratio of 9:3:3:1 in second-generation hybrid offspring reflects inheritance based on two independently assorting gene pairs. Although variations on these ratios are now known to occur, none has refuted Mendel's most important insight: *The two alleles of a given gene pair segregate from each other during gamete formation.*

What about Mendel's concept of independent assortment of different gene pairs? Later work showed that many gene pairs are indeed assorted independently of one another, so that any of a number of possible gene combinations can occur in gametes. Others do not assort independently. They are physically located on the same chromosome in such a way that they almost always travel together into the same gamete, thereby introducing variations into Mendelian phenotypic ratios. Yet here again, Mendel's insight provided a basis for interpreting events at the genotypic level. The concept of independent assortment has been limited, not discarded.

It is the concept of dominance that has undergone the greatest modification. Not all phenotypic traits are as clear-cut as those Mendel studied. In any population, most traits show continuous variation, which does not lend itself so readily to simple measurements. Continuous variation arises not only through interactions between alleles of single genes. It also arises through concurrent interactions among different gene pairs. Today we have these modifications to Mendel's concept of dominance:

---

1. Gradations of dominance exist between two alleles for a given gene locus, so that the expression of one or both may be fully dominant, or one may be incompletely dominant over the other.

2. A hierarchy of dominance can exist among all the alternative allelic forms that may exist for a given gene locus.

3. The activity of a single gene may have major or minor effects on more than one trait.

4. The activity of a gene in space and time may be influenced by other genes, with a sum total of their positive and negative actions producing some effect on phenotype.

5. The environment has profound influence over the expression of all genes and their contribution to phenotype.

Readings

Avers, C. 1980. *Genetics.* Revised edition. Boston: Willard Grant Press. One of the best introductions to genetics. Modern in organization, clearly written, very good genetics problems with answers included.

Ayala, F., and J. Kiger. 1980. *Modern Genetics.* Menlo Park, California: Benjamin/Cummings. Another current introduction to genetics. Clearly written; no answers given in book to genetics problems.

Crow, J. 1979. "Genes That Violate Mendel's Rules." *Scientific American* 240(2):134–146.

Dunn, L. 1965. *A Short History of Genetics.* New York: McGraw-Hill.

Mendel, G. "Experiments in Plant Hybridization." Translation in J. Peters (editor), *Classic Papers in Genetics.* 1959. Englewood Cliffs, New Jersey: Prentice-Hall.

Singer, C. 1962. *A History of Biology to About the Year 1900.* New York: Abelard-Schuman.

Stern, C., and E. Sherwood (editors). 1966. *The Origin of Genetics.* San Francisco: Freeman. Includes a modern translation of Mendel's paper and correspondence.

Witkop, C., Jr. 1975. "Albinism." *Natural History* 84(8):48–59. Good account of the various forms of albinism—their biochemical and genetic bases and their phenotypic manifestations.

Review Questions

1. State the Mendelian principle of segregation. Does segregation occur during mitosis or meiosis?

2. Distinguish between the following terms:
   a. Gene, allele, and gene pair
   b. Dominant trait and recessive trait
   c. Homozygote and heterozygote
   d. Genotype and phenotype

3. Give an example of a self-fertilizing organism. What is cross-fertilization?

4. Distinguish between monohybrid, dihybrid, and trihybrid crosses. What is a testcross, and why is it valuable in genetic analysis?

5. State the Mendelian principle of independent assortment. Does independent assortment occur during mitosis or meiosis? Does independent assortment of gene pairs always occur?

6. How does polygenic inheritance differ from the notion of "blending" of heritable traits?

7. Contrast continuous and discontinuous variation, and outline the genotypic basis for both.

8. Mendel's concept of dominance was based on observations of inheritance patterns in clearly contrasting traits. How has this concept since been modified?

9. List five main factors influencing the expression of phenotype.

10. What does epistasis mean?

Genetics Problems (Answers appear in Appendix II)

1. One gene has alleles A and a; another gene has alleles B and b. For each of the following genotypes, what type(s) of gametes will be produced?
   a. $AA\ BB$
   b. $Aa\ BB$
   c. $Aa\ bb$
   d. $Aa\ Bb$

2. Referring still to the preceding problem, what genotypes will be present in the offspring from the following matings? (Indicate the frequencies of each genotype among the offspring.)
   a. $AA\ BB \times aa\ BB$
   b. $Aa\ BB \times AA\ Bb$
   c. $Aa\ Bb \times aa\ bb$
   d. $Aa\ Bb \times Aa\ Bb$

3. In one experiment, Mendel crossed a true-breeding pea plant having green pods with a true-breeding pea plant having yellow pods. All of the F_1 plants had green pods.
   a. Which trait (green or yellow pods) is recessive? Can you explain how you arrived at your conclusion?
   b. Suppose the F_1 plants are self-pollinated and 135 F_2 plants are produced. What phenotypes should be present in the F_2 generation, and how many of the plants in that generation should show each of those phenotypes?

4. Being able to curl up the sides of your tongue into a U-shape is under the control of a dominant allele at one gene locus. (When there is a recessive allele at this locus, the tongue cannot be rolled.) Having free earlobes is a trait controlled by a dominant allele at a different gene locus. (When there is a recessive allele at this locus, earlobes are attached at the jawline.) The two genes controlling tongue-rolling and free earlobes assort independently. Suppose a woman who has free earlobes and who can roll her tongue marries someone who has attached earlobes and who cannot roll his tongue. Their first child has attached earlobes and cannot roll the tongue.
   a. What are the genotypes of the mother, the father, and the child?
   b. If this same couple has a second child, what is the probability that it will have free earlobes and be unable to roll the tongue?

5. In addition to the two genes mentioned in Problem 1, assume you now study a third gene having alleles C and c. For each of the following genotypes, indicate what type (or types) of gametes will be produced:
   a. $AA\ BB\ CC$
   b. $Aa\ BB\ cc$
   c. $Aa\ BB\ Cc$
   d. $Aa\ Bb\ Cc$

6. A man is homozygous dominant for ten different genes, which assort independently. How many genotypically different types of sperm could he produce? A woman is homozygous recessive for eight of these ten genes, and she is heterozygous for the other two. How many genotypically different types of eggs could she produce? What can you conclude regarding the relationship between the number of different gametes possible and the number of heterozygous and homozygous genes that are present? For a

species (or population), what might be the biological benefits, if any, of possessing a large number of heterozygotes?

7. Recall that Mendel crossed a true-breeding tall, purple-flowered pea plant with a true-breeding dwarf, white-flowered plant. All the F_1 plants were tall and purple-flowered. If an F_1 plant is now self-pollinated, what is the probability of obtaining an F_2 plant heterozygous for the genes controlling height and flower color?

8. Assume that a new gene was recently identified in mice. One allele at this gene locus produces a yellow fur color. A second allele produces a brown fur color. Suppose you are asked to determine the dominance relationship between these two alleles. (Is it one of simple dominance, incomplete dominance, or codominance?) What types of crosses would you make to find the answer? On what types of observations would you base your conclusions?

9. The ABO blood system has often been employed to settle cases of disputed paternity. Suppose, as an expert in genetics, you are called to testify in a case where the mother has type A blood, the child has type O blood, and the alleged father has type B blood. How would you respond to the following statements of the attorneys:
   a. "Since the mother has type A blood, the type O blood of the child must have come from the father, and since my client has type B blood, he obviously could not have fathered this child." *(Made by the attorney of the alleged father)*
   b. "Further tests revealed that this man is heterozygous and therefore he must be the father." *(Made by the mother's attorney)*

10. In mice, epistasis is observed for two independently assorting genes that influence coat color. At one gene locus, a dominant allele produces a nonalbino, and a recessive allele produces an albino. At the second gene locus, a dominant allele produces an agouti and a recessive allele produces a black coat. (An agouti mouse has a mixture of gray, yellow, and brown colors in its coat.) When a mouse is homozygous recessive for the first gene, it is an albino regardless of the alleles present at the second gene locus. Only when the mouse is *not* homozygous recessive for the first gene is it agouti or black.
   a. If a completely homozygous recessive albino mouse mates with a completely homozygous dominant agouti mouse, what phenotypes would be expected in the F_1 offspring, and at what frequencies?
   b. If the F_1 mice mate with each other, what phenotypes would be expected in the F_2 offspring, and at what frequencies?

11

EMERGENCE OF THE CHROMOSOMAL THEORY OF INHERITANCE

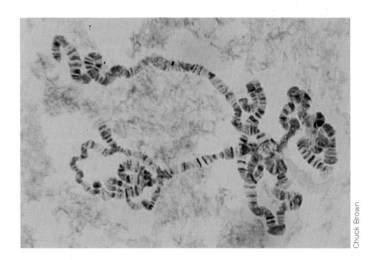

Chuck Brown

Figure 11.1 Polytene chromosomes from a salivary gland cell of *Drosophila*, an insect that played a key role in the development of the chromosomal theory of inheritance.

RETURN OF THE PEA PLANT

The year was 1884, Mendel's published paper on plant hybridization had been gathering dust in at least a hundred libraries for nearly two decades, and Mendel himself had just passed away. Ironically, separate streams of research were even now flowing around him—and moving toward the same principles of inheritance he had stated so carefully in that ignored, forgotten paper. *Cytology,* the study of cell structure and function, was about to converge with genetic analysis.

Interest in the cellular basis of inheritance had been renewed at midcentury by new developments in microscopy (Chapter Four). Through microscopic studies, cytologists were beginning to suspect that hereditary material resides in the cell nucleus. By 1882, Walther Flemming reported seeing threadlike bodies—chromosomes—in nuclei of dividing salamander cells. He called the division process mitosis, after the Greek word for thread. Wilhelm Roux had a hunch that the chromosomes weren't performing their elaborate divisional ballet for no purpose at all. *What if those threadlike chromosomes were the hereditary material?*

Further studies showed that each sperm or egg has *one* set of chromosomes, whereas a fertilized egg has *two.* In 1887, August Weismann proposed that a special division process must reduce the number of chromosomes by half during gamete formation. Sure enough, in that same year Flemming identified the process, which became known as meiosis. About this time, Weismann began to promote his theory of heredity: (1) in multicelled plants and animals, the chromosome number is halved during meiosis; (2) the original chromosome number is restored when sperm and egg nuclei fuse; and (3) half the hereditary material in offspring is therefore paternal in origin, and half maternal. His views became well known and hotly debated, and the debates drove researchers into devising ways to test the theory. Throughout Europe there was a flurry of quantitative, experimental crosses—just like the ones by Mendel.

Thus in 1900, Carl Correns of Germany, Erich Von Tschermak of Austria, and Hugo De Vries of Holland published papers on their independent studies of plant hybridization. Each acknowledged that a literature search for related studies revealed that Mendel had arrived at the same results with garden peas, and had reached the same conclusions more than three decades before. Through these and other studies, Mendel's concept of segregation became reinforced. Flemming's "threads" were likely candidates for being the carriers of Mendel's "units" of inheritance. The convergence of insights foreshadowed an explosion of research into the physical basis of inheritance.

THE CHROMOSOMAL THEORY

In this chapter, we will outline the nature of observations, experiments, and hypotheses about hereditary mechanisms that unfolded in the decades after the rediscovery of Mendel's work. Taken together, they represent impressive evidence in support of what is now called the **chromosomal theory of inheritance**:

---

1. The chromosome is the vehicle by which hereditary information is physically transmitted from one generation to the next.

2. Each chromosome carries a linear sequence of genes, the units of hereditary information that govern the development of phenotype.

3. Diploid organisms have two chromosome sets, one from each parent. One gene for a given trait resides on a chromosome derived from one parent, and its allelic partner resides on the homologous chromosome derived from the other parent.

4. During meiosis, each member of a pair of homologous chromosomes becomes separated from the other, then is assorted into gametes. Because whole chromosomes are assorted independently of one another, there can be *different combinations* of chromosomes from both parents in different gametes.

5. The genes on one chromosome of a homologous pair tend to be inherited *as a group*. However, during meiosis I, *homologous chromosomes exchange parts as a result of crossing over.* Thus the combination of alleles on any given chromosome that ends up in a gamete may not be the same as that in either parent.

6. A chromosome can also undergo structural changes, such as deletion, duplication, inversion, and translocation of parts. All such changes are considered to be chromosomal mutations.

7. Other chromosomal mutations involve the wayward movement of whole chromosomes or chromosome sets, which changes the chromosome number in resulting gametes.

8. *Crossing over, independent assortment of whole chromosomes, chromosomal mutations*—such events produce new genotypic combinations. The new genotypes in turn give rise to new phenotypes upon which selective agents can act. In short, these chromosomal events are wellsprings of diversity and evolutionary change.

CLUES FROM THE INHERITANCE OF SEX

Enter the Fruit Fly

The growing speculation that genes might be carried on chromosomes was first confirmed by Thomas Hunt Morgan and his students at Columbia University. Morgan had weighed the advantages and disadvantages of using different kinds of organisms for breeding experiments. To his mind, the fruit fly *Drosophila melanogaster* would be a better choice than the plants and animals that had been used before. These small flies are commonly observed in summer and fall, when they hover over ripe and rotting fruit. They require no special care in the laboratory; they can be grown in bottles on nothing fancier than bits of rotting fruit and yeast. A female can lay hundreds of eggs in a few days, and her offspring reach reproductive age in less than two weeks. This meant that Morgan could track hereditary traits through nearly thirty generations of thousands of flies in the space of a year. Before long, his laboratory was glutted with bottles of fruit flies.

Sex Determination

At the time Morgan began his *Drosophila* experiments, microscopic studies had already revealed that the male and female of most animal and some plant species differ in their chromosome sets. Although most of the chromosomes were clearly homologous pairs, some differed in number or in kind between males and females. They were called **sex chromosomes**, for they probably were associated with the development of maleness or femaleness. All other chromosomes became known as **autosomes**: they are of the same number and kind in both males and females.

For example, cytologists found that one chromosome in male grasshopper cells doesn't have a homologous partner. They called it the X *chromosome.* They also found that female grasshopper cells have two of these chromosomes. Females were designated XX, and the males XO (the "O" signifying the absence of a homologue). In other species, the X chromosome in males has a partner—but the partner is often smaller and shaped differently. The unlike partner came to be called the Y *chromosome.* For instance, in *D. melanogaster* the females are XX, and the males XY (Figure 11.2). This is by far the most common pattern among animals. Sex chromosomes are rarely found in plants.

For most animal species, the sex chromosome pattern is XX (female) and XY (male).

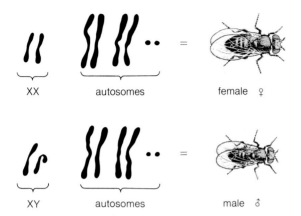

Figure 11.2 Sex chromosomes and autosomes of *Drosophila melanogaster*. Together they represent a diploid number of eight (four chromosome pairs).

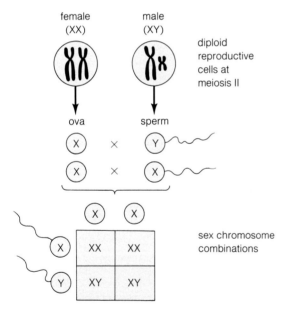

Figure 11.3 Sex determination as it occurs in most animal species. (The chromosomes depicted here are from human diploid reproductive cells.) Only the sex chromosomes are shown here; each ovum and sperm also carries a haploid set of autosomes. Males transmit their Y chromosome to their sons, but none to their daughters. Males receive their X chromosome only from their mothers.

It became evident that whether a zygote is destined to become male or female can be explained in terms of Mendelian genetics. If a female parent is an XX homozygote, each normal gamete she produces will carry one X chromosome. If a male parent is an XY heterozygote (with the X and Y acting as homologues during meiosis), then half the gametes he produces will carry an X and the other half will carry a Y chromosome. When an X-bearing sperm fuses with an X-bearing egg, the zygote develops into a female. When a Y-bearing sperm fuses with an egg, the zygote develops into a male (Figure 11.3). This is the meaning of the segregation pattern:

The inheritance of a clearly recognizable phenotypic difference—maleness versus femaleness—is associated with specific chromosomes.

Why was this association considered to be so important? If a certain trait—say, eye color—were manifest only in males or only in females of an experimental group, *then perhaps the genes coding for those traits could be assigned to specific sex chromosomes.* This would provide strong evidence that genes are indeed located on chromosomes. Gathering such evidence is what Morgan and his students set out to accomplish.

Sex-Linked Traits

Individual fruit flies vary in such traits as eye color, eye size, body color, and wing size. Such variations arise from multiple allele systems of the sort described in Chapter Ten. In natural populations, the most common allele in the series is called the normal, or **wild-type allele**. *D. melanogaster* normally is homozygous for two wild-type alleles that code for red eyes.

When Morgan began his studies, all of the flies being produced had red eyes. One day, he observed a *white-eyed* male in one of the bottles. Apparently, the variant form arose through a spontaneous mutation in a gene controlling eye color. Morgan crossed the male with a red-eyed female. As Mendel would have predicted, all of the first-generation offspring had red eyes; and red-eyed and white-eyed individuals appeared in a 3:1 ratio in the second-generation offspring. Crosses between white-eyed flies showed that the mutant strain was true-breeding. (Here, "true-breeding" indicates that the individuals are homozygous for the trait under consideration.)

However, Morgan discovered some patterns that did not seem to fit with Mendel's rules of inheritance. True, the 3:1 ratio was manifest in the second-generation offspring. But all of the *females* had red eyes. Half of the *males* had red eyes and the other half had white—and all of these second-generation males were true-breeding! Another curious pattern emerged in offspring of the second-generation females. Half of these females produced all red-eyed offspring. The rest produced $\frac{1}{2}$ red-eyed and $\frac{1}{2}$ white-eyed males. What was going on in these crosses?

Morgan had an idea. Female fruit flies obviously inherit one X chromosome from each parent. Males (XY) inherit their single X chromosome *only* from their maternal parent. If the eye-color gene locus were on the X chromosome, the first-generation females with red eyes must have been heterozygous for eye color. (They must have carried the red-eye allele on one X chromosome and the recessive white-eye allele on the other X chromosome.) According to the Mendelian segregation rule, the alleles had been separated from each other during gamete formation. Sexual fusion produced these combinations of sex chromosomes:

Female gamete: X × X = XX

Male gamete: X × Y = XY

But what if there were no eye-color gene on the Y chromosome? If only X chromosomes carried the gene being studied, then it would be expressed in males regardless of whether it were dominant or recessive!

By identifying a specific gene that is linked only to a specific sex chromosome, Morgan was able to explain the seemingly curious dominant-to-recessive ratios that appeared among the second-generation offspring of these crosses. Figure 11.4 shows the results that can be expected when the idea of a sex-linked gene is combined with Mendel's concept of segregation. The predicted outcomes match the actual results.

To check his hypothesis, Morgan performed various testcrosses. In one, he backcrossed a red-eyed first-generation female to its white-eyed male parent. As Morgan anticipated, white-eyed *females* appeared among the offspring. Because only homozygous recessive females could be white-eyed, the results confirmed his hypothesis. Figure 11.5 shows why this is so.

Morgan's initial work confirmed the existence of sex-linked genes, which are located only on an X chromosome and have no alleles on the Y chromosome.

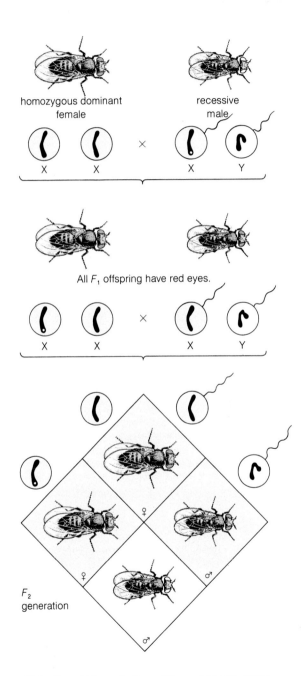

homozygous dominant female   recessive male

X   X   ×   X   Y

All F_1 offspring have red eyes.

X   X   ×   X   Y

F_2 generation

Figure 11.4 One of Morgan's *Drosophila* experiments, which suggested that a specific gene (for eye color) is carried only on the X chromosome, not on the male's Y chromosome. White dots on chromosomes indicate a recessive allele.

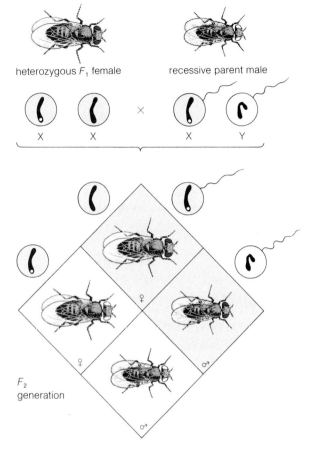

heterozygous F_1 female   recessive parent male

X   X   X   Y

F_2 generation

Figure 11.5 Morgan's backcross between an F_1 female *Drosophila* heterozygous for eye color (one dominant red allele and one recessive white allele) and the mutant white-eyed parental male. The recessive allele (depicted here by the white dot) must be carried on the X chromosome only, given the correlation between eye color and sex in the F_2 generation. Thus a male can carry only one recessive allele, whereas a female can carry two for this (or any other) sex-linked trait.

In later studies, Calvin Bridges and others found evidence that sex differences between males and females are not the exclusive domain of sex chromosomes. Genes that influence the expression of maleness *versus* femaleness occur on autosomes as well. In most diploid organisms, major sex-determining genes are concentrated on the sex chromosomes. In humans and other mammals, the Y chromosome carries a gene that is necessary for the development of the testis (a male reproductive organ). However, the overall male or female phenotype is an outcome of many interactions of different gene products (hormones) with autosomal and with X-linked gene loci.

LINKAGE GROUPS AND THE NUMBER OF CHROMOSOMES

With so many thousands of new flies being churned out in the *Drosophila* bottles, Morgan's group was able to collect a significant number of spontaneously mutated individuals for use in dihybrid cross experiments. By 1915, more than eighty types of mutants had been isolated.

Results from some of the dihybrid crosses conformed to Mendel's concept of independent assortment. Individuals showing mutant forms of two traits were crossed with wild-type individuals. The mutant forms did not manifest themselves in the first generation, and they reemerged in the second generation as if the two traits being studied had been assorted independently of each other into gametes.

However, other dihybrid crosses yielded an unexpected result. Genes coding for certain traits invariably ended up together in the *same* gamete. For instance, a fly mutant for both wing shape and body color was crossed with a wild-type fly. Wild-type individuals have straight, flat wings (which can be designated C) and a gray body (B). One mutant form had curly wings (c) and a black body (b). If these genes assorted independently, then a cross between heterozygous flies ($CcBb$) would yield offspring in about a 9:3:3:1 ratio (compare, for example, Figure 10.8). Yet the actual ratio was closer to 3:1. *It was as if the experimenters had been tracking only a single gene that produced two separate phenotypes.* The two genes for wing shape and body color obviously were not assorting independently.

Through many such experiments, Morgan and his colleagues realized that there are four groups of apparently linked genes in *D. melanogaster*. The four groups probably corresponded to its haploid set of four chromosomes. The term **linkage** eventually was applied to the group of genes that are physically located on the same chromosome. All the genes located on a given chromosome are now said to make up a **linkage group**.

Independent assortment, as Mendel perceived it, can occur when genes coding for different traits are located on different chromosomes. When genes that are physically located on the same chromosome travel together into the same gamete, they are said to be linked.

Different genes located on different chromosomes can assort independently of each other into gametes.

Genes physically located on the same chromosome might end up together in the same gamete; they might not assort independently.

RECOMBINATION AND LINKAGE MAPPING OF CHROMOSOMES

More surprises were still to come. Some genes are physically linked on the same chromosome and stay together most of the time—but some of the time they end up in *different* gametes! To explain this puzzle, Morgan's group turned to the recent findings of cytologist F. Janssens. During his studies of salamander cells undergoing meiosis, Janssens had observed that two nonsister chromatids of homologous chromosomes can cross each other. As you read in Chapter Nine, this event is now called *crossing over:* two nonsister chromatids of homologous pairs of chromosomes exchange corresponding segments at breakage points. Its consequence is a form of genetic recombination. New combinations of alleles end up in a chromosome, hence in the new individual destined to carry that chromosome (Figure 11.6).

Alfred Sturtevant, one of Morgan's students, suggested that the puzzling separation of linked genes might be related to crossing over. He reasoned that (1) genes occur in a linear sequence on chromosomes, and (2) the farther apart on a chromosome two linked genes may be, the more likely that crossing over can disrupt the original combination of linked genes.

Through the work of Morgan and Sturtevant, the following picture has emerged. Crossing over apparently can occur at any point in the array of genes on each chromatid. *But the probability of crossing over and recombination occurring at a point somewhere between two genes located on the same chromatid is proportional to the distance that separates them.* If two genes are located very close together, in nearly all cases they will end up in the same gamete; they are tightly linked. If two genes are relatively far apart, crossing over will occur between them much more often than it will between tightly linked genes. Even so, in more than half the gametes formed, they will still be together on the same chromatid. Such genes are loosely linked. Finally, if two genes are very far apart on a chromatid, crossing over and recombination can occur between them so often that they act as if they had assorted independently—even though they are located on the same chromosome.

The relationship between the organization of genes on chromosomes and their segregation patterns during meiosis is so regular that it can be used to determine the positions of genes relative to one another on a given chromosome. Plotting their positions is called **linkage mapping** of genes.

For example, Sturtevant constructed linkage maps for *Drosophila,* based on the relative frequencies with which

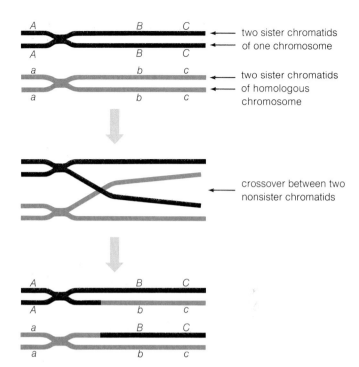

Figure 11.6 Genetic recombination as a result of crossing over between nonsister chromatids of homologous chromosomes during meiosis I.

different genes tend to undergo crossing over. For the unit of measure, Sturtevant used one crossover per hundred gametes as the standard map unit. Thus, five map units separate genes showing a five percent crossover frequency, ten map units separate genes showing ten percent crossover frequency, and so on. Figure 11.7 is an example of a gene map that has been plotted on the basis of crossover percentages. Because the map unit is an arbitrarily selected standard, the distances between genes are relative, not actual.

Of the several thousand genes contained in the four chromosomes of *Drosophila,* the positions of about 1,000 have been mapped—and *Drosophila* is one of the most intensively studied organisms. There are surely many more genes in a haploid set of human chromosomes, very few of which have been identified and their positions mapped. We have a long way to go in the mapping of the physical basis of heredity. But work to date has yielded undeniable proof that genes are carried on chromosomes—*and that they are carried in linear array.*

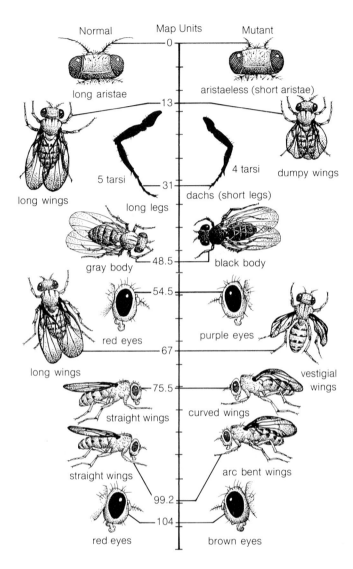

Normal · Map Units · Mutant

- long aristae / 0
- aristaeless (short aristae) / 13
- 5 tarsi / 4 tarsi
- long wings / dumpy wings
- long legs / 31 / dachs (short legs)
- gray body / 48.5 / black body
- red eyes / 54.5 / purple eyes
- long wings / 67 / vestigial wings
- straight wings / 75.5 / curved wings
- straight wings / arc bent wings
- red eyes / 99.2 / brown eyes
- 104

Figure 11.7 Genetic mapping of genes on a segment of chromosome 2 in *D. melanogaster.* Such maps don't show actual physical distances between genes. Rather they show relative distance between gene locations that undergo crossing over and other chromosomal rearrangements. Only if the probability of crossing over were equal along the chromosome's length (which it is not) would it be possible to calculate physical distance exactly.

Here, distances between genes are measured in map units, based on the frequency of recombination between the genes. Thus, if the frequency turns out to be 10 percent, the genes are said to be separated by 10 map units. The amount of recombination to be expected between "vestigial wings" and "curved wings," for instance, would be 8.5 percent (75.5 − 67). This works for genes close together on the map, but not for distant genes.

VISUALIZATION OF CHROMOSOMES

Morgan's work ushered in the golden age of *cytogenetics*, which relates gene behavior to chromosome features that can be observed through the microscope. Later refinements in electron microscopy provided even more precise means for tracking and interpreting what was going on in the chromosome sets that form the basis of inheritance.

In the 1930s cytologists first observed **polytene chromosomes**, the unusually large chromosome structures in salivary gland cells of several insect species. At one stage of the life cycle, these cells do not divide. But each chromosome is replicated over and over again, and the many replicas remain packed together in parallel. Some regions of the fibers are more condensed than others, and the variations show up as differences in staining intensity. The outcome is a banding pattern of the sort shown in Figure 11.1.

The distinct banding patterns proved to be the same in all normal chromosomes of a given type. Cytologists now had a means of visually identifying specific chromosome regions associated with specific phenotypic traits. As you will see, the banding pattern can change as a result of certain chromosomal mutations, and the changes can be correlated with changes in phenotype.

Visualizing chromosomes other than polytene "giants" proved to be more difficult. Until the late 1960s, micrographs of chromosomes from other animals and plants had to be grouped on the basis of chromosome length and centromere location. However, some chromosomes were almost identical in these two features, so it was sometimes difficult to distinguish among chromosome types in a given group. Then a new staining method revealed that chromosomes of some plants and all vertebrates also have distinct bands. (The method was named G-banding after the Giemsa stain.) Because chromosomes can be more clearly identified, they are now usually numbered rather than referred to by group.

Through the work in cytology, chromosomes of a given type can be distinguished from all others present in the dividing nucleus of a cell at metaphase. The chromosome complement of the cell (hence the organism) can be characterized exactly by such features as the number of chromosomes present, their relative lengths, and their banding patterns. Such characteristics are used in creating a **karyotype**: a visual representation of a chromosome set in which individual chromosomes are ordered and arranged relative to one another, from largest to smallest. Figure 11.8 shows a karyotype for human male metaphase chromosomes. The

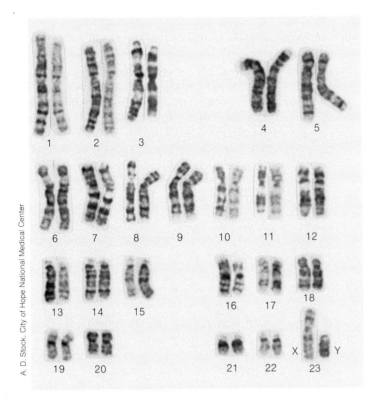

Figure 11.8 Karyotype of a human male. Normally, human cells have a diploid chromosome number of 46. The nucleus contains 22 pairs of autosomes and one "pair" of sex chromosomes (X and Y). Each chromosome of a given type has already undergone replication.

These chromosomes were prepared for microscopy by G-staining. The unique bands identify chromosomes as being of a given type.

chromosome complement shown here numbers forty-six (twenty-three pairs). Figure 11.9 shows how karyotypes can be prepared.

CHANGES IN CHROMOSOME STRUCTURE

Discovery of the distinct banding patterns in plant and animal chromosomes opened up new horizons in cytogenetic research. Although gross structural changes had been observed before in rare abnormal chromosomes, the banding patterns provided a means for analyzing the genetic basis of the ensuing phenotypic disorders. Cytological comparisons of altered chromosomes with their normal counterparts gave insight into how genetic systems are organized—and they proved beyond doubt that genes are carried in linear array on chromosomes. Four major kinds of structural changes in chromosomes were identified through this work. They are called deletions, duplications, inversions, and translocations.

A **deletion** is the loss of a segment of chromosome. A deletion can arise when viral attack, irradiation, or chemical action causes two breaks in a chromosome region. Enzymes

can repair such breaks, but a piece of the chromosome may inadvertently be left out during the repair process. When the damaged chromosome undergoes synapsis with its homologue during meiosis I, its partner has nothing to pair with in the region corresponding to the deletion. The normal homologue has to buckle outward from the unmatchable part:

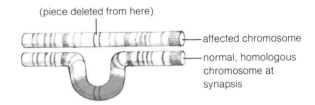

(piece deleted from here)

—affected chromosome

—normal, homologous chromosome at synapsis

The buckling can cause problems during what would otherwise be an orderly separation of homologues during meiosis. There are almost always problems when the damaged chromosome is transmitted to offspring, for genes that control one or more traits can be lost entirely.

A **duplication** is a repeat of a particular DNA sequence in the same chromosome or in nonhomologous ones. Like deletions, a duplication can rise when viral attack, irradia-

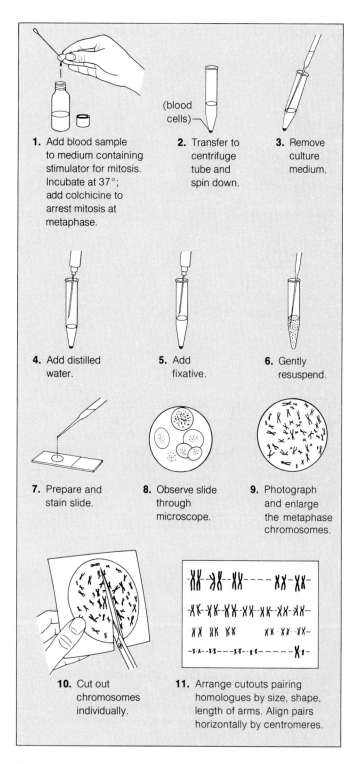

1. Add blood sample to medium containing stimulator for mitosis. Incubate at 37°; add colchicine to arrest mitosis at metaphase.

2. Transfer to centrifuge tube and spin down.

3. Remove culture medium.

(blood cells)

4. Add distilled water.

5. Add fixative.

6. Gently resuspend.

7. Prepare and stain slide.

8. Observe slide through microscope.

9. Photograph and enlarge the metaphase chromosomes.

10. Cut out chromosomes individually.

11. Arrange cutouts pairing homologues by size, shape, length of arms. Align pairs horizontally by centromeres.

Figure 11.9 How to prepare a karyotype.

tion, or chemical action introduces two breaks in a chromosome. It also can arise through *unequal* crossing over. When homologous chromosomes approach each other during synapsis, their pairing and attachment depend on a point-by-point matching of corresponding regions. Sometimes, though, the DNA sequence is very similar in neighboring regions of the chromosome, and homologues can pair at the wrong stretch. When segments break and are exchanged during crossing over, one chromosome might end up with both copies of a segment in the mispaired region, whereas its partner might end up with none:

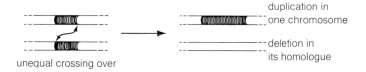

unequal crossing over

duplication in one chromosome

deletion in its homologue

It may be that duplications provide a hedge against malfunctioning in the segments that they repeat. If genes in some segment later become altered or lost, repeats can cover their functions.

An **inversion** is a chromosome segment that has been excised and rejoined at the same place—but backward. Although an inversion doesn't change the number of genes or the amount of nucleoprotein in a chromosome, the position and sequence of the genes involved do change. When inversions occur, there is a flip-flop in banding patterns in the region corresponding to the change.

Some inversions may have figured in the evolution of primates (monkeys, apes, and humans). In many ways, the chromosomes of humans and chimpanzees are astonishingly alike. They are nearly identical in the case of chromosome 17. However, the centromere is located in the middle of chimpanzee chromosome 17. In humans, there seems to have been an inversion, with the centromere position flopped so that it is halfway between the middle and the end of the chromosome. Comparative studies suggest that inversions involving shifts in centromere location have also occurred in three other human chromosomes.

On occasions when chromosomes break, still another aberration can result. In a **translocation**, a chromosome segment can be permanently transferred to a nonhomologous chromosome. Translocations produce peculiar configurations at the recombination stage of meiosis I. A homologue still pairs with the remainder of the original chromosome—and it also pairs with the translocated part, wherever it ends up. *Transposition* is another term for a simple translocation. Some transpositions are due to remarkable DNA sequences called transposable elements, or "jumping genes," which often leave a copy of themselves behind when they move to a new location. Transpositions may be a source of considerable structural variation among individuals of a population. This concept was advanced by Barbara McClintock, the pioneer in eukaryotic transposition studies.

CHANGES IN CHROMOSOME NUMBER

With the exception of gametes, all cells of a multicelled eukaryote usually have the same number of chromosomes in their nuclei. From time to time, though, whole chromosomes or chromosome sets go astray when the meiotic nucleus divides. The resulting gametes end up with more or fewer chromosomes than they were supposed to have. So do the resulting new individuals—*if* they survive the change. For most animal species, an altered chromosome number is typically harmful, and often fatal. For many plants, such alterations have proved beneficial (or at least harmless), and the new chromosome number has become characteristic of a population, even of a species.

Changes in chromosome number have been a focus of studies into the mechanisms of inheritance. In the course of these studies, it has also become apparent that changes of this sort may have played a major role in evolutionary history, especially for land plants.

Missing or Extra Chromosomes

Aneuploidy refers to a condition in which a chromosome of a given type is either absent entirely, or present three or more times in the diploid chromosome set. Aneuploidy can arise when homologous chromosomes fail to separate at meiosis, so that both end up in the same nucleus. Such failures to separate properly are known as *nondisjunctions.*

For example, the normal chromosome complement of a diploid nucleus is $2n$. Nondisjunction in meiosis I can lead to a gamete having an extra chromosome $(n + 1)$. Upon sexual fusion with a normal gamete, the number becomes $(n + 1) + (n)$, or $2n + 1$. During growth and development, each cell arising through mitotic cell divisions will be $2n + 1$. This condition, in which three chromosomes of the same kind are present in the chromosome set, is called *trisomy.* Similarly, the gamete deprived of a chromosome is $(n - 1)$; and the individual arising through sexual fusion with a normal gamete is $(n - 1) + (n)$, or $2n - 1$. This condition is called *monosomy.* Chapter Fifteen gives some examples of these abnormalities in humans.

Three or More Chromosome Sets

From earlier discussions, you know that most eukaryotic cells are diploid. They have two sets of chromosomes in the nucleus. Yet many eukaryotes—incuding about half of all flowering plant species—have three or more *sets* of chromosomes. This condition is known as **polyploidy**. It can occur in certain tissues only, or it can occur in all somatic (body) cells of the individual.

Polyploidy comes about in several ways. For example, failure of homologous chromosomes to separate completely at meiosis sometimes leads to diploid instead of haploid gametes. Fusion of a $2n$ gamete with a normal one produces a *triploid* $(3n)$ individual. Fusion of two $2n$ gametes produces a *tetraploid* $(4n)$ individual, and so on.

As another example, chromosome replication in somatic cells may not be followed by cell division. If such doublings occur in plant tissues that develop into reproductive organs, diploid gametes will result. If the plant is self-fertilizing, the offspring will be tetraploid. If cross-fertilization with a normal plant occurs, triploid offspring will result.

Triploid individuals are usually sterile. In fact, any polyploid having an *uneven* number of chromosome sets $(3, 7, 9, . . .)$ is likely to be sterile, because it produces gametes with incomplete sets of chromosomes. For instance, during meiosis in a triploid nucleus, there are three sets of chromosomes, not two. Three homologous chromosomes can synapse with each other along different segments. Skewed chromosome configurations result, and disjunction of the three homologues is abnormal. The chromosomes are randomly distributed into gametes. When these gametes take part in sexual reproduction, fusion leads to an individual having an unbalanced chromosome complement. This means the individual might have too many of some genes and not enough (or none at all) of others. Because growth and development depend on a full set of hereditary instructions, the individual usually cannot function normally.

Polyploidy is more common among plants than animals. One reason is that plants generally have no sex chromosomes; for animals, polyploidy can disturb the balance between autosomes and sex chromosomes that is essential for proper development. Also, many plants can self-fertilize, whereas most animals cannot. (Thus a gamete with an abnormal chromosome number is more likely to meet up with a similarly abnormal counterpart from the same parent.) In addition, many plants can still propagate themselves asexually even if they are sterile. Finally, plant development

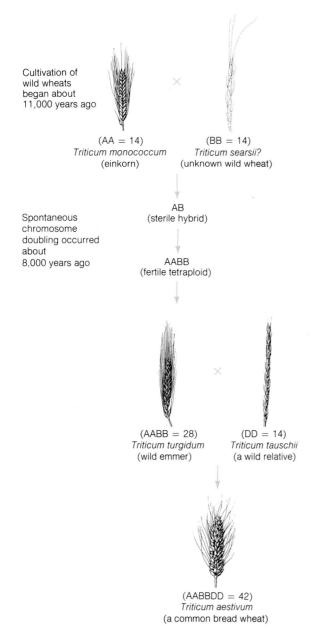

Cultivation of
wild wheats
began about
11,000 years ago

(AA = 14)
Triticum monococcum
(einkorn)

(BB = 14)
Triticum searsii?
(unknown wild wheat)

AB
(sterile hybrid)

Spontaneous
chromosome
doubling occurred
about
8,000 years ago

AABB
(fertile tetraploid)

(AABB = 28)
Triticum turgidum
(wild emmer)

(DD = 14)
Triticum tauschii
(a wild relative)

(AABBDD = 42)
Triticum aestivum
(a common bread wheat)

Figure 11.10 Proposed hybridizations in wheat that led to chromosome doublings and polyploidy.

Wheat grains dating from 11,000 B.C. have been found in the Near East. Several species of wild diploid wheat still grow there. They have 14 chromosomes (two sets of 7, designated AA). Also growing in the region is a wild grass with 14 chromosomes, designated BB. They differ from the A chromosomes, judging from their failure to pair with them at meiosis. One tetraploid wheat species has 28 chromosomes; analysis during meiosis shows that they are AABB. The A chromosomes pair with A's, and the B chromosomes pair with B's. A hexaploid wheat has 42 chromosomes (six sets of seven). Its chromosomes are AABBDD, the last set (DD) coming from *Triticum tauschii*, another wild grass. (After Jensen and Salisbury, *Botany: An Ecological Approach*, 1972)

is less complex than that of most animals. Therefore, changes in cell structure and function associated with polyploidy may not have as drastic an effect on survivability. This may be one of the reasons why hybridization between different plant species occurs widely. Chromosome doublings and amplified polyploidy apparently figured in the hybridizations that gave rise to common bread wheat, one of our most important crops (Figure 11.10 and *Commentary*).

This brings us to an interesting point. Polyploidy does have its advantages for some kinds of plants. Winesap apples (triploid) and potatoes, peanuts, and coffee plants (tetraploids) are larger and hardier than their diploid ancestors. The commercial banana (a sterile triploid) does not have the tooth-jarringly hard, inedible seeds of its diploid parent stock.

Plant breeders use experimental procedures for inducing polyploidy. **Colchicine** is a chemical derived from the autumn crocus (*Colchicum autumnale*). As one of its effects, colchicine inhibits microtubule assembly. Without microtubules, spindles can't form during nuclear division. Without a spindle apparatus, chromosomes can't separate during meiosis or mitosis. By adjusting colchicine concentrations and the length of exposure to it, plant breeders can produce nuclei with variable numbers of duplicated chromosome sets. When these cells are freed from colchicine exposure, they go on to divide and lead to polyploid cells. These cells may produce polyploid gametes.

Just how potent are the effects of colchicine? If you bathe an onion cell in colchicine for ninety-six hours, its nucleus ($2n = 16$) may end up with as many as a thousand chromosomes!

Chromosome Fission and Fusion

Some changes in chromosome number do not lead to changes in the amount of hereditary material present in offspring. Rather, the hereditary material becomes rearranged into fewer or more separate chromosome structures. In **chromosome fusion**, two nonhomologous chromosomes are physically fused together. The alteration is permanent; thereafter, the chromosome functions as a single strand. In **chromosome fission**, one chromosome splits in two.

Comparative studies of related species suggest that fusion has occurred often in the evolution of many groups of plants and animals. For instance, within the genus *Drosophila*, different species have much the same genetic material but different haploid chromosome numbers (ranging from six to three). Most deer have twenty-five pairs of chromo-

COMMENTARY

Cytogenetics, Mr. Sears, and a Lot More Bread

In the 1950s, Ernest Sears set out to apply the methods of cytogenetics to a problem of no small concern. He wanted to make one of the world's major food crop plants, the common bread wheat *Triticum aestivum*, more resistant to the attacks of a parasitic fungus. The fungus is a rust that destroys an appalling amount of wheat before it can be harvested.

Sears knew that a wild grass, *Aegilops umbellulata*, is genetically equipped to resist the fungal attacks. Could this rust-resistant species be crossed with bread wheat to produce a rust-resistant hybrid wheat? Not directly. The chromosome complements of the two species were mismatched, meiosis could not proceed properly, and fertile gametes could not be produced. In one of the classic experiments in genetic engineering, Sears circumvented the problem through the <u>bridging cross</u>. He indirectly performed the cross between these two sexually incompatible species by first introducing the chromosomes of one into an intermediate species that can successfully interbreed with both.

Triticum dicoccoides, one of the bread wheat's wild relatives, served as the go-between. It is a tetraploid (4 × 7 = 28) whose chromosomes are designated AABB. The rust-resistant wild grass is diploid (2 × 7 = 14), with chromosomes CC. The bridging cross produced hybrid ABC offspring, but they were sterile triploids (3 × 7, or 21 chromosomes).

Undaunted, Sears judiciously applied colchicine to the growing tips of the sterile hybrid seedlings. Chromosome doubling followed, so that ensuing mitotic cell divisions now produced cells with 42 chromosomes (AABBCC). Eventually some cells divided and differentiated into reproductive structures, which gave rise to gametes that could cross-fertilize with *T. aestivum*.

Like the hybrids just produced, *T. aestivum* has 42 chromosomes—but they are a little different. They are designated AABBDD (Figure 11.11). The cross between the hybrids and this bread wheat produced offspring of genotype AABBCD. Almost all the offspring were

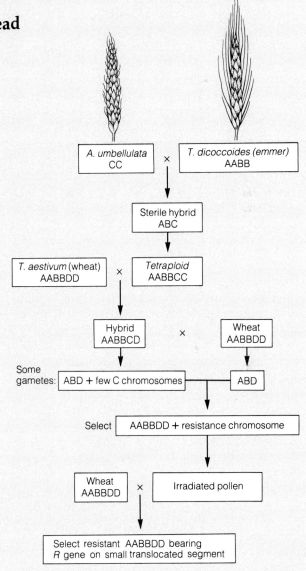

Summary of Sears' experiment to transfer rust resistance from a wild grass to common bread wheat. *R* indicates the gene (or genes) whose expression confers resistance to the fungus. (From D. Suzuki, A. Griffiths, and R. Lewontin, *An Introduction to Genetic Analysis*, Second edition. Copyright © 1981 by W. H. Freeman and Company. All rights reserved.)

sterile, because the C and D chromosome sets couldn't pair properly at meiosis. But Sears kept crossing the chromosomal misfits to wheat, and a *few* of the seeds resulting from the crosses germinated. They not only germinated, they grew into hybrid wheat plants that displayed rust resistance. Analysis showed that the new resistant strain had 43 chromosomes. Apparently, abnormal meiotic segregation had produced a gamete with 22 chromosomes—one of which was the C chromosome from the wild grass.

On that C chromosome was the gene (or genes) conferring rust resistance. But also on that C chromosome were genes conferring some not-so-great characteristics, from an agricultural standpoint. The new strain grew more like a raggedy weed than the tall (and easily harvestable) wheat, and its edible parts were scanty by comparison. The trick, then, was to get the "good" genetic material out of the otherwise undesirable chromosome. Sears decided to try inducing chromosomal breaks in the C chromosome by irradiating pollen grains from the new strain. He succeeded: many breaks occurred. And one result was exactly what he was looking for. The C chromosome segment carrying the resistant genetic material was inserted into a bread wheat chromosome! Sears used the pollen to fertilize AABBDD plants. The offspring were AABBDD with rust resistance—and with all the growth patterns and vigor characteristic of the parent wheat stock.

This example should not lead you to believe that all experiments turn out so fortuitously all of the time; plant breeding is complex business. But it does underscore the tremendous potential of genetic engineering for solving food production problems—a potential that keeps experimenters at the chromosomes and colchicine.

somes, but one species in India has only three. Apes (gibbons, orangutans, gorillas, chimpanzees) have twenty-four chromosome pairs. Humans have twenty-three. Human chromosome 2 contains just about the same amount of hereditary material found in two chimpanzee chromosomes. Somewhere in evolutionary time, it may have arisen through chromosome fusion in the ancestral primate stock from which humans arose.

Readings

Avers, C. 1980. *Genetics.* Revised edition. Boston: Willard Grant Press. Especially good coverage of chromosome abnormalities.

Ayala, F., and J. Kiger. 1980. *Modern Genetics.* Menlo Park: Benjamin/Cummings. Excellent discussions of the inheritance of sex and sex chromosome abnormalities.

Feldman, M., and E. Sears. 1981. "The Wild Gene Resources of Wheat." *Scientific American* 244(1):102–112.

Garber, E. 1972. *Cytogenetics: An Introduction.* New York: McGraw-Hill.

McKusick, V. 1971. "The Mapping of Human Chromosomes." *Scientific American* 224(4):104–113.

Morgan, T., A. Sturtevant, H. Muller, and C. Bridges. 1915. *The Mechanism of Mendelian Heredity.* New York: Holt. For those who like to browse through original research papers.

Strickberger, M. 1976. *Genetics.* Second edition. New York: Macmillan. This is the most comprehensive introductory genetics book presently available, a classic in its own time.

Sturtevant, A. 1965. *A History of Genetics.* New York: Harper & Row.

White, M. 1973. *Animal Cytology and Evolution.* Third edition. New York: Cambridge University Press.

Review Questions

1. State the difference between sex chromosomes and autosomes. In humans, _____ designates female, and _____ designates male.

2. Why did Morgan decide that *Drosophila* was a good candidate for cytogenetic studies? What did he hope to prove through his studies of sex inheritance in the fruit fly?

3. Explain how a linkage group is related to chromosome number. What is the meiotic basis of independent assortment as Mendel perceived it? How does linkage affect assortment of genes into gametes?

4. Using the Punnett square method, show how Morgan's *Drosophila* cross between a male recessive for white eyes and a female homozygous dominant for red eyes confirmed the existence of sex-linked genes through the phenotypic results in second-generation offspring.

5. The probability of crossing over and recombination occurring at a point somewhere between two genes located on the same chromosome is directly proportional to _____.

6. How is the frequency of crossing over between any two genes used in constructing a linkage map of chromosomes? Look at Figure 11.7 before giving your answer.

7. Cytogenetics is a wedding of cytology (the study of cell structure and function) and genetic analysis (the study of gene behavior and its phenotypic outcomes). Why has the development of G-banding been so important in cytogenetic studies of mammalian chromosomes?

8. Say that you are preparing a karyotype from a human blood sample in a laboratory. After arranging the photographic images of the metaphase chromosome pairs relative to one another, from 1 to 23, you realize that there are one Y and two X chromosomes in the sample. How might this abnormal chromosome number have arisen?

9. Deletions, duplications, inversions, and translocations are four kinds of changes in chromosome structure. What are some agents that induce the chromosome breaks that allow such changes to occur? Can you say why any one of these abnormalities helped prove that genes are carried in linear array on chromosomes?

10. Define aneuploidy, and give an example of how aneuploidy can arise. What is the difference between trisomy and triploidy?

11. Define polyploidy, and explain why it might occur more commonly among plants than animals.

12. How does polyploidy arise? Why are even-numbered polyploids more likely to survive and produce fertile offspring than odd-numbered polyploids?

13. State the eight main points of the chromosomal theory of inheritance.

Genetics Problems (Answers appear in Appendix II)

1. Recall that human sex chromosomes are XX for females and XY for males.
   a. Does a male child inherit his X chromosome from his mother or father?
   b. With respect to an X-linked gene, how many different types of gametes can a male produce?
   c. If a female is homozygous for an X-linked gene, how many different types of gametes can she produce with respect to this gene?
   d. If a female is heterozygous for an X-linked gene, how many different types of gametes can she produce with respect to this gene?

2. One human gene, which may be Y-linked, controls the length of hair on men's ears. One allele at this gene locus produces nonhairy ears; another allele form produces rather long hairs (hairy pinnae).
   a. Why would you *not* expect females to have hairy pinnae?
   b. If a man with hairy pinnae has sons, all of them will have hairy pinnae; if he has daughters, none of them will. Explain this statement.

3. Suppose that you have linked genes 1 and 2 with alleles A,a and B,b respectively. An individual is heterozygous for both genes, as in the following:

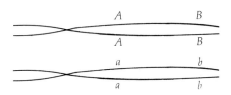

For each of the following crossover frequencies between these two genes, what genotypes would be expected among gametes from this individual, and with what frequencies?
   a. 0 percent
   b. 10 percent
   c. 25 percent

4. Assume the two genes mentioned in Problem 3 are separated by 10 map units. If the double heterozygous individual mates with an individual who is homozygous recessive for these same two genes, what genotypes would you expect among their offspring, and with what frequencies?

5. In *D. melanogaster,* a gene influencing eye color has red (dominant) and purple (recessive) alleles. Linked to this gene is another that determines wing length. A dominant allele at this second gene locus produces long wings; a recessive allele produces vestigial wings. Suppose a completely homozygous dominant female having red eyes and long wings mates with a male having purple eyes and vestigial wings. First-generation females are then crossed with purple-eyed, vestigial-winged males. From this second cross, offspring with the following characteristics are obtained:

252	red eyes, long wings
276	purple eyes, vestigial wings
42	red eyes, vestigial wings
30	purple eyes, long wings
600	offspring total

Based on these data, how many map units separate the two genes?

6. Suppose you cross a homozygous dominant long-winged fruit fly with a homozygous recessive vestigial-winged fly. Shortly after mating, the fertilized eggs are exposed to a level of x-rays known to cause chromosomal deletions. When these fertilized eggs subsequently develop into adults, most of the flies are long-winged and heterozygous. However, a few are vestigial-winged. Provide a possible explanation for the unexpected appearance of these vestigial-winged adults.

7. Individuals afflicted with Down's syndrome typically have an extra chromosome 21, so their cells have total of 47 chromosomes. However, in a few cases of Down's syndrome, 46 chromosomes are present. Included in this total are two normal-appearing chromosomes 21, and a longer-than-normal chromosome 14. Interpret this observation and indicate how these few individuals can have a normal chromosome number.

8. Refer to Figure 11.10. *Triticum turgidum* should produce gametes having 14 chromosomes (AB), and *T. tauschii* should produce gametes with 7 chromosomes (D). When these gametes combine, offspring having 7 + 14 = 21 chromosomes should be produced. How, then, did *T. aestivum* originate having 42 chromosomes (AABBDD)? If *T. aestivum* is backcrossed to *T. turgidum,* how many chromosomes would be present in the offspring? Would these offspring be fertile?

12

THE RISE OF
MOLECULAR GENETICS

Figure 12.1 James Watson and Francis Crick posing in 1953 by their newly unveiled model of DNA structure. (A. C. Barrington Brown © 1968 by J. D. Watson)

One might have wondered, in the spring of 1868, why the physician Johann Miescher was collecting quantities of cells from the pus of open wounds and, later, the sperm of a fish. Miescher knew what he was doing. Both kinds of cells are almost entirely nuclear in composition, with very little cytoplasm. Cell physiology was the doctor's research focus, and he was attempting to gather a large enough sample of nuclear material to identify its chemical composition. What he succeeded in isolating was a highly acidic substance, one that contained considerable phosphorus. Both properties seemed peculiar, compared with what was known about the composition of other organic substances. This substance was something different; Miescher called it "nuclein." He had discovered what came to be known as deoxyribonucleic acid, or DNA.

The discovery caused scarcely a ripple through the scientific community. At the time, only a few researchers were beginning to suspect that hereditary controls might be centered in the cell nucleus, and that an understanding of nuclear structure and composition might reveal the nature of those controls. As the century drew to a close, scattered work continued on various cell substances, "nuclein" included. Chemical analysis showed it to be composed of two kinds of nitrogen-containing bases and one kind of five-carbon sugar. No one thought much about it. In fact, from such inauspicious beginnings, seventy-five years would pass before DNA would be recognized as a substance of profound biological importance.

THE SEARCH FOR THE HEREDITARY MOLECULE

In the 1900s genetics and cytology converged, and led the way to new insights into the physical basis of inheritance (Chapter Eleven). Genetic researchers were probing more deeply than ever before into the nature of life. Microscopy and genetic analysis had pointed to the gene as the unit of heredity. Studies of plants and animals had provided strong evidence that genes are carried in organized, linear array on chromosomes. Messages of inheritance, then, had to be encoded in the molecules of those threadlike strands!

The genetic basis of an individual's phenotype is encoded in the molecular composition and organization of chromosomes.

If the molecular structure of chromosomes could be deduced, then perhaps it would be possible to discover how hereditary instructions are actually duplicated from one generation to the next. Yet how could details of chromosome structure be probed at the molecular level? One of the first approaches was devised by Fred Griffith during his work with bacteria. Let's look briefly at this work, for it figured in the development of our understanding of the molecular basis of inheritance. It also is a good example of how control groups can be used to advantage in biological experiments.

The Puzzle of Bacterial Transformation

In 1928, Griffith isolated two distinct strains of *Diplococcus pneumoniae,* a bacterium that causes the lung disease pneumonia. He called one strain the "S" form, because its colonies had a smooth appearance. The other strain was called the "R" form, because of the rough surface appearance of its colonies (Figure 12.2). Griffith tested the effects of S and R forms on laboratory mice.

Living S cells served as one control group. When they were injected into mice, the mice promptly contracted pneumonia and died. Blood samples from the dead mice were teeming with bacteria; the S form had to be a disease-causing strain. Living R cells served as a second control group. When they were injected into mice, nothing happened; the R cells were harmless.

Armed with these results, Griffith began experimenting. He killed S cells by heating them, injected them into mice—and nothing happened. Then he mixed live R cells with *dead* S cells, and injected them into mice. Incredibly, the combination led to pneumonia and death—and blood samples from the dead mice were teeming with *live* S cells!

What was going on? Maybe heat-killed S cells weren't really dead. But if that were true, then the mice injected with heat-killed S cells alone (the first experimental group) should have contracted the disease, too. Or maybe R cells had mutated into killer forms. But if that were true, why didn't the same thing happen in the control group of mice receiving only living R cells? It had to be that the dead S cells transferred their ability to cause infection to the harmless R cells. Through further experiments, it became clear that the "harmless" cells had become permanently transformed—for all their offspring also caused infections. *The transformation had to involve a change in the bacterium's hereditary system itself.*

Griffith's discovery was a door to the molecular world of heredity. He showed that hereditary material could be passed between organisms in a nonconventional manner—one that could be subject to **assay** (chemical testing to determine the presence and amount of components of a system).

News of Griffith's results reached an American bacteriologist, Oswald Avery, and his colleagues. For a decade they worked on identifying the biochemical nature of the "transforming principle" underlying the permanent change in the bacterial hereditary system. In 1944, they reported that their assays pointed to DNA as the molecule by which this heritable feature was transmitted through generations.

Their evidence was not widely publicized. It was ahead of its time and people generally had no idea of what it meant. Besides, the scientific community was adhering to a notion (by then a generation old) that only proteins could serve as hereditary molecules. Proteins, after all, are diverse and complex. In contrast, nucleic acids were thought to have a simple repeating-unit structure, like starch or cellulose. How, then, could nucleic acids encode all the instructions necessary to build and maintain any living organism?

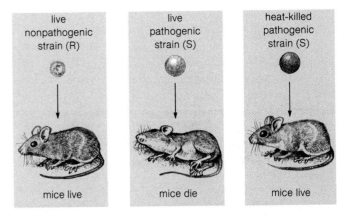

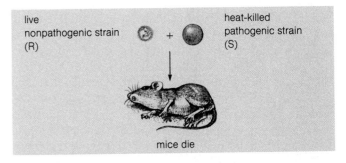

Figure 12.2 Griffith's experiments with harmless (R) strains and disease-causing (S) strains of *Diplococcus pneumoniae*, as described in the text. (You may be wondering why the S form is deadly, and the R form harmless. The killer S form shrouds its cell wall with a smooth protective capsule, which resists attack by the host cell's normal defenses. The R form has no such capsule; hence the host's defense system destroys the R form before it can cause the disease.)

Despite this prevailing notion, Avery's message did not go entirely unnoticed. The biochemist Erwin Chargaff, among others, came under its influence. As you will see, his studies yielded more information about DNA.

Bacteriophage Studies

In the 1940s, Max Delbrück, Alfred Hershey, and Salvador Luria formed a core group for research into the hereditary system of a class of viruses called **bacteriophages**. All viruses are disease-causing agents composed only of nucleic acid and protein. Bacteriophages infect only specific types of bacterial cells. To Delbrück's mind, bacteriophages were the most stripped-down reproductive package of all, and the bacteria they infected were among the simplest of all living organisms. He assumed, correctly, that studies of the bacteriophage hereditary system would yield insights into the molecular nature of heredity in general. Let's look at just one set of bacteriophage experiments conducted during this period. These experiments were based on using a bacteriophage infectious cycle as a research tool.

Like all viruses, bacteriophages do not deliberately go about ambushing potential victims. They haven't any means whatsoever of moving about on their own. The only way they can infect their target host is to bump accidentally into it. Bacteriophages have receptor molecules that are complementary to bacterial cell surface recognition factors (Chapter Five). Once contact is made and binding occurs, the infectious cycle begins.

Think about what happens in the infectious cycle of "T-even" bacteriophages. First, the bacteriophage injects its contents into the host (Figure 12.3). Within sixty seconds, the bacterium stops making most of the things it normally would make. It produces modified enzymes or entirely new enzymes. Subsequently, all of its enzyme-mediated activities are devoted to building new bacteriophages! In less than half an hour, the virus reproduces itself a hundred-fold. Then the infected bacterium undergoes lysis: its cell wall is degraded (by bacteriophage-prescribed enzymes), and the cell bursts. By subverting the host's biosynthetic machinery, the bacteriophage reproduces and liberates new infectious particles for encounters with new, living hosts.

In considering the reproductive outcome of this infectious cycle, Hershey and his colleague Martha Chase asked an intriguing question. What was the bacteriophage injecting into the host? Whatever it was, it had to be the chemical blueprint specifying "build bacteriophages." Knowing that a bacteriophage contains only DNA and protein, they nar-rowed their question to whether the injected substance was protein, DNA, or both. To find the answer, they relied on a chemical difference between DNA and protein.

Protein contains sulfur but no phosphorus. DNA contains phosphorus but no sulfur. Both chemical elements have radioactive isotopes (Chapter Three). When bacterial cells are grown on a culture medium containing radioactive sulfur, they must use this isotope in one of the amino acid building blocks in protein assembly. Suppose bacteriophages infect these cells. Following lysis, new bacteriophage particles would contain labeled protein. Why? They can be built *only* of materials (in this case, including radioactive ones) available from their hosts. If these labeled particles are used to infect unlabeled bacteria, it should be possible to determine whether the radioactive sulfur is left outside the host or is injected into it. The same kind of experiment can be used to determine the destination of radioactive phosphorus, hence DNA.

Hershey and Chase performed these experiments. As Figure 12.4 shows, they found that the radioactive sulfur remained mostly outside the bacterial cells, as part of bacteriophage bodies. The radioactive phosphorus ended up inside the host cells. They also found that radioactive phosphorus was present in the DNA of certain members of the next bacteriophage generation—but that the radioactive sulfur-labeled protein was not. Here was proof that bacteriophage transmits DNA, not protein, to the next generation. This evidence strongly suggested that DNA is the hereditary molecule.

Later work showed that RNA rather than DNA is the hereditary molecule in some viruses. For all *cells* studied to date—and this includes cells of many species from all five kingdoms—the following is true:

Encoded in the molecular structure of DNA are instructions for producing all heritable traits.

THE RIDDLE OF THE DOUBLE HELIX

Now the search was on to find out precisely how a DNA molecule is structured. From earlier studies, it was known that the molecule contains only four different kinds of nucleotides. A **nucleotide** is the structural unit of all nucleic acids. It is composed of a sugar molecule, a phosphate group, and a nitrogen-containing molecule called a base.

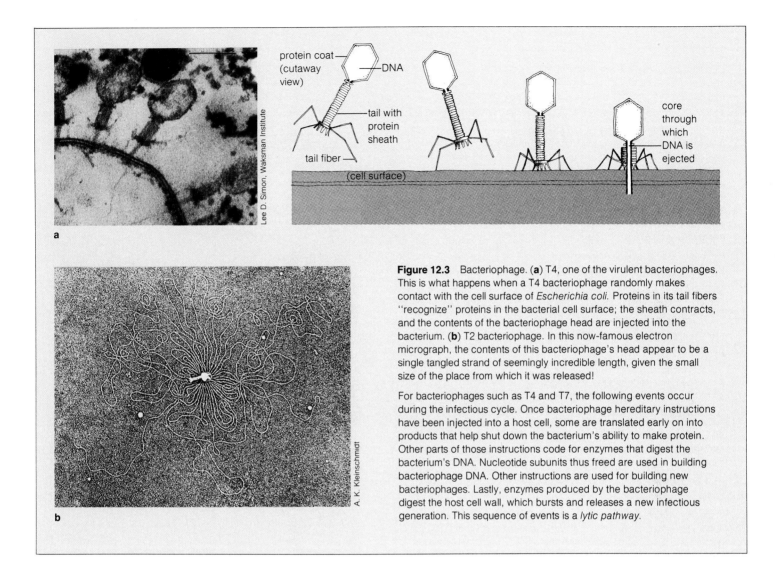

Figure 12.3 Bacteriophage. (**a**) T4, one of the virulent bacteriophages. This is what happens when a T4 bacteriophage randomly makes contact with the cell surface of *Escherichia coli*. Proteins in its tail fibers "recognize" proteins in the bacterial cell surface; the sheath contracts, and the contents of the bacteriophage head are injected into the bacterium. (**b**) T2 bacteriophage. In this now-famous electron micrograph, the contents of this bacteriophage's head appear to be a single tangled strand of seemingly incredible length, given the small size of the place from which it was released!

For bacteriophages such as T4 and T7, the following events occur during the infectious cycle. Once bacteriophage hereditary instructions have been injected into a host cell, some are translated early on into products that help shut down the bacterium's ability to make protein. Other parts of those instructions code for enzymes that digest the bacterium's DNA. Nucleotide subunits thus freed are used in building bacteriophage DNA. Other instructions are used for building new bacteriophages. Lastly, enzymes produced by the bacteriophage digest the host cell wall, which bursts and releases a new infectious generation. This sequence of events is a *lytic pathway*.

All four nucleotides of DNA have the five-carbon sugar, deoxyribose, and a phosphate group:

However, each nucleotide has one of four different bases. Two of these bases are single-ring *pyrimidines,* called **cytosine** and **thymine**. The other two are both double-ring *purines,* called **adenine** and **guanine**:

Figure 12.4 Hershey-Chase experiments to determine the destination of DNA and protein from T2 bacteriophage during infection of *E. coli*.

(**a**) One population of bacterial cells was grown on a medium containing a radioactive isotope of phosphorus (^{32}P), a building block for DNA but not for protein. Another population was grown on a medium containing a radioactive isotope of sulfur (^{35}S), a building block usually found in protein but not in DNA. The molecules in which ^{32}P and ^{35}S became incorporated were thereby tagged, or radioactively labeled. They could be distinguished, by certain methods, from unlabeled molecules in the cells being studied. In the diagrams, the green dots and black dots represent the label (radioactivity).

(**b**) Bacterial cells so labeled were exposed to and infected by T2 bacteriophages, which entered the lytic pathway (Figure 12.2).

(**c**) The bacteriophage progeny released upon lysis were radioactively labeled, for their protein and DNA had to have been assembled only from molecules available in the host cells.

(**d**) The labeled progeny were allowed to infect fresh, unlabeled bacteria. During infection, they remained attached to the host cell surface, as shown in Figure 12.2.

(**e**) Suspensions of cells bearing their attackers were osmotically shocked by being churned rapidly in a kitchen blender. The shearing forces caused the bacteriophage bodies to break away from the cell surface. In the first experiment, analysis showed that the bacteriophage body, not the host cell, contained the ^{35}S. In the second experiment, the bacterial cells contained ^{32}P; the labeled DNA had been injected into the host cells.

(**f**) In other samples of the infected cells, the bacteriophage life cycle was allowed to proceed.

In the first experiment, analysis showed that bacteriophages released upon lysis contained very little ^{35}S. In the second experiment, however, bacteriophage contained radioactive DNA. The DNA, not protein, was being transmitted through generations of bacteriophages.

(These experiments did leave some room for doubt, for a small amount of protein is injected into bacterial cells along with DNA during the normal infection process. Later experiments used bacteria stripped of their cell walls, and pure labeled DNA stripped from bacteriophage. The results of these "clean" experiments did confirm Hershey and Chase's conclusion that DNA is the genetic material.)

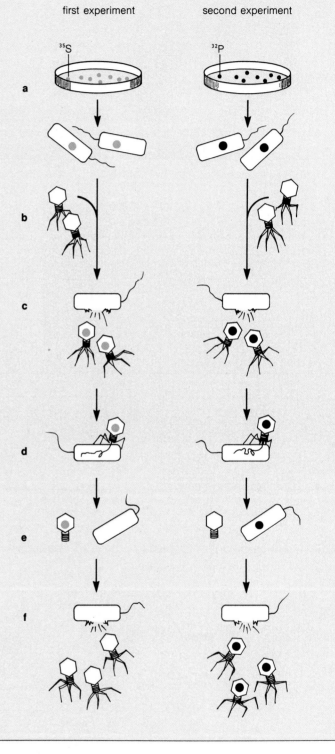

first experiment   second experiment

purines (double rings)

adenine (A)

guanine (G)

The asterisks indicate where a bond forms between each base and the sugar ring structure. In flat formula, the three components of all nucleotides show the same general bonding pattern:

(phosphate group is attached to carbon 5′)

NH_2

$O = C$

$HO - P - O - CH_2$

(base is attached to carbon 1′)

OH

Here, the small numerals identify the positions of atoms making up the ring structures of the sugar and the base. (The carbon atoms of the sugar are numbered 1′, 2′, 3′, and so forth simply to distinguish them from the numbering of atoms in the base.) The phosphate group of a nucleotide such as the one shown above can be linked to the carbon 3′ position on the sugar ring structure of another nucleotide. A DNA molecule is composed of many different nucleotides linked together in this manner. Figure 12.5 suggests how four could be joined in part of a DNA strand.

By the early 1950s, this much was known about the molecular structure of DNA. Chargaff's work added two more insights:

1. The four bases in DNA may vary greatly in relative amounts from one species to the next. Yet the relative amounts are always the *same* among members of the same species.

2. The amount of adenine present equals the amount of thymine, and the amount of cytosine equals the amount of guanine (A = T, and C = G).

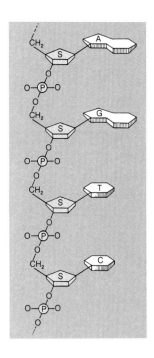

Figure 12.5 How nucleotides can be linked together in a DNA strand. The S designates the sugar components, which are linked with phosphate groups into a sugar-phosphate backbone. Notice how the bases project from the backbone. (Here, A indicates adenine; G, guanine; T, thymine; and C, cytosine.)

At about the same time, Maurice Wilkins and his associates were using **x-ray diffraction** methods to determine DNA structure. The atoms in a crystal of any substance can bend a narrow x-ray beam. When the atoms are arranged in a repeating pattern, they will bend an x-ray beam in a regular way. When a piece of film placed behind the crystal is exposed by the x-rays, a pattern of dots and streaks shows up on it. Each dot represents a beam that has been diverted by a given kind of repeating atomic unit. By itself, the dot pattern doesn't reveal the molecular structure. But the distances and angles between these dots can be used to calculate the position of atomic groups relative to one another in the crystal.

One of Wilkin's coworkers, Rosalind Franklin, obtained some especially clear x-ray diffraction images of oriented molecules of DNA. Her analyses of those images strongly suggested three things. First, the molecule had to be long and thin, with a uniform 2-nanometer diameter. Second, DNA had to be highly repetitive: some structural element was being repeated every 0.34 nanometer, and another every 3.4 nanometers. Third, the molecule had to be helical, with an overall shape like a circular stairway.

If the DNA molecule were helical, would its three-dimensional structure turn out to resemble that of protein chains? Linus Pauling had only recently identified certain

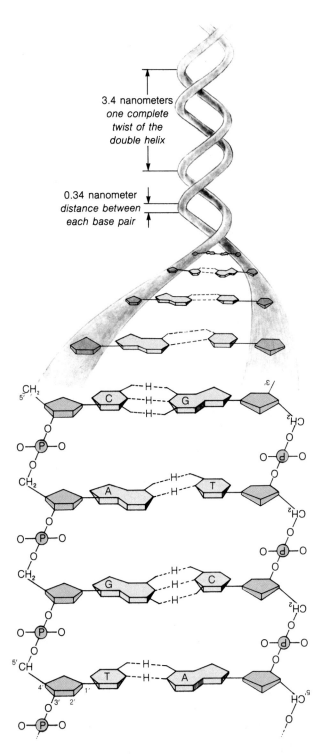

3.4 nanometers
one complete twist of the double helix

0.34 nanometer
distance between each base pair

Figure 12.6 Representation of a DNA double helix. Notice how the two sugar-phosphate backbones run in opposite directions. This is the only arrangement in which one nucleotide base can become aligned with and bonded to its complementary base in the DNA molecule.

protein chains as being a single helical coil, held in place by hydrogen bonds. In the early 1950s, James Watson (a postdoctoral student from Indiana University) teamed up with Francis Crick (a young Cambridge researcher), and together they came up with the answer. They deduced that the DNA molecule is indeed coiled into a helix—*but that the helix is double, with two DNA strands wound one around the other.*

Patterns of Base Pairing

Watson and Crick had puzzled over the question of how nucleotides are arranged in DNA. They knew the arrangement couldn't be random. If it were, then the molecule would bulge in regions where the double-ring purines were abundant. It also would narrow down in regions where the single-ring pyrimidines were abundant. However, diffraction data suggested that DNA has a uniform diameter. Watson and Crick also knew that in terms of relative amounts, A = T and G = C. Purines probably were *physically paired* with pyrimidines in DNA. What was the pairing arrangement?

The two researchers shuffled and reshuffled paper cutouts of the nucleotides. They consulted with Jerry Donahue, a chemist, who provided insights into the structure and possible bonding sites of each kind of nucleotide. They discovered that in a certain orientation, adenine and thymine form a pair of hydrogen bonds with each other. In a very similar orientation, guanine and cytosine form three hydrogen bonds with each other.

If *two* DNA chains were arranged so that their nucleotide bases faced each other, then hydrogen bonds could easily bridge the gap between them, like rungs of a ladder (Figure 12.6). Watson and Crick constructed scale models of how this "ladder" might look. The only arrangements possible in their model were purine-pyrimidine pairs: A—T and G—C. The constancy of the two purine-pyrimidine arrangements is now called the **principle of base pairing**.

In the ladder model, the only way that purine-pyrimidine pairs align is to have two strands running in *opposing directions* and twisted together into a helix (Figure 12.1). Because the model was built to scale with known atomic sizes, it could be calculated that there was a base pair every 0.34 nanometer and a complete twist of the helix every 3.4 nanometers. Also, the helix diameter came out to be 2 nanometers. Thus the model fit all existing data.

With such base pairing, cytosine would always be present in proportions equal to guanine, and thymine in proportions equal to adenine. Yet there could be variation in the total amount of A—T relative to the total amount of G—C present in the DNA of different species. Why? Any pair could follow any other in the DNA double helix, which means that the number of different sequences possible for these two kinds of base pairs is staggering! For instance, even in one small DNA region, the sequence might be:

```
...T A T...   ...C T A...   ...G G C...   ...G T G...
   | | |   or    | | |   or    | | |   or    | | |
...A T A...   ...G A T...   ...C C G...   ...C A C...
```

and so on. Thus the Watson-Crick model of DNA structure reflected at once the twin properties of unity and diversity inherent in the molecule of inheritance:

There is constancy in base pairing (adenine to thymine, guanine to cytosine) between the two DNA strands of a double helix.

There can be variation in which kind of base follows the next in a DNA strand.

Unwinding the Double Helix: The Secret of Self-Replication

Once DNA structure had been deduced, Watson and Crick immediately saw how the DNA molecule might be duplicated prior to cell reproduction (Chapter Nine). If the two DNA strands were unwound from each other, their bases would become exposed to the nuclear environment. Such unwinding could occur readily enough, given that only relatively weak hydrogen bonds hold the two strands together. Assuming that appropriate enzymes were present, the strands could be separated, then free nucleotides in the surroundings could become attached to exposed bases on the two parent strands. If the attachments followed the patterns of base pairing, *then the only sequence that could be assembled on one parent strand would have to be an exact duplicate of the base sequence occurring on the other parent strand.*

Figure 12.7 illustrates this view of DNA replication. As you can see, when a region of the double helix is unwound, the two separated DNA strands can act as a pair of templates (structural patterns); each is the complement of the other. *Each parent strand remains intact, and a new companion strand is assembled on each one.* One parent strand then winds up with a new partner, forming a double helix. The other parent strand winds up with a new partner also, forming another double helix. In each of the two double helices, one "old" DNA strand has been conserved.

Many experiments have been conducted to test this view of DNA replication. One of the most impressive, per-

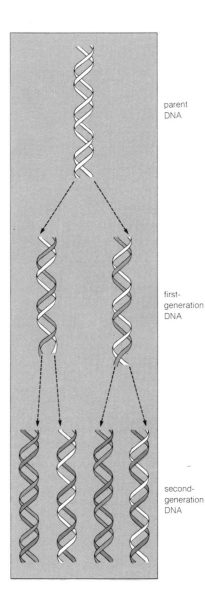

Figure 12.7 Semiconservative nature of DNA replication, through two generations. The original two-stranded DNA molecule is shown in white. Two new strands (blue) are assembled on them. The new strands in the second generation are shown in dark brown.

formed by Matthew Meselson and Frank Stahl, is described in Figure 12.9. Through such experiments, conducted with many different kinds of organisms, this mode of replication is now known to be the near-universal basis of DNA duplication.

Prior to cell division, the double-stranded DNA molecule unwinds and is duplicated through semiconservative replication: each of the two parent strands remains intact—it is conserved—and a new companion strand is assembled on each one. Two "half-old, half-new" DNA molecules result.

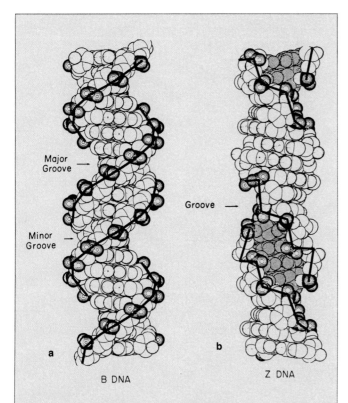

Figure 12.8 New twists in the double helix.

In the Watson-Crick model of DNA (shown in **a**), the molecular structure is highly uniform. Base pairs are regularly spaced, and the double helix curves smoothly as it twists to the right. This double helix, which occurs in fully hydrated surroundings, is known as the *β-form* of DNA.

Over the past three decades, it has become clear that DNA structure can be much more varied. Bases can tilt at different angles, they can stack together more closely, and the double helix can be wound up more tightly. In fact, DNA shows great variation throughout its length! The variations might be related to solution conditions (which dissolved ions are present, and in what concentrations), and on which bases are present in a given region of the double helix.

For instance, in some DNA, the sugar-phosphate backbone zigzags to the left, as shown in (**b**). For this reason, left-handed DNA is called the *Z-form*. Here, bases are positioned more at the periphery and are more exposed to the surroundings. Being more exposed, bases in Z-form stretches of DNA might interact more readily with enzymes and proteins. Z-form stretches might thus be important regions of control over gene expression. (Illustration courtesy Alexander Rich from computer graphics program developed by Gary J. Quigley)

DNA REPLICATION

Meanwhile, Back at the Forks . . .

Semiconservative replication is simple in theory: the two strands of a DNA double helix are separated, and each is used as a template for a new strand of complementary nucleotides. But stop to think about what is going on, and where it is taking place. For instance, *Escherichia coli* is a relatively simple prokaryote. Although its typical body length is a mere 2 micrometers, its circular DNA molecule is about 1,360 micrometers long (Figure 12.10). The DNA double helix turns about 400,000 times on its long axis. Each strand has about 4,000,000 nucleotides. For replication to occur, the entire double helix has to be separated into two strands. Separation requires that the double helix be untwisted so that new nucleotides can base-pair and become joined together in precise order on each parent strand. The newly forming double-stranded molecules must then form two separate helices, without getting tangled with each other. All of the untwisting, strand separation, assembly of a duplicate strand, and twisting up again can be finished in less than thirty minutes!

To get a better sense of how this activity is accomplished, let's address three questions. First, where on the DNA molecule does replication actually start? Second, in what direction does strand assembly proceed? Third, what is the actual assembly mechanism?

Origin and Direction of Replication: In prokaryotes, most double-stranded DNA molecules are closed circles. For replication to begin, an enzyme nicks the circle at a specific initiation site. This site is a particular base sequence called the **origin**. Other enzymes unzip the DNA double helix on each side of the nick. Thus replication is **bidirectional**: it proceeds simultaneously in two directions from an origin of replication (Figure 12.11). All eukaryotes (and some viruses) have linear rather than circular DNA. Replication of a linear double helix is also bidirectional, but there are many origins spaced along the length of eukaryotic DNA. Replication proceeds in both directions from each of these origins.

Strand Assembly: From the work of John Cairns, we know now that DNA synthesis occurs at **replication forks**. In these limited V-shaped regions, some enzymes are separating the two complementary strands of the parent double helix, and other enzymes are simultaneously assembling new nucleotides on the separated strands. We can depict a replication fork in the following manner:

Figure 12.9 Meselson and Stahl's use of density-gradient centrifugation for testing whether DNA strands are separated and new ones formed upon each one during replication.

Density-gradient centrifugation is used to separate molecules of different densities. A centrifuge is a power-driven spinning device with tubes attached to its rotating arms. Typically these tubes are filled with concentrated solutions of heavy salts such as cesium chloride. High-speed spinning creates a force that drives the densest molecules to the bottom of the tubes, intermediate-density molecules toward the middle, and least dense molecules in some region closer to the top.

Meselson and Stahl grew bacteria on a medium containing a heavy isotope of nitrogen (a component of DNA). Some of these cells were transferred to a medium containing a lighter isotope of nitrogen. DNA was extracted from cells of the parent generation and the F_1 generation; DNA was also extracted from F_2 generation cells.

By choosing a solution that has the same density as ordinary DNA, the researchers knew that centrifugation would cause DNA of lighter weight to band in one part of the tube, and DNA of heavier weight to band in another. If DNA replication did involve the separation of parent strands and the formation of new, complementary strands upon them, then the first-generation DNA would be composed of one heavy and one light strand. The density of these hybrid molecules would be between the heavy DNA and light DNA bands in the centrifuge tube. The results agreed exactly with these expectations.

b. *DNA is extracted from cells at each stage, mixed with cesium chloride solution, and placed in centrifuge tube:*

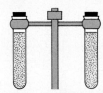

c. *Solution is centrifuged for two days. Centrifugal force drives cesium chloride toward the tube's base. But this is counteracted by diffusion. Thus a density gradient is created in the tube. DNA molecules band in regions where their density matches that of the cesium chloride solution:*

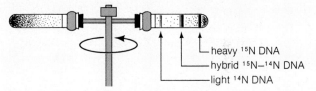

— heavy ^{15}N DNA
— hybrid ^{15}N–^{14}N DNA
— light ^{14}N DNA

d. *Results from tests on labeled DNA of cells taken from parent generation, F_1 and F_2 generations:*

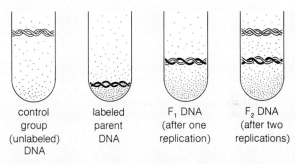

| control group (unlabeled) DNA | labeled parent DNA | F_1 DNA (after one replication) | F_2 DNA (after two replications) |

Compare these results with the control group (unlabeled DNA) shown to the left in this series.

a. *Bacteria are grown on ^{15}N-containing medium, then transferred to one containing ^{14}N:*

| ^{15}N | ^{14}N | ^{14}N |
| parent cells | F_1 cells | F_2 cells |

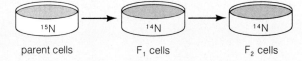

3′ replication fork 5′
direction of separation
5′ 3′

Reiji Okazaki was the first to realize DNA synthesis is not the same on both strands in a replication fork. On one, nucleotides are assembled continuously, one after another. (The continuously formed chain is the "leading" strand.) But on the other, short stretches of nucleotides are first assembled, then enzymes link them together. (The discontinuously formed chain is the "lagging" strand.) It's

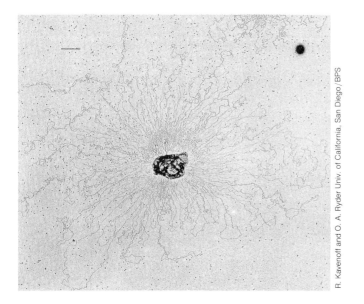

Figure 12.10 A single molecule of a DNA double helix from the bacterium *Escherichia coli*. All that remains of the bacterial owner are the plasma membrane fragments near the center of the micrograph.

R. Kavenoff and O. A. Ryder Univ. of California, San Diego / BPS

something like boxcars being assembled behind a series of engines on a railroad track, with workers (enzymes) later coupling the boxcars together into a long, continuous train.

As Figure 12.12 suggests, new nucleotides are not added any which way. For both strands, *overall* growth has to be in the 3′ → 5′ direction. Enzymes can add a new nucleotide only where an —OH group projects from the 3′ carbon atom of a nucleotide that is already positioned on the "track."

Enzymes of DNA Replication and Repair

The task of accurately assembling new DNA for each new cell generation is entrusted to a battery of enzymes and related proteins. Dominating the replication events are DNA polymerases. All of the DNA polymerases are construction enzymes, and they function in one or both of these roles:

1. Assembling nucleotide segments into a continuous DNA strand on a parent template, in a sequence that is complementary to the template.

2. "Proofreading" the growing DNA chain for mismatched base pairs, and replacing them with correct bases.

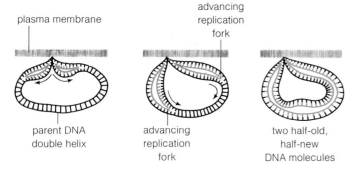

Figure 12.11 Bidirectional replication from the membrane-attached initiation site of a circular prokaryotic DNA molecule.

Figure 12.12 Direction of growth of newly forming DNA strands. Nucleotides can be added only in the 5′ ⟶ 3′ direction, as the yellow strand indicates. Bases projecting from the parent strand dictate which kind of nucleotide will follow the next in line. But an exposed —OH group must be available on the growing end of the new strand if enzymes are to catalyze the addition of more nucleotides.

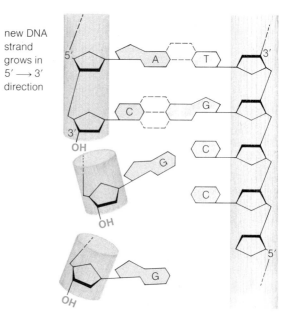

The proofreading function of some DNA polymerases is one of the reasons why replication is so phenomenally accurate. On the average, for every 9 or 10 *billion* base pairs formed, only *one* mistake creeps in!

There are many other replication enzymes. But here we will comment on just one more, for it plays another role in the recombination mechanisms to be described shortly. **DNA ligase** is a coupling enzyme: it links together the short DNA fragments into one continuous polynucleotide strand. It works only when the "boxcars" are already hydrogen bonded (base-paired) to the DNA template strand. Because of its coupling action, DNA ligase is also able to close nicks that occur in DNA.

This brings us to an important point. Your own life, and the life of all other organisms, depends on the *long-term stability* of chemical messages encoded in DNA, as well as on the faithful replication of those messages. Yet DNA is not in itself a particularly stable molecule. It is highly vulnerable to damage by chemical agents, viral attacks, and radiation of wavelengths that are far more energetic than those of the visible light spectrum. The same enzymes that govern replication, however, safeguard the integrity of the DNA molecule.

Summary of DNA Replication

From what we have covered so far in this unit, we can piece together the following summary of DNA replication:

1. Encoded in DNA are chemical messages for building all the enzymes and other proteins necessary to reproduce a particular set of organic materials that make up each kind of cell.

2. It follows that a new daughter cell must receive a copy of the parent DNA. For this to happen, DNA must be replicated before a parent cell divides by binary fission, mitosis, or meiosis.

3. DNA replication is *semiconservative*. Each parent strand of a double helix remains intact (is conserved), and a new companion strand is assembled on each one. Two "half-old, half-new" molecules result.

4. DNA replication is *bidirectional*. It proceeds in two directions at the same time from one or more origins (start points). Only one origin exists in a prokaryotic DNA molecule. Many thousands exist in eukaryotic DNA, so bidirectional replication proceeds simultaneously at many places along the eukaryotic DNA molecule.

5. Replication proceeds only at a *replication fork*. In this limited V-shaped region, enzymes unzip the parent molecule and simultaneously assemble new DNA on the exposed regions of the parent strands.

6. DNA synthesis is *continuous* on one parent strand but *discontinuous* on the other. (In discontinuous assembly, short stretches of nucleotides are first positioned at intervals on one parent strand, then enzymes link the short stretches together into a continuous chain.)

7. Replication requires unwinding, construction, coupling, and proofreading enzymes. Many of the enzymes also repair damage inflicted on the DNA molecule by chemical agents, viruses, and harmful radiation. Thus replication enzymes help assure the long-term stability of the DNA molecule as well as its accurate duplication.

DNA RECOMBINATION

Molecular Basis of Recombination

Earlier chapters described how homologous chromosomes undergo breakage and swap segments at meiosis. The event is a form of crossing over, and its outcome is genetic recombination. Now that we've looked at the molecular nature of the hereditary material, we can expand on that initial picture of meiotic crossing over. As you will see, the same enzymes governing DNA replication and repair take part in recombination events. Their action results in **recombinant DNA**: whole molecules or fragments that incorporate parts of two different parent DNA molecules.

Genetic recombination depends in large part on the same enzymes that govern DNA replication and repair.

Let's start with what is known about the molecular events of crossing over between nonsister chromatids of homologous chromosomes. At the cytological level, crossing over is said to occur at a particular frequency between two given genes on a chromatid (Chapter Nine). However, when you stop to think about it, why couldn't segments also be swapped *within* the boundaries of a single gene? Studies at the molecular level indicate that, on very rare occasions, such intragenic recombination does indeed occur. It has not yet been possible to identify all the activities

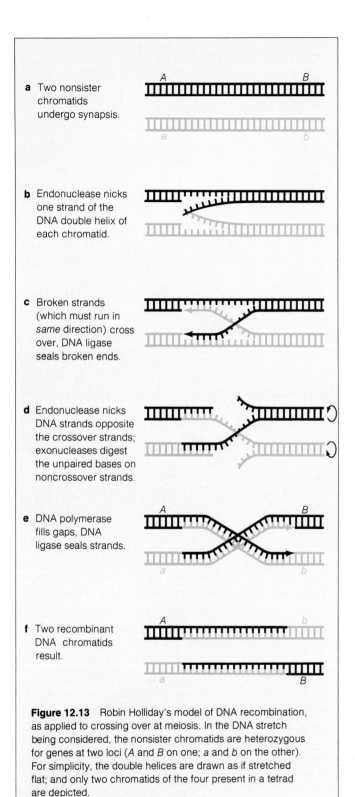

a Two nonsister chromatids undergo synapsis.

b Endonuclease nicks one strand of the DNA double helix of each chromatid.

c Broken strands (which must run in *same* direction) cross over, DNA ligase seals broken ends.

d Endonuclease nicks DNA strands opposite the crossover strands; exonucleases digest the unpaired bases on noncrossover strands.

e DNA polymerase fills gaps, DNA ligase seals strands.

f Two recombinant DNA chromatids result.

Figure 12.13 Robin Holliday's model of DNA recombination, as applied to crossing over at meiosis. In the DNA stretch being considered, the nonsister chromatids are heterozygous for genes at two loci (*A* and *B* on one; *a* and *b* on the other). For simplicity, the double helices are drawn as if stretched flat; and only two chromatids of the four present in a tetrad are depicted.

associated with this event, but there is general agreement on the manner in which the activities unfold.

First, in both nonsister chromatids, enzymes called **endonucleases** nick (or cleave) one strand of the double helix. They do this by hydrolyzing phosphate bonds between nucleotides. Hydrogen bonds unzip in the nicked region, and part of the strand is displaced from the double helix (Figure 12.13). Its free end invades the nicked strand on the nonsister chromatid. With this invasion, two single-stranded regions of DNA are attached to *both* chromatids. DNA polymerase now assembles complementary bases on the single-stranded regions, and DNA ligase seals the ends.

Among bacteria, recombination can occur during conjugation, transformation, and transduction. In *conjugation,* DNA is transferred between bacteria of two different mating strains that have made cell-to-cell contact. The transfer involves the main circular DNA molecule—and it involves small circles of double-helical DNA that may also be present in the cytoplasm.

For example, some extra DNA circles are known as **episomes**. One kind controls the production of conjugation tubes (cytoplasmic bridges) that can form between *E. coli* cells. Bacterial cells containing this episome are called F+; those without it are F−. Contact between cells of the two types triggers the formation of a conjugation tube between them (Figure 12.14). When conjugation occurs, the episome undergoes replication. Enzymes nick one strand of the episome double helix, and one separated strand unrolls through the tube. DNA synthesis proceeds on the separated strands in both the donor cell and the recipient cell (Figure 12.15). Once replicated inside the receiving cell, the episome can undergo crossing over with the host's main DNA molecule and become incorporated into it. Once incorporated, it can promote conjugation with F− cells through the DNA-directed synthesis of proteins from which conjugation tubes are assembled.

In *transduction,* bacterial DNA fragments accidentally become packaged in a viral coat when the circular DNA molecule breaks apart following bacteriophage attack. The fragments are carried into a new bacterial host cell as if they were viral DNA. When the particle injects its contents into a new host cell, the DNA may undergo recombination with the host DNA molecule.

In *transformation,* bacterial cells become exposed to DNA fragments from ruptured cells of a different bacterial strain, or from an entirely different organism. Some fragments are taken up by the bacterium and undergo random recombination with the bacterial DNA. Griffith and then Avery were among the first to treat bacterial cells with

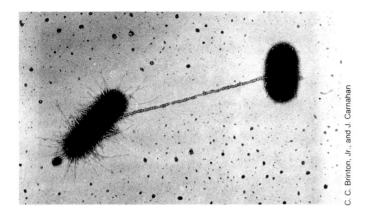

Figure 12.14 Conjugation bridge between a recipient (F⁻) cell, shown to the right, and a donor (F⁺) cell of *E. coli*. The bridging structure between them is called a pilus; it originates from the F⁺ cell.

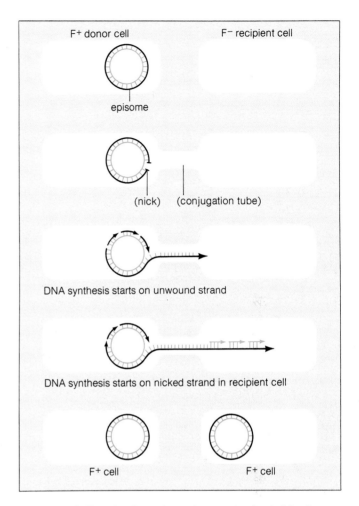

Figure 12.15 Transfer of an episome between two bacterial cells during conjugation. For simplicity, the main DNA molecule is not shown.

extracts obtained from different bacterial strains, and to observe the manner in which genetic transformation can affect phenotype. Here, as in transduction, the length of DNA being transferred to the host DNA is quite small compared with the length of the main bacterial chromosome. As you will now see, these small packages of DNA play a key role in recombinant DNA research.

Recombinant DNA Research

Is there, in the natural world, a DNA double helix that is not already a recombinant molecule? Given the exchange mechanisms of the sort just outlined, we probably would be hard-pressed to find one. Viruses, bacteria, fungi, plants, animals—all are subject to DNA shufflings. It isn't even that recombinations are limited to members of the same species. Among flowering plants, for example, DNA of one species becomes integrated into the DNA of another during gamete formation following hybridization. Viral DNA routinely invades the DNA molecules of bacterial, plant, and animal hosts. Biochemists and molecular geneticists have been identifying mechanisms by which DNA from different species undergoes recombination. Knowledge of these mechanisms has opened up the frontier of recombinant DNA technology.

Recombinant DNA research involves (1) joining a piece of DNA onto another DNA molecule and (2) putting the recombined molecule of two DNAs from different sources into a cell in which it can be duplicated. Recom-

bination methods require precise identification of the gene to be transferred, and this requires the manufacture of suitable probes to find the right genes. They also require appropriate vectors: regions of DNA that contain the nucleotide sequence necessary to introduce a newly isolated gene from some species into a new, host species.

A common laboratory method uses **plasmids**, a kind of small DNA circle that can occur independently of the main DNA molecule in bacterial cells. Plasmids are similar to the episome described in Figure 12.15. In the plasmid insertion method, restriction endonucleases cleave a plasmid double helix. These enzymes are found in bacteria, where they are thought to defend against the invasion of

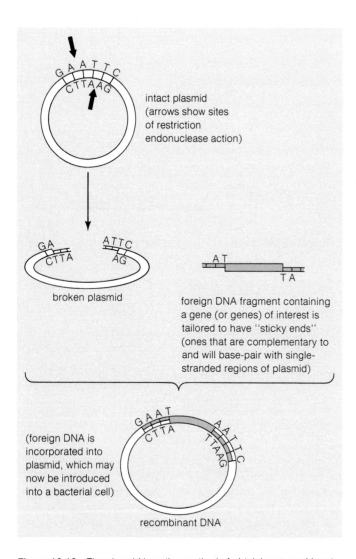

foreign DNA. (For example, they cleave nucleic acids that bacteriophages inject into *E. coli.*) The endonucleases act only in double-helical regions where a particular sequence of bases is an exact reversal of the sequence adjacent to it on the other strand. For instance, one kind of enzyme recognizes the following sequence of base pairs:

$$
\begin{array}{c}
\ldots \text{G A A T T C} \ldots \\
\mid \; \mid \; \mid \; \mid \; \mid \; \mid \\
\ldots \text{C T T A A G} \ldots
\end{array}
$$

Enzymes make staggered cuts in this sequence (Figure 12.16). Other enzymes are used to clip off more nucleotides from the ends of the nicked strands, thereby making the complementary single-stranded regions even longer. Thus primed, a stretch of foreign DNA can be inserted into the plasmid.

Restriction endonucleases are used to cleave the DNA molecule that contains the nucleotide stretch to be inserted into the plasmid. As a result, the plasmid DNA and the foreign DNA fragment have "sticky ends": they are complementary and can base-pair when mixed together. When mixed in the presence of DNA ligase, one can be bonded covalently to the other. The recombinant DNA produced this way can be picked up by a bacterial host cell. The bacterium, with its twenty- or thirty-minute reproductive cycle, is like a manufacturing plant. With repeated doublings of its offspring on a controlled culture medium, millions of genetically identical copies, or **clones**, of the purified DNA fragments can be produced overnight.

Cloned populations can be used as factories to produce specific proteins in quantities that can be used in research, agricultural, and medical applications. They also can be used to map the sequence of bases in the DNA fragment and to study how its genes are expressed in different environments.

A different method must be used to introduce DNA fragments into mammalian cells. (Mammalian cells typically do not tolerate some plasmid sequences, and therefore the recombinant DNA is not retained in the cell.) The main method is one of packing DNA fragments in solid calcium phosphate and putting it next to a cell. Cell membrane surrounds the fragment, which is transferred to the cytoplasm. When the cargo is delivered during mitotic division (when the nuclear membrane has disappeared), the fragments are incorporated into daughter nuclei, then into daughter cells.

Techniques of the sort just outlined have transported recombinant DNA research into a new era. Consider that foreign genes inserted into cells are not only being accepted,

Figure 12.16 The plasmid insertion method of obtaining recombinant DNA. A randomly fragmented segment of DNA from some organism is inserted into a plasmid. The plasmid is then introduced into a bacterial host cell. Each cell playing host to the recombinant DNA is grown on a nutrient-rich culture medium. Through reproduction, each cell produces its own colony of genetically identical cells. The clone populations can be tested to identify which particular DNA segment was obtained from the original donor organism.

they are being expressed by host cells. Bacterial factories are now mass-producing enzymes and hormones by means of instructions encoded in human genes, which have become incorporated into the bacterial DNA. Until recently, hormones used in treating certain human genetic diseases have been difficult to stockpile. Insulin (a hormone that may be absent or deficient in diabetics) was extracted from the pancreas of cattle and pig cadavers. Growth hormone is obtained from pituitary glands of human cadavers. The bacterial factories possible with recombinant DNA technology would be less expensive and more reliable sources, to say the least. At this writing, insulin produced by such technology is now being marketed.

Or consider that recombinant DNA research has accelerated the prospects for **genetic engineering**: bypassing normal sexual or asexual processes that restrict the transfer of genes between entirely different species. By using recombinant DNA methods, plant breeders hope to modify food crops for disease resistance, for greater yields, and for enhanced nitrogen uptake. For example, corn and wheat are the main food crops for the human population. Presently these crops depend on expensive nitrogen-containing fertilizers. Atmospheric nitrogen is abundant, but it is in a chemical form that can be converted to a usable form by only a few kinds of soil microorganisms (Chapter Seven). Through genetic engineering, this capability might be transferred to food crops.

Recombinant DNA research has placed powerful tools in the hands of humankind. And questions have been raised about our ability to control these tools and use them wisely. There is some concern that the release of new combinations of DNA may have serious effects on human health and the environment. What, for example, would happen if bacteria or viruses carrying recombinant DNA of a potentially hazardous sort were to escape from the laboratory? Such risks have not yet been accurately estimated. But neither have the benefits—and the potential benefits are enormous.

Most scientists agree that recombinant DNA research is safe, as long as proper guidelines are followed. For instance, researchers should use weakened strains of bacteria that are unable to survive at all in the absence of conditions that would not exist outside the laboratory. Strict physical isolation is required for research involving disease-causing microorganisms. Both nonscientists and scientists have a vested interest in resolving the ethical issues raised by recombinant DNA research. At best, a careful balance will be struck between protecting public and environmental safety, and protecting the freedom of scientific inquiry that holds such tremendous potential for our well-being.

CHANGE IN THE HEREDITARY MATERIAL

Let's reflect, for a moment, on what has been presented so far on sources of variation in the hereditary material. Earlier chapters described *crossing over and recombination* at the cytological level. The present chapter has described these events at the molecular level. The outcome, again, is a novel combination of genetic information from two different DNA molecules. Chapter Eleven also described *chromosomal mutations* that change the structure or number of chromosomes in a eukaryotic cell. There is one more category of change, and it can occur in any molecule of inheritance. It concerns heritable alterations in the amount or sequence of as few as one or two nucleotides. It is called the *gene mutation.*

Mutation at the Molecular Level

As Table 12.1 indicates, a **gene mutation** may arise when one kind of base pair within a stretch of DNA is replaced by another. It may also arise when one or more extra pairs get inserted into the DNA sequence, or when one or more base pairs gets clipped out entirely.

Less than one-fourth of all gene mutations are *base-pair substitutions.* They can occur when chemicals or other agents alter the atomic structures of a base. In its altered form, the base may form hydrogen bonds with the wrong kind of partner. In other words, C will pair with A, or G will pair with T. Enzymes of DNA replication and repair can recognize the mismatch. They may excise one or the other base. As one alternative, the enzymes will reinstate the DNA sequence to what it should be for a normal allele. The other alternative will introduce a different base pair into the DNA sequence.

More than three-fourths of all spontaneous gene mutations involve the insertion or deletion of one to several base pairs in a DNA sequence. They are called *frameshift mutations.* Because "letters" are added or subtracted from the messages encoded in the DNA sequence, a frameshift mutation can scramble some or all of the instructions for building a protein. You will read more about frameshift mutations in the next chapter.

In the natural world, spontaneous mutations are rare, chance events. It is impossible to predict exactly when, and in which particular organism, they will appear. They are also inevitable. (For example, as long as sunlight reaches the earth, some ultraviolet rays will scramble bonds in some DNA.) Mutations at the molecular level are almost

Table 12.1 Sources of Change in the Hereditary Material: A Summary

Level of Analysis		Outcome	Occurs in
Crossing Over and Recombination*			
Cytological		New allelic combinations in a chromosome	Viruses, prokaryotes, eukaryotes
Molecular		New base-pair sequence in a stretch of DNA	
Chromosomal Mutation			
Cytological	Deletion	Segment lost from a chromosome	Eukaryotes
	Duplication	Chromosome segment repeated more than once in a chromosome set	
	Inversion	Chromosome segment flip-flopped	
	Translocation	Chromosome segment transferred to a nonhomologous chromosome	
	Transposition	Chromosome segment moves to new location in same or different chromosome	
	Aneuploidy	Single chromosome of a given type absent, or present three or more times, in a chromosome set	
	Polyploidy	Three or more chromosome sets present	
	Centric fusion	Fusion of two nonhomologous chromosomes into one	
	Centric fission	One chromosome splits into two	
Gene Mutation			
Molecular	Base substitution	One purine replaced by another, or one pyrimidine replaced by another	Viruses, prokaryotes, eukaryotes
		One purine replaced by a pyrimidine, or vice versa	
	Frameshift	One to several extra base pairs inserted into DNA sequence	
		One to several base pairs lost entirely from DNA sequence	

*In cytological studies, crossing over and recombination occur *between* genes. At the molecular level, crossing over and recombination are known to occur also *within* a single gene.

always ferreted out. They seldom escape recognition by the enzymes that work throughout the life cycle to preserve the letter-by-letter messages encoded in genes. Chromosome mutations are another matter. Enzymes can do some molecular patching here, but the extent of change is largely beyond their reach.

What determines whether a mutation will turn out to be beneficial, harmful, or trivial? It depends on how the mutant phenotype is received in the environment, and on how the change meshes in the coordinated workings of the entire set of DNA (Chapter Eleven). Because of these two variables, most mutations don't bode well for the organism. Each organism has a set of alleles which selective agents have fine-tuned for a given range of operating con-

ditions. A mutant allele is likely to be less functional, not more so, under those conditions. Given this prospect, DNA replication and repair enzymes probably evolved as adaptive mechanisms, which counter mutational disruptions in a genetic package having a history of survival value. The precise action of these enzymes has protected the overall stability of the slender, vulnerable DNA molecules that have been replicated through billions of years.

Yet every so often through that immense time span, mutations have appeared at the right moment, in the right organism. Either they provided their bearers with advantages, or they did their bearers no harm. Selection processes have worked to perpetuate mutations having adaptive consequences. Other mutations, it seems, have persisted as "rusting hulks." They are DNA regions that have no currently assignable function, but that are still replicated along with everything else. After more than three billion years, molecular descendants of the first strands of DNA are replete with mutations. Each is a patchwork molecule, with variant numbers and kinds of genes stitched into it.

PERSPECTIVE

DNA—deoxyribonucleic acid—is the hereditary molecule of every living cell. It is the helically twisted, double-stranded blueprint inside all prokaryotes and all eukaryotes. Every DNA molecule is composed of only three kinds of substances: a sugar, a phosphate group, and nitrogen-containing bases (adenine, thymine, guanine, and cytosine). Every DNA molecule is assembled according to the same rules. When the time comes for new bases from the cellular environment to become paired with old bases sticking out from a DNA sugar-phosphate backbone, adenine normally pairs only with thymine, and guanine only with cytosine.

What this means is that every living thing on earth shares the same fundamental chemical heritage with all others. Your DNA is made of the same kinds of substances, and follows the same base-pairing rules, as the DNA of earthworms in Missouri and grasses on the Mongolian steppes. Your DNA is replicated in much the same way as theirs. Occasional mistakes in its replication are repaired much the same way as theirs. In the evolutionary view, the reason you don't *look* like an earthworm or a flowering plant is largely a result of mutations and recombinations. Mistakes and shufflings in base-pair sequences made their entrance during the past $3\frac{1}{2}$ billion years—$3\frac{1}{2}$ billion years that led, in their unique divergent ways, to the three of you. Thus the *sequence* of base pairs along the DNA molecule has come to be different in the three of you.

Dinosaur DNA, too, was presumably assembled from the same chemical stuff as yours. But the mutations and recombinations that gave rise to the unique sequences of base pairs that specified "build dinosaurs" made those creatures unsuitable, when environmental conditions changed, for continuing their journey.

We have, in this chapter, introduced evidence for three concepts of profound importance. *First, DNA is the source of the unity of life. Second, mutations and recombinations in the structure and number of DNA molecules are the source of life's diversity. And finally, the changing environment is the testing ground for the success or failure of products specified by each novel DNA sequence and assortment that appears on the evolutionary scene.*

Readings

Anderson, W. F., and E. Diacumakos. 1981. "Genetic Engineering in Mammalian Cells." *Scientific American* 245(1):106–118.

Bernstein, H., G. Byers, and R. Michod. 1981. "Evolution of Sexual Reproduction: Importance of DNA Repair, Complementation, and Variation." *The American Naturalist* 117(4):537–549. Excellent review article. Summarizes arguments that sexual reproduction evolved as a DNA repair process and that an advantage of diploidy is protection against expression of harmful mutations.

Cairns, J., G. Stent, and J. Watson (editors). 1966. *Phage and the Origins of Molecular Biology.* Cold Spring Harbor, New York: Cold Spring Harbor Laboratories. Collection of essays by the founders of and converts to molecular genetics. Gives a sense of history in the making—the unfolding insights, the wit, the humility, the personalities of the individuals involved.

Cooke, R. 1982. "Engineering a New Agriculture." *Technology Review* 22–28. Describes technology and prospects for gene transfers in food crops.

Davies, R. 1981. "Gene Transfer in Plants." *Nature* 291:531–532.

Hopkins, R. 1981. "Deoxyribonucleic Acid Structure: A New Model." *Science* 211: 289–291.

Karp, G. 1979. *Cell Biology.* New York: McGraw-Hill.

Mays, L. 1981. *Genetics: A Molecular Approach.* New York: Macmillan.

Ruddle, F. 1981. "A New Era in Mammalian Gene Mapping: Somatic Cell Genetics and Recombinant DNA Methodologies." *Nature* 294:115–120. Excellent state-of-the-art review article.

Streyer, L. 1981. *Biochemistry.* Second edition. San Francisco: Freeman. Good summary of the enzymes of DNA replication and repair.

Taylor, J. (editor). 1965. *Selected Papers on Molecular Genetics.* New York: Academic Press. Contains papers on major concepts forwarded by Avery, Hershey and Chase, Watson and Crick, Arthur Kornberg, Meselson and Stahl.

Watson, J. 1978. *The Double Helix.* New York: Atheneum. A highly personal view of scientists and their methods, interwoven into an account of how DNA structure was discovered.

Wetzel, R. 1980. "Applications of Recombinant DNA Technology." *American Scientist* 68(6): 664–675. Very good summary article.

Review Questions

1. How did Griffith's use of control groups help him deduce that the transformation of harmless *Diplococcus* strains into deadly ones involved a change in the bacterium's hereditary system?

2. What is a bacteriophage? In the Hershey-Chase experiments, how did bacteriophages become labeled with radioactive sulfur and radioactive phosphorus? Why were these particular elements used instead of, say, carbon or nitrogen?

3. DNA is composed of only four different kinds of nucleotides.

Name the three molecular parts of a nucleotide. Name the four different kinds of nitrogen-containing bases that may occur in a nucleotide. What kind of bond holds nucleotides together in a single DNA strand?

4. What kind of bond holds two DNA chains together in a double helix? Which nucleotide base pairs with adenine? Which pairs with guanine? Do the two DNA chains run in the same or opposite directions?

5. The four bases in DNA may *vary* greatly in relative amounts from one species to the next—yet the relative amounts are always the *same* among all members of a single species. How does the concept of base pairing explain these twin properties—the unity *and* diversity—of DNA molecules?

6. When regions of a double helix are unwound during DNA duplication, do the two unwound strands join back together again after a new DNA molecule has formed?

7. Name some of the molecules that monitor DNA duplication. What kind of tasks do they help perform? How do you suppose some of these molecules can be used as research tools in the study of DNA?

8. What is a recombinant DNA molecule? What are some of the potential hazards of recombinant DNA research? What are some of the potential benefits? Would you mind living next door to a laboratory where such research is going on? Would your answer be the same if you happen to be one of the millions of individuals afflicted with diabetes or some other genetic disease?

9. If genetic information were transmitted precisely from generation to generation, organisms would never change. What are some of the DNA mutations that give rise to phenotypic diversity?

10. How is your DNA like the DNA of earthworms, grasses, and (presumably) dinosaurs? How is your DNA different?

DNA is like a book of instructions that each cell carries inside itself. The alphabet used to create the book is simple enough: A, T, G, and C. However, merely knowing the letters doesn't tell us how they give rise to the language of life, with words (genes) evoking precise meanings (proteins). And the letters alone can't tell us how or why a cell selectively reads some DNA passages and skips others at any particular moment. The more we learn about DNA, the more we realize it is no simple book. It was put together over a time span of epic proportions, and it is correspondingly complex. It is known to contain passages of great clarity and precision. It contains long stretches of unknown function. It even contains genetic gibberish, arising from the random tamperings of mutations and recombinations.

What can be said about an evolving, ancient language that is not fully deciphered? All we can do here is outline some current ideas about how genetic instructions encoded in the letters of that language are translated into proteins.

PREVIEW OF THE STEPS AND PARTICIPANTS IN PROTEIN ASSEMBLY

Recall, from Chapter Nine, that heritable traits arise through the action of enzymes and other proteins. Proteins are first assembled as polypeptide chains (strings of amino acids). The particular amino acid sequences for given proteins are encoded in DNA. But the amino acids are not strung together directly on DNA. Instead, the information content of certain DNA stretches (genes) is used to build molecules of **ribonucleic acid**, or RNA.

Like DNA, an RNA molecule is assembled as a linear, unbranched chain of nucleotides. Like DNA, each RNA nucleotide consists of a sugar ring structure, a phosphate group, and a nitrogen-containing base. However, as its name implies, the sugar in the ribonucleic acid chain is riose, not deoxyribose. And in place of the base thymine, RNA has **uracil** (U). Uracil behaves chemically like thymine, for it can form hydrogen bonds with adenine. This means that RNA nucleotide bases can match up with those found in a DNA double helix. It also means that a complementary RNA strand can be assembled on a DNA template.

There are three kinds of RNA. **Messenger RNA** (mRNA) carries genetic instructions away from DNA to protein construction sites in the cytoplasm. **Transfer RNA** (tRNA) and **ribosomal RNA** (rRNA) participate directly in the construction of polypeptide chains.

The assembly of RNA on DNA is called **transcription**. The RNA-directed synthesis of polypeptide chains is called **translation**. Both are subject to genetic controls (Figure 13.1).

13

FROM DNA TO PROTEIN: HOW GENES FUNCTION

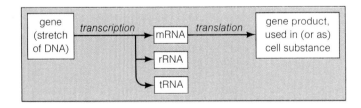

Figure 13.1 Summary of steps in protein synthesis.

The processes of transcription and translation are the subjects of this chapter. Before considering their details, let's look briefly at a few of the experiments that led to our understanding of how they occur.

EARLY IDEAS ABOUT GENE FUNCTION

In 1908 no one knew much about genes, other than that discrete units of inheritance probably existed and gave rise to an individual's physical traits. But in that year Archibald Garrod, an English physician, reported what he thought gene function must be. Garrod had studied many cases of childhood diseases. He decided that in some families, there had to be a heritable basis for certain diseases that recur in particular patterns. What did the diseases have in common? Garrod inferred that within the cells of afflicted persons, one of the steps of a metabolic pathway was being blocked. How could he make this inference? Garrod knew his biochemistry. Normally, a substance is converted into several intermediate compounds before the cell ends up with a required product. If one of the intermediate steps is blocked, there may be an absence of the compound that normally forms after that step, and a buildup of the compound before it:

normal pathway: A ⟶ B ⟶ C ⟶ D

blocked pathway: A ⟶ B   B ⟶✗ C

At some point, it's possible to detect a buildup of the compound immediately preceding the blocked pathway. For instance, an oxidation product of phenylalanine accumulates in excess amounts in the disease phenylketonuria (Chapter Fifteen). The excess can be detected in urine samples. In the disease alkaptonuria, individuals suffer from inflammation of the joints. In this case, the intermediate alkapton builds up in the body. The excess can be detected by analyzing the urine.

Garrod called such disorders **inborn errors of metabolism**, arising from the absence or deficiency of a vital enzyme. He speculated that each enzyme must be specified by a single unit of inheritance—and that if the unit is defective, then the enzyme will be defective.

Studies of Neurospora Mutations. Thirty-three years later, research began that supported Garrod's hypothesis.

At that time, the geneticist George Beadle and the biochemist Edward Tatum were studying effects of mutations on metabolic pathways leading to observable traits. For several reasons, they had figured that *Neurospora crassa,* a red bread mold, would be a good candidate for tracking mutation effects on enzyme activities:

1. Large populations of *Neurospora* can be cultured easily.

2. It takes only ten days for each new generation to reach reproductive age. Hence mutation effects could be observed quickly.

3. The conspicuous body of the life cycle is haploid, with only a single gene for each trait. There would be no masking of a mutant gene by a functional allelic partner (as there would be in a diploid organism).

4. *Neurospora* can reproduce asexually. Hence many genetically identical copies of a mutant could be produced and readily detected.

5. When *Neurospora* reproduces sexually, a diploid zygote forms in a long spore sac, then undergoes division into eight spore cells. The sac is so narrow that the division products line up and stay put in a predictable order. The ordering reflects chromatid segregation patterns present during meiosis. By tracking crossover frequencies, mutations can be assigned to genes on specific chromatids.

Beadle and Tatum knew that *Neurospora* will survive on a minimal medium containing only sucrose, mineral salts, and biotin (one of the B vitamins). Every other substance the organism needs—other vitamins, amino acids—*it can synthesize for itself.* The biochemical steps in the assembly of some of these substances were already known. If the enzyme catalyzing one of these steps were defective, then individuals carrying the defective enzyme would not be able to grow on the minimal medium. Lack of growth would be evidence of a mutation.

The researchers collected asexual spores from the bread mold and bombarded them with x-rays to step up the mutation rate. Then the spores were allowed to grow into large colonies on a complete medium that included all known vitamins and amino acids. Hence the spores were assured of having each of the nutrients they might no longer be able to synthesize. Afterward, part of each colony was transferred to a minimal medium. As Figure 13.2 shows, not all colonies thrived. Some could not grow at all on the minimal diet, so they were probably nutritional mutants.

How did Beadle and Tatum determine which substance could not be synthesized by the mutants? They set up a series of test tubes. One contained the minimal medium; spores placed in it would be the control group. Others contained the minimal medium plus (for example) one kind of vitamin. It turned out that one mutant strain could grow only when vitamin B_6 supplemented the culture medium. Another could grow only when vitamin B_1 was added. Also, analysis of mutant cell extracts revealed a defective enzyme in one strain, and different defective enzymes in other strains. *Each separately inherited mutation corresponded to a different defective enzyme.*

Through genetic analysis, Beadle and Tatum traced the pattern of inheritance for each mutation. In each case, they observed Mendelian segregation patterns that strongly implicated the malfunctioning of a single gene. On the basis of their findings, they formulated the "one gene, one enzyme" hypothesis: that a single gene codes for one kind of enzyme.

At the time, it was known that enzymes are proteins. It was also known that not all proteins are enzymes. (For instance, some are hormones, others are structural molecules such as collagen.) The idea that genes also code for other proteins quickly surfaced. For a while, the more inclusive "one gene, one protein" hypothesis guided research. But this concept, too, was destined for slight modification.

Electrophoresis Studies. Better understanding of the link between genes and proteins came through studies of sickle-cell anemia. This heritable disease, recall, arises from the presence of abnormal hemoglobin molecules (HbS instead of HbA). In 1949, James Neel and E. Beet proposed that a mutant allele causes the disease. That same year, Linus Pauling and his colleagues thought that differences between HbS and HbA molecules might be detectable through *electrophoresis*. This technique can be used to measure the rate and direction of movement of organic molecules in response to an electric field (Figure 13.3). Analysis showed that hemoglobin from normal persons (HbA/HbA) moved toward the negative end of the electric field. HbS/HbS molecules moved in the opposite direction. The difference was attributed to a slightly smaller number of negatively charged R groups in the abnormal hemoglobin molecule. Now, a hemoglobin molecule contains four polypeptide chains (two identical alpha- and two identical beta-chains). Where, in this assortment, did the abnormality reside?

A few years later, Vernon Ingram discovered that the difference between HbA and HbS arises from a mutation in one of the 146 amino acids in the beta-chain. At position 6

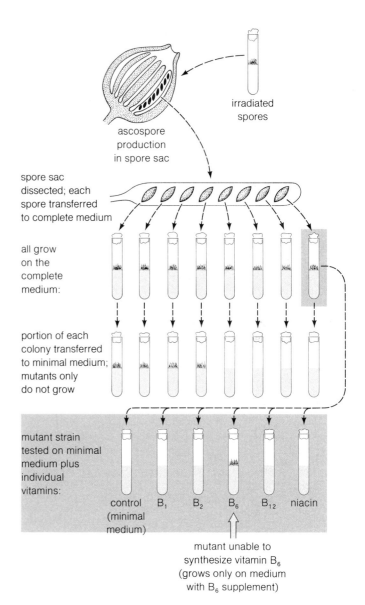

Figure 13.2 One of Beadle and Tatum's experiments with nutritional mutants of *Neurospora crassa*, as described in the text.

of the abnormal beta-chain, valine is substituted for glutamate (Figure 13.4). The R group of glutamate has a negative charge—but valine has no net charge. Thus HbS (with two abnormal chains) would have two fewer negative charges than HbA—which would account for the different rates of movement in the electric field. The results clearly suggested that the gene coding for HbA chains had to be different from the gene coding for the HbS chains.

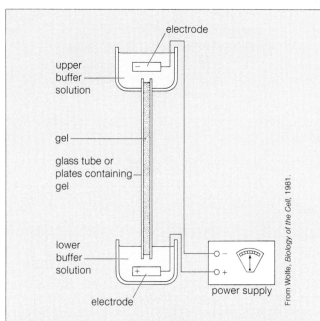

Figure 13.3 Electrophoresis: a technique used to measure the rate and degree of migration of organic molecules in response to an electric field.

Often the electric field is established in a glass tube containing a gel. The tube ends project into two containers of salt solutions, which can conduct an electric current. When current flows through the tube, one end carries a positive charge; the other, a negative charge.

Suppose that a sample containing a mixture of different proteins is placed in the gel. Each protein molecule will move toward one end of the tube or the other. The rate and direction of movement depend in part on a molecule's net surface charge. They also depend on the molecule's size and shape. For example, larger molecules show more resistance to moving through the gel.

Ingram proposed that the same thing had to apply to other proteins containing more than one polypeptide. Thus the Beadle and Tatum hypothesis came to be amended as the **one gene, one polypeptide** hypothesis: a gene codes for the amino acid sequence of one polypeptide chain, and one or more such chains (which may or may not be identical) comprise a protein molecule.

One gene codes for the precise amino acid sequence in each kind of polypeptide chain.

THE GENETIC CODE

By this time, researchers suspected that the route by which genes become translated into polypeptide chains must be an indirect one. They knew that the protein-building instructions of DNA are sequestered in the nucleus (or, in prokaryotes, the nucleoid), yet gene products are assembled in the cytoplasm. In some way, the messages of genes had to be physically moved away from the genes themselves.

Genes are carried on DNA, but the products they specify are not assembled on DNA.

Most likely, RNA figured in the route from genes to proteins. Considerable indirect evidence supported the possibility. First, RNA is abundant in cells that are specialized for protein secretion (such as pancreatic cells). But little RNA is present in cells such as those of muscle and kidney, which do not export proteins. Second, RNA can be detected in both the nucleus and cytoplasm. In fact, radioactive labeling experiments showed that RNA is produced in the nucleus and *moves into* the cytoplasm.

Even so, because the arrangement of nucleotides in RNA is complementary to that of DNA, researchers were still left with the central question. *How does a linear sequence of nucleotides specify a linear sequence of amino acids in proteins?*

Consider that there are only four kinds of nucleotides in DNA and RNA, but that twenty kinds of amino acids commonly occur in proteins. Obviously, each nucleotide doesn't call for only one type of amino acid; that would be only four choices. Two nucleotides in a row would give only sixteen choices, not twenty. With three nucleotides in a row, sixty-four choices would be possible—far more than the twenty required. Are nucleotide bases read in an overlapping way, then, or do different nucleotide sequences specify the same thing?

For the answer let's consider, as Francis Crick and Sidney Brenner once did, the effects of nucleotide deletions and insertions on gene function. (Such gene mutations give rise to defective enzymes, which can be detected because of the diminished amount or absence of their products.) Brenner discovered that one or two extra nucleotides inserted in the middle of a gene made the protein it specified completely defective. Yet, sometimes when a third nucleotide was inserted near the first two, gene function was partly restored! Why was the presence of three extra nucleotides less serious than the addition of one or two?

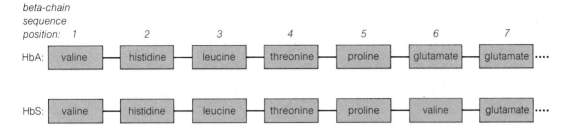

beta-chain sequence position:

	1	2	3	4	5	6	7
HbA:	valine	histidine	leucine	threonine	proline	glutamate	glutamate ....
HbS:	valine	histidine	leucine	threonine	proline	valine	glutamate ....

Figure 13.4 A substitution of one amino acid for another in a polypeptide chain—the clinical consequences.

In sickle-cell hemoglobin, valine is substituted for glutamate at position 6 of the beta polypeptide chain. Glutamate is highly polar. Valine is nonpolar, and its incorporation into the amino acid sequence at this particular position puts a "sticky" hydrophobic patch on the surface of a hemoglobin S molecule.

When oxygen concentrations in the blood are high, the sticky patches are masked and HbS molecules can't interact. When oxygen concentrations are low, the molecules interact and aggregate into long rods. These are the rods that distort red blood cells and cause them to clump in blood vessels (Chapter Ten).

Crick and Brenner sensed that the results probably revealed the nature of the **genetic code**: the relationship between the nucleotide sequence in DNA (or RNA) and the amino acid sequence in a polypeptide chain. *These results would be expected if the genetic code consists of nucleotide bases that are read linearly, three at a time, with the sequence of each triplet signifying an amino acid.*

Assume that the nucleotides of a gene are read linearly, from start to finish. If one extra nucleotide were inserted in a gene, the "reading frame" would be modified from that point on. And the protein to be assembled would end up with the wrong amino acid sequence. Figure 13.5 shows why this is so. A second insertion wouldn't improve matters. A third insertion, though, would restore the reading frame. Because the region between the first and third extra bases would still be wrong, the corresponding stretch of the amino acid sequence would be defective. However, the sequence coded for by the regions on either side of the insertions would be normal. Hence the protein product could be partially functional.

The reading frame for the genetic code is nonoverlapping, with each amino acid specified by a base triplet (three nucleotide bases in a row).

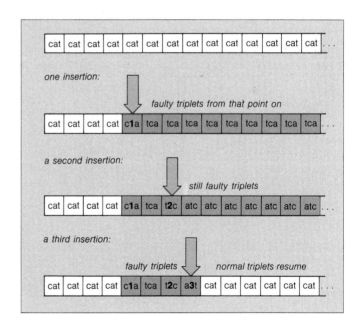

Figure 13.5 Crick's interpretation of Brenner's base insertion experiments. If translation of the genetic code depends on reading adjacent nucleotides three at a time, insertion of one or two extra nucleotides will change the sequence (hence the meaning) of all subsequent base triplets. But a third addition will restore much of the normal sequence.

First Letter	Second Letter				Third Letter
	U	C	A	G	
U	phenylalanine	serine	tyrosine	cysteine	U
	phenylalanine	serine	tyrosine	cysteine	C
	leucine	serine	stop	stop	A
	leucine	serine	stop	tryptophan	G
C	leucine	proline	histidine	arginine	U
	leucine	proline	histidine	arginine	C
	leucine	proline	glutamine	arginine	A
	leucine	proline	glutamine	arginine	G
A	isoleucine	threonine	asparagine	serine	U
	isoleucine	threonine	asparagine	serine	C
	isoleucine	threonine	lysine	arginine	A
	(start) methionine	threonine	lysine	arginine	G
G	valine	alanine	aspartate	glycine	U
	valine	alanine	aspartate	glycine	C
	valine	alanine	glutamate	glycine	A
	valine	alanine	glutamate	glycine	G

Figure 13.6 The genetic code. Each codon consists of three nucleotides. The first nucleotide of any triplet is given in the left column. The second is given in the middle columns; the third, in the right column. Thus we find (for instance) that tryptophan is coded for by the triplet U G G . Phenylalanine is coded for by both U U U and U U C All such nucleotide triplets (codons) are strung one after another in messenger RNA molecules. Different sequences of triplets call for different protein chains.

Through the work of H. Gobind Khorana, Marshall Nirenberg, Robert Holley, and others, we now know that the genetic code consists of sixty-four combinations of nucleotide triplets. Sixty-one triplets actually specify amino acids. The remaining three act like punctuation points. Their occurrence in a genetic message signifies that the addition of amino acids to a growing polypeptide chain must be terminated.

In an mRNA molecule, each nucleotide triplet that codes for an amino acid (or for chain termination) is called a **codon**. Of the twenty common amino acids, there are two that are specified by only one codon. They are tryptophan (with its codon UGG) and methionine (AUG). As Figure 13.6 indicates, the other eighteen can be specified by two or more different triplet combinations. For instance, CCU, CCC, CCA, and CCG *all* specify proline. Different triplets that code for the same amino acid are called "synonyms." Most differ only in the last base of the triplet.

The genetic code is universal for all cells. Codons that specify particular amino acids in bacteria specify the same amino acids in all the different protistans, fungi, plants, and animals studied so far. In fact, this universal code is one of the reasons why DNA recombination between different species is possible.

All living cells studied to date use the same genetic code as the language of protein synthesis.

TRANSCRIPTION OF DNA INTO RNA

Now that we have looked at the triplet nature of the genetic code, we are ready to consider how this code is used in *transcription*: the process by which genetic information is actually transferred from a DNA template to an RNA molecule. The word transcription means "to make a copy"—although it might help to keep in mind that the transcript is *complementary* to, not an identical copy of, the DNA region on which it is formed.

In some ways, RNA synthesis is like DNA synthesis. In both cases, base pairs in an unzipped region of the DNA double helix are a template for assembling a complementary sequence of base pairs into a new nucleotide chain. In both cases, a new strand is assembled in the 5' → 3' direction, in the manner shown earlier in Figure 12.12.

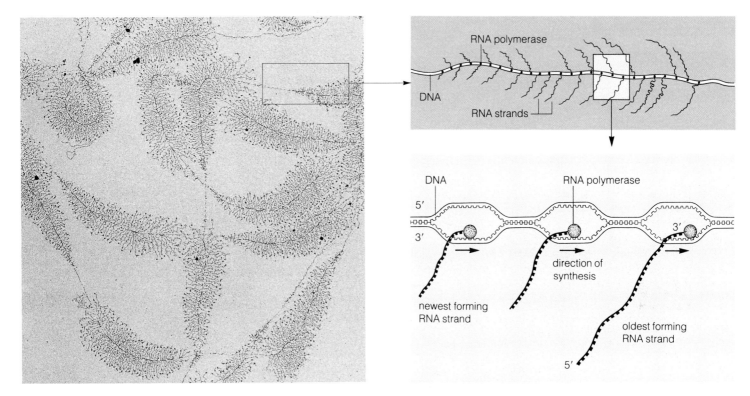

Figure 13.7 Transcription: the transfer of genetic information from DNA to RNA. The micrograph shows genes isolated from a maturing egg of the spotted newt *(Triturus viridescens)*. The short RNA strands are in early stages of synthesis; the longer are nearing completion. 27,000×. (Oscar Miller and Barbara Beatty, 1969, "Visualization of Nucleolar Genes," *Science,* 164:955–957. Copyright 1969 by the American Association for the Advancement of Science)

How do DNA and RNA synthesis differ? *First,* in RNA synthesis, the only enzymes responsible for chain elongation are **RNA polymerases**, and the molecules they assemble are called **RNA transcripts**. *Second,* RNA is almost always assembled on only one of the two strands of an unzipped DNA region. (Which of the two strands acts as the template varies from region to region. For instance, enzymes may be putting together an RNA molecule on one DNA strand and, farther down the double helix, enzymes may also be putting one together on the other strand.) *Third,* several RNA polymerases may run single-file down the same DNA stretch, one after another, so that multiple copies of the same RNA molecule are rapidly assembled.

Transcription starts at specific locations on a DNA strand. These locations, called *promoters,* are sites at which RNA polymerases can bind and initiate transcription. They contain a specific sequence of base pairs, which occur a little bit ahead of the first nucleotide to be transcribed. As Figure 13.7 suggests, one RNA polymerase synthesizes an entire transcript. Ribonucleotides are matched to bases on the DNA template. They are joined together, one after another, until RNA polymerase reaches and transcribes a "stop" signal—a specific base sequence that brings transcription to a close. The RNA molecules so produced are released and are now available for the cell's program of protein synthesis.

MESSENGER RNA TRANSLATION

In *translation,* the information content of an mRNA molecule is used in the synthesis of a specific polypeptide chain. The events of translation depend on interactions between mRNA, tRNA, and rRNA.

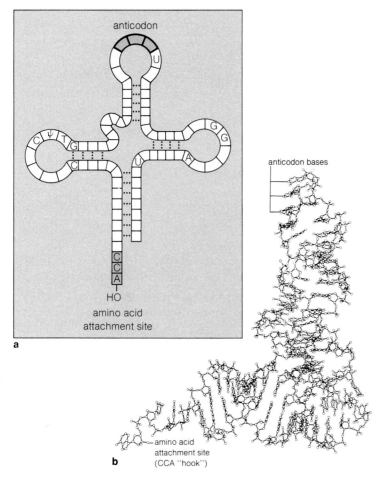

Figure 13.8 (**a**) Structural features that all tRNA molecules hold in common. Notice how the ribonucleotide strand folds back on itself into hairpin loops, which are held in place by hydrogen bonding between complementary stretches of bases. (**b**) Three-dimensional structure of one tRNA molecule, as determined by computer analysis. (Courtesy of Sung Hou Kim)

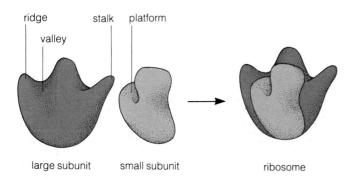

Figure 13.9 A current model of the two-part structure of ribosomes.

Codon-Anticodon Interaction. Messenger RNA serves as the template for protein synthesis. To keep things simple, the mRNA template can be portrayed in this way:

To this template, individual tRNA molecules attach specific amino acids. Each kind of tRNA contains an **anticodon**: a template recognition site which is complementary to (and therefore can hydrogen-bond with) a specific mRNA codon. An anticodon consists of some combination of three nucleotide bases, positioned at one end of the tRNA molecule. At the opposite end is a molecular "hook," an attachment site for an amino acid. Figure 13.8 gives an idea of its molecular structure. For the sake of clarity in later illustrations, the structure of the tRNA molecule can be portrayed in this simplified way:

The first two bases of an anticodon must be precisely complementary to an mRNA codon for binding to occur. However, recognition of the *third* codon base is often less precise. Some tRNA molecules can form hydrogen bonds with more than one kind of codon. (For instance, yeast alanine tRNA can bind to three codons: GCU, GCC, or GCA.) This freedom in codon-anticodon pairing at the third base is called the "wobble" effect.

A codon (base triplet of mRNA) is a hydrogen-bonding site for an anticodon (complementary base triplet of tRNA).

Codon-anticodon recognition is precise between their first two base pairs. At the third base, some tRNA molecules can form hydrogen bonds with more than one kind of base; hence they can recognize more than one codon.

Ribosome Function in Protein Assembly. All codon-anticodon interactions take place on the surface of the

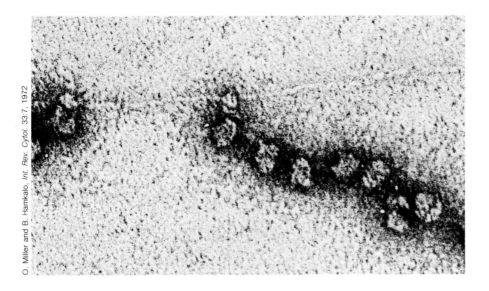

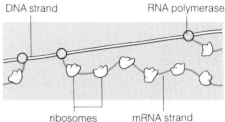

DNA strand   RNA polymerase

ribosomes   mRNA strand

Figure 13.10 A group of ribosomes (a polysome) positioned on an mRNA molecule, which was formed from the *E. coli* DNA molecule running from the left to the right edge of the micrograph. 361,200×. (O. Miller and B. Hamkalo, *Int. Rev. Cytol.*, 33:7, 1972)

O. Miller and B. Hamkalo, *Int. Rev. Cytol.* 33:7, 1972

ribosome, the cytoplasmic structure on which amino acids are linked into polypeptide chains. Ten thousand ribosomes can be present in one prokaryotic cell; a eukaryotic cell may contain many tens of thousands. At its widest dimension, a ribosome is only twenty-five nanometers (about a millionth of an inch). Electron microscopy shows it is anchored in the cytoplasmic lattice in eukaryotic cells.

Each ribosome consists of two parts. A small subunit consists of one rRNA molecule and twenty-one different proteins. As Figure 13.9 shows, the small subunit has a platform. Apparently, an mRNA molecule binds to this platform, then a procession of tRNAs binds to the mRNA. The large subunit of the ribosome consists of two rRNA molecules and thirty-four different proteins. This large subunit seems to contain the enzymes that catalyze the linkage between the amino acids that tRNAs have delivered to the ribosome.

An mRNA molecule may be translated simultaneously by several ribosomes. The term **polysome** refers to a cluster of ribosomes bound to the same mRNA (Figure 13.10). Polypeptide chain elongation proceeds independently at each ribosome in the cluster.

Initiation Stage. Translation of mRNA into a polypeptide chain proceeds through three stages: initiation, elongation, and termination. In *initiation,* an mRNA molecule becomes positioned on a ribosome in a way that enhances the reading of its genetic messages. First, the mRNA, some proteins (which assist in initiating the process), and guanosine triphosphate (an energy carrier) bind to a small ribosomal subunit. A special initiator tRNA then binds to the start codon of mRNA. This complex now binds with a large ribosomal subunit, and chain elongation can begin.

Chain Elongation Stage. The position of a start codon in an mRNA strand defines the reading frame for *chain elongation:* the peptide linkages of a genetically specified series of amino acids. Elongation begins when a second tRNA molecule becomes positioned at the so-called A site on the ribosomal platform (Figure 13.11). Once the second tRNA is aligned with the initiator tRNA, the two amino acids attached to them become linked into a dipeptide. Now the bond between the first tRNA and its amino acid is broken, and the decoupled tRNA is ejected from the platform. The tRNA remaining moves from the A site to another binding

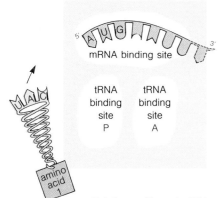

mRNA binding site

tRNA binding site P

tRNA binding site A

amino acid 1

a *Relative positions of mRNA and tRNA binding sites on a platform region of the small ribosomal subunit. An initiator tRNA is shown to the left; it can recognize and bind to the start codon (in this example, AUG).*

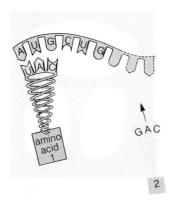

amino acid 1

GAC

2

b *During initiation, the initiator tRNA becomes positioned in the P site. A second tRNA is approaching the ribosome.*

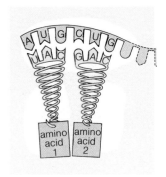

amino acid 1

amino acid 2

c *Chain elongation proper begins when the second tRNA moves into the A site and base-pairs to the second mRNA codon. As it does, its attached amino acid aligns with the amino acid that is attached to the initiator tRNA.*

Figure 13.11 Simplified picture of the polypeptide chain elongation stage of protein synthesis.

site (Figure 13.11e). The mRNA molecule moves over also, so that a third codon becomes aligned with the vacated A site. A third tRNA with its amino acid cargo moves in, and the steps are repeated.

Elongation mechanisms are repeated over and over, from delivery of the second tRNA to the ribosome until delivery of the last. In this way, polypeptide chains are assembled from a set of the twenty common amino acids. Each chain has its own sequence of from 20 to 3,000 amino acid subunits.

Termination Stage. *Chain termination* is the final step of polypeptide chain synthesis. When the mRNA codon aligned with a vacated A site is UAG, UAA, or UGA, a tRNA molecule usually will not move into it. These three triplets apparently are "stop" codons. Stop codons are recognized by proteins called release factors. When one of these factors becomes attached to a stop codon, it leads to hydrolysis of the bond between the newly formed chain and the tRNA occupying the A site. When this bond is broken, the chain falls away from the ribosome.

SUMMARY OF PROTEIN SYNTHESIS

What we have been describing here are the elements of an information-processing system for putting DNA instructions to work. These elements may be summarized in this way:

1. A source of systematically arranged information *(the linear sequence of nucleotide triplets in DNA).*

2. An encoding process, or some means of assembling bits of that information into a coherent, transmittable message. *(Here we are talking about specific enzymes of transcription and their interactions with DNA regions.)*

3. The encoded message itself *(messenger RNA).*

4. Decoding mechanisms *(ribosomal RNA, transfer RNA, enzymes of translation and other proteins).*

5. An information receiver *(cytoplasmic substances and cell organelles).*

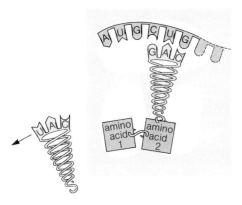 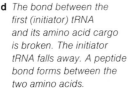 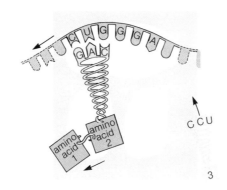 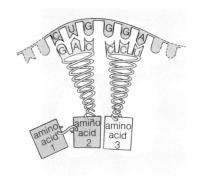

d *The bond between the first (initiator) tRNA and its amino acid cargo is broken. The initiator tRNA falls away. A peptide bond forms between the two amino acids.*

e *The vacated P site is now filled, when the second tRNA moves into it. The mRNA molecule also moves, so that the second codon is aligned with the P site. A third tRNA is approaching the ribosome.*

f *The third tRNA base-pairs with the third codon (which has moved so that it is aligned with the A site). A peptide bond forms between the second and third amino acids. In this way, a polypeptide chain will grow until a stop codon in the mRNA message is reached; then the chain will be released from the ribosome.*

Let's review the roles of these elements in transcription (the prelude to protein synthesis) and translation (actual protein synthesis). In transcription, the base sequence on an exposed DNA region serves as a template for assembling a complementary sequence of ribonucleotide bases. The result is an RNA transcript. First, enzymes open up the two strands of a DNA double helix, in a region corresponding to the gene about to be transcribed. With the assistance of a small protein, an RNA polymerase attaches to the exposed stretch of one or the other DNA strands. Then the enzyme alone catalyzes RNA chain elongation. The ribonucleotides become linked into one of three kinds of RNA molecules (mRNA, tRNA, or rRNA).

Translation, again, is the RNA-directed synthesis of a polypeptide chain. "Polypeptide chain" is the same thing as "protein primary structure." Here, the three kinds of RNA molecules transcribed from DNA interact with each other, and with enzymes and other proteins. Only the mRNA carries polypeptide-building instructions. These instructions are encoded in nonoverlapping mRNA base triplets (codons), with each triplet specifying one amino acid. The other two kinds of RNA function in decoding the mRNA message. Decoding requires three stages: initiation, chain elongation, and chain termination.

Initiation involves the convergence of several elements into an intact, two-part ribosome to which an mRNA molecule is attached. An initiator tRNA binds to a start codon in the mRNA strand. This codon defines the reading frame for chain elongation. Here, a series of tRNAs deliver amino acids to the ribosome. Each tRNA has an anticodon (a base triplet complementary to a codon, by which it recognizes and hydrogen-bonds with mRNA). Two tRNAs at a time are positioned on the ribosome surface. When they align with each other, a peptide bond forms between their attached amino acids. The codon sequence of mRNA specifies which amino acids will be bound, one after another, into a polypeptide chain.

The occurrence of a stop codon in the sequence of an mRNA message signals when the chain must be terminated. The polypeptide chain is now released and falls away from the ribosome. It will twist and fold into some chemically prescribed, three-dimensional shape (Chapter Three). In its final configuration, it will play some role in (or as) a cell substance.

Meanwhile, Back at the Mitochondrion . . .

In the evolutionary view, the genetic code probably dates back to the most ancient cells from which all existing species arose. First, the code appears to be identical for all living species, from bacterial to human. Second, the absence of variation from one species to the next suggests that the genetic code predates the divergences into separate evolutionary lines. Once the code had been established, variation would have been nearly impossible. (One variant triplet alone could alter the functioning of many different proteins, depending on where and how many times it specified a given product in an amino acid sequence. Most such variations would be harmful or lethal.)

It happens, though, that a slightly variant code does exist—in the mitochondrion. A mitochondrion, recall, is an organelle specialized in aerobic energy metabolism. It has its own DNA, which is replicated independently of the cell DNA. This DNA governs synthesis of at least some RNA and proteins that the organelle requires in its specialized tasks. Although the mitochondrial code is almost the same as it is for cells, a *few* codons have different meanings. (For instance, UGA is a punctuation point in most genetic messages; for mitochondria, it specifies tryptophan. AUA, which generally codes for isoleucine, codes for methionine.)

With its variant codons, the mitochondrion is genetically isolated from the rest of the eukaryotic cell. What is the significance of this isolation? Many biologists suspect that the original ancestors of mitochondria were free-living cells, similar to some modern bacteria. In some way, these bacteria took up permanent residence inside the cytoplasm of other kinds of cells (Chapter Thirty-One). The guest and the host cell became locked in a symbiotic relationship, with each gaining some benefit from the activities of the other (Chapter Thirty-Seven). Over time, the "guest" lost the means to perform some function that the host cell was performing for it—hence it lost the capacity for independent existence.

If this is what happened, then the mitochondrial code might be a vestige of a primitive code from an entirely separate species, long since vanished. However, it might also be true that the variant code arose only *after* the joint living arrangement became permanent. Mutations leading to a slightly variant code would have been advantageous, for there would henceforth be no accidental role-swapping between nuclear and mitochondrial genes that code for different proteins.

Readings

Benzer, S. 1962. "The Fine Structure of the Gene." *Scientific American* 206(1):70–84.

Clark, B., and K. Marcher. 1968. "How Proteins Start." *Scientific American* 218(1):36–42. Available as Offprint 1092.

Crick, F. 1966. "The Genetic Code: III." *Scientific American* 215(4):55–62.

Lake, J. 1981. "The Ribosome." *Scientific American* 245(2):84–97. Presents a three-dimensional model for ribosome structure.

Miller, O., Jr. 1973. "The Visualization of Genes in Action." *Scientific American* 228(3):34–42. Available as Offprint 1267.

Nirenberg, M. 1963. "The Genetic Code: II." *Scientific American* 208(3): 80–94.

Rich, A., and S. Kim. 1978. "The Three-Dimensional Structure of Transfer RNA." *Scientific American* 238(1):52–62.

Stryer, L. 1981. *Biochemistry.* Second edition. San Francisco: Freeman. Chapters 25 through 28 are a good place to start for an introduction to protein synthesis.

Yanofsky, C. 1967. "Gene Structure and Protein Structure." *Scientific American* 216(5): 80–94. Available as Offprint 1074.

Review Questions

1. Are the products specified by DNA assembled *on* the DNA molecule? If so, state how. If not, tell where they are assembled, and on which molecules.

2. How is a linear sequence of nucleotides in DNA translated into a linear sequence of amino acids in a protein?

3. Name the process by which RNA of three different types is assembled from the parent DNA code. Name the process by which the three different types of RNA cooperatively assemble a sequence of amino acids.

4. If sixty-one triplets actually specify amino acids, and if there are only twenty common amino acids, then more than one nucleotide tirplet combination must specify some of the amino acids. How do triplets that code for the same thing usually differ?

5. Is the same basic genetic code used for protein synthesis in all living organisms? What significance is attached to that fact by most biologists?

6. Describe the general structure and function of the three types of RNA. What is a codon? An anticodon? Where is each physically located?

7. If you view protein synthesis as an information-processing system for putting DNA to work, then what are the elements of this system? (List each information-processing step, and name the molecules or structures that each represents.)

TYPES OF GENE CONTROLS

Each living cell in your body contains the same hereditary instructions as all the others. Your brain cells contain the information needed in building skin cell proteins; your skin cells contain the information needed in building brain cell proteins. Nevertheless, each cell type builds *only* those particular proteins that it will require throughout its life span. Even then, the same cell type does not always produce the same kinds of proteins in unvarying amounts. Certain white blood cells can build proteins called antibodies, which bind and lead to inactivation of bacterial invaders of your body. But they produce these proteins *only* when they actually make contact with specific bacterial targets. *These cells, and all others, have the means to control which gene products appear, at what times, at what rates, and in what amounts.*

In this chapter, we will consider some mechanisms by which cells selectively read their genetic library and thereby control protein synthesis. As Figure 14.2 suggests, five general kinds of control systems are necessary:

Transcriptional controls govern whether enzymes of transcription have access to a given structural gene. (A *structural gene* is that portion of DNA coding for a particular polypeptide or RNA molecule.) These controls influence the amounts and kinds of RNA transcripts assembled on structural genes.

Post-transcriptional controls act on RNA transcripts after they peel off the structural genes. For example, some transcript regions can be snipped out; other regions can be modified chemically before the transcript reaches a ribosome for translation.

Translational controls govern which available RNA transcripts will actually be translated at a given time. For example, the nuclear envelope is positioned between structural genes and the ribosomes where genetic instructions are translated into proteins. The nuclear envelope serves as a control point by preventing passage of transcripts into the cytoplasm until receiving signals that say, in effect, it is time for them to be processed. Translational controls also can be exerted on RNA transcripts in the cytoplasm. Levels of certain kinds of enzymes can be varied, and the variations can influence how fast different transcripts are translated.

Post-translational controls modify the protein or RNA products of genes. For instance, before some proteins become fully functional, a phosphate group must be attached to them. Such modifications can be made at controlled rates by controlling the availability of enzymes required in the phosphorylation step.

Finally, *controls over enzyme activity* slow down, speed up, or degrade enzymes whose actions directly or indirectly

14

CONTROLS OVER GENE EXPRESSION

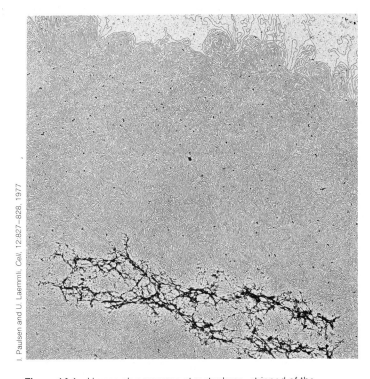

I. Paulsen and U. Laemmli, *Cell*, 12:827–828, 1977

Figure 14.1 Human chromosome at metaphase, stripped of the proteins that normally hold it in its condensed form. Notice the tremendous amount of DNA that must be coiled up in controlled ways.

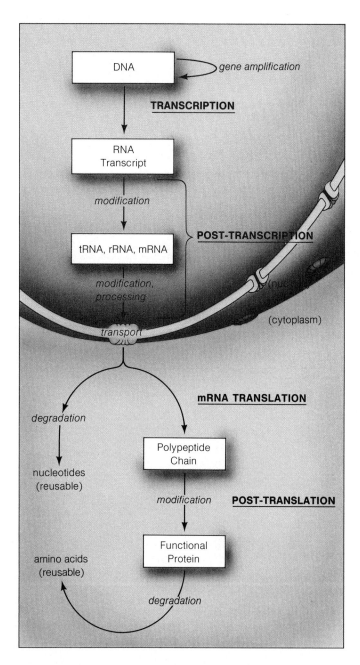

DNA → *gene amplification*

TRANSCRIPTION

RNA Transcript

modification

tRNA, rRNA, mRNA

POST-TRANSCRIPTION

modification, processing

transport

(nuc...)

(cytoplasm)

mRNA TRANSLATION

degradation

nucleotides (reusable)

Polypeptide Chain

modification   **POST-TRANSLATION**

amino acids (reusable)

Functional Protein

degradation

Figure 14.2 Control of gene expression: steps at which regulatory mechanisms can be brought into play. (Here, the steps are superimposed on a sketch of nuclear and cytoplasmic regions of a eukaryotic cell.) In addition to the mechanisms summarized in this illustration, controls over enzyme activity are brought into play at all steps leading to protein synthesis.

affect protein synthesis. These controls include substrate concentrations, pH levels, and a host of other factors characteristic of the cell environment. For example, from earlier chapters you know that enzyme activity can be influenced by feedback inhibition mechanisms, which limit the number of enzymes available to perform some task. You also know that internal pH can be regulated through active and passive transport mechanisms built into cell membranes. Hence, by controlling internal pH, cells control enzyme activity and, partly, protein synthesis.

Both prokaryotes and eukaryotes depend on the kinds of controls outlined above. When we turn to specific examples of these controls, though, we find major differences between these two categories of organisms:

Prokaryotes and eukaryotes depend on short-range controls over gene expression that are responses to immediate environmental conditions.

Eukaryotes alone also depend on long-range controls over the events of development and differentiation.

GENE REGULATION IN PROKARYOTES

The Operon: Coordinated Unit of Transcription

The first evidence for controls over transcription came from studies of *Escherichia coli,* a bacterial resident of the mammalian gut. In newborn mammals, this type of bacterium is destined to encounter an abrupt change in diet. For a few weeks or months, the host in which *E. coli* resides takes in nothing but milk, which contains large amounts of the sugar lactose. Once the weaning period is over, most mammalian hosts never take in milk again. (The only exceptions are ourselves and a few of our pets.) During the first part of the mammalian life cycle, then, *E. coli* present in the gut must be able to metabolize a sugar that subsequent *E. coli* generations never will encounter. Those later bacterial generations will have no need to make thousands of copies of lactose-degrading enzymes.

Three French biologists, André Lwoff, François Jacob, and Jacques Monod, looked into this intriguing aspect of *E. coli* nutrition. Jacob and Monod grew bacteria on a culture medium that contained no lactose whatsoever. They found that the bacteria produced no lactose-degrading enzymes. Then they abruptly switched the bacteria to a medium in which lactose was the only energy source. Within minutes, the bacteria produced thousands of molecules of the lactose-degrading enzymes! Such enzymes obviously were not synthesized until the cells had need of them. The presence of lactose had somehow induced transcription of structural genes coding for exactly those enzymes that could disassemble lactose molecules.

Through genetic studies of mutant bacteria, Jacob and Monod discovered that the structural genes coding for the lactose-metabolizing enzymes are adjacent to one another in the DNA molecule. More importantly, they found that three DNA control elements govern the transcription rate for these three genes:

regulator   *a gene coding for a <u>repressor</u> protein*

promoter   *a noncoding sequence of nucleotides to which RNA polymerase can bind; initiation site for transcription*

operator   *a noncoding sequence of nucleotides to which repressor protein can bind and thereby block transcription of a set of structural genes*

With these discoveries, Jacob and Monod put together the first operon model of transcriptional control. The term **operon** was coined to signify a set of structural genes which are transcribed as a coordinated unit under the direction of a single set of DNA control elements. Let's look briefly at this model and at one of the more recent ones.

Induction-Repression

Figure 14.3 outlines the Jacob-Monod model of induction and repression of gene transcription for the lactose operon. In this model, lactose operon functioning depends on a regulator, promoter, operator, and three structural genes. Transcription of the regulator proceeds to the extent that some repressor proteins are always present in the bacterial cytoplasm. Each of these repressor proteins has two binding sites. One is for lactose (here, the inducer molecule that turns on transcription). The other is for the operator.

When *E. coli* is not feeding on lactose, inducer molecules are not around, and repressor proteins are free to diffuse along the DNA molecule. When one reaches the operator, it binds rapidly to it. The repressor happens to be a rather bulky molecule. When bound to the operator, it overlaps the adjacent promoter (Figure 14.3b). The overlapping means that the binding site for RNA polymerase is blocked. Hence transcription is *repressed* in the absence of inducer molecules, and lactose-degrading enzymes (which are not needed) are not produced.

When lactose *is* entering the bacterial cell, it binds to repressor proteins. The binding *induces* conformational changes in the repressor protein, such that the repressor cannot bind to the operator. Therefore, RNA polymerase is able to bind to the promoter, and transcription proceeds (Figure 14.3c).

For the inducible lactose operon, transcription rates depend on the proportion of repressor molecules to inducer molecules. With increased lactose concentrations in the cytoplasm, most of the repressor molecules are inactivated. As a result, transcription and the subsequent production of lactose-degrading enzymes are rapid. When lactose concentrations fall, the number of repressor molecules free to bind with the operator rises—and enzyme production slackens.

Repressor protein is a <u>negative control</u> over the inducible lactose operon: it <u>prevents</u> transcription when lactose concentrations are low.

Corepression

In *E. coli*, another operon codes for five enzymes necessary to build the amino acid tryptophan. Five structural genes are transcribed simultaneously into one mRNA chain. Translation into a polypeptide (which is snipped into five different tryptophan-assembly enzymes) begins even before transcription is completed. In fact, a tryptophan mRNA only lasts about three minutes before it is degraded! This means that *E. coli* can turn on or shut off tryptophan assembly with amazing speed, depending on cellular conditions.

Rapid control over the tryptophan operon is possible because of a mechanism called corepression. By itself, the repressor protein for this operon can't bind to the operator. First it must become complexed tightly with a tryptophan molecule. When tryptophan is bound to it, the repressor undergoes a change in shape that allows it to bind to the operator. This complex blocks access of RNA polymerase to the initiation site for transcription. Here, the end product (tryptophan) is the corepressor. It helps shut down its own synthesis when present in enough quantity to do so. When tryptophan concentrations fall, repressor proteins do not become bound with a control partner. The operator remains clear, and transcription proceeds.

Corepression provides <u>negative feedback</u> control over the tryptophan operon: the <u>end product</u> of transcription (tryptophan) becomes bound to repressor protein, and the tryptophan-repressor complex shuts down transcription.

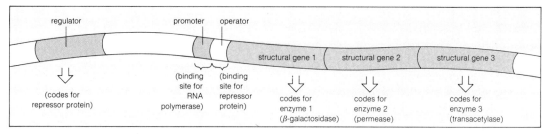

a *Structural genes and control elements of the lactose operon*

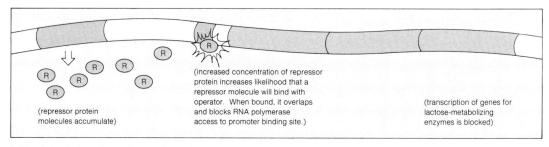

b *When lactose is absent from environment (repression occurs)*

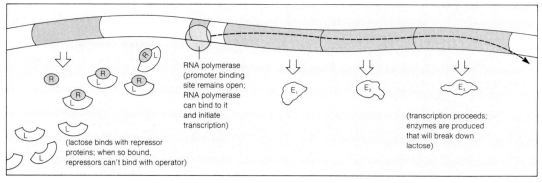

Figure 14.3 Induction and repression of gene transcription for the lactose operon, as described in the text. (Illustrations based on conversations with Robert Robbins, Michigan State University)

c *When lactose is present in the environment (induction occurs)*

Other Prokaryotic Control Mechanisms

In *E. coli*, operon controls of transcription are the most prevalent. Compared with straightforward transcription, though, operon control is an energetically expensive mechanism. Its use is limited to those metabolic events which, on balance, are worth the cost of building and maintaining DNA regions that do not directly yield useful cell products. Thus, being adaptive to changes in lactose availability means survival in a certain environment and is worth the cost.

For many genes, more economical mechanisms control the rate of transcription. Most of these mechanisms entail modification of RNA polymerase or its binding site, the promoter. For example, not all promoters are equally open-armed in their chemical invitation to RNA polymerase. Through variations in their nucleotide sequence, some promoters are better at binding this enzyme. We would expect the structural genes under their control to have a higher output, and their products to be required in greater amounts.

Prokaryotes also appear to depend somewhat on translational controls over the rate at which protein products are assembled. For instance, parts of mRNA transcripts might be folded up tightly, which would make them less accessible to translation enzymes.

GENE REGULATION IN EUKARYOTES

Comparison of Prokaryotic and Eukaryotic DNA

The haploid DNA complement characteristic of a cell (or species) is called its **genome**. Structural genes make up the bulk of prokaryotic genomes. Each is an uninterrupted stretch of nucleotides that contains the information for building a polypeptide or RNA molecule. For the most part, these structural genes have unique base sequences that occur only once in the genome. In other words, prokaryotic genomes are largely *single-copy DNA*.

Repetitive DNA Sequences. When we turn to eukaryotes, we find that their genomes are more complex than those of prokaryotes. Even though a large part of the eukaryotic genome is also single-copy DNA, many of the nucleotide sequences are not: *they occur more than once.* For example, fifteen percent of some eukaryotic genomes are repeated sequences. Thirty percent of your own genome consists of repeated nucleotide sequences.

The term *moderately repetitive DNA* refers to identical (or nearly identical) sequences that are repeated over and over, tens to hundreds of times. As an example, hundreds of copies of the genes coding for rRNA occur one after the other in the nucleolar region of chromosomes. Several thousand different kinds of moderately repetitive sequences can be present in a eukaryotic genome. *Highly repetitive DNA* consists of short, simple stretches repeated thousands or millions of times. In general, highly repetitive DNA is not transcribed. Some studies show that it is concentrated at centromere regions of chromosomes. The localization suggests that highly repeated sequences might function in aligning chromosomes for movement during mitotic and meiotic division (Chapter Nine).

Currently, the sequence organization of eukaryotic DNA is an enormous puzzle. Studies using recombinant DNA methods have revealed that only a small part of the genome of complex eukaryotes becomes translated into proteins. (For instance, it has been estimated that a mere five percent of the *Drosophila* genome are protein-coding genes. For humans, the estimate is less than two percent.) To complicate matters, nearly every structural gene in complex eukaryotes is *not* one continuous sequence of protein-coding information. To give an extreme example, the structural gene coding for collagen is interrupted more than fifty times by DNA sequences that never do get translated!

Introns and Exons. Noncoding nucleotide sequences that are positioned within a structural gene are called *intervening DNA*, or *introns* for short. The coding portions of a structural gene (which are expressed) are called *exons*. All introns and exons that occur between the start codon and stop codon for the gene are transcribed into RNA. As a result, the transcript contains far more information than is needed to build a particular product. Such transcripts are found in the nucleus during all stages of the life cycle—but they are never found in the cytoplasm. Their intron-derived portions are snipped out and degraded before leaving the nucleus. The exon-derived portions are spliced together into a mature RNA transcript, by mechanisms that will be described next.

Given the points made so far, we can make the following generalizations about prokaryotic and eukaryotic genomes:

Prokaryotic genomes are largely single-copy DNA sequences, most of which are protein-coding structural genes. Each structural gene in prokaryotes is an uninterrupted stretch of nucleotides.

Eukaryotic genomes contain single-copy, moderately repetitive, and highly repetitive DNA sequences. Protein-coding genes make up only a small part of the genome. Nearly all protein-coding genes are fragmented by intervening nucleotide sequences (introns) whose functions are unknown.

Transcript Processing

Let's now take a look at how introns are snipped out of RNA transcripts that are destined to leave the nucleus. From the time it peels off a gene until it reaches a nuclear gateway to the cytoplasm, an RNA transcript associates with proteins. The proteins seem to take part in post-transcriptional modifications to the newly formed RNA molecule, which contains coding regions (exons) and intervening sequences (introns). As Figure 14.4 shows, the transcript gets capped at its beginning, and a string of about 200 adenine nucleotides (a "poly-A tail") is attached to the end. Two other post-transcriptional modifications are called **RNA processing**. Here, introns are excised from the initial transcript, then the exons are spliced together to form a continuous sequence of genetic information for assembling a polypeptide chain.

Enzymes execute the splicing. But how do they know where to cut? How do they know that the end of one exon is supposed to be spliced to the start of another exon that is

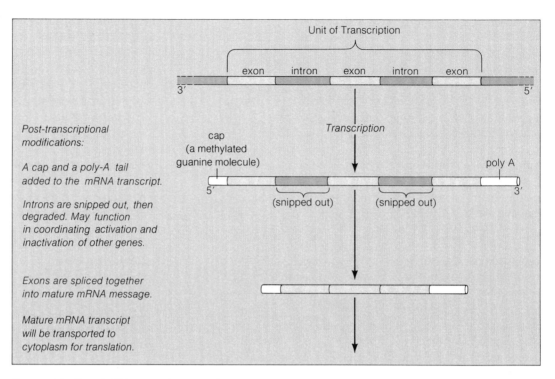

Figure 14.4 Steps in RNA-transcript processing.

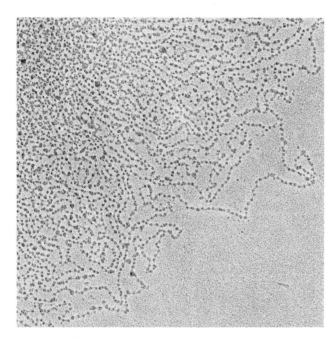

Figure 14.5 Nucleosomes of chromatin from *Drosophila melanogaster*. 102,500×. (From O. Miller, Jr., and Steve McKnight, University of Virginia)

(for example) seven or eight *thousand* nucleotides downstream in the transcript? After all, even though some introns are a mere 10 nucleotides long, others are 10,000 long! If the enzymes slip up by so much as one nucleotide, they can destroy the normal reading frame for the transcript, and a defective protein can result.

This actually happens in the rare genetic disease known as β^+ *thalassemia*. Individuals afflicted with the disease cannot produce enough of the beta-chain subunits of globin (a blood protein). The disease arises from a single mutation in an intron. With this mutation, the intron sequence becomes CTATTAG. It happens that this sequence resembles a normal recognition site for splicing enzymes (CCCTTAG). More than ninety percent of the abnormal RNA transcripts produced in the red blood cells of afflicted individuals are cut here. A result of the abnormal cuts is that the reading frame for the transcript shifts, and it is impossible to translate the message into functional protein.

Abnormal recognition sites aside, enzymes do process RNA transcripts with remarkable fidelity. This suggests that not all portions of the introns are gibberish. Indeed, most introns have quite similar nucleotide stretches near the splicing junctions, almost all begin with the sequence

GT, and almost all end with AG. However, a question remains: Is the *bulk* of an intron nonfunctional? The picture is still sketchy, except for the results of a few studies. The studies suggest that *both splicing and intron organization might be part of a broader mechanism for coordinating the expression of more than one gene.*

Chromosome Organization and Gene Activity

An intriguing puzzle, still to be solved, is how chromosome structure figures in gene control. It seems that eukaryotic DNA and its RNA transcripts are cloaked in proteins that figure in this puzzle.

Nucleosome Packaging. Chromosome structure arises from a combination of DNA and a class of structural proteins called *histones*. (Other, nonstructural proteins such as enzymes are also associated with chromosome assembly and gene activity. They are collectively called "nonhistones.") The histones don't vary much in overall composition from one chromosome to the next, from one cell type to the next, even from one species to the next. They also vary little in amino acid sequence from one histone to the next, compared with most other classes of proteins. Such uniformity suggests that histones have long been central to chromosome structure.

DNA and histones become organized into nucleoprotein fibers. When stretched out, a nucleoprotein looks like a beaded chain (Figure 14.5). Each "bead" in the chain is a

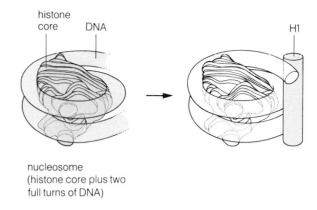

nucleosome
(histone core plus two
full turns of DNA)

Figure 14.6 Model of the nucelosome, showing how DNA loops around a core of eight histone molecules, and is "locked" in place by another histone (H1).

nucleosome, the basic unit of chromosome structure. A nucleosome consists of 146 base pairs of DNA, wound around a core of eight histone molecules (Figure 14.6). Once the DNA makes two loops around a nucleosome, another histone (called H1) holds it in place. This histone is critical in further chromosone condensation. Figure 14.7 is one model of how nucleosomes might be packed in metaphase chromosomes. Figure 14.1, which shows a metaphase chromosome that is stripped of its histones, gives an idea of the extraordinary extent of the actual packaging.

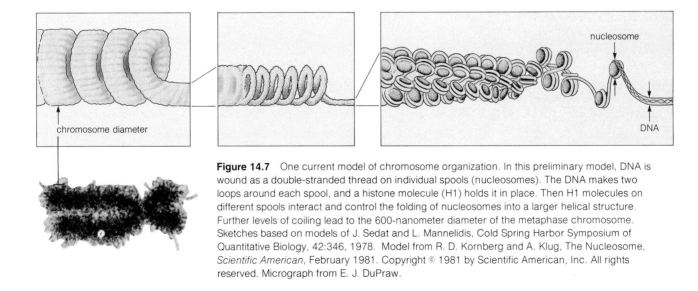

Figure 14.7 One current model of chromosome organization. In this preliminary model, DNA is wound as a double-stranded thread on individual spools (nucleosomes). The DNA makes two loops around each spool, and a histone molecule (H1) holds it in place. Then H1 molecules on different spools interact and control the folding of nucleosomes into a larger helical structure. Further levels of coiling lead to the 600-nanometer diameter of the metaphase chromosome. Sketches based on models of J. Sedat and L. Mannelidis, Cold Spring Harbor Symposium of Quantitative Biology, 42:346, 1978. Model from R. D. Kornberg and A. Klug, The Nucleosome, *Scientific American*, February 1981. Copyright © 1981 by Scientific American, Inc. All rights reserved. Micrograph from E. J. DuPraw.

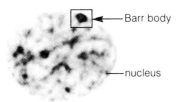

Figure 14.8 Barr body from a cell of a mammalian female. (Murray L. Barr)

Experiments suggest that nucleosome packaging arrangements might be related to gene activity in particular cells at particular times. In several species, researchers have discovered chromosome regions that become highly sensitive to enzymes when structural genes are about to become active. One such region is the "TATA box" (which always has a double thymine-adenine sequence). It is about thirty nucleotides upstream from a gene initiation site. Another hypersensitive region, the "CAT box," is about eighty nucleotides upstream. Harold Weintraub has calculated that with one turn of DNA around a histone core, a TATA and a CAT box would end up side by side. With another turn, both would end up right next to another known hypersensitive region. Do such three-dimensional arrangements actually occur in the condensed chromosome—and might they be control points for gene transcription? That is not known.

X Chromosome Inactivation. Some controls over gene expression operate through shifts in the degree of chromosome condensation. Quite simply, the bases of condensed DNA are less accessible to enzymes and other transcription agents than are bases where DNA coiling is more relaxed. Consider chromosome behavior just before nuclear division. About that time, chromosomes condense and gene activity (transcription) generally cannot be detected. Activity resumes when the compact chromosome becomes stretched out in the nucleus following division.

In some cases, the whole chromosome remains tightly condensed between divisions. For example, there are two X chromosomes in cells of mammalian females. Both are required for normal development of oocytes (hence for female fertility). But oocytes are the only cells in an adult female in which genes on both X chromosomes are active. During early development, one X chromosome is inacti-

vated. It remains condensed, and most of its genes are never transcribed. The condensed form is called a **Barr body** after its discoverer, Murray Barr (Figure 14.8). Alleles on the homologous X chromosome are the ones that are expressed.

Which of the two chromosomes becomes turned on in a given cell seems to be a matter of chance. Once the cell has made its random chemical choice, though, the same choice is made by all of its descendants that come to form a given body tissue region. Mary Lyon was the first to deduce what was going on, hence the process has become known as **Lyonization**.

Consider what the process means for human males (XY) and human females (XX). Cells of *both* sexes have only one active X chromosome. Depending on which of the two is active in a given tissue region, this also means that female tissues are actually a "mosaic" of sex-linked traits. The mosaic effect is most evident in calico cats. These animals are heterozygous for black and yellow coat-color alleles, which reside on the X chromosome. Coat color in a given body region thus depends on which of the two X chromosomes has been loosened up so that its particular alleles are available to agents of transcription (Figure 14.9).

What controls the chromosome condensations of the sort just described? Here again, there are no answers. Clearly, much remains to be learned about the relationship between chromosome condensation and gene activity in eukaryotes.

VARIABLE GENE ACTIVITY IN EUKARYOTIC DEVELOPMENT

The prokaryotic life cycle is basically one of growing and dividing, growing and dividing, and growing again. As the first part of this chapter suggested, even this simple flow of living matter requires many controls at the genetic level. By comparison, genetic controls over eukaryotes as complex as multicelled plants and animals are awesome. They must coordinate the development of a single-celled zygote into all the specialized cells and structures of the adult form! *Thus eukaryotic gene controls extend through longer spans of time and over intricate cellular arrangements in space.*

In general, the word **development** means an ordered unfolding of the potential of the genome. It is a controlled process whereby genetic instructions for building a structurally and functionally organized system become progressively expressed. The word applies to single cells; it applies to multicelled organisms. During eukaryotic development, cells also undergo **differentiation**. Cells or cell regions become specialized in appearance, composition, function, and (in multicellularity) position according to the genetic program for the species.

In plants, fungi, and animals, all cells have the same genetic makeup, for they are all descended from the same single-celled zygote. Many experiments have shown that differentiated cells in these organisms selectively use a common set of hereditary instructions to build diverse cell types.

Differentiation among cells that carry the same set of hereditary instructions arises from selective gene expression (activation of some parts of the DNA and suppression of other parts in a given cell type).

The patterns of selective gene expression are astonishingly varied. In differentiated cells, some genes might be turned on only once. Some genes might be turned on several times or left on continually. Others are switched on and off throughout the individual's life. Some are never activated at all. (For instance, almost none of the genome is expressed in red blood cells. At a late stage of differentiation, there are about 4,000 different RNA transcripts in the nucleus of these cells. Fewer than 100 become processed and sent out of the nucleus. Of these, almost all are concerned with hemoglobin synthesis.)

The selective reading of hereditary instructions in differentiated cells involves three levels of controls, which can be summarized this way:

In multicelled eukaryotes, gene controls operate within cells, between cells, and between cells and the environment.

Later chapters will give details of the developmental outcomes of variable gene activity in plants and animals. Here, a few examples will give you an idea of how variability can arise through gene controls.

Case Study: The Not-So-Simple Slime Molds

Dictyostelium discoideum, one of the cellular slime molds, is said to be about as simple a eukaryote as you can get. At one stage of its life cycle, *D. discoideum* produces spores. Each spore gives rise to a single-celled amoeba, which divides into two amoebas, then four, and perhaps many more.

Jack Carey

Figure 14.9 Random inactivation of X chromosomes in the female calico cat. One X chromosome carries a black allele for coat color and the other carries a yellow allele. In different body regions, random patches of these two colors occur, depending on which of the two chromosomes has been inactivated. (The white patches result from interaction with another gene locus—the so-called spotting gene—that determines whether any color appears at all.)

The amoebas feed on bacteria. As long as this food source is abundant, the amoebas keep on growing and dividing. But what happens when the bacterial population dwindles? Then the amoebas begin streaming toward one another. Sometimes only a dozen or so are around to congregate; sometimes the number exceeds a hundred thousand. The mass of cells assumes the shape of a slug (Figure 14.10). This slug actually crawls around as a coordinated body! Then it differentiates in a remarkable way. Some of its cells are destined to form a vertical stalk, which will be strengthened with fibrils of cellulose. The stalk will support a sporocarp, a mature fruiting body from which new spores will be discharged. There might be hundreds, even thousands of spores perched on a stalk. Air currents disperse them. When they land on damp, warm soil, each gives rise to one amoeba—and the cycle begins again.

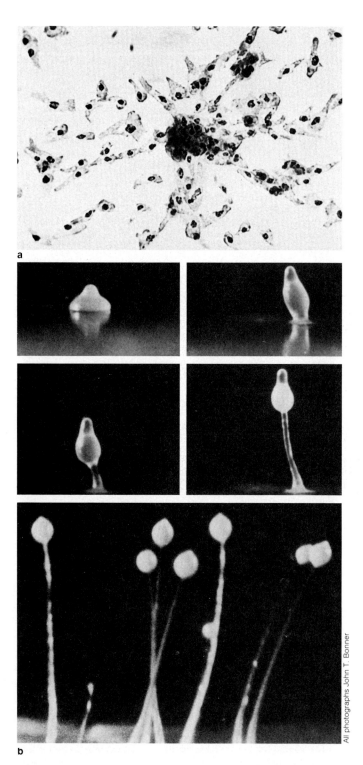

a

b

Figure 14.10 (a) Clumping of amoebas, preceding differentiation in *Dictyostelium discoideum*. (b) Formation of the mature fruiting body. The last photograph shows spores being discharged.

All photographs John T. Bonner

You may be wondering about what coordinates the movement and self-assembly of previously dispersed cells into a differentiated, multicelled body. First, the declining food supply serves as an environmental trigger. When amoebas are starving, their surfaces become exceedingly sticky. Obviously, then, environmental change influences internal metabolic activities that govern the kinds of materials present at the cell surface. Another metabolic change is evident. Some cells start secreting cyclic adenosine monophosphate (cyclic AMP). They do so at intervals of about five minutes, with some cells being faster than others. The dispersed amoebas start moving in the direction where the intervals are shortest (hence where secretions are becoming most concentrated). Cell after cell moves along the chemical gradient, displaying a behavior called chemotaxis.

When one amoeba adheres to another, the contact activates membrane surface receptors that send messages into the cytoplasm. These signals must be transmitted through the cytoplasm to genes residing in the nucleus—specifically, to genes that control cellular differentiation. This much has been deduced from studies of amoebas raised in isolation. When they are not allowed contact with other amoebas, they cannot receive such signals. Their genetic program continues to specify only those enzymes and other gene products required for growth and division. And the isolated cells never do differentiate!

With contact, then, there is chemical communication between cells that the environment has already primed into becoming sticky. Stick together they do, and their developmental fate is sealed according to where, in the newly forming slug, each cell happens to end up. The cells at the leading end are the ones that are most exuberant in their production of cyclic AMP; they are the ones that differentiate into prestalk cells. The rest differentiate into prespore cells. Apparently, the developmental signal is the cyclic-AMP gradient that exists from the leading end to the tail end of the migrating slug. A slug can be cut in two, and each half cut in two again—and a gradient still forms, provided the fragments are given enough time to migrate. Supporting the idea of a biochemical signal for development is the fact that isolated amoebas exposed to high concentrations of cyclic AMP differentiate—into prestalk cells.

The two cell types differ morphologically and biochemically. For example, only the prespore cells develop a certain kind of cytoplasmic vacuole. Perhaps more importantly, for our present purposes, the two cell types also differ in their protein composition—*which suggests that different genes are being transcribed in the differentiated cell types.*

From this example of slime mold development, it is possible to draw the following conclusion:

Both environmental signals and interactions between cells can influence the activities of genes necessary for differentiation.

Case Study: Acetabularia

Acetabularia, an alga, provides another good example of variable gene activity within cells. This single-celled alga thrives in shallow tropical waters. The nucleus resides in the rhizoid, a tiny structure that anchors the cell to the seafloor. From this structure, a graceful stalk extends upward and then terminates in a caplike structure. In the species *A. crenulata,* the cap vaguely resembles a daisy. In the species *A. mediterranea,* the cap looks like an umbrella blown inside out.

In a series of experiments conducted in the 1930s, Joachim Hämmerling studied the interactions between the cytoplasm and nucleus of the two algal species. In one experiment, the stalk and cap were removed from the rhizoid of a mature daisylike alga about to undergo asexual reproduction. A stalk from *A. mediterranea* was grafted onto it. As Figure 14.11 shows, a daisylike cap was regenerated—a cap characteristic of the species from which the nucleus was derived. Similarly, when the stalk of *A. crenulata* was grafted onto the rhizoid of an alga of the blown-out umbrella sort, the cap regenerated looked like a blown-out umbrella.

Clearly, hereditary instructions in the nucleus from one cell had taken over cytoplasmic differentiation in the recipient cell. RNA transcripts had been produced, had moved into the cytoplasm, and had become translated into those particular proteins necessary for producing a different kind of cap. It is known that inhibitors of RNA synthesis injected into the rhizoid prevent such cap regeneration.

Observations of Variable Gene Activity

The differentiation observed in *Dictyostelium* and in *Acetabularia* provides only indirect evidence of variable gene activity. More direct evidence has been obtained from cytological studies of *Drosophila*. In *Drosophila* salivary glands, polytene chromosomes form when DNA is duplicated repeatedly and all the duplicated strands stick together in parallel array. A distinct banding pattern is characteristic of these "giant" chromosomes.

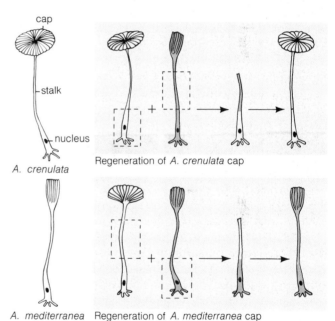

Figure 14.11 *Acetabularia* grafting experiments implicating the nucleus as the control center for regeneration of cellular structures.

Each band is composed of homologous regions of tightly massed DNA. Each mass represents the location of one or perhaps several genes. In their highly condensed form, the DNA regions are relatively inaccessible to agents of transcription. However, during different developmental stages, some of the bands uncoil into loops. Open loops from homologous bands extend outward and form a **chromosome puff** (Figure 14.12).

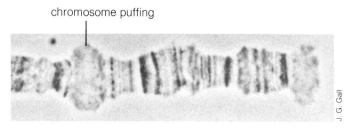

chromosome puffing

Figure 14.12 Chromosome puffing. The phase-contrast micrograph shows a prominent puff near the end of chromosome 3 from *Drosophila melanogaster*.

J. G. Gall

Transcription in cells containing polytene chromosomes has been correlated with how large and diffuse these puffs become in appearance. Labeled precursors of uracil (a marker for RNA synthesis) have been tracked and have been shown to become concentrated in puff regions. Hence transcription is proceeding actively where puffing occurs.

Chromosome puffs also provide a way of observing the effects of environmental agents on gene transcription. Consider, for example, some effects of a hormone called **ecdysone**. Many insect life cycles progress through larval stages, in which the shedding of a hardened, outer body layer of fixed size alternates with periods of body growth and morphological change. The shedding phase is a form of *molting*, a genetically prescribed replacement of old body parts for new. Suppose that you inject ecdysone into a *Drosophila* larva during a nonmolting phase. You will be able to observe shifts in the puff patterns of the larva's polytene chromosomes. Certain bands loop outward, others condense inward. And they do so in a pattern that is identical with the one you would observe during a normal molting phase. When you stop the injections, the puffed regions corresponding to molting subside. Resume the injections, and the puff pattern emerges once more. You can even inhibit puffing entirely during a molting phase with applications of actinomycin (which inhibits nucleic acid synthesis). Such experiments provide evidence that agents outside the nucleus influence transcription of specific gene regions in specific cell types.

More of what is known about variable gene activity comes from studies of **lampbrush chromosomes**. The lampbrush configuration can be observed during oogenesis in many animals. This configuration occurs when the oocyte has entered a tremendous growth phase. Meiosis is not yet complete at this phase, and sister chromatids are still attached (Chapter Nine). Together, the two chromosomal axes form a backbone from which hundreds or thousands of paired loops (one loop per chromatid) extend. These loops are illustrated in Figure 14.13. In this state, the chromosome resembles bristle brushes that were once used to clean oil lamps (hence the name).

The appearance of lampbrush chromosomes heralds intense transcriptional activity. Dense clusters of RNA polymerases appear among the loops once they have formed. Soon, giant RNA transcripts peel off the loops. At least some of the RNA assembled on lampbrush chromosomes direct initial developmental events. Experiments have shown that early embryonic cells exposed to chemical inhibitors of gene transcription are still able to build most proteins. Instructions for doing so occur in RNA transcripts stockpiled earlier, in the oocyte.

CANCER: WHEN CONTROLS BREAK DOWN

Throughout the eukaryotic life cycle, variable gene activity is controlled through mechanisms of the sort described in this chapter. These controls are essential in the coordinated functioning of the whole organism. Under some circumstances, however, the controls are subject to breakdown. Although such breakdowns are rare, when they do occur the results can be devastating.

Consider what happens when nuclei from frog brain cells are transplanted into a frog zygote that has had the nucleus removed. In a normal zygote, DNA duplication and cell division proceed rapidly; in a mature brain cell, they normally do not proceed at all. Almost from the moment of transplantation, though, brain cell nuclei respond to signals from the egg cytoplasm. Within five minutes, DNA duplication begins and the nuclei prepare for division!

Unfortunately, such gross modification of cell behavior is not merely a laboratory curiosity. Sometimes in humans, a single nondividing, differentiated cell undergoes this kind of change. Instead of devoting itself to the normal program of gene expression, this differentiated cell begins duplicating its DNA and growing. Then it divides. It divides again and again. Soon the progeny of this one cell begin to crowd surrounding cells, exerting increasing pressure on them and interfering with cellular functions. One single cell has gone out of control and has spawned a tumor.

A **tumor** is an abnormal growth and massing of new tissue in some region of the body. It results from the breakdown of normal genetic control mechanisms. It is not that the affected cells grow and reproduce at some phenomenal rate. It is that they have lost the controls that tell them when to stop. If the tumorous growth is not removed, it can continue to destroy the surrounding tissues and it may bring about death of the individual.

If the only regulatory controls being modified are those governing cell growth and division, the situation is less serious than it might otherwise be. A tumor resulting from cells dividing more than they should is considered a **benign tumor**. When the abnormal mass is surgically removed, its threat to the individual ceases.

The situation can be far more serious when modifications in the control system lead to changes in the cell surface. Recall that membrane surface recognition factors identify a given cell as being of a certain type (Chapter Five). Such factors enable differentiated cells of like type to recognize each other chemically and interact with one another. Through these interactions, they remain bound together in tissues and organs. When something suppresses the genes coding for a given set of recognition factors, the cell loses its identity. It also shows a disposition to adhere indiscriminately to any other cell type it encounters. **Malignant cells**, or **cancer**, characteristically have lost surface properties necessary for proper intercellular communication, and they characteristically show unchecked growth.

Curiously, cancer cells have something in common with prokaryotic cells. As long as environmental conditions remain favorable, both cell types simply go on dividing indefinitely. For instance, in 1951 a population of cancerous human cells was placed in culture—and today their descendants are still dividing, in cell culture laboratories all over the world. (These are the **HeLa cell** lines, an abbreviation of the name of the woman donor.)

Malignant cells that have lost their normal surface markers can invade and destroy surrounding tissues. Not all malignant cells grow into one solid tumor. Some are capable of dispersal, or **metastasis**. In leukemia, white blood cells become malignant and divide, unchecked, in the bloodstream. Sometimes, too, cells slip away from a malignant tumor and enter the bloodstream; sometimes they wander through body tissues. They might become lodged in a variety of different tissues, there to begin multiplying and producing secondary tumors. Cancer cells exhibiting metastasis are more difficult to treat. Surgery in one region is not likely to remove all the malignant cells that might be present in the body. A tumor can be removed from one site, but another might appear elsewhere. Treatments other than surgery must then be used. Such treatments include specific chemical agents, radiation, or both. As you will read in Chapter Twenty-Four, however, the treatments carry their own hazards. They must be administered with utmost caution in order to destroy cancer cells without

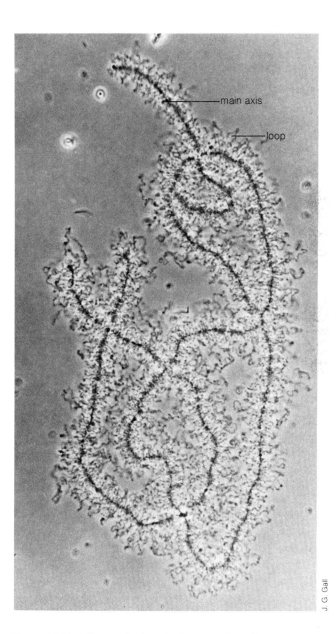

Figure 14.13 Micrograph of a pair of synapsed lampbrush chromosomes. These chromosomes were taken from an oocyte of a female newt (*Triturus viridescens*). Notice how the loops project laterally from the main chromosomal axis. The sketch depicts three pairs of these loops emerging from the main axis.

destroying normally dividing cells (such as those which form blood).

What causes such traumatic changes in cellular controls? There are many known factors, and often they act in concert. Viruses cause cancer in experimental animals such as birds (see Chapter Twenty-Four). Some viruses have been implicated in certain types of human cancer. Very rarely, common viruses normally associated with mild disease symptoms can initiate the loss of normal cellular controls. Malignancies can also be triggered by other than infectious agents. Chemicals, environmental pollutants of many sorts, continuous exposure to sunlight, and constant physical irritation of some tissue are a few examples. All can lead to an increased susceptibility to (if not cause) some form of cancer.

Because we do not yet understand in detail the controls over the differentiated state in eukaryotic cells, neither do we understand in detail the changes that occur in cancerous transformations of those cells. However, progress is being made in identifying the processes involved, and many biologists are predicting that some presently unmanageable forms of cancer might be brought under control within the next few decades.

PERSPECTIVE

In this chapter, you have been introduced to controls over which gene products can appear in a cell, when they can appear, at what times, at what rates, and in what amounts. You have seen that these controls work during transcription of a structural gene and, afterward, on the RNA transcripts themselves. They work during and after translation of the transcripts into gene products. And they work on enzyme activity at every stage of protein synthesis.

In later units, we will look at examples of gene controls over animal and plant growth, maintenance, and development. In reading about these examples, keep in mind that we have yet to discover how all the diverse cells in a complex eukaryote read the same genetic library in their own selective way and thereby become unique. Somehow these cells respond not only to changes induced by the extracellular environment, but also to internal genetic cues. Somehow they exchange chemical signals that modify the cytoplasm. In turn, the cytoplasm of a given cell generates a new set of signals to the nucleus embedded within it, signals that cause some genes to be turned off and others to be turned on. That cell may then send out new signals, telling neighboring cells that it is time for them to change their patterns of structure and behavior.

Thus eukaryotic cells embark on a most ambitious journey: they come into existence equipped with genetic controls specifying which species they are, where they are in relation to other cells, where they are headed, and what time it is as they move on a prescribed course of development. It is a journey that has its pathways—perhaps even its ultimate destination—encoded in the complex structure of eukaryotic DNA.

Readings

Breathnach, R., and P. Chambon. 1981. "Organization and Expression of Eukaryotic Split Genes Coding for Proteins." *Annual Review of Biochemistry* 50:349–383. Excellent state-of-the-art review on sequence organization of split genes and on RNA processing.

Davidson, E., and R. Britten. 1979. "Regulation of Gene Expression: Possible Role of Repetitive Sequences." *Science* 204:1052–1059.

Gilbert, W. 1981. "DNA Sequencing and Gene Structure." *Science* 214:1305–1313.

Gurdon, J. 1974. *The Control of Gene Expression in Animal Development.* Cambridge, Massachusetts: Harvard University Press.

Klug, A., et al. 1981. "A Low-Resolution Structure of the Histone Core of the Nucleosome." *Nature* 287:509–515.

Kornberg, R., and A. Klug. 1981. "The Nucleosome." *Scientific American* 244(2):55–64.

Review Questions

1. Cellular life depends on controls over which gene products are synthesized, at what times, at what rates, and in what amounts. List the five general kinds of control systems, then give an example of how one kind works.

2. What is the basic difference between controls over gene expression in prokaryotes and eukaryotes?

3. Define a structural gene. List and define three control elements that govern the transcription rate of many structural genes in prokaryotes.

4. Define intron and exon. What happens to introns before an RNA transcript of a structural gene leaves the nucleus?

5. Somatic cells of human females have two X chromosomes. During what developmental stage are genes on *both* chromosomes active? Can you explain what happens to one of those chromosomes after this stage?

6. Define development and differentiation.

7. A plant, fungus, or animal is composed of diverse cell types. How does this diversity arise, given that all of its cells have the *same* set of hereditary instructions?

8. What is a benign tumor, and why is it less serious than one exhibiting metastasis?

Peas, beans, corn, flies, molds, bacteria—these are organisms that have been truly accommodating in genetic studies. They grow and reproduce in small quarters, under contrived and controlled conditions. They also reproduce rapidly and in abundance, giving rise to many offspring through successive generations that are far shorter in duration than the life span of the geneticist who observes them. In short, they lend themselves to genetic analysis.

In contrast, humans live in enormously varied and variable environments. They tend not to stay put. Generally they get together and reproduce by preference, not by dictum. Human subjects live just as long as the geneticists studying them, so tracking traits through generations is a long, drawn-out process. Besides that, humans don't produce families in sizes large enough to make meaningful statistical inferences about the transmission and distribution of traits.

Despite all such obstacles to analysis, human genetics is a burgeoning field. Pedigrees are now constructed according to standardized procedures that provide more accurate ways of organizing data and tracking family traits through several generations. Many different families in which the same trait is manifest are studied together, as a means of increasing the numerical information on which statistical analyses are based. Data gathered on large populations throughout the world are pooled for comparative analyses.

The information being gathered does more than help satisfy our curiosity about ourselves. It forms a basis for making decisions that affect the well-being of individuals and society at large. Consider that more than 20,000 human diseases have already been traced to genetic disorders. Many of the diseases can be readily diagnosed and treated. However, actual treatments are presently limited to **phenotypic cures**, in which certain practices are followed that compensate for phenotypic defects. (For instance, some prevent harmful alleles from being expressed, so that the disease symptoms themselves cannot be expressed. Others compensate for a nonfunctional allele by providing the body with the missing gene product.)

Phenotypic cures do alleviate individual suffering. They also circumvent the process of natural selection. Harmful alleles not only can be perpetuated, they can become represented with increased frequency in a population with the passage of many generations. When afflicted persons have children, they may pass on their disorder to the next generation. The "cure," in other words, is illusory.

On the horizon are **genotypic cures**, in which defective alleles will be chemically modified or replaced. For instance,

15

HUMAN GENETICS

if a harmful allele is identified in prospective parents, it theoretically can be isolated, excised, and replaced microsurgically in sperm or eggs by a functional allele obtained with recombinant DNA methods (Chapter Twelve). Thus a genotypic cure could be brought about before fertilization.

This chapter will focus initially on some human genetic disorders. The examples selected are necessarily limited, but they will give you an idea of the diversity of genetic problems that we deal with as individuals and as members of society. They will also provide a framework for considering some practical and ethical aspects of genetic screening, counseling, and treatment programs.

AUTOSOMAL RECESSIVE INHERITANCE

Galactosemia is a disease that arises from an inability to metabolize a component of milk. It occurs at a frequency of about 1 in 100,000 individuals. Afflicted infants suffer from malnutrition, diarrhea, and severe vomiting. Often the eyes, liver, and brain are damaged. Without treatment, galactosemic individuals usually die.

The disease has been traced to a mutant allele, which leads to the absence or nonfunctioning of one enzyme. The normal allele codes for an enzyme that takes part in a metabolic pathway by which the milk sugar lactose is degraded (Figure 15.1). In individuals who are homozygous recessive for the allele, lactose cannot enter the glycolytic pathway (Chapter Eight). Instead, an intermediate formed just before the blocked metabolic step accumulates in the blood. In large concentrations, the intermediate is toxic.

Galactosemia is a disease that can be cured phenotypically. Abnormally high amounts of galactose can be detected in the urine. When diseased infants are detected early enough, they are placed on a diet that includes milk substitutes. By drinking lactose-free "milk" and avoiding other sources of galactose, they can grow up symptom-free.

Studies of many families indicate that galactosemia is an example of *autosomal recessive inheritance,* for the following reasons:

1. Both males and females can carry the recessive allele.

2. The recessive allele is not expressed in heterozygotes of either sex, but it is expressed in homozygotes of both sexes.

3. Two heterozygous parents produce disease-free and diseased infants in about a 3:1 ratio. But all of the offspring of two homozygous, galactosemic parents are diseased.

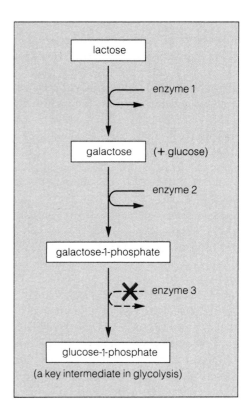

Figure 15.1 Step at which lactose metabolism is blocked in galactosemia, a genetic disease arising from the absence or nonfunctioning of one allele coding for one kind of enzyme.

By constructing Punnett squares, you can see that the first two observations indicate that the gene locus resides on an autosome, not a sex chromosome. You can also see that the last observation indicates that the allele is transmitted according to the rules of simple Mendelian inheritance.

SEX-LINKED RECESSIVE INHERITANCE

Hemophilia

The term **hemophilia** refers to one of several genetic disorders that lead to abnormalities in the body's ability to stop bleeding from injury or stress. A series of proteins takes part in the normal blood-clotting mechanism. Mutations can occur in any one of the individual genes coding for these proteins. In classical hemophilia (called hemophilia A), one of the genes carried on the X chromosome is affected. It codes for a defective protein (or none at all).

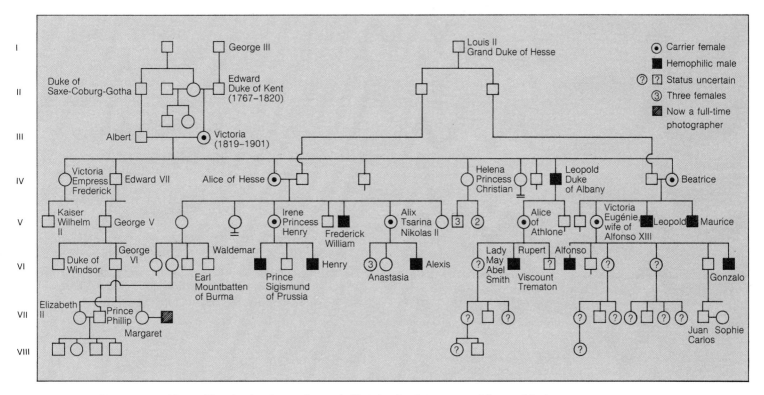

Figure 15.2 Descendants of Queen Victoria, showing carriers and afflicted males that possessed the sex-linked gene conferring the disorder hemophilia A. Many individuals of later generations are not shown in this family pedigree. (After V. McKusick, *Human Genetics.* Second edition, copyright 1969. Reprinted by permission of Prentice-Hall, Inc., Englewood Cliffs, N.J.)

Hemophilia A is an example of *sex-linked recessive inheritance:* the recessive allele can be carried by but not expressed in females, and the male almost always is the one who is afflicted with disease symptoms. In a woman who is heterozygous for the gene, blood-clotting time is essentially normal, because the nonmutated allele on her other X chromosome codes for enough of the normal protein. But if that woman gives birth to a son, there is a fifty-percent probability that he will inherit the X chromosome bearing the mutant allele. In human males, recall, the X chromosome is paired with a Y chromosome. Hence, if the mutant allele *is* inherited, it will be the only one that the male has for this trait. He will be unable to produce the functional blood-clotting protein. Without medical attention, cuts, bruises, or internal bleeding could lead to death.

The mutant allele for hemophilia is rare in the human population. Many more males than females are afflicted by its phenotypic consequences. (Only when a female who is a carrier of the defective allele marries a hemophilic male can daughters be born with the disease. Because the allele occurs so rarely, such births are not likely to occur unless hemophilic males marry close relatives.)

Hemophilia was a recurrent disorder among the royal families of Europe during the nineteenth century. Queen Victoria of England was a carrier of the mutant allele. At one time it was calculated that, of her sixty-nine descendants, eighteen were afflicted males or female carriers of the mutant allele. The family inheritance pattern clearly showed that the mutation is sex-linked. If the mutant allele were on the Y chromosome, father and son would always show the same trait, and this simply did not occur.

One of Victoria's descendants, Crown Prince Alexis of Russia, was hemophilic (Figure 15.2). His affliction and the cast of characters it indirectly drew together—Czar Nicho-

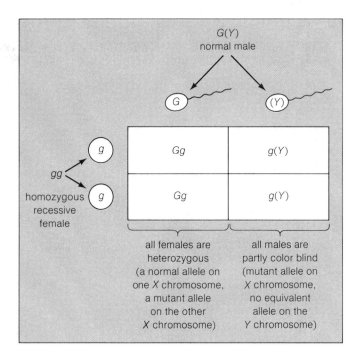

Figure 15.3 Phenotypic outcome among offspring of a female who is homozygous *(gg)* for the recessive green-weakness allele and a male who is normal *G(Y)*. All female children will be heterozygous (carriers), and all males will be afflicted with the disorder.

las II, Czarina Alexandra (a granddaughter of Victoria and a carrier), the power-hungry monk Rasputin who manipulated the aggrieved family to his political advantage—helped catalyze events that brought an end to dynastic rule in the Western world. The historical novel *Nicholas and Alexandra* is a poignant account of these individuals and the afflicted child.

Green Color Blindness

Another example of sex-linked recessive inheritance is called **green weakness**, a partial color blindness that arises because of a reduced amount of retinal pigment that is sensitive to light of green wavelengths. In northern Europe, about five percent of white males show this trait. To them, bright greens appear to be tan colors, olive greens appear to be brown, and reds appear to be reddish browns.

The green-weakness allele *(g)* occurs on the X chromosome. Hence the trait shows up in homozygous females *(gg)*. In heterozygous *(Gg)* females, the dominant allele codes for

enough pigment to permit near-normal color vision. The trait shows up in all males with the recessive allele. When an afflicted male and a female who is heterozygous for the recessive allele have children, the green-weak trait will show up in an average of one child in two (half of the sons, half of the daughters). For a normal male and a homozygous recessive female, all daughters will be normal and carry the recessive allele, whereas all sons will be blind to the color green (Figure 15.3).

CHANGES IN CHROMOSOME NUMBER

As you read in Chapter Eleven, the number of chromosomes can change as a result of nondisjunction and other chromosomal mutations. Among humans, the phenotypic consequences are usually severe and often lethal. Here we will consider just a few examples of this kind of genetic disorder.

Down's Syndrome

Sometimes nondisjunction at meiosis leads to the presence of two copies of chromosome 21 in a gamete. Fusion of this gamete with a normal one produces a trisomic $(2n + 1)$ individual. The condition is called *trisomy 21*, and it leads to a condition called **Down's syndrome**. (The word "syndrome" means a set of symptoms that typically occur together and that characterize some particular disorder.) In its most extreme form, Down's syndrome is characterized by severe mental retardation. Most often, trisomic 21 embryos are lost through miscarriage. (They are expelled spontaneously from the uterus before completion of the first six months of pregnancy.) For every 700 individuals born, though, one is destined to develop Down's syndrome.

Women who conceive past age forty run a much greater risk of giving birth to a trisomic 21 infant than do women in their early twenties (see, for example, Figure 15.4). Apparently, nondisjunction of chromosome 21 in female reproductive cells occurs more frequently with increased age.

Turner's Syndrome

Turner's syndrome is a *sex chromosome abnormality* that probably arises through nondisjunction at meiosis. It is a monosomic $(2n - 1)$ condition, with afflicted individuals having only one X and no Y chromosome. The syndrome occurs about once in every 5,000 live births. Its frequency is lower than for other common sex chromosome abnormalities, probably because almost ninety-eight percent of all afflicted embryos are miscarried early in pregnancy.

This genetic disorder leads to a female phenotype, but the phenotypic distortions are pronounced. The females are always sterile. Their ovaries are nonfunctional, and secondary sex characteristics fail to develop at puberty. At least one-fourth of these females suffer from a defective aorta (a major blood vessel leading away from the heart); they have deformed kidneys, and two ureters instead of one for each kidney. Often these individuals age prematurely and have shortened life expectancies.

Trisomy XXY and XYY

Nondisjunction produces other sex chromosome abnormalities. Some individuals are **trisomic XXY** (they have two X and one Y chromosomes). The phenotype is male. Some XXY males are mentally retarded. They are always sterile, their testes develop to only about one-third their normal size, body hair is sparse, and the deposition of body fat follows female patterns. There may also be some breast enlargement.

About 1 in every 1,000 males born are **trisomic XYY**. Although they are phenotypically normal for the most part, it has been pointed out that 2 in every 100 males in prisons are trisomic XYY. However, the idea that XYY males are inevitably destined to become criminals is a shaky proposition, because it has also been pointed out that only about four percent of all XYY males in the general population end up in prisons, compared to about two-tenths of a percent for all other prisoners of all other genotypes.

PROSPECTS AND PROBLEMS IN HUMAN GENETICS

Chances are, you personally know of someone who suffers the symptoms of a genetic disorder. Of all individuals being born, possibly one percent will be afflicted with pronounced problems arising from a chromosomal mutation. Between one and three percent more will suffer because of mutant genes that either cannot code for vital products or code for defective ones. Of all patients in children's hospitals, between ten and twenty-five percent are being treated for problems that arise from genetic abnormalities. As you have seen from the preceding examples, the phenotypic consequences of these abnormalities can be severe.

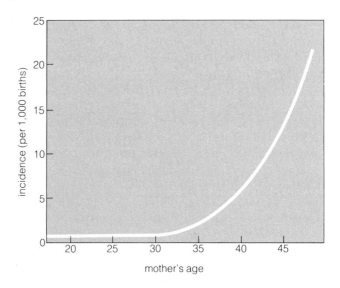

Figure 15.4 Relationship between frequency of Down's syndrome and the age of mothers. These are the results from a study of 1,119 children afflicted with the disorder who were born in Victoria, Australia, between 1942 and 1957. (After Collmann and Stoller, *American Journal of Public Health*, 52, 1962)

Considerable effort is being devoted to developing diagnostic tools and treatments for genetic disorders. However, some of the work is controversial. Genetically based diseases apparently cannot be approached in the same manner as infectious diseases (such as influenza, measles, and polio). Infectious agents are enemies from the environment, so to speak, that attack without much warning. We have had no qualms about mounting counterattacks through immunizations and antibiotics, which either eliminate these agents or at least bring them under control. With genetic disorders, the problem is inherent in the hereditary material of individual human beings.

How do we attack an "enemy" within? Do we institute regional, national, even global programs to identify afflicted individuals? Do we inform those so identified that they are defective in particular ways, and that they might bestow the defect on one or all of the children they might wish to have? Should there be concern about the increased frequency of harmful alleles in the human population as phenotypic cures allow afflicted individuals to survive and reproduce? Who decides which alleles are "harmful"? What do we say to a pregnant woman who has been diagnosed as carrying a trisomic 21 embryo that will suffer Down's syndrome? Should society bear the cost of treating genetically based diseases? If so, should society also have some say in whether embryos diagnosed as having some genetic defect will be born at all, or aborted?

These questions are only the tip of an ethical iceberg. Answers to any one of them have not yet been worked out in a way that can be called universally acceptable. Until such time as permanent, genotypic cures are a reality, however, the questions will remain with us.

The rest of this chapter describes current approaches to treating genetically based diseases. As Table 15.1 suggests, these approaches fall into two general categories: therapeutic measures and preventive measures.

Treatments for Phenotypic Defects

Currently, individuals who already suffer from a genetic disorder are treated at the phenotypic level only. In other words, the genetic disorder itself cannot be eliminated, but often its phenotypic expression can be circumvented. Treatments include diet modifications, adjustments to the environment, surgery, and chemotherapy.

Diet Modification. The outward symptoms of several genetic disorders can be suppressed or minimized by controlling the diet. Galactosemia, described earlier, can be controlled this way. So can **diabetes**, a disease that arises from an inability to produce sufficient amounts of the hormone insulin. This hormone is vital for cellular absorption of glucose. Without it, cells become starved for nutrients, and glucose levels rise in the blood. Symptoms may progress from weight loss to eventual brain damage, coma, and death. At present, insulin cannot be taken orally, because the body's digestive enzymes degrade it before it can reach individual cells. The hormone must be injected directly into veins—a procedure that must be faced daily.

Environmental Adjustments. Some therapeutic treatments for genetically based diseases require adjustments to surrounding conditions. Phenotypic defects such as impaired vision or hearing can be circumvented by such devices as eyeglasses or hearing aids. True albinos avoid direct sunlight. Sickle-cell anemics, recall, suffer from impaired oxygen and carbon-dioxide transfers because of a mutant allele that codes for a variant form of hemoglobin, the oxygen-carrying protein in blood (Figures 10.13 and 13.3). They should avoid strenuous activity in environments where oxygen levels are low (such as high altitudes and unpressurized aircraft cabins). At the extreme are the rare children whose immune system does not function at all. They must be raised in complete sterile confinement to avoid any encounter with infectious agents.

Surgical Correction. Many phenotypic defects can be corrected or at least minimized by surgical reconstructions. For example, **harelip** is a developmental defect of the upper lip. A vertical fissure is present at the lip midsection and often extends into the palate (the roof of the mouth). Surgery can usually correct the defect in terms of appearance and function.

Chemotherapy. Knowledge of the molecular basis of genetic disorders is being used to chemically modify gene products and to compensate for the absence of gene products. For example, **Wilson's disease** arises from an inability to utilize copper, which is essential for the action of several enzymes. Copper deposits build up in tissues and can lead to brain and liver damage. Convulsions and death are the outcome. Yet with a combination of dietary restrictions of copper-containing foods (such as chocolate) and drug administration, individuals who are diagnosed early enough can lead relatively normal lives. One of the drugs (a penicillin derivative) binds with copper in the body, and it is flushed from the body by way of the urinary system.

Genetic Screening

The therapeutic measures described so far are used to assist individuals who are already born and already suffering the consequences of genetic disorders. Preventive measures are also being used to allow early detection and treatment of genetic disorders, before disease symptoms can develop. Others are used to identify carriers who show no outward symptoms but may give birth to diseased children.

Genetic screening usually refers to large-scale programs to detect afflicted persons in a given population. One of the most extensive programs began in the late 1950s and continues today as a means of detecting the disease **phenylketonuria**, or PKU. With this disorder, a mutant allele codes for a defective enzyme. The normal enzyme converts phenylalanine (an amino acid) to tyrosine (another amino acid). In individuals homozygous for the defective allele, phenylalanine accumulates in the body. In large amounts, it is diverted to other pathways, which produce compounds in high enough concentrations to interfere with normal body functioning. One of the compounds, phenylpyruvic acid, can be detected in the urine. In children afflicted with PKU, high concentrations of this compound can damage the nervous system and lead to mental retardation. If diagnosed early enough, the disease symptoms can be alleviated. The individual simply is placed on a diet that provides only as much phenylalanine as required for protein synthesis. Thus the body is not called upon to dispose of excess amounts. Aside from having a restricted diet, afflicted persons can lead normal lives. Most hospitals in the United States routinely screen all newborns for PKU, so outward signs of the disease are rapidly disappearing from the population.

Genetic Counseling and Prenatal Diagnosis

Sometimes prospective parents are concerned that they will have a severely afflicted child. Their first child may have suffered a hereditary disease and the parents now wonder if future children will suffer the same defect. How are such individuals counseled? Typically, several different consultants are required, including medical specialists, geneticists, and social workers who can give emotional support to families into which severely afflicted children are born.

Counseling begins with an accurate diagnosis of a particular disorder in the parental genotypes. Biochemical tests can be performed to detect many metabolic disorders. Family pedigrees are constructed as completely and accurately as possible to aid in the diagnosis. For disorders that follow simple Mendelian inheritance patterns, it is possible to predict the likelihood of producing afflicted children—but not all disorders follow Mendelian inheritance patterns. Even those that do can be influenced by other factors, some identifiable, others not. Even when the extent of risk has been determined with some confidence, it is important that the prospective parents understand that the risk is the same for *each* pregnancy. For example, if there is one chance in four that the child will be born with a genetic disorder, there is one chance in four that the next child will be also.

What happens when a female is already pregnant? For example, suppose a woman forty-five years old has just become pregnant. She may want to know whether she will give birth to a child who will suffer Down's syndrome. Through prenatal diagnosis, it is possible to detect this and more than a hundred other disorders in early pregnancy.

A major detection procedure is based on **amniocentesis**, a sampling of the fluid surrounding the embryo in the mother's uterus (Figure 15.5). The thin needle of a syringe is carefully inserted through the mother's abdominal wall and into the fluid-filled sac (amnion) containing the embryo. Floating in this fluid are skin cells that have been shed from the embryo. Some of the fluid, with its sample of embryonic cells, is withdrawn by the syringe. These cells can be cultured, and can undergo mitosis. Through

Table 15.1	Some Therapeutic and Preventive Measures Used in Treating Genetically Based Diseases
Therapeutic Measures:	
Diet modification	*Providing substances that the body cannot produce for itself, or restricting intake of substances that the body cannot tolerate*
Environmental adjustment	*Using corrective devices (such as eyeglasses for visual defects), or avoiding environmental conditions that the body cannot tolerate (for example, low oxygen levels at high altitudes in the case of sickle-cell anemics)*
Surgical correction	*Surgically repairing deformities (such as cleft lips, heart defects)*
Chemotherapy	*Using chemicals (such as drugs) to modify or inhibit gene expression or gene product function*
Preventive Measures:	
Mutagen reduction	*Avoiding or eliminating environmental substances (such as many industrial wastes) that can induce mutations*
Genetic screening	*Methodically searching through populations and identifying individuals afflicted with (or heterozygous for) a particular genetic disorder*
Genetic counseling	*Conveying information about genetic disorders, as well as the social and medical options available, to afflicted individuals and their families*
Prenatal diagnosis	*Detecting chromosomal mutations and metabolic disorders at the embryonic stage*
Gene replacement*	*Substituting normal alleles for mutant alleles in sperm or eggs*

*Research stage only.

various tests, including karyotype analysis of metaphase chromosomes, abnormalities can be diagnosed early in pregnancy. Amniocentesis is also being used to test for biochemical defects that lead to a host of genetic diseases, such as sickle-cell anemia.

Unfortunately, there presently is no cure for disorders arising from abnormalities in chromosome structure or number. If the embryo is diagnosed as having a severe dis-

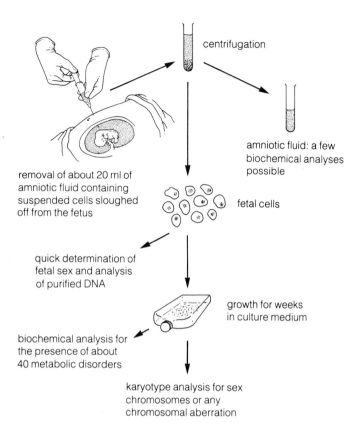

Figure 15.5 Steps in amniocentesis, a procedure used in prenatal diagnosis of many genetic disorders.

order such as Down's syndrome, the parents might elect to request an abortion (an induced expulsion of the embryo from the uterus). Such decisions are bound by ethical considerations. The role of the medical community should be to provide information that the prospective parents need in order to make their own choice. But that choice in turn must be consistent with their own values, within the broad constraints imposed by society.

Gene Replacement

It is not yet possible to replace defective alleles with normal ones in humans. However, recombinant DNA technology has raised hopes that gene replacement therapy may be possible. In fact, gene replacement has already been accomplished in experiments with laboratory mice. The mice were carriers of an allele coding for abnormal hemoglobin,

COMMENTARY

A Holistic View of Human Genetic Disorders

(By Vernon Tipton, Brigham Young University, Provo, Utah)

The sound of carts rolling over cobblestone streets was commonplace in towns and villages of the fifteenth and sixteenth centuries. Ordinarily, it would have served only to break the early morning silence. But the heavy and terrible loads the carts carried lent an ominous tone to the sound, and charged the atmosphere with morbid anticipation. Methodically and inexorably, the carts made their rounds to carry away those dead of smallpox and plague.

Samuel Pepys captured the mood of the times in this brief expression of gratitude: "This day I am by the blessing of God, 34 years old, in very good health and mind's content, and in condition of estate much beyond whatever my friends could expect of a child of theirs. This day, 34 years. The Lord's name be praised! And may I be thankful for it." Life expectancy for Pepys and his contemporaries was about one-third of what it is today, primarily because of the ravages of communicable diseases.

Most of our afflictions fit into one of three categories: communicable diseases (such as plague, tuberculosis, and common colds), degenerative diseases (such as atherosclerosis and diabetes), and behavioral diseases (including alcoholism). The ten current leading causes of death contrast sharply with those of Pepys' era. Today, few die of plague, tuberculosis, or influenza, and smallpox has been eradicated. Today, most die because of heart diseases, cancer, cerebrovascular disease, accidents, emphysema, and suicide. Thus, *during the past two centuries, there has been a dramatic shift from communicable diseases to degenerative and behavioral diseases, many of which are genetic in origin.*

The causes of the shift are many, but included among them are changes brought about by the industrial revolution, advances in medical technology, mass education, and major changes in life styles. This shift, dramatic and profound, suggests two questions: What is its significance to the individual? What impact does it have on the total population?

The shift from external to internal causation of diseases places a greater burden of responsibility on the individual, who must consider the care of the body as a stewardship that cannot be delegated to others. However, the trend has been in the opposite direction: toward the institutionalization of health care and the abdication of individual responsibility. The trend has now reached immense proportions, as described by Leon Kass: "All kinds of problems now roll to the doctor's door, from sagging anatomies to suicides, from unwanted childlessness to unwanted pregnancies, from marital difficulties to learning difficulties, from genetic counseling to drug addiction, from laziness to crime." It is apparent that an increasing number of attitudes and forms of behavior have become defined as illnesses, the treatment of which is regarded as belonging within the jurisdiction of medicine and its practitioners.

Society has become enormously dependent on medicine, an outgrowth of the "one germ, one disease, one therapy" concept that originated in the latter part of the nineteenth century. There is, however, growing realization that most diseases have multiple causes. John Knowles has suggested that "personal behavior, food, and the nature of the environment around us are prime determinants of health and disease." He further indicates that between 1900 and 1966, life expectancy at age sixty-five increased by 2.7 years, as a result of the efforts of organized medicine. At the same time, it has been possible for the sixty-five year old to extend life expectancy eleven years by practicing good health habits.

The collective impact of the shift from communicable to degenerative and behavioral diseases is more difficult to document, mainly because of the time frame required for genetic changes to become clearly manifest. However, it is reasonable to assume that selective pressures exerted by diseases today are considerably different from those existing two centuries ago. Undoubtedly, the net effect is both positive and negative. The harsh environmental conditions of earlier times produced a high incidence of communicable diseases and an extremely high infant mortality rate that gradually eliminated from the population those most susceptible to disease. Very likely, those suffering genetic abnormalities were among those highly susceptible to communicable diseases. Those who escaped genetic abnormalities and communicable disease became susceptible to chronic degenerative disorders simply by virtue of living longer than those who did not.

During the past thirty years, particularly in Europe and the United States, communicable diseases have not been significant in terms of selective pressure on populations. Thus, many more individuals are reaching reproductive age than in former times. Does this mean that the incidence of genetic abnormalities is increasing? The full significance of the historical shift from communicable to degenerative and behavioral diseases cannot be fully understood without the added perspective that the time factor provides. When selective pressures change over time, the genetic composition of populations also changes.

Some questions for debate:

1. Pyloric stenosis, a genetically based disorder, is manifest in some infants. Their pyloric valve is closed, which prevents food from moving from the stomach to the small intestine. Simple surgery corrects the defect; without it, infants would die within a few days. To what extent have such advances changed the genetic composition of populations?

2. Environmental conditions in undeveloped countries are often harsh, and their citizens are exposed to many disease agents which most North Americans seldom (if ever) encounter. In the event of a major disaster requiring prolonged existence in a "nonsanitized" environment, which group would be the more durable? What are some long-term implications of exporting high-technology medicine to undeveloped countries?

3. Why is a cure for cancer (which apparently has a genetic basis) more elusive than the cures for diseases such as polio?

the oxygen-carrying pigment of red blood cells. Red blood cells are produced in bone marrow. Cells from bone marrow tissue were extracted, a normal allele was introduced into their DNA, and the recombinant cells were reestablished in the mouse body. Many generations of the progeny of these cells have continued to express the foreign allele and produce normal hemoglobin!

The problems associated with inserting the right gene in the right place and in the right cells are enormous. It seems likely that the most promising results will come from gene replacement in individual reproductive cells—sperm and eggs—before the zygote embarks on a course of cell division and differentiation, with all of the associated complexities of gene controls (Chapter Fourteen).

Readings

Anderson, A., and E. Diacumakos. 1981. "Genetic Engineering in Mammalian Cells." *Scientific American* 245(1):106–121.

Council of the Environmental Mutagen Society. 1975. "Environmental Mutagenic Hazards." *Science* 187:503–514.

Fuchs, F. 1980. "Genetic Amniocentesis." *Scientific American* 242(6): 47–53. Excellent summary article of a major diagnostic procedure.

Kass, L. 1975. "Regarding the End of Medicine and the Pursuit of Health." *The Public Interest* 40:11.

Knowles, J. 1977. "The Responsibility of the Individual." *Daedalus* 106(1):57–60. Issue entitled "Doing Better and Feeling Worse: Health in the United States."

Lubs, H., and F. de la Cruz (editors). 1977. *Genetic Counseling.* New York: Raven Press. Includes material on the frequency of genetic diseases and a review of studies of genetic counseling.

Mange, A., and E. Mange. 1980. *Genetics: Human Aspects.* Philadelphia: Saunders. Outstanding textbook; highly recommended for the personal reference library of serious students.

Pimentel, D. 1961. "Animal Population Regulation by the Genetic Feedback Mechanism." *The American Naturalist* 95(881):65–79.

Genetics Problems (Answers in Appendix II)

1. In hemophilia A, the body's blood-clotting mechanism is defective. This condition has been traced to a recessive allele of an X-linked gene. Refer now to Figure 15.2. Why are only the females shown as carriers of the recessive allele? If Victoria had married Leopold (also in generation IV), what phenotypes would have been expected among their children, and with what probabilities?

2. Huntington's chorea is due to a dominant autosomal allele. Usually this disorder does not manifest itself until after age thirty-five. Individuals having Huntington's chorea are almost always heterozygous. As a genetic couselor, you are visited by a twenty-year-old woman. Her mother has Huntington's chorea but her father is normal. What is the probability that this woman will develop Huntington's chorea as she grows older? Suppose, at her present age, she marries someone with no family history of the disorder. If they have a child, what is the probability that it will have Huntington's chorea?

3. A woman heterozygous for color blindness (Gg) marries someone who has normal color vision. What is the probability that their first child will be color blind? Their second child? If they have two children only, what is the probability that both will be color blind?

4. A person afflicted with Turner's syndrome has only a single sex chromosome (X only), yet may survive. In contrast, a person having a single Y chromosome and no X chromosome cannot survive. What does this tell you about the genetic contents of the X and Y chromosomes?

5. Fertilization of a normal egg by a sperm that has no sex chromosomes (male nondisjunction) can lead to Turner's syndrome. Also, fertilization of an egg that has no sex chromosomes (female nondisjunction) by a sperm carrying one X chromosome can lead to the same disorder. Suppose a hemophilic male and a carrier (heterozygous) female have a child. The child is nonhemophilic and is afflicted with Turner's syndrome. In which parent did nondisjunction occur?

6. The trisomic XXY condition is also called Klinefelter's syndrome. How could this syndrome arise if nondisjunction occurred in the female parent of an afflicted individual? How could it arise if nondisjunction occurred in the male parent?

7. If nondisjunction occurs for the X chromosomes during oogenesis, then some eggs having two X chromosomes and others having no X chromosomes are produced at about equal frequencies. If normal sperm fertilize these two types of eggs, what genotypes are possible?

8. Phenylketonuria (PKU) is an autosomal recessive condition. About 1 of every 50 afflicted individuals is heterozygous for the gene but displays no symptoms of the disorder.
   a. If you select a symptom-free male at random from the population, what is the probability that he will be heterozygous?
   b. If you select a symptom-free female at random from the population, what is the probability that she will be heterozygous?
   c. If you select a symptom-free male and a symptom-free female at random, what is the probability that both will be heterozygous? What is the probability that they could have a child afflicted with PKU?

9. Laws restricting marriage between close relatives (consanguineous matings) are widespread, the rationale being that such marriages generally lead to an increase in the incidence of genetic defects among offspring. Suppose you are a carrier (heterozygous) for PKU. If you pick a potential mate at random from the population, what is the probability that he or she would also be a PKU carrier? If you marry your first cousin, do you think he or she would have the same probability of being a PKU carrier as your randomly selected mate? Why?

PLANT SYSTEMS AND THEIR CONTROL

16

PLANT CELLS, TISSUES, AND SYSTEMS

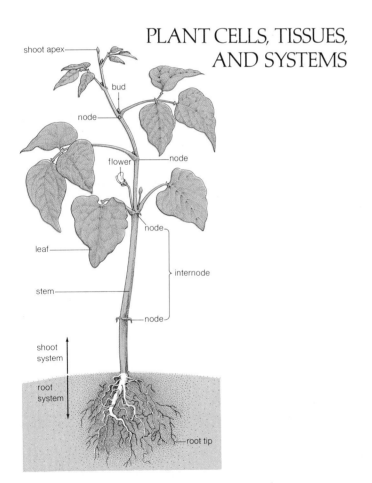

shoot apex

bud

node

flower

node

node

leaf

stem

internode

node

shoot system

root system

root tip

Figure 16.1 Basic body plan of a typical vascular plant, the bean plant *Phaseolus*.

On a summer morning in 1883, a cataclysmic explosion literally blew the small South Pacific island of Krakatoa out of the water. All life there abruptly came to an end. Only the peak of the volcanic cone remained, smoldering with lava, and buried in hot ashes and pumice. For about a year, the island was essentially sterile. But winds and water were carrying inadvertent visitors to it from nearby islands. In time, when the island cooled, some of the visitors settled down and survived. At first, only algae formed mats on the volcanic rocks. Then airborne spores of mosses and ferns took hold in the algal mats. Seeds of flowering plants germinated; grasses thrived in the sunlight and tropical rains streaming down on the volcano's flanks. Over the years, the remains of plants gradually enriched the soil. By 1896, wild sugarcane and delicate orchids were established. Coconuts and other tree seeds drifted over on the ocean currents and took root. All the while, birds and other animals were visiting the island—and carrying seeds from such plants as figs and papayas in their digestive tracts. Half a century after the explosion, Krakatoa was cloaked with a thick forest.

In the spring of 1980, Mount Saint Helens in southwestern Washington exploded violently. Within minutes, hundreds of thousands of mature trees near the volcano's eastern flank were blown down like matchsticks. Thick ashes and pumice turned the once-thick forest below into a scarred, barren sweep of land. Since that time, plants have been repopulating the area, as they did on Krakatoa.

Events of this magnitude dramatize our dependence on plants. We could no more survive without them here on earth than we could survive on the rock-strewn surface of the moon. What characterizes these remarkable organisms that make the land habitable for us? Can we identify general patterns of structural organization among them? Do they, like animals, have complex organ systems that carry out such functions as circulation, gas exchange, and nutrition? How do plants reproduce? What governs their growth and differentiation? These are questions addressed in this unit.

THE PLANT BODY: AN OVERVIEW

On "Typical" Plants

By now, you know about the pitfalls of using a "typical" plant as a textbook example of all plants. A plant can be a tiny string of cells or a giant redwood. It can live in fresh water, seawater, on land—even high above a forest floor, attached to the woody stem of another plant. Some plants, such as trees and grasses, are **vascular**. They have well-developed conducting tissues through which water and solutes are transported to different body regions. Other plants (the algae and bryophytes) are **nonvascular**. They have no internal transport systems, or what they do have is rudimentary. Most nonvascular plants live in water or in moist land settings, and their body plans generally are filamentous or sheetlike. With such body plans, water and solutes can reach individual cells by diffusion alone (Chapter Five). We will look at the nonvascular plants in Unit Seven. Our focus here will be on two kinds of familiar vascular plants: **gymnosperms** (chiefly conifers such as pines, junipers, and redwoods) and **angiosperms** (flowering plants such as roses, cherry trees, corn, and dandelions).

Flowering plants can be divided into two major classes: Monocotyledoneae and Dicotyledoneae. It's easier to think of them as **monocots** and **dicots**. (The names refer to the number of cotyledons, or seed leaves, present in the seeds of these plants. Monocots have one such leaf, dicots have two.) Figure 16.1 shows the organization of a bean plant, which can be used to illustrate the body plan of flowering plants in general. This plant body differentiates into three kinds of vegetative organs: the root, stem, and leaf. All roots present constitute the *root system*. Together, all stems and leaves constitute the *shoot system*. At some point in the life cycle, flowers appear and constitute the *reproductive system*. The structure and functioning of flowers will be described in the next chapter.

How Plant Tissues Arise

Like animals, the multicelled plant follows a prescribed program of growth and development from a single-celled zygote. Mitotic divisions, elongation, growth, and differentiation of cells give rise to tissues and organs with specialized functions. As in animals, genetic controls and environmental cues influence the developmental program. However, even though plants and animals are alike in having the same kind of controls over development, they are not alike in *how* they develop.

For animals, all but a few cell types are already committed to being one particular type of cell even before birth. (For example, all the nerve cells you ever will have were already formed during embryonic development.) In contrast, *plants have the property of open growth.* In other words, even at "maturity," many regions of the vegetative body are composed of undifferentiated cells. These undifferentiated tissue regions are known as **meristems**. They continue to give rise to new cells that go on to become specialized for one task or another.

The tips of roots and shoots have dome-shaped *apical meristems*, where new cells form through mitosis. *All other plant tissues are derived directly or indirectly from apical meristems.* The new cells at these tip regions differentiate into three other meristematic tissues—protoderm, ground meristem, and procambium—which in turn produce the primary plant body (Table 16.1).

The vegetative body of a vascular plant shows continued growth through the activity of several regions of undifferentiated tissues, collectively called meristems.

Continued growth from meristematic regions makes it impossible to assign precise boundaries between parts of the primary plant body. Where does a root end and the

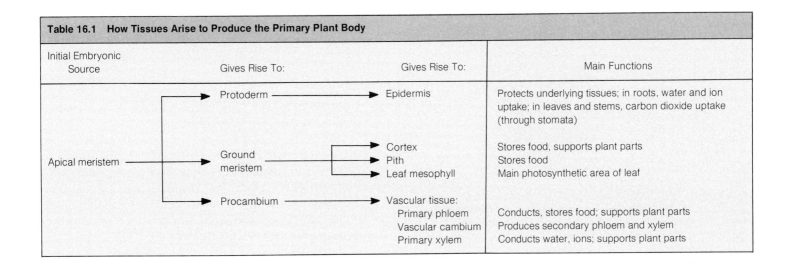

Table 16.1 How Tissues Arise to Produce the Primary Plant Body			
Initial Embryonic Source	Gives Rise To:	Gives Rise To:	Main Functions
Apical meristem	Protoderm	Epidermis	Protects underlying tissues; in roots, water and ion uptake; in leaves and stems, carbon dioxide uptake (through stomata)
	Ground meristem	Cortex Pith Leaf mesophyll	Stores food, supports plant parts Stores food Main photosynthetic area of leaf
	Procambium	Vascular tissue: Primary phloem Vascular cambium Primary xylem	Conducts, stores food; supports plant parts Produces secondary phloem and xylem Conducts water, ions; supports plant parts

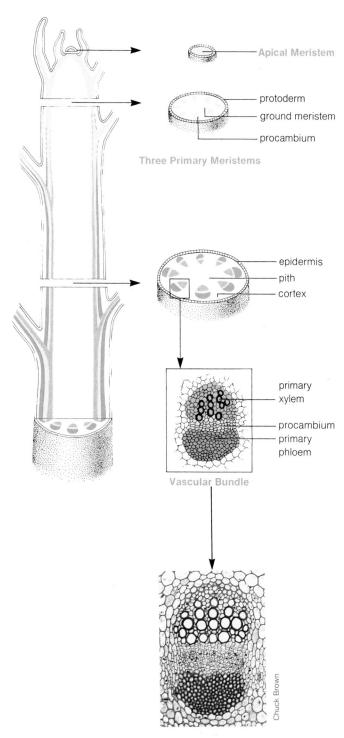

Apical Meristem

protoderm
ground meristem
procambium

Three Primary Meristems

epidermis
pith
cortex

primary
xylem

procambium
primary
phloem

Vascular Bundle

Chuck Brown

Figure 16.2 Pattern of stem development for dicots, a class of vascular plants. To the left, the stem is sliced in half lengthwise to show the location of developing vascular tissue. Apical meristems give rise to the three primary meristem tissues, which in turn produce the tissues of the primary plant body.

stem begin? Where does a stem end and a leaf or flower begin? *The same tissue systems are produced in all parts of the vascular plant.* In roots, stems, leaves, and flowers, protoderm gives rise to the **dermal system**, which consists largely of protective coverings on the plant's outer surface. Ground meristem gives rise to the **ground system**, which makes up most of the primary plant body. Procambium gives rise to the **vascular system**, which includes food-conducting and water-conducting tissues. Table 16.1 summarizes the developmental sequence leading to the primary plant body.

All parts of the vascular plant body are composed of three main tissue systems: the dermal, ground, and vascular systems.

In most plant stems, vascular tissue is organized in clusters of strands called **vascular bundles**. The bundles are embedded in ground tissue and generally run parallel with the long axis of stems. In monocots, vascular bundles are distributed throughout the stem ground tissue:

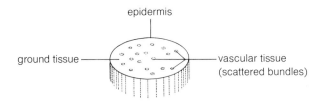

epidermis
ground tissue
vascular tissue
(scattered bundles)

In dicots, vascular bundles are organized in a ring. The ground tissue inside the ring is known as *pith*. The ground tissue between the ring and the dermal surface layer is known as the *cortex*:

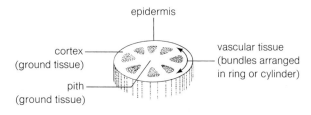

epidermis
cortex
(ground tissue)
pith
(ground tissue)
vascular tissue
(bundles arranged in ring or cylinder)

Figure 16.2 illustrates the vascular system of dicot stems at different stages of stem development.

In many plants, other tissues are added after the primary plant body has formed. This secondary growth increases the thickness of the body. Secondary growth arises from meristems called *vascular cambium* and *cork cambium* in roots and stems. Later, we will look more closely at the events of primary and secondary growth. First, however, let's consider the types of cells and tissues that are produced during these events.

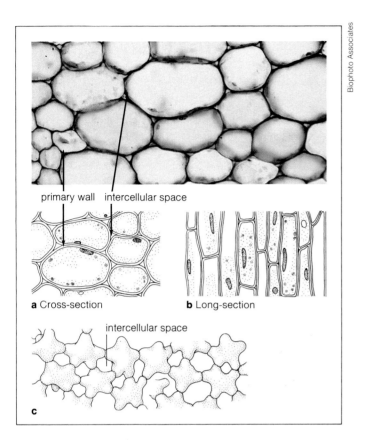

Figure 16.3 Parenchyma. (**a,b**) This is parenchymal tissue from the stem of a sunflower (*Helianthus*). (**c**) In photosynthetic regions of leaves and stems, abundant air spaces exist between parenchyma cells known as mesophyll.

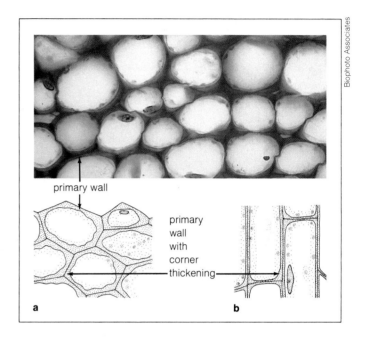

Figure 16.4 Collenchyma from a sunflower stem. The sketches show the cells in cross-section (**a**) and long-section (**b**).

PLANT TISSUES AND THEIR COMPONENT CELLS

Parenchyma: Photosynthesis, Food Storage

Parenchyma is the main cell type of ground tissue systems. Parenchyma cells form continuous tissues in the stem and root cortex and in stem pith. They also form the photosynthetic tissue, or *mesophyll,* between the upper and lower dermal tissue of leaves and floral parts. Parenchyma cells even occur in vascular systems. As Figure 16.3 suggests, parenchyma cells vary in size, shape, and wall structure.

Even though parenchyma cells become specialized in such tasks as food storage and photosynthesis, many do not lose the ability to divide. These are the cells responsible for healing wounds and for regenerating plant parts (even whole plants, in experimental situations). By forming an interconnecting mass of new cells, they are involved in as-

suring successful grafts, whereby one plant part is joined to another plant at an incision made in a stem or root.

Collenchyma: Supporting Young Plant Parts

Beneath the epidermis of many stems and leaves is a thick-walled yet flexible tissue called **collenchyma**. For example, those strong, pliable ribs of a celery stalk contain collenchyma cells joined together into long fibers. Collenchyma cells have unevenly thickened primary walls built up in several patterns (Figure 16.4). When a shoot is first developing, the cell walls expand in surface area, and they become thickened with cellulose and pectin. Being hydrophilic, pectin attracts water into the walls. Partly because the walls contain considerable water, they remain pliable. Hence stems and leaves elongate even while gaining structural support from collenchyma cells.

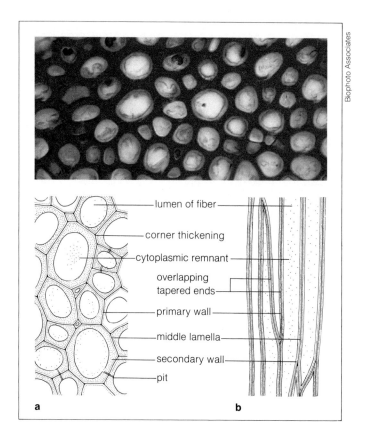

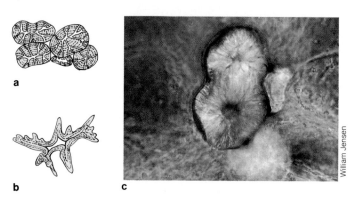

Figure 16.6 Examples of sclerenchyma cells. Stone cells, sketched as if sliced through their midsections (**a**) and under the microscope (**c**). Star sclereid, with its arms radiating from a central body (**b**). Stone cells and star sclereids are in the sclereid category.

Figure 16.5 Sclerenchyma from a sunflower stem. The sketches show the cells in cross-section (**a**) and long-section (**b**).

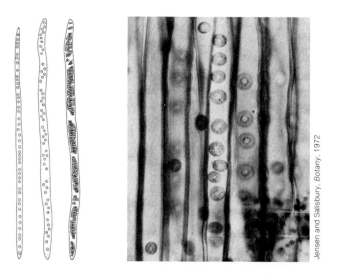

Figure 16.7 Examples of tracheids. The micrograph shows tracheids with bordered pits; these come from a pine tree.

Sclerenchyma: Strengthening Mature Plant Parts

Sclerenchyma is found in mature plant parts. It is especially abundant in fruits and seeds. Sclerenchyma cells have thick secondary walls, which are deposited inside the primary walls (Figure 16.5). The cells themselves are usually dead at maturity, with only their strong walls remaining. Sclerenchyma cells occur individually or as small clusters in the dermal, ground, and vascular systems.

Sclerenchyma cells are of two sorts: sclereids and fibers. The diverse *sclereids* include cells resembling stones, hourglasses, columns, hairs, and stars. Stone cells (Figure 16.6) give the flesh of pear fruit its gritty texture. Stone cells typically have very thick secondary walls impregnated with lignin. *Fibers* are long cells having somewhat flexible walls. These cells support plant parts that have ceased growing. Strands of fibers have great commercial value. They are used in papermaking, in textile and thread manufacture, and in rope-making.

Xylem: Water Transport, Storage, and Support

Xylem is a vascular tissue that extends continuously through the plant. During growth of the primary plant body, xylem develops as strands parallel with the long axis of roots and stems. In plants showing secondary growth of roots, stems, and larger branches, secondary xylem forms what we call

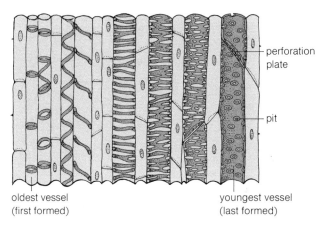

oldest vessel
(first formed)

youngest vessel
(last formed)

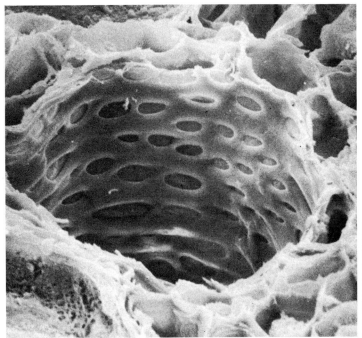

J. Troughton and L. A. Donaldson

Figure 16.8 Scanning electron micrograph of a vessel member from a cucumber stem. Notice the pits on the side walls. Sketch shows the appearance of primary xylem during stem development. The oldest (first-matured) cells are the most stretched, having developed during rapid primary growth. The youngest (last-matured) cells developed after elongation ceased; their wall regions will not be stretched further. Vessels in between reflect decreased stretching that corresponds to a decrease in stem elongation. Secondary-wall depositions are shown in dark color. Such depositions prevent collapse as water under tension is pulled through the vessel member.

wood. Depending on the species, xylem contains most or all of the following cell types:

vessel members
tracheids   } *conduction of water, dissolved mineral ions*

parenchyma   *food, water storage*

fibers
sclereids   } *mechanical support*

The **vessel members** and **tracheids** are more or less elongated cells with lignin-impregnated secondary walls. Each cell type is dead at maturity, and the cavity that the cytoplasm once occupied serves passively as a water pipeline. However, the two cell types differ to some extent in the way that they conduct water. To understand the difference, we must first look at how their primary and secondary walls are laid down.

Usually, primary cell walls vary in thickness. In vessel members and tracheids, the secondary cell wall is not deposited over the thinner areas of primary walls. The uneven deposition creates *pits* (depressions) in the secondary wall. Figures 16.7 and 16.8 are examples of pits in the walls of xylem cells. Typically, a pit in one cell matches up with a pit in its adjacent cell neighbor. In such regions, the two ad-

jacent pits are said to be a pit-pair. The pit-pairs in mature xylem cells do not offer much resistance to water flow. When the cells start to die and become functional as a pipeline, the materials here are partly hydrolyzed and only a thin primary wall remains:

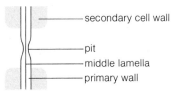

In overlapping tracheids as well as vessel members, water can be conducted from one cell to the next through pit-pairs. In vessel members alone, water also can be conducted through holes that generally occur through the end walls. The part of the wall bearing these holes is called a *perforation plate* (Figure 16.8). Such plates occur where vessel members are joined end to end in long, continuous tubes called *vessels*. Because water flows more rapidly through these tubes, vessel members are more efficient than tracheids at water conduction. They occur in most flowering plants; most other vascular plants rely on tracheids only.

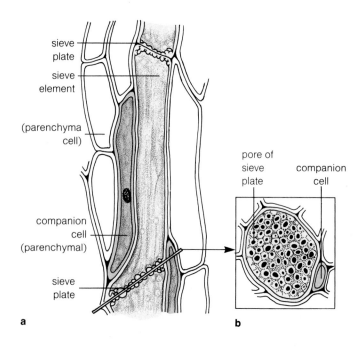

Figure 16.9 (**a**) Mature sieve-tube member and companion cell, sliced lengthwise through their midsections. (**b**) Face view of a sieve plate. Dark regions represent the sieve pores. (After Salisbury and Ross, *Plant Physiology*, 1978)

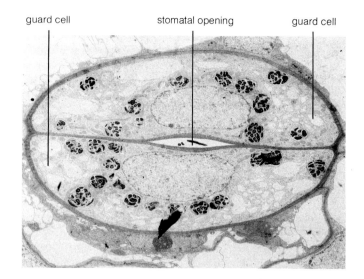

Figure 16.11 Paired guard cells of a stoma on the stem of a beavertail cactus *(Opuntia)*. Stomata open and close in response to environmental conditions, thereby enhancing the movement of carbon dioxide into the plant, and limiting water loss during drought or at night. (From W. Thomson, "Studies on the Ultrastructure of the Guard Cells of Opuntia," *Amer. J. Bot.* 57(3):309–316, 1970)

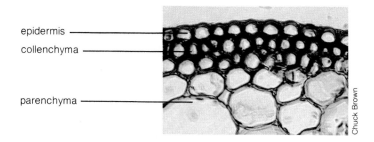

Figure 16.10 Section through the stem of corn *(Zea mays)*, showing the epidermal layer.

Phloem: Food Transport, Storage, and Support

In all vascular plants, another tissue is laid down initially in strands and then is expanded during secondary growth. This tissue, called **phloem**, runs in directions parallel with the xylem strands. The following cell types occur in phloem:

sieve elements	*food conduction*
companion cells	*accessory role in food conduction*
parenchyma	*food storage*
fibers sclereids	*mechanical support*

Unlike many xylem cells, **sieve elements** are alive at maturity. The word "sieve" refers to clusters of wall pores that match up between adjacent cells. In some sieve elements, the pores are small and uniform in all wall regions. In others, called *sieve-tube members*, larger pores also occur on the end walls. Flowering plants have sieve-tube members joined end to end as continuous pipelines. Here, the abutting regions with large pores are known as *sieve plates* (Figure 16.9).

Sieve-tube members are functionally linked with specialized, adjacent parenchyma cells. These so-called **companion cells** play an accessory role in moving food from photosynthetic regions to other plant parts by way of the phloem pipelines. Although the nucleus has been digested away in the mature sieve member, the companion cell nucleus remains functional and may direct activities of *both* cells. Apparently, companion cells help load and unload the phloem pipelines. They move sugars into adjacent sieve elements, *against* concentration gradients. Chapter Seventeen explains how such gradients are at the heart of the phloem pipeline operation.

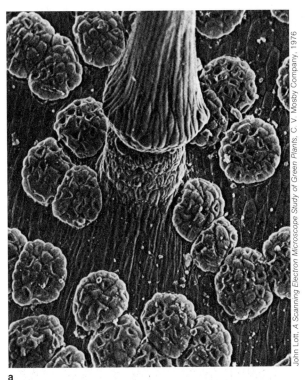

a

b

c

Figure 16.12 Epidermal adaptations to the environment, as seen in the venus flytrap. These plants grow in nitrogen-poor soil. Their two-lobed leaves open and close like a clam shell; the leaf margin is fringed with spines that intermesh when the lobes close. (**a**) Suppose an insect lands on the leaf and moves against one of the long epidermal hairs (the base of one is shown here). The movement triggers cellular changes at the leaf midrib, and the leaf closes up (**b, c**). Glandlike epidermal cells (the pincushion-like structures in the micrograph) secrete enzymes that digest the proteins of the trapped insect. Nitrogen is released from the proteins so kindly provided.

Epidermis and Periderm: Interfaces With the Environment

Figure 16.10 shows part of a section through a stem. The outermost cell layer is the **epidermis**. The epidermis covers the plant, usually as a single, compact, and continuous layer of cells. However, the epidermis varies in structure and function, depending on the kind of plant and the nature of the external environment.

For example, some thin-walled epidermal cells in roots form protuberances that grow in length. Such so-called **root hairs** enhance absorption of water and essential nutrients from the surrounding soil by increasing the available cell surface area. On aerial plant parts, the outer walls of epidermal cells are impregnated with waxes and a mixture of substances called cutin. These substances form a **cuticle**: a noncellular surface coating. In plants, the cuticle restricts water loss from the plant and may confer some resistance to microbial attack.

The epidermal layer contains highly specialized cells that represent further adaptations to environmental con-

ditions. In all aerial parts, numerous pairs of **guard cells** flank tiny openings through the epidermis (Figure 16.11). Each opening is a **stoma** (plural, stomata). Stomatal openings permit the movement of carbon dioxide into the leaf. The cuticle and stomatal closure limit the movement of water out of the leaf, in ways that will be described in Chapter Seventeen. Leaf epidermis in such plants as mint, lavender, and peppermint contain oil-secreting structures. Hair cells and scales are also common in epidermis. In the epidermis of insect-eating plants are structures that secrete sticky mucopolysaccharides as well as digestive enzymes (Figure 16.12). Saltbush and tamarisk plants have epidermal glands that collect excess salts in the plant body and secrete them to the outside. Many flower parts, stems, and leaves contain nectaries (tissues or glands that secrete sugar-rich fluid derived from phloem and xylem). Many more epidermal specializations occur, including such adaptations against predators as hooks on cells that impale insects, and cells that secrete foul-tasting chemicals.

In the thickening stems and roots of gymnosperms and flowering plants undergoing secondary growth, a protective

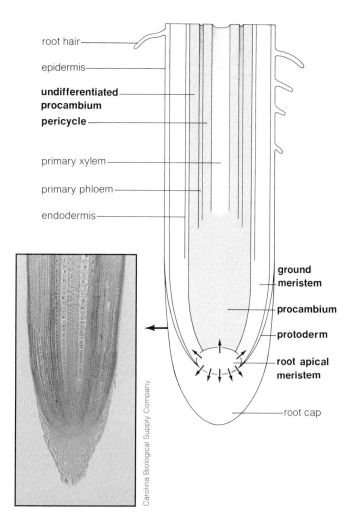

root hair

epidermis

undifferentiated procambium

pericycle

primary xylem

primary phloem

endodermis

ground meristem

procambium

protoderm

root apical meristem

root cap

Carolina Biological Supply Company

Figure 16.13 Generalized sketch of a root tip, sliced lengthwise. The undifferentiated procambium can develop into vascular cambium. The pericycle can develop into vascular cambium, cork cambium, and can also form branch roots. (From Marian Reeve) The boxed inset is a micrograph of an onion *(Allium)* root tip that shows the meristematic zone. (Carolina Biological Supply Company)

THE ROOT SYSTEM

The most important function of any root system is absorption of water and dissolved mineral salts. Root systems penetrate a large volume of soil and absorb a tremendous amount of water from it. Two common systems are called taproot and fibrous root systems.

In gymnosperms and dicots, the first (primary) root develops from the apical meristem at the root tip of the embryo (Figure 16.13). In some cases the primary root increases in length and diameter, and other roots arise laterally from it. This primary root and its lateral branchings represent a **taproot system**. A carrot has a taproot system, but not all taproot systems resemble a carrot. Branch roots can enlarge and the primary root can stop growing, so that the roots superficially look the same.

In other cases, the primary root is replaced by roots that arise as numerous extensions from the base of the seedling. These replacements are a form of *adventitious* roots. (The term "adventitious" refers to any structure arising at an unusual location, such as roots that grow from stems or leaves.) Adventitious roots also become branched, but all the roots are somewhat alike in length and diameter. They form a **fibrous root system**.

Root Primary Structure

The roots of both taproot and fibrous root systems have much the same internal organization during primary growth. Covering the root apical meristem is a dome-shaped cell mass called a **root cap** (Figure 16.13). The cap protects delicate young tissues from being torn apart as growth forces the root to advance through the soil. Behind the root cap, cells arising from the apical meristem differentiate into dermal, ground, and vascular systems.

In the absorptive regions of a mature root, epidermis with root hairs surrounds the cortex, which surrounds several columns of vascular tissue. The cortex makes up most of the primary root. This tissue consists almost entirely of relatively undifferentiated parenchyma cells that function in food storage. Root epidermis functions in absorption as well as protection. Water and dissolved salts pass readily through the epidermal cells, which have thin walls and no cuticle. All but a few species of seed-bearing plants depend on epidermal root hairs, which increase the root absorptive surface by about threefold.

Within the root cortex, a one-cell-thick cylinder called the **endodermis** surrounds the vascular column. The endodermis helps control the movement of water and dissolved

cover replaces the epidermis. This cover is **periderm**. Its component cells arise from a type of meristem called **cork cambium**. The outermost cells formed are not alive at maturity. However, their walls form a tissue called **cork**. (Cork isn't the same thing as "bark," a nontechnical term that applies to all living and nonliving tissues formed outside the vascular cambium.) The walls of the cork are impregnated with suberin, a waxy substance that functions in waterproofing.

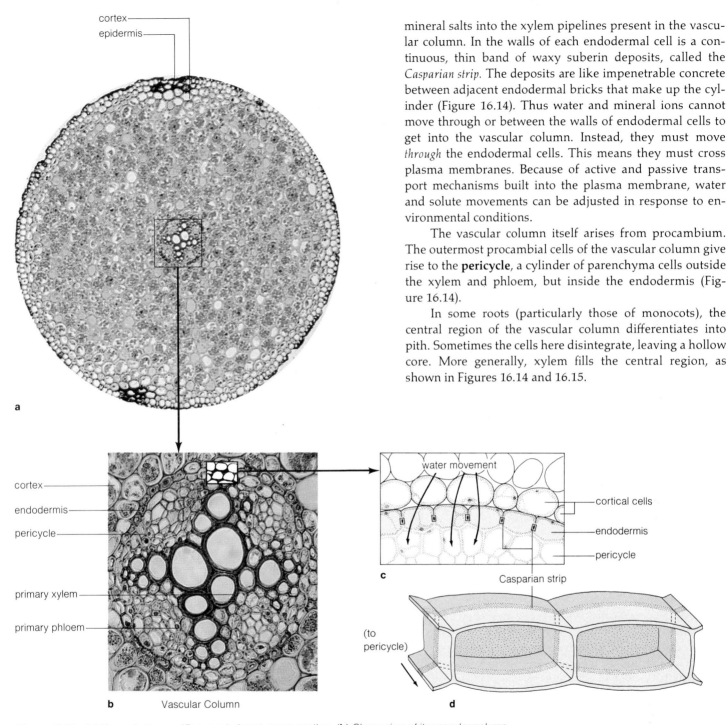

mineral salts into the xylem pipelines present in the vascular column. In the walls of each endodermal cell is a continuous, thin band of waxy suberin deposits, called the *Casparian strip*. The deposits are like impenetrable concrete between adjacent endodermal bricks that make up the cylinder (Figure 16.14). Thus water and mineral ions cannot move through or between the walls of endodermal cells to get into the vascular column. Instead, they must move *through* the endodermal cells. This means they must cross plasma membranes. Because of active and passive transport mechanisms built into the plasma membrane, water and solute movements can be adjusted in response to environmental conditions.

The vascular column itself arises from procambium. The outermost procambial cells of the vascular column give rise to the **pericycle**, a cylinder of parenchyma cells outside the xylem and phloem, but inside the endodermis (Figure 16.14).

In some roots (particularly those of monocots), the central region of the vascular column differentiates into pith. Sometimes the cells here disintegrate, leaving a hollow core. More generally, xylem fills the central region, as shown in Figures 16.14 and 16.15.

Figure 16.14 (**a**) Young buttercup (*Ranunculus*) root, cross-section. (**b**) Closer view of its vascular column. (**c**) Location of the Casparian strip. Water moving into the root wets the cellulose walls of cells until it reaches the Casparian strip. Water cannot penetrate this suberized strip, and must cross the cytoplasm of endodermal cells. (**d**) Three-dimensional view of two endodermal cells; the Casparian strip is shown in gold. (a,b Chuck Brown; c,d Weier et al., *Botany*, sixth edition, Wiley, 1982)

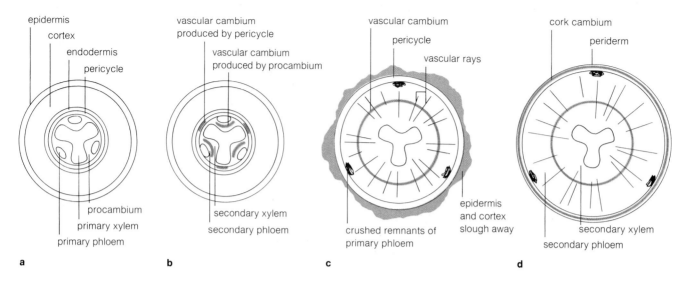

Figure 16.15 An alfalfa root, sliced crosswise, in different developmental stages. (**a**) Primary growth has given rise to components of the three basic tissue systems (dermal, vascular, and ground). (**b**) Secondary growth begins when the vascular cambium lying between primary xylem and phloem undergoes division. New, secondary xylem and phloem arise from the vascular cambium. (**c**) The root grows in diameter as cell divisions proceed parallel and perpendicular to the vascular cambium. The cortex ruptures as diameter increases. (**d**) Epidermis is replaced by periderm. (From Marian Reeve)

Secondary Growth in Roots

Gymnosperms and most flowering plants undergo secondary growth, which increases root (and stem) diameter. In the roots of these plants, secondary growth begins at narrow strips of procambium that occur between the primary xylem and phloem (Figure 16.15b). The procambial cells develop into a lateral meristem called **vascular cambium**, a continuous layer of single cells that give rise to secondary xylem and phloem.

As cell divisions and enlargements increase the volume of new xylem, the vascular cambium is pushed toward the root periphery. Part of the tissue between the xylem and endodermis begins dividing soon afterward. This tissue region is the pericycle (compare Figures 16.15a and c). Cells of the pericycle become aligned with the vascular cambium; together they form a continuous layer of active cambium, one cell thick. This cambium produces layer after layer of secondary xylem and phloem, which lead to thickened roots.

As you might imagine, the burgeoning mass of new tissue inside the root causes the cortex and outer phloem to rupture. Parts of the cortex split away and carry epidermis with them. However, pericycle cells continue to divide, keeping pace with the enlarging vascular tissue. Its divisions produce periderm, the corky covering that replaces the epidermis. In some plants, secondary growth of this sort occurs year after year and produces massive, woody roots.

THE SHOOT SYSTEM

Shoot systems, again, consist of stems and leaves. The **stems** of vascular plants serve several functions. They are structural frameworks for upright growth that gives leaves favorable exposure to light. Their phloem and xylem provide routes for moving water, minerals, and organic molecules between roots and leaves. Food storage occurs in parenchyma cells in various stem regions. Stems also bear the reproductive structures.

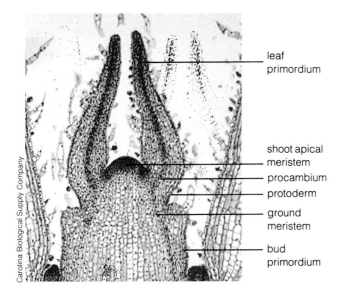

leaf
primordium

shoot apical
meristem
procambium
protoderm
ground
meristem
bud
primordium

Carolina Biological Supply Company

Figure 16.16 Shoot apical meristem of *Coleus*, longitudinal section.

Stem Primary Structure

By comparing Figures 16.13 and 16.16, you can see that meristems have much the same arrangement in shoots as they do in roots. As in roots, the shoot apical meristem gives rise to procambium, protoderm, and ground meristem, which in turn give rise to the primary plant body. However, shoots are structurally more complex than roots. At specific points along the stem axis, tissues are differentiated into leaves or side branches. These points are *nodes;* the stem lengths between them are *internodes*. In the angles where leaves are attached to stems, masses of undifferentiated cells (bud primordia) can grow and differentiate, creating a branched plant body. The buds arising in these angles are **axillary buds**. Those at stem or branch tips are **terminal buds** (Figure 16.17).

Stems also have structural differences that are associated with different environments. Stems grow underground, in air, and in water. Some stems are thick and free-standing. Others creep along the ground or below it. Still others climb upward by elongating in ways that allow them to wrap around the stems of other plants.

a

c

b

d

All photographs E. R. Degginger

Figure 16.17 Terminal bud of a dogwood tree, showing its growth and differentiation into leaves and the spectacular dogwood flower.

In the case of flowering plants, stem structure follows not one but two general patterns. Monocot stems usually show uniform thickness along their length; dicot stems usually taper. Most monocot stems do not undergo secondary growth; many dicot stems do. As you have seen, the primary vascular tissues in monocot and dicot stems are arranged differently. Figure 16.18 provides a closer look at the two arrangements.

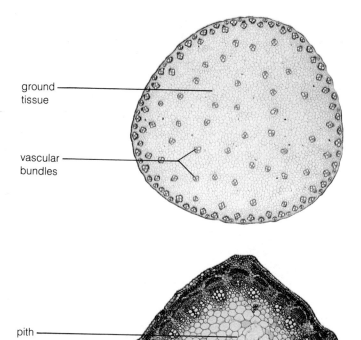

ground tissue

vascular bundles

pith

cortex

vascular bundles

Figure 16.18 Vascular bundle arrangements in monocot and dicot stems. (**a**) Section through the stem of a corn plant, a monocot. (Gene Cox/Bruce Coleman Ltd.) (**b**) Section through the stem of alfalfa, a dicot. (Ray F. Evert)

Leaf Structure

During primary growth of a stem, lobelike tissue masses called *leaf primordia* form at genetically prescribed intervals on the flanks of a developing apical meristem (Figure 16.16). These masses give rise to leaves. Each **leaf** is an individual organ, an integrated unit of cells and tissues performing a common task. Most are sites of photosynthesis. A leaf has a large external surface area and even larger internal surface areas afforded by its individual cells. Its structure enhances the interception of sunlight and the rapid uptake of carbon dioxide from the surrounding air, even by the innermost photosynthetic cells. Throughout the leaf, cells are serviced by a vascular system composed of **veins** (Figure 16.19). The veins are continuous with stem vascular bundles.

Figure 16.20 shows the tissue layers common to many leaves. Uppermost is a protective epidermis, with its outer surface covered by cuticle. Next comes *palisade mesophyll,* a loosely packed tissue of parenchyma cells that are capable of photosynthesis. Below the palisade tissue is even more loosely packed *spongy mesophyll,* which also is photosynthetic. Between thirty and fifty percent of a leaf consists of air spaces around spongy mesophyll and around most of each palisade cell wall. Below the spongy mesophyll is another cuticle-covered epidermal layer. This layer often contains most of the stomata that permit movement of carbon dioxide into the leaf and also influence water loss from it.

Leaf structure varies considerably among plant species. For example, succulents are plants with fleshy, water-storing

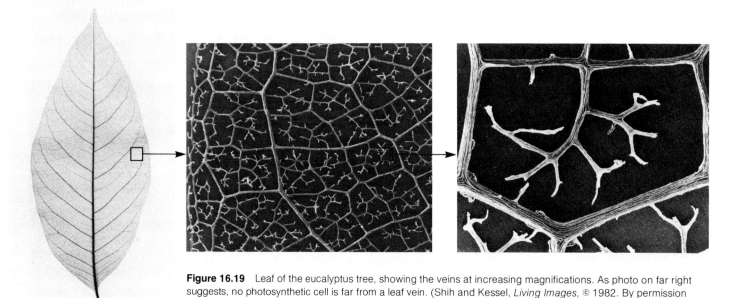

Figure 16.19 Leaf of the eucalyptus tree, showing the veins at increasing magnifications. As photo on far right suggests, no photosynthetic cell is far from a leaf vein. (Shih and Kessel, *Living Images,* © 1982. By permission of Jones and Bartlett Publishers, Inc., Boston)

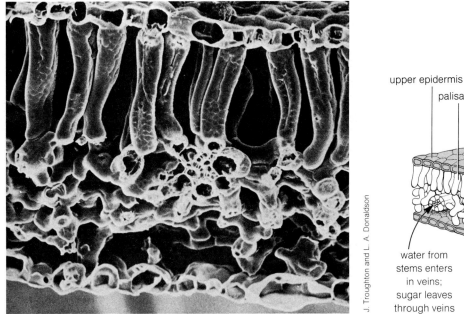

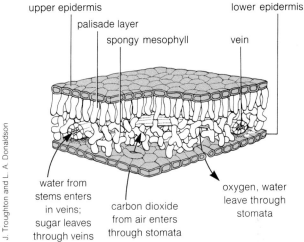

upper epidermis

palisade layer

spongy mesophyll

lower epidermis

vein

water from stems enters in veins; sugar leaves through veins

carbon dioxide from air enters through stomata

oxygen, water leave through stomata

J. Troughton and L. A. Donaldson

Figure 16.20 Example of leaf structure. The scanning electron micrograph shows a slice through a mature broadbean leaf. The sketch identifies the different leaf cells, and shows their arrangement.

leaves or stems. Succulent leaves have large, water-storing parenchyma cells and thick cuticles for water conservation. Succulents, grasses, and conifers have no distinct palisade and spongy mesophyll layers in their leaves.

Plants can bear one, two, or a ring of leaves at each stem node. Solitary leaves develop from the stem in different directions. The overall arrangement is a spiraling of one leaf after another as they appear at nodes along the stem. Some plants have *simple leaves,* each with a single blade. Apple leaves are like this. In other plants, blades are divided into leaflets; rose bushes and ash trees have *compound leaves* of this sort. Even with all the diversity, almost all leaves are alike in being fairly short-lived organs. Even in evergreen plant species, leaves drop away from the stem during certain times of year. In evergreen species, not all leaves drop at the same time, so the plant is not periodically devoid of leaves (as deciduous species are).

Secondary Growth in Stems

When stems begin secondary growth, vascular cambium that is present between vascular bundles becomes active. So does vascular cambium between the xylem and phloem of individual bundles. The vascular cambium will produce secondary xylem and phloem. As in roots, two kinds of meristematic cells occur in the vascular cambium. The vertically elongated *fusiform initials* produce xylem and phloem cells that are arranged parallel with the stem long axis (Figure 16.21). Their products make up the **vertical system** of secondary vascular tissues. The vertical system conducts food and water up and down the stem. The *ray initials* are shorter, brick-shaped cells. They produce the **ray system** of (mostly) parenchyma cells that act as horizontal conduits and food storage centers in wood. Through the ray system, water from secondary xylem is fed laterally into the vascular cambium and secondary phloem. Also through this system, food from secondary phloem moves into the vascular cambium and the still-living cells of secondary xylem.

In regions having prolonged dry spells or cool winters, vascular cambium becomes inactive during parts of the year. The first xylem cells produced at the start of the growing season tend to have fairly large diameters and thin walls; they represent *early wood.* As the season progresses and less water is available, the cell diameters become smaller and the walls thicker; these cells represent the *late wood.* The last-formed, small-diameter cells of late wood will end up next

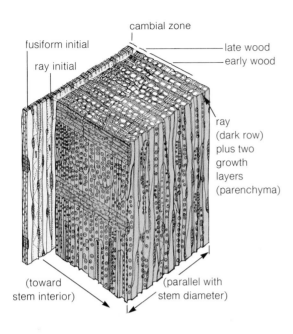

fusiform initial
ray initial
cambial zone
late wood
early wood

ray
(dark row)
plus two
growth
layers
(parenchyma)

(toward
stem interior)

(parallel with
stem diameter)

a

vascular ray (tangential cut)

Ray F. Evert

b

vascular ray (cross-section)

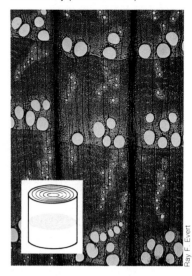

Ray F. Evert

c

Figure 16.21 (**a**) Block diagram of a section through white cedar, showing the cells of the vascular cambium that give rise to the ray systems of wood. (**b**) Tangential cut in the hardwood of a red oak (*Quercus rubra*). (**c**) Cross-section through the same hardwood shows vascular rays as dark, vertical lines.

to the first-formed, large-diameter cells of the next season's growth. Although we don't see individual cells with the naked eye, there is enough difference in light reflection from a stem cross-section to reveal the alternating light bands (early wood) and dark bands (late wood). These alternating bands represent annual growth layers, which often are called "tree rings" (Figure 16.22).

In some wet tropical regions, there is a continuous growing season. The annual growth layers of tropical woody plants are either faint or nonexistent. The more pronounced the shifts in seasons, the more pronounced the annual growth layers.

As the mass of xylem increases season after season, it crushes the thin-walled phloem cells from the preceding year's growth, leaving only the thick-walled fibers. New rings of phloem cells must be produced each year, outside the growing inner core of xylem. As you can see from Figure 16.22, phloem in older trees is confined to a thin zone beneath the periderm. If this narrow band of phloem is stripped all the way around a tree's circumference, the tree will die. When the phloem cells in this region are stripped away, there is no way to transport photosynthetically derived food down to roots, which will starve to death. Dis-

ruptions of this sort increase our awareness of the functional interrelationships among different plant regions, which is a topic that will occupy our attention in the chapter to follow.

Readings

Bold, H., C. Alexopoulos, and T. Delevoryas. 1980. *Morphology of Plants and Fungi.* Fourth edition. New York: Harper & Row. Comprehensive reference book for the serious student.

Cutter, E. 1969. *Plant Anatomy: Experimental and Interpretation.* Reading, Massachusetts: Addison-Wesley. Also available in paperback.

Esau, K. 1977. *Anatomy of Seed Plants.* Second edition. New York: Wiley. Excellent, well-illustrated book, a standard reference in the field.

Ray, P. 1972. *The Living Plant.* Second edition. New York: Holt.

Shih, G. and R. Kessel. 1982. *Living Images.* Boston: Science Books International, Jones and Bartlett Publishers. Extraordinary scanning electron micrographs of plant structures.

Weier, T., C. Stocking, and M. Barbour. 1982. *Botany: An Introduction to Plant Biology.* Sixth edition. New York: Wiley. Time-tested introduction to the world of plants, very well-written and clear illustrations.

a

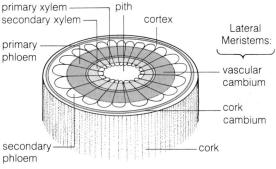

epidermis — | — primary xylem

pith — | — primary phloem

cortex — | — vascular cambium

b *Beginnings of secondary growth*

primary xylem — | — pith

secondary xylem — | — cortex

primary phloem — | — Lateral Meristems:

vascular cambium

cork cambium

secondary phloem — | — cork

c *Secondary growth underway*

Review Questions

1. Define meristem. Which meristem regions produce the primary plant body? Which two kinds of active cambium give rise to layers of secondary xylem and phloem?

2. With a sheet of paper, cover the column entitled "Main Functions" in Table 16.1. Can you now state the primary function of each tissue listed?

3. Distinguish between the following:
   a. xylem and phloem
   b. tracheid and vessel member
   c. epidermis and endodermis

4. What is the functional relationship between endodermis and the Casparian strip?

5. Sketch the stem of a monocot and a dicot in cross-section. Can you label the main tissue regions of each, and describe the functions of their cellular components? Do the same for a cross-section of a root.

6. How are annual growth layers formed in woody stems? If you were to strip away a narrow band of phloem from a tree's circumference, what would happen to the tree?

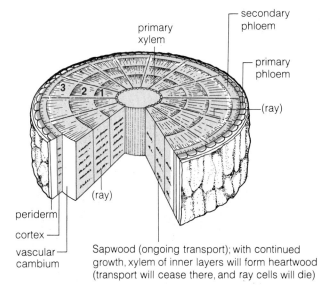

primary xylem

secondary phloem

primary phloem

(ray)

periderm

cortex

vascular cambium

(ray)

Sapwood (ongoing transport); with continued growth, xylem of inner layers will form heartwood (transport will cease there, and ray cells will die)

d *Stem after three years of growth*
Numbers refer to annual growth layers (secondary xylem)

Figure 16.22 (**a**) Annual rings of a pine tree, in cross-section. (**b-d**) Stages during secondary growth of a woody plant.

17

WATER, SOLUTES, AND PLANT FUNCTIONING

It took you eighteen years or so to grow to your present height. A corn plant can exceed that in three months! Yet how many of us stop to think that corn or any other kind of plant actually does anything at all impressive? Being endowed with remarkable mobility, intelligence, and varied emotions, we tend to be endlessly fascinated with ourselves —and somewhat indifferent to the immobile and expressionless plants around us. Besides, from our own experiences and educational biases, we simply have acquired more knowledge about animals than we have about plants. But look around and you see at once that it is not animal life but *plant* life that dominates the earth's surface. Plants, not animals, sustain whole communities of life by serving as initial food producers in complex feeding relationships among organisms.

Like other organisms, land plants grow and reproduce only as long as they acquire raw materials from the environment. For plants, the necessary materials are water, carbon dioxide, and assorted minerals. Obtaining these materials is not a simple task. Most soils are frequently rather dry. Atmospheric concentrations of carbon dioxide average about 330 parts per million of air, which is scarce, to say the least. Minerals also are scarce and must be accumulated against concentration gradients.

Many aspects of plant structure and function can be explained in terms of the low concentrations of environmental resources. An example is the thin, broad shape of leaves, which present a large surface area not only for sunlight interception but also for gas absorption. Another example is the large central vacuole within individual cells of roots and shoots. Vacuoles are an energetically "cheap" way of increasing cell volume. In a mature, living plant cell, a vacuole can take up about ninety percent of the space (see, for example, Figure 4.9). This organelle is mostly water, a material that is energetically inexpensive to accumulate, compared with other cytoplasmic substances. With the minimal energy outlay required for assembling a vacuole, cell volume is increased considerably—which increases the cell surface area in contact with the surroundings.

Plant roots are adapted in other ways to low concentrations of raw materials. Consider that the concentration of potassium alone is often fifty times greater in the plant body than it is in soil water. This means that plant roots must actively mine the soil. Broad, leaflike roots would have a large surface area to do this, but they could scarcely force their way through soil during growth. (Imagine trying to push a sheet of paper through the soil.) Instead, plants have cylindrically shaped roots—which collectively offer a large surface area and individually present less resistance to the surrounding soil.

Table 17.1		Essential Elements for Most Complex Land Plants		
Element	Symbol	Form Available to Plants	Percent Concentration in Dry Tissue	
Carbon	C	CO_2	45	} 96% of total
Oxygen	O	O_2, H_2O, CO_2	45	} dry weight
Hydrogen	H	H_2O	6	
Nitrogen	N	NO_3^-, NH_4^+	1.5	
Potassium	K	K^+	1.0	
Calcium	Ca	Ca^{++}	0.5	
Magnesium	Mg	Mg^{++}	0.2	
Phosphorus	P	$H_2PO_4^-$, HPO_4^{--}	0.2	
Sulfur	S	SO_4^{--}	0.1	
Chlorine	Cl	Cl^-	0.010	
Iron	Fe	Fe^{++}, Fe^{+++}	0.010	
Boron	B	H_3BO_3	0.002	
Manganese	Mn	Mn^{++}	0.0050	
Zinc	Z	Zn^{++}	0.0020	
Copper	Cu	Cu^+, Cu^{++}	0.006	
Molybdenum	Mo	MoO_4^-	0.00001	

Of course, increased surface area is only part of the picture. Because water and minerals are so dilute in soil, a plant (which is stationary) must have some means of extending through as large a volume of soil as possible. The expansion of root systems in different directions increases the contact between absorptive surface areas and moist soil locations.

Leaves and roots are structures that expose a large surface area of the plant body to a large volume of environmental space, thereby enhancing the uptake of dilute raw materials.

Sending out extensions of the plant body through a large volume of the environment requires still other kinds of adaptations. As roots grow through soil and stems grow upward, the transport of water and food from one plant organ to another becomes more of a necessity. In most land plants, we find extensive vascular systems that serve all parts of the body.

How plant systems function in response to the environment is the focus of *plant physiology*. From Chapter Seven, you have already become acquainted with how plants acquire energy from environmental sources, then produce and use their own food with the aid of that energy. These two aspects of plant function are called photosynthesis and aer-obic respiration. In this chapter, we will look at how plants actually acquire the raw materials—water, carbon dioxide, and minerals—that are directly or indirectly used in photosynthesis and all other cell activities. We will also look at how photosynthetic products and other organic molecules are selectively distributed through the plant body.

ESSENTIAL ELEMENTS AND THEIR FUNCTIONS

Oxygen, Carbon, and Hydrogen

Most plants require sixteen essential elements to grow and reproduce, although most studies have been carried out with crop plants only. These elements include oxygen, carbon, and hydrogen, which are the basic building blocks for all organic compounds (carbohydrates, lipids, proteins, and nucleic acids). Oxygen is incorporated into organic compounds that make up the plant's dry weight. It comes from three sources: water, gaseous oxygen (O_2), and carbon dioxide (CO_2) in the air. Hydrogen is obtained from water molecules. Together, oxygen, hydrogen, and carbon account for about ninety-six percent of the plant's dry weight—and much more if we look at a normal plant that still contains seventy to eighty percent water.

Dennis Brokaw

Figure 17.1 Sunlight filtering through a grove of California coast redwoods—representing the tallest organisms on earth. How are water and essential nutrients transported to the tops of such giant trees? How are photosynthetically derived organic molecules distributed from leaves to all parts of the massive plant body, even down to the roots? These are questions that will be addressed in this chapter.

Table 17.2   Role of Mineral Elements in Plant Function

Element	Function	Deficiency Symptoms
Macronutrients:		
Nitrogen	Synthesis of amino acids, proteins, chlorophyll, nucleic acids, and coenzymes	Stunted growth, delayed maturity, light green older leaves; lower leaves turn yellow and die
Potassium	Sugar and starch formation, protein synthesis, enzyme reactions, growth of meristematic tissue, water balance*	Reduced yields; mottled, spotted or curled older leaves; marginal burning of leaves; weak root system, weak stalks
Calcium	Cell walls, cell growth and division; nitrogen assimilation. Cofactor for some enzymes	Deformed terminal leaves, reduced root growth. Dead spots in dicot leaves. Terminal buds die
Magnesium	Essential in chlorophyll; photosynthesis; respiration; formation of amino acids and vitamins. Essential in formation of fats and sugars	Plants usually chlorotic (interveinal yellowing of older leaves); leaves may droop
Phosphorus	Used in proteins, nucleoproteins, ATP, ADP, photosynthesis and respiration. Component of phospholipids	Purplish older leaves, stems, and branches; reduced yields of seeds and fruits, stunted growth
Sulfur	Essential in some amino acids and vitamins	Light green or yellow leaves, including veins; reduced growth. Weak stems. Similar to nitrogen deficiency
Micronutrients:		
Chlorine	Not much known except that it aids in root and shoot growth. Required for growth and development	Plants wilt. Chlorotic leaves. Some leaf necrosis. Bronzing in leaves
Iron	Catalyst in synthesis of chlorophyll. Involved in electron transport during photosynthesis and aerobic respiration	Paling or yellowing of leaves (chlorosis) between veins at first. Grasses develop alternate rows of yellowing and green stripes in leaves
Boron	Affects flowering, pollen germination, fruiting, cell division, nitrogen metabolism, water relations, hormone movement	Terminal buds die, lateral branches begin to grow, then die. Leaves thicken, curl, and become brittle
Manganese	Chlorophyll synthesis; acts as coenzyme for many enzymes	Network of major green veins on light green background. Leaves later become white and fall off
Zinc	Used in formation of auxins, chloroplasts, and starch	Abnormal roots; mottled bronzed or rosetted leaves. Interveinal chlorosis
Copper	Constituent in enzymes, chlorophyll synthesis, catalyst for carbohydrate and protein metabolism	Terminal leaf buds die. Chlorotic leaves. Stunted growth. Terminal leaves die
Molybdenum	Essential in enzyme-mediated reactions that reduce nitrate	Plants may become nitrogen deficient. Pale green, rolled or cupped leaves, with yellow spots

Data from Hartmann et al. *Plant Science*, 1981.
*All solutes contribute to the osmotic solute and ion balance.

Mineral Elements

Thirteen other elements essential in plant functioning are minerals. A mineral, recall, is any naturally occurring inorganic substance in the earth, with the exception of water. Table 17.1 lists the forms in which a plant takes up these elements, along with the approximate tissue concentrations necessary for adequate growth. As you can see from the third column of this table, minerals become available to plants as ions, dissolved in soil water.

Table 17.2 lists the main functions of the mineral elements, along with symptoms that are associated with their deficiency. The first six listed are called *macronutrients;* they are present in amounts that are at least a tenth of a percent of the total dry weight. The rest are *micronutrients,* or trace elements; they represent only a few parts per million of the plant dry weight. The plant cannot get along without these traces of minerals.

Gaseous nitrogen (N_2) represents about seventy-eight percent of all the molecules present in air. Plants can't use it, because they don't have the metabolic machinery for breaking apart the strong bonds holding these molecules together. Insufficient nitrogen frequently limits plant growth. However, some microorganisms that live independently of plants in the soil can break the bonds and use gaseous nitrogen (see Chapter Thirty-Seven). So can microorganisms that live in nodules of the roots of legumes and other plants (Figure 17.2). These nodule residents convert some of the N_2 first to ammonia (NH_3), then use the nitrogen in assembling their own amino acids, proteins, and nucleic acids. They leave most of the ammonia and amino acids for the plants in which they reside, in exchange for organic molecules transported to them from the leaves.

Potassium ranks behind oxygen, carbon, hydrogen, and nitrogen in terms of abundance. Like most of the minerals listed in Table 17.2, potassium serves two important functions. First, it activates enzymes involved in protein synthesis, starch synthesis, photosynthesis, and aerobic respiration. Second, like other less abundant ions, potassium sets up an osmotic gradient across the plasma membrane. Water moves down such gradients, into cells and their vacuoles (Chapter Five). **Turgor pressure** (the internal pressure applied to the walls as water is absorbed into the cell) accomplishes one of two things. If the walls are still soft, they expand and the cell grows. If the walls can no longer stretch, the resulting pressure simply allows the plant to sustain a nonwilted form (Figure 17.3).

Mineral ions function in the formation and activation of plant enzymes. They also are important because their absorption into cells sets up an osmotic gradient. Hence water necessary for growth and for maintaining plant shape also moves into cells.

WATER UPTAKE, TRANSPORT, AND LOSS

Water Absorption by Roots

In Chapter Sixteen, you read about the absorptive properties of root epidermis, particularly in root hair regions. The extent of the root system that develops is genetically and environmentally controlled. Generally, monocots (grasses, including corn) have highly branched, fibrous root systems near the soil surface. Most dicots have a tap root system

Figure 17.2 Root nodules, where symbiotic nitrogen-fixing bacteria live. In many plants, groups of nitrogen-fixing bacteria occur within cells of such nodules. Most nodules develop close to the soil surface, where more air (hence more gaseous nitrogen) is present.

Figure 17.3 Plant wilt. Turgor pressure allows nonwoody plant parts to retain their normal form. However, plants wilt when evaporation exceeds water uptake from dry soil. You can observe the effects of a drop in turgor pressure by pouring a concentrated salt solution into a pot containing tomato plants. Water follows the osmotic gradient, from roots into the salty soil. Water from the stems and leaves then follows, and wilting is the result. The severe wilting shown here occurred in less than thirty minutes.

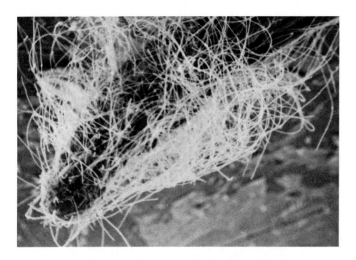

Figure 17.4 Mycorrhiza (fungus-root) of a lodgepole pine tree. White threads are fungal strands. When you dig up and move a plant to another location, try to include some native soil with the roots. The soil probably contains the proper mycorrhizal fungus. Without it, transplants are frequently retarded in their growth. (J. Mexal, C. Reid, and E. Burke, Botanical Gazette, 140: 3, 1979. University of Chicago)

F. B. Reeves

Figure 17.5 Effect of mycorrhizal fungi on plant growth. The six-month-old juniper seedlings on the left were grown in sterilized, low-phosphorous soil in a growth chamber inoculated with a mycorrhizal fungus. The seedlings on the right were grown without the fungus.

that can penetrate more deeply into the soil. The branch roots of both systems develop and are replaced as conditions change in different locations. It is not that the roots "explore" the soil in search of water. Rather, outward root growth (hence growth of the entire plant) is stimulated in moist, mineral-rich soils.

Millions, sometimes billions, of root hairs can develop in a root system. In addition, nearly all vascular plants bene-

fit from **mycorrhizae**, or "fungus-roots." Figure 17.4 shows a mycorrhiza on a lodgepole pine tree. Mycorrhizae represent a mutually beneficial association between a fungus and a young root. The vegetative body of these symbiotic fungi is an extensive mat of very thin filaments. Collectively, the filaments have a tremendous surface area for contact with a large volume of the surrounding soil. Thus, the fungus is most efficient at accumulating water (and dissolved mineral ions). The root draws on some of the water that the fungal mat absorbs. In turn, the fungus absorbs some sugars and nitrogen-containing compounds in roots (Figure 17.5).

Especially in regions of root hairs and mycorrhizae, water from the soil diffuses passively through the thin-walled epidermal cells of roots. Once inside the walls of epidermal cells, water apparently is conducted along the cortex walls, which are highly permeable. Once water reaches the one-cell-thick column of endodermis that surrounds the vascular tissue, it encounters the waterproof, suberized Casparian strip (Chapter Sixteen). At this point, water movement is funneled directly into the cytoplasm of the endodermal cells, rather than along wall material. Once water enters the vascular column, its movement up through the xylem is governed by tensile forces, of the sort to be described next.

Transpiration

Liquid water moves from roots to the stems, then into leaves. Some is used for growth (through cell enlargement) and in metabolism, but most evaporates into the air. **Transpiration** is the name for evaporation from stems and leaves. Transpiration, of course, depends on the presence of water in stems and leaves. But how does water get there in the first place? What could possibly make water move upward, to the top of even the tallest tree? *It appears that water is pulled upward by continuous tensions that extend downward from the leaf to the root.*

First, the (usually) dry air around a plant causes evaporation from leaf mesophyll cell walls. As some water molecules escape, others diffuse out of the cell cytoplasm and into the walls as replacements. When they do, still other water molecules move into the mesophyll cells from the xylem pipeline system running through leaf veins. *Second,* when water moves from xylem's tracheids and vessels, water is pulled out of cells connected to them in the xylem system. Because of the pulling action, water inside all of these dead conducting cells is in a state of tension (negative pressure), compared with the positive pressure in living

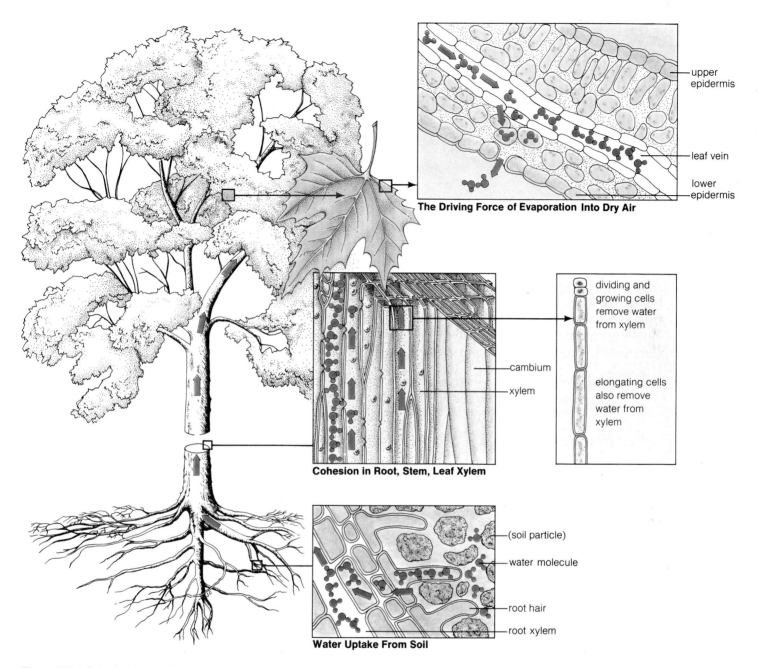

Figure 17.6 Cohesion theory of water transport. Tensions in xylem extend from leaf to root. These tensions are caused by transpiration, cell divisions, and cell enlargements. As a result of the tensions, columns of water molecules that are hydrogen-bonded to one another are pulled upward, much like tiny ropes being pulled up the stem.

Labels within figure:
- upper epidermis
- leaf vein
- lower epidermis
- **The Driving Force of Evaporation Into Dry Air**
- dividing and growing cells remove water from xylem
- elongating cells also remove water from xylem
- cambium
- xylem
- **Cohesion in Root, Stem, Leaf Xylem**
- (soil particle)
- water molecule
- root hair
- root xylem
- **Water Uptake From Soil**

cells. (The pressure typical of each cell type is maintained by its strong cell walls.) *Third,* replacement water molecules move into the xylem from living root cells, even when the soil is somewhat dry. When water moves into the xylem, more soil water is drawn in, following its osmotic gradient. This inward movement will continue until the soil becomes so dry that the osmotic gradient no longer exists. Figure 17.6 illustrates the way that water is pulled from roots to leaves.

Cohesion Theory of Water Transport

Water moves as a continuous, fluid column through the xylem pipelines. This might seem puzzling, given all the tension that the molecules are under. Why doesn't the "stretching" cause the molecules to snap away from each other? Some time ago the Irish botanist Henry Dixon came up with an explanation, which has since been named the **cohesion theory of water transport**. According to this theory, hydrogen bonding allows water molecules to cohere tightly enough to keep from breaking apart as they are pulled up through the plant body. Dixon had no way of measuring how much tension exists in xylem (and therefore of convincing skeptics that it really exists). Confirmation of his explanation came much later. In any event, the points to remember are these:

1. The drying power of air causes transpiration (evaporation of water from stems and leaves).

2. Transpiration causes a state of tension (negative pressure) in xylem that is continuous from leaves, down through the stems, to roots.

3. As long as water molecules continue to vacate transpiration sites, replacements are pulled up along the negative pressure route.

4. Because of the cumulative strength of hydrogen bonds between water molecules that are confined in the narrow, tubular xylem, water can be pulled up as continuous columns to stem and leaf transpiration sites.

The Paradox in Water and Carbon Dioxide Movements

We have been describing the way that transpiration alone can pull up water through a plant body. However, as the plant physiologist Herman Wiebe points out, *any process that uses water in a shoot system can pull up water and develop a tension in the xylem.* For example, you know that water molecules are used up in photosynthesis as sources of hydrogen ions and electrons. As another example, cell divisions and enlargements remove considerable water from the xylem. In fact, transpiration competes with photosynthesis and other water-requiring activities! When transpiration is excessive (as it can be during hot, dry weather), cell enlargement is diminished and growth is reduced. As it is, of the

water moving into a leaf, only about two percent is available for cell activities; the rest is lost through transpiration.

Transpiration competes with photosynthesis, cell division, cell enlargement, and other water-requiring processes.

Now, if plants were like people, they would have a fairly watertight surface covering that would restrict water loss; and they would have internal vascular systems that circulate essential solutes. Indeed, a cuticle does cover the aerial parts of all land plants. Water inside the plant body can barely penetrate the cuticle's waxy layers (see, for example, Figure 3.15). Without a cuticle, land plants would rapidly wilt and die during hot, dry weather. The cuticle, however, is not watertight. If it were, it would be disastrous for plant functioning. *The reason is that carbon dioxide—so essential in photosynthesis—has almost as much trouble getting past a cuticle and into a leaf as water does getting out of it.*

As you read in the preceding chapter, numerous stomata penetrate the cuticle, and these are the sites where carbon dioxide enters the leaves and stems. But the price of carbon dioxide acquisition is water loss through transpiration. It is a paradoxical situation that requires a tricky balancing act, as you will see.

Transpiration competes with the vital uptake of carbon dioxide, which is present only in dilute concentrations in air. When stomata are open and carbon dioxide is moving into the plant, water is free to move out.

Stomatal Action

Flanking each stoma are two guard cells (Figure 17.7). When the guard cells are swollen with water, turgor pressure so distorts their shape that they move apart. The separation produces a gap between them. When the water content of the guard cells dwindles, turgor pressure drops and the gap closes. Stomata typically open during daylight hours, when carbon dioxide is being used in the formation of starch and sugars.

Although the processes involved are not completely understood, this much is clear: *A stoma opens and closes according to how much water and carbon dioxide are present in the two guard cells.* When the sun comes up, photosynthesis begins and carbon dioxide is used up. As carbon dioxide

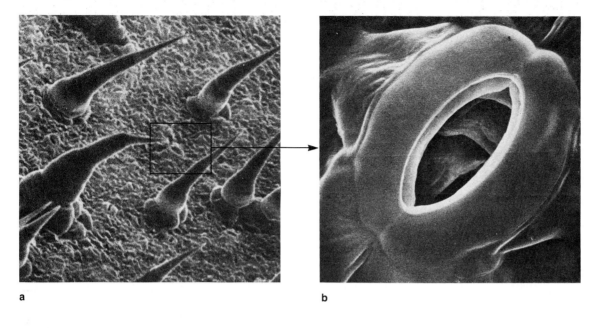

a

b

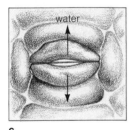 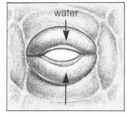

c

Figure 17.7 Where stomata occur on a typical dicot leaf, and how they function. (**a**) Stomata are found among hairlike structures on a cucumber leaf's lower epidermis. The box identifies one of the stomata. (**b**) Closer look at stomatal structure. Here, we can peer through the gap between the stomatal guard cells and view parts of mesophyll cells inside the leaf. (**c**) Sketches of a closed stoma and one opened as guard cells swell up. (a, b from John Troughton and L. A. Donaldson)

concentrations dwindle in guard cells, potassium ions are actively pumped into them from surrounding epidermal cells (Figure 17.8). As these ions accumulate inside, the osmotic gradient across the guard cell plasma membrane shifts accordingly, and water also moves in. The resulting increase in turgor pressure causes the guard cells to swell and stomata to open. Transpiration proceeds, and so does carbon dioxide movement into the leaf. Photosynthesis keeps carbon dioxide concentrations low, so the plant continues to lose water and gain carbon dioxide during the day.

When the sun goes down, photosynthesis stops. Carbon dioxide is no longer used, but it is still being released during aerobic respiration. As a result, carbon dioxide accumulates in all cells. Much of the potassium that had accumulated inside guard cells now moves out, and water follows it. Turgor pressure decreases, stomata close, transpiration is greatly reduced, and water is conserved.

 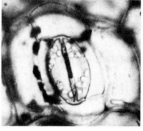

a

b

Figure 17.8 Evidence for potassium accumulation in stomatal guard cells undergoing expansion. Strips from the leaf epidermis of a dayflower *(Commelina communis)* were immersed in solutions containing dark-staining substances that bind preferentially with potassium ions. (**a**) In leaf samples having opened stomata, most of the potassium was concentrated in the guard cells. (**b**) In leaf samples having closed stomata, very little potassium was in guard cells; most was present in normal epidermal cells. (a and b from T. A. Mansfield)

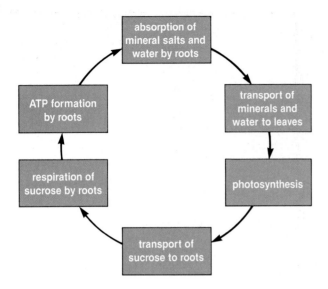

Figure 17.9 Interrelated processes that influence the coordinated growth of roots, stems, and leaves. When one process is rapid, the others also speed up. Any environmental factor limiting one process eventually slows growth of all plant parts.

As long as soil is moist, stomata can remain open during daylight. When soil is dry and the air is also dry and hot, the stomata of land plants close and little water is absorbed. Although photosynthesis (and growth) slows as a consequence, the plants still survive short drought periods. They can do so repeatedly. Briefly, such stressful conditions trigger the production of a chemical signal—a plant hormone called **abscisic acid**. The hormone is synthesized faster when a leaf is water stressed. When abscisic acid accumulates in a leaf, it somehow causes guard cells to give up potassium ions, hence water—so the stomata close.

UPTAKE AND ACCUMULATION OF MINERALS

Active Transport of Mineral Ions

Water uptake by roots is a passive process, dependent on an osmotic gradient. Yet if a cell in roots (or in any other part of the plant) is to retain water, it must maintain a higher overall solute concentration than exists in its surroundings, so that an osmotic gradient can be produced. This means that a cell must expend energy and actively *accumulate* solutes, particularly dissolved mineral ions. Without energy outlays, diffusion would equalize the solute concentrations on both sides of a plasma membrane. Energy from ATP drives the membrane pumps involved in active transport. These pumps are membrane-bound proteins that move substances into the cell even against a concentration gradient, as described in Chapter Five.

In photosynthetic cells, ATP necessary for the membrane pump operation is formed during both photosynthesis and aerobic respiration. What about nonphotosynthetic cells, such as those in roots? How do they get all the ATP necessary for active transport? Here, ATP is formed through aerobic respiration in the mitochondria of individual cells (Chapter Eight).

Feedback Controls Over Ion Absorption

Solute absorption and accumulation are two activities that must be coordinated throughout the plant. To give one example, root cells receive sugars (commonly sucrose) from leaves—especially during daylight, when photosynthesis is rapid. These cells absorb oxygen from air in the soil (unless the ground is really waterlogged or flooded). When soil is sufficiently moist, dissolved ions move rapidly to roots, where active transport moves them from cell to cell into the xylem. When the soil is quite dry, more air is present and more oxygen can be absorbed. However, insufficient water limits growth and ion absorption no matter how much oxygen is present. In addition, dry soil causes complete or partial closure of stomata. As a consequence, leaves absorb less carbon dioxide when water and ions are in short supply. Photosynthesis and growth slow down—and leaf cells cannot send as much sucrose to roots. Without enough sucrose, aerobic respiration slows down in roots—and so does ion absorption.

The feedback relationships that exist among plant organs are summarized in Figure 17.9. The figure illustrates part of what is known about coordinated growth between different plant regions.

Mineral ion absorption and accumulation are coordinated throughout the plant body in ways that have profound influences on growth.

TRANSPORT OF ORGANIC SUBSTANCES THROUGH PHLOEM

Leaves are the main organs in which organic molecules are assembled. Organic molecules not used by the leaf cells themselves are transported to roots, stems, flowers, and fruits, which also require these molecules for growth. Many of the organic molecules are also stockpiled in the form of starch, fats, and proteins.

Starch is the dominant storage form (Chapters Three and Four). Yet starch is a large molecule—much too large to cross the plasma membranes of cells in which it is stored. Besides, starch is too insoluble for transport in water to other regions of the plant body.

Fat stores are especially prevalent in many seeds. These energy-rich stores are used by the root and shoot that develop when a seed germinates. However, fats also are insoluble in water, and they cannot be transported out of their plant cell storage sites. In general, leaves store little or no fat; rather, starch is the main form of stored energy in these organs.

Proteins are stored in granules in many seeds and grains. Before they can be transported through the plant body, the storage proteins must be converted to soluble amino acids and amides. In addition, functional proteins in old leaves and other organs must be converted to soluble units that can be transported to and reused in new cells as organs die.

The energy and building blocks inherent in starch, fats, and proteins are made available through different chemical reactions. For example, starch molecules are hydrolyzed into soluble, transportable subunits. In most plants, the subunit is sucrose.

Transport of organic substances through the plant requires that storage starch, fats, and proteins be converted to smaller subunits that are soluble and transportable.

Translocation

How do soluble organic molecules travel from photosynthesis sites or storage sites to organs that require them? Here we must turn to a process known as **translocation**. In botany, the word can mean the relatively long-distance transport of water or solutes, but most often it is used to signify the transport of sucrose through phloem. As you read earlier, sieve elements of the phloem are joined into

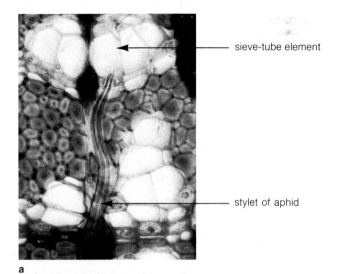

sieve-tube element

stylet of aphid

Figure 17.10 (**a**) Naturally occurring research tool: the aphid stylet, here penetrating a sieve-tube element. (**b**) Honeydew droplet at the tail end of a well-fed aphid. (Martin Zimmerman, *Science*, 133:73–79, 1961. Copyright 1961 by the American Association for the Advancement of Science)

long, interconnecting pipelines (Figure 16.9). The pipelines lie side by side in overlapping array within vascular bundles, and they extend from leaf to root. Unlike xylem cells, sieve elements are alive at maturity. Water and organic molecules are transported rapidly through their numerous wall perforations at rates up to 100 centimeters an hour.

Interestingly, the feeding habits of small insects called aphids tell us something about translocation. An aphid feeds on leaves and stems. It forces a mouthpart (stylet) into sieve elements, which contain sugary fluid. Although aphids are often called sucking insects, they are actually passive feeders. Sieve element contents are under such high pressure—often five times as much as in an automobile tire—that some "honeydew" seems to be forced right through the aphid gut and clear out the other end (Figure 17.10). Park your car under trees being attacked by aphids and it might get a spattering of sticky honeydew droplets, thanks to sieve-tube pressures.

In some experiments, feeding aphids were anesthetized with carbon dioxide. Then their bodies were severed from their stylets, which were left embedded in the sieve tubes that the aphids had been attacking. Analysis of the fluid being forced out of the tubes verified that sucrose is the main carbohydrate being transported through the plant body in most species.

Pressure Flow Theory

Organic molecules in phloem travel up, sideways, and down through the plant body. The direction of transport is from a *source region* (photosynthesis sites and storage organs such as carrot roots) to sink regions. A *sink region* is any tissue where organic molecules are being used in growth or metabolism, or where they are being stockpiled. Young leaves, fruits, seeds, and roots are examples of sink regions.

Obviously, a plant doesn't "know" which way it should be translocating organic molecules through the phloem. But what causes the directional movement? According to the **pressure flow theory**, translocation through the phloem depends on pressure gradients in the sieve-tube system. The pressure gradients are seen to arise by osmosis, which occurs when sucrose is actively transported into the sieve tubes at a source region. Companion cells, adjacent to the sieve-tube members, apparently aid in the loading process. These cells actively transport sucrose into the tubes and thereby maintain high solute concentrations in the loading regions (Chapter Sixteen).

To understand the points of the pressure flow theory, let's consider what happens when sucrose is actively transported into sieve elements in a leaf. Energy from ATP drives the loading process. Solute concentrations rise accordingly in the tubes. Water that the xylem has delivered to the leaf moves into the tubes, down the osmotic gradient. The resulting increase in local pressure causes water to flow to regions where pressure in the tube system is lower—which may be upward as well as downward from the leaf. Everything dissolved in the water also flows along, if it is small enough to penetrate the wall perforations in sieve elements. Molecules of sucrose, fatty acids, glycerol, amino acids, and amides are small enough.

What maintains the low pressure at the other end of the phloem pipelines? If pressure were to build up there, the osmotic gradient that assures translocation would disappear. Cells maintain low pressures when they use up the organic molecules being delivered to them. For example, some sucrose is converted into cell wall polysaccharides and storage starch; some is used in aerobic respiration. All such cell activities lower the water pressure in sink regions, because a low concentration of dissolved solutes means that less water can be held osmotically. Growth also lowers the water pressure. Internal pressure forces cell walls to expand, and the expansion causes pressure to drop.

By analogy, think of what happens when you water a garden with a hose. The water in the hose has been used up when you first open the faucet valve; it is a low-pressure region. Water in the pipeline behind the faucet valve is a high-pressure region—and it flows through the hose even when you raise the hose far above the faucet line.

The key points of the pressure flow theory can be summarized this way:

---

1. Translocation of organic molecules through the plant occurs in pipelines of living cells (sieve elements) in the phloem.

2. Translocation is driven by differences in water pressure between source regions (photosynthesis sites or storage organs) and sink regions (any metabolically active or growing tissue).

3. Organic molecules such as sucrose are actively transported into sieve elements present in source regions. Water follows osmotically because the loading of organic molecules increases solute concentrations in the sieve elements. Hence osmotic pressure builds up here.

4. Solutes in the phloem are moved to sink regions as water moves down its gradient. In sink regions, organic molecules are unloaded by transport mechanisms that move them into individual cells.

5. The movement of solutes into cells lowers the internal water concentration, so water moves passively out of the pipeline system and into cells. Also, cell growth lowers the internal water concentration and pulls more water out. In such ways, low-pressure regions are maintained in sink regions.

6. Thus active transport (through ATP expenditure) and osmotic gradients between source and sink regions are the basis for translocation of organic molecules in the phloem.

Readings

Apfel, R. 1972. "The Tensile Strength of Liquids." *Scientific American* 227(6):58–71. A fairly simple treatment of theory and experiments providing evidence that liquids can exist under tension as well as pressure.

Epstein, E. 1973. "Roots." *Scientific American* 228(5): 48–58.

Galston, A., P. Davies, R. Satter. 1980. *The Life of a Green Plant.* Englewood Cliffs, New Jersey: Prentice-Hall. A simplified treatment of much of plant physiology.

Hewitt, E., and T. Smith. 1975. *Plant Mineral Nutrition.* New York: Wiley. Techniques and results in studies of plant mineral nutrition.

Leopold, A., and P. Kriedemann. 1975. *Plant Growth and Development.* New York: McGraw-Hill. A thorough treatment of these subjects, with emphasis on experimental results.

Mayer, A., and A. Poljakoff-Mayber. 1981. *The Germination of Seeds.* Third edition. New York: Pergamon Press. A simple treatment of seed biology, and effects of light and other environmental factors on seed germination.

Peel, A. 1974. *Transport of Nutrients in Plants.* New York: Wiley. A short, simple treatment of transport processes occurring in xylem and phloem.

Salisbury, F., and C. Ross. 1978. *Plant Physiology.* Second edition. Belmont, California: Wadsworth. Excellent, comprehensive book covering most plant functions.

Torrey, J., and D. Clarkson (editors). 1975. *The Development and Function of Roots.* New York: Academic Press. One of the few modern treatments of root structure and function.

Review Questions

1. Give examples of the features that enable land plants to absorb water and nutrients from their surroundings, which have dilute concentrations of these required substances.

2. What three elements make up most of the dry weight of a land plant? Which six elements are considered macronutrients for land plants?

3. Describe some of the specific roles that mineral salts play in plant functioning. How does solute absorption and accumulation affect plant growth?

4. Define mycorrhiza. Why is it important to include some of the native soil around roots when transplanting a plant from one place to another?

5. Describe transpiration. State how the cohesion theory of water transport helps explain what is going on in this form of water movement.

6. Transpiration competes with other water-requiring cell processes. Can you name some of these processes?

7. Look at Figure 17.9. Then, on your own, diagram the feedback relations that influence the coordinated growth of stems, roots, and leaves.

8. Sucrose transport from one plant organ to another is called translocation. Can you explain how it works in terms of the four key points of the pressure flow theory? How did aphids help show that sucrose is indeed the main substance being transported through the phloem pipelines?

18

PLANT REPRODUCTION AND EMBRYONIC DEVELOPMENT

Although it is probably not something you think about very often, flowering plants engage in sex. They produce sperm and egg cells, as humans do. They, too, have elaborate reproductive systems that protect and nourish sex cells during their formation. As in human females, the female organs of flowering plants house the embryo during its early development. Those exquisite and varied forms called flowers are, in effect, exclusive or open invitations to third parties—pollinating agents—that function in getting sperm and egg together (Figure 18.1). Long before humans ever did, flowering plants were using tantalizing colors and seductive fragrances in improving the odds for sexual success. Long before prospective brides discovered that a way to a man's heart is through his stomach, flowering plants were plying the stomachs of pollinators with nectar.

Plants also do something that humans cannot do (at least not yet). They can reproduce asexually. As you know, there are two central events in sexual reproduction. One is meiosis (which halves the parental number of chromosome sets for forthcoming sex cells, or gametes). The other is fertilization (whereby the number of chromosome sets doubles when the nuclei of two gametes fuse). Asexual reproduction is so named because sex cells and fertilization are not involved; a new multicelled body can be formed from mitotic divisions of either unfertilized sex cells or somatic cells of a parent body.

Both sexual and asexual reproduction occur in plant life cycles, and the reproductive details vary considerably among the diverse species of the plant kingdom. We will look at the nature of these variations in Chapter Thirty-Three, which is an evolutionary survey of plant diversity. Here, let's start with sexual reproduction and embryonic development as it occurs among angiosperms—those fascinating flowering plants.

SEXUAL REPRODUCTION OF FLOWERING PLANTS

Overview of Key Reproductive Events

The roots, stems, and leaves described in the preceding chapters are vegetative organs of the **sporophyte**, or spore-producing plant (Chapter Nine). In flowering plant life cycles, sporophytes alternate with **gametophytes**, the gamete-producing bodies. The gametophytes of these plants are relatively small structures, compared with the sporophyte. They form right on the vegetative parent body and remain attached to it during the reproductive phase of the life cycle.

In flowering plants, the production of flowers marks the onset of the reproductive phase. Then, vegetative growth of the sporophyte is permanently or temporarily interrupted, depending on the plant species. For *annuals,* the life cycle is completed within one growing season and the sporophyte dies. For most *perennials* (plants that live from year to year), vegetative growth of the sporophyte resumes after the reproductive phase.

Figure 18.2 shows the relationship between the vegetative and reproductive phases of flowering plant life cycles. Typically, the following events constitute the reproductive portion:

---

1. **Microspore formation.** Reproductive cells develop and undergo meiosis into microspores in male reproductive organs. Microspores develop into pollen grains (immature male gametophytes). Pollen grains later develop into mature, sperm-bearing gametophytes.

2. **Megaspore formation.** Reproductive cells develop and undergo meiosis into megaspores in female reproductive organs. Megaspores develop into egg-bearing female gametophytes.

3. **Pollination.** Pollen grains are transferred to female parts (stigma) of the flower.

4. **Pollen tube growth.** A pollen grain with its pollen tube is a mature male gametophyte. Growth of a pollen tube through female tissues conveys sperm to the egg.

5. **Fertilization.** Egg and sperm nuclei fuse, and a zygote forms. Formation of endosperm (reserve food tissue of the forthcoming seed) is triggered.

6. **Embryo development.** Genetic and cytoplasmic controls transform the zygote into a plant embryo.

7. **Seed, fruit formation.** The embryo becomes packaged in seed and fruit tissues that aid in its dispersal from the parent plant.

8. **Dispersal, germination.** Seeds and fruits are dispersed (by wind, water, animals). At the proper time and on suitable substrates, the seeds germinate (begin growth), which will lead to a mature sporophyte.

Floral Structure

The first seven events just described take place in a **flower:** a cluster of reproductive (fertile) and nonreproductive (sterile) organs. All of these organs are generally regarded as

highly modified leaves. Typically, the leaf parts are arranged in whorls on a modified stem tip called a *receptacle* (Figure 18.3). The outermost whorl consists of *sepals.* Usually sepals are green (as in roses); sometimes they are brightly colored (as in *Clematis*). The next whorl consists of the *petals.* Often, petals are conspicuously colored structures that function in attracting bird and insect pollinators, in ways that will be described shortly.

a

b

Figure 18.1 Reproductive systems called flowers. Many of these exquisite structures have coevolved with animals, such as the hummingbird shown in (**a**), which serve as pollination vectors in the reproductive process. (**b**) The orchid *Lealia.*

277

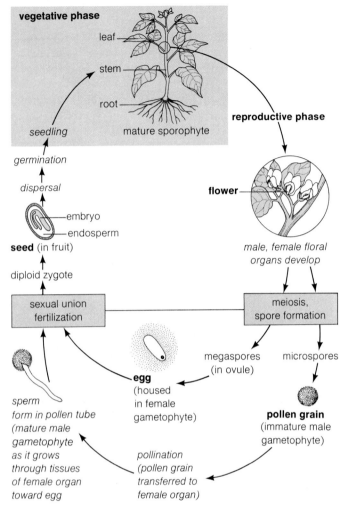

Figure 18.2 Phases in which vegetative and reproductive structures typically occur in the life cycle of a flowering plant.

Labels in figure:

vegetative phase
leaf
stem
root
seedling
germination
mature sporophyte
dispersal
reproductive phase
embryo
endosperm
seed (in fruit)
flower
diploid zygote
male, female floral organs develop
sexual union fertilization
meiosis, spore formation
egg (housed in female gametophyte)
megaspores (in ovule)
microspores
sperm form in pollen tube (mature male gametophyte as it grows through tissues of female organ toward egg
pollination (pollen grain transferred to female organ)
pollen grain (immature male gametophyte)

Stamens, the male reproductive organs, are enclosed in the petals of a flower. Commonly, the stamens consist of pollen-bearing structures called *anthers,* each perched on top of a single stalk, or filament. **Carpels** are the female reproductive organs. The central whorl of modified leaves in the flower consists of one or more carpels, depending on the species.

A carpel usually has three parts. The expanded base is the **ovary**, which eventually ripens into fruit tissue. A stalk, called the **style**, is continuous with the ovary and extends above it. Topping the style is a sticky region, called the **stigma**. A stigma is a landing platform for pollen. Its surface proteins are complementary to those of pollen grains from plants of the same species.

The flower just described is a "perfect" flower, having both stamens and one or more carpels. Some plant species have "imperfect" flowers, with only stamens or only carpels. Often they are called male and female flowers. In some species, such as corn, male and female flowers appear on the same plant. In other species, such as holly and cottonwoods, they occur on separate plants.

GAMETE FORMATION

Microspores to Pollen Grains

When the anther is first developing, mitotic divisions produce local masses of cells called *microspore mother cells.* Following meiosis in a diploid mother cell, four haploid meiospores are produced (Figure 18.4). The meiospores of male floral organs are called **microspores**. A microspore divides

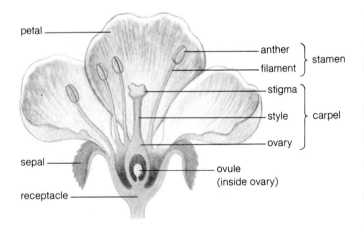

Figure 18.3 General arrangement of floral organs. Shown here, the cherry flower (*Prunus*).

Labels in figure:
petal
anther
filament
stamen
stigma
style
carpel
ovary
sepal
ovule (inside ovary)
receptacle

E. R. Degginger

mitotically into a two-celled **pollen grain**, which is the immature male gametophyte. The tube cell of the pollen grain gives rise to a pollen tube. Following pollination, growth of a pollen tube transports sperm cells to the egg. The generative cell of a pollen grain produces the sperm nuclei that function in fertilization.

A tough wall develops around the pollen grain. This wall will protect the male gametophyte from drying out when it leaves the anther and is transported through the air to a stigma. As Figure 18.5 suggests, the walls have elaborate surface patterns that correlate with those of stigmas of the same species. When pollen lands on a compatible stigma, the pollen tube cell is stimulated to grow into the style tissue below the stigma. When pollen lands on an incompatible stigma, it does not receive the stimulatory signals that trigger its growth.

Megaspores to Eggs

When a plant ovary is first developing, one or more dome-shaped cell masses form on its inner wall or on its inner partitions. Each mass is the start of an **ovule**, a structure that eventually becomes a seed. Figure 18.6 shows the arrangement of ovules within the ovary of one type of flowering plant. In some species, only one ovule is present. In others, hundreds or thousands of individual ovules are packed inside ovaries.

a

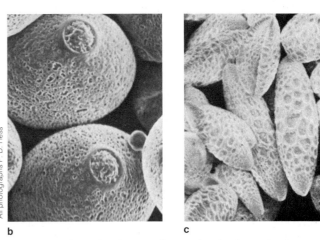

All photographs F. D. Hess

b   c

Figure 18.5 Scanning electron micrographs of pollen grains from (**a**) ragweed, 750×, (**b**) cucumber, 900×, and (**c**) day lily, 350×.

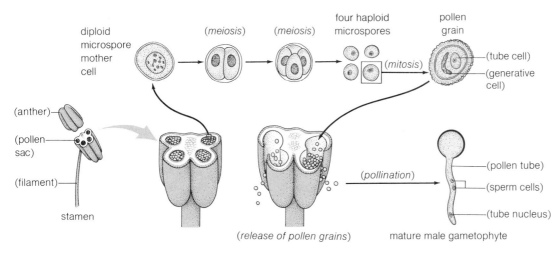

Figure 18.4 Stages in the development of a male gametophyte, beginning with microspore production in the anther. Maturation of the male gametophyte and formation of sperm depend on successful pollination.

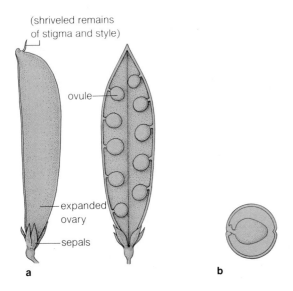

Figure 18.6 Attachment of ovules to tissues of the ovary, at the lower part of a carpel in a flower. Beans and peas have a single carpel, and ovules are attached to the margins of the ovarian wall. In (**a**), a nearly mature garden pea is opened to reveal the vertical arrangement; in (**b**), the arrangement is shown in cross-section.

The outermost cells of the early ovule develop into one or two protective layers called *integuments*. Only a tiny tip of the dome-shaped ovule does not become covered with integuments. This tiny opening (the *micropyle*) is most often the site of pollen tube penetration into the ovule.

While the integuments are developing, mitotic divisions increase the inner cell mass of the ovule. One of the internal cells is a *megaspore mother cell*. A single layer of cells surrounds this cell, which enlarges in preparation for meiosis. Following meiosis, four haploid meiospores form; in female plant parts, they are called **megaspores**. For the majority of plants, three of the four megaspores now disintegrate. One enlarges and develops into a **female gametophyte**, or **embryo sac**. This development involves mitotic divisions that produce eight nuclei.

Cytokinesis does not occur right after the formation of the eight nuclei. First, the nuclei migrate to specific locations. When cytoplasmic division does occur, the result is a seven-cell, eight-nucleate embryo sac. Three of the cells end up near the micropyle; one is the egg. Three end up at the opposite end of the embryo sac. In between is a single binucleate cell, called the *endosperm mother cell.* It will help give rise to a mass of tissue that will surround the forthcoming embryo.

Figure 18.7 illustrates some of the structures we have been describing so far, and shows when they develop in the life cycle of a representative plant.

POLLINATION AND FERTILIZATION

Pollination and Pollen Tube Growth

The word **pollination** refers to the transfer of pollen grains to stigmatic surfaces. Once a pollen grain has been deposited on a compatible stigma, pollen tube formation commences. The generative cell of the pollen grain divides and two sperm cells form before or during tube growth. The pollen tube grows down through stigmatic and ovarian tissues on its journey to the egg. The rate of growth varies. The journey takes only a few hours through the very long style (silk) of corn. In wheat, it takes only one or two days for the pollen tube to reach the egg. In some oaks, it takes nearly a year.

Fertilization and Endosperm Formation

Upon reaching the ovarian chambers, a pollen tube grows toward an ovule. Typically it enters the micropyle, penetrates the surrounding tissues, and nears the female gametophyte. Apparently the tip of the pollen tube ruptures and the sperm are released.

In most organisms, fusion of egg and sperm is a singular event in the reproductive phase of the life cycle. In flowering plants, **double fertilization** occurs. One sperm nucleus fuses with that of the egg, and a zygote forms. The other sperm nucleus usually fuses with the endosperm mother cell. This second fusion results in a **primary endosperm cell**, with a single *triploid* (3*n*) nucleus. Double fertilization marks the beginning of a new sporophyte. Before looking at how embryonic development proceeds in this new sporophyte individual, however, let's take a closer look at the relationship between floral structure and the pollinators necessary for a new generation to begin.

Coevolution of Flowering Plants and Their Pollinators

Flower-bearing plants grow in alpine regions, in forests, in deserts, even in water. More than any other group of plants, they have spread across the earth's surface and have become extremely diverse. Their adaptive success had its beginnings in the Cretaceous Period of the Mesozoic, about 125 million years ago. Before then, wind-pollinated gymnosperms were

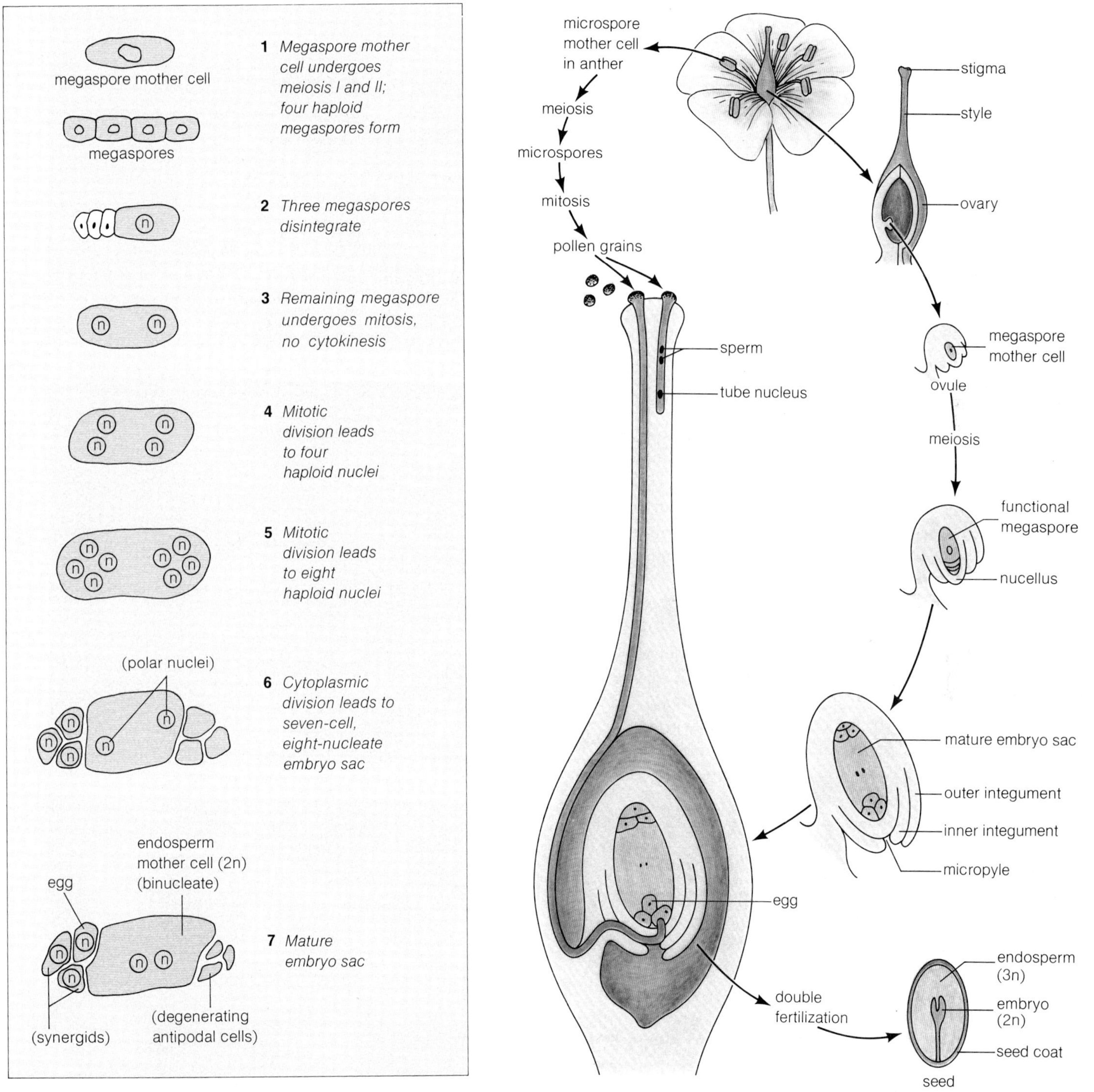
megaspore mother cell
megaspores
1 Megaspore mother cell undergoes meiosis I and II; four haploid megaspores form
2 Three megaspores disintegrate
3 Remaining megaspore undergoes mitosis, no cytokinesis
4 Mitotic division leads to four haploid nuclei
5 Mitotic division leads to eight haploid nuclei
(polar nuclei)
6 Cytoplasmic division leads to seven-cell, eight-nucleate embryo sac
egg
endosperm mother cell (2n) (binucleate)
7 Mature embryo sac
(synergids)
(degenerating antipodal cells)
n
microspore mother cell in anther
meiosis
microspores
mitosis
pollen grains
stigma
style
ovary
sperm
tube nucleus
megaspore mother cell
ovule
meiosis
functional megaspore
nucellus
mature embryo sac
outer integument
inner integument
micropyle
egg
double fertilization
endosperm (3n)
embryo (2n)
seed coat
seed

Figure 18.7 Details in the life cycle of a flowering plant. The boxed inset shows the events of embryo sac development as it occurs in the majority of flowering plant species.

the dominant land plants. By that time, however, flowering plants appeared and had begun to take hold. By the close of the Mesozoic, about 65 million years ago, they had expanded in numbers and kinds through diverse environments. And this period of rapid expansion was paralleled by expansion among insect groups.

During the early Mesozoic, some beetles apparently were already feeding on pollen or other parts of wind-pollinated plants. They probably visited plants on a haphazard basis, just as beetles do today. Hence they might have been secondary in importance as inadvertent pollinating agents. Yet, we can imagine that plants being slightly more conspicuous or tasty would attract more insects—and pollen dispersal would have been more effective because of the increased visits. There would have been selective advantage in having ample pollen, special glands that secreted nectar, and flamboyant floral advertisements. However the interactions actually developed, diverse species of insects and flowering plants were locked in interdependence by the dawn of the Cenozoic, some 65 million years ago.

Flowers attract beetles, bees, wasps, butterflies, moths, flies, birds, and bats. They attract people, who sometimes specialize in plant hybridization and propagation. The attracting factors are the arrangement of flower parts, the patterns in which parts fuse or remain distinct, coloration, odor, nectar, and size (Figure 18.8). It is true that many successful plants are wind-pollinated; grasses, oaks, birches, and some maples are like this. Their flowers typically do not have nectar or perfume and tend to lack colorful petals. But many flowering plants depend on animals to disperse their pollen. Color is an important attractant for many of these animals. For instance, bird-pollinated flowers tend to be red, a wavelength to which bird eyes are sensitive. Bee-pollinated flowers tend to be blue, yellow, or yellow-orange, with prominent ultraviolet components. Odors, too, can attract pollinators from great distances.

Once a pollinator locates a flower, color patterns and petal shapes guide it to the nectar. These visual cues also channel the pollinator's movements in ways that aid pollination. For instance, petals of hummingbird-pollinated flowers form a tube that often corresponds to bill length and shape (Figure 18.1). These flowers often exclude other potential pollinators (such as heavy bumblebees that cannot feed during flight).

Some orchids mimic the female form and coloration of pollinating insects. The male insects attempt to mate with flower after flower. They spread pollen about as they are led ever onward by this deception. Eventually a real female comes along, so the insects do keep reproducing, and the orchids do keep getting pollinated.

a
R. Taggart

b
Edward S. Ross

c
Ted Schwartz

Figure 18.8 Pollination through reliance on visual cues, winds, deceit, spring traps, and tasty inducements. Close-range guides to nectar in (**a**) a passion flower, *Passiflora caerulea,* and (**b**) a composite, *Arctotis acaulis.* The strong fragrance of white-flowered stephanotis (**c**) attracts night-flying moths. (**d**) Some orchids resemble females of pollinating species, and males attempt to mate with the flowers. Others look like rival male bees vibrating in winds; then, territorial male insects attack (and pollinate) the flowers. Wind-pollinated flowers include cattails (**e**) and grasses (**f**). Scotch broom (**g**) is an ''explosive'' flower. The pollinator's weight forces the flowers open, and pollen-laden stamens (positioned to strike against the insect's body) are thereby released. (**h**) Flowers of the bird-of-paradise, *Strelitzia reginae,* are yellow-orange and bright blue, colors that attract bees. (**i**) Glorybower, with suspended flowers, is pollinated by hummingbirds. (**j**) In return for sips of nectar, the gila woodpecker carries pollen from blossom to blossom of the saguaro cactus.

EMBRYONIC DEVELOPMENT

From Zygote to Plant Embryo

When the flowering plant zygote first forms, it is still attached to the parent plant. Even before it begins the mitotic divisions that will produce the multicelled embryo, this single cell already has undergone **polarization**: cytoplasmic substances located at one end of the cell are different from cytoplasmic substances located at the other. As an example, Figure 18.9 shows polarization in a *Capsella* zygote. Notice how most organelles, including the nucleus, reside in the top half. A vacuole takes up most of the lower half. When the cell does divide, lower cells give rise only to a simple row of cells that transfer nutrients from the parent plant to the embryo. This cell row is called the *suspensor*. The upper cells undergo divisions that give rise to the mature, multicelled embryo. Both the suspensor and the embryo arise from a common predecessor cell, the zygote. Thus they both must contain the same hereditary instructions. The only initial difference between them is the polarization of cytoplasmic substances, which is itself a heritable attribute. Thus, we might well conclude that inherited differences in the cytoplasm of the plant zygote contribute to later differences in structure and function. Thereafter, differentiation is a result of interactions between cells and between cells and the environment (Chapter Fourteen).

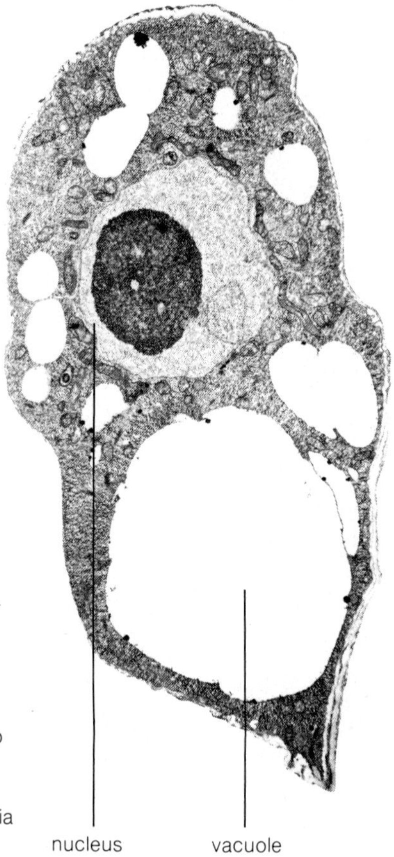

Figure 18.9 Elongate, single-celled zygote of *Capsella* (shepherd's purse), showing the polarization of cytoplasmic components. This inherited cytoplasmic difference leads to differentiation during the first mitotic divisions that produce the multicelled embryo. (Patricia Schulz)

nucleus vacuole

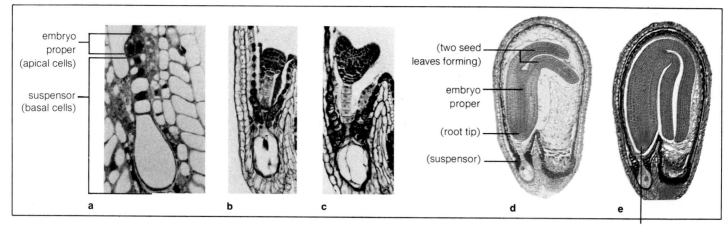

Figure 18.10 A few stages in the embryonic development of *Capsella*, a dicot. All of the micrographs are in long section. (**a**) The embryo after several mitotic divisions, with apical cells differentiated to form the embryo proper, and basal cells differentiated to form the suspensor. (**b**) Globular stage, showing differentiated cells that will make up the epidermal layer. (**c**) Embryo at the heart stage, in which some cells are beginning to differentiate and form seed leaves (primary organs in these plants). (**d**) Continued divisions lead to an elongate embryo. (**e**) The embryo at maturity. (Micrograph a from Patricia Schulz; b, c from Ray F. Evert; d, e from Ripon Microslides)

Seed and Fruit Formation

Following double fertilization, the ovule of a flowering plant undergoes expansion. Integuments thicken and harden. Inside, the zygote develops into a diploid embryo. The triploid primary endosperm nucleus divides repeatedly and forms endosperm. A fully mature ovule is a **seed**; its integuments are the seed coat.

In some seeds, the endosperm serves as a food storage tissue, which is used during early growth when the seed germinates. In this case, the embryos develop **cotyledons**, or seed leaves. The cotyledons remain thin but may produce enzymes that aid in transferring stored food from the endosperm to the germinating seedling. The endosperm in these seeds are filled with proteins, fats, oils, and starch. In other seeds, the embryo develops cotyledons that absorb the endosperm and that function in food storage. Figure 18.10 shows the two cotyledons of a mature seed of shepherd's purse, a dicot. Figure 18.11 shows the single cotyledon of a mature seed of corn, a monocot.

While an ovule is developing into a seed, the ovary surrounding it is developing into most or all of the structure called a **fruit**. As Figure 18.12 shows, sometimes the shriveled sepals and stamens are still present on the mature fruit. The largest mature fruit is that of *Coco-de-mer*, a double coconut that weighs twenty kilograms. The smallest seeds are the dustlike particles in orchids; several million seeds can be housed in a single fruit!

Figure 18.12 Fruit formation on an apple tree. Successful fertilization is usually indicated by the dropping of petals from the flower. Expansion of the ovary follows. Sepals and stamens can still be observed on the mature fruit.

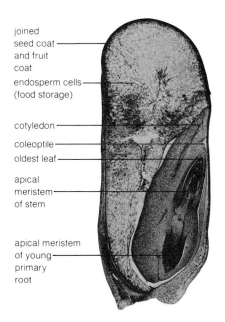

joined seed coat and fruit coat

endosperm cells (food storage)

cotyledon

coleoptile

oldest leaf

apical meristem of stem

apical meristem of young primary root

Figure 18.11 Elongated seed of corn (*Zea mays*), a monocot. Most of the seed volume is composed of endosperm cells that store starch and protein. The embryo has a single cotyledon that, upon germination, secretes digestive enzymes into the endosperm and absorbs digested products in return. These products are transported to the young root and shoot tips. The coleoptile will enclose and protect the young leaves as they grow upward through the soil. (Bracegirdle and Miles, *An Atlas of Plant Structure*, Heinemann Educational Books, 1977)

Table 18.1 Kinds of Fruits of Some Flowering Plants		
Type	Characteristics	Some Examples
Simple (formed from single carpel, or two or more united carpels of one flower)	1. Fruit wall *dry; split* at maturity	pea, magnolia, tulip, mustard
	2. Fruit wall *dry; intact* at maturity	sunflower, wheat, rice
	3. Fruit wall *fleshy*	cherry, peach, olive, lemon
Aggregate (formed from numerous but separate carpels of single flower)	*Aggregate* (cluster) of matured ovaries (fruits), all attached to common receptacle (modified stem end)	strawberry, blackberry, raspberry
Multiple (formed from carpels of several associated flowers)	*Multiple* matured ovaries, grown together into a mass; may include accessory structures (such as receptacle, sepal, and petal bases)	pineapple, fig, mulberry

We tend to think of fruits as juicy edible structures, as indeed many are. But fruits are any matured or ripened ovary, with or without accessory parts (Table 18.1). Grains and nuts are dry fruits; tomatoes are fleshy fruits. A raspberry is an aggregate of many fruits from one flower that later separate. In a pineapple, several flowers form a cluster of multiple units that remain together at maturity. A maple fruit wall is dry and intact at maturity.

Dispersal and Germination

What is the function of the diverse fruit structures that occur among flowering plants? *Fruits, be they edible structures, small capsules, or a variety of other forms, are adaptations for seed protection and dispersal in specific environments.* Thus, for example, the lightweight, tiny seeds of the orchid fruit can be widely dispersed on air currents when the ovarian walls rupture. Maple fruits have winglike extensions. When the fruit drops, the wings cause it to spin sideways—and in this way, seeds can be dispersed to new locations, where they will not have to compete with the parent plant for soil water and minerals. Many fruits have hooks, spines, hairs, and sticky surfaces. By such means they adhere to feathers and fur of animals that brush against them—and thereby can be taxied to new locations.

Fleshy fruits such as strawberries and cherries are well adapted for moving through the animal gut, which contains powerful digestive enzymes. The enzymes remove just enough of the hard seed coats to enhance the likelihood of successful germination when the indigestible seeds are expelled from the body.

How long does a plant embryo remain locked within its seed coat and still retain the ability to give rise to a mature sporophyte? That is a subject of the next chapter.

ASEXUAL REPRODUCTION OF FLOWERING PLANTS

The sexual reproductive modes we have just described are the most prevalent among flowering plants. This is not to say they are the only ones. Sporophytes also can be reproduced asexually by several means (Table 18.2). For example, a strawberry plant can reproduce sexually. It also can send out horizontal aboveground stems called *runners.* Along such runners, new roots and shoots develop at every other node. As another example, oranges can reproduce every so often by *parthenogenesis:* the development of an embryo from an unfertilized egg. In some plants, parthenogenesis is stimulated when pollen contacts a stigma even when the pollen tube never does grow down the style. There is evidence that hormones (either formed in the stigma or produced by pollen grains) diffuse down to the unfertilized egg and stimulate embryogenesis. These embryos become $2n$ by fusion of products of egg mitosis, or a $2n$ cell outside the gametophyte may be stimulated to form an embryo.

Vegetative reproduction occurs among plants that show wound responses. For example, when a leaf falls or is torn away from a jade plant, a new plant can develop from meristematic tissue in vascular bundles just inside the wound.

Vegetative propagation also occurs with a little help from humans. For example, a whole orchard of individual pear trees might have been grown from cuttings or buds of a parent tree. Obviously, the "offspring" have the same DNA instructions as the parent. Any organism reproduced asexually in such a way that it is genetically identical with its parent is called a **clone**. Many of our food crops are clones.

Vegetative propagation can also be induced in the laboratory. In 1958, Frank Steward and his colleagues propagated carrot plants from *tissue cultures.* They isolated small clumps of cells from differentiated parenchyma tissue in a carrot root. They placed the cells in a nutrient-rich liquid medium that was constantly rotated and aerated. The procedure led to a milky suspension of separate cells. The researchers discovered that individual cells in the suspension

Table 18.2 Asexual Reproductive Modes of Flowering Plants

Mechanism	Representative Species	Characteristics
Reproduction on modified stems:		
1. Runner	Strawberry	New plants arise at nodes of an aboveground horizontal stem
2. Rhizome	Bermuda grass	New plants arise at nodes of underground horizontal stem
3. Corm	Gladiolus	New plant arises from axillary bud on short, thick, vertical underground stem
4. Tuber	Potato	New shoots arise from buds on tubers (enlarged tips of slender underground rhizomes)
5. Bulb	Onion, lily	New bulb arises from axillary bud on short underground stem
Parthenogenesis	Orange, rose	Embryo develops without nuclear or cellular fusion (e.g., from unfertilized haploid egg; or adventitiously, from tissue surrounding embryo sac)
Vegetative propagation	Jade plant, African violet	New plant develops from tissue or organ (e.g., a leaf) that drops or is torn from plant
Tissue culture propagation	Carrot, corn, wheat, rice	New plant arises from cell in parent plant that is not irreversibly differentiated; laboratory technique only

could grow and develop into a normal embryo—even into an entire carrot plant, given the proper environmental conditions. In other words, cells from the parent tissue were not irreversibly differentiated; they were able to give rise to a new plant by repeating the developmental program. Such induced vegetative propagations are also accomplished with shoot tips or other parts of individual plants. The technique is particularly useful when an advantageous mutant arises. For example, one such mutant might show resistance to a disease that is particularly crippling to wild-type plants of the same species. Through tissue culture propagation, hundreds and even thousands of identical plants can be propagated from that one specimen. The method is already being used in efforts to improve major food crops, such as corn, wheat, rice, and peas.

Readings

Jensen, A., and F. Salisbury. 1983. *Botany: An Ecological Approach.* Second edition. Belmont, California: Wadsworth. Authoritative, well-illustrated introduction to plant biology.

Proctor, M., and P. Yeo. 1973. *The Pollination of Flowers.* London: Collins. Beautifully illustrated introduction to pollination.

Raven, P., R. Evert, and H. Curtis. 1981. *Biology of Plants.* Third edition. New York: Worth. Outstanding illustrations.

Salisbury, F., and C. Ross. 1978. *Plant Physiology.* Second edition. Belmont, California: Wadsworth.

Weier, T., C. Stocking, and M. Barbour. 1974. *Botany: An Introduction to Plant Biology.* Fifth edition. New York: Wiley.

Review Questions

1. Sketch a flower and label its sterile and reproductive parts. Explain floral function by relating some floral structures to events in the life cycle.

2. Distinguish between these terms:
   a. Megaspore and microspore
   b. Pollination and fertilization
   c. Pollen grain and pollen tube
   d. Ovule and female gametophyte
   e. Runner and rhizome

3. Observe the kinds of flowers growing in the area where you live. On the basis of what you have read about the likely coevolutionary links between flowering plants and their pollinators, can you perceive what kinds of pollinating agents your floral neighbors might depend upon?

4. Describe the steps involved in the formation of an eight-cell, seven-nucleate embryo sac.

5. Describe what happens to the endosperm mother cell and the egg following fertilization.

6. Give some specific examples of adaptations that enhance seed protection and dispersal.

19

PLANT GROWTH AND DEVELOPMENT

So far in this unit, we have looked at some basic aspects of plant structure. We have also looked at some aspects of plant functioning, such as the stomatal controls that help maintain internal conditions in the plant body. Let us now extend the picture in time, by looking at adaptations that allow the plant to follow its genetically prescribed program of growth and development through seasonal change.

Think about just a few of the more familiar kinds of flowering plants—corn, maple trees, the grasses used for lawns. You have probably observed that environmental conditions influence their development. Here we are talking about more than responses to short-term shifts in external conditions (such as fluctuations in mineral ion concentrations). Daylength, temperature, and moisture vary cyclically with the seasons. They trigger such major developmental events as seed germination, leafing out in spring, flowering, and leaf drop in autumn. What internal mechanisms govern these events, and what kind of environmental signals set them in motion? In this chapter, we will consider some answers to these questions—along with some best guesses.

PLANT GROWTH: ITS NATURE AND DIRECTION

Genetic Controls Over Development

Within a seed, embryonic cells start churning out specific proteins when it is time to grow and divide. Undifferentiated cells at the growing tip of a shoot become committed to a

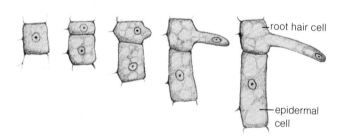

Figure 19.1 Scanning electron micrograph of root hair cells. 46×. The sketch above shows cytoplasmic division in the differentiation of immature cells in the root epidermis of a flowering plant. The unequal division, which has a genetic basis, helps dictate the formation of a root hair cell and an ordinary epidermal cell.

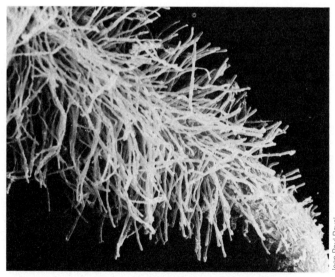

developmental track that will lead to a leaf, or a flower, or simply more stem. For species that go dormant in autumn, some cells respond to signals that cause the genes governing growth and division to idle. Development, in short, involves controlled activation and deactivation of genes.

Among flowering plants, we also find evidence of inherited cytoplasmic effects on early development. While flowering plant zygotes are forming, recall, they are still attached to the parent plant. (They may, for example, be housed inside a ripening apple on the parent tree.) Even before such a zygote begins dividing mitotically, it has undergone *polarization.* The nucleus, mitochondria, ribosomes, and other organelles have become positioned at one end of the cell, and a vacuole has formed which occupies most of the cell volume at the other end. Such polarization is a heritable trait, and it is a basis for early differentiation of the plant embryo (Chapter Eighteen).

When the plant embryo germinates, it divides and daughter cells grow in ways that lead to roots, stems, and leaves. Typically these mitotic divisions are unequal, as they are in immature cells that give rise to specialized root tissues (Figure 19.1). Unequal divisions lead to further variations in the way that cytoplasmic substances are distributed in the growing mass of cells. Beyond this, cells divide in different planes and expand in different directions. These differences lead to mature tissues and organs of diverse shapes. Some structural and chemical differences exist among these cells, differences that give insight into the nature of their variations.

First, by this time, individual cells vary in the number of microtubules present in the cytoplasm. Microtubules, recall, are assembled from protein subunits, with the aid of still other proteins (enzymes). *Hence transcription and translation of the genes coding for these proteins, as well as enzyme activity, are variable in different parts of the developing plant.*

Second, we can assume that by this time, the massed-together cells are interacting chemically and physically, in ways that influence cell shape and function. For example, even during early development, chemical messenger molecules called **hormones** are synthesized and released from certain cells, then move through the body until they encounter and induce changes in target cells. By definition, a *target cell* is one that has receptor sites for a particular hormonal message. Hormones have inhibitory or stimulatory effects on protein synthesis within target cell types.

Through gene controls, specific enzymes required in the formation of cell structures and cell substances (such as hormones) are produced at particular times in a developmental program.

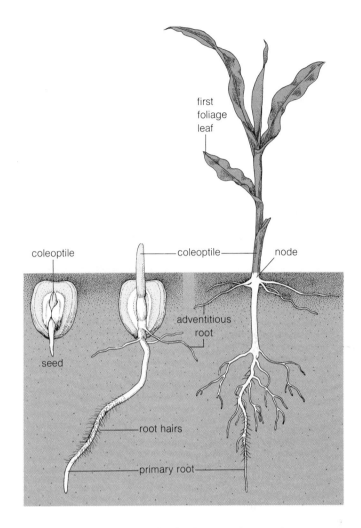

Figure 19.2 A few stages in the development of a corn plant (*Zea mays*), a monocot. When the seed germinates, the coleoptile enclosing the young leaves protects them as the shoot grows upward through soil. Adventitious roots develop from the first-formed node at the coleoptile base. The larger seedling shows branch roots, which form from the primary root.

Patterns of Cell Enlargement

Actual growth—permanent increase in size—begins in the seed. Exactly where in the seed does growth occur, and what causes it? Obviously, the whole seed doesn't grow much. Rather, it simply swells with incoming water molecules, which have been attracted into the seed by hydrophilic groups on proteins and polysaccharides. Once that happens, the plant embryo begins to burgeon. To get an idea of what goes on, let's follow the course of growth for two different plants—corn and soybean (Figures 19.2 and 19.3).

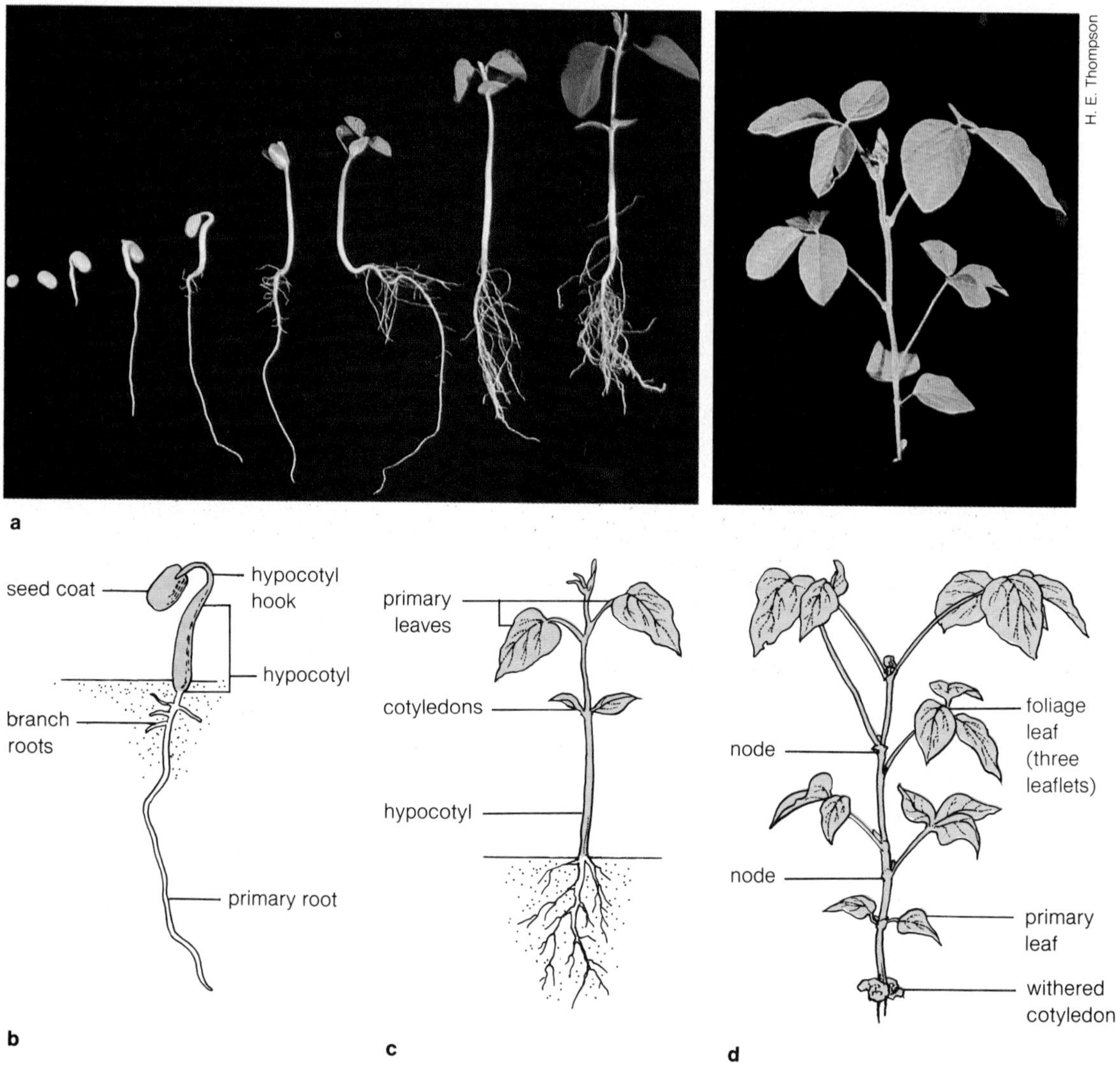

Figure 19.3 A few stages in the development of a soybean plant. (**a**) Germination and early seedling development. In soybean, the common bean, and many other dicots, the food-storing cotyledons are carried aboveground by elongation of cells making up the hypocotyl (**b**). The hypocotyl forms a hook, which makes a channel through the soil as it grows. In this channel, cotyledons are pulled up by growth of the hypocotyl without being torn apart. At the soil surface, light causes the hook to straighten. The cotyledons become photosynthetic for several days, and then wither and fall from the plant body. In (**c**) and (**d**), the first (primary) leaves of soybean are shown to be positioned opposite each other on the stem, and the leaf structure itself is not divided. Afterward, all other foliage leaves are divided into three leaflets. In (**d**), flowers are developing on axillary buds at the four upper nodes.

As is typical of nearly all seeds, the first cells to grow in corn and soybean seeds are found in the embryonic root, which is called the **radicle**. Growth is mainly in a longitudinal direction. The outcome is a slender **primary root** composed of somewhat elongated cells. When this root visibly protrudes from the seed coat remnant, germination is considered to be complete. Later, some cells in the primary root grow in branching directions. The lateral roots that are formed also branch, and the branchings branch again. Such growth can lead to hundreds or millions of roots in a mature plant, depending on its size and species.

Plants grow because their individual cells grow. Cell division in itself does not constitute growth, because the volume of newly formed daughter cells is about the same as that of the parent cell (Figure 19.4). On the average, though, about half the daughter cells formed undergo enlargement—often by twenty times! Thus, cell division increases the capacity for overall growth. The remaining daughter cells remain meristematic; they grow no larger than the parent cell, then probably divide again.

This concept can be summarized in this manner:

In itself, cell division does not constitute growth; it increases the capacity for overall growth through enlargement of about half of the newly formed cells.

Cell growth, recall, is driven by increased solute concentrations, water uptake, and the ensuing turgor pressure against the cell wall (Chapter Seventeen). In some ways, the growth process is like a balloon being blown up with air. Balloons with soft walls are easy to inflate; cells with soft walls grow rapidly under little turgor pressure. An important difference is that the balloon wall gets thinner as it "grows," but the cell wall does not.

To a large extent, the arrangement of polysaccharides in cell walls dictates the direction in which the wall yields under turgor pressure. Therefore, just how the wall polysaccharides are oriented governs whether a cell becomes long and slender, or short and broad. If most cells in a plant organ are elongated, so is the organ. This is true of roots and stems. If most are spherical, so is the organ. This is true of many fruits.

In some elongated root and stem cells, cellulose microfibrils of the primary wall are arranged like barrel hoops around the long axis of the cell. In spherical cells, the microfibrils are randomly arranged in all directions, so that resistance to expansion under turgor pressure is equal in all directions.

The arrangement of cellulose microfibrils in a cell wall controls the direction of cell growth. Cell shapes that result from directional growth help dictate plant form.

Earlier, Figures 3.11 and 4.24 showed examples of the ways that cellulose microfibrils become oriented during the formation of cell walls. What controls the directions in which these fine strands are deposited? That is not known, although microtubules might play a role.

Once primary cell walls are formed, they exhibit two kinds of expansive properties. First, the walls can be *elastic* and stretch reversibly. After stretching, they return to their original shape (much like a filled balloon when the air is released). Second, the cell walls can be *plastic* and become irreversibly stretched. After stretching, they stay stretched (like a blown-up bubble of bubble gum when the air has been let out). Guard cells are examples of highly elastic cells. They swell during stomatal opening, then return to their original size and shape during stomatal closure. The walls of cells exhibiting true growth are somewhat elastic, but they also stretch plastically and thus retain much of their stretched shape. This allows true growth.

The expansive properties of primary cell walls permit cell enlargement.

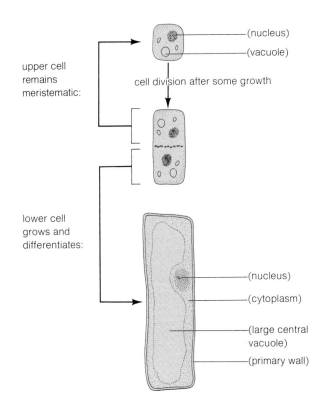

Figure 19.4 The nature and direction of plant cell growth. Through divisions, meristems provide new cells for growth. At a stem tip, small meristematic cells double in size, then divide at right angles to the stem's long axis. The upper cell remains meristematic. The lower cell grows into a mature parenchyma cell of pith or cortex, for example. Tiny vacuoles present in young cells absorb water, fuse, and form the large central vacuole of mature parenchyma cells.

PLANT HORMONES

Types of Plant Hormones

Plant growth, like the growth of other multicelled organisms, is influenced in powerful but poorly understood ways by plant hormones. In response to environmental conditions, hormone-secreting cells in particular plant tissues send out messages that reach target cells and induce them to change activities.

Five hormones (or groups of hormones) are known to exist in vascular plants, and evidence of others is accumulating. The five are auxins, gibberellins, cytokinins, abscisic acid, and ethylene (Table 19.1).

Table 19.1	Main Plant Hormones and Some Known (or Suspected) Effects
Auxins	Promote cell elongation in coleoptiles and stems; long thought to be involved in phototropism and gravitropism
Gibberellins	Promote stem elongation (especially in dwarf plants); might help break dormancy of seeds and buds
Cytokinins	Promote cell division; promote leaf expansion and retard leaf aging
Abscisic acid	Promotes stomatal closure; might trigger bud and seed dormancy, and abscission of leaves, flowers, and fruits; might be involved in root gravitropism
Ethylene	Promotes fruit ripening; promotes abscission of leaves, flowers, and fruits; might play a role in thigmomorphogenesis
Florigen (?)	Arbitrary designation for as-yet unidentified hormone (or hormones) thought to cause flowering

Auxins are best known for their ability to stimulate elongation of stem cells. They have other effects, which will be considered later. The main auxin is *indoleacetic acid,* or *IAA.* Many investigators believe that IAA is the only auxin in plants, so they use "auxin" and "IAA" interchangeably. However, there is some evidence that at least one other compound, *phenylacetic acid,* performs similar roles. It is more abundant than IAA in plants, but many of its effects are not as pronounced. Several compounds synthesized by chemists behave much like natural auxins. They are used by homeowners, farmers, and horticulturists. One of the most common is *2,4-D* (2,4-dichlorophenoxyacetic acid). When sprayed on the foliage at proper concentrations, this compound is a potent killer of dicot weeds and has little effect on grasses.

Gibberellins, like auxins, are best known for their promotion of stem elongation. More than fifty kinds have been identified in plants and fungi. Each differs chemically from the others in a small way. The most familiar is *gibberellic acid.* It is widely used in growth experiments, because of its potency and because a certain fungus serves as an inexpensive factory for its production.

Cytokinins were named for their ability to stimulate cytoplasmic division (the name refers to "cytokinesis"). But leaf cells also grow larger in the presence of these hormones. All cytokinins are similar in structure to adenine, a normal component of nucleotides. The most common and abundant cytokinin seems to be *zeatin,* first isolated from immature seeds of *Zea mays* (corn).

Abscisic acid (ABA) is important in promoting stomatal closure. It also promotes seed and bud dormancy. The hormone was once thought to be of importance in *abscission* (the loss of flowers, fruits, and leaves from the plant body), but this effect might not be that common.

Ethylene (C_2H_2) is a simple hydrocarbon gas that stimulates fruit ripening. Ancient Chinese knew that a bowl of fruit would ripen faster when incense was burned in the same room, although they didn't know that ethylene present in the smoke was responsible. The notion that plants might produce something that promotes ripening was first mentioned in a 1910 report to the Jamaican Agricultural Department. Oranges, the report stated, should not be stored near bananas on freighters, because some emanation from the oranges caused the bananas to become overripe. Almost surely, the "emanation" was ethylene.

It is not yet possible to distinguish clearly between hormonal effects and environmental effects on plant development. One of the reasons is that the environment also controls the amount and distribution of hormones! Nevertheless, let's take a look at what *is* known by following the development of those corn and soybean plants shown in Figures 19.2 and 19.3.

Examples of Hormonal Action

Hormones are known to govern coleoptile growth in corn and other grasses. A **coleoptile** is a hollow, cylindrical organ that protects tender young leaves growing within it (Figure 19.2). Without a coleoptile, young corn leaves would be torn apart by soil particles during early growth. While underground, both the coleoptile and the tightly curled oldest leaf grow in a coordinated fashion. Once exposed to sunlight, however, the coleoptile stops elongating. Its task is completed. The leaf now breaks through the protective coleoptile cylinder, uncurls, absorbs sunlight, and provides organic molecules for the plant parts below.

In a corn coleoptile and leaf, the youngest cells are at the base, not at the tip. Cells between the base and tip elongate under the stimulation of auxins. Through experiments of the sort described in Figure 19.5, we know that *growth of a coleoptile is controlled by IAA synthesized in its tip.* This hormone moves down the coleoptile and changes

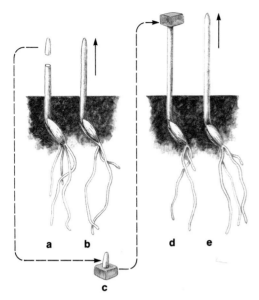

Figure 19.5 Experiment showing that IAA made in the tip of grass coleoptiles promotes elongation of cells below. In (**a**), an oat coleoptile tip is cut off. Compared with a normal coleoptile (**b**), the stump doesn't elongate much. When the excised tip is placed on a tiny block of gelatin for several hours (**c**), IAA moves into the gelatin. When the gelatin block is placed on another de-tipped coleoptile (**d**), elongation proceeds about as fast as it does in an intact coleoptile (**e**).

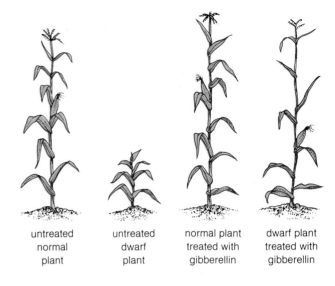

untreated normal plant untreated dwarf plant normal plant treated with gibberellin dwarf plant treated with gibberellin

Figure 19.6 Influence of gibberellin on the height of a normal corn plant and a mutant plant that differs in only one gene.

metabolic activities of cells below the tip. As a result of these changes, cell wall plasticity is increased—and the plasticity encourages elongation.

What about growth of a soybean stem? Like all dicots, soybeans have an apical meristem and young, growing cells near the stem tip. Cells at the stem base are older and larger. Auxin is synthesized near the stem tip, especially in very young leaves being formed there. Experiments show that a dicot stem stops elongating when the tip is cut off. When auxin is applied to the cut stump, growth resumes. Thus, *auxin synthesized at a dicot stem tip promotes growth of cells below.*

What about the effects of other plant hormones? In the stems of many normal plants with tips intact, cells often elongate faster after application of gibberellin. Apparently, *growth of stems that elongate slowly is especially influenced by gibberellin.* Consider dwarf varieties of corn which have short stems. Often, cells of the dwarf plants have a mutant allele that codes for a defective enzyme. Unlike the normal enzyme, the mutant form cannot catalyze an important step in gibberellin production. Gibberellin applications to the dwarfs promote stem elongation. However, they have little effect on a normal corn variety (Figure 19.6).

In contrast to coleoptiles and dicot stems, *root and leaf cells themselves synthesize most or all of the hormones that they require.* Normal roots and leaves show little response to hormone applications.

HORMONES, THE ENVIRONMENT, AND PLANT DEVELOPMENT

Effects of Temperature

Whether a given plant species grows in a particular place depends partly on prevailing temperatures, which affect the growth of coleoptiles, stems, roots, and leaves. Environmental temperatures have considerable effect on cell metabolism, and on the transport of water, minerals, and organic molecules through the plant body.

In general, it's possible to predict the optimum temperature range for a given species by observing where it grows best. Corn and soybean plants grow best in warm regions. The optimum temperature range for many grasses other than corn is lower than that for many dicots. Some plants,

Figure 19.7 Two plants adapted to different land environments. (**a**) The snow buttercup (*Ranunculus adoneus*) grows right up through the edge of a melting snowbank in spring—here, high above timberline in the Colorado Rocky Mountains. (**b**) The creosote bush (*Larrea divaricata*) tolerates extreme conditions of hot, dry deserts of North America. Neither one of these plants will survive in the environment that is favorable for growth and development of the other.

such as cacti, grow best in hot deserts. They are adapted to high air temperatures, high heat absorption, and low soil moisture. Still other plants are adapted to cold environments. Typically, such plants outcompete others at high elevations or in northern latitudes. Most are short, perennial, and grow rapidly during perhaps only one to three months of a cool summer (Figure 19.7).

Tolerance to both cold and hot temperatures is not a suddenly acquired attribute in any individual plant. Besides numerous mutations that have conferred tolerance on a given species, an individual plant even of a cold-tolerant species can die when it is suddenly transferred from a hot-

summer to a cold-winter environment. Thus, survival somehow relates to gradual temperature changes during fall and spring.

Effects of Sunlight

When you stop to think about it, temperature changes are somewhat unreliable guides to what season is approaching, because weather can be fickle. Much better guides are the lengths of day and night—which each year are nearly constant at the same day of the month in a given region. Plants have mechanisms that detect and respond to daylength. In effect, plants can anticipate the coming of winter. Many form flowers and seeds, develop dormant buds, attain more cold hardiness, and shed their leaves—all in response to the shorter daylengths of late summer and early fall. Later in the chapter, you will read about how these remarkable responses might be accomplished. Here, let's take a look at some molecular mechanisms by which sunlight affects plant growth.

Phytochrome is a blue-green pigment molecule that is a receptor for light energy. It is central to controls over plant growth. *Phytochrome seems to be a modulator for hormone activities governing leaf expansion, stem branching, stem length and, in many plants, seed germination and flowering.* Phytochrome is most active when stimulated by light of red wavelengths. Before the sun rises, phytochrome exists mainly in an inactive form (abbreviated Pr) that responds to red light. When Pr absorbs red wavelengths, it is converted to the active form (Pfr). At night, and in shade or at sunset (when far-red light predominates), Pfr reverts to Pr. With the reversible reaction to the inactive form of phytochrome, plant responses promoted by red light are curtailed. The reactions can be summarized in the following way:

$$
Pr \underset{\textit{far-red light}}{\overset{\textit{red light}}{\rightleftharpoons}} Pfr
\begin{cases}
\text{seed germination} & (+) \\
\text{stem elongation} & (-) \\
\text{leaf expansion} & (+) \\
\text{stem branching} & (+) \\
\text{flowering} & (+ \text{ or } -)
\end{cases}
$$

Plants shaded by others are exposed largely to green and far-red wavelengths, because photosynthesizing leaves above them absorb most of the blue and red wavelengths. Thus shaded plants deprived of red light are Pfr deficient. Plants adapted to sunlight but exposed to darkness or shade put more resources into stem elongation and less into leaf expansion or stem branching (Figure 19.8).

How does Pfr promote or inhibit growth of different plant parts? Phytochrome molecules are thought to reside largely in cell membranes. It might be that conversion of Pr to Pfr controls whether hormones bind to (or are transported across) the plasma membranes of target cells.

The Many and Puzzling Tropisms

Plant **tropisms** are familiar but as yet unexplained growth responses. In these responses, an environmental stimulus acts more strongly on one side of an organ than on the opposite side, and the plant responds with a faster rate of cell elongation on one side or the other.

Phototropism. Have you ever noticed how the flat leaf surfaces of houseplants turn toward the light from a nearby window? This response is a form of **phototropism**: growth toward or away from light coming in mainly toward one side of the organism. Stems curve toward light; the flat surface of a leaf blade becomes perpendicular to the light (Figure 19.9).

In the 1800s, Charles Darwin showed that curvature of coleoptiles is much more rapid when light strikes the tip than when it strikes the bending region below. In the 1920s, Frits Went discovered that a growth promoter exists in the coleoptile tip. He called it auxin, after the Greek word mean-

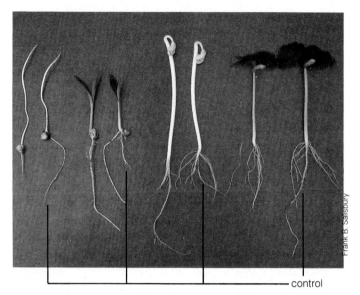

Figure 19.8 Effects of the absence of light on young corn and bean plants. The plant at the right of each group served as a control; it was grown in a greenhouse. The others were grown in darkness for eight days. Dark-grown plants were yellow; they could form carotenoid pigments but not chlorophyll in darkness. They also had longer stems, smaller leaves, and smaller root systems. (Why do you suppose roots of dark-grown plants grow less, considering that those of light-grown plants aren't exposed to light, either?)

Figure 19.9 Phototropism in bean, pea, and oat seedlings. These plants were grown in darkness, then exposed to light from the right side for a few hours before being photographed. Notice that curvature in the bean and pea seedlings occurs mainly in young (upper) cells that are still growing rapidly. Curvature in oat seedlings occurs in the leaves, where the youngest (still-growing) cells are those near the leaf base.

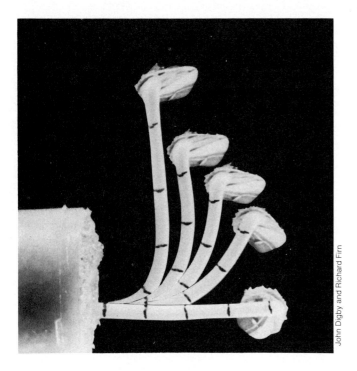

Figure 19.10 Composite time-lapse photograph of gravitropism in a dark-grown sunflower seedling. In this plant, the two cotyledons emerge aboveground, because the stem portion just below the cotyledons elongates. Just before this five-day-old plant was positioned horizontally, it was marked at 0.5-centimeter intervals. After thirty minutes, upward curvature was detectable. The most upright position shown was reached within two hours.

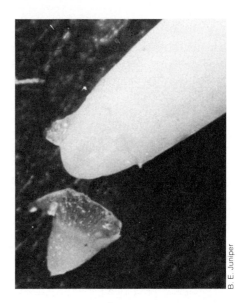

Figure 19.11 Young corn root cap, shown removed from the root tip. When the cap is removed, cells just behind the apical meristem grow faster. When the cap is replaced, their growth slows. These and many other experiments suggest that the root cap synthesizes a growth inhibitor, and that transport of the substance to lower growing portions of a horizontal root causes the downward curvature responsible for gravitropism.

ing "to increase." Went showed that the substance moves down toward shaded elongating cells and causes curvature toward light. Today we know that Went's auxin is IAA. It moves from an illuminated side of a coleoptile to the shaded side, then downward, where it especially promotes elongation of epidermal cells. We also know that blue wavelengths are the most important stimulus for phototropism.

A large, yellow pigment molecule called **flavoprotein** absorbs blue light. Apparently, this pigment absorbs the light that causes phototropic bending. Flavoprotein contains riboflavin (vitamin B_2), which is tightly complexed with a protein molecule. How light absorption by this pigment causes IAA to move horizontally across a coleoptile is not understood.

Gravitropism. The term **gravitropism** (or geotropism) refers to a response to the earth's gravitational force. It is apparent after seed germination, when the plant root curves downward soon after it breaks through the seed coat and

when the coleoptile or stem curves upward. Slower cell growth on the lower side of a horizontally growing root leads to its downward curvature. Because root cells are cemented together at primary walls and middle lamellae, the root curves as a unit. Greatly decreased cell elongation on the upper side of a horizontally growing stem, often with increased elongation on the lower side, leads to its upward curvature (Figure 19.10), even in the dark.

Gravitropic responses seem to govern growth of the first (primary) root and main stem of all seedlings. Yet branch roots usually grow somewhat horizontally through more fertile (upper) soil regions. Also, in shrubs and trees, branches grow more horizontally than the main stem, thereby exposing aerial plant parts to more light and carbon dioxide.

Which plant hormones, if any, take part in gravitropism? For a long time, IAA was thought to move from one side of a stem or root to the other in response to gravity. To be sure, IAA is transported from the upper to the lower side of horizontally positioned coleoptiles and dicot stems. But so are gibberellins. It now seems unlikely that transport of either hormone is fast enough and in sufficient amounts to cause the differential elongation. (Epidermal cells on the lower side of a stem might step up their own hormone production and directly speed their elongation.)

Gravitropism in roots might be related to the root cap. When a root cap is surgically removed, a horizontally oriented root does not curve downward. When the cap is reinstated, curvature is restored. Removing the root cap doesn't prevent cells of the elongating region from growing. If anything, they elongate faster. This suggests that a growth inhibitor is removed along with the cap. Evidence favors the idea that gravity somehow causes the inhibitor to accumulate in cells on the lower side of horizontally positioned root caps. When the inhibitor moves out of the cap, toward the elongating cells, it inhibits their growth (Figure 19.11). At one time, abscisic acid was considered to be the most likely candidate for the inhibitor of root gravitropism. However, recent experiments are calling this idea into question.

Thigmotropism. Unequal growth resulting from physical contact with environmental objects is called **thigmotropism**. Stems of peas, beans, and many other climbing vines show this response. These plants are generally so long and slender that they cannot grow upright without support. Suppose one side of a pea or bean stem grows against a solid object—a fencepost, a supporting stick in a greenhouse pot, the stem of a nearby woody plant. Cells stop elongating on the contacting side, and within minutes the stem begins to curl around the contacted object. It might do so several times before cells on both sides of the stem begin elongating at about the same rate once again. How contact affects elongation is a mystery, although auxin seems to be involved.

Thigmomorphogenesis. Plant growth also is affected by mechanical stress. **Thigmomorphogenesis** is a response to mechanical stress, the result generally being an inhibition of overall plant growth. Contact with rain, grazing animals, farm machinery, even air molecules disturbed during winds causes this plant response. Shaking a plant daily for a brief period can do the same thing, depending on the species. Figure 19.12 shows what happens when you shake tomato plants each day.

Thigmomorphogenesis helps explain differences between indoor and outdoor plants of the same species. Often, the plants grown outdoors are shorter, have thicker stems, and are more resistant to winds. These characteristics appear to be adaptive responses to wind stress. The response mechanism is not yet known.

Figure 19.12 Thigmomorphogenesis in tomato plants. The plant to the far left is an untreated control. It was grown in a greenhouse, protected from wind and rain. The center plant was mechanically shaken thirty seconds at 280 rpm for twenty-eight consecutive days. The plant to the far right received two such shaking periods daily, for twenty-eight days.

THE FLOWERING PROCESS

As a flowering plant matures, its physiological processes become directed toward the production of flowers, seeds, and fruits. In corn, soybeans, and peas, this activity occurs after only a few months of growth. These plants are **annuals**: they live only one growing season. An extreme example is the so-called century plant, for which ten years or so pass before flowering occurs. This plant is a **perennial**: it lives year after year. Still other species produce only roots, stems, and leaves the first growing season, die back to soil level in autumn, then grow a new flower-forming stem from a bud that remains alive in a protected stem region underground (Chapter Eighteen). Such plants typically live through two growing seasons and are called **biennials**. They include many garden vegetables such as cabbages, carrots, and turnips. Perennial grasses in lawns, rangelands, and pastures form flowering stems each year, but they also die back and regrow in spring from buds near the soil level.

Daylength and temperature are the strongest stimuli for flowering of land plants. Low-temperature stimulation of flowering is called **vernalization** (after a Latin term meaning "to make springlike"). Unless buds of some garden biennials and perennials are exposed to cold winter temperatures, flowers do not form on the new spring stems.

All photographs Jan Zeevaart

Figure 19.13 Effect of day length on flowering of short-day plants (SDP) and long-day plants (LDP). In each photograph, the plant on the left was grown under short-day conditions; the plant on the right was grown under long-day conditions.

Daylength is a highly reliable cue for flowering and reproduction of many species. Flowering plant species can be categorized on the basis of responsiveness to daylength:

Long-day plants flower when the daylength becomes longer than some critical value, often in spring. The critical value itself can be longer or shorter than twelve hours.

Short-day plants flower when the daylength becomes shorter than some critical value, often in late summer or early autumn. However, the critical value itself can be longer or shorter than twelve hours.

Day-neutral plants flower irrespective of daylength whenever they become mature enough to do so.

The long days of late spring promote flowering of winter wheats and most biennials. Many other species also are adapted to long days and reproduce early in summer. Autumn-flowering species are short-day plants attuned to shorter daylengths of late summer. Some day-neutral species grow near the equator, where daylength essentially remains nearly constant. Corn, peas, tomatoes, and other crop plants are often day-neutral. They have for many generations undergone artificial selection for variants that can flower under a wide range of conditions. Figure 19.13 shows some flowering plants that can respond in different ways to long and short days.

Cocklebur, a short-day plant, somehow measures time with uncommon sensitivity. For cockleburs and other short-day plants, adequate night length is the key. A single night *longer than* $8\frac{1}{2}$ hours is enough to cause flowering of a cocklebur. When a long night is experimentally interrupted with even a minute or two of light, flowering is reduced or prevented. For cockleburs and all other short-day plants, red light is the most effective color in interrupting the long night, and red light is detected by phytochrome. In short-day plants, Pfr inhibits flowering if it is formed during the dark period. (Remember that red light causes formation of Pfr.) In long-day plants, Pfr is also the active pigment, but extended daylengths provide Pfr for longer periods. As a result, there is faster flowering or more flowers per plant.

We have no idea of how Pfr controls flowering. In theory, at least, Pfr promotes the synthesis of a transportable hormone (or group of hormones) involved in the process. In anticipation of its discovery, the elusive hormone thought to control flowering was designated **florigen** more than forty years ago. Much evidence for its existence comes from cocklebur experiments. Only the main stem tip, branch tips, and lateral buds can form flowers. Before they do, they stop producing young leaves. Although the meristematic regions *respond* to reduced daylength by forming flower cells instead of leaf cells, only the leaves *detect* the length of day and night.

Presumably, detection involves production of florigen and its transport from leaves to buds. There, young leaves stop forming and flowering begins. If all but one leaf is trimmed from a cocklebur plant, and if this leaf is covered with black paper for at least $8\frac{1}{2}$ hours, the plant will flower. But if the leaf is cut off at once after the dark period, the plant will not flower. Apparently, florigen is still in the discarded leaf.

Such experiments suggest that "florigen" does indeed exist, and that it is similar or identical in both short-day and long-day plants.

SENESCENCE

Growth of flowers, fruits, and seeds of all plants places strong demands on roots, stems, and leaves for nutrients—nutrients that will sustain seedlings of the next generation. The demands are so strong that reproductive organs actually withdraw nutrients from vegetative organs through connecting sieve elements. In older leaves, newly formed enzymes degrade proteins, chlorophyll, and other large organic molecules. The breakdown products are transported, along with mineral ions, to reproductive organs. There they form energy reserves of fats, starches, and proteins in seeds of a new generation (Chapter Eighteen). In annuals and most perennials, plants are left with tan-colored, dead leaves depleted of most nutrients. In deciduous trees (which shed leaves at the end of each growing season), nutrients are also transported to parenchyma cells in twigs, stems, and roots prior to abscission. There they are stored until spring growth begins.

What makes the leaves of deciduous trees fall off, or abscise? Studies suggest that ethylene, formed in cells near the break points, activates an enzyme that breaks down cell walls in a narrow zone, causing abscission of leaves, flowers, and fruits. Abscisic acid might also contribute to abscission, perhaps because it causes cells to produce more ethylene. Adequate auxin from the leaf prevents the ethylene from forming.

The sum total of processes leading to death of a plant or any of its organs is called **senescence**. One stimulus for senescence could be the drain of nutrients during the growth of reproductive organs. Consider that when each newly formed flower is removed from a soybean plant, the leaves and stems remain green and healthy much longer than they otherwise would (Figure 19.14). Gardeners maintain vegetative growth in many plants by removing flower buds.

The loss of nutrients from vegetative organs isn't the only cause of senescence. If a cocklebur is induced to flower, its leaves will yellow regardless of whether the young flowers are pinched off or left on. It is as if some signal formed during short days causes both flowering and senescence of the cocklebur. More evidence for a death signal comes from experiments with soybeans. Such a signal must counteract the effects of cytokinins, which delay senescence. At least, when the surface of a mature leaf is painted with a cytokinin solution (which increases the leaf's cytokinin content), the leaf often remains green longer, as Figure 19.15 suggests.

Figure 19.14 Delay of senescence in soybean plants through the daily removal of flower buds. (From A. C. Leopold et al., *Plant Physiology*, 1958, 34:570)

flowers removed   control group

Figure 19.15 Effect of localized cytokinin applications on senescence in a bean plant. The first two (oldest) bean leaves form on opposite sides of the stem; they are called primary leaves. Normally, the oldest leaves of any plant are the first to senesce. Here, primary leaf senescence was delayed by covering their upper surfaces at four-day intervals with a cytokinin solution. This caused the leaves immediately above to senesce and probably to transport nutrients into both primary leaves, allowing them to stay green and healthy longer. Presumably, cytokinins synthesized by leaves or transported to them from other plant parts normally delay leaf senescence. (From A. C. Leopold and M. Kawase, *American J. of Botany*, 1964, 51:294–298)

Figure 19.16 Effect of the relative length of day and night on Douglas fir plant growth. The plant at the left was exposed to twelve-hour light and twelve-hour darkness for a year; its buds became dormant because daylength was too short. The plant at the right was exposed to twenty-hour light and four-hour darkness; buds remained active and growth continued. The middle plant was exposed to twelve-hour light, eleven-hour darkness, and one-hour light in the middle of the dark period. This light interruption of an otherwise long dark period also prevented bud dormancy. Such light causes Pfr formation at an especially sensitive time in the normal day-night cycle. (From R. J. Downs in T. T. Kozlov, ski, ed., *Tree Growth,* The Ronald Press, 1962)

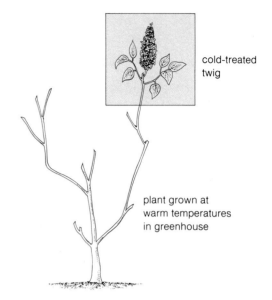

Figure 19.17 Effect of cold temperature on breaking bud dormancy in many woody plants. In this experiment, one branch (boxed portion) of a lilac plant was positioned so that it protruded from a greenhouse during winter; the rest of the plant remained inside, at warm temperatures. Only the buds on the branch exposed to low outside temperatures grew again in spring. This experiment suggests that low-temperature effects are localized.

DORMANCY

As autumn approaches and days grow shorter, stem growth slows or stops in many evergreen trees, deciduous trees, and perennial herbaceous plants. It stops even if temperatures are still warm, the sun is bright, and enough water is available. This surprising response occurs largely because apical meristem cells in each bud stop forming new stem cells. These buds become tolerant of lower temperatures, and ordinarily they will not grow again until spring. When any plant stops growing under physical conditions that are actually quite suitable for growth, it is said to have entered a period of **dormancy.**

What controls bud dormancy? Short days and long nights are two environmental cues. We can demonstrate that these cues cause bud dormancy in Douglas fir plants by interrupting their exposure to a long night with a short period of light—especially of red wavelengths. The plants now behave as if they were exposed to short nights (long days) and continue to grow taller (Figure 19.16).

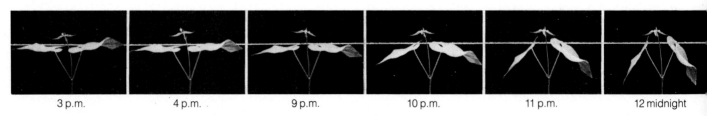

3 p.m.   4 p.m.   9 p.m.   10 p.m.   11 p.m.   12 midnight

Figure 19.18 Leaf movements in bean plants.

Phytochrome (Pr) is involved in this response. In this case, conversion of Pr to Pfr by red light during the night prevents dormancy. It may be that buds go dormant because less Pfr can form during the decreasing daylengths of late summer. It may also be that in the absence of Pfr, leaves synthesize a dormancy-triggering hormone (perhaps abscisic acid) that is transported to buds.

If short days and long nights increase bud dormancy in trees, what breaks dormancy in spring? After all, spring temperatures and daylengths are similar to those prevailing when buds became dormant the previous fall! Between fall and spring, though, a major *dormancy-breaking mechanism* is at work. This mechanism is exposure to low temperature for hundreds of hours (Figure 19.17). The actual temperature and exposure time varies among species. For instance, Delicious apples grown in Utah require 1,230 hours near 43°F (6°C); apricots grown there require only 720 hours. Generally, tree varieties growing in the southern United States require less cold exposure than those growing in northern states and Canada. So if you live, say, in Colorado and order a young peach tree from a Georgia nursery, the tree might start spring growth too soon and be killed by a late frost or heavy snow.

Both gibberellin and abscisic acid may help control dormancy. When gibberellins are applied to dormant buds, dormancy is often broken. Abscisic acid extends dormancy and partially counteracts the effects of gibberellins. These and other results suggest that the following may be true: *Abscisic acid movement from leaves to buds in late summer may trigger dormancy, and abscisic acid breakdown along with gibberellin accumulation in buds in late autumn and winter may end dormancy.*

Seeds of most native species also exhibit dormancy, which suggests that dormancy may have survival value. (In contrast, dormancy is rare in seeds of highly selected agricultural crops.) The mechanisms by which seed dormancy develops and ends are variable. In some species such as honey locust and alfalfa, hard seed coats are formed.

These coats prevent absorption of water and oxygen. Dormancy ends when the seed coat is abraded (perhaps as strong winds and rains drive the seed across sand), when it is chemically digested (by bacteria, by fungi, or in the gut of a bird or mammal), perhaps even when fire burns it away.

For species such as lilacs, apples, peaches, plums, and cherries, moistened seeds must be exposed to low temperatures for weeks or months before dormancy ends. Such seeds are shed from the plant in autumn. Built-in controls prevent their germination before spring; without these controls, the seedlings would be killed by frost. In many of these species, gibberellins are known to break dormancy, and abscisic acid is known to prolong it.

Finally, many seed types depend on red wavelengths to end dormancy. As you might suspect, phytochrome once again is the essential pigment involved in light detection, and Pfr is the active form. Only in the past few decades have we learned about the importance of phytochrome in germination and so many other still-puzzling responses.

BIOLOGICAL CLOCKS IN PLANTS

Plant growth and development—indeed, nearly all activities of plants—are influenced by **biological clocks** that lie somewhere within their cells. Such clocks are time-measuring devices that allow all eukaryotes to anticipate and adjust to environmental changes. For example, the ability of cockleburs to measure the length of night helps assure reproductive success. Cockleburs flower and set seeds only in late summer, when nights become shorter. Late flowering means that seeds will remain dormant in winter and germinate under favorable spring conditions.

Leaves of many species, especially those in the legume family, display their leaves horizontally during daylight and more vertically at night (Figure 19.18). The remarkable

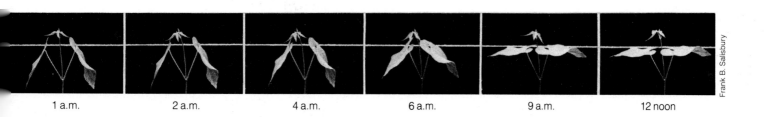

1 a.m.   2 a.m.   4 a.m.   6 a.m.   9 a.m.   12 noon

Frank B. Salisbury

thing about these movements is that they continue for a few days even in constant light or constant darkness. Thus, a plant kept in constant light and constant temperature folds its leaves into the sleep position in the evening hours to which it has been conditioned, even though no night will follow. It anticipates that night is coming! Clearly, the plant must have a mechanism of measuring time that is somewhat independent of light-on (sunrise) and light-off (sunset) signals. Rhythms that continue for a while in an apparently constant environment are said to be **endogenous** (controlled from within) rather than exogenous (controlled externally). Those rhythms that occur daily are called **circadian** (from the Latin *circa,* meaning about; and *dies,* meaning day). Although sleep movements are among the best-studied rhythms that verify the existence of a biological clock, we are still uncertain as to their ecological advantage. One idea is that the sleep position prevents bright moonlight from being absorbed by phytochrome in the leaves. Moonlight could otherwise interrupt a dark period necessary for induction of flowering. Another idea is that the sleep position is important to slow heat loss from leaves, because such leaves radiate heat to each other rather than to a cold sky.

Case Study: From Embryogenesis to the Mature Oak

Where the ocean breaks along the central California coast, the land rolls inward as steep and rounded hills. Sixty-five million years ago, these sandstone hills had their genesis on the floor of the Pacific. At that time, violent movements in the earth's crust caused parts of the submerged continental shelf to begin crumpling upward into a jagged new coastal range. Since then, the rain and winds of countless winters have played across the crumpled land, softening the stark contours and sending mineral-laden sediments down into the canyons. Grasses have come to cloak the inland hills, and their organic remains have accumulated and gradually enriched the soil. On these hillsides, in these canyons, the coast live oak—*Quercus agrifolia*—began to evolve more than ten million years ago.

Quercus agrifolia is a long-lived giant. Some trees reach heights of a hundred feet; their evergreen branches may spread wider than that. Some individuals are known to be three hundred years old. In this species, male and female flowers appear on the same tree. In early spring, when the reproductive cycle commences, microspores in the anthers of male flowers develop into pollen grains. The pollen-

bearing flowers, clustered together as golden catkins, droop pendulously from the leafy branches. Inconspicuous female flowers also appear among the leaves in small clusters near branch tips. Wind carries pollen from the catkins to receptive parts (stigmas) of female flowers on the same or neighboring trees. From each pollen grain, a sperm-bearing pollen tube emerges and elongates through the style, toward the ovary where the eggs reside. Eventually the pollen tube reaches an ovule in the ovary. There, fusion of a sperm nucleus with an egg nucleus leads to formation of a diploid zygote. As the zygote begins dividing, polarization of its cytoplasmic substances leads to differences in the rate and direction of division. Cells divide again and again, giving rise to root and shoot apices, and to large cotyledons that represent most of the embryo. At the same time, integuments of the ovule form the seed coat, and ovary walls develop into a shell. By early fall, the seed reaches maturity and is shed from the tree as a hard-shelled acorn.

Three centuries ago, long before Gaspar de Portóla sent landing parties ashore to found colonies throughout Upper California, the oaks were shedding the seeds of a new generation. Suppose it was then that a scrubjay, foraging at the foot of a hillside, came across a worm-free acorn. In storing away food for leaner days, that bird used its beak to scrape a small crater in a moist spot, dropped in the acorn, and scraped back just enough soil to cover the prize. Although a scrubjay might remember many such hiding places most of the time, this particular acorn lay forgotten. Within a few days, it germinated.

From the moment of germination, the oak seed embarked on a journey of dynamic, continued growth. At one end of the embryo, the root apical meristem gave rise to cells whose divisions created the primary root. At the other end, the shoot apical meristem gave rise to cells that would create the primary shoot. These meristem-derived cells divided repeatedly. And they enlarged. They grew longer; they increased in diameter. Water pressure drove the enlargement—water taken up osmotically as ions accumulated in the newly forming roots, and as hormones caused a softening of cell walls that otherwise would have been too strong to allow expansion under pressure. Differentiation produced the root cap that would protect the primary root as growth forced it down through the soil. Differentiation produced cortex and epidermis, as well as a vascular cylinder through which water and ions would flow. From the pericycle (ground tissue just inside the root's endodermis), lateral roots arose under the influence of growth regulators. As these new roots continued to elongate, the plant's absorptive surfaces increased. Even before the shoot developed, the primary root

Figure 19.19 From germination to the mature oak (*Quercus agrifolia*).

had already pushed down considerable distances through the soil. When the primary shoot did begin its upward surge, separate vascular bundles appeared first near the shoot periphery. Later, activity of the vascular cambium would consolidate these into a continuous cylinder of secondary xylem and phloem.

In parenchyma cells of the developing roots, stems, and leaves, large central vacuoles formed. Vacuole enlargement caused the cytoplasm to be pressed outward as a thin zone against the cell wall. In this way, cytoplasmic contact with the environment was enhanced; essential ions, gases, and water were harvested rapidly in spite of their relatively dilute concentrations in the surrounding air and soil. Mycorrhizae—fungal strands symbiotically interlocked with the roots—enhanced the absorption process. In leaves, stomates developed and regulated carbon dioxide movement into each leaf's interior.

As the seedling grew, the xylem pipelines came to form a system that provided functional links among all parts of the plant body. In dead tracheid and vessel elements, thick secondary walls did not collapse under the highly negative water pressure within them. Through xylem, water and minerals moved from roots to stems and leaves. The living phloem cells—sieve tube elements—had no lignified secondary walls. Their primary walls were strong enough to prevent cells from bursting under the strong positive pressures within them. Through the phloem, carbohydrates—sucrose especially—moved upward and downward from leaves to regions where food was being used or stored. Through phloem, various amino acids, amides, and essential elements were redistributed from one part of the oak to another.

At the whim of a scrubjay, the seed actually had sprouted in a well-drained, sandy basin at the foot of several steep hills, in full sunlight. Rainwater accumulated there each fall and winter, and kept the soil moist enough to encourage luxuriant growth during the spring and even through the dry summers. Out in the open, abundant red wavelengths of sunlight activated phytochrome pigments in the seedling. So stimulated, the phytochrome triggered hormonal events that encouraged stem branching and leaf expansion. All the while, delicate hormone-mediated responses were being made to the winds, the sun, the tug of gravity, the changing seasons. Lignin and cellulose strengthened secondary cell walls in secondary xylem and phloem. With this strengthening came resistance to the strong winds racing through the canyon. As the oak matured, phytochrome detected the subtle shifts in daylength throughout the year, which helped the plant respond to changing seasons. The shorter days of late summer promoted bud dormancy, hence resistance to winter cold.

As the oak seedling matured into the adult plant form, more and more roots developed and snaked through a tremendous volume of the moist soil. Branch after branch spread out beneath the sun. Leaves proliferated—leaves where the oak put together its own food from water, carbon dioxide, the few simple inorganic substances it mined from the soil, and the sunlight energy it harnessed to drive the synthesis reactions. Continued activity of vascular cambia increased the girth of roots and branches; with each new spring, terminal and lateral meristems increased the tree's height and diameter. Thus the oak increased in size every season, year after year, century after century. On their way to the gold fields, prospectors of the California Gold Rush rested in the shade cast by its immense canopy. The great earthquake of 1906 scarcely disturbed the giant, anchored as it was by a root system that spread out eighty feet in diameter through the soil. By chance, the brush fires that periodically sweep through California's coastal canyons did not seriously damage this particular tree. Fungi that could have rotted its roots never took hold; the soil was too well-drained and the water table too deep. Leaf-chewing insects were kept in check not only by protective chemicals in the leaves but also by the bird predators abounding in the lush growth of the canyon.

During the 1960s, human population underwent a tremendous upward surge in California. The land outside the cities began to show the effects of population overflow as the wild hills gave way to suburban housing. The developer who turned the tractors on the canyon in which the giant oak had grown was impressed enough with its beauty that the tree was not felled. Death came later. How could the new homeowners, newly arrived from the east, know of the ancient, delicate relationships between the giant trees and the land that sustained them? Soil was graded between the trunk and the drip line of the overhanging canopy; flower beds were mounded against the trunk; lawns were planted beneath the branches and sprinklers installed. Overwatering in summer created standing water next to the great trunk—and the oak root fungus (Armillaria) that had been so successfully resisted until then became established. With its roots rotting away, the oak began to suffer the effects of massive disruption to the feedback relationships among its roots, stems, and leaves. Eventually it had to be cut down. In their fifth winter, in their red brick fireplace, the homeowners began burning three centuries of firewood.

Readings

Leopold, A., and P. Kriedemann. 1975. *Plant Growth and Development.* New York: McGraw-Hill.

Mayer, A., and A. Poljakoff-Mayber. 1975. *The Germination of Seeds.* Second edition. New York: Pergamon Press. A simple treatment of seed biology, and effects of light and other environmental factors on seed germination.

Nickell, L. 1982. *Plant Growth Regulators: Agricultural Uses.* New York: Springer-Verlag. Concise explanations of agricultural practices that include use of growth regulators.

Salisbury, F., and C. Ross. 1978. *Plant Physiology.* Belmont, California: Wadsworth. Chapter 20 explains in detail selected examples of time measurement and what we know and don't know about the nature of the biological clock.

Sweeney, B. 1969. *Rhythmic Phenomena in Plants.* New York: Academic Press. A concise book that clearly illustrates several plant rhythms matching periodicities of day and night, month, and season.

Villiers, T. 1975. *Dormancy and the Survival of Plants.* London: Edward Arnold. A short book summarizing major dormancy mechanisms.

Vince-Prue, D. 1975. *Photoperiodism in Plants.* New York: McGraw-Hill. Excellent discussion of daylength effects on plant growth and development.

Review Questions

1. List the five known plant hormones (or groups of hormones) and the main functions of each.

2. Which of the following plant cells or organs synthesize most or all of the hormones required in normal growth and development: coleoptiles, dicot stems, root cells, and leaf cells. Describe one experiment that tells us which ones do this, or which ones don't.

3. Explain how sunlight exposure influences leaf expansion, stem elongation, and stem branching during primary growth.

4. What is phytochrome, and what is its role in plant growth?

5. Define plant tropism. How is unequal growth in different parts of the same organ associated with phototropism and thigmotropism?

6. Why are plants grown outdoors often shorter, thicker, and more wind-resistant than plants of the same species grown indoors?

7. Define annual, biennial, and perennial plants. Then describe the difference between long-day, short-day, and day-neutral plants.

8. Which factors apparently trigger dormancy, and which factors may help break dormancy?

UNIT FIVE

ANIMAL SYSTEMS AND THEIR CONTROL

20

SYSTEMS OF CELLS AND HOMEOSTASIS

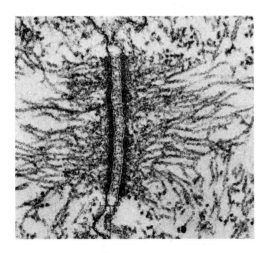

Figure 20.1 What sorts of structures hold animal cells together in tissues? One example: an adhering junction between two cells from the skin of a newt, 22,000×. (Wolfe, *Biology of the Cell*, 1981)

SOME CHARACTERISTICS OF ANIMAL CELLS AND TISSUES

Beneath the surface of the world's oceans and seas are animals called sponges. These animals are attached to rocks and coral outcroppings, and they feed on microorganisms floating past. In body plan, sponges are like vases with holes in the sides. Food-laden water flows into the holes, then out through the opening at the top. Although multicelled, the sponge body is only a loose aggregation of cells in a gelatin-like ground substance. Some of the cells of the interior body wall surface have sticky collars, which collect food. Inside the ground substance, amoebalike cells transport some of the collected food to other cell types that make up the body wall. The sponge mode of reproduction is not what you would call well developed; the amoebalike cells serve as the reproductive cells as well as food caterers. Not much else happens in sponges. In fact, if we define a **tissue** as a group of cells of a particular type (or types) that are united in form and function, then the sponge body is only a rudimentary tissue, at best.

In the 1960s, the developmental biologists Tom Humphreys and Aron Moscona thought they might learn something about animal tissues in general by experimenting with the rudimentary tissues of sponges. They forced sponges of two different species through a fine sieve. All that remained of the sponge bodies were isolated cells and tiny clumps of cells. The remains were mixed together in a medium that contained nutrients and ions. Cells proceeded to move about and bump into one another. And they began *adhering* to one another. Their reunion was not random. Collared cells began adhering in patterns characteristic of the intact sponge body. Equally intriguing, the mixed-together cells sorted themselves out according to their species! Such experiments provided the first verification of the following fact:

Individual cells in animal tissues have properties that promote molecular recognition between similar cells and their adhesion to one another.

In complex animals, body tissues are said to be composed of **somatic cells**. ("Somatic" comes from the Greek *soma*, meaning body.) The only other animal cells are **germ cells**, which develop into gametes. Fusion of two gametes leads to formation of a single-celled zygote, which divides mitotically to form the developmental stage called the animal **embryo**.

Soon after an embryo embarks on its course of development, cells become aggregated into primordial tissue layers, which differentiate into all the specialized tissues that make up the animal body. For instance, in humans and other vertebrate embryos, three embryonic tissue layers form:

1. **Ectoderm** gives rise to tissues of the outer layer of skin and the nervous system.

2. **Mesoderm** gives rise to tissues of muscles, the skeleton, and the circulatory system, the inner layer of skin, the kidney, and the reproductive tract.

3. **Endoderm** gives rise to tissues lining the gut and to tissues of digestive glands.

Through biochemical and electron micrograph studies, we now know that surface receptors of the plasma membrane promote cell aggregations into such tissues. Once the cells become clustered together, one or more kinds of junctions form between them. These cell-to-cell junctions serve the following functions:

1. *Tight junctions* bar the free passage of molecules across the tissue layer.

2. *Adhering junctions* hold adjacent cells in place and permit them to function collectively as a structural unit.

3. *Gap junctions* are open channels for rapid communication between cells.

Tight junctions occur in epithelial tissues (which cover the external and internal body parts of most animals). Adhering junctions are found between cells of all tissues, and between cells of different but adjacent tissues. Gap junctions are the routes by which signals, nutrients, or both are rapidly exchanged in a coordinated way. Gap junctions are known to occur between nerve cells; they are profuse in muscle, and in liver, mammary, and salivary gland tissues. Figures 20.1 and 20.2 give examples of some cell-to-cell junctions.

During the development of all animals other than sponges, tissues become arranged into organs. An **organ** is a structure of definite form and function that is composed of two or more different tissues. Organs take on their indi-

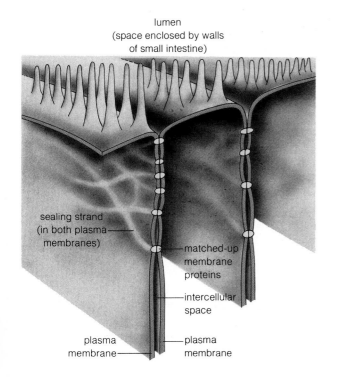

lumen
(space enclosed by walls
of small intestine)

sealing strand
(in both plasma
membranes)

matched-up
membrane
proteins

intercellular
space

plasma
membrane

plasma
membrane

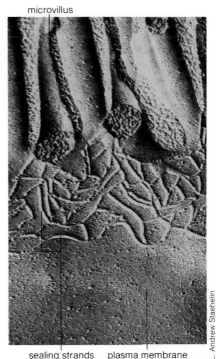

microvillus

sealing strands   plasma membrane

L. Andrew Staehelin

Figure 20.2 How epithelial cells are stitched together at tight junctions. Rows of membrane proteins match up and form sealing strands between such cells in the small intestine. The criss-crossed strands form a barrier between all adjacent cells in the epithelial tissue. To be absorbed into the body, nutrients traveling through the digestive tract must pass through the cells themselves. The electron micrograph shows a tight junction near the base of microvilli (which extend into the intestinal lumen).

Table 20.1   Classification of Some Covering and Lining Epithelium

Category	Structural Features	Main Functions	Some Common Locations
Simple epithelium:			
Squamous	Single sheet of large cells shaped like flat floor tiles	Filtration of substances found in body fluids	Lines heart, blood vessels; forms one-layer-thick capillaries and air sacs in lungs; lines body cavities; covers many organ surfaces (such as air sacs in lungs, kidney regions)
Cuboidal	Single sheet of cube-shaped cells	Secretion and absorption	Covers eye regions, kidney regions, ovary surfaces, many ducts
Columnar	Single sheet of column-shaped cells; some with microvilli or cilia on surfaces exposed to fluids	Secretion and absorption; ciliated forms move mucus and other fluids	Lines stomach, intestines, gall bladder, digestive glands; ciliated forms line parts of respiratory system and, in females, oviducts
Stratified epithelium:			
Squamous	Several cell layers; surface cells shaped like flat floor tiles, deeper layers have cube- and column-shaped cells	Protection	Lines mouth, esophagus, vagina; the outer layers of skin
Cuboidal	Two layers (or more) of cube-shaped cells	Protection	Sweat gland ducts
Columnar	Several layers of many-sided cells, with column-shaped cells at surface layer only	Secretion and protection	Lines some large ducts

vidual character from the kinds of differentiated tissues present, and from the way they are combined and arranged. For instance, organs that show considerable movement in different directions (such as the stomach) typically contain layers of muscle tissues, oriented at different angles. Delicate organs such as capillaries are typically cushioned by connective tissue, which also helps hold them in place.

At the most complex level of structural organization, organs are components of organ systems. An **organ system** has two or more organs that are interrelated physically, chemically, or both and serve some common function. For example, the human digestive system includes organs called the mouth, salivary glands, pharynx, esophagus, stomach, liver, gall bladder, pancreas, small intestine, large intestine, rectum, and anus. All are necessary for a common task: the ingestion and preparation of food for absorption by individual cells, as well as elimination of the food residues.

In chapters to follow, we will consider the structure and function of organs and organ systems. In anticipation of those discussions, let's look first at the tissues that compose them and give them their unique properties.

KINDS OF ANIMAL TISSUES

Somatic cells become differentiated into the components of four main types of animal tissues. The four are called epithelial, connective, muscular, and nervous tissue.

Epithelial Tissues

Epithelial tissues (or, more simply, *epithelia*) play many roles, ranging from protection to absorption and secretion. This type of tissue covers external body surfaces, body cavities, and some internal organs. It also forms the secretory portion of glands.

All epithelial tissues are continuous sheets of densely packed cells, with little space or intercellular material at the tight junctions between them. The greater the number of tight junctions, the less freely permeable the tissue. Also, the more interconnected they are, the more the tissue can resist tearing in response to stress associated with expansion and stretching movements. This is important, because all epithelia are subjected to wear and tear daily.

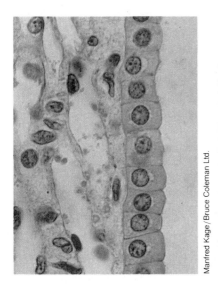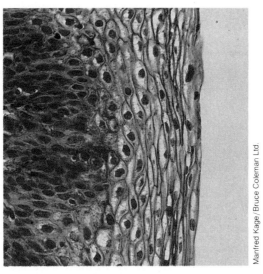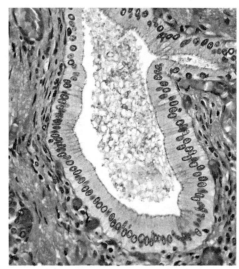

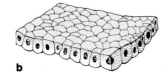

Figure 20.3   Basic cell shapes in epithelial tissues: (**a**) squamous, (**b**) cuboidal, and (**c**) columnar.

In structural terms, epithelia can be classified by number of layers and by the predominant shape of cells in those layers. *Simple epithelium* consists of a single sheet of cells. *Stratified epithelium* consists of cells stacked into several layers. Both kinds of tissues can contain cells shaped like flat floor tiles (squamous epithelium), cubes (cuboidal epithelium), or columns (columnar epithelium). These three cell shapes are illustrated in Figure 20.3. The main varieties of simple and stratified epithelium are summarized in Table 20.1, along with some of their locations and specialized functions.

In functional terms, epithelium serves either as a covering tissue or as a glandular tissue. Single-layered epithelium that covers body and organ surfaces functions in filtration. It is thin enough to facilitate passage of substances across the tissue. For instance, carbon dioxide and oxygen move readily across single-layered epithelium in the air sacs of the lungs. Fluid from the blood readily filters across single-layered epithelium lining certain kidney regions. Epithelial coverings that are multilayered (stratified) provide protection to underlying tissues. The uppermost portion of skin is an example of a stratified epithelial covering.

Epithelial coverings are considered to be glandular epithelium when they contain the single-celled or multicelled secretory structures called *glands*. There are two kinds of glands: endocrine and exocrine. Generally, an **endocrine gland** secretes hormones directly into the bloodstream. (Hormones can be defined as endocrine cell products that travel the bloodstream and trigger specific cellular reactions in tissues and organs some distance away.) In contrast, an **exocrine gland** secretes its products through ducts that empty at an epithelial surface. Exocrine cell products include mucus, saliva, wax, oil, milk, and digestive enzymes.

Single-celled exocrine glands occur in some of the epithelial coverings of the digestive, urinary, and reproductive systems. An example is the *goblet cell,* which secretes mucus that lubricates the tissue surface. Multicelled exocrine glands can be shaped like simple tubes or flasks. (See, for example, Figure 20.4.) Some have an unbranching duct and others have a branched duct above the secretory portion.

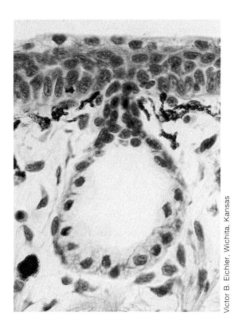

Figure 20.4 An example of an exocrine gland, shown in longitudinal section. 110×.

Victor B. Eichler, Wichita, Kansas

Connective Tissues

Connective tissues are the most widely distributed of all systems of cells. Some of these tissues provide support for soft, flexible body parts. Others bind different structures together. Often, connective tissues are classified as four groups: connective tissue proper, cartilage, bone, and blood. Table 20.2 summarizes the characteristics of these groups.

Connective Tissue Proper. Unlike epithelium, **connective tissue proper** has a more or less fluid intercellular substance (called the ground substance) in which several kinds of cells are embedded. The predominant cell type is the fibroblast, which gives rise to protein fibers and the intercellular substance.

In *loose connective tissue*, the ground substance contains a weblike scattering of thin, strong, flexible protein fibers (collagen) and some highly elastic protein fibers (elastin). An example of this tissue is shown in Figure 20.5a. Loose connective tissue is like packing material. It supports and holds in place blood vessels, nerves, and internal organs even while according them some freedom of movement. It

Table 20.2 Classification of the Main Types of Connective Tissue			
Category	Structural Features	Main Functions	Some Common Locations
Connective tissue proper			
Loose connective tissue	Semifluid ground substance; scattered cells and protein fibers (of collagen, elastin)	Support, elasticity	Layer beneath skin; pads blood vessels, nerves, other organs
Dense connective tissue	Parallel bundles of collagen fibers; fibroblasts in rows between bundles	Flexible, strong connections between structures; encapsulates some organs	Tendons, ligaments; around muscles; capsules around heart, kidney, liver
Adipose tissue	Dense clusters of large cells (each with one fat storage vacuole)	Energy reserve, insulation, support and protection of some organs	Under skin; padding in different body regions
Cartilage	Large fibers in rubbery ground substance secreted by cartilage cells	Firm, flexible support; shape maintenance; shock absorption	Nose, ear regions; larynx, trachea, intervertebral disks
Bone (osseous) tissue	Collagen fibers; abundant mineral deposits between widely spaced bone cells (osteoblasts, osteoclasts)	Firm support, protection of internal organs; rigidity necessary for leverage in movements	Vertebrate skeleton
Blood	Plasma (fluid portion); red blood cells, white blood cells, platelets	Transports substances to and from body cells; transport medium for infection-fighting proteins and cells; contains buffers that stabilize pH	Heart, blood vessels

also binds muscle cells together and binds skin to underlying tissues.

In *dense connective tissue,* coarser collagen fibers are bundled together in parallel array (Figure 20.5b). Fibroblasts occur in rows between the bundles, and little space is left for intercellular ground substance. This structural organization imparts great strength and some flexibility to the tissue. Dense connective tissue is the main component of tendons (which attach muscle to bone) and ligaments (which hold bones together at skeletal joints). Sheets of this tissue also surround muscles and hold them in place.

In *adipose tissue,* large cells derived from fibroblasts and specialized for fat storage occur in dense clusters. The fat accumulates in a single vacuole in each cell. Adipose tissue is an energy reserve region. It also pads some organs, and it insulates the body against rapid loss of heat generated by metabolism.

Cartilage. The connective tissue called **cartilage** cushions body parts and provides a framework for maintaining the shape of body regions. In this tissue, living cartilage cells are clustered in small chambers within a rubbery ground substance that the cells themselves secrete. Cartilage occurs on the ends of bones in many joints and in parts of the nose. It serves as a framework for the tip of the nose and the external ear. One kind of cartilage forms shock pads (such as intervertebral disks of the backbone). Embryonic skeletons are cartilage and are replaced with bone tissue during development.

Bone (Osseous) Tissue. Almost all vertebrates have a skeleton that is composed of a connective tissue called **bone.** Together with muscles, limb bones form a leverlike system that provides a means for mechanical movement of the body. Some bone tissue forms flat plates and other structures that support and protect softer tissues, including those of the brain, spinal cord, and lungs. Bone is also a production site for blood cells, and a storage site for minerals. Calcium phosphate and calcium carbonate deposits make up sixty-seven percent of the weight of mammalian bones; collagen fibers make up most of the remainder.

There are two kinds of tissues in bone: spongy and compact. **Spongy bone tissue** is latticelike rather than dense. In the spongy bone tissue found in the ends of long bones, the spaces are filled with red marrow. *Red marrow* is a major region of blood cell formation. The interior cavity of long

Chuck Brown

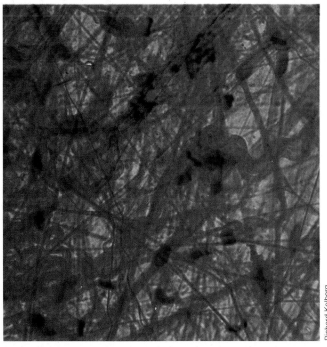

Richard Kolberg

Figure 20.5 Examples of connective tissue. (**a**) Scanning electron micrograph of dense connective tissue in ligaments. Parallel, tightly packed collagen fibers give rise to this structural organization. (**b**) Light micrograph of loose connective tissue, showing the weblike scattering of cells and fibers in the semifluid ground substance.

a   b

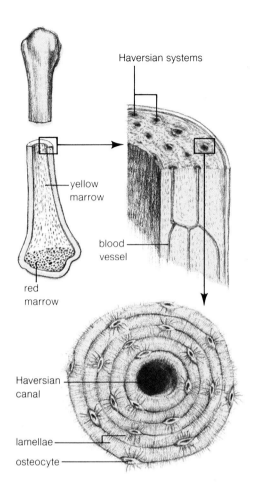

Haversian systems

yellow marrow

blood vessel

red marrow

Haversian canal

lamellae

osteocyte

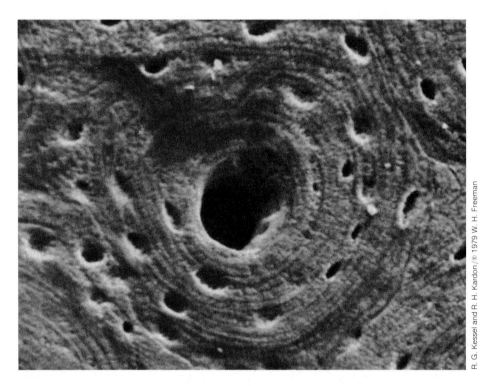

R. G. Kessel and R. H. Kardon / © 1979 W. H. Freeman

Figure 20.6 Scanning electron micrograph of a Haversian system in compact bone. The sketches show a long bone of a mammal with its distinct marrow regions and organized Haversian systems through which living bone cells receive nourishment and integrative signals (from hormones) by way of blood vessels.

bones sometimes contains spongy tissue and is filled with yellow marrow. *Yellow marrow* is a reserve tissue. Whenever blood is lost, as it can be during bodily injury, this tissue assists the red marrow in producing red blood cell replacements.

Compact bone tissue occurs as a dense layer over spongy bone tissue. Compact bone functions in support and protection and helps long bones withstand mechanical stress. In long bones, mineral deposits form thin, concentric layers (lamellae). The lamellae are laid down around small channels called Haversian canals. The channels are interconnected and run more or less parallel to the bone (Figure 20.6). Haversian canals contain blood vessels (which service living bone cells) and nerve cells (which regulate blood vessel function).

New bone formation (or ossification) is the task of bone cells called *osteoblasts.* In the developing embryo, they use the cartilage skeleton as a template for future bone. Osteo-

blasts secrete collagen fibers that form a framework for mineral deposits. The intercellular deposits become so abundant that the osteoblasts become widely separated. Gradually, some become imprisoned in their own secretions and lose their bone-forming ability. Once this function is lost, the mature, still-living cells are known as *osteocytes.* As cartilage cells degenerate during bone formation, the cavities they once occupied become invaded by blood vessels. The blood vessels nourish the imprisoned bone cells and carry away their metabolic wastes.

During the life cycle of many animals, bone size and shape undergo change. For example, such changes are necessary for your own growth and development. Bone remodeling as well as bone maintenance requires that calcium deposition be balanced with calcium removal. *Osteoclasts* are bone cells whose hydrolytic enzymes can break down the calcium deposits in bone tissue. Their action is balanced by the bone-forming action of the osteoblasts. During remodeling, their joint action removes old bone and provides replacements. Their joint action also allows bone to serve as the body's calcium reserve. Calcium, recall, is vital in many cellular activities, including muscle contraction, nerve function, and blood clotting. Bone calcium is distributed through the body by way of the bloodstream when there is insufficient calcium in the diet; and it carries dietary calcium to the bone when bone mass begins to dwindle.

Blood. Some of the properties of blood are summarized in Table 20.2. Understanding the nature of this tissue and its diverse functions depends on prior understanding of the organ system of which it is part. For that reason, details of blood and the vascular tissue in which it is typically contained are postponed until Chapter Twenty-Four.

Nerve Tissues

The plasma membranes of all cells are alike in a critical respect: they work at maintaining polarity of charge between the cytoplasm and the extracellular environment. A detected energy change (stimulus) can disrupt this polarity and cause a chemical or physical response. In all living things, such disruptions are the basis of *membrane excitability*, which in turn is the basis of the cell's ability to receive and respond to signals about environmental change.

Nerve tissue contains cells that specialize in keeping the multicelled body informed of environmental change and in helping control body responses to those changes. **Neurons**, or individual nerve cells, are organized in functional pathways that extend throughout the body. Their organization is such that the neuron receives and initiates signals in response to specific kinds of change, and conducts messages to other neurons, muscles, or glands. We will be taking a closer look at the neuron in the next chapter.

Muscle Tissues

Muscle tissue serves three functions: movement, heat production (which helps maintain body temperature), and maintenance of posture. Like nerve cells, muscle cells display excitability. Unlike nerve cells, they also display an ability to contract in response to stimulation. Tissues containing these cells can actively shorten and passively lengthen. They can be stretched, then return to their original shape.

There are three kinds of muscle tissues: smooth, skeletal, and cardiac. All are highly contractile. Both skeletal

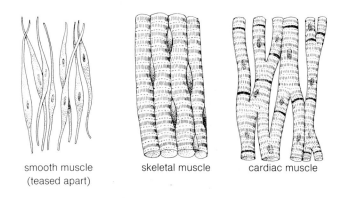

smooth muscle (teased apart)   skeletal muscle   cardiac muscle

Figure 20.7 Three kinds of muscle tissue.

and cardiac muscle tissue are *striated* (striped), with alternating light and dark bands (Figure 20.7).

Smooth muscle tissue is composed of spindle-shaped cells, each with a single nucleus. Dense connective tissue holds these cells together in layers. Smooth muscle tissue occurs in the walls of hollow internal structures, such as ducts, blood vessels, the stomach, and the intestines. In vertebrates, smooth muscle is said to be *involuntary*, because its contraction usually is not under conscious control.

Skeletal muscle tissue generally attaches by tendons to the vertebrate skeleton. This tissue is responsible for voluntarily controlled movements that can be both rapid and intermittent. Skeletal muscle tissue contains many long, cylindrical cells called *muscle fibers*. Some of the muscle fibers in your body are up to thirty centimeters (twelve inches) long. Typically, a number of skeletal muscle cells are enveloped in connective tissue; together they form a muscle bundle. Several bundles are usually enclosed in a tougher connective tissue sheath and form the functional contractile units called individual muscles. We will be returning to the structure and functioning of skeletal muscle tissue in Chapter Twenty-Three.

The contractile tissue of vertebrate hearts is called **cardiac muscle tissue**. Cardiac muscle cells are branched and are considerably shorter than most skeletal muscle cells. Also, membranes of adjacent cardiac muscle cells are fused, end to end, at regions called intercalated disks. Because of these fusion points, the cells do not function on an independent basis. Rather, when one receives a signal to contract, its neighbors are excited and also contract in a manner to be described in Chapter Twenty-Four.

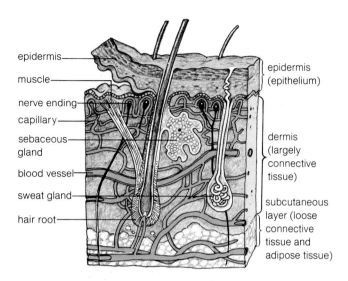

epidermis
muscle
nerve ending
capillary
sebaceous gland
blood vessel
sweat gland
hair root

epidermis (epithelium)

dermis (largely connective tissue)

subcutaneous layer (loose connective tissue and adipose tissue)

Figure 20.8 A section through vertebrate skin and the underlying (subcutaneous) layer. Skin is a two-layered organ, with a thin outer portion (the epidermis) and a thicker, underlying portion (the dermis). (J. Creager, *Human Anatomy and Physiology*, Wadsworth, 1982)

OVERVIEW OF ORGAN SYSTEMS AND THEIR FUNCTION

Having reviewed the basic types of animal tissues, we can begin thinking about how different tissues are combined in organs, then in systems of organs. Let's consider the two-layered organ called **skin**, which is the outer body covering of all vertebrates. Figure 20.8 is an example of a section through this kind of organ.

Vertebrate skin offers resistance to mechanical injury. It prevents loss of internal fluids. It also acts as a line of defense against microorganisms and other foreign particles. Some of its components play roles in the regulation of body temperature. Others sense changes in environmental temperature and pressure.

The outer skin layer is **epidermis**. In humans and other land vertebrates, the outermost epithelial tissues of this layer consist of flattened, dead, and dried-out squamous cells. Keratin is a fibrous protein component of these cells. It is highly resistant to mechanical injury and chemical

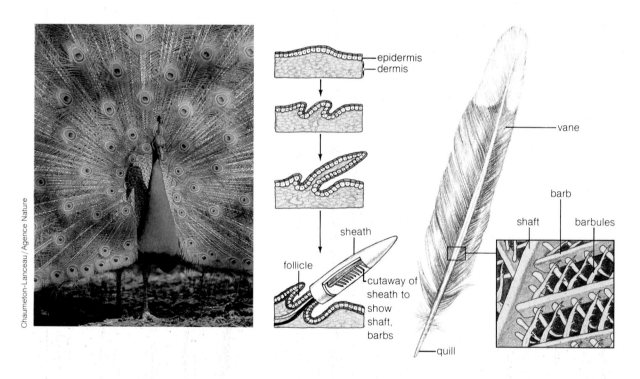

epidermis
dermis

vane

barb

shaft

barbules

sheath

follicle

cutaway of sheath to show shaft, barbs

quill

Figure 20.9 Differentiation of a region of epidermal tissue into the organ we call a feather. The photograph shows a courtship display of a peacock, which relies on spectacularly specialized feathers to capture the attention of a peahen. (Sketches after T. Storer et al., *General Zoology*, sixth edition, 1979, McGraw-Hill)

Chaumeton-Lanceau / Agence Nature

breakdown and is one of the reasons why skin provides such good protection against environmental stress. Keratin is also regionally concentrated in hair and fingernails, feathers and scales, beaks and claws. All of these structures arise from differentiated epidermal cells. (Figure 20.9 is an example of this type of cell differentiation.) Deeper epithelial tissues of the epidermis are sites of active mitotic divisions that push replacement cells to the surface. The replacement process goes on all the time (although we usually do not notice it except during the accelerated activity associated with dandruff or sunburned skin).

Beneath the epidermis but tightly connected to it is the **dermis**, a dense layer composed mostly of connective tissue. Sweat glands and sebaceous (oil) glands are located in this tissue. There may be cylindrical epithelial regions called follicles embedded in the connective tissue and extending to the epidermal surface. Follicles are narrow evaginations in which hair or feathers grow. Muscle, nerve, and vascular tissue penetrate the dermis. Here, too, sensory neurons receive information about touch, temperature, and pain.

Connective tissue fibers that originate in the dermis anchor skin to the subcutaneous layer, which is composed of loose connective tissue and adipose tissue. The subcutaneous layer is not part of skin; it is the tissue by which skin is firmly connected to underlying tissues and organs.

Skin, in short, is a specialized organ composed of a combination of several different tissues. Nails, hair, glands, claws, feathers, and parts of sensory receptors are examples of specialized organs derived from different tissues of the skin. Together, skin, its derivatives, and the underlying subcutaneous layers constitute an organ system that is called an **integumentary system**.

In this unit of the book, we will look at the major organ systems of animals and at how those systems work together in keeping the animal alive in specific environments. The organ systems are more or less integrated in the representative animal sketched in Figure 20.10. Some assortment of these systems occurs in animals of almost all major phyla. These are their main functions:

Body covering or integumentary system Protection from the external environment, protection from loss of internal fluids, body temperature regulation, elimination of some wastes, reception of external stimuli

Nervous system Together with endocrine glands or system, integration of body functioning, detection of stimuli from the environment, control over responses to stimuli

Endocrine glands or system Internal chemical control; together with the nervous system, integration of body functions

Skeletal system Support and protection of some body parts, determination of some body shapes; in many animals, muscle attachment sites, blood cell production sites, calcium and phosphorus storage sites

Muscular system Movement of internal body parts, movement of whole body through environment, maintenance of posture, heat production

Circulatory system Internal transport of materials to and from cells, pH and temperature stabilization

Defense system Protection against foreign substances and agents, such as those causing infection

Respiratory system Supplying body cells with oxygen, removal of carbon dioxide wastes produced by them, pH regulation

Digestive system Ingestion and preparation of food molecules for absorption, elimination of residues of digestion

Reproductive system Production of new individuals

Excretory glands or system Disposal of certain metabolic wastes; regulation of salts and fluids in cellular environment

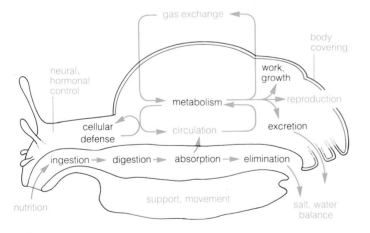

Figure 20.10 Simple portrayal of the basic functions in animals. In some animal groups, some of these functions (such as gas exchange) are accomplished only by individual cells. In the more complex animal groups, organs and organ systems carry out the tasks indicated.

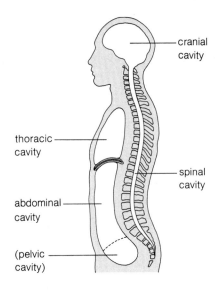

Figure 20.11 Four major body cavities in humans.

Many organs of the systems we have been describing are located in body cavities of one sort or another. For example, the human body has four major cavities, as shown in Figure 20.11. We will have occasion to refer to these regions throughout this unit; they occur in other animals as well.

HOMEOSTASIS AND SYSTEMS CONTROL

The Internal Environment

In the nineteenth century, the physiologist Claude Bernard made an important observation: All body cells interact with **extracellular fluid**, a medium through which substances are continuously exchanged between cells. In vertebrates, extracellular fluid falls into two categories. Most is **interstitial fluid**, which fills spaces between cells and tissues. The remainder is **plasma**, the fluid portion of blood. Vertebrate blood constantly exchanges oxygen, nutrients, and metabolic products with the interstitial fluid, which then exchanges substances with the cells that it bathes.

In vertebrates, most extracellular fluid is interstitial (occupying spaces between cells and tissues). The remainder is blood plasma (which is contained in blood vessels and the heart).

Extracellular fluid is the medium through which substances move from cell to cell, and from one body region to another.

For relatively simple animals such as marine sponges, the extracellular fluid bathing each cell is the sea. For more complex animals, the "sea" has been internalized. In its composition, extracellular fluid resembles seawater, especially in its high concentration of sodium ions. It also resembles seawater in its concentrations of hydrogen, potassium, calcium, and other ions. Indeed, the resemblance was one of the first clues that the early forms of life probably evolved in the ancient seas.

Homeostatic Control Mechanisms

Through his studies of body functioning, Bernard came to realize that ". . . all the vital mechanisms, varied as they are, have only one object, that of preserving . . . the conditions of life in the internal environment." For instance, he discovered that the liver absorbs many of the nutrients carried to it by blood, and converts some of them to complex storage forms, such as glycogen. When nutrient levels fall below a certain point in the blood—hence in extracellular fluid—the liver degrades glycogen. The nutrients so released are distributed through the body and help maintain its cells.

In other studies, Bernard showed that the amount of blood being supplied to different body regions can be regulated by the contraction and relaxation of small blood vessels. Blood carries oxygen and nutrients that sustain all body cells. Through controls over blood distribution, blood can be diverted to body regions whose maintenance and functioning require increased amounts of oxygen and nutrients at any particular moment.

Much later, the physiologist Walter Cannon extended Bernard's line of thinking. Maintaining internal conditions, he said, is possible only through coordinated **homeostatic systems** that operate to keep some physical or chemical aspect of the body within some tolerable range.

In multicelled bodies, homeostatic control systems maintain physical and chemical aspects of the internal environment within some range of tolerance.

Many homeostatic controls are based on feedback mechanisms. The word "feedback" means any circular situation in which information is fed back into a system. The most common are **negative feedback mechanisms**, whereby the initial condition that causes a change is reversed. Examples of negative feedback occur at all levels of biological activity, from biochemical reactions of the sort described in Chapter Five, to ecological disturbances of the biosphere.

How does negative feedback work? By way of analogy, consider how a thermostatically controlled furnace works. A thermostat is a device that senses air temperature and that activates other devices in the furnace control system when temperature changes from a preset point. When the temperature falls below that point, the thermostat detects the change. Then the thermostat signals an integrating device, which turns on the heating unit. When air temperature has been raised to the prescribed level, the thermostat detects the change and signals the integrating device, which shuts off the heating unit. Similar controls are at work in the human body. For example, feedback mechanisms maintain internal body temperature near 37°C (98.6°F) even during extremely hot or cold weather.

Homeostatic feedback in organ system interactions requires three basic components: receptors, integrators, and effectors (Figure 20.12). Sensory cells or tissues act as the **receptors** for some particular stimulus. The stimulus can be changes in light or heat energy, sound wave energy, pressure, or chemical energy. Whatever the form, the energy of the stimulus is translated into electrochemical energy by the body's receptors. This energy form is the signal sent to an **integrator**, a control point where different bits of information are pulled together in the selection of a response. (In some animals, the integrating center is little more than some nerve cells clustered at the head end. In others, the integrating center is a spinal cord and brain.) The integrating center then sends signals to muscles and glands, which are **effectors** in most animals.

In the brain, integrative centers receive information that indicates not only how the system *is* operating (the information from sensory receptors), but also how it *should be* operating (information from a "set point" that is sometimes built into the center itself). The difference between these two bits of information helps determine how the integrating center will respond in increasing or decreasing the activity of effectors in bringing the system back to its operating range.

Under some circumstances, **positive feedback mechanisms** operate. These mechanisms set in motion a chain of events that *intensify* the original input. Positive feedback is associated with instability in a system. For example, sexual

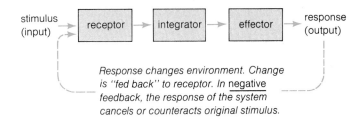

Response changes environment. Change is "fed back" to receptor. In <u>negative</u> feedback, the response of the system cancels or counteracts original stimulus.

Figure 20.12 Components necessary for negative feedback at the organ level.

arousal demands increased stimulation, which demands more stimulation, and so on until an explosive, climax level is reached (Chapter Twenty-Nine). As another example, during childbirth, pressure of the fetus on the uterine walls stimulates production and secretion of the hormone oxytocin. Oxytocin causes muscles in the walls to contract, which increases pressure on the fetus, and so on until expulsion of the fetus from the mother's body.

In addition to negative and positive feedback mechanisms, animals also have **feedforward mechanisms**, which generally are parallel inputs to integrating centers. For example, sensory cells in human skin can detect a drop in air temperature, and send parallel messages to the brain before the blood temperature changes. The brain sends signals to metabolic and muscular systems that can function in raising internal body temperature. With feedforward control, corrective measures can sometimes begin even before a change in the external environment significantly alters the internal environment.

What we have been describing here is a general pattern of monitoring and responding to a constant flow of information about the external and internal environments. During this activity, organ systems operate together in coordinated fashion. Throughout this unit, we will be asking the following questions about organ system functioning:

1. What physical or chemical aspect of the internal environment are organ systems working to maintain as conditions change?

2. By what means are organ systems kept informed of change?

3. By what means do they process incoming information?

4. What mechanisms are deployed in response?

With these questions in mind, we will now turn to the two systems under whose dominion all others must fall—those of neural and endocrine control.

Readings

Barnes, R. 1974. *Invertebrate Zoology.* Third edition. Philadelphia: Saunders. Good descriptions of organs and organ systems in invertebrate groups.

Bloom, W., and D. Fawcett. 1975. *A Textbook of Histology.* Tenth edition. Philadelphia: Saunders. Outstanding reference text.

Greaves, M. 1975. *Cellular Recognition.* New York: Halsted-Wiley. Part of the Outlines in Biology series.

Hickman, C., et al. 1979. *Integrated Principles of Zoology.* Sixth edition. St. Louis: Mosby.

Kessel, R., and R. Kardon. 1979. *Tissues and Organs: A Text-Atlas of Scanning Electron Microscopy.* San Francisco: Freeman. Oustanding, unique micrographs and well-written descriptions of major tissues and organs.

Romer, A., and T. Parsons. 1977. *The Vertebrate Body.* Fifth edition. Philadelphia: Saunders. A classic in zoology; an authoritative reference for your personal library.

Storer, T., et. al. 1979. *General Zoology.* Sixth edition. New York: McGraw-Hill.

Vander, A., J. Sherman, and D. Luciano. 1980. *Human Physiology: The Mechanisms of Body Function.* Third edition. New York: McGraw-Hill. Perhaps the clearest, in-depth introduction to human organ systems and their functioning.

Review Questions

1. What is an animal tissue? An organ? An organ system?

2. Are there a few tissue types, or a great diversity of tissues? How can a bird wing and a human arm look and function so differently when they are constructed of the same basic tissues?

3. Name some of the functions of epithelium. What is the difference between simple and stratified epithelium? What shapes of cells are found in both types?

4. Describe the structure and function of one of these types of connective tissue: loose connective tissue, dense connective tissue, adipose tissue.

5. Can you describe how cartilage differs from bone? What roles do osteoblasts and osteoclasts play in bone formation and maintenance? In calcium storage and distribution?

6. Describe skeletal, cardiac, and smooth muscle tissue.

7. List the major organ systems that occur in animals, along with their main functions.

8. Define homeostasis. What are the three components of homeostatic control systems?

9. What is interstitial fluid? What function does it serve in the vertebrate body? How is it functionally related to blood?

10. What are the differences between negative feedback, positive feedback, and feedforward controls?

From time to time, the human body has been likened to a city, or state, or some other social unit composed of separate but independent parts. These analogies are wonderfully optimistic about our capacity for social organization. In truth, our cities and states don't begin to approach the degree of functional integration of any complex animal. Whether the animal is asleep, relaxed, or alert to danger, some body parts are being called into action in coordinated ways even as activities of other parts are being suppressed. Throughout the animal's life, activities of each body part are monitored and evaluated—not for its sake alone but for how it is contributing to working patterns of the whole. In this chapter and the next, we will look at the neural and endocrine systems by which activities are integrated and controlled in the animal body. Here, we will begin with the **neuron**, the highly differentiated nerve cell that is present in almost all animals.

21

INTEGRATION AND CONTROL: NERVOUS SYSTEMS

THE NEURON

What Neurons Do. All cells show some degree of excitability, in that their plasma membranes receive and respond to signals about environmental change. However, neurons can do more than this. They can respond in the following ways to specific forms of chemical, electrical, or mechanical stimulation:

1. *Integrate* (simultaneously add up) many incoming signals about change.

2. *Propagate* excitation as a pulse of information along the plasma membrane, from one location to another.

3. *Transmit* information about change to other neurons, muscles, or glands.

Signals can be integrated and propagated because of mechanisms built into the plasma membrane, as you will read shortly. Messages can be transmitted to specific locations because neurons are organized and connected in communication pathways. Only small junctions (synapses) separate them. Throughout the body, signals about change are received, integrated, and relayed across the junctions. The communication pathways for these signals are the key parts of what we call nervous systems.

Classes of Neurons. There are three functional classes of neurons, as the sketch on page 320 suggests.

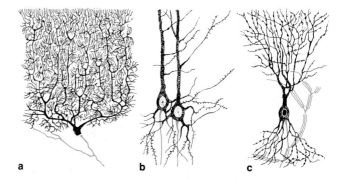

Figure 21.1 Examples of structural diversity in neurons. Those shown occur in the brains of mammals. Axons are shaded in blue. The profuse branches and tufts are dendrites.

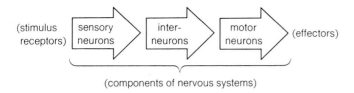

(stimulus receptors) → sensory neurons → inter-neurons → motor neurons → (effectors)

(components of nervous systems)

Sensory neurons relay information about environmental change *into* integrating centers (such as the spinal cord and brain). These neurons receive information in one of two ways. Epithelial receptor cells detect specific environmental changes and activate adjacent sensory neurons. Also, some sensory neurons have specialized regions that serve directly as receptors (Chapter Twenty-Three).

Interneurons are the main components of integrating centers. They integrate information arriving on incoming communication lines, and they influence other neurons in turn. The vast majority of neurons are interneurons.

Motor neurons carry information *away* from integrating centers, to the body's effectors (muscle and gland cells). The messages they carry can alter activity in effector cells.

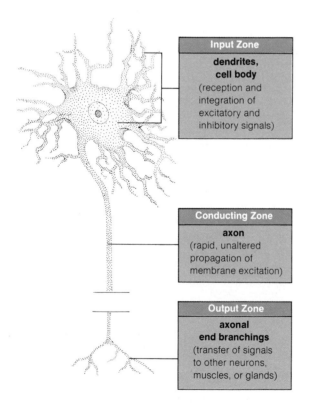

Input Zone

dendrites, cell body
(reception and integration of excitatory and inhibitory signals)

Conducting Zone

axon
(rapid, unaltered propagation of membrane excitation)

Output Zone

axonal end branchings
(transfer of signals to other neurons, muscles, or glands)

Figure 21.2 Main information-processing zones of a motor neuron.

In nervous systems, the neurons just described are intimately associated with Schwann cells and other assorted cells, collectively called **neuroglia**. In vertebrates, neuroglial cells represent at least half the volume of the nervous system. Despite their abundance, the function of most neuroglial cells is not clearly understood. Some, however, are thought to be metabolically associated with neurons, in that they aid in their nutrition. Schwann cells surround the axons of many neurons, and may influence how fast a message travels.

Structure of Neurons. Neurons vary in size. They also vary in the number and length of their cytoplasmic extensions, which collectively are called nerve cell "processes." A typical motor neuron has short, branched processes called **dendrites** (Figure 21.1). It also has a long, fiberlike process called an **axon**. The cell body proper houses the nucleus, with its genetic instructions for maintaining neural structure and metabolic systems.

In most neurons, the dendrites (and often the cell body) generally are *input zones*, where information is received and integrated (Figure 21.2). Axons are *conducting zones*. Here, membrane excitation travels rapidly, without alteration, from the start of the axon to its branched endings. The endings of axons are *output zones*. Most commonly, the excitation causes chemical substances to be released from output zones. Whether adjacent neurons, muscles, or glands are excited or inhibited depends on the nature of the released substance and on the properties of the adjacent cell.

MESSAGE CONDUCTION

Like all cells, the neuron has a differentially permeable plasma membrane. Some substances can diffuse passively across the membrane, down their concentration and electric gradients. Other substances cannot diffuse across the membrane at all. And some substances can be actively transported against gradients.

In neurons, membrane permeability to sodium ions (Na^+) and potassium ions (K^+) plays a key role in message conduction. Sodium and potassium ions both carry positive electric charge, and their flow across the plasma membrane can make one side more positive than the other. For neurons, there is indeed a charge separation across the plasma membrane, in that the inside is negative with respect to the outside. Neural "messages" are successive *reversals* in the polarity of charge, brought about by sodium and potassium movements across the membrane:

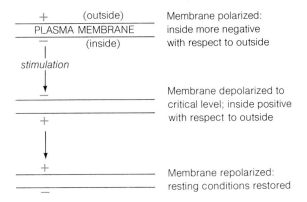

Let's first take a look at how this polarity of charge is established. Then we can consider the mechanisms by which polarity is reversed, and subsequently restored.

The Neuron "At Rest"

A neuron is said to be at rest when it is not conducting signals. In this state, there usually is a steady voltage difference across the plasma membrane, with the inside about seventy millivolts more negative than the outside. (What, you might ask, is a "millivolt"? It is simply a unit for measuring a *voltage difference:* the amount of potential energy between two differently charged regions.) What we have, then, is an electric gradient across the plasma membrane of a resting neuron. The voltage difference along this gradient is called the **resting membrane potential**.

The electric gradient depends largely on the distribution of sodium and potassium ions across the membrane. The interstitial fluid has far more sodium and far less potassium than the cytoplasm:

		interstitial fluid
K+	**Na+**	
		plasma membrane
K+	Na+	
		cytoplasm

where large letters denote which side of the membrane has the greatest concentration. (As an example of the magnitude of this difference, consider a neuron from a cat. For every 150 potassium ions in a given volume of cytoplasm, there are only 5 in the same volume of fluid outside.

For every 15 sodium ions on the inside, there are 150 on the outside.)

The ion distributions and the voltage difference across the resting membrane are established by two processes:

---

1. A pumping process actively transports sodium and potassium across the resting membrane, and thereby establishes the ion distributions. The **sodium-potassium pump** is a cotransport mechanism, in that both sodium and potassium are exchanged at the same time by the same membrane-bound enzyme system (Figure 21.3).

2. Leaks of sodium and potassium ions establish the voltage difference. The term "leaks" refers to diffusion of these ions across the membrane, down their concentration gradient.

Now, you may wonder how a "polarity of charge" can be established when both sodium and potassium ions are positively charged. The main reason is that the resting membrane happens to be permeable to potassium but not to large, negatively charged ions present in the cytoplasm. Thus, when potassium ions diffuse out of the cell and leave these negative ions behind, the inside becomes more negative. To some extent, inward leaks of sodium counteract this charge separation. However, the resting membrane is much less permeable to sodium than to potassium, so the negativity is only partly countered.

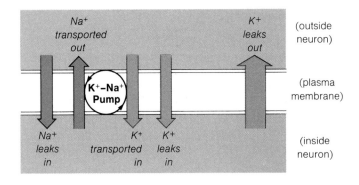

Figure 21.3 Balance between pumping and leaking processes that maintain the distribution of sodium and potassium ions across the plasma membrane of a neuron at rest. The relative widths of the arrows indicate the magnitude of the movements. As you can see, the combined effect of leaks (in response to concentration and electric gradients) and of active transport by the pump is that the inward movement equals the outward movement for each kind of ion when the neuron is not being stimulated.

Under resting conditions, a balance between pumping and leaking processes maintains the membrane potential at about seventy millivolts. The effect of sodium ions leaking in is countered by sodium pumping in the opposite direction. Some potassium ions are leaking out, but the pumping process is bringing others back in. Potassium also is attracted back by the greater negativity of the cytoplasmic side. Here, potassium pumping and the inward diffusion of potassium down an electric gradient counters the outward-leaking potassium (Figure 21.3). *Overall, there is no net movement of sodium and potassium ions into or out of the resting neuron.*

Changes in Membrane Potential

When a resting membrane is stimulated, its permeability to sodium and potassium is altered. The charge distribution across the membrane is disturbed, and changes in membrane potential are the result.

Most incoming signals arrive at dendrites or the cell body of the neuron. Each can produce a **graded potential** by means of a small, local current flow across the membrane. Many graded potentials acting together can significantly change the voltage difference across the membrane. When they reduce it enough, membrane voltage suddenly undergoes a dramatic reversal in the polarity of charge, called an **action potential**. Let's consider the action potential first, for it is better understood.

Action Potentials

Neural excitation arises largely through stimulus-induced changes in membrane permeability to *sodium*. Sodium ions, recall, do not freely move in significant amounts across the resting membrane. Under certain conditions, though, they *can* move rapidly through special transmembrane channels. These special sodium channels have molecular "gates," which are shut tightly during resting conditions. Under strong stimulation, these gated channels open to the extent that membrane permeability increases by several hundredfold. Sodium then diffuses down its steep concentration and electric gradients, into the neuron.

When positively charged sodium ions pass through the gated channels, the voltage on the inside becomes more positive. The positive voltage causes more gates to open, which admits more sodium, which increases the positivity inside, and so on. The escalating flow of sodium

is an example of *positive feedback,* whereby an original event is increasingly intensified as a result of its own occurrence. It is the increased movement of sodium into the neuron that leads to an action potential. An action potential can occur in many types of nerve and muscle cells, which are equipped with voltage-sensitive sodium gates.

When the stimulus is strong enough, the membrane potential reaches a critical **threshold value**. This value is the minimum voltage change needed to trigger an action potential (Figure 21.4). Once threshold is reached, membrane permeability no longer depends on stimulus strength, because of the positive feedback cycle that causes the inward rush of sodium. Thus, action potentials are **all-or-nothing events**: either all of the associated membrane permeability changes occur, or they do not occur at all.

Once a strong stimulus causes sodium gates to open, sodium moves in and the potential energy is released automatically, like the energy released when a trap door opens beneath some rocks that have been piled on it. Thus the amount of energy released during the action potential is not at all related to the strength of the stimulus, any more than the effect of dynamite depends on the size of the match that lit the fuse.

Duration of an Action Potential. Each action potential lasts only a few milliseconds. Several hundred can occur in a neuron in a single second. Certainly billions of action potentials occur in your nervous system during the time it takes you to read about a single one of them.

Why does an action potential end so abruptly? There are two reasons. First, there is a mechanism that rapidly shuts off the sodium influx. This mechanism is *another* gate, on the cytoplasmic side of the gated sodium channel. When voltage inside goes from negative to positive during an action potential, this second gate slams shut and closes off the sodium flow. Second, halfway through the action potential, membrane permeability to potassium increases. Potassium moves out of the neuron (through gated protein channels) at the same time that sodium entry decreases. These movements automatically restore the voltage across the membrane to its original value.

Even though the voltage is restored, the sodium and potassium gradients are ever so slightly reduced in size at the end of an action potential. These tiny reductions in the concentration gradients must be countered, otherwise the ability of the neuron to respond to stimuli would gradually disappear. Restoration of the gradients is achieved by the ongoing sodium-potassium pumping process described earlier.

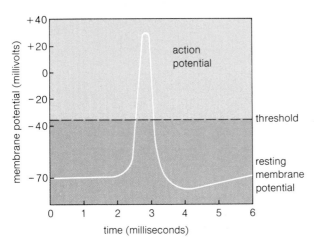

Figure 21.4 Recording of an action potential, or nerve impulse. Figure 21.5 describes how such recordings can be made.

Propagation of Action Potentials. Once an action potential has been triggered, it is self-propagating. The electrical disturbance alters the permeability of adjacent membrane regions (Figure 21.6). There, sodium moves into the neuron and potassium moves out. The new disturbance affects the permeability of the next adjacent region, and so it goes, away from the original stimulation point. These alterations in voltage across the membrane constitute the "message" that is propagated along the neuron.

Action potentials always travel in a direction away from the stimulation site. There is no backflow, largely because each action potential is followed by a **refractory period**. This is a time during which the membrane is insensitive to stimulation. It occurs while sodium gates are shut tight and potassium gates are wide open during restoration of the membrane potential. After the resting membrane potential has been restored, the electrical disturbance has moved far enough away that it no longer can cause sodium gates to open in the region of the original action potential.

In unsheathed axons, action potentials travel most rapidly when the axon diameter is large (and thereby does not show as much resistance to current flow). In many vertebrates, however, sheathed axons can propagate nerve impulses even faster, at 120 meters per second! This high-speed propagation is due to an arrangement between the neurons and **Schwann cells** (a kind of neuroglial cell). Schwann cells wrap their plasma membranes many times

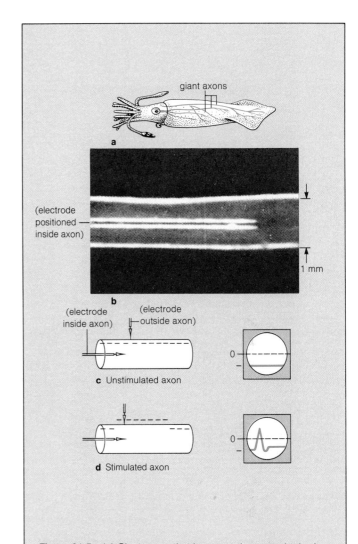

Figure 21.5 (**a**) Giant axons that innervate the muscular body wall (mantle) of the squid *Loligo*. These axons are a millimeter in diameter. The sketch shows their approximate location in the squid body. (**b**) The micrograph shows the axon diameter relative to the size of an electrode, a device used in measuring voltage changes. Being large enough to accommodate such devices, the giant axon was used in early studies of nerve functioning. (From A. L. Hodgkin, *J. Physiology*, London, 1956, volume 131)

Two recording electrodes can be used to measure change in electric potential across the axonal plasma membrane. One electrode penetrates the axon; the other is positioned outside. Both connect to a voltmeter and to an oscilloscope, a device by which voltage fluctuations can be briefly visualized as a wave form on a fluorescent screen. (**c**) In a resting neuron, the oscilloscope shows that the inside of the axon is negative with respect to the outside. When the electrodes detect an action potential, a wave form of the sort depicted in (**d**) appears on the oscilloscope screen.

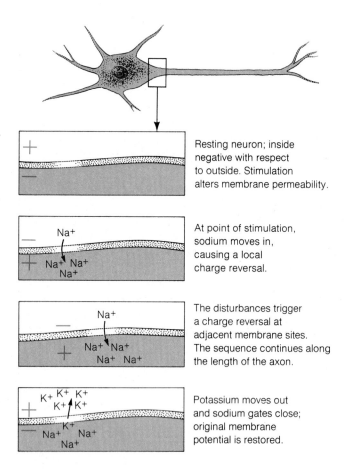

Resting neuron; inside negative with respect to outside. Stimulation alters membrane permeability.

At point of stimulation, sodium moves in, causing a local charge reversal.

The disturbances trigger a charge reversal at adjacent membrane sites. The sequence continues along the length of the axon.

Potassium moves out and sodium gates close; original membrane potential is restored.

Figure 21.6 Simplified picture of how action potentials are propagated along the axon of a neuron.

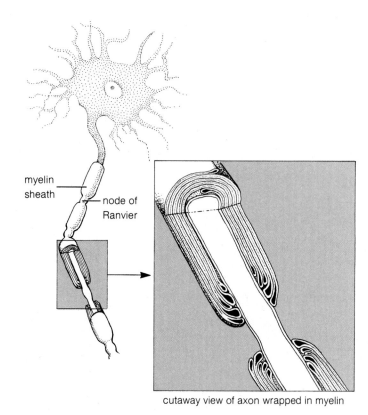

cutaway view of axon wrapped in myelin

Figure 21.7 Myelinated axon of a motor neuron.

around a single axon, like large narrow straps. The membrane layers of Schwann cells form a lipid-rich *myelin sheath* (Figure 21.7). Each Schwann cell is separated from the next by a *node of Ranvier:* a small gap where the axon is exposed to interstitial fluid.

The lipid-rich regions between nodes of Ranvier have a high electrical resistance. This means that current cannot move readily across the neural membrane where the wrappings occur. Hence action potentials cannot be triggered in the sheathed regions. However, current can be conducted through cytoplasm and interstitial fluid with little decay. (Because these fluids contain many mobile ions, they offer little resistance to current flow.) Thus the current can still trigger an action potential at the next node in line (about a millimeter away). In this manner, an action potential "jumps" from one node to the next in line. The rapid, node-to-node hopping via conducting fluids is called *saltatory* conduction, after the Latin word meaning "to jump."

Summary of Message Conduction Mechanisms

So far, we have considered several aspects of neuron functioning. Let's put a few of the key aspects in perspective:

1. The outside of a neuron has far more sodium ions and far fewer potassium ions than the inside.

2. The ion distributions impose concentration and electric forces on the ions themselves. In response to these forces, potassium and sodium ions leak in and out, in ways that create a voltage difference across the membrane.

3. The voltage difference is maintained by a balance between (1) leaks of sodium and potassium down their gradients, and (2) the action of sodium-potassium pumps that operate against the gradients.

4. Because of the leaking and pumping processes, the inside of a resting neuron stays more negative by about 70 millivolts with respect to the outside. This voltage difference is a store of potential energy.

5. The potential energy can be tapped when a stimulus affects sodium gates in the membrane. Energy is released when sodium moves through the gates, into the neuron.

6. The energy released can generate two types of signals: graded potentials or action potentials.

7. Strong stimulation can bring the membrane to the threshold of an *action potential:* an accelerated opening of voltage-sensitive sodium gates through a positive feedback cycle. The feedback cycle causes a dramatic reversal of the polarity across the membrane.

8. Action potentials are self-propagating because of the positive feedback mechanism; they do not decay with distance.

9. Each action potential ends abruptly when sodium gates slam shut, and when gated potassium channels open and potassium moves out of the neuron. These two events restore the resting membrane potential. They also prevent message backflow (the membrane is insensitive to stimulation while they occur).

10. *Graded potentials* are due to local, nonpropagated current flows that vary in strength, depending on the stimulus.

11. A neuron can be influenced by signals arriving from many different communication lines. The individual graded potentials that these signals generate can be summed.

12. In some cases, summation is not enough to bring the membrane to threshold, so the current decays. In other cases, summation is strong enough to lead to an action potential, whereby the signal is propagated.

MESSAGE TRANSFERS

Synaptic Transmission Between Neurons

Now that we have looked at message conduction along the individual neuron, let's turn to message transmission from one neuron to another. The specialized junction where an axon (or some other part) of one neuron terminates right next to another neuron is called a **synapse**. At this junction, activity in the first neuron can alter the activity in the second. Most often, the terminal endings of the neuron sending the signal are slightly swollen, or knoblike (Figure 21.8). A small extracellular space separates the synaptic knob and the membrane of the receiving neuron. This space is the **synaptic cleft**.

The separation between a sending and a receiving neuron means that an action potential cannot be directly propagated from one to the other. However, when an action potential reaches the end of the sending neuron, it increases membrane permeability to calcium ions. Calcium enters the sending neuron and acts on small vesicles that are stored in the synaptic knobs. The vesicles move toward and fuse with the plasma membrane. Through exocytosis, their contents are expelled into the synaptic cleft. The contents are molecules of **transmitter substances**, which cause changes in the membrane potential of a receiving neuron. Acetylcholine, dopamine, norepinephrine, and epinephrine are examples of transmitter substances.

Transmitter substances can change the membrane permeability of a receiving neuron, which alters its activity level in one of two ways. Either the receiving neuron's activity is enhanced, or it is inhibited. The outcome depends largely on the kinds of ions involved in the permeability change and on the state of the receiving neuron (for instance, on how close graded potentials have brought it to threshold).

At an **excitatory synapse**, a transmitter substance produces changes in the receiving cell that bring the membrane *closer* to threshold. When transmitter molecules combine with receptor sites on the receiving cell membrane, permeability to sodium and several other ions increases. Sodium moves into the neuron, and the voltage difference across the membrane is diminished. This local current flow in a receiving neural membrane is a graded potential. In combination with other excitatory signals, it can help initiate an action potential.

At an **inhibitory synapse**, a transmitter substance produces changes in the receiving cell that drive the membrane potential *away* from threshold. In this case, the transmitter substance increases membrane permeability to potassium

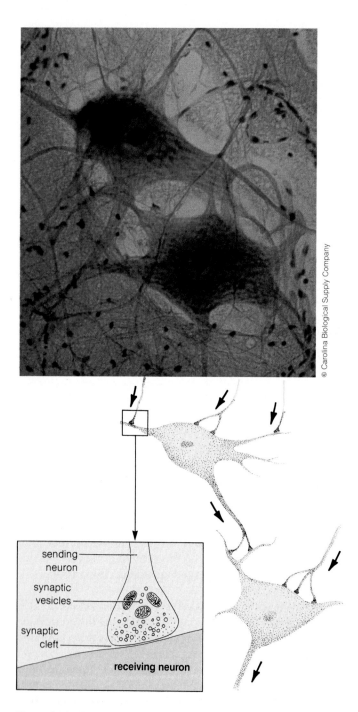

Figure 21.8 Synapses between sending neurons and receiving cells. Messages typically spread outward from each active synapse on the membrane surface of a receiving neuron. Hence a large area of the neuron surface, not just a process or two, can become excited. The *direction* in which a given message flows through the body depends on the way neighboring neurons and their processes are organized relative to one another, as the arrows suggest.

Labels in figure:
- sending neuron
- synaptic vesicles
- synaptic cleft
- receiving neuron

ions, chloride ions, or both. When potassium follows its gradient out of the neuron, the voltage difference across the membrane rises, so it would take an even greater increase in sodium permeability than usual to trigger an action potential. The same thing happens when chloride follows its gradient, into the neuron. The graded potentials at inhibitory synapses lessen the likelihood that the receiving cell membrane will reach threshold.

Most of the time, a lone excitatory synaptic event cannot trigger an action potential. The reason is that it takes an excitatory input of up to twenty-five millivolts to drive a resting membrane to threshold—but a graded potential at an excitatory synapse provides only about half a millivolt. The input of hundreds of graded potentials at a time must be summed before a receiving neuron will respond to a stimulus with action potentials of its own.

At each neuron in a nervous system, there is a constant interplay between excitatory and inhibitory signals. Imagine what this means on the scale of your own nervous system, with its 100 billion neurons. Action potentials shoot toward your brain on a remarkable number of specific communication lines. At each synapse along the way, some signals are excitatory and others are inhibitory. At each neuron, excitatory and inhibitory signals generate graded potentials, which are summed. Hence each convergence point for incoming messages represents a relay station where information may be reinforced and sent on, or suppressed.

Integration is, in its most fundamental sense, the moment-by-moment summation of all excitatory and inhibitory signals acting on a neuron.

Junctional Transmission Between Neurons and Muscle Cells

Recall that muscle cells also have voltage-sensitive sodium gates and can produce action potentials. Muscle cells receive signals from motor neurons. Axons of motor neurons branch into terminal endings that lie next to the muscle cell membrane in a region called a **neuromuscular junction**. At this junction, a synaptic cleft separates the two cells (Figure 21.9). In this case, acetylcholine is the transmitter substance that diffuses across the synaptic cleft. Acetylcholine increases membrane permeability to ions (including sodium ions), and the increased permeability leads to a

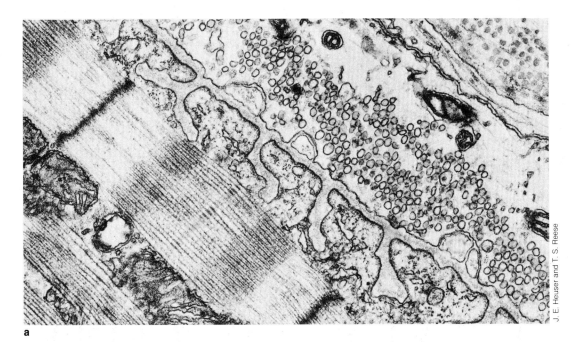

a

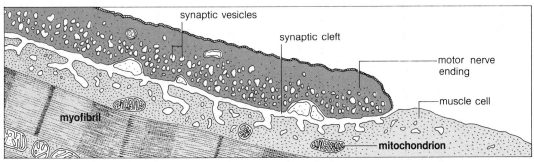

synaptic vesicles

synaptic cleft

motor nerve
ending

muscle cell

myofibril

mitochondrion

b

Figure 21.9 Transmission electron micrograph (**a**) and sketch (**b**) of a neuromuscular junction. The axon of this motor neuron terminates in a slight depression on the muscle cell surface. A narrow space (the synaptic cleft) separates the nerve ending from the muscle cell. Notice how the part of the nerve cell facing this space is not wrapped in a protective myelin sheath. Notice also how channels from the main synaptic cleft penetrate the region of the muscle cell membrane. An as-yet unidentified substance fills all these channels. And it is through this substance that chemical messages may travel from the nerve to bring about muscle contraction.

J. E. Heuser and T. S. Reese

graded potential. With enough stimulation, the muscle cell membrane is brought to threshold. An action potential is generated and the muscle cell contracts, an event that is described in Chapter Twenty-Three.

THE REFLEX ARC: FROM STIMULUS TO RESPONSE

Now that we have considered mechanisms by which neural messages are conducted and transmitted, we can consider how these messages flow through nerve pathways. One of the simplest pathways is called a **reflex arc**. It coordinates a fixed (stereotyped) sequence of stimulus-induced events, including the response to the stimulus. The components of a neural reflex typically include receptors, sensory neurons, interneurons, motor neurons, and effector cells.

Consider the pathway that mediates a **stretch reflex**. Here, a muscle contracts automatically whenever conditions cause an increase in its length. For vertebrates, the stretch reflex assures a rapid and uncomplicated response. For instance, even when you aren't aware of the stretch reflex, it is at work helping you maintain an upright posture despite small shifts in your balance.

As Figure 21.10 shows, length-sensitive receptors are located within skeletal muscles. These receptors, called

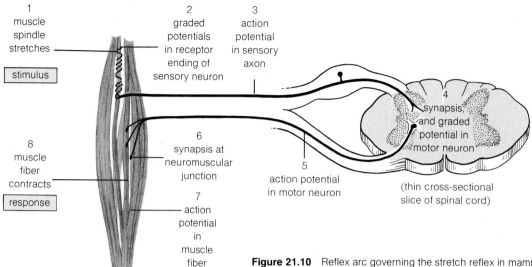

Figure 21.10 Reflex arc governing the stretch reflex in mammals. Other inputs and outputs exist, but they are omitted here for the sake of clarity.

muscle spindles, are made of small muscle cells enclosed in a sheath that runs parallel with the muscle itself. Sensory neurons connect with different muscle spindles. When a spindle is stretched, action potentials are triggered in the sensory axon. These potentials are conducted rapidly toward the spinal cord. There, axonal endings of the sensory neuron synapse with (among other things) motor neurons—which have axons leading right back to the muscle that was stretched. Under enough stimulation, action potentials are generated in each motor neuron. They travel to its axonal endings, there to activate the muscle membrane. This motor neuron activity leads to muscle contraction, as described in the preceding section. Thus the stretch reflex maintains a degree of tension in the muscle.

This example of a reflex arc is simplified, for we have looked at just one synapse (sensory neuron to motor neuron). But even such one-to-one connections are subject to intervention by input from many interneurons. Say that you are standing up and someone stomps on your foot. Muscles in your leg cause your knee to bend rapidly in response. The injured foot is thereby lifted in the air—which is opposite to the motor response of the stretch reflex. Other branches of the sensory neuron also spread out in the spinal cord region and make other connections, leading (for instance) to the brain.

NERVOUS SYSTEMS: INCREASING THE OPTIONS FOR RESPONSE

Evolution of Nervous Systems

What are the simplest pathways of message transmission in animals? Sponges are among the simplest animals, in anatomical terms. But sponges do little more than contract slowly in response to mechanical stimuli (such as a pinprick). The response is diffuse and never more than a few millimeters away from the point of irritation. Not until we turn to the cnidarians do we find a system of neurons organized into reflex arcs.

Sea anemones, hydras, jellyfishes—all such animals are water-dwelling cnidarians. Some forms attach themselves to the seafloor; others are free-floating. Regardless of whether they float or sit, all cnidarians face similar challenges and respond in similar ways. For them, food and danger are likely to appear not on the water's surface or on the bottom, but anywhere in between (Figure 21.11). The systems by which cnidarians sense and respond to the environment show **radial symmetry**. The term means that the components are arranged radially about a central axis, much like the spokes of a bike wheel.

In the cnidarian systems, many neurons are arranged in **nerve nets**: pathways between receptors and muscle

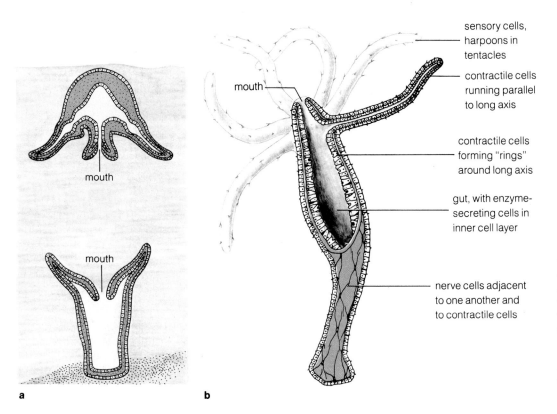

sensory cells, harpoons in tentacles

contractile cells running parallel to long axis

contractile cells forming "rings" around long axis

gut, with enzyme-secreting cells in inner cell layer

nerve cells adjacent to one another and to contractile cells

mouth

mouth

mouth

a

b

Figure 21.11 (**a**) Where cnidarians are in relation to their environment. Whether sedentary or free-floating, these animals have a radially symmetrical system of responding to food or danger that can come from any direction. (**b**) System of sensory reception and response in *Hydra,* arranged radially about mouth and gut—and suggestive of evolutionary pressures for efficient food-getting as a major impetus for the development of nervous systems.

tissue that are concerned with diffuse message conduction and response. (For instance, one reflex pathway controls contractile tissues that extend from sensory receptors in tentacles to the mouth.) Some components of nerve nets are well developed. For example, cnidarians have receptors, called statocysts, that sense which way is up (Chapter Twenty-Three). They have **ganglia**: concentrations of nerve cell bodies encased in connective tissue and forming integrative centers.

Cnidarians provide a model for the evolutionary beginnings of integration. Typically, offspring of some modern-day cnidarians do not look at all like their parents. Each is a *planula:* a ciliated larval form. At first, a planula swims or crawls by using its cilia as motile structures. Then it settles down on one end, and a mouth forms at the other. It becomes a polyp, a form typified by the lower left sketch in Figure 21.11. The planulas survive if they happen to settle where food is plentiful. They don't survive if they settle where food is scarce, for the polyp form can't pick up and move on.

Suppose that long ago, mutations in some planulas blocked the developmental signals to stop crawling. Suppose that other mutations led to the opening of the mouth on the underside of the body rather than at one end. Such a mutant would resemble an existing animal: the flatworm. It would at once have selective advantages. At its mouth would be living microorganisms and the remains of others, in amounts more concentrated than food floating through the water. And with its "feet," it could move to regions of organic feasts!

Such forward-crawlers would have been candidates for **cephalization**: an increasing concentration of nervous structures and coordinative functions at the "front" end, or head. Consider that the end going first would encounter food (and danger) more frequently. Variant individuals with sensory organs located at the front end could sense and turn toward food (and away from danger) more quickly than others. Cephalization would thus offer survival advantages.

Forward-crawlers would also have been candidates for **bilateral symmetry**: the left and right halves of the body

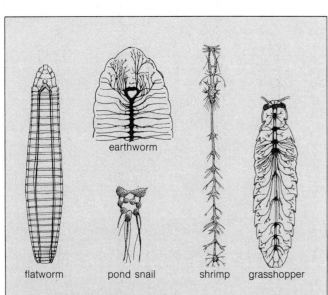

flatworm   pond snail   shrimp   grasshopper

earthworm

Figure 21.12 Examples of central and peripheral nervous systems from a few invertebrates. The sketches are not to scale relative to one another, the point being merely to show that even these supposedly simple animals have neurons organized into nerves as well as a brain and other ganglia. (Adapted from Bullock et al., 1977)

In flatworms, a small brain tops a pair of longitudinal nerve cords. The cords are connected to each other by nerves that branch laterally in the body. The same branching pattern has echoes in the multiple body segments of annelids (such as earthworms) and arthropods (such as shrimps, crabs, and grasshoppers). Even the nerves branching from your own spinal cord have this segmental patterning. A ganglion in each segment modulates reflex activities for that segment and for its immediate neighbors.

In mollusks such as abalone and snails, the central nervous system is a ring of paired ganglia to which peripheral nerves connect. In this group are the most advanced invertebrate nervous systems, those of the squid and octopus. Their central nervous system is dominated by a brain composed of a concentrated mass of ganglia—and there are regional differences in brain function. Some regions control internal organs such as the heart. Others control movements of eyes, head, and tentacles. One region governs the ability of these animals to retain information—they show both short-term and long-term memory—and to learn from it!

would evolve in roughly equivalent directions. Consider that food and danger would most likely be encountered on both sides, not just one. Thus, there would be selection pressure for the body's right half to develop in much the same ways as the left.

The evolutionary importance of cephalization is obvious. What significance can be attached to the evolution of bilaterally symmetrical bodies? Perhaps this:

A shift from radial to bilateral symmetry could have led, in some evolutionary lines of animals, to paired nerves and muscles, paired sensory structures such as eyes, and paired brain regions.

Cephalization and bilateral symmetry—today these are features of all animals except sponges and cnidarians. Some parts of the nervous system are clustered in a central region, with the part exercising the most control concentrated at the head end. Other parts are in the body's outlying regions, or periphery, but they have connections leading into and from the neural control center (Figure 21.12).

In vertebrates, the brain and spinal cord (or nerve cord) represent the **central nervous system**. It contains specialized interneurons and cell bodies of motor neurons. All neurons (or parts of neurons) outside the spinal cord and brain are the **peripheral nervous system**. Differences that do exist among vertebrates relate more to brain size and its degree of control over the rest of the nervous system. For no matter how specialized a nervous system has become, the same basic principles apply:

1. Information flows over short distances by way of *graded potentials* (as in receptors and at synapses) and over long distances by *action potentials* (along axons).

2. There are pathways of *divergence*. A message can travel through branched endings of one neuron and activate many other neurons. Processes of those neurons may branch in different directions and thus can disperse messages to different body regions.

3. There are pathways of *convergence*. Typically, each neuron receives both excitatory and inhibitory signals from many other neurons.

4. For all bilaterally symmetrical animals, each through-conducting pathway is oriented in one direction only: all sensory axons lead toward the central nervous system, and all motor axons lead away from it.

5. Excitatory and inhibitory signals are summed at each synaptic transfer.

6. Signals about internal and external events are sent to the brain. When modification in response is required, the brain sends out command signals. The brain's action represents the highest level of integration yet developed.

CENTRAL NERVOUS SYSTEM

```
brain          spinal cord
```

PERIPHERAL NERVOUS SYSTEM

```
sensory neurons        motor neurons
(afferent)             (efferent)
```

SOMATIC NERVOUS SYSTEM	AUTONOMIC NERVOUS SYSTEM
(control of skeletal muscles; usually voluntary)	*(involuntary control of smooth muscles, cardiac muscles, glands)*

```
sympathetic        parasympathetic
nerve pathways     nerve pathways
```

Figure 21.13 Divisions of the vertebrate nervous system.

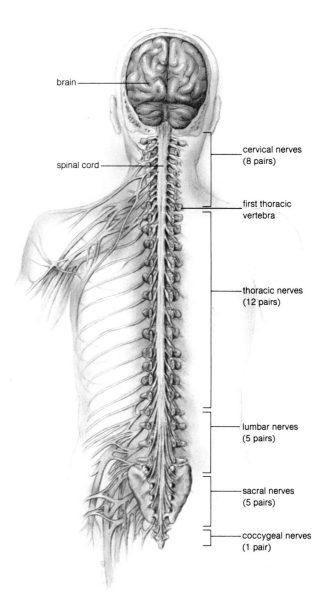

brain

spinal cord

cervical nerves (8 pairs)

first thoracic vertebra

thoracic nerves (12 pairs)

lumbar nerves (5 pairs)

sacral nerves (5 pairs)

coccygeal nerves (1 pair)

Figure 21.14 Human nervous system, showing how paired nerves run into the spinal cord at different levels.

The divisions of the vertebrate nervous system are illustrated in Figure 21.13, and will now be described.

Central Nervous Systems

In most vertebrates, the central nervous system is enclosed in bony chambers and cushioned with fluid. Bony plates joined together form a skull, which protects the brain. A series of hard, bony segments joined into a vertebral column (backbone) protects the spinal cord.

In functional terms, the spinal cord is in part a region of local integration and reflex connections. Pair after pair of communication lines lead into and out from different levels of the spinal cord (Figure 21.14). In relatively simple vertebrates, these communication lines and their interconnections in the cord are largely autonomous in handling reflex responses. For instance, a frog with its brain destroyed surgically can still maintain normal body position. It can even use its legs to kick away an irritant placed on its skin!

In cross-section, the brain and spinal cord have two distinct regions, one white and the other gray (Figure 21.15). The *white matter* is white because the axons are sheathed with fatty myelin. White matter is the through-conducting zone between levels of the spinal cord or the brain, and between the spinal cord and brain. The *gray matter* is the synaptic zone.

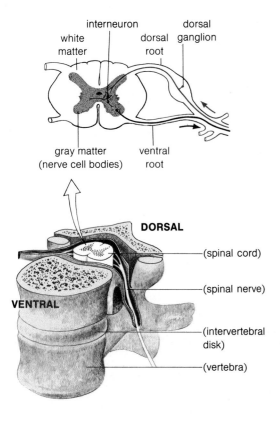

interneuron
white matter
dorsal root
dorsal ganglion
gray matter (nerve cell bodies)
ventral root

DORSAL
—(spinal cord)
—(spinal nerve)
VENTRAL
—(intervertebral disk)
—(vertebra)

Figure 21.15 Organization of white matter and gray matter of the vertebrate spinal cord. Compare this sketch with Figure 21.10 to get a better picture of the flow of information during reflex activity.

In all vertebrates, the brain represents the most complex level of neural organization and integration. It includes the following regions, which begin as a continuation of the spinal cord:

hindbrain   *medulla oblongata and cerebellum*

midbrain   *optic lobes*

forebrain   *thalamus, hypothalamus, cerebrum*

The **hindbrain** is an enlarged continuation of the upper spinal cord (Figure 21.16). The lower hindbrain region is called the *medulla oblongata.* Part of the medulla receives and integrates information from the spinal cord and from many brain regions. It contains reflex coordinating centers for breathing, swallowing, vomiting, and cardiovascular control. Other parts are concerned with sleep and arousal. The hindbrain region called the *cerebellum* is concerned with

coordinating the motor activity necessary for refined limb movements, for maintaining posture, and for spatial orientation. The cerebellum integrates signals from the forebrain and from organs of equilibrium (located in the inner ear). It sends the summation of these signals to motor control regions of the brain and to skeletal muscles. The vital role of this hindbrain region becomes evident when we observe humans who suffer from its damage. Uncontrollable tremors affect all of their attempts at movement—walking, speaking, even breathing.

Early in vertebrate history, the **midbrain** developed as a major integrative center. Here, nerve pathways converge on a pair of *optic lobes,* structures concerned with visual reception. In the fish and amphibian midbrain, sensory information from different sources is integrated: it is the primary "association center." It is also the source of motor responses. In reptiles, birds, and mammals, the midbrain is reduced in importance. Messages still converge and are integrated in the midbrain, but they are sent on to the forebrain for further neural processing.

The **forebrain** consists of the cerebrum, thalamus, and hypothalamus. The *cerebrum* is characterized by a thickened mass of gray matter divided into two halves (the cerebral hemispheres). It represents the highest level of control over the integration of sensory signals and the selection of motor responses. The functions of this region will be described later, in the section on the human brain. The *hypothalamus* is a region that coordinates many of the activities of the nervous system and endocrine system (Chapter Twenty-Two). The hypothalamus also contains centers concerned with body temperature regulation and with salt and water balance. Cells in the hypothalamus influence many forms of behavior, including those associated with hunger, thirst, aggression, sex, pleasure, and pain. The *thalamus* lies in the pathway to the cerebral hemispheres. From here, impulses concerning sight, sound, taste, position, movement, and pressure are sent on to appropriate regions of the cerebrum. The thalamus also coordinates much of the outgoing motor activity.

Peripheral Nervous Systems

In most vertebrates, peripheral nervous systems consist of various nerve processes that connect the brain and spinal cord with receptors, muscles, and glands. Sensory neurons are the incoming communication lines from receptors; motor neurons are the outgoing lines to effectors (Figure 21.13). The motor neurons are subdivided into two categories, called the somatic and autonomic nervous systems.

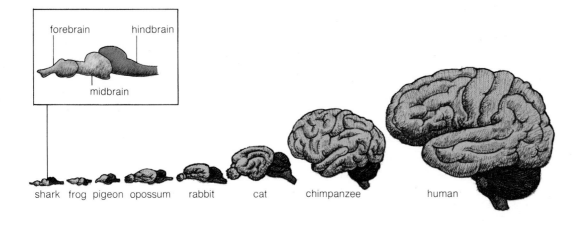

forebrain
hindbrain
midbrain

shark   frog   pigeon   opossum   rabbit   cat   chimpanzee   human

Figure 21.16 Brains of different vertebrates, drawn to the same scale. (From J. Eccles, *Understanding of the Brain*, 1977, McGraw-Hill) The inset shows the three divisions of the vertebrate brain, and its component structures.

Somatic Nervous System. The motor neurons making up a somatic nervous system convey signals from the brain and spinal cord to skeletal muscles. In complex vertebrates, some of these communication lines can be consciously controlled. When somatic neurons stimulate skeletal muscle cells, the muscle cells contract.

Autonomic Nervous System. The motor neurons making up an autonomic nervous system convey signals from the brain and spinal cord to smooth muscles, cardiac muscles, and glandular tissue. The autonomic neurons affect such functions as heartbeat, glandular secretions, blood vessel constriction, and muscle movements of the digestive system. The word autonomic means "self-managed." It indicates that the autonomic nervous system is generally not under conscious control. Signals from the brain and spinal cord do influence its activities, but the influence is automatic.

The motor neurons of the autonomic nervous system are further subdivided into two kinds of pathways, called *sympathetic nerves* and *parasympathetic nerves*. Many organs are innervated by both (Figure 21.17). When such dual innervation exists, signals conveyed by one nerve pathway generally increase organ activity, and the other nerve pathway conveys signals for decreasing organ activity. Depending on the organ, the nerves conveying the stimulatory signals can be either sympathetic or parasympathetic.

Parasympathetic nerves are concerned mostly with organ functions that supply and conserve energy. For example, under normal body conditions, parasympathetic nerves are dominant over smooth muscle contraction of the digestive tract. (Food digestion and absorption supply the body with energy.)

In contrast, sympathetic nerves are concerned mostly with organ functions that demand energy outlays. Under normal conditions, they balance the parasympathetic nerves only enough to maintain body functioning. During times of danger, excitement, or even heightened awareness, they dominate and the parasympathetic nerves are inhibited, as the following case study suggests.

Fight-or-Flight Response: A Case Study. One of the most ancient, rapid, and thoroughly integrated responses of the nervous system is known as the fight-or-flight response. Under signals from sympathetic nerves, pupils of the eyes dilate, heartbeat accelerates, blood vessels constrict in skin and smooth muscle, and all other blood vessels open wide. The effects of these responses can be conveyed by the following brief example.

Imagine yourself snorkeling through the warm waters of a tropical reef. In the shadow of a coral ledge, a brightly colored sea anemone catches your eye. You find a handhold and pull yourself toward it. Suddenly, out of the corner of your eye, you see glistening needlelike teeth—*MORAY!* Your arms and legs explode into action, and your body shoots away from the danger. By violating a prime rule of diving—by allowing part of your body to touch a place you had not yet examined carefully—you had come within a fraction of a second of losing your hand.

In that one instant, your body had become mobilized for supernormal speed and strength. Your eyes registered

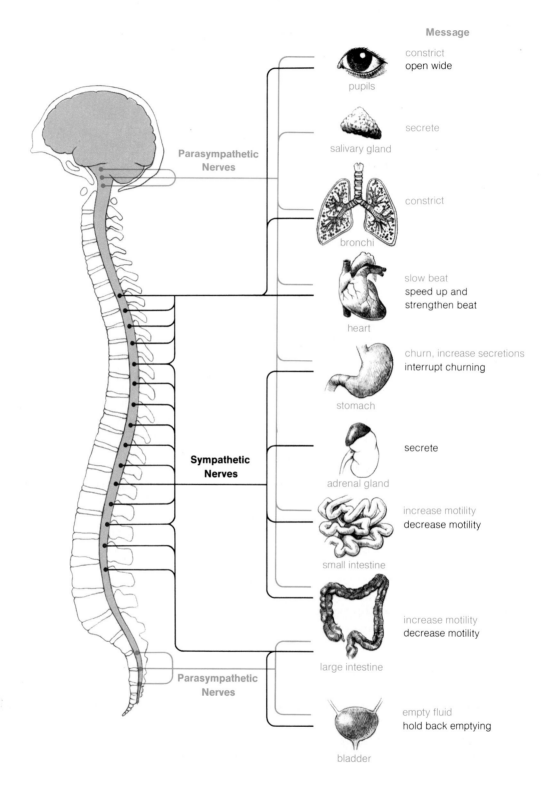

Figure 21.17 Autonomic pathways of the human nervous system.

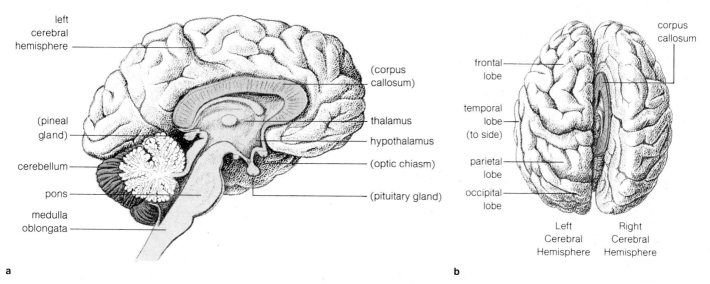

left cerebral hemisphere

(pineal gland)

cerebellum

pons

medulla oblongata

(corpus callosum)

thalamus

hypothalamus

(optic chiasm)

(pituitary gland)

a

corpus callosum

frontal lobe

temporal lobe (to side)

parietal lobe

occipital lobe

Left Cerebral Hemisphere

Right Cerebral Hemisphere

b

Figure 21.18 (**a**) Main components of the brain, sliced through the midsection. (**b**) Looking down on major regions of the cerebral hemispheres of the human brain, portrayed as if the main nerve tract connecting them (the corpus callosum) has been split so that the two hemispheres can be moved apart.

a glimpse of flashing teeth. As soon as action potentials traveled from eye regions to your brain, they were processed and interpreted. Their meaning: *DANGER!*

Signals shot to the hypothalamus and other regions dealing with emotions. From the motor cortex, commands traveled to the pituitary, motor neurons, and skeletal muscles, and along sympathetic and parasympathetic nerves. Neural and hormonal signals reached every key organ. Epinephrine and norepinephrine signaled the heart to beat stronger and faster, thereby accelerating blood flow. They signaled muscle cells in respiratory tubes to relax, and more oxygen flowed into your lungs. Your pupils dilated. Glucose and fatty acid from your liver and adipose tissue entered the bloodstream and became available as urgently needed energy.

At the same time, epinephrine and norepinephrine closed off blood vessels in your skin and gut wall. Thus they diverted blood from organs that would play no part in the response to those that would. They caused blood vessels supplying skeletal muscles to open wide. Thus nourished, muscles could now respond with maximum speed and strength to urgent commands descending from your brain.

With all systems alerted, your brain ran through its memory banks, searching for information stored away during earlier diving lessons. "Don't panic!" "If it's a shark, freeze!" *"If it's a moray eel, get out of there!"*

And now your cerebrum selected and initiated the correct detailed program of response. From there, action potentials flowed down the spinal cord and out the motor neurons in precisely the right sequence and frequency needed to activate muscles into producing a powerful swimming stroke. *And all of this happened in a fraction of a second!*

Your nervous system does more than work constantly to maintain your body in a homeostatic state. It also prepares your body to modify internal conditions in an instant. The fight-or-flight response is an extremely rapid response to stress. It is not unique to humans. All mammals display it whenever a sudden confrontation demands an immediate, unequivocal response.

THE HUMAN BRAIN

Regions of the Cortex

In the human brain, as in the brains of other vertebrates, the cerebral hemispheres are the most complex constellations of neurons. Inside each hemisphere is a core of white matter (axonal pathways connecting the rest of the central nervous system with the brain's surface layer). The surface layer, the **cerebral cortex,** is gray matter about three millimeters thick (Figure 21.18).

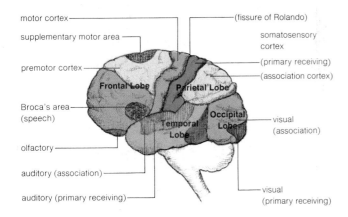

Figure 21.19 Primary receiving and association areas for the human cerebral cortex. Signals from receptors on the body's periphery enter primary cortical areas. Sensory input from different receptors is coordinated and processed in association areas. The text describes the main cortical regions. Also shown here are the *premotor area,* involved in intricate motor activity (as typified by a concert pianist performing); the *supplementary motor area,* which helps coordinate sequential voluntary movements; and *Broca's area,* which coordinates muscles required for speech. (After N. Lassen, D. Ingvar, and E. Skinhøj, "Brain Function and Blood Flow," *Scientific American,* October 1978)

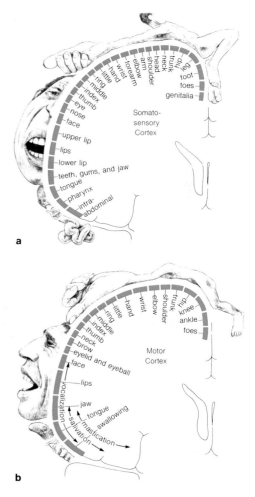

Figure 21.20 (**a**) Body regions represented in the somatosensory cortex. This region is a strip a little over an inch wide, running from the top of the head to just above the ear on the surface of each cerebral hemisphere. The sketch is a cross-section through the right hemisphere of someone facing you. (**b**) Body regions represented in the motor cortex, a region just in front of the somatosensory cortex. (After Penfield and Rasmussen, *The Cerebral Cortex of Man.* Copyright © 1950 Macmillan Publishing Co., Inc. Renewed 1978 by Theodore Rasmussen)

Different cortical regions have specific functions (Figure 21.19). Some are primary receiving centers for signals from receptors at the body's periphery. Some are association centers, where sensory information is coordinated and processed. Others are motor centers, where instructions for motor responses are coordinated.

Some neurons in the *motor cortex* act as direct channels from the brain to motor neurons. Stimulation of different points on the motor cortex triggers contractions of muscle groups in different body parts. There isn't a one-to-one relationship between muscle size and the motor cortex area devoted to it. But there is a relationship between function and the size of cortical area. For instance, a relatively large area is devoted to muscles that control thumb and tongue movements (Figure 21.20b). This you might expect, given the control that is required for intricate hand movements and verbal expression.

Just behind the motor cortex is the *somatosensory cortex,* a synaptic zone for signals coming from receptors in the skin and joints. When such signals stimulate your somatosensory cortex, you experience sensations of touch, pressure, heat, cold, pain, and changes in body position.

Visual information and auditory information arise in different cortical regions. Sensory pathways from your eyes terminate in a primary receiving center, the *visual cortex.* The visual cortex lies in the occipital lobe of each cerebral hemisphere (Figure 21.19). Sensory pathways from your ears terminate in the *auditory cortex.* Each temporal lobe contains a small region of auditory cortex. You will read about these two pathways in Chapter Twenty-Three.

Also lying outside the motor and somatosensory regions, but connected to them by neural pathways, are regions of *association cortex.* These largely unmapped regions are thought to give rise to conscious awareness of changing events in the surrounding world.

Information Processing in the Cortex

Earlier, you read that all neural signals have virtually the same electrical basis. If that is so, then how does the cerebral cortex distinguish one kind of stimulus from another? For example, how do odorless, tasteless, and colorless action potentials give rise to sensations of smell, taste, and color? Part of the answer is that distinctions are made on the basis of the type and location of the stimulus.

Where in the body does a specific communication line originate? Activity along a specific neural pathway provides information about a specific type of stimulus. For example, even in the dark, you can "see stars"—experience visual sensations—when you accidentally poke your eye. The poke triggers visual receptors in an unusual way, but your brain doesn't interpret the incoming signals as "pressure" or "pain." It always interprets stimulation of those particular receptors as "light."

As another example, sometimes a person whose legs have been amputated will suffer leg pains. The stumps of nerves that once ran from the legs to the brain apparently respond to pressure and send signals to the brain. The brain interprets signals from those particular communication lines as "pain"—as if the legs were still there. And the sensation of pain is referred to where the "pain" receptors once were.

Perception of the type of stimulus is determined by signal flow along particular nerve pathways, which have fixed origins and destinations.

Because of the way that nerve pathways are organized, it is also possible to pinpoint stimulus location. Your body's receptors are distributed through different tissue regions. One or more receptors of the same kind connect with a single sensory neuron. Together, the receptors and neuron form a sensory unit, and the tissue region they sample is called a **receptive field.** Pinpointing stimulus location depends on the size of each receptive field, and on the overlapping of adjacent receptive fields.

For instance, you are able to distinguish between the pressure of your thumb and that of your thumbnail even when you press them into the same tissue region of your

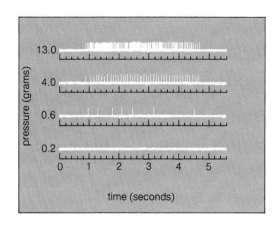

Figure 21.21 Impulses recorded from a single pressure receptor on the human hand, which correspond to variations in stimulus strength. A rod one millimeter in diameter was pressed against the skin with the force indicated. Vertical bars above each thick horizontal line correspond to the number of impulses. Notice the increase in impulse frequency which corresponds to increased stimulus strength. (From Hensel and Boman, *J. Neurophysiology,* 1960, 23:564–568)

fingertips. The variation is recorded through small, overlapping receptive fields that are abundant in fingertips. One reason why you have trouble localizing pain in your gut is that the walls of internal organs have fewer sensory processes and broader receptive fields, with less overlap, than those found in your skin. We will look at some examples of receptive fields in Chapter Twenty-Three. For now, the point is this:

Neural messages on specific communication lines contain information about stimulus location, coded in the signals from receptive fields in a given tissue region.

How does the cerebral cortex distinguish between stimuli of the same type but of differing intensities? For instance, how do action potentials convey to your brain the difference between a throaty whisper and a wild screech? After all, action potentials are all-or-nothing events; their amplitude cannot be varied to indicate differences in stimulus strength. Part of the answer is that variations in stimulus strength are encoded in the *frequency* of action potentials traveling along a particular pathway. Sights, movements, sounds, temperature changes, taste—the perceived strength of such sensations depends largely on how often receptors in a tissue are being activated. Figure 21.21

Figure 21.22 From signaling to visual perception.

Parts of the brain concerned with vision contain arrays of neurons, stacked in columns at right angles to the brain's surface. Connections run between neurons in each column and between different columns. Each column apparently analyzes only one kind of stimulus, received from only one location. The transformations from signaling to visual perception have actually been traced through eight levels of synapses.

What do eight synaptic levels tell us, given the *billions* of synaptic connections in the brain? Perhaps a great deal. In spite of their immense numbers, neurons in the brain's surface layer fall into a few basic categories. And those of each category seem to be tripped into action in the same way. For instance, excitatory signals from neurons climbing up through the brain's surface layer or running parallel to its surface activate particular neurons, which send out inhibitory commands to other neurons even as they themselves are being stimulated. Because of the precise vertical organization of these interactions, the excitatory and inhibitory feedback loops between neurons form narrow bands of activity—*the effect of which is a highly focused pattern of excitation through specific columns of neurons.*

Some experiments of David Hubel and Torsten Wiesel tell us something about this focusing. They implanted electrodes in individual neurons in the brain of an anesthetized cat. After the cat woke up, they positioned it in front of a small screen, then projected images of different shapes (such as a bar) onto the screen. Changes in electrical activity that accompanied different visual stimuli were recorded. As the above sketches suggest, the strongest signals were recorded for one kind of neuron when the cat observed an image of a vertical bar. When the bar image was tilted, electrical activity was reduced in frequency. When the image was tilted past a certain point, electrical activity stopped. Another neuron fired only when a block image was moved from left to right across the screen; still another fired when the image was moved from right to left. Such experiments suggest that the key to visual perception resides in the organization and synaptic connections between columns of neurons in the brain. (Sketches from Kuffler and Nicholls, *From Neuron to Brain*)

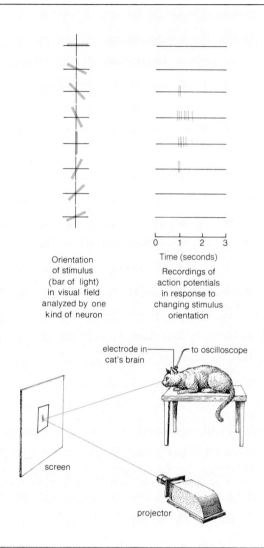

Orientation of stimulus (bar of light) in visual field analyzed by one kind of neuron

Time (seconds)

Recordings of action potentials in response to changing stimulus orientation

electrode in cat's brain — to oscilloscope

screen

projector

gives examples of frequency variations that correspond to differences in sustained pressure applied to human skin.

Variations in stimulus intensity are also detected because of variations in the *number* of nerve fibers bearing the incoming action potentials. A stronger stimulus usually acts on more nerve processes. The messages of a very strong stimulus can even be carried by one or more **nerves** (bundles of axons). Thus, the intensity of the message carried by a nerve is proportional to (1) the number of neurons in the bundle that have been stimulated and (2) the frequency of action potentials in each neuron.

Neural messages contain information about stimulus intensity, coded in the number of neurons activated and the frequency at which they are firing.

The cerebral cortex is the most complex integrative center in the living world. As Figure 21.22 suggests, we are only beginning to understand the levels of information processing that lie between the signaling of some environmental change and the brain's perception of that change.

Conscious Experience

Our two cerebral hemispheres are strapped together deep inside the cleft between them by a thick tract of white matter, the **corpus callosum**. The corpus callosum consists of axons running from one hemisphere to the other (Figure 21.18). Thus you might assume that it functions in communication between the two hemispheres. Indeed, experiments such as those performed by Roger Sperry and his coworkers showed that this is the case. They also demonstrated some intriguing differences in perception between the two halves!

The body's right and left sides have the same kinds of sensory nerves. These nerves enter the spinal cord or brainstem, then run in parallel to the brain. Similarly, sensory nerves from the left eye and ear run in parallel with sensory nerves from the right eye and ear toward the brain. The signals carried by these nerves reach the left or right cerebral hemisphere. But the signals are not all processed on the same side as the nerves. Instead, much of the information is projected onto the opposite hemisphere. In other words, *many of the nerve pathways leading into and from one hemisphere deal with the opposite side of the body.*

Knowing this, Sperry's group set out to treat severe cases of epilepsy. Persons afflicted with severe epilepsy are wracked with seizures, sometimes as often as every half hour of their lives. The seizures have a neurological basis, analogous to an electrical storm in the brain. What would happen if the corpus callosum of afflicted persons were cut? Would the electrical storm be confined to one cerebral hemisphere, leaving at least the other to function normally? Earlier studies of animals and of humans whose corpus callosum had been damaged suggested that this might be so.

The surgery was performed. And the electrical storms subsided, in both frequency and intensity. Apparently, cutting the neural bridge between the two hemispheres put an end to what must have been positive feedback loops of ever intensified electrical disturbances between them. Beyond this, the "split-brain" individuals were able to lead what seemed, on the surface, entirely normal lives.

But then Sperry devised some elegant experiments to determine whether the conscious experience of these individuals was indeed "normal." After all, the corpus callosum is a tract of no less than 200 million through-conducting axons; surely *something* was different. Something was. "The surgery," Sperry later reported, "left these people with two separate minds, that is, two spheres of consciousness. What is experienced in the right hemisphere seems to be entirely outside the realm of awareness of the left."

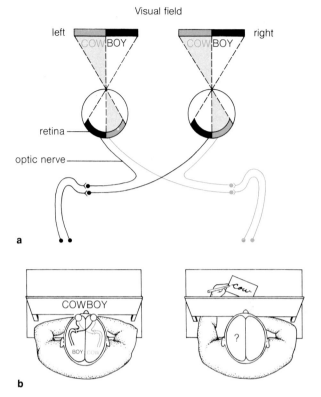

Figure 21.23 (**a**) Optic nerve pathways into the left and right cerebral hemispheres. These nerve pathways cross, so that they inform each hemisphere of what is happening on the opposite side of the body. These pathways are not affected when the corpus callosum is cut, but the ability of the two hemispheres to coordinate the separate visual input is essentially lost. (**b**) The kind of experiment testing the perceptual abilities of split-brain individuals, as described in the text. (a based on Vander et al., *Human Physiology*, third edition. © 1980 by McGraw-Hill. Used by permission.)

In Sperry's experiments, the left and right hemispheres of split-brain individuals were presented with different stimuli. Recall that visual connections to and from one hemisphere are mainly concerned with the opposite visual field. Sperry projected words—say, COWBOY—onto a screen. He did this in such a way that COW fell only on the left visual field, and BOY fell on the right (Figure 21.23). The subject reported seeing the word BOY. (The left hemisphere, which received the word, controls language.) However, when asked to write the perceived word with the left hand—a hand that was deliberately blocked from view—the subject wrote COW. The right hemisphere, which "knew" the other half of the word, had directed the left hand's motor response. But it couldn't tell the left hemisphere what was going on because of the severed corpus callosum. The subject knew that a word was being written, but could not say what it was!

The functioning of our two cerebral hemispheres has been the focus of many more experiments. Taken together, the results have revealed the following information about our conscious experience:

---

1. Each cerebral hemisphere can function separately, but it functions in response to signals mainly from the opposite side of the body.

2. The main association regions responsible for spoken language skills generally reside in the *left* hemisphere.

3. The main association regions responsible for nonverbal skills (music, mathematics, and other abstract abilities) generally reside in the *right* hemisphere.

Memory

Conscious experience is far removed from simple reflex action. It entails *thinking* about things—recalling objects and events encountered in the past, comparing them with newly encountered ones, and making rational connections based on the comparison of perceptions. Thus conscious experience entails a capacity for **memory**: the storage of individual bits of information somewhere in the brain.

The neural representation of information bits is known as a **memory trace**, although no one knows for sure in what form a memory trace occurs, or where it resides. So far, experiments strongly suggest that there are at least two stages involved in its formation. One is a *short-term* formative period, lasting only a few minutes or so; then, information becomes spatially and temporally organized in neural pathways. The other is *long-term* storage; then, information is put in a different neural representation that lasts more or less permanently.

Observations of people suffering from **retrograde amnesia** tell us something about memory. These people can't remember anything that happened during the half hour or so before experiencing electroconvulsive shock or before losing consciousness after a severe head blow. Yet memories of events before that time remain intact! Such disturbances temporarily suppress normal electrical activities in the brain. These observations may mean that whereas short-term memory is a fleeting stage of neural excitation,

long-term memory depends on *chemical or structural* changes in the brain.

In addition, information seemingly forgotten can be recalled after being unused for decades. This means that individual memory traces must be encoded in a form somewhat immune to degradation. Most molecules and cells in your body are used up, wear out, or age and are constantly being replaced—yet memories can be retrieved in exquisite detail after many years of such wholesale turnovers. Nerve cells, recall, are among the few kinds that are *not* replaced. You are born with billions, and as you grow older some 50,000 die off steadily each day. Those nerve cells formed during embryonic development are the same ones present, whether damaged or otherwise modified, at the time of death.

The part about being "otherwise modified" is tantalizing. *There is evidence that neuron structure is not static, but rather can be modified in several ways.* Most likely, such modifications depend on electrical and chemical interactions with neighboring neurons. Electron micrographs show that some synapses regress as a result of disuse. Such regression weakens or breaks connections between neurons. The visual cortex of mice raised without visual stimulation showed such effects of disuse. Similarly, there is some evidence that intensively stimulated synapses may form stronger connections, grow in size, or sprout buds or spines to form more connections! The chemical and physical transformations that underlie changes in synaptic connections may correspond to memory storage.

Sleeping and Dreaming

Between the mindless drift of coma and total alertness are many *levels* of conscious experience, known by such names as sleeping, dozing, meditating, and daydreaming. Through this spectrum of consciousness, neurons in the brain are constantly chattering among themselves. This neural chatter shows up as wavelike patterns in an **electroencephalogram** (EEG). An EEG is an electrical recording of the frequency and strength of potentials from the brain's surface. Each recording shows the contribution of thousands of neurons.

EEG Patterns. Figure 21.24 gives examples of EEG patterns. The prominent wave pattern for someone who is relaxed, with eyes closed, is an *alpha rhythm*. In this relaxed state of wakefulness, potentials are recorded in trains of about ten per second. Alpha waves predominate during the state of meditation. With a transition to sleep, wave trains gradually become longer, slower, and more erratic. This *slow-wave sleep* pattern shows up about eighty percent of the total sleeping time for adults. It occurs when sensory input is low and the mind is more or less idling. Subjects awakened from slow-wave sleep usually report that they were not dreaming. If anything, they seemed to be mulling over recent, ordinary events. However, slow-wave sleep is punctuated by brief spells of *REM sleep.* The name refers to the *Rapid Eye Movements* accompanying this pattern (the eyes jerk about beneath closed lids). Also accompanying REM sleep are irregular breathing, faster heartbeat, and twitching fingers. Most people who are awakened from REM sleep say that they were experiencing vivid dreams.

With the transition from sleep (or deep relaxation) into wakefulness, EEG recordings show a shift to low-amplitude, higher frequency wave trains. Associated with this accelerated brain activity are increased blood flow and oxygen uptake in the cortex. The transition, called *EEG arousal,* occurs when individuals make a conscious effort to focus on external stimuli or even on their own thoughts.

The Reticular Formation. What brain regions govern changing levels of consciousness? Deep in the brainstem, buried within ascending and descending nerve pathways, lies a mass of nerve cells and processes called the **reticular formation**. This mass forms connections with the spinal cord, cerebellum, and cerebrum, as well as back with itself. It constantly samples messages flowing through the central nervous system. The flow of signals along these circuits—and the inhibitory or excitatory chemical changes accompanying them—has a great deal to do with whether you stay awake or drop off to sleep. For example, when certain areas of the reticular formation of sleeping animals are electrically stimulated, long, slow alpha rhythms are displaced by high-frequency potentials associated with arousal. Similarly, damage to the reticular formation leads to unconsciousness and coma.

Within this formation are neurons collectively called the **reticular activating system** (RAS). Excitatory pathways connect the RAS to the thalamus (the forebrain's switching station). Messages routed from the RAS arouse the brain and maintain wakefulness.

Also in the reticular formation are *sleep centers.* One center contains neurons that release the transmitter substance serotonin. This chemical has an inhibitory effect on RAS neurons: high serotonin levels are associated with drowsiness and sleep. Another sleep center, in the part of the reticular formation that lies in the pons, has been linked to REM sleep. Chemicals released from the second center

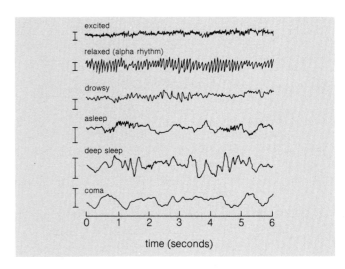

Figure 21.24   Examples of EEG wave patterns. The vertical bars indicate fifty millivolts each, with the irregular horizontal lines indicating the response with time. (After H. Jasper, 1941)

counteract the effects of serotonin. Hence its action allows the RAS to maintain the waking state.

DRUG ACTION ON INTEGRATION AND CONTROL

Each day can bring some minor frustration or disappointment, some pleasure or small triumph—and the brain responds to the shadings of environmental stimuli with delicate interplays among the activities of norepinephrine, dopamine, and the like. These interplays translate into changing emotional and behavioral states. When stress leads to physical or emotional pain, the brain apparently deploys other substances—**analgesics**, or pain relievers that the brain produces itself.

Receptors for natural analgesics have been identified on neural membranes in many parts of the nervous system, including the spinal cord and limbic system. (The limbic system includes structures bordering the cerebral hemispheres, at the top of the brainstem.) When bound to receptors, the pain relievers seem to inhibit neural activity. *Endorphins* (including *enkephalins*) are brain analgesics that may have this inhibitory effect. High concentrations of en-

Table 21.1 Endorphins and Enkephalins

Name of Substance	Effects
ACTH 4-10	Improves memory and concentration in normal individuals; helps mentally retarded individuals comprehend situations; improves memory of senile individuals
Beta-endorphin	Has powerful analgesic effect in mice and rats; in small sample of human trials countered depression and anxiety in mentally disturbed individuals, reduced hallucinations in some individuals suffering from schizophrenia; being studied for alleviation of pain in terminal cancer and for reducing withdrawal symptoms of opiates
Alpha-endorphin	Has analgesic and tranquilizing effect in rats
Gamma-endorphin	Produces violence, increased irritability, and increased sensitivity to pain in rats
Methionine-enkephalin and leucine-enkephalin	Appear to be body's natural pain-relieving molecules; synthetic compounds similar to these have caused long-lasting pain relief in rats; natural enkephalins improve memory, induce pleasure, and in rats can initiate epilepsy

(From J. Creager, *Human Anatomy and Physiology*, Wadsworth, 1982)

dorphins ("internally produced morphines") occur in brain regions concerned with our emotions and perception of pain (Table 21.1).

Emotional states—joy, elation, anxiety, depression, fear, anger—are normal responses to changing conditions in the complex world around us. Sometimes, through imbalances in transmitter substances, one or another of these states becomes pronounced. For instance, schizophrenic persons become despairing; they withdraw from the social world and focus obsessively on themselves. In an extreme form of the disorder (paranoid schizophrenia), afflicted persons suffer delusions of persecution or grandeur. Yet by administering certain synthetic tranquilizers, the symptoms can be brought under control. It appears that the tranquilizers affect norepinephrine, dopamine, and serotonin levels in the brain, in ways that depress the activity of neurons utilizing these transmitter substances.

Tranquilizers, opiates, stimulants, hallucinogens—such drugs are known to inhibit, modify, or enhance the release or action of chemical messengers throughout the brain (Table 21.2). Yet research into the effects of drugs on integration and control is in its infancy. For the most part, we don't understand much about how any one drug works. Given the complexity of the brain, it could scarcely be otherwise at this early stage of inquiry.

Table 21.2 Examples of Drug-Induced Disruptions of Neural Functions

Messenger	Regions Where Identified	Known Effects	Some Known Drug-Induced Disruptions
Norepinephrine	Secreted by some neurons in brain, by sympathetic neurons, and by adrenal medulla cells (derived embryonically from neurons)	Excitatory or inhibitory, depending on the target	*Amphetamines:* increase brain activity; increase heart action, respiration; decrease REM sleep
Epinephrine	Secreted by some neurons in brain; forms 80 percent of adrenal medulla's secretions		*Antidepressants:* possibly work by blocking receptors for the neurotransmitter histamine
Dopamine	Mostly motor system		*Phenothiazines (major tranquilizers):* block dopamine receptor sites, prevent uptake of norepinephrine and serotonin; inhibit sensory input to reticular activating system; induce relaxation and calm
Serotonin	Central nervous system, especially hypothalamus and limbic system, parts of reticular activating system		*LSD:* may inhibit effects of serotonin and enhance activity of norepinephrine; extreme perceptual distortion and hallucination (ranging from "mind-expanding" to terrifying)

Despite our ignorance of drug effects, one of the major problems in the modern world is drug abuse—the self-destructive use of drugs that alter emotional and behavioral states. The consequences show up in unexpected places—among seven-year-old heroin addicts; among the highway wreckage left by individuals whose perceptions were skewed by alcohol or amphetamines; among victims of addicts who steal and sometimes kill to support the drug habit; among suicides on LSD trips who were deluded into believing that they could fly, and who flew off buildings and bridges.

Each of us possesses a body of great complexity. Its architecture, its functioning are legacies of millions of years of evolution. It is unique in the living world because of its nervous system—a system that is capable of processing far more than the experience of the individual. One of its most astonishing products is language—the encoding of *shared* experiences of groups of individuals in time and space. Through the evolution of our nervous system, the sense of history was born, and the sense of destiny. Through this system we can ask how we have come to be what we are, and where we are headed from here. Perhaps the sorriest consequence of drug abuse is its implicit denial of this legacy—the denial of self when we cease to ask, and cease to care.

Readings

Axelrod, J. 1974. "Neurotransmitters." *Scientific American* 230(6):58–71.

Bullock, T., R. Orkand, and A. Grinnell. 1977. *Introduction to Nervous Systems.* San Francisco: Freeman. Outstanding source book, and by far the best illustrated.

Eccles, J. 1977. *The Understanding of the Brain.* New York: McGraw-Hill. Excellent, well-written account of neural activity in the brain; the descriptions of research into states of consciousness convey the excitement and frontier aspect of ongoing research. Paperback.

Gazzaniga, M. 1967. "The Split Brain in Man." *Scientific American* 217(2):24–29.

Hubel, D., and T. Wiesel. 1974. "Sequence Regularity and Geometry of Orientation Columns in the Monkey Striate Cortex." *Journal of Comparative Neurology* 158:267–294.

Kuffler, S., and J. Nicholls. 1977. *From Neuron to Brain.* Sunderland, Massachusetts: Sinauer. Unusual perspective; follows recent developments emerging from a few selected lines of research. Excellent discussions on neural signaling and the neural organization underlying visual perception.

Lassen, N., D. Ingvar, and E. Skinhøj. 1978. "Brain Function and Blood Flow." *Scientific American* 239(4):62–72. New maps of the cerebral cortex, based largely on radioactive isotope tracings of changes of blood flow in different cortical regions during different states of activity.

Penfield, W., and T. Rasmussen. 1952. *The Cerebral Cortex of Man.* New York: Macmillan. Fascinating account of early mappings of cortical regions.

Romer, A., and T. Parsons. 1977. *The Vertebrate Body.* Fifth edition. Philadelphia: Saunders. Chapter 16 contains detailed pictures of vertebrate nervous systems. Excellent reference book.

Shepherd, G. 1978. "Microcircuits in the Nervous System." *Scientific American* 238(2):93–103. For almost a hundred years message conduction has been described largely in terms of axonal pathways. This article describes recent discoveries of inhibitory feedback loops between dendrites only.

Sherrington, C. 1947. *Integrative Action of the Nervous System.* New Haven, Connecticut: Yale University Press. Sherrington was an outstanding neuroscientist, and a poet as well; his writing is near-lyrical, and his insights still rewarding.

Sperry, R. 1970. "Perception in the Absence of the Neocortical Commissures." *Perception and Its Disorders.* Research Publication of the Association for Research in Nervous and Mental Diseases, vol. 48.

Vander, A., J. Sherman, and D. Luciano. 1980. *Human Physiology: The Mechanisms of Body Function.* Third edition. New York: McGraw-Hill. Contains very good introductions to what is known about information processing in the human brain.

Review Questions

1. Describe the functional zones of a neuron.

2. Two major concentration gradients exist across a neural membrane. What are they, and how are they maintained?

3. An electrical gradient also exists across a neural membrane. Explain what the electrical and concentration gradients together represent. What is a nerve message?

4. Distinguish between an action potential and a graded potential. What is meant by "all-or-none" and "self-propagating" messages?

5. Define sensory neuron, interneuron, and motor neuron.

6. What is a synapse? Explain the difference between an excitatory and an inhibitory synapse. Then define neural integration.

7. What is a reflex? Describe the sequence of events in a stretch reflex.

8. Contrast radially and bilaterally arranged nervous systems in terms of responsiveness to the environment.

9. Six basic principles govern the functioning of all nervous systems, from the simplest to the most complex. What are these principles?

10. Make a list of the main parts of the vertebrate nervous system. Can you define the main functions of each?

11. How do sympathetic and parasympathetic nerves regulate the autonomic pathways?

22

INTEGRATION AND CONTROL: ENDOCRINE SYSTEMS

HORMONE FUNCTION

Comparison of Neural and Endocrine Cell Secretions

In nervous systems, coordination and control of body activities depends on message transmission along clearly prescribed communication pathways. The transmitter substances secreted from any neuron travel only a short distance to the next cells in line. The messages they carry to their targets is this: "It's time to change a particular activity." All of these transmitter substances are released in tiny amounts, they rapidly trigger change in the membrane potential of an *adjacent* cell, then they are quickly degraded by enzymes or taken up by the cells that secrete them. Transmitter substances function, for a fleeting moment, as information carriers.

Some nerve cells release different kinds of information carriers, called **neurosecretory hormones**. These secretions also trigger changes in membrane potential of their targets. But they travel more slowly and they travel farther, by way of interstitial fluid or the bloodstream, to many *nonadjacent* cells. In anatomically simple animals (cnidarians, annelids, probably flatworms), neurosecretory hormones are practically the only physiological controls over cells and tissues concerned with growth and reproduction.

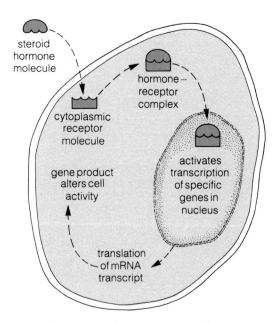

Figure 22.1 Proposed mechanism of steroid hormone action on target cells.

Animals ranging from mollusks to humans depend on transmitter substances and neurosecretory hormones. They also depend on **true hormones**, which are information carriers secreted only by endocrine cells (Chapter Twenty). Some endocrine cells function individually; others are organized in secretory structures called glands. All endocrine cells secrete hormone molecules into interstitial fluid. From there, the molecules move into the bloodstream and are transported for some distance through the body. Then they move out of the bloodstream and diffuse through interstitial fluid, and are picked up by specific target cells. *By definition, hormones are endocrine products that are transported by body fluids and that regulate specific reactions in cells of nonadjacent tissues and organs.*

Through their action, some hormones stimulate or inhibit the growth, development, and activity of various tissues. Others help control metabolism. Still others have profound effects on behavior. No hormone acts as rapidly as neural secretions, which take effect within milliseconds. Minutes, hours, even days pass between the time of hormonal secretion and the start of a response. In some cases, the response to hormonal action continues long after its initiation, as happens during development. In general, endocrine controls come into play when the concentration of some cell substance must be maintained at a prescribed level in the body or when prolonged stimulation or inhibition of cell activity is required.

Hormones are endocrine products that help maintain the internal environment and that help bring about long-term growth and development.

Mechanisms of Hormone Action

The "targets" of a particular hormone are those cells which have membrane receptor sites for molecules of that hormone. Some kinds of hormones have widespread effects, because nearly all body cells have receptor sites for them. The growth hormone secreted by the pituitary gland has such a pervasive effect. Other kinds of hormones have highly specific effects, because only a limited number of cell types have receptor sites for them. For instance, the hormone gastrin diffuses throughout the body, but only certain stomach cells respond to it.

The most common hormones are steroid, peptide, or amine compounds. These compounds induce changes in target cells in different ways. Being lipids, the **steroid hor-**

mones can pass readily through the plasma membrane of a target cell. Once inside the cytoplasm, the steroid combines with a protein molecule that serves as a cytoplasmic receptor (Figure 22.1). Then the steroid-protein complex enters the cell nucleus, where it triggers transcription of specific genes into specific messenger-RNA molecules. When the messenger-RNA is translated in the cytoplasm, the protein product molecules alter cell activity in specific ways, as described in Chapter Thirteen.

Many **polypeptide hormones** are unable to penetrate the plasma membrane of the target cell. They rely on functional partners—second messengers—which mediate the hormone action for them inside the cell. Some polypeptide hormones bind with a receptor site on the plasma membrane (Figure 22.2). The binding activates adenyl cyclase, an enzyme that transforms ATP present in the cytoplasm to **cyclic AMP**. (The full name is cyclic adenosine monophosphate. "Cyclic" indicates that the phosphate group is bound between the 3' and 5' carbon atoms of the sugar component of the molecule, which thereby becomes a ringlike structure.) Cyclic AMP acts on protein kinases, which add

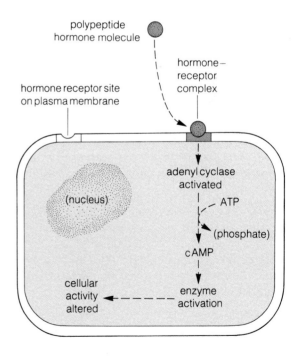

Figure 22.2 Proposed mechanism of action of some polypeptide hormones on target cells.

or remove phosphate groups from proteins involved in diverse cellular responses. For instance, protein kinases must activate the enzymes required for breaking down carbohydrates and lipids.

Through hormonal action, the formation or the activity of a specific enzyme is accelerated or slowed down in target cells.

Factors Influencing Hormone Levels in the Bloodstream

The concentration of a hormone in blood plasma depends on several factors, including the following:

1. *Availability of chemical precursors.* The precursors are obtained from the diet or from body cells; they enter the bloodstream and are picked up by the cells in which the hormones are synthesized.

2. *Hormone secretion rate.* Endocrine cells secrete hormones when they are stimulated by neural input, other hormones, or plasma concentrations of certain ions or nutrients. In cases where the secretion of one hormone controls the secretion of another, a negative feedback relationship may exist between the target endocrine cell and the controlling endocrine cell. (For example, the anterior pituitary releases the hormone ACTH, which stimulates the adrenal cortex into releasing the hormone cortisol. Plasma concentrations of cortisol rise, and the increased level acts on the anterior pituitary in such a way that further ACTH release is inhibited.) In most (if not all) cases, the central nervous system also exerts controls over secretion rates, in ways that will be described shortly.

3. *Hormone activation rate.* Some hormones are not fully activated when released from endocrine cells, and they cannot exert their effects without further processing. For instance, coenzymes in target cells must convert the steroid hormone testosterone to dihydrotestosterone before the hormonal response can be effected.

4. *Rate of hormone removal from bloodstream.* Following their action, hormone molecules do not accumulate in the body. Some are inactivated by the target cells themselves. Most, however, are inactivated by the liver or excreted from the body via the kidneys and the urinary ducts.

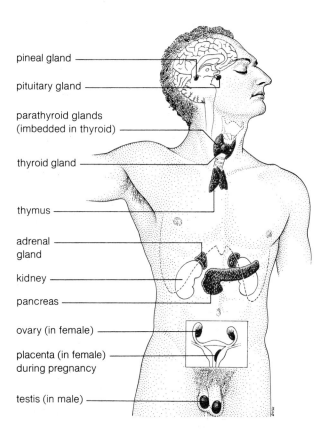

Figure 22.3 Location of endocrine glands and endocrine elements in the human body. Glandular epithelium of the gastrointestinal tract also serves endocrine functions.

COMPONENTS OF ENDOCRINE SYSTEMS

Most vertebrates have the following assortment of glands and other endocrine elements, which together constitute an endocrine system:

    Pituitary gland
    Pineal gland
    Adrenal glands (two)
    Thyroid gland
    Parathyroid glands (two)
    Gonads (two)
    Pancreatic islets (multiple)
    Glandular epithelium of gut (multiple)
    Kidneys (two)
    Thymus gland

The position of these endocrine elements in the body has not changed much during the course of vertebrate evolution. Hence a sketch of their location in the human body will give you an idea of their location in other vertebrates as well (Figure 22.3).

The remainder of this chapter will present a brief overview of the components of the human endocrine system. Subsequent chapters will include details of specific hormonal products and will describe their roles in elegant feedback mechanisms that control the functioning of specific organ systems.

NEUROENDOCRINE CONTROL CENTER

On Neural and Endocrine Links

In looking at Figure 22.3, you might conclude (as researchers did for a long time) that the vertebrate "endocrine system" is not much of a system at all. After all, its component cells, tissues, and organs are physically separated. They secrete diverse polypeptide, amine, and steroid hormones. And they often act on targets located nowhere near them! What possibly could link the system's components together? The answer may lie in their ancient origins. It is possible that many endocrine elements evolved as specialized regions of nervous systems in animals not much more complex than flatworms.

Suppose that long ago, mutations in a sending or a receiving neuron led to the production of transmitter substances that were not degraded in the synaptic cleft between them. Molecules of the substance might have started to diffuse through surrounding tissues. They might even have begun slipping into and out of the bloodstream. Suppose their surface configuration enabled them to stick to or penetrate cells in distant body parts and that the association altered metabolic activity in those cells. If the alterations somehow enhanced cell function, then the mutation would have conferred advantages on the individual. Over time, the mutant cells and their inadvertent targets might have become modified in ways that promoted long-distance action; they would have been forerunners to endocrine cells and tissues.

If complex endocrine elements did indeed evolve from neurosecretory beginnings, we might suspect that they still must retain close connections with the nervous system. Today we know that neurosecretory cells are the main source of hormones in many invertebrate groups. Given its pervasive presence throughout the animal kingdom, we can

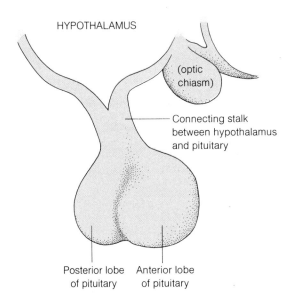

Figure 22.4 Location of the pituitary gland relative to the hypothalamus.

conclude that neurosecretion is an ancient functional link between nervous and endocrine systems. In complex vertebrates also, both the nervous system and the body's endocrine elements produce and secrete chemical messengers that influence the output of target cells. Autonomic nerves directly control the secretion of certain endocrine elements. Neurosecretory hormones act on certain endocrine elements, and some endocrine secretions influence the nervous system's activity. Most bodily states—and this includes mental and behavioral states—depend on their interaction.

The functioning of most endocrine elements is mediated directly by a separate nerve supply or indirectly by secretions from control centers in the nervous system.

Interactions Between the Hypothalamus and Pituitary

The hypothalamus, recall, is an information-processing region of the central nervous system. The **pituitary** is a compound gland, about the size of a small jellybean in adult humans. A slender stalk attaches it to the floor of the hypothalamus (Figure 22.4). The connecting stalk and the pituitary's *posterior lobe* are nervous tissue. The posterior lobe is

Table 22.1 Summary of Known Major Controls of Hormone Secretion

Control Element	Directly Controls Release of:
Hypothalamic neurons	Hypothalamic-releasing factors Oxytocin (from posterior pituitary) Antidiuretic hormone (from posterior pituitary)
Hypothalamic-releasing factors	Anterior pituitary hormones: Growth hormone Thyroid-stimulating hormone (TSH) Adrenocorticotropic hormone (ACTH) Gonadotropic hormones (FSH and LH)
Anterior pituitary hormones	Thyroid hormone Cortisol (from adrenal cortex) Gonadal hormones (estrogen and progesterone in females, testosterone in males)
Autonomic neurons	Epinephrine, norepinephrine (from adrenal medulla) Renin (from kidney) Insulin, glucagon (from pancreas) Gastrointestinal hormones
Ion concentrations, nutrient concentrations in blood plasma	Parathyroid hormone Insulin, glucagon (from pancreas) Aldosterone (from adrenal cortex) Calcitonin (from thyroid glands)

Data from Vander et al. *Human Physiology*, 1980.

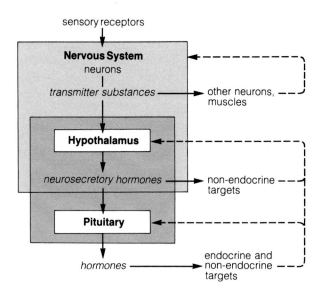

Figure 22.5 Main pathways leading to and away from the neuroendocrine control center. Secretory pathways are shown in solid lines. Broken lines indicate negative feedback loops brought about by changing activities in the cells that are targets for the secretions indicated.

they function as brain analgesics (Chapter Twenty-One). Is there also a hormonal role for endorphins? That is not known.

Taken together, the hypothalamus and pituitary are now being viewed as the **neuroendocrine control center**, which integrates neural and endocrine activities. The hypothalamus governs many behavioral patterns that require an interplay of neural and hormonal input; it is also of central importance in regulating the internal environment. In the hypothalamus, stimulatory and inhibitory signals from the cerebral cortex are summed. Both the hypothalamus and pituitary respond to shifts in blood plasma concentrations of hormones, certain ions, and nutrients. Table 22.1 and Figure 22.5 give an indication of the extent of the control relationships we are outlining here.

All vertebrates have a neuroendocrine control center, which consists of the hypothalamus and pituitary.

Because its secretions affect many other endocrine elements, the pituitary is traditionally thought of as the "master gland." But the hypothalamus controls the pituitary. And the hypothalamus itself is influenced by the cerebral cortex and by concentrations of hormones, ions, and nutrients in the bloodstream.

a holding station for two neurosecretory hormones that are produced in the hypothalamus. The *anterior lobe* of the pituitary is mostly glandular tissue. It produces and secretes at least six hormones, and it controls the secretion of several more from other endocrine elements.

The pituitary also has an *intermediate lobe,* which is not as well developed as the other two. Cells in the intermediate lobe secrete melanocyte-stimulating hormones, which in many vertebrates function in determining the amount and distribution of melanin pigments in the skin. (The function of these hormones in humans is not well understood.) Both the intermediate and the anterior lobes contain endorphins. Endorphins, recall, are also present in brain regions, where

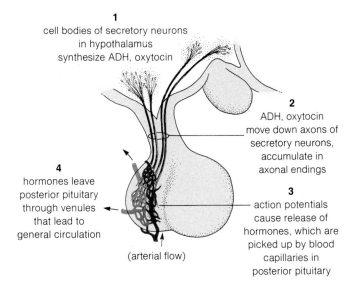

1
cell bodies of secretory neurons
in hypothalamus
synthesize ADH, oxytocin

2
ADH, oxytocin
move down axons of
secretory neurons,
accumulate in
axonal endings

4
hormones leave
posterior pituitary
through venules
that lead to
general circulation

3
action potentials
cause release of
hormones, which are
picked up by blood
capillaries in
posterior pituitary

(arterial flow)

Figure 22.6 Functional links between the hypothalamus and the posterior lobe of the pituitary.

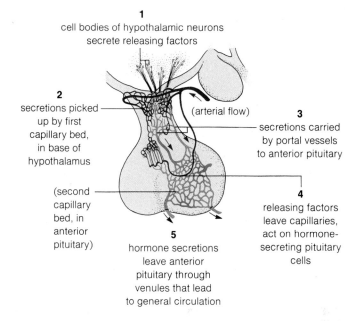

1
cell bodies of hypothalamic neurons
secrete releasing factors

2
secretions picked
up by first
capillary bed,
in base of
hypothalamus

(arterial flow)

3
secretions carried
by portal vessels
to anterior pituitary

(second
capillary
bed, in
anterior
pituitary)

5
hormone secretions
leave anterior
pituitary through
venules that lead
to general circulation

4
releasing factors
leave capillaries,
act on hormone-
secreting pituitary
cells

Figure 22.7 Functional links between the hypothalamus and the anterior lobe of the pituitary.

Posterior Lobe Secretions. Cells in the hypothalamus produce two neurosecretory hormones. One of these hormones is *oxytocin,* which plays a key role in mammalian reproduction. The other is *antidiuretic hormone,* or ADH. This hormone functions mainly in controls over water levels in the body, and it thereby indirectly influences salt concentrations as well. (ADH is also called vasopressin, a name that relates more to the role this hormone plays in vasoconstriction.) In mammals, oxytocin and ADH are stored in axonal endings of the hypothalamic neurons that produce them. The cell bodies of these neurons are clustered in two distinct areas of the hypothalamus, as Figure 22.6 suggests. Their axons pass down the stalk that connects the hypothalamus and the pituitary, and they terminate in the posterior lobe. In response to neural, hormonal, or metabolic input, action potentials are generated in these hypothalamic neurons. Action potentials travel down their axons and stimulate release of ADH or oxytocin molecules, which are picked up by capillaries present in the posterior lobe. These capillaries empty into venules that lead to the general circulation.

Anterior Lobe Secretions. In diverse regions of the hypothalamus are cell bodies of secretory neurons that produce two kinds of proteins, called releasing and inhibiting factors. The **releasing factors** stimulate the secretion of specific anterior lobe hormones; the **inhibiting factors** suppress their secretion.

The axons of this particular assortment of secretory neurons do not terminate directly on the anterior lobe of the pituitary. Rather, they terminate at the base of the hypothalamus, right next to an intricate network of blood capillaries (Figure 22.7). These capillaries converge into **portal vessels** present in the stalk between the hypothalamus and pituitary. ("Portal" refers to vessels that connect two distinct capillary beds.) The portal vessels then diverge into another capillary bed, in the anterior lobe.

In response to neural, hormonal, or metabolic signals, releasing factors or inhibiting factors are secreted from the hypothalamic neurons. They are picked up by blood capillaries, transported down through portal vessels to the second capillary bed, and move into the interstitial fluid. From there, they interact with specific target cells in the anterior pituitary, and these cells respond by altering their hormonal output.

At least seven hypothalamic factors are conveyed by portal vessels to the anterior lobe, where they regulate secretion of the following hormones:

Table 22.2 Animal Hormones Produced by the Hypothalamus and Pituitary

Source	Hormone	Target	Primary Actions
Hypothalamus (production) and posterior pituitary (storage, secretion)	Oxytocin	Uterus	Stimulates uterine contractions
		Mammary glands	Stimulates milk movement into secretory ducts
	Antidiuretic hormone (ADH); also called vasopressin	Kidney	Promotes water reabsorption
Anterior pituitary	Adrenocorticotropic hormone (ACTH)	Adrenal cortex	Stimulates adrenal hormone secretion
	Thyroid-stimulating hormone (TSH)	Thyroid gland	Stimulates thyroid hormone secretion
	Gonadotropins:		
	Follicle-stimulating hormone (FSH)	Ovaries, testes	In females promotes follicle growth, helps stimulate estrogen secretion, ovulation. In males promotes testosterone secretion, spermatogenesis
	Luteinizing hormone (LH)	Ovaries, testes	In females stimulates corpus luteum. In males promotes testosterone secretion, spermatogenesis
	Growth hormone; also called somatotropin	Most cells	Induces mitotic cell division and protein synthesis underlying growth
	Prolactin	Mammary glands	Stimulates milk production

Adrenocorticotropin (ACTH)
Thyroid-stimulating hormone (TSH)
Follicle-stimulating hormone (FSH)
Luteinizing hormone (LH)
Growth hormone
Prolactin

The targets of these hormones are indicated in Table 22.2. All but the last two hormones listed above influence the activity of other endocrine glands. *Prolactin,* which acts on exocrine glands in breast tissue, stimulates milk production. *Growth hormone* (or somatotropin) acts on most cells in the body. Growth hormone governs bodily growth by stimulating mitotic cell division and protein synthesis. It also figures in the metabolism of protein as an alternative energy source when carbohydrate supplies are low (as during periods of fasting).

Growth hormone is one of many hormones that are secreted on a distinctly cyclic basis. Normally, little if any growth hormone is secreted during the daytime. Just after a person falls asleep, signals are generated in sleep centers in the brain (Chapter Twenty-One). Neurons carrying these signals synapse with hypothalamic neurons that secrete growth-hormone releasing factors. The outcome is one or more prolonged bursts of growth hormone secretion from the anterior pituitary. The cyclic secretion rate is most pronounced during adolescence, the period during childhood when the body grows most rapidly. Individuals who produce deficient amounts of growth hormone during childhood suffer *dwarfism:* an adult body that is similar in proportion but extremely reduced in size, compared with a normal adult. Excessive production of growth hormone leads to *gigantism:* an adult body that markedly surpasses normal body size.

Table 22.3 lists the secretions of endocrine elements other than the pituitary gland. We will briefly consider the nature of these secretions here. The functional relationships between these endocrine elements and the nervous system will be traced in later chapters, so you may find it useful to scan this table as an overview of things to come.

Table 22.3   Other Main Animal Hormones, Their Sources, and Their Action

Source	Hormone	Target	Primary Actions
Adrenal cortex	Glucocorticoids (cortisol and others)	Most cells	Raise blood sugar level; control lipid, carbohydrate, protein metabolism; mediate responses to stress
	Mineralocorticoids (aldosterone and others)	Kidney	Promote sodium reabsorption, salt and water balance
	Sex hormones (androgens, estrogens)	General	Influence sexual characteristics, general growth
Adrenal medulla	Epinephrine (adrenalin)	Liver, cardiac muscle	Raises blood sugar level by stimulating glucose production
		Adipose tissue	Raises blood fatty acid levels
	Norepinephrine	Smooth muscle of blood vessels	Vasoconstriction
Gonads:			
Testis	Testosterone (an androgen)	General	Stimulates development of genital tract; development, maintenance of accessory sex organs and secondary sex traits; general effect on metabolism, growth; essential for spermatogenesis
Ovary	Estrogen	General	Stimulates thickening of uterine lining for pregnancy; essential for oogenesis; other actions same as above
	Progesterone	Uterus, breasts	Prepares, maintains uterine lining for pregnancy, stimulates breast development
Thyroid	Thyroxin	Most cells	Regulates carbohydrate, lipid metabolism; growth, development
	Calcitonin	Bone	Lowers calcium levels in blood by inhibiting calcium reabsorption from bone
Parathyroids	Parathyroid hormone	Bone, kidney, gut	Elevates calcium levels in blood by stimulating calcium reabsorption from bone, kidneys, and absorption from gut
Pancreatic islets	Insulin	All cells except neurons in brain and red blood cells	Lowers blood sugar by stimulating glucose uptake by cell; fat storage; protein synthesis
	Glucagon	Liver, muscle, adipose tissue	Raises blood sugar by stimulating glucose production
Glandular epithelia of stomach, small intestine	Includes gastrin, cholecystokinin, secretin	Stomach, small intestine	Part of controls over gastrointestinal secretion, motility
Thymus	Includes thymosin	Lymphocytes, plasma cells	Promote development of infection-fighting abilities and lymphocyte function in immune surveillance
Kidney	Erythropoietin*	Bone marrow	Stimulates red blood cell production
	Angiotensin*	Adrenal cortex, arterioles	Control of blood pressure

*These hormones are not produced in the kidneys but are formed when enzymes produced in the kidney activate specific plasma substrates.

OTHER ENDOCRINE ELEMENTS

Adrenal Glands

Above each of the two kidneys in the vertebrate body is a compound adrenal gland. The outer layer, the **adrenal cortex**, develops embryonically in close association with the reproductive organs. It secretes three types of hormones: glucocorticoids, mineralocorticoids, and sex hormones. The *glucocorticoids* (such as cortisol) help regulate carbohydrate, lipid, and protein metabolism. They also combat tissue damage. The *mineralocorticoids* (including aldosterone) influence salt and water concentrations in the body. Two classes of sex hormones, the *androgens* and *estrogens,* are also secreted in small amounts by the adrenal cortex.

The inner region of the adrenal gland, the **adrenal medulla**, is derived embryonically from nerve tissue. Its cells are actually modified neurons, which reinforce sympathetic activity. The adrenal medulla secretes *epinephrine* and *norepinephrine;* both help control blood circulation and carbohydrate metabolism. Brain centers (including the hypothalamus) govern their secretion by way of sympathetic nerves. Normally, the adrenal medulla releases both hormones in small amounts.

Thyroid and Parathyroid Glands

At the base of your neck, just below and in front of your windpipe, is a two-lobed **thyroid gland**. It stores and releases hormones that help govern growth, development, and metabolic rates throughout the body. Under the direction of the anterior pituitary, the thyroid gland secretes *thyroxin,* which increases the metabolic rate of cells. Special cells located in the thyroid secrete *calcitonin,* which inhibits the release of calcium from bone storage sites when calcium levels rise in blood plasma.

Embedded in the back surface tissues of the thyroid are four **parathyroid glands**. Their secretion, *parathyroid hormone,* counterbalances the effects of calcitonin by promoting the release of calcium from bone storage sites when calcium levels drop in blood plasma. Calcium, recall, is vital in many cellular reactions. For example, nerve and muscle cell excitability depends on carefully regulated amounts of calcium ions.

Gonads

The **gonads** are the primary sex structures known as testes (in males) and ovaries (in females). Gonads give rise to gametes. They also secrete hormones that prepare accessory reproductive structures (ducts, glands, and tissues) for reproduction. In the female, gonadal secretions help prepare the uterus for implantation and embryonic development. Some gonadal secretions are listed in Table 22.3. The gonads themselves are described in Chapter Twenty-Nine, as are the effects of their hormones.

Glandular Tissues of the Pancreas, Stomach, and Small Intestine

The pancreas is largely an exocrine gland that secretes digestive enzymes. However, about 2 million endocrine cell clusters, called **pancreatic islets**, are also scattered in the pancreas. In response to plasma concentrations of glucose and amino acids, these cells produce and secrete the hormones insulin and glucagon. *Insulin* takes part directly or indirectly in glucose, lipid, and protein metabolism throughout the body. *Glucagon* counterbalances some aspects of insulin action by stimulating the breakdown of glycogen (a storage polysaccharide) into glucose monomers.

Glandular epithelium in the gastrointestinal tract also produces hormones. These hormones help control digestion by stimulating the release of digestive enzymes and bile. Among the hormones produced by the gastrointestinal tract are *gastrin, cholecystokinin,* and *secretin.*

Hormone Functions of Kidneys

The **kidneys** are paired organs positioned in the back of the abdominal wall. They are concerned with balancing salt and water concentrations in the internal environment. They also take part in hormonal controls over blood pressure and red blood cell production.

Special cells lining the arterioles in kidneys produce and secrete an enzyme called renin. When circulating in the bloodstream, renin acts on a plasma protein (which the liver produces). The protein becomes converted to a hormone called *angiotensin.* This hormone is a powerful vasoconstrictor, and its effects are widespread on arterioles throughout the body. More importantly, angiotensin acts on the adrenal cortex, stimulating it into releasing the hormone aldosterone. This hormone is a major control over sodium levels in the body and, indirectly, over blood volume.

Some cells in the kidney secrete a glycoprotein that activates a plasma substrate to form *erythropoietin.* This hormone stimulates bone marrow to produce oxygen-carrying red blood cells.

Pineal Gland and Thymus Gland

The pineal gland and thymus have endocrine functions, but they are not usually listed among the major endocrine glands. The **pineal gland** takes part in reproductive physiology, although its precise role in the human body has not been identified. In other vertebrates, the pineal gland senses change in the length of daylight associated with changing seasons and causes alterations in how fast certain hormones are produced and released. (This response to cyclic variations in light stimuli is a form of *photoperiodism*.)

The **thymus** is a two-lobed gland located behind the breastbone and between the lungs. The thymus figures in the maturation of white blood cells called lymphocytes, which defend against infection and form a surveillance system by which damaged or malignant cells are detected and eliminated. The thymus also secretes a group of hormones collectively called *thymosin*. These hormones are thought to affect the functioning of certain lymphocytes.

Prostaglandins

Prostaglandins are not hormones in the traditional sense. Rather, they are a grab-bag of "local hormones." They are present in tissues throughout the body—lungs, gut, liver, and the prostate gland in males. Prostaglandins may act as mediators between membrane receptors and the enzymes that activate cyclic AMP in diverse cell types. Some have profound effects on reproduction. Prostaglandins also influence nerve function, respiration, digestion, blood clotting, and the immune response. The analgesic and fever-reducing actions of aspirin are due to aspirin's ability to inhibit the action of prostaglandin.

Readings

Frieden, E., and H. Lipner. 1971. *Biochemical Endocrinology of the Vertebrates.* Englewood Cliffs, New Jersey: Prentice-Hall. Structure and action of hormones are described.

Ganong, W. 1979. *Review of Medical Physiology.* Ninth edition. Los Altos, California: Lange Medical Publications. Advanced reading, but an authoritative source of information on endocrinology.

Hickman, C., et al. 1979. *Integrated Principles of Zoology.* Sixth edition. St. Louis: Mosby. Good introduction to the evolution of endocrine systems in Chapter Thirty-Three.

McEwen, B. 1976. "Interactions Between Hormones and Nerve Tissue." *Scientific American* 235:48–58. Traces steroid hormones secreted by gonads and adrenal cortex to target cells in the brain.

Pastan, I. 1972. "Cyclic AMP." *Scientific American* 227(2):97–105.

Turner, C., and J. Bagnara. 1976. *General Endocrinology.* Sixth edition. Philadelphia: Saunders. Perhaps the best single reference on endocrine structure and function. Very well illustrated.

Review Questions

1. Name the main endocrine glands and state where each is located in the human body.

2. Define the difference between transmitter substances and neurosecretory hormones.

3. Define hormone. What functions do hormones serve? How do these functions differ from those of transmitter substances?

4. There are two general classes of hormones: steroid and polypeptide. In molecular terms, how is each thought to act on a target cell?

5. Describe four factors that may influence the concentration of a hormone in the bloodstream at a given time.

6. The hypothalamus and pituitary are considered to be a neuroendocrine control center. Can you describe some of the functional links between these two organs?

7. How does the hypothalamus control secretions of the posterior lobe of the pituitary? The anterior lobe?

8. Name five endocrine glands and a substance that each one secretes. What are the main consequences of their secretion?

9. Which hormone secreted by the anterior pituitary has an effect on most body cells rather than on a specific cell type? What are the clinical consequences of too little or too much secretion of this hormone?

23

RECEPTION AND MOTOR RESPONSE

No matter where an animal lives, survival means adjustment to change. In complex animals, adjustments fall under neural and endocrine controls of the sort described in the preceding chapters. Yet how does information about change actually reach the nervous system? In what ways are commands for motor response actually implemented? These questions bring us to sensory and motor adaptations for interacting with the environment. At first glance, some of these adaptations may seem bizarre. However, there is an underlying logic to the ways that animals sense and respond to their surroundings. To discover it, we must think about where the animal lives and where its probable forerunners evolved.

For example, consider the bat. This winged mammal has a terrifying face, it hides by day and emerges at dusk to swoop in the gathering darkness. Its appearance and its habits caused it to be placed in the company of demons, witches, and other suspect figures of the human imagination. Where do bats live? What were conditions like when their ancestors were evolving? How are bat senses tuned to the environment?

Bats live everywhere except in polar regions and on a few oceanic islands. One species or another lives in forests, grasslands, and deserts, although they are most abundant and diverse in the tropics. Regardless of where they live, all bats are essentially immobile during the day. When the sun is up they roost upside-down in caves, barns, branches, or rocky cliffs. All become active at dusk, when they take to the air in search of fruit, pollen, nectar, or (depending on the species) insects, frogs, lizards, fish, even other bats. Thus bats forage when the skies are cleared of the flights and sounds of almost all birds. Birds happen to eat the same kinds of foods as bats.

What sensory adaptations enable bats to dominate the nighttime skies that birds leave vacant? How can bats detect food then, and why don't they fly smack into trees,

Figure 23.1 Above: Portrait of a moustached bat on the wing. (Timothy Strickler and Terry Vaughan) Below: This bat is listening to echoes of self-produced ultrasonic noises as they bounce back from objects in the environment.

Merlin D. Tuttle, Milwaukee Public Museum

cliffs, and other obstacles? For possible answers, consider that bats generally are social animals. Sometimes they live in colonies that number in the millions. They also fly together in the dark. Given the sheer numbers of these groups, you might expect bats to have some means of keeping far enough apart to avoid midair collisions. They do. Bats make numerous sounds by which they communicate their location to one another. In addition, male bats make explosive, throaty calls that attract females during the breeding season. In other words, they use sound waves for social communication.

Perhaps long ago, social communication was a basis for the evolution of sensory adaptations that allow most present-day bat species to forage in the dark. Bats **echolocate**: they emit high-frequency sound waves, and echoes from the waves bounce back to their ears from objects in the surroundings (Figure 23.1). In this way, bats orient themselves toward prey and away from obstacles. Bats and birds evolved concurrently many millions of years ago, and competition for the same foods would have been fierce. Thus it is possible that bats and birds came to coexist in the same places by dividing up the day-into-night cycle—with echolocation providing the competitive edge at night.

Thus some bats have big lips which they purse up during flights, like a megaphone, to give off echolocating pulses. The echoes of those pulses return to extremely sensitive ears. Some bats have a horseshoe-shaped structure around the nostrils that projects pulses straight ahead, much like a flashlight beam, for pinpointing objects. Bats that dine on small vertebrates have immense ears and (for a bat) large eyes, perhaps the better to hear faint rustlings and to observe stealthy movements of prey. Such exaggerated features of bat faces have nothing to do with intimidating other animals. They are the sensory structures with which these particular animals have become adapted to the world.

SENSING ENVIRONMENTAL CHANGE

Primary Receptors

The only link between the nervous system and events going on within and around the animal body are **primary receptors**: sensory nerve processes or specialized epithelial cells that detect specific kinds of stimuli. A **stimulus** is any form of energy change in the environment (or any variation between energy forms) that the body actually detects. If there were no such detection of change or variation, the world would seem perpetually devoid of detail. What you see as

a blue flower in a yellow wheat field is, in essence, variations in wavelengths of light energy—a difference in color between two regions of space. What you hear as sound are waves of change in air pressure—mechanical energy changes over time.

A stimulus is any detected form of energy change, or variation between energy forms, in the environment. Receptors translate stimulus energy into electrochemical messages that can be dealt with by the nervous system.

Receptors reside in body surface tissues, muscles and tendons, and internal organ walls. Often they are arranged in epithelial and connective tissue to form sensory organs, such as the eye. **Sensory organs** amplify and focus stimulus energy during its transformation into nerve signals. *Stimulus amplification* helps many animals to detect weak but potentially important signals in the distance—for instance, to see or hear danger approaching. In addition, sensory organs provide information about *stimulus direction.* Thus, for example, your brain can estimate the source of some sound by comparing signals being sent to it from receptors in each of your two ears.

Receptors are classified according to the type of stimulus energy that they selectively detect:

Chemoreceptors detect impinging chemical energy (ions or molecules that have become dissolved in body fluids next to the receptor). They include odor and taste receptors, and internal receptors such as those sensitive to blood glucose levels.

Mechanoreceptors detect mechanical energy associated with changes in pressure, position, or acceleration. They include receptors for touch, stretch, hearing, and equilibrium.

Photoreceptors detect photon energy of visible light and ultraviolet light.

Thermoreceptors detect radiant energy associated with temperature changes. They include infrared receptors.

Electroreceptors detect currents (movement of electrical energy). They include receptors for electrical fields generated passively by external objects (such as prey), or for externally induced disturbances in a self-generated electric field around the animal body (as in electric eels).

Nocireceptors detect energy changes that are injurious or painful to the body.

Here, we will focus on only a few examples of these receptors to illustrate how information is channeled into the nervous system. Other examples will be described in later chapters.

Chemical Reception

Olfaction, the detection of odors, is one of the most ancient senses. In fact, most of the forebrain of the earliest vertebrates was devoted to processing olfactory signals. Olfactory receptors are present in epithelium that lines nasal cavities. The receptors are specialized columnar epithelial cells, each with hairline projections on its free surface (Figure 23.2). These cells are unique among receptors in that their axons continue right into the olfactory bulb of the central nervous system, rather than synapsing with sensory neurons.

Olfactory receptors sample odors from food present in the mouth, but they also function in the sense of taste. (That is why food seems tasteless when your nose is stopped up from a cold.) In functional terms, odor and taste receptors seem to differ only in their sensitivity to different classes of molecules; taste receptors are about four times more sensitive. Molecules reach both kinds of receptors by dissolving first in mucus or other fluids that coat the surface epithelium in which the receptors reside.

In structural terms, taste receptors are more complex than olfactory receptors. For example, **taste buds** are barrel-shaped organs that are abundant in the mouth and pharynx of most animals. In mammals, taste buds are concentrated mostly on the tongue. Each taste bud is a cluster of columnar epithelial cells. Some are supporting cells; others are specialized as receptors, with hairlike projections that sample the environment (Figure 23.3). These receptors synapse with sensory nerve fibers that carry signals to the brain.

Highly specialized chemoreceptors occur in insects. For instance, chemoreceptors on antennae of male silk moths *(Bombyx mori)* can sense one molecule of bombykol in 1,000,000,000,000,000,000 molecules of air! About forty chemoreceptors receiving only one molecule per second can trigger an action potential, through stimulus amplification. What is the adaptive value of this astonishing sensitivity? Bombykol is a **pheromone**: an exocrine gland product whose targets lie outside the body of the animal that secretes it. Female moths secrete bombykol as a sex attractant. Chemoreception of bombykol permits the male to *find* a female, even in the dark, and even more than a kilometer upwind.

Mechanical Reception

Tactile and Stretch Receptors. Sensory nerve processes that detect mechanical distortion at or near the body surface are **tactile receptors**. The nerve processes thread through skin connective tissue. Tactile receptors occur in almost all surface body parts of birds and mammals; they are scarce in amphibians and nonexistent in fishes. Their presence or absence corresponds to the extent of mechanical pressure that the environment imposes on the body. Animals living on land are more likely to interact with solid surfaces (the ground, for instance) than are animals suspended in water.

Stretch receptors, of the sort shown earlier in Figure 21.10, occur in muscles of all animals with legs. Action potentials from these receptors help the brain determine the state of muscle contraction and the position of body parts in space.

How does pressure or stretching trigger action potentials in these two types of receptor cells? One proposal is that strong mechanical pressure deforms the plasma membrane enough to open the gated sodium channels that span the membrane. The inward rush of sodium triggers the sudden change in electric potential across the membrane (Chapter Twenty-One). Experiments with lobster axons show that stretching the plasma membrane does indeed increase membrane permeability to sodium ions.

Vibrations, Hearing, and Equilibrium. Mechanical energy detected by tactile and stretch receptors is fairly steady and intense in quality. Some forms of mechanical energy are not as constant or as intense. Consider the **vibration**, a wavelike change in stimulus strength. When you clap, you compress many molecules together in the air between your hands. With the increased density, molecules bump together more often. Because of the clapping force, they also bump together more rapidly. Molecules fly outward and collide with more distant molecules, which bounce even farther away, and so on away from your hands. Meanwhile, back at your hands, the disturbed molecules keep jostling each other with less and less energy until they return to equilibrium density.

Each time air molecules are forced together, a high-pressure region is created. At the same time, crowding them together means that there won't be as many left in the place they came from; a low-pressure region is also created. Such alterations in air density can be propagated, batch after batch, for long distances. They are a series of *longitudinal waves*—a form of mechanical energy transmitted outward from a stimulus source by molecules of air, water, or solids.

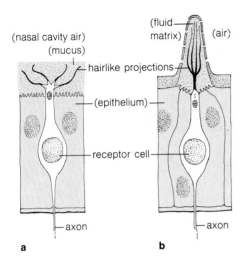

Figure 23.2 Structure of an olfactory receptor cell in the epithelium of a vertebrate (**a**) and of an insect (**b**). (After Steinbrecht in C. Pfaffman, ed., *Olfaction and Taste,* vol. 3, Rockefeller University Press, 1969)

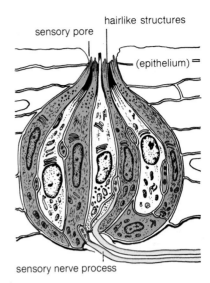

Figure 23.3 Structure and innervation of a taste bud, shown in long-section. Notice the different elongated cells with specialized hairlike structures at the tip. (After R. Murray and A. Murray, *Taste and Smell in Vertebrates,* 1970, Churchill)

Sound is a form of vibration. It is the perception of periodic compressional waves, typically airborne, that are processed by specialized receptors. The perceived loudness, or *amplitude* of sound, depends on the density difference between areas of high and low pressure in the wave trains. The more packed together the molecules are in each compressed region, the louder the sound. The perceived pitch, or *frequency* of sound, depends on how fast the wave changes occur. The faster the vibrations, the higher the sound.

Sound is a perception of periodic compressional waves. Typically there is variation in rate and density between the high- and low-pressure regions of the wave trains.

Which animals are attuned to sound as a stimulus? The ones with ears, you might say, thinking of the flexible cartilage flaps on the sides of your head. But organs for sound reception are not always so readily apparent. Web-building spiders have no ears, yet they are attracted to vibrations of a tuning fork. So are mosquitoes. Crabs and shrimp produce growls, grunts, creaks, and rasping noises that evoke predictable behavioral responses in others of their species.

Thus they not only produce but perceive sounds—even though they have nothing that remotely resembles vertebrate sound receptors.

As a land vertebrate, you live where sound waves spread out through air, hence become weaker with distance. Your ears have membranes and bony structures that amplify weak signals. Figure 23.4 outlines how the amplification occurs. The human ear can detect 400,000 different sounds reaching it. Some sounds are barely perceptible. Others are extremely intense and cause structural damage to inner ear regions. Examples include prolonged exposure to sounds of jet planes taking off, prolonged exposure to amplified music, and prolonged industrial noise. Such recent developments have outstripped the functional range of the evolutionarily ancient mechanoreceptor cells in the ear. These mechanoreceptors are **hair cells**: they have hairlike vibration receivers at one end. Figure 23.5 illustrates how extremely loud sounds can damage them.

Sound perception is a recently acquired function of the ear. In ancestral water-dwelling vertebrates, its main function apparently was to detect body movements in different planes of space: it was an organ of equilibrium. An animal perceives itself to be in **equilibrium** when the forces acting

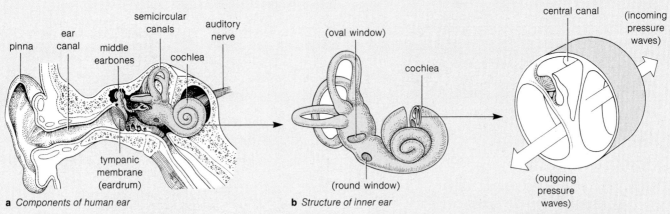

a *Components of human ear*

b *Structure of inner ear*

c *Section through the three canals of the cochlea*

Figure 23.4 Case study: the human ear.

Your own perception of sound begins with a system of compressional wave amplifiers and receivers. Your external ear collects sound waves and channels them to the *ear canal* (**a**). The channeled waves arrive at a thin *eardrum*, the entrance to the middle-ear cavity. The eardrum bows inward slightly, under bombardment by a compressional wave, then springs back. (With rapid changes in altitude, pressure differences can distort the membrane enough to cause pain. This can happen when you are in an ascending or descending airplane or elevator.) Attached to the back of the eardrum are three *middle earbones* (the hammer, anvil, and stirrup). The earbones amplify and transmit vibrations to the *oval window*, a membrane-covered gateway to the inner ear. The oval window is about twenty-five times smaller than the eardrum, hence mechanical energy of sound waves is greatly concentrated here. The energy so concentrated passes into the *cochlea*, a coiled tube vaguely reminiscent of a snail shell (**b**). Inside this inner ear region are three fluid-filled canals (**c**). As shown in (**d**), there are two pathways for energy flow through these canals, depending on the pressure-wave frequency. Very low-frequency waves take the long way around: across the oval window, down an incoming canal, into an outgoing canal, then all the way up to the membrane-covered *round window*. Through this "window," any energy remaining is dissipated. The other pathway is a shortcut taken by higher frequency waves: from the incoming canal, then across a central canal and out the round window.

How are pressure waves sorted out this way in the inner ear? The answer lies in the way that one of the cochlear membranes, the *basilar membrane*, is constructed. At the cochlea's entrance it is narrow and somewhat rigid. But it gradually becomes broader and more flexible deep in the coil. High-frequency waves, which carry more energy, cause the greatest displacement of the stiff region of the membrane. Most of their energy becomes transformed at once into membrane vibrations here, and these waves die out before traveling farther down the coil. Low-frequency waves also set up vibrations in this region, but the vibrations are lower in amplitude. As a result, the low-frequency waves continue into the more elastic regions.

Precisely where along the basilar membrane these vibrations occur determines which mechanoreceptors in the ear will be stimulated. For

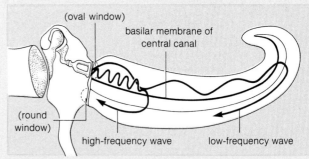

d *Distribution of sound waves of different frequencies in the cochlea (shown here as if it were partially uncoiled)*

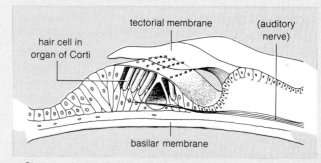

e *Close-up of hair cells in the organ of Corti, which is attached to the basilar membrane*

it happens that perched on the basilar membrane, in the fluid-filled central canal, is the *organ of Corti*. And here we find *hair cells*: mechanoreceptors having hairlike vibration receivers at one end (**e**). As pressure waves travel inward, they displace the basilar membrane so that it moves. With this displacement, the hair cell processes are made to move in relation to an overhanging flap, the *tectorial membrane*. This movement is thought to change the permeability of the hair cell membrane, leading to excitation of the associated sensory neuron.

hair cell

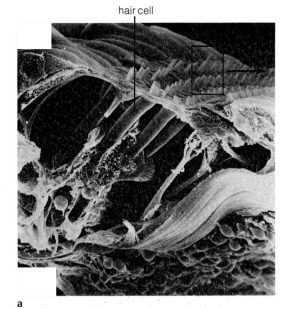 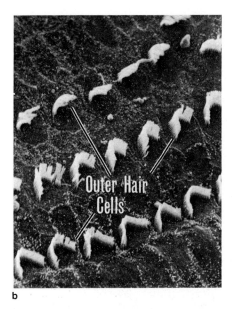 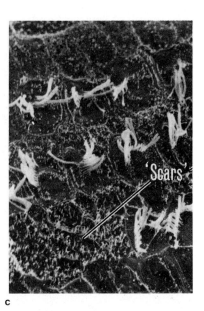

a   b   c

Figure 23.5 Effect of intense sound on inner ear. Normal organ of Corti from a human (**a**) and from a guinea pig (**b**), showing three rows of outer hair cells. (**c**) Organ of Corti after twenty-four-hour exposure to noise levels approached by loud rock music (2,000 cycles per second at 120 decibels). (a, Dr. Göran Bredburg, Uppsala, Sweden; b, c, Robert E. Preston micrograph, courtesy Joseph E. Hawkins, Kresge Hearing Research Institute, University of Michigan Medical School)

on its body are so balanced that there is no change in position or acceleration relative to some direction.

How do organs of equilibrium work? The internal ear contains a closed system of fluid-filled sacs and canals. In this system are mechanoreceptors—hair cells again, with their threadlike processes encased in a jellylike mass called a cupula. **Semicircular canals** (Figure 23.4) contain structures that detect vertical balance, acceleration, and rotation. As your body moves in a given plane in space, fluid in the canal corresponding to that plane is displaced and pushes against a cupula. Fluid pressure bends the hair cell processes encased in the cupula. Because of the orientation of these processes, turning the body in one direction triggers excitatory signals in an associated sensory neuron. Turning in the opposite direction decreases the rate of firing. Neural signals reach the cerebellum, where they are integrated with other information related to normal body position.

Other organs of equilibrium are present in vertebrate ears. These organs, too, depend on specialized hair cells. The cupula for these cells is thickened by deposits of cal-

cium carbonate crystals. Such thickened structures are **ear stones** (otoliths). When the head is tilted or when the body accelerates in a straight line, the weighty ear stones press against hair cells, which signal the shift out of equilibrium. Similar organs occur in some invertebrates (Figure 23.6).

Light Reception

Photoreception and Vision. Light is a flow of discrete energy packets known as **photons**. Each photon is a bit of energy that has escaped from an excited atom. Here we are talking about atoms not only from an original light source, such as the sun, but atoms of objects in the environment. Trees, rocks, rabbits—the surfaces of all such objects absorb photons, the added energy raises electrons in atoms to higher energy levels, and the excited atoms give up new photons. Regardless of the source, photons always travel the same way. *Photons travel through air in a straight line.* Almost all animals have sensory adaptations to this property. Being able to sense the direction of light energy from the sun, or another organism, or some other object enables an animal to move toward or away from it with some precision.

Reception of light energy depends on absorptive properties of pigment molecules embedded in membranes of photoreceptor cells. In **photoreception**, photon absorption briefly alters the structure of pigment molecules. Through this alteration, photon energy becomes transformed into the energy of a nerve signal.

Photoreception is *not* the same thing as vision. All organisms, whether they see or not, are sensitive to light wavelengths. Shine a bright light on a single-celled amoeba that is moving about and it will stop abruptly in its pseudopodial tracks. Neither photoreceptors nor pigments have been found in some small invertebrates, yet they display **phototaxis**: they orient toward or away from the direction of incoming light.

What we call "vision" depends on highly developed sensitivity to light. A **visual system** includes (1) structures that focus patterns of light energy onto a dense layer of photoreceptors, and (2) a neural network in the brain that can deal with those patterns. In the brain, different aspects of a visual stimulus (such as its position, brightness, shape, and distance) are processed.

A key part of most visual systems is a lens. Typically, a **lens** is a spherical or cone-shaped body of transparent protein fibers, which channel incoming light energy to photoreceptor cells located behind it. A lens alone does not lead to vision. Some invertebrates have eyes equipped with lenses, yet they cannot see as we do. Their lenses channel light either in front of or behind their photoreceptors, the result being a very diffuse kind of stimulation. These invertebrates detect a general change in light intensity, as might occur when another animal passes overhead in the water. But they can't discern the size or shape of moving or motionless objects.

Vision requires precise light focusing onto a photoreceptor cell layer that is dense enough to sample details concerning the light stimulus, followed by visual information processing in the brain.

Invertebrate Photoreception. Ocelli, or **eyespots**, occur in many invertebrates, such as the jellyfish *Aurelia* (Figure 23.6). These organs function in photoreception, but image formation does not follow. Eyespots are simple clusters of

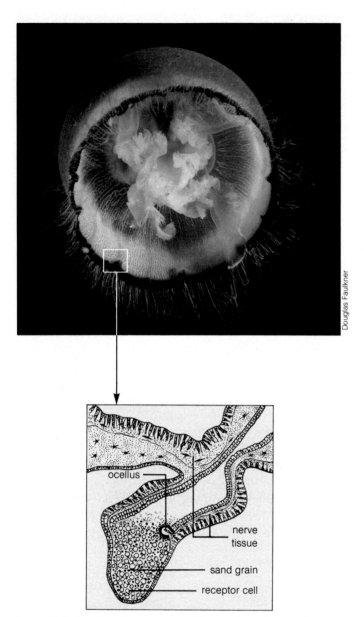

ocellus

nerve tissue

sand grain

receptor cell

Douglas Faulkner

Figure 23.6 Invertebrate organs of equilibrium. Along the margin of the bell-like crown of the jellyfish *Aurelia* are a number of small sensory organs. Each contains a *statocyst:* a hollow organ containing sand grains that move when the body shifts in position relative to gravity. When the sand grains move, they stimulate receptor cells lining the organ.

Often, equilibrium receptors are ciliated, as they are in lobster statocysts. Resting on these hairlike projections is a *statolith*, a small mass of stuck-together sand grains or calcium crystals that weighs more than the surrounding water. When the lobster body is tilted, the statolith stimulates receptor cells on the downslope side. This causes a steady firing of their sensory processes, which synapse with muscle cells in a reflex arc that corrects body position.

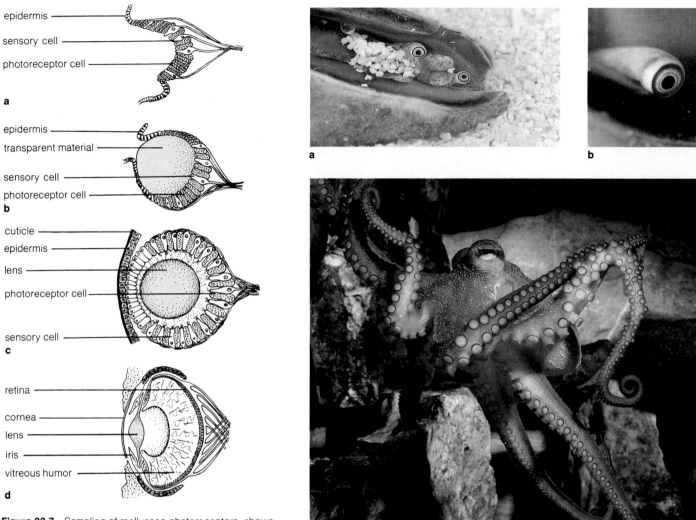

Figure 23.7 Sampling of molluscan photoreceptors, shown as if sliced lengthwise through the middle. (**a**) Limpet eyespot, no more than a shallow epidermal depression; (**b**) abalone eye, with secreted material that may serve as a lens; (**c**) land snail eye; and (**d**) octopus eye. (After M. Gardiner, *The Biology of Invertebrates*, 1972, McGraw-Hill)

Figure 23.8 The well-developed eyes of mollusks. (**a,b**) A red-mouthed conch (*Strombus*) peering about the Great Australian Barrier Reef. (**c**) Slit eye of an octopus. (a, b, Keith Gillett / Tom Stack & Associates; c, J. Grossauer / ZEFA)

photosensitive cells, usually arranged in a cuplike depression in epidermis. In these cells, pigment-containing membrane is often folded into **microvilli** (tiny, fingerlike projections of surface membrane). This membrane pattern also occurs in vertebrate photoreceptors.

In anatomical terms, mollusks are the simplest animals having **eyes**: well-developed photoreceptor organs that allow some degree of image formation. Some molluscan eyes are closed, fluid-filled vesicles (Figure 23.8). The vesicles have a transparent lens, a **cornea** (transparent cover), and a **retina** (a tissue containing densely packed photoreceptors).

One group of mollusks (the cephalopods) include squids, cuttlefishes, and octopuses. All are fast-moving

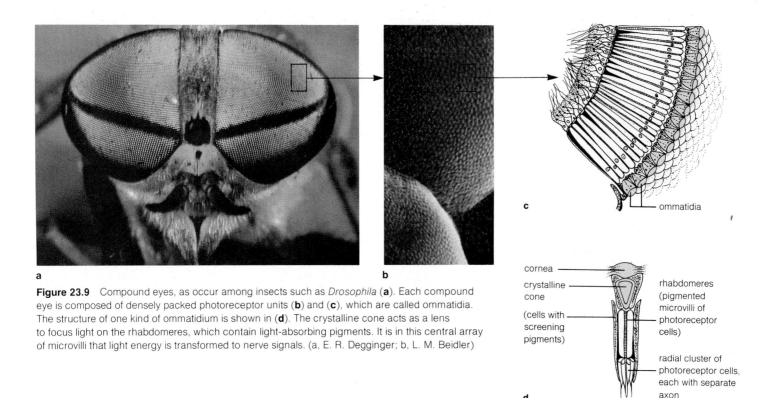

Figure 23.9 Compound eyes, as occur among insects such as *Drosophila* (**a**). Each compound eye is composed of densely packed photoreceptor units (**b**) and (**c**), which are called ommatidia. The structure of one kind of ommatidium is shown in (**d**). The crystalline cone acts as a lens to focus light on the rhabdomeres, which contain light-absorbing pigments. It is in this central array of microvilli that light energy is transformed to nerve signals. (a, E. R. Degginger; b, L. M. Beidler)

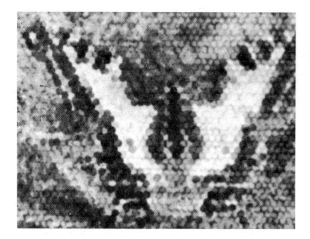

Figure 23.10 An approximation of light reception in the insect eye. This image of a butterfly was actually formed when a photograph was taken through the outer surface of a compound eye that has been detached from an insect. However, it may not be what the insect actually "sees." Summation of potentials being sent to the brain from many ommatidia can strengthen some signals and inhibit others to produce a more crisply defined image. The representation shown here is useful insofar as it suggests how the overall visual field may be *sampled* by separate ommatidia. (G. A. Mazokhin-Porshnykov (1958). Reprinted with permission from *Insect Vision*, © 1969 Plenum Press)

predators that live in dimly lit underwater worlds. All have large, paired eyes capable of effective image formation. Their eyes are positioned just behind prey-grabbing tentacles. Both eyes are used in aligning the tentacles at the correct striking distance from prey. Muscles control movements of both the eyeball and an **iris**, an adjustable ring of contractile and connective tissues within the eye. The open center of this contractile ring (the *pupil*) can be varied in size to admit more or less light. At the base of each eye is a retina of densely packed photoreceptors.

Bright light causes the cephalopod pupil to shrink in size—not into a tiny circle (as it does in your eyes) but into a narrow slit. In case you are snorkeling or diving and happen to stumble over a large octopus, you might like to know that the pupils of its already large eyes can flare open suddenly, one or both at a time, in response. The effect is startling and no doubt adaptive. The octopus is known to use its enormous stare in securing the attention of a potential mate and possibly to warn away a potential enemy.

The **compound eyes** of insects and crustaceans (crabs, shrimp, and the like) contain up to many thousands of closely packed photosensitive units. These units are called *ommatidia* (singular, ommatidium). Usually, each unit has a hexagonal cornea and a cone-shaped, crystalline lens below that. Light entering through the lens is absorbed by pigment in one to a dozen photoreceptor cells arranged radially below the cone (Figure 23.9). Light absorption in microvilli of these cells triggers action potentials, which travel directly to the optic lobe from each photoreceptor. How the signals are processed to form visual images is not understood. According to the **mosaic theory** of image formation, each ommatidium detects information about only one small region of the visual field. An image is built up according to signals about different light intensities detected by all the ommatidia, with each contributing a separate bit to the whole visual mosaic (Figure 23.10).

Vertebrate Photoreception. Almost all vertebrates have eyes capable of effective image formation. The eyeball itself has a lens, a **sclera** (a tough outer coat), then a **choroid** (a dark-pigmented tissue through which blood vessels course), and a densely packed retina. A transparent, light-focusing cornea is continuous with the sclera. It covers the front surface of the eye. Choroid tissue extends inward from the front of the eye to form an iris. The iris is richly endowed with light-screening pigments, and with radial and circular muscle fibers used in controlling how much light enters. A clear fluid (aqueous humor) fills the space between the cornea and iris. A lens is positioned behind the iris, and a jellylike substance (vitreous body) fills the chamber behind the lens. Figure 23.11 shows the arrangement of these structures in the human eye.

Among vertebrates, variations occur in the means by which light rays from both distant and close-up objects are made to converge precisely onto retinal photoreceptors. Convergence begins in the cornea. When light rays enter its curved surface, they are bent so that they funnel toward some focal point. (Here you might want to review the description of light refraction in Figure 4.4.) But it is in the lens that *adjustments* are made. If the angle of bending is not great enough, the focal point will end up behind the retina. If it is too great, the focal point will end up in front. The lens helps bring the image into focus.

In the vertebrate eye, lens adjustments assure that the focal point for a given batch of light rays will land on the retina.

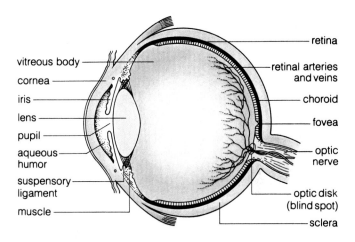

Figure 23.11 Main components of the human eye.

The term **accommodation** refers to lens adjustments that bring about precise focusing onto the retina. For example, fishes use eye muscles that move the entire lens forward or backward, thereby adjusting the distance from the retina. Increasing the distance moves the focal point forward; decreasing the distance moves it back. In other vertebrates, lens shape is adjusted under the coordinated stretching and relaxation of eye muscles and fibers attached to the lens (Figure 23.12). Birds that depend on rapid, complex maneuvers during flight have the means for rapid accommodation. The bird lens is highly elastic and ringed with muscles. The same is true for the lens in humans and other highly active mammals.

The retina is well developed in birds and mammals. Its basement layer, composed of pigmented epithelium, covers the choroid. These pigments help prevent light scattering. Hence they prevent diffuse stimulation that could create blurred images. Resting on the basement layer is nerve tissue containing both photoreceptors and sensory neurons. Figure 23.13 shows how this arrangement works in photoreception by the human eye.

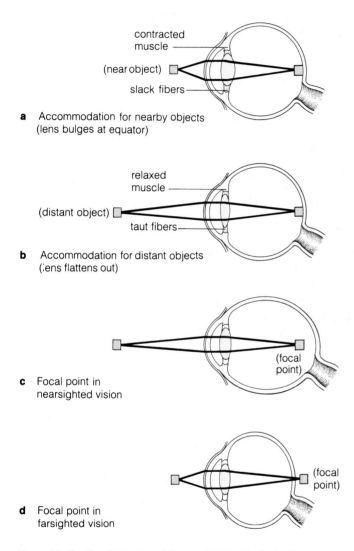

a Accommodation for nearby objects
(lens bulges at equator)

b Accommodation for distant objects
(lens flattens out)

c Focal point in
nearsighted vision

d Focal point in
farsighted vision

Figure 23.12 Visual accommodation, as it occurs in the human eye.
(**a**) Close objects are brought into focus when eye muscles contract
enough to slacken certain fibers interposed between them and the lens,
which causes the lens to thicken in width at its equator. (**b**) Distant
objects are brought into focus when these muscles relax, which puts
tension on the fibers and stretches the lens into a flatter shape.

(**c**) People who are *nearsighted* have eyes in which the retina is too far
behind the lens; light from distant objects is focused in front of the
retina. (**d**) Those who are *farsighted* have light from nearby objects
focused behind the retina.

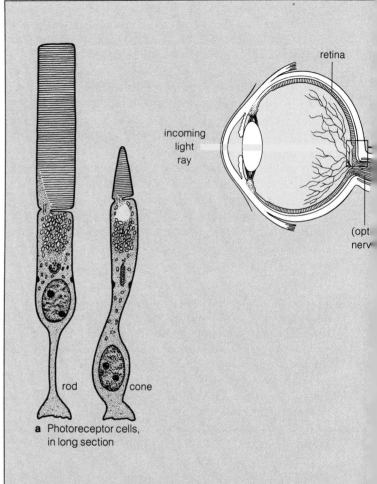

a Photoreceptor cells,
in long section

Figure 23.13 Case study: photoreception in the human eye.

Two kinds of photoreceptor cells are intermingled in the retina's
photoreceptive fields. They are called rods and cones because of
their shape (**a**). A *rod cell* is concerned with perception of very dim
light, and with coarse perception of changes in light intensity that occur
with movements across a visual field. Rods typically are packed in the
retina's periphery. A *cone cell* is stimulated only by high-intensity light.
It's concerned with sharp daytime vision and usually color perception.

Three types of cone cells have been identified. Each contains
photopigments most sensitive to wavelengths corresponding to what
we perceive as the colors red, green, and blue. (Colors in between
are perceived when graded potentials from two or three different
types of cones are summed at synapses. Thus excitation of both
"red" and "blue" cones means we see the color purple.) In the
human eye, cones are most densely packed in the fovea. The *fovea* is a
funnel-shaped pit near the retina's center, where overlying nerve
tissue is thinned away. This pit is only a millimeter across. Yet
photoreceptors clustered here provide the greatest visual acuity
(precise discrimination between adjacent points in space).
What happens to nerve signals generated in rods and cones? They

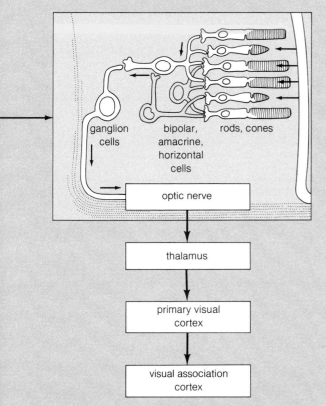

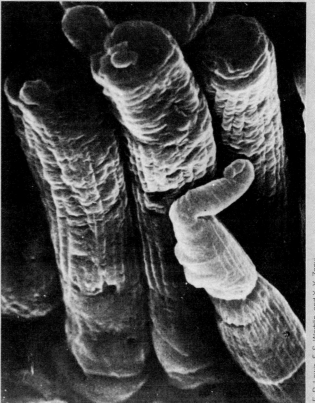

b Pathways from photoreceptors to the human brain

c

move along at least two types of communication lines to the brain. In *through-conducting pathways*, only a few photoreceptor cells synapse with a few so-called bipolar cells, which relay signals to a ganglion cell (**b**). Axons of the ganglion cells lead out from the nerve tissue layer, and converge to form the optic nerve. From there, potentials travel to the thalamus, then on to visual processing centers in the cerebral cortex.

For the most part, signals from cones travel the direct lines. That's why cones provide precise detailing; their messages remain relatively unmixed. Signals from many rods typically converge onto a few bipolar and ganglion cells. This convergence is one reason why rods can trigger an action potential even when light intensity is too low to excite cones. It's a reason why light-sensitive yet somewhat fuzzily signaling rods let you sense where things are in a room too dark to activate their pointy-headed counterparts.

In the human retina, receptive fields for ganglion cells are circular. Some overlap, and they number in the hundreds. Stimulating different fields (even different parts of the same field) excites ganglion cells in specific ways. For instance, light falling on an inner circle of receptors in an "on-center" field triggers increased firing of the cells. Light

falling on the surrounding ring of receptors triggers a decrease in firing. Activity in an "off-center" field is reversed, and has the opposite effects. The organization of cells in such fields enhances our ability to see the boundaries between objects.

Also, lateral connections between retinal cells bring about graded, localized potentials. These messages, recall, decay unless amplified by other messages. Thus the *frequency* of firing in a given ganglion cell is modified by changes in size, location, or intensity of a light stimulus.

In this manner, the brain receives signals about different shapes and movements detected by receptors in a visual field—signals about lines of sight, orientations of those lines, their edges and contours, and their location over time (Chapter Twenty-One). *Thus photoreception in the retina is more than an "on-off" activity. Preliminary integration also occurs here, even before messages about that activity course down the optic nerve and on to the brain.*

(a from "Visual Cells" by Richard W. Young, *Scientific American*, October 1970. Copyright © 1970 by Scientific American, Inc. All rights reserved.)

Table 23.1 Main Categories of Motor Systems	
Type	Representative Animals
Antagonistic muscle system	Sea anemone
Hydraulic skeletons:	
1. Body fluid + soft body wall	Earthworm, octopus, sea star
2. Body fluid + rigid body part	Spider (hind legs only)
Rigid skeletons:	
1. Exoskeleton	Beetle, grasshopper, crab
2. Endoskeleton	Frog, snake, bird, human

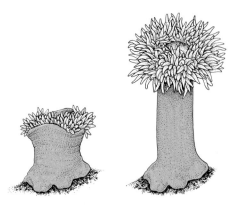

Figure 23.14 Antagonistic muscle system of the sea anemone. In the lengthened body, contractile proteins arranged in rings around the central axis have contracted. In the shortened body, contractile proteins arranged longitudinally to the central axis have contracted.

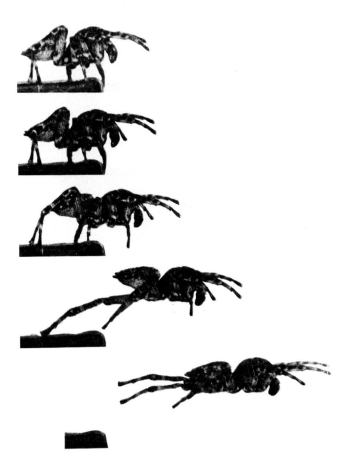

Figure 23.15 Hydraulic leap of the jumping spider (*Sitticus pubescens*), which can soar ten centimeters through the air to pounce on prey. The leap is based on the hydraulic extension of the hind legs when blood surges into them under high pressure. (D. A. Parry, *Journal of Experimental Biology,* 1959, 36:654)

MOVEMENT IN RESPONSE TO CHANGE

Motor Systems

The sensory systems just described range from simple arrays of photoreceptors to networks that sample the surroundings with great precision. Paralleling the sensory spectrum are motor systems of response to a range of stimuli. Almost all motor systems are based on contractile proteins, which can shorten under stimulation and then relax. The most prevalent of these proteins are actin and myosin. All motor systems are based on the presence of some medium or structural element against which force can be applied. Table 23.1 lists the main types of motor systems.

All motor systems require the presence of some medium or structural element against which force can be applied.

Chapter Four described the motor "systems" of single cells, many of which use motile structures (cilia and flagella) in a liquid medium. Here we will make acquaintance with some motor systems that occur among different animals.

Invertebrate Motor Systems. The motor system of the sea anemone is little more than a network of T-shaped cells in the body wall, with each cell containing contractile proteins. Some cells are positioned longitudinally through one tissue layer. When they contract, the body shortens and becomes thicker. Other contractile cells in another tissue layer are positioned circularly about the central body axis. When they contract, the body lengthens (Figure 23.14). The longitudinal and circular muscle layers work as an **antagonistic muscle system**: action of one motor element opposes the action of another.

Annelids such as earthworms depend on a different arrangement. These worms are segmented: the body cavity is divided *into* a series of compartments, each with a flexible wall surrounding a fluid-filled chamber. Each segment has a set of longitudinal and circular muscles. First the contractile force of the circular muscles is applied against the fluid-filled interior. Because fluid resists compression, the fluid interior acts as a **hydraulic skeleton**. In all hydraulic systems, body fluids are used to transmit force. As circular muscles contract in the earthworm, fluid is squeezed down the body, much like toothpaste being forced down a tube. When that happens, longitudinal muscles are made to stretch. Now sets of bristles (setae) projecting from the body grip the ground, acting like toeholds for the stretched-out worm. When the longitudinal muscles contract, their force is applied against the bristles and the body is pulled forward.

There are some intriguing variations on the hydraulic theme. For example, spiders have no muscles that can be used to extend the leg. However, a rapid surge of blood under high pressure can extend the hind leg spines. Figure 23.15 illustrates how one jumping spider uses blood pressure as a hydraulic source for leaping at prey.

Insects, crabs, and other arthropods also have segmented body plans. Each body segment is covered by a hardened *cuticle*: a noncellular body cover formed from chitin, protein, and sometimes lipid secretions (Chapter Thirty-Four). The hardened cuticle forms an external skeleton, or **exoskeleton**, for a network of antagonistic muscles that bridge the gaps between segments. The cuticle between body segments remains pliable and acts like a hinge when muscles move it in different directions.

Vertebrate Motor Systems.   Vertebrates have an internal skeleton, or endoskeleton. Your own endoskeleton consists of bone and cartilage (Figure 23.16). Bone cells are arranged to form hollow tubes—structures that are lightweight yet afford strength (Chapter Twenty). The **endoskeleton** functions in movement, support, and protection of internal organs. Even its ribs and the muscles between them function in maintaining upright posture.

The *axial portion* of an endoskeleton includes the skull and facial bones, vertebral column, and rib cage. The *ap-*

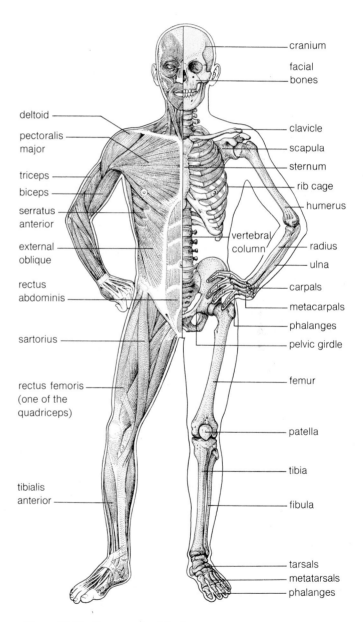

Figure 23.16 Components of the human motor system.

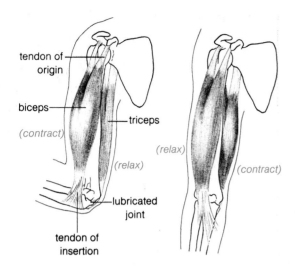

Figure 23.17 Antagonistic muscle movement, showing how two muscles of a pair can contract and relax in opposition to each other.

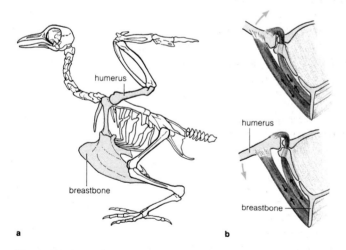

a   b

Figure 23.18 (a) Skeletal system of a bird, showing the thin bones, the flight-stabilizing heavy breastbone, and bone fusions in the breast, pelvic girdle, and backbone—all adaptations for flying. (b) The rope-and-pulley type of mechanism between powerful antagonistic muscles that help raise and lower the bird wing. The main muscle mass lies low in the body, which also helps stabilize flight. (a reprinted by permission from *Ornithology in Laboratory and Field* by O. S. Pettinghill, 1970, Burgess Publishing Company; b from T. Storer et al., *General Zoology*, sixth edition, 1979, McGraw-Hill)

pendicular portion includes the arms, legs, pelvic girdle, and pectoral girdle. The appendicular portion acts as a system of levers for moving the body. Webs of muscles stretch over the skeletal framework. Tough connective tissue strands (tendons) attach muscles firmly to skeletal bones. Connective tissue fibers (ligaments) form flexible connections between bones at joints.

Skeletal muscles contract and relax along one axis only. But the animal body requires movement in multiple directions. Such movement is possible because of reciprocal reflex connections that exist between *pairs* of muscles. Muscles in body limbs are arranged in antagonistic pairs, such as the biceps and triceps shown in Figure 23.17. Notice how these muscles bridge both the elbow and shoulder joints. When one member of this antagonistic pair (the biceps) contracts, the elbow joint flexes (bends). As it relaxes and its partner (the triceps) contracts, the limb extends and straightens out again. Their coordination results from **reciprocal innervation** in the spinal cord, whereby inhibitory signals to one motor neuron prevent the contraction of one muscle of a pair while the other muscle is being excited.

Thus, when a biceps contracts, inhibitory interneurons simultaneously act on the motor neurons of its partner, the triceps, which relaxes. When a triceps contracts, inhibitory signals simultaneously act on motor neurons of its partner. Such reciprocal innervation is the basis for coordinated movements in various skeletal-muscle systems, including those of birds (Figure 23.18).

In a skeletal-muscle system, reciprocal innervation of motor neurons to antagonistic muscle pairs is the basis for coordinated contraction.

Reciprocal innervation can be overridden. You can contract your biceps and triceps at the same time, when (for example) you hold your arm upright like a stiff pillar.

Muscle Contraction

Contractile tissue is most highly developed in cells called muscle fibers. Recall that muscle fibers are organized together in three kinds of muscle tissue: skeletal, smooth, and cardiac muscle tissue. All three tissues take part in motor responses. In vertebrates, only skeletal muscle is concerned with moving the body through the environment. Smooth muscle occurs primarily in internal organs such as those of the digestive system. It is involved in propelling or regulating the movement of substances within the body (Chapter

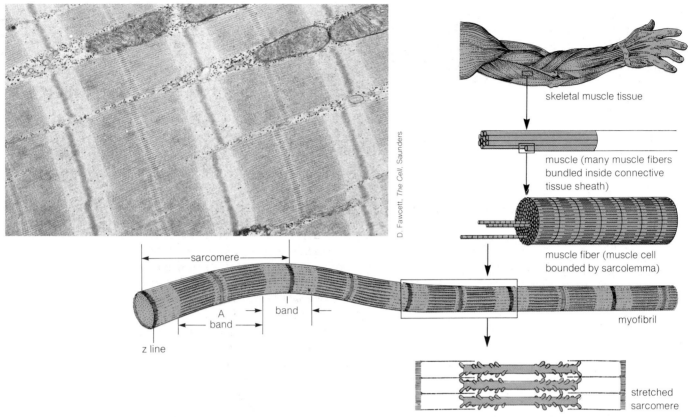

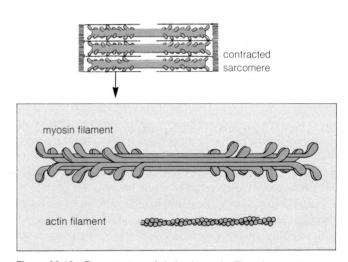

Figure 23.19 Fine structure of skeletal muscle. The micrograph shows a slice through several myofibrils, running diagonally from the lower left to the upper right corner. Interactions between actin and myosin filaments are the basis of skeletal muscle contraction.

Twenty-Six). Cardiac muscle occurs only in walls of the heart, and will be described in Chapter Twenty-Four. Here we will focus on contraction of skeletal muscle.

Motor Units. A skeletal muscle contains between a few hundred and a thousand muscle fibers. Connective tissue holds muscle fibers together in bundles, which are attached to bone. Each skeletal muscle fiber is functionally connected to a motor neuron, in the manner described in Chapter Twenty-One. At a neuromuscular junction, the muscle fiber membrane is differentiated into a **motor end plate**. ATP-producing mitochondria are abundant in this region.

Each motor neuron has several branched axonal endings, which can form neuromuscular junctions with many separate muscle fibers. Excitatory signals from one motor neuron can thus cause the simultaneous contraction of all the muscle fibers connected to it. The term **motor unit** refers to a motor neuron and all of the muscle fibers that it controls.

Fine Structure of Skeletal Muscle. A muscle fiber consists of finer, threadlike structures called **myofibrils** (Figure 23.19). A myofibril is made of actin and myosin filaments. Each *actin filament* looks like two beaded chains twisted around each other; the "beads" are ball-shaped actin molecules. Each *myosin filament* is really 200 or so myosin molecules, lying in parallel. A globe-shaped head extends from each of these rod-shaped molecules. The myosin head has a binding site that is complementary to multiple binding sites that occur in series on the actin filament.

Repeating bands of actin and myosin filaments translate into a light-dark-light repeating unit that gives skeletal muscle its striped appearance. Between each repeating unit are darker regions known as *Z lines.* The Z lines are the fibrous anchoring for the actin filaments, and they define the sarcomere. The **sarcomere** is the fundamental unit of contraction (Figure 23.19).

Mechanism of Muscle Contraction.   The only way that skeletal muscles bring about movement of body parts to which they are attached is to shorten. When a skeletal muscle shortens, its component muscle fibers are shortening. When a muscle fiber shortens, its component sarcomeres are shortening. *The combined decreases in length of the individual sarcomeres account for contraction of the whole muscle.*

The question becomes this: How does a sarcomere alternately contract and relax? Are the actin and myosin filaments assembled and disassembled, in the manner of microtubules? It appears not. According to the **sliding-filament model**, actin filaments physically slide over myosin filaments, moving toward the center of the sarcomere during contraction, and moving away from the center when the sarcomere is relaxing.

For the sliding movement to occur, myosin heads must first attach to binding sites on the actin filaments. When attached, the myosin heads are *cross-bridges* between the two types of filaments. Look at Figure 23.19, which shows that there are two sets of actin filaments, each attached to one end of a sarcomere. The myosin filament has two sets of myosin heads, each set pointing away from the sarcomere center during resting conditions. When cross-bridges between actin and myosin are activated, the myosin heads tilt inward in a short power stroke. Because the actin filaments are attached to cross-bridges they move slightly inward, also. The myosin heads then detach, reattach at the next actin binding site in line, and move the actin filaments a little bit more. A single contraction of the sarcomere takes a whole series of these power strokes.

ATP energy is used in changing the angle of attachment of cross-bridges during the sliding movements. The heads of myosin filaments show enzyme activity: they can catalyze the hydrolysis of ATP. When a muscle is relaxed, each myosin head has picked up an ATP molecule and has hydrolyzed it into ADP and phosphate. These products, however, are not released. As long as they remain locked in place, the myosin head is energized—like a loaded, pulled-back spring of a mousetrap. When ATP is hydrolyzed, the energy of the products (ADP and inorganic phosphate) is less than that in the reactants (ATP and water). The energy difference is used to bring about changes in the shape of the myosin head. The change results in the power stroke. Only then does the myosin head release the bound products. It picks up a new ATP molecule, and the cycle begins again.

In the absence of ATP, cross-bridges never do detach. The muscle becomes rigid, a condition known as *rigor.* Following death, ATP production stops along with other metabolic activities. Cross-bridges remain locked in place and all skeletal muscles in the entire body become rigid. This condition, called *rigor mortis,* lasts up to sixty hours after death.

Clearly, ATP is necessary for muscle contraction. As you might expect, muscle tissue is richly endowed with mitochondria, in which considerable ATP is produced through aerobic respiration. In a resting muscle, energy is stored in the form of **creatine phosphate**. This compound readily gives up phosphate to ADP and thereby helps replace the ATP that has been used up in cross-bridge movements. When oxygen concentrations are low in muscle tissue (as they are during strenuous exercise), some ATP also forms through anaerobic metabolism. This alternate route cannot be followed for long. Build-up of lactate (the end product of the anaerobic route) leads to muscle aching.

Control of Muscle Contraction.   To understand how muscle contraction is controlled, we have to consider the connections between three types of membranes:

sarcolemma	*the plasma membrane that surrounds the entire muscle fiber*
sarcoplasmic reticulum	*a continuous system of membrane-bound chambers that surround myofibrils within the muscle fiber, and that store calcium ions*
transverse tubule system	*a system of tubular membranes that extend from the sarcolemma all the way through the muscle fiber, and that are in intimate contact with the sarcoplasmic reticulum*

Figure 23.20 shows the arrangement of these membranes in a section from a muscle fiber.

As indicated in Chapter Twenty-One, action potentials are the stimulus for contraction, and they begin at junctions between the sarcolemma and motor neurons. At these neuromuscular junctions, a motor neuron releases acetylcholine. This neurotransmitter interacts with receptors on the sarcolemma, producing graded potentials. Under strong enough stimulation, the summation of these potentials can generate an action potential. An action potential self-propagates along the sarcolemma and invades the interior of the muscle by way of the tubule system. There, it increases the membrane permeability of the sarcoplasmic reticulum to calcium ions, which simply diffuse into the cytoplasm. *These calcium ions clear the binding sites on actin filaments, allowing cross-bridges to form.*

Under resting conditions, binding sites for the myosin heads are blocked by rod-shaped *tropomyosin* molecules, which are proteins associated with the actin filament. However, also associated with the actin filament are *troponin* molecules—globular proteins to which calcium ions can become attached. When they are attached, the troponin changes shape in the manner shown in Figure 23.21. The change happens to displace the rod-shaped proteins—thus clearing the actin binding sites for cross-bridge formation.

When a muscle is at rest, calcium ions are actively taken up and stored in the sarcoplasmic reticulum. Removal of calcium ions causes the muscles to relax after contraction; the release of calcium ions from the sarcoplasmic reticulum leads to contraction. Now, the nervous system controls which motor neurons will carry action potentials, and at what frequency. By controlling the action potentials that reach the sarcoplasmic reticulum in the first place, the nervous system controls calcium ion levels in muscle tissue—and thereby exerts control over contraction.

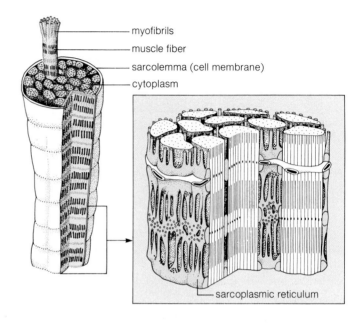

Figure 23.20 Location of sarcoplasmic reticulum, the calcium ion storage site within muscle fibers. (Inset L. D. Peachey, *J. Cell Biology*, 1965, *25*:222)

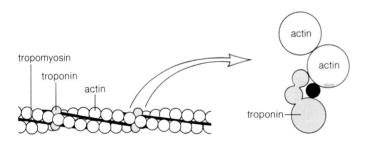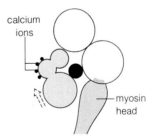

a Components of actin filament (actin molecules, rod-shaped proteins called tropomyosin, and globular proteins called troponin). The proteins, together with calcium ions, regulate the formation of cross-bridges between an actin filament and a myosin filament.

b Cross-section of an actin filament at rest. Tropomyosin (black) blocks attachment site for myosin head. Cross-bridge cannot form between actin filament and myosin filament.

c Calcium ions bind to troponin, change its shape; position of tropomyosin shifts and attachment site is cleared. A cross-bridge can form between actin and the myosin head.

Figure 23.21 Role of calcium ions in the formation of cross-bridges between actin and myosin filaments. (Adapted from Eckert and Randall, 1983)

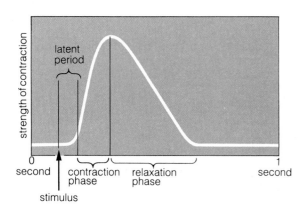

Figure 23.22 Recording of a muscle twitch.

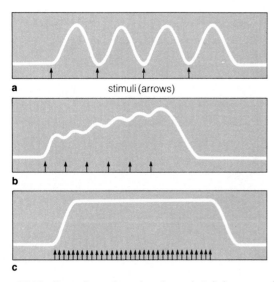

Figure 23.23 Recordings of a series of muscle twitches caused by about two stimulations per second (**a**); recording of a summation of twitches resulting from about six stimulations per second (**b**); and a tetanic contraction resulting from about twenty stimulations per second (**c**).

Summary of Muscle Contraction

Now that we have considered the different aspects of muscle contraction, we can briefly summarize the events involved and how they are controlled:

1. A muscle fiber is composed of fine strands called myofibrils. The length of a myofibril is functionally divided into small segments called sarcomeres, the basic units of muscle contraction.

2. A sarcomere contains actin filaments and myosin filaments, which interact through a sliding mechanism that shortens each sarcomere.

3. Contraction of a sarcomere depends on the arrival of action potentials from motor neurons. Action potentials stimulate the release of calcium ions from the sarcoplasmic reticulum (membranous chambers surrounding the myofibrils).

4. Calcium ions diffuse across the short distance to actin filaments. There they attach to troponin (a protein associated with actin). In response, the troponin changes shape. When it does, it displaces tropomyosin (another protein associated with actin), which otherwise blocks the binding sties where actin and myosin can interact.

5. Once a binding site is cleared, the head of a myosin filament can attach to the adjacent actin filament. The myosin head is in an energized state, having earlier hydrolyzed ATP without letting go of the high-energy products (ADP and phosphate).

6. Cross-bridge formation causes energy inherent in the bound products to be released, and the myosin head changes shape. The change results in a short power stroke that moves the attached actin filament.

7. The deenergized myosin head picks up another ATP, becomes energized, then reattaches at the next binding site in line. A single contraction of the sarcomere requires a repetitive series of power strokes.

8. ATP energy is necessary for the power stroke underlying muscle contraction.

9. Calcium ions are necessary to clear the binding site where the power stroke occurs.

10. Because the nervous system controls the release of calcium ions from the sarcoplasmic reticulum, it exerts control over contraction itself.

Types of Muscular Responses to Action Potentials

Twitch Contraction. Each muscular contraction initiated by a single action potential is known as a **twitch**. The twitch contraction consists of a latent period, actual contraction, then relaxation (Figure 23.22). The muscle does not respond at once to the action potential. A short time (the latent period) passes between stimulation and the onset of contraction. The contraction builds up gradually to a peak strength, after which it gradually diminishes. The strength of the twitch contraction is proportional to the strength of the stimulus. Individual twitches are not ordinarily observed during normal muscle contractions.

Tetanic Contraction. When a muscle is restimulated before the twitch response is completed, the muscle contracts again. The contraction strength generally is proportional to the *summation* of the first and second changes in electric potential across the membrane. Relaxation does not occur at all during frequent stimulation. Then, the muscle is maintained in a state of contraction called **tetanus** (Figure 23.23). Tetanus is the normal mode of contraction in skeletal muscle.

Contractions in different motor units are commonly sustained in the tetanic state. They are smoothed out by neural commands from the spinal cord. Some motor units are made to relax and others to contract at the same time, so that the overall muscle action is smooth rather than jerky.

To some extent, sustained contraction occurs even in muscles that seem to be resting. The low level of tetanic contraction is called **muscle tone**. The spinal cord coordinates this continual state of contraction.

Neuromotor Basis of Behavior

In Chapter Twenty-One, you read about the stretch reflex, the simplest sort of reflex arc. Few neuromotor responses are as well understood. In most responses, integrative centers and memory banks in the brain intervene in many ways. Genetic programming has its effect; so do physiological states, diverse environmental changes, and learning. Thus there can be a range of variation within the same category of motor response. Its intensity, how rapidly it is carried out, and how long it lasts depend on external and internal cues—both of which vary. Integration of sensory, genetic, and neural factors leads to the coordinated output called animal behavior. It is a topic that we will consider in a later unit.

Readings

Bennett, T. 1978. *The Sensory World.* Monterey, California: Brooks/ Cole.

Bullock, T., R. Orkand, and A. Grinnell. 1977. *Introduction to the Nervous System.* San Francisco: Freeman.

Eckert, R., and D. Randall. 1978. *Animal Physiology.* San Francisco: Freeman. Advanced reading. Chapter Seven gives a detailed picture of how sensory signals are actually processed. Chapter Nine is an excellent account of the sliding-filament model of muscle contraction.

Hildebrand, M. 1982. *Analysis of Vertebrate Structure.* Second edition. New York: Wiley. Outstanding introduction to the vertebrate body; interprets structure on the basis of function. Notably clear writing.

Lissman, H. 1963. "Electric Location by Fishes." *Scientific American* 208(3):50–59. Also available as Offprint 152. A specialized topic, not covered in this chapter, but one which you might find interesting as supplemental reading.

Miller, W., W. Ratliff, and H. Hartline. 1961. "How Cells Receive Stimuli." *Scientific American* 205(3):222–238. Also available as Offprint 99.

Young, R. 1970. "Visual Cells." *Scientific American* 223(4):80–91. Also available as Offprint 1201.

Review Questions

1. What is a stimulus? Receptor cells detect specific kinds of stimuli. When they do, what happens to the stimulus energy?

2. Give some examples of chemoreceptors and mechanoreceptors. What kind of mechanoreceptor occurs repeatedly in sensory organs of different kinds of animals?

3. What is sound? How are amplitude and frequency related to sound? Give some examples of animals that apparently perceive sounds.

4. How does vision differ from photoreception? What sensory apparatus does vision require?

5. How does the vertebrate eye focus the light rays of an image? What is meant by nearsighted and farsighted?

6. What are the two basic components of any motor system? Distinguish between a hydroskeleton, exoskeleton, and endoskeleton.

7. What is antagonistic muscle action? Why is reciprocal inhibition of reflexes necessary in producing coordinated contractions?

8. Describe the fine structure of muscle fibers. Explain how the muscle fiber components interact in muscle contraction.

9. Name five factors that together shape the neuromotor responses called animal behavior.

24

CIRCULATION

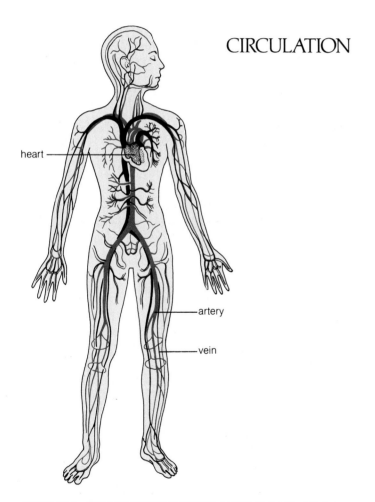

heart

artery

vein

Figure 24.1 One type of blood circulation system, as it occurs in the human body.

INTERNAL DISTRIBUTION STRATEGIES

In terms of their activity and internal organization, sponges, cnidarians, and flatworms are among the simplest animals. Because their bodies are not massive, materials can be distributed to and from cells simply by diffusion through tissue fluid. Because sponges, cnidarians, and flatworms are not highly active, they have a low metabolic rate that does not require an abundant flow of nutrients and gases.

In contrast, most invertebrates and all vertebrates are more active, more massive, and more structurally complex. For such animals, nutrients and gases are distributed by a system of tubes that thread through each body region (Figure 24.1). The tubes are constructed of epithelial, connective, and muscular tissues. They are regionally differentiated into transport vessels (arteries, capillaries, veins, and the like) and some kind of pumping mechanism (heart). **Blood**, a highly specialized fluid connective tissue, circulates within the system.

Blood transports nutrients and oxygen to cells of all tissue regions and transports cellular products and wastes from them. In vertebrates, blood serves additional functions. Vertebrate blood contains infection-fighting and scavenger cells, which are circulated to tissue regions that are injured or under attack. Blood serves as the highway for most hormones. By virtue of its composition, blood helps stabilize internal pH. In warm-blooded birds and mammals, blood also helps equalize body temperature by distributing heat from regions of high metabolic activity (such as skeletal muscles) through all body parts.

A circulatory system, and the blood it transports through the animal body, carries vital materials to cells, carries products and wastes from them, and helps maintain an internal environment that is favorable for cell activities.

Many invertebrates, including insects, have **open circulation systems**. Here, blood is pumped from the heart into one or more blood vessels, which open directly into tissue spaces. Blood flows freely around cells making up the tissues, then seeps sluggishly back to the heart. The blood distribution and circulation rate are not controlled much in these invertebrates. Either their life-styles do not demand more efficient metabolic support, or other systems assist in transport functions. For example, insects have respiratory tubes that bypass the bloodstream and channel oxygen directly to body tissues.

Some invertebrates and all vertebrates have **closed circulation systems**. The circulation path is defined by the continuously connected walls of blood vessels and one or more hearts, so that there is functional separation between circulating blood and interstitial fluid. Closed systems have an advantage, in that blood can be moved quickly to tissue regions that must have high metabolic output when changing conditions demand it. At any given time, blood flow can be increased to active regions and decreased to less active ones through controls over the constriction and dilation of blood vessel diameters.

It is not that "closed" circulation systems are completely sealed off. Materials continually pass between capillaries and the surrounding tissues. A small amount of fluid, too, leaves the capillaries. A supplementary network of tubular vessels, the **lymph vascular system**, picks up the overflow and returns it to the circulation system. Reclamation of water and proteins squeezed out of the bloodstream is one of the main functions of the lymph vascular system.

In this chapter, you will focus on the closed circulation systems of vertebrates and on the supplementary lymph vascular system. As you will see, both play diverse yet interconnected roles in assuring homeostasis.

COMPONENTS OF BLOOD

Blood Composition and Volume

Vertebrate blood has four components: red blood cells, white blood cells, platelets, and plasma. Red blood cells constitute all but one percent of the cellular portion. About fifty-five percent of a given blood sample is plasma. The plasma portion of blood is mostly water, which functions as a solvent. Within plasma are sixty or so different kinds of proteins that function in such tasks as infection fighting, blood clotting, and lipid transport.

Blood volume varies with body size, and with changes in water and ion concentrations. On the average, an adult human male weighing 70 kilograms (about 150 pounds) has a blood volume of about 5 liters (a little more than 5 quarts).

Types of Blood Cells and Their Function

Red Blood Cells. Erythrocytes, or **red blood cells**, function primarily in transporting oxygen to cells. A mammalian red blood cell is a biconcave disk, thicker around the rim than in the center (Figure 24.2). The shape enhances red blood cell function in two ways. First, compared with a round cell, the ratio of plasma membrane to cell volume is increased. Second, the surface membrane is brought close to the cytoplasm, which contains hemoglobin.

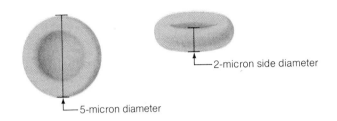

Figure 24.2 Biconcave structure of a red blood cell. (See also Figure 10.13a for a scanning electron micrograph of red blood cells.)

Hemoglobin, recall, is an iron-containing protein that gives red blood cells their characteristic color (Figures 3.20 and 3.21). A heme group occurs in association with each of the four polypeptide chains of the hemoglobin molecule. Each heme contains one iron atom, which can rapidly combine with one oxygen molecule. When oxygen dissolves in blood, it quickly binds with the iron and thus forms a substance called **oxyhemoglobin**. Blood that is rich in oxyhemoglobin is bright red. Blood somewhat depleted of oxygen is darker and appears bluish when observed through blood vessel walls.

Hemoglobin also can transport carbon dioxide, a by-product of aerobic metabolism. Although most of the carbon dioxide is dissolved or is carried as bicarbonate in the bloodstream, about eleven percent binds with amino groups of the hemoglobin molecule. The resulting substance is known as **carbaminohemoglobin**.

The red blood cell forms in red bone marrow (Chapter Twenty). During its formation, it uses cell-building instructions contained in nuclear DNA. As the cell matures, the nucleus disappears and hemoglobin becomes dispersed in the space it once occupied. Although the nucleus is absent in mature cells, the enzymes it specified earlier remain functional. A red blood cell can last for about four months.

A small portion of red blood cells dies off and is removed from circulation on a continuing basis. However, the **cell count** (the number of cells of a given type in each microliter of blood) remains fairly stable. The red blood cell count averages 5.4 million in healthy adult males, and 4.8 million in females. The red blood cell population is maintained by feedback mechanisms. When oxygen levels in tissues are low, the kidneys secrete a substance that acts enzymatically on a plasma protein, converting it to a hor-

red blood cells (erythrocytes)	platelets (thrombocytes)

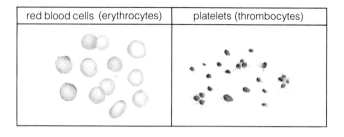

white blood cells (leukocytes)

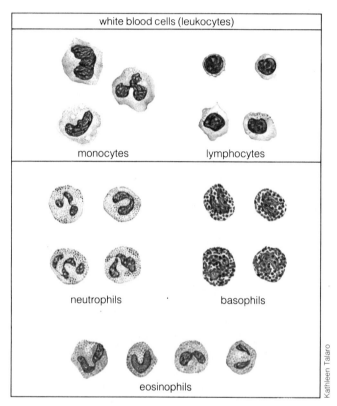

monocytes   lymphocytes

neutrophils   basophils

eosinophils

Kathleen Talaro

Figure 24.3 Cellular components of vertebrate blood. There are two classes of white blood cells. The "granular" cells (neutrophils, basophils, and eosinophils) have grainy particles in the cytoplasm. The "agranular" cells (monocytes and lymphocytes) do not.

mone (erythropoietin). The hormone travels to red bone marrow and stimulates an increase in red blood cell production. New cells enter the circulation. Within a few days, their oxygen-carrying capacity assures that more oxygen will reach tissues. When tissue oxygen levels are raised sufficiently, hormone activation dwindles and red blood cell production decreases.

White Blood Cells. White blood cells, or **leukocytes**, function in defense responses to tissue damage or infection by foreign agents, and as scavengers (for example, some destroy dead or worn-out cells). All are derived from stem cells in bone marrow. **Stem cells** are immature cells that are not yet fully differentiated. Some are "uncommitted" and can differentiate into one of several mature cell types. Others are "committed" genetically to differentiating into one cell type only.

Five types of white blood cells can be distinguished on the basis of size, nuclear shape, staining characteristics, and the presence or absence of dark-staining granules in the nucleus. The cell types are lymphocytes, neutrophils, monocytes, basophils, and eosinophils (Figure 24.3).

Lymphocytes account for twenty to forty percent of the white blood cells in a blood sample. There are two kinds of lymphocytes, called T-cells and B-cells. Both are central to immune responses, which are described later in the chapter. During such responses, the B cells differentiate into *plasma cells,* which secrete proteins (antibodies) that bind to extracellular invaders and mark them for destruction.

Neutrophils are highly mobile. Many can squeeze between the cells of capillary walls and move, amoebalike, into infected or damaged tissue regions. Neutrophils are also highly phagocytic. They chemically track down, ingest, and destroy bacteria. *Monocytes,* too, are highly mobile and phagocytic. They follow the neutrophils into damaged tissue regions, where they ingest bacteria, other foreign matter, and dead cells.

Only two to four percent of the white blood cells are *basophils* and *eosinophils.* Both contain enzymes that help destroy bacteria. Basophils also contain substances that are important in blood clotting and anticlotting mechanisms. (The term "clotting" refers to a reaction in which blood cells clump together in a sticky net, as around puncture wounds.) Eosinophils are phagocytic and can ingest particles that have been chemically earmarked for destruction by other white blood cells. Eosinophils might be involved in controlling allergic reactions.

Normally, each microliter of human blood contains between 5,000 and 11,000 white blood cells. The number varies, depending on whether the body is highly active, in a state of health, or under siege. For example, the white blood cell count increases during bacterial infections, and it can drop below 5,000 during viral infections.

Platelets. Thrombocytes, or **platelets**, are actually cell fragments that are produced in bone marrow. They are bits of cytoplasm pinched off giant cells (megakaryocytes). About 300,000 platelets are present in each microliter of blood. These cytoplasmic fragments contain substances that aid in blood clotting. Hence platelets function in controls over blood loss from damaged blood vessels.

Plasma. The straw-colored, liquid portion of blood is called **plasma**. Its components can be summarized this way:

water	91.5 percent
plasma proteins	7.0 percent
ions, sugars, lipids, amino acids, vitamins, hormones, dissolved gases	1.5 percent

Plasma proteins include albumin, globulins, and fibrinogen. The concentration of plasma proteins is important in controls over the water distribution between blood and interstitial fluid. *Albumin* is the most important in this respect, for it represents sixty percent of the total amount of plasma proteins. *Alpha globulin* and *beta globulin* are transporters of lipids and fat-soluble vitamins. *Gamma globulins* function in immune responses. *Fibrinogen* is necessary in blood clotting.

Plasma contains ions, simple sugars (such as glucose), amino acids, vitamins, hormones, and dissolved gases (mostly oxygen, carbon dioxide, and nitrogen). Some ions are released during metabolism; others are absorbed from the digestive tract. These diverse ions have many functions, such as maintaining extracellular pH and fluid volume, and conducting messages (in nerve and muscle cells). The lipids present in plasma include fats, phospholipids, and cholesterol. They are generally complexed with proteins into *lipoproteins*. Lipoproteins are the form in which lipids are transported from the liver to different body regions.

STRUCTURE AND FUNCTION OF BLOOD CIRCULATION SYSTEMS

Systemic and Pulmonary Circulation

In all vertebrates, blood flows from the heart into arteries, which branch into smaller diameter arterioles. The arterioles branch into enormous networks of capillaries, called capillary beds. Blood flows from capillary beds into venules, then veins, which carry blood back to the heart.

In fishes, blood travels in a *single* circuit from the heart to gills, then to body organs, then back to the heart (Figure 24.4a). Fish gills have capillary beds where oxygen is picked

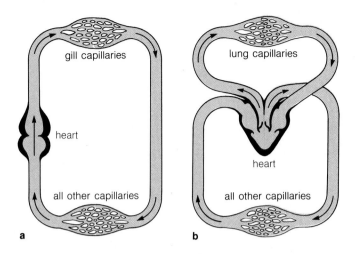

Figure 24.4 Comparison of the single circuit for blood delivery in fishes (**a**) with the dual circuit in birds and mammals (**b**). Figure 24.5 shows a few more details of the dual circuit arrangement, as it occurs in humans.

up from the surrounding water (Chapter Twenty-Five). Capillary beds also occur in other body regions. This means that all blood flows through two systems of small-diameter capillary beds. Accordingly, there are two regions of high resistance to fluid flow that the pumping action of a single heart must overcome.

In contrast, blood flows in a *dual* circuit through birds and mammals. This dual route depends on a heart that is divided internally into two halves. One circuit is called **pulmonary circulation**. Blood from the right side of the heart moves to the lungs (where blood is oxygenated), then back through veins that lead into the left side of the heart. The other circuit is called **systemic circulation**. Here, the oxygenated blood moves from the left side of the heart, through the rest of the body (where oxygen is used), then back through veins that lead to the right side of the heart. As Figure 24.4b and 24.5 show, there is complete separation of the delivery of oxygen-poor blood to the lungs and oxygen-enriched blood to the rest of the body.

Chapter Thirty-Four explores the evolution of dual circulation systems, including the environmental pressures that are thought to have fostered them. For now, let's look at the structure and function of this system as it occurs in humans, beginning with the heart.

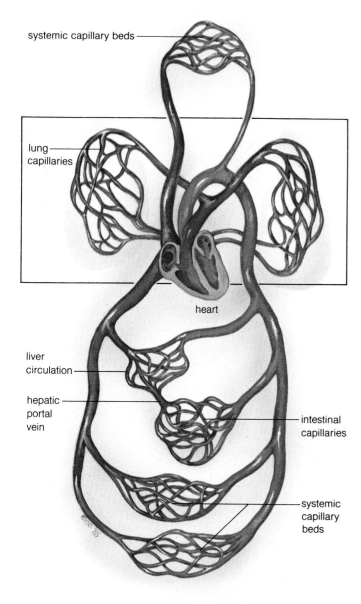

systemic capillary beds

lung capillaries

heart

liver circulation

hepatic portal vein

intestinal capillaries

systemic capillary beds

Figure 24.5 Dual circulation system in the human body. The pulmonary circuit is indicated by the boxed region; all other blood vessels make up the systemic circuit.

The Human Heart

Heart Structure. In humans and other mammals, the **heart** is a four-chambered muscular organ (Figure 24.6). Its protective outer covering (pericardium) is made of tough, fibrous connective tissue. The thick midlayer (myocardium) consists of cardiac muscle tissue that provides the contractile force behind blood flow through the heart. The smooth inner lining (endocardium) is made of epithelial and connective tissues.

Inside, the heart is divided in two halves. Each half is further divided into a thin-walled **atrium** (plural, atria) and a thick-walled **ventricle**. Oxygenated blood from the lungs enters the left atrium, moves into the left ventricle, and is pumped into the *aorta,* the main artery leading to the rest of the body. Deoxygenated blood being returned from the body enters the right atrium, moves into the right ventricle, then is pumped into the *pulmonary artery,* which leads to the lungs.

The heart has four sets of membranous flaps that serve as **valves**. The coordinated opening and closing of the valves permits blood to move in one direction, so that backflow is prevented as blood is being circulated. An **atrioventricular valve** is located at the passageway between the atrium and ventricle of each half of the heart. One **semilunar valve** is located at the passageway leading from the left ventricle to the aorta; another is located between the right ventricle and the pulmonary artery (Figure 24.6).

Cardiac Cycle. During a seventy-year life span, the heart beats some $2\frac{1}{2}$ billion times. It rests only during the brief interval between heartbeats. Each heartbeat is a sequence of muscle contractions and relaxation, called the **cardiac cycle**. During a cardiac cycle, the walls of the four heart chambers contract in coordination, causing pressure within the chambers to rise and fall in a rhythmic way. Heart valves passively close and open in response to the pressure gradient.

Blood from veins flows into the heart when both atria are relaxed. As blood fills the atrial chambers, the pressure inside becomes greater than the pressure within the relaxed ventricles. Thus the atrioventricular valves are open and blood flows into the ventricles even before the atria contract. When the atria do contract, atrial pressure rises sharply and forces much of the remaining blood into the ventricles. Both atria now relax. This part of the cardiac cycle is called atrial **systole** and atrial **diastole**. ("Systole" means a contraction and "diastole" means a relaxation of the heart chamber wall.)

Another part of the cardiac cycle involves contraction and relaxation of the ventricles (ventricular systole and diastole). When ventricles contract, the atrioventricular valves snap shut and prevent the backflow of blood. The contraction also causes pressure inside the ventricles to rise sharply above the pressure in the aorta and pulmonary veins. The increase forces open the semilunar valves leading to those vessels. The valves remain open until the ven-

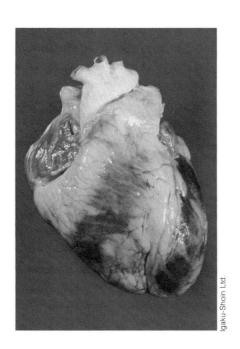

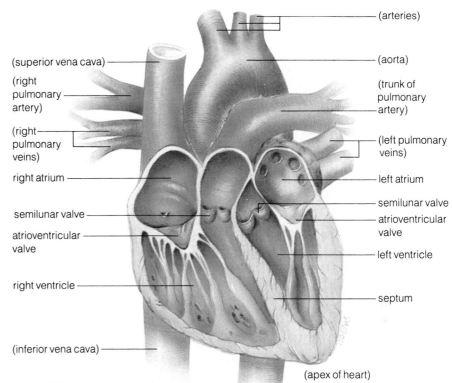

(arteries)

(superior vena cava)

(aorta)

(right pulmonary artery)

(trunk of pulmonary artery)

(right pulmonary veins)

(left pulmonary veins)

right atrium

left atrium

semilunar valve

semilunar valve

atrioventricular valve

atrioventricular valve

right ventricle

left ventricle

septum

(inferior vena cava)

(apex of heart)

Figure 24.6 The human heart. The sketch is a cutaway view of this muscular organ, showing its four chambers (left atrium, left ventricle, right atrium, right ventricle). The photograph and sketch both show the position of the heart as it would be in a person facing the viewer.

tricles are almost empty and ventricular pressure has dropped. The ventricles relax and some arterial blood flows back toward them, causing the semilunar valves to slam shut (Figure 24.7). *Thus, during a cardiac cycle, ventricles are relaxed when atria are contracting; and atria are relaxed when ventricles are contracting.*

Blood and heart movements generate vibrations that produce a "lub-dup" sound. The sound can be heard at the chest wall. Each "lub" marks the closure of atrioventricular valves. The "dup" marks the closure of the semilunar valves behind blood leaving the heart.

Heart Muscle Contraction. Like skeletal muscle, the cardiac muscle of the myocardium is striated. It contains parallel bands of thin actin filaments and thick myosin filaments, arranged into the contractile units called sarcomeres (Figure 23.19). Unlike skeletal muscle, cardiac muscle fibers branch and abut with each other at muscle fiber endings.

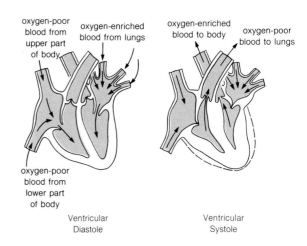

oxygen-poor blood from upper part of body

oxygen-enriched blood from lungs

oxygen-enriched blood to body

oxygen-poor blood to lungs

oxygen-poor blood from lower part of body

Ventricular Diastole

Ventricular Systole

Figure 24.7 Blood flow through the human heart during contraction (systole) and relaxation (diastole) of muscle tissue in the walls of ventricles.

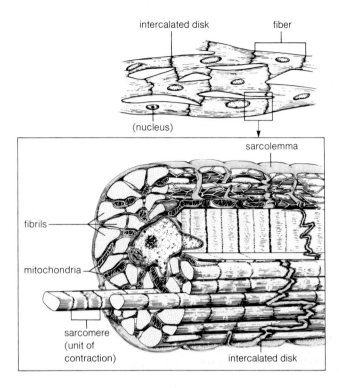

Figure 24.8 Intercalated disk between abutting heart muscle fibers. (From E. Braunwald et al., *New England Journal of Medicine*, 1967, 277:794. Reprinted by permission.)

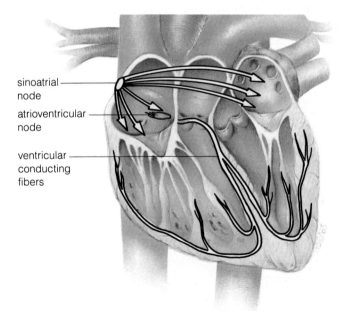

Figure 24.9 Location of conducting muscle fibers that make up the cardiac conducting system.

Each end-to-end region of cell membrane is called an **intercalated disk** (Figure 24.8). Cell membranes of adjacent fibers are fused together here and for some distance along both fibers, producing strong cohesion between cells. Electron micrographs show that despite the membrane fusion, each muscle fiber remains a separate cell with its own nucleus.

Gap junctions span each intercalated disk and provide rapid communication between cells (Chapter Five). At these junctions, ions are transferred directly from one cell to the other, causing the changes in membrane potential that lead to contraction. Thus the gap junctions permit the rapid spread of excitation from one fiber to another. The muscle tissue contracts as a unit, *as if* it were one large mass of unseparated cells.

Because of strong cohesion and rapid chemical communication at intercalated disks between individual fibers, cardiac muscle tissue contracts as a single unit.

Cardiac Conduction System. Heartbeat is under the control of the autonomic nervous system. However, autonomic nerves control only *changes* in the rate of contraction. Even when all autonomic nerves leading to the heart are severed, the heart keeps on beating! What causes the heart to beat?

Just beneath the endocardium are highly modified cardiac muscle fibers that are self-excitatory. These fibers specialize in conducting excitation through all parts of the myocardium, and they are the basis of the **cardiac conduction system**.

Heart excitation originates in the **sinoatrial node**, a region of the conducting fibers where major veins enter the right atrium (Figure 24.9). Here, changes in membrane potentials occur repeatedly, without any stimulation from the outside. One wave of excitation follows another, seventy or eighty times a minute. The rhythmic excitation begins soon after heart muscle cells first appear in the developing animal embryo, and thereafter it is responsible for all muscle contractions through the entire myocardium. Although all cells of the conducting system are self-excitatory, the sinoatrial node comes to threshold first. Thus the sinoatrial node is the **cardiac pacemaker**: its rhythmic firing is the basis for the normal rate of heartbeat.

First, each wave of excitation from the pacemaker spreads over the two atria. So stimulated, the atria contract almost simultaneously. The atrial and ventricular muscle tissues are separated by nonconducting connective tissue, so the wave of excitation does not pass directly into the ventricle walls. The delay allows the atria to empty and the ventricles to fill with blood.

During the delay, the excitation passes to the **atrioventricular node**, which consists of conducting fibers located in the floor of the right atrium (Figure 24.9). This node is the *only* conduction pathway between atrial and ventricular muscle tissue.

From the atrioventricular node, bundles of conducting fibers carry excitation through the ventricles. Because these fibers branch extensively throughout the inner walls of both ventricles, all parts of the walls contract simultaneously in response to the excitation. Because contractile muscles in the ventricle walls are arranged in whorls (Figure 24.10), the walls contract with a wringing movement that squeezes blood into the aorta and pulmonary arteries.

The sinoatrial node is the cardiac pacemaker. Its spontaneous, repetitive excitation spreads along a system of special conducting muscle fibers that stimulate contractile tissue in the atria, then the ventricles, in a rhythmic cycle.

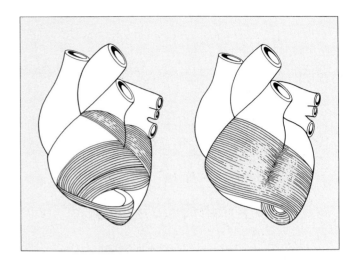

Figure 24.10 Arrangement of cardiac muscle in the myocardium. Contraction of the two opposing whorls of muscle creates a wringing motion from the heart apex (tip) upward, such that blood is forced into arteries. (From *Human Anatomy and Physiology,* second edition, by John W. Hole, Jr. © 1978, 1981 Wm. C. Brown Publishers, Dubuque, Iowa. All rights reserved. Reprinted by permission.)

Blood Vessels

Now that we have considered the pumping mechanism of blood circulation, let's take a look at the different vessels that transport blood to and from all body regions. As you will see, these vessels offer varying degrees of resistance to the blood that is flowing under pressure through them.

Arteries and Arterioles.   Arteries carry blood away from the heart. An **artery** has thick, impermeable walls containing smooth muscle and distensible connective tissue (Figure 24.11). Because of these components, the artery can expand under the surges of fluid pressure from blood leaving the heart. It also can recoil elastically, a movement that forces blood onward. Arteries branch into smaller tubes, or **arterioles**. Smooth muscle fibers form rings around these tubes (Figure 24.11).

The smooth muscles in the walls of both arteries and arterioles are under control of the autonomic nervous system. Excitatory signals traveling along sympathetic nerves keep these muscles in a state of partial contraction. Increases in sympathetic nerve signals cause further contraction, which shrinks the blood vessel diameter. This motor response is called **vasoconstriction**. Decreases in sympathetic nerve signals allow the muscles to relax, which enlarges the

blood vessel diameter. This motor response is called **vasodilation**. The coordinated vasoconstriction and vasodilation of arterioles directs blood to regions of greatest metabolic activity. The more active the cells in a given region, the greater the flow of blood that reaches them.

Although neural controls can lead to redistribution of blood flow, the controls are concerned mostly with maintaining blood pressure. Local controls are more important in the distribution of blood flow. These controls are exerted by chemical changes in rapidly metabolizing tissues and organs (such as the heart and skeletal muscle). These changes also cause arterioles to dilate. Decreases in oxygen concentration, and increases in carbon dioxide, hydrogen ion, and potassium ion concentrations, serve as local regulators of blood flow. Such chemical changes act on smooth muscle in arterioles, causing them to relax and thereby increasing blood flow to specific regions.

In summary, we can say this about the role of arterioles in blood distribution:

Through controls over their musculature, arterioles can be used in varying the resistance to blood flow along different routes; hence these blood vessels function in controlling blood flow distribution through the body.

Capillaries. A **capillary** is a blood vessel with such a small diameter that red blood cells squeeze through it single file. Capillary walls consist of a single layer of epithelial cells. Because these thin walls are permeable to many materials, capillaries represent the functional zone in which materials are exchanged between blood and the surrounding tissue.

With their thin walls and vast numbers, capillaries represent an immense surface for exchange of materials between blood and interstitial fluid.

In each capillary bed, nutrients, gases, and metabolic by-products move between the bloodstream and interstitial fluid (Figure 24.12). Diffusion along concentration gradients accounts for most of the movements. In addition, water is exchanged across capillary walls.

Two opposing forces govern water movement. First, because of the higher plasma protein concentrations in the capillaries, water is less concentrated in the blood than in interstitial fluid. This creates an inward-directed force of osmotic pressure. Second, because of the fluid pressure generated by heart contractions, there is an outward-directed hydrostatic force. At the arteriole end of the capillary, hydrostatic pressure is greater than the osmotic pressure. Thus, more fluid leaves the capillaries than enters (Figure 24.12). The term **filtration** refers to this kind of transmembrane movement as a result of hydrostatic pressure.

By the time blood reaches the venule end of a capillary, filtration has reduced the water concentration inside. Also, the small-diameter capillary has presented enough resistance to blood flow that hydrostatic pressure is reduced. Here, the inward-directed osmotic pressure gradient exceeds hydrostatic pressure, and the net water movement is inward.

In any given tissue, the density of capillaries is directly related to metabolic output of the tissue. For example, cardiac muscle uses large amounts of oxygen (in ATP-generating metabolism). Not surprisingly, the heart is serviced by extensive capillaries. These capillaries are part of the heart's own blood transport system, called **coronary circulation**. The first two branches of the aorta (the coronary arteries) supply blood to capillaries in the myocardium. Here, as much as eighty percent of the oxygen flowing through moves out of the bloodstream and diffuses through interstitial fluid to heart muscle cells. (In contrast, only about thirty percent of the oxygen being transported through other body tissues moves out of the capillaries.)

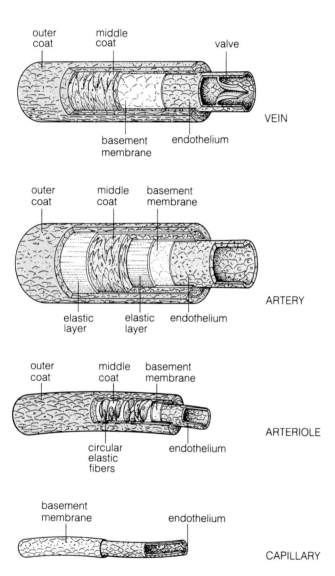

Figure 24.11 Structure of blood vessels. The outer coat consists of loose connective tissue. The middle coat contains elastic fibers and smooth muscle. The basement membrane consists of loose connective tissue and elastic connective tissue. (Based on A. Spence, *Basic Human Anatomy*, Benjamin/Cummings)

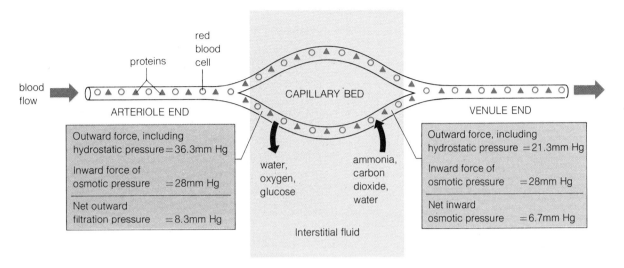

Figure 24.12 Forces underlying movements of substances between capillaries and interstitial fluid. Notice the difference in net inward and outward pressures, resulting in net filtration. (From *Human Anatomy and Physiology*, second edition, by John W. Hole, Jr. © 1978, 1981 Wm. C. Brown Publishers, Dubuque, Iowa. All rights reserved. Reprinted by permission.)

Sympathetic nerves and local chemical changes that influence arteriole diameter also affect **precapillary sphincters**: tiny rings of smooth muscle at the capillary entrance. Only when a sphincter is dilated can red blood cells squeeze through the lumen. (A "lumen" is the space within a tube, such as a blood vessel.) Thus precapillary sphincters also play a role in the distribution of blood flow.

Veins and Venules. Capillaries merge into **venules**, which then merge into **veins**—the vessels that return blood to the heart after materials have been delivered to and picked up from body cells. Venule walls are only a little thicker than those of capillaries (Figure 24.11). Compared with arteries, the walls of veins do not have much smooth muscle, and they are readily distended. A vein is distended when internal pressure is high.

Veins are under neural controls, which can cause considerable vasoconstriction. Also, the walls of veins servicing the body's limbs have **venous valves**: tissue folds that project into the lumen, in the direction of flow. When fluid starts moving backward, it pushes the folds into the lumen, thereby closing off the vessel and preventing backflow (Figure 24.13).

Both venules and veins serve as a temporary reservoir for blood volume, precisely because they are so highly distensible. When the body's metabolic activity is low, blood volume is high in these vessels. When metabolic activity increases, the venous return from the reservoir is increased.

With their great distensibility, veins and venules function as blood volume reservoirs.

Blood Pressure and the Distribution of Flow

Blood pressure can be defined as the fluid pressure, generated by heart contractions, that keeps blood circulating. Blood always flows from high-pressure regions to low-pressure regions. Blood flow through the pulmonary and systemic circulation routes depends on the high pressures created by heart contractions. As blood courses first through arteries, then arterioles, the decreasing diameters of the vascular tubes present more and more resistance to flow. Along these routes, fluid pressure drops. The magnitude of the pressure drop depends on the amount of resistance that the flowing blood has encountered.

The magnitude of pressure in large arteries depends on two independent variables: the rate at which the heart pumps blood into them (cardiac output), and the resistance to blood flow out of them, as offered by the small arteries and arterioles (total peripheral resistance). Let's begin with the pressure required to keep blood circulating.

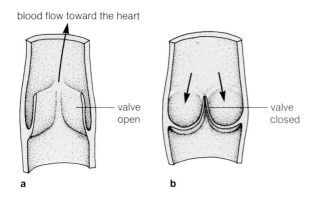

Figure 24.13 Venous valve structure when internal pressure is high (**a**) and low (**b**).

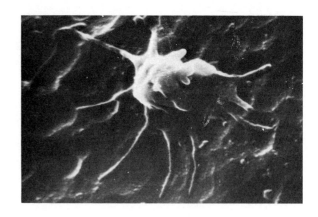

Figure 24.14 Scanning electron micrograph of a spiny blood platelet.

T. Hovig, Oslo University

Blood pressure is generally measured at large arteries of the systemic circulation, such as the ones in your upper arms. First a systolic reading is taken of the highest pressure generated by heart contractions. In young adults at rest, systolic pressure is about 120mm Hg. (This is the distance, expressed in millimeters, that a column of mercury, or Hg, will rise when subjected to the specified amount of pressure.) Next, a diastolic reading is taken of the lowest pressure in the artery, just before blood is pumped out of the heart again. Diastolic pressure is generally about 80mm Hg. Thus the difference between systolic and diastolic readings (the so-called *pulse pressure*) is 120 − 80, or 40mm Hg.

The volume of blood returning to the heart is the same as the volume of blood being pumped out. *However, blood pressure is not the same at the start and end of the circuit.* This is important, because if there were no pressure difference, blood would go nowhere. Instead, when blood leaves the heart, its pressure is high. By the time blood has traveled back through the veins and has arrived at the right atrium, blood pressure is virtually zero. What happens is this: The arterial system, which channels blood toward capillaries, serves as a **pressure reservoir**. Thick-walled arteries are elastic, but only enough to partially smooth out pressure oscillations caused by heart contractions. Farther down the circuit, muscular arterioles control blood flow to one body region or another. For any given arterial pressure, the blood flow through a tissue will be greater as the diameters of the arterioles in that tissue are greater. Under neural signals and local chemical signals, arterioles constrict or dilate, the result being variations in blood flow that meet the chang-

ing demands of different tissues. Even farther down the circuit, entrances to capillaries continually open and close. During periods when the body is resting, only five to ten percent of all capillaries are open at any one time. During periods of increased metabolic activity, such as exercise, many more are open.

The venous system is a low-pressure volume reservoir that contains more than half the total blood volume. What forces venous blood back to the heart? Heart contractions are the main force, keeping a finite although low pressure in the venous reservoir and lowering the pressure in the atria by emptying the atrial chambers. Limb muscle movements, and expansion of the rib cage during breathing, also reinforce the pressure gradient that causes blood to flow through the venous system. So do skeletal muscle contractions, which compress adjacent veins. The forces acting on the venous system can be summarized this way:

The pressure gradient that heart contractions establish is aided by pressure generated by muscle action and by respiration. These forces together work to return venous blood to the heart.

Hemostasis

Suppose you are paring an apple and the knife slips just enough to pare part of your thumb, too. Your blood, being under higher pressure than your surroundings, promptly flows outward. At the sight of such outpourings, have you ever wondered for one spinning moment what keeps your body fluids from draining away completely?

In many invertebrates and all vertebrates, bleeding is stopped by several mechanisms that include blood vessel spasm, platelet plug formation, and blood coagulation. The collective action of these mechanisms is called **hemostasis**. It occurs in response to *hemorrhage,* a bulk flow of blood from damaged vessels. Hemostasis is most effective in capillaries, arterioles and venules, which have small diameters compared with arteries and veins.

Hemostasis proceeds through the following events when a small blood vessel is ruptured or cut:

1. Constriction of smooth muscle in walls of the damaged vessel, in an extended spasm that may curtail blood flow

2. Adherence and clumping of platelets, a response that temporarily plugs the rupture

3. Prolongation of the muscle spasm when the clumped platelets release serotonin (a vasoconstrictor)

4. Clot formation as blood becomes coagulated (converted to a gel)

5. Clot retraction into a compact mass, which draws ruptured walls back together

First, injury triggers a *muscle spasm:* smooth muscle in the blood vessel wall constricts and curtails blood flow at once. The spasm occurs partly as a reflex reaction to stimulation of pain receptors in affected tissues. This reflex lasts only a few minutes. However, the spasm also occurs as a direct response to mechanical stimulation, and this response can continue for as long as half an hour.

During the extended muscle spasm, *platelet plug formation* begins. Platelets, recall, circulate in the bloodstream. When they reach a damaged vessel, the platelets take on a spiny appearance (Figure 24.14). The spines are pseudopodia, formed by microtubular growth. Through chemical recognition, the pseudopodia spread out and adhere to exposed collagen fibers in damaged walls. When attached to collagen, platelets release ADP—which attracts still more platelets. They also release calcium ions, which promote clumping into a plug. Such plugs can seal tiny ruptures. The platelets also release serotonin, a vasoconstrictor that helps prolong the spasm.

Clot formation refers to coagulation of blood at the damaged site. The primary means of blood coagulation is called the **intrinsic clotting mechanism**. It is initiated when the epithelial surface of blood vessels is damaged to the extent that underlying collagen fibers are exposed. Exposure in the

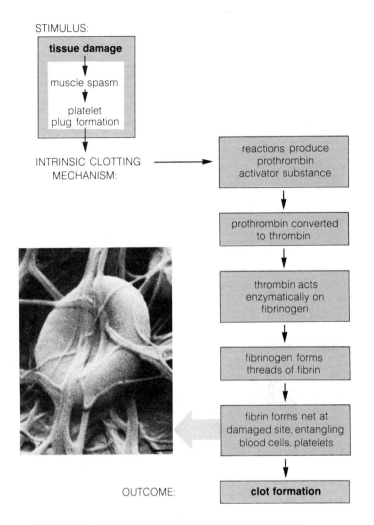

Figure 24.15 Intrinsic clotting mechanism leading to blood coagulation at cut or ruptured blood vessel tissues. The scanning electron micrograph shows a red blood cell trapped in a fibrin net. (From Emil Bernstein, *Science,* volume 173 cover, 27 August 1971. Copyright 1971 by the American Association for the Advancement of Science)

presence of calcium ions activates a plasma protein (Figure 24.15). In activated form, this protein triggers a series of reactions leading to the formation of prothrombin activator. The activator, in the presence of calcium ions, converts an alpha globulin (called prothrombin) into the enzyme thrombin. This enzyme acts on large, rodlike proteins (fibrinogen) that are produced in the liver and that circulate in blood plasma. The proteins adhere to each other, end to end and side by side. They form long, insoluble polymers called fibrin threads. The growing threads stick to exposed collagen on the damaged vessel wall, forming a net that entangles blood cells and platelets. The mass is a blood clot. Figure 24.15 summarizes these intrinsic clotting events.

Blood also can coagulate through an **extrinsic clotting mechanism**. The contribution of this mechanism to hemostasis is unclear. However, it is definitely involved in walling off bacterial infections and thereby preventing the spread of bacteria from invaded tissue regions. The mechanism is triggered by the release of chemical substances from the damaged tissue itself. The damage stimulates tissues into releasing a substance which, in the presence of calcium ions, phospholipids, and proteins, is converted to prothrombin activator. The remaining steps parallel those shown in Figure 24.15.

What could be the advantage of such an involved series of steps in clot formation? Perhaps it provides the opportunity for built-in control points, which would guard against abnormal clot formation. The bloodstream contains many substances that promote coagulation, and some anticoagulants that inhibit it. Under normal conditions, anticoagulation predominates. Blood clotting depends on the balance that exists between the two processes. With multiple control points in the clotting mechanism, there is less likelihood of abnormal clot formation. This is important, for abnormal clots can cause serious circulatory problems (see *Commentary*).

LYMPHATIC SYSTEM

During capillary exchange, more fluid leaves the bloodstream than enters. The reason is that hydrostatic pressure forces out slightly more water than osmotic pressure drives in (Figure 24.12). Given the tremendous number of capillaries in the human body, considerable water and dissolved substances could accumulate in interstitial regions if it were not for a vascular network that supplements pulmonary and systemic circulation. This network is part of the **lymphatic system**, which functions in returning excess tissue fluid to the bloodstream and in the body's defenses against injury and attack. The transport tubes constitute a lymph vascular system. When tissue fluid has moved into these transport tubes, it is called **lymph**. The organs of the lymphatic system (lymphoid organs) take part in defense responses. These organs are connected with both the blood and lymph vascular systems.

COMMENTARY

On Cardiovascular Disorders

During certain types of increased physical activity, systolic pressure rises because the heart rate accelerates and a greater volume of blood leaves the heart. Thus pulse pressure rises. Sometimes arterial walls undergo structural changes, and this, too, leads to increased pulse pressure.

One of the most prevalent of all cardiovascular disorders is hypertension, a gradual increase in arterial blood pressure brought on by factors that are, in most cases, unknown. Hypertension has been called the silent killer, because afflicted individuals may show no outward symptoms; in fact, they feel healthy. Often they are neither "hyper" nor "tense." Thus, even when their high blood pressure has been detected, some hypertensive individuals tend to resist corrective changes in diet, exercising, and medication. Of 23 million Americans who are hypertensive, most are not undergoing treatment. About 180,000 will die each year as a result.

In arteriosclerosis, calcium salts and fibrous tissue gradually build up within arterial walls, leading to a "hardening of the arteries." As arteries become less and less compliant, they cannot expand under increased blood flow, and pressure builds up in the arterial system. If arterial blood pressure is high enough, small blood vessels supplying brain cells rupture, which is one cause of a brain stroke. If the brain cells deprived of oxygen and nutrients are in a region governing the coordination of body movements, paralysis may follow. If they are in regions controlling the vital function of breathing, death will follow.

In Chapter Three, you read that lipids such as fats and cholesterol are insoluble in water. Such lipids are transported in the bloodstream, where they are bound to protein carriers that keep them suspended in the plasma. In atherosclerosis (the major type of arteriosclerotic disease), abnormal smooth muscle cells multiply in arterial walls. Then lipids are deposited within them and in the surrounding extracellular space. Calcium salts are deposited on top of the lipids, and a fibrous net forms

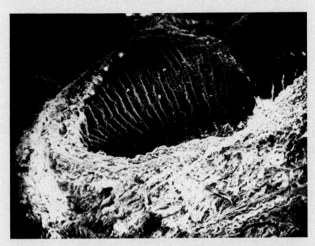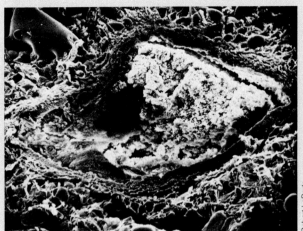

To the left, a normal artery; to the right, an artery clogged with plaques.

Robert LaPorta

over the whole mass. This so-called plaque sticks out into the lumen. Sometimes platelets become caught on rough plaque edges, and are stimulated into secreting some of their chemicals. When they do, they initiate clot formation. As the clot and plaque grow, the artery can become blocked. This shuts off blood flow to tissues that the artery supplies. Heart muscles are supplied by coronary arteries, which branch off the aorta. A coronary occlusion may build up slowly, as it does from atherosclerosis. Or it may occur suddenly, as when clots dislodged from the coronary or other arteries travel to one of these heart supply lines and plug the passageway. Heart attacks may result.

Not all heart attacks are fatal. Survival depends on how much heart tissue is deprived of its blood support system, and on where the damage occurs. Survival also depends on immediate care. A pumping machine can be attached to a leg artery and synchronized with the victim's heartbeat, so that the heart has to work only to sixty percent of its normal capacity. If the victim is confined to bed rest, the heart may recover.

What causes cardiovascular disorders? Cholesterol, obviously, is under suspicion. When transported through the bloodstream, it is bound to one of two kinds of protein carriers: high-density lipoproteins (HDL) and low-density lipoproteins (LDL). Evidence is accumulating that high levels of LDL are related to a tendency toward heart trouble. It appears that LDLs, with their cholesterol cargo, show a greater penchant for infiltrating arterial walls. It may be that HDLs can attract cholesterol out of the walls and transport it to the liver, where it can be metabolized. Atherosclerosis is uncommon in rats; rats have mostly HDL. In monkeys, pigs, and humans, which generally have mostly LDL, atherosclerosis is not uncommon.

Behavior patterns, too, may trigger conditions that lead to cardiovascular disorders. Some individuals are so-called Type A personalities: they tend to be competitive, aggressive, and impatient; they are least stressed when their lives are most organized. Type A individuals tend to become acutely stressed when some aspect of their life—personal or professional—swings out of control. And the stress may lead to behavioral and physiological precursors to heart and vascular disorders. Type B personalities are more relaxed about themselves and about life; they seem to be less prone to cardiovascular troubles. Intriguingly, Robert Nerem and Fred Cornhill of Ohio State University reported in 1979 on a most unusual effect of their studies of drug action on high-cholesterol diets. Rabbits were the subjects. One group of rabbits was cuddled and played with; the other group received impersonal care. Arterial tissue samples from both groups showed that atherosclerosis was less prevalent by half in the cuddled rabbits. The experiment was repeated; the results were the same. Might we chalk one up for tender loving care?

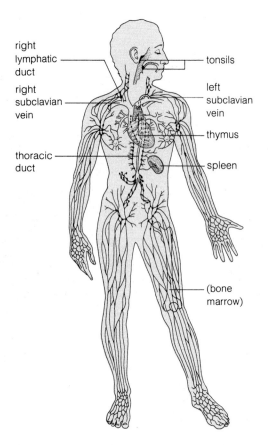

Figure 24.16 Lymphatic system, which includes the lymph vascular network and the lymphoid organs. Although bone marrow is not a lymphoid organ, it is the site of many cells that end up residing in lymphoid organs.

Lymph Vascular System

The **lymph vascular system** includes lymph capillaries, lymph vessels, and collecting ducts. This vascular system has the following functions:

1. Return of excess filtered fluid to the blood

2. Return of a small amount of proteins that normally move out of the capillaries

3. Transport of fats absorbed from the digestive tract

4. Transport of foreign particles and cellular debris to disposal centers (lymph nodes)

The lymph vascular system originates as *lymph capillaries*, which are no larger in diameter than blood capillaries. These small vessels occur in the tissues of almost all organs. They are "blind-end" tubes, in that they have no entrance at the end residing in interstitial regions; the only opening is one that merges with larger lymph vessels. The lymph capillary walls consist of only a single layer of epithelial cells. They seem to be permeable to all substances dissolved in interstitial fluid. Specialized lymph capillaries extend through intestinal villi and transport absorbed fats away from the digestive tract to the bloodstream.

Lymph vessels are structurally similar to veins. They have an external layer of connective tissue, a midlayer of smooth muscle and elastic fibers, and an inner epithelial lining. Flaplike valves in these vessels prevent backflow. Lymph vessels converge into collecting ducts, which drain into veins in the lower neck. The *right lymphatic duct* drains lymph from the upper right quadrant of the body; the *thoracic duct* drains the rest (Figure 24.16).

Lymph movement depends on the pumping action of skeletal muscles on adjacent lymph vessels and on expansion of the rib cage during breathing. Because of the lymph vessel valves, the flow is in one direction only.

Lymphoid Organs

The **lymphoid organs** include the lymph nodes, spleen, thymus, tonsils, and patches of lymphoid tissue in the small intestine. These organs function as production centers for infection-fighting cells and as sites for some defense responses.

Lymph nodes are located at intervals along lymph vessels (Figure 24.16). All lymph trickles through at least one of these nodes before being delivered to the bloodstream. Each node has an outer capsule of fibrous connective tissue (Figure 24.17). Partitions from this capsule extend into the node itself. The spaces between are packed with lymphocytes and plasma cells. Macrophages in the node help clear the lymph of bacteria, cellular debris, even dust.

The *spleen* is located behind the stomach and beneath the diaphragm, in the left part of the abdominal cavity. The spleen is the largest lymphoid organ, but in structure it is similar to a lymph node. Partitions of its outer capsule extend inward and divide the organ into chambers. Unlike lymph nodes, the chambers are filled with blood rather than lymph. Red and white "pulp" fills the spleen chambers. The red pulp contains a large store of red blood cells and macrophages. This region is a production site for red blood cells in developing human embryos. In adults, lymphocytes derived from bone marrow differentiate and mature in the white pulp of the spleen.

The spleen serves as a filtering station for blood and as a holding station for lymphocytes. It also serves as a blood reservoir. When blood circulation slackens during times of rest, some blood is stored here. During exercise or in response to hemorrhage, some of the stored blood is rapidly emptied into the circulation.

The *thymus* is another major organ where lymphocytes differentiate and mature. The thymus is a key organ in the immune response. It also serves as an endocrine gland, in that it secretes hormones concerned with the activity of lymphocytes (Chapter Twenty-Two).

NONSPECIFIC DEFENSE RESPONSES

External Barriers to Invasion

Survival, for animals, includes more than response to tissue injury. It also includes prevention of attack on cells. Most animals have skin and mucous membranes that provide important passive barriers against invasions from bacteria, viruses, and foreign substances. Few bacteria can penetrate intact skin. Also, exocrine glands in surface epithelium secrete substances (such as a component of saliva) that can kill some bacteria on contact. Mucous membranes lining respiratory tubes are like sticky traps for bacteria and assorted foreign particles, which can be swept from the tubes and expelled from the body.

Inflammatory Response

Even under normal conditions, some foreign agents enter the body every day. Their penetration triggers reactions of two sorts: specific and nonspecific defense responses. *Nonspecific responses are vital in first-time contacts as well as later encounters with the same kind of foreign matter.* It is not that invaders are recognized as being, say, a unique virus or bits of dirt brought in by a splinter. Rather, during nonspecific responses there is only general mobilization against the presence of something foreign in the tissue.

Phagocytosis and inflammation are nonspecific responses. Phagocytic cells help clean up local tissues that are damaged, cluttered with debris, or under siege by just about anything. These cells can individually patrol a region, or they can become mobilized and travel in force during **inflammation**: a series of homeostatic events that restore

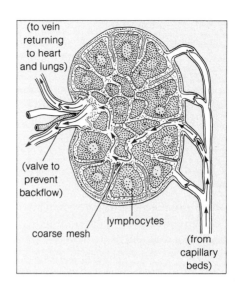

Figure 24.17 A lymph node, as it might appear when sliced lengthwise.

damaged tissues and intercellular conditions. From the time of invasion or injury, the inflammatory response proceeds through these events:

1. Under local chemical signals, blood vessels dilate, which increases blood flow to the local tissue region.

2. Local capillaries become "leaky" to plasma proteins, including about fifteen different circulating proteins called **complement**.

3. Phagocytic white blood cells actively migrate out of the blood vessel and into the damaged tissue.

4. Complement amplifies defense responses. Some complement proteins enhance blood vessel dilation and permeability. Others can release phagocyte-attracting chemicals. Others coat invaders, thereby making them "tastier" to the phagocytes.

How do we know when an inflammatory response is proceeding? Two outward symptoms are warmth and redness caused by vasodilation. Another is local swelling. The swelling occurs when water moves into the tissue as a result of increased hydrostatic pressure in capillaries and increased osmotic pressure in the interstitial fluid due to protein leakage from capillaries. The swelling, along with chemicals released during the tissue damage, stimulate local receptors that give rise to sensations of pain.

SPECIFIC DEFENSE RESPONSES: THE IMMUNE SYSTEM

In addition to nonspecific responses to invasion and injury, vertebrates have specific mechanisms for recognizing and disposing of invaders in a highly discriminatory way. These mechanisms constitute the vertebrate immune system.

Evolution of Vertebrate Immune Systems

Among single-celled organisms, phagocytosis is a means of ingesting food. During animal evolution, this nutritive function probably proved adaptive in defense. In multi-celled bodies, some of the cells were able to ingest and destroy potentially harmful organisms and substances that worked their way into tissues. When circulatory systems developed in some invertebrates, phagocytic cells apparently took to the blood and lymph highways and began patrolling all tissue regions.

Later, among vertebrates, specialized cells appeared that could recognize individual types of invaders. In addition, cell products emerged that could neutralize invaders, or hasten their elimination. Thus there arose lines of phagocytic white blood cells, with appetites ranging from broad to specific—the granulocytes, monocytes, and macrophages ("big-eaters," derived from the monocytes). There also arose the pickier lymphocytes. And there arose derivative lines, including plasma cells, which assist in battles by way of chemical secretions. All of these cells, and their products, together constitute the **vertebrate immune system**.

Cells of the vertebrate immune system are responsible for *defense* against foreign agents such as bacteria, viruses, and fungi. They are also responsible for *extracellular housekeeping*, in that they help maintain the tissue environment by eliminating worn-out or damaged body cells and structures. Through events called *immune surveillance*, they also remove mutant and cancerous cells—as well as foreign cells of solid tissues that have been surgically transplanted from one individual to another.

The vertebrate immune system is concerned with recognizing microbial invaders as well as worn-out, damaged, or mutant cells—and with selectively eliminating or neutralizing them.

Where do cells of this system reside? They are strategically dispersed through the body. Many patrol blood and lymphatic vessels. Some stand guard over the respiratory, digestive, and urinary membranes exposed to the outside environment. Whole populations are found in tissues of the lymphatic system.

Specific immune responses amplify nonspecific defense responses. They defend the body against particular foreign agents or substances, which can be of a nearly unlimited range of configurations. Thus they offer a refinement on the broad distinction between "self" and "nonself." This expansion of the immune arsenal occurs indirectly through chemical warfare agents and directly through lymphocytes sensitized for the kill.

Killer T-Cells and the B-Cell Ways of Chemical Warfare

Two distinct lymphocyte populations carry out specific immune responses. The lymphocytes are called **T-cells** and **B-cells**. Both kinds arise from stem cells in bone marrow. Some of the stem cell progeny move into the thymus (hence their name, "T"-cells). In the thymus, they acquire specific receptors on the cell surface. The receptors will be a complementary "fit" with some surface region of a given type of invader. In other words, T-cells are *precommitted* to do highly discriminatory battle. The B-cells also become precommitted, but no one knows for sure where B-cells mature and acquire their cell-surface receptors.

Primary Immune Response. What triggers T-cells and B-cells into action? Recall that during a first-time invasion, macrophages mount a nonspecific counterattack. Once invaders are ingested by macrophages, they become enclosed within membranous sacs in the cytoplasm. The sacs contain hydrolytic enzymes that degrade the invaders into harmless molecular bits. A few bits, though, end up on the macrophage surface. In some way, lymphocytes taste these chemical crumbs and become activated. Also, foreign matter that invades the bloodstream and lymphatic vessels accumulates in lymph nodes. There, it collects in chambers that house the lymphocytes. This contact, too, invites lymphocytes to join the fray.

Only lymphocytes that are precommitted to a specific invader become sensitized and move into action. They divide in a series of clonings that produce a whole army of cells (Figure 24.18). Some T-cell clones differentiate into killer T-cells, which *directly* attack their targets. Others, known as "helper" T-cells, somehow assist in B-cell maturation. B-cell clones *indirectly* attack their targets. First, B-cells differentiate into plasma cells. Then plasma cells secrete protein molecules called **antibodies**, which are

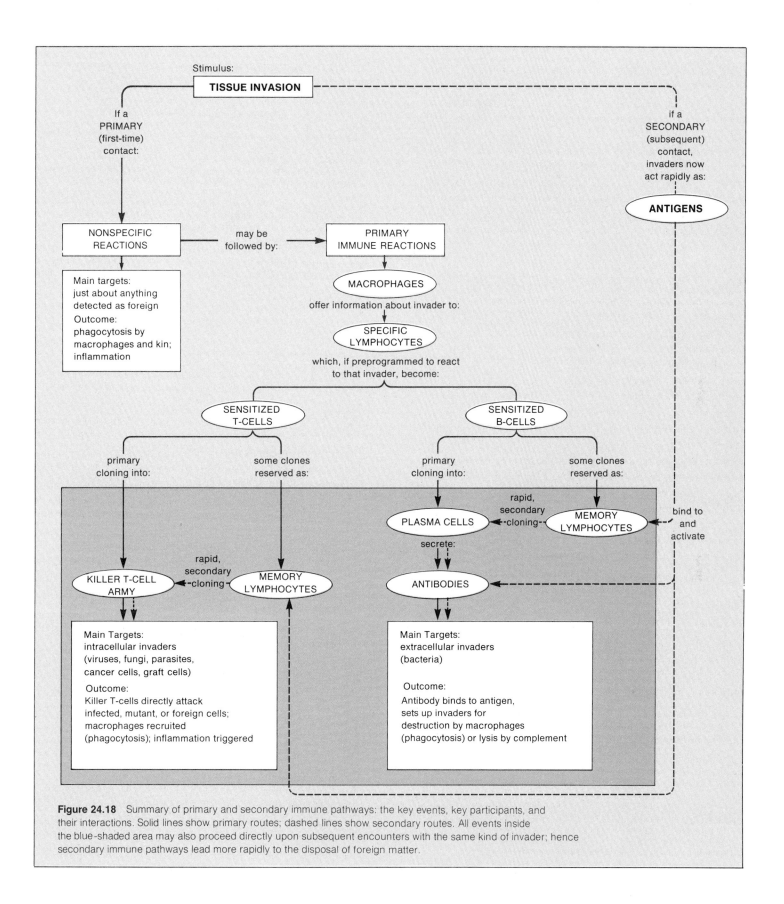

Figure 24.18 Summary of primary and secondary immune pathways: the key events, key participants, and their interactions. Solid lines show primary routes; dashed lines show secondary routes. All events inside the blue-shaded area may also proceed directly upon subsequent encounters with the same kind of invader; hence secondary immune pathways lead more rapidly to the disposal of foreign matter.

distributed by the circulation. An antibody can bind to the surface of its target. When it does, the invader is marked for disposal by other forces (Figure 24.18). Any invader that triggers antibody production is an **antigen** (*anti*body *gen*erator).

From nonspecific defense responses, to specific T-cell and B-cell clonings, then on through their direct and indirect counterattacks—this is the **primary immune pathway**. It is the route taken during a first-time contact with an antigen. A primary immune response usually takes about five or six days from the first general battle to successfully mobilize the body's more specific defenses.

Secondary Immune Response.   What happens when the same kind of antigen turns up again? Then the body typically relies on the **secondary immune pathway**. The secondary route only becomes available after an initial battle has run its course. When T-cells and B-cells undergo initial clonings, some of the clones do not join the battle. Instead they are held in reserve as **memory lymphocytes**. Unlike the rest of the army, memory lymphocytes can last for years—even decades, in some cases. Subsequent contacts with the same antigen can directly trigger memory lymphocytes into large-scale clonings. Thus a plasma cell army can rapidly proliferate, and antibodies can be rapidly churned out in abundance. Similarly, a T-cell army can be raised at once.

Because memory lymphocytes are already present and primed for action, antigens are often destroyed before they can take hold and cause disease symptoms. It is not that subsequent antigen attacks are any different, or that response mechanisms of the secondary immune pathways are all that different. *It is that the response mechanisms are* <u>*amplified*</u>.

Immunization.   Specific immune responses can also be triggered by deliberately introducing a particular antigen into the body. Following the introduction, the body is expected to mount a counterattack and develop an army of memory lymphocytes. The army will rapidly destroy antigens of this type that might later invade the body. Deliberately provoking the production of memory lymphocytes is called **immunization**. The preparation used to provoke their appearance is known as a **vaccine**. Typically, preparations of some killed or weakened antigen are injected into the body or taken orally. For instance, Sabin polio vaccine is prepared from live but weakened poliovirus. Other vaccines are prepared from the toxic by-products of dangerous organisms. Such preparations offer protection against bacteria that cause tetanus, to give one example.

COMMENTARY

Cancer, Allergy, and Attacks on Self

The immune system is a marvel of surveillance, a restorer of homeostatic balances that have been upset by all manner of threats. Here is a system that defends the body against myriad viruses and bacteria, fungi and parasites. Here is a system that sweeps out bits of dirt and old cell structures, the debris of day-to-day living. Here is a system that monitors and disposes of malignant cells, which slip from their tissue niche, lodge in improper places, and crowd normal cells to death with their abnormal growth and division. The amazing thing is how *well* the immune system works, given the diversity and unpredictable nature of the tissue invasions to which it responds. Yet the more we learn about the extent of its functioning, the more formidable seems the challenge of setting things right when the system breaks down.

Immune Surveillance.   Consider that cancer cells might arise in your body at any time as a result of mutations induced by events such as viral attack, chemical bombardment, or irradiation. "Cancer" refers to cells that have (1) lost controls over cell division and (2) lost their identity because surface recognition factors are absent or altered. Through their berserk divisions, cancer cells destroy surrounding tissues. Without proper markers for intercellular identification, cancer cells can migrate and establish themselves throughout the body (Chapter Fourteen).

As fast as cancer cells arise, they normally are destroyed before they can multiply enough for anybody to detect them. That, anyway, is the essence of the <u>immune surveillance theory</u>. The mutant cells move past circulating lymphocytes, which become sensitized to them. The activated lymphocytes proliferate rapidly. Some become killer T-cells and others release lymphokines—substances that arouse macrophages. Once macrophages become activated, they go on the rampage against any invaders and mutants—including cancer cells.

Sometimes, though, cancer cells slip through the surveillance net. Maybe the mutation doesn't affect cell surface recognition factors; or maybe the factors are

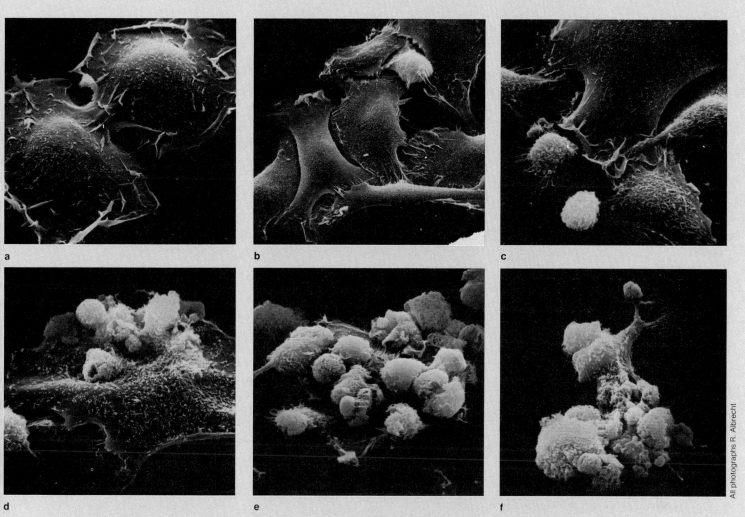

Scanning electron micrographs of the birth and immune-mediated death of cancer cells. (**a**) These cancer cells, dividing in a culture dish, are magnified about 2,000 times. (**b**) After fifty-six hours, their progeny are crowding each other. (**c**) Even with cancer cells all around them, macrophages (smaller spheres) ignore the invaders; they have not yet been turned on. (**d,e**) Activated macrophages cluster around a tumor cell. Recent work by John Hibbs at the University of Utah suggests that macrophages transfer some substance into the invader. (**f**) One or two days after the transfer, the cancer cell dies—and the macrophages ingest the leftovers. (After Krahenbuhl and Remington, 1978)

altered so slightly that cells escape detection. Perhaps surface markers become chemically disguised. Perhaps they are even released from the cell surface and begin circulating through the bloodstream—and lead the immune fighters down false trails. Sometimes, too, individuals are not genetically equipped to respond to a particu-lar antigen. The age of the individual and the overall state of health also seem to play a role in resistance to cancer.

Immune Therapy. At present, surgery, drug treatment (chemotherapy), and irradiation are the only weapons against cancer. Surgery is effective when a tumor has not spread, but surgery alone offers little hope when cancer cells have begun their wanderings. When used by themselves, chemotherapy and irradiation destroy good cells as well as bad. Immune therapy is a promising prospect. The term refers to methods of inducing mobilization of the body's own immune system by deliberately introducing agents that will set off the general immune alarm.

Interferons, a group of small proteins, are candidates for immune therapy. Trials with laboratory animals show that interferons display antiviral activity. Most cells produce and release interferon following viral attack. The interferon binds to the plasma membrane of other cells in the body and induces resistance to a wide range of viruses. Interferon is a species-specific substance; hence you can't use interferon from other organisms to fight viruses in humans. However, with standard gene-splicing methods (Chapter Twelve), enough interferon is now being produced for cancer research. The goal is to develop interferon molecules with tailored specificity and activity against cancer-inducing viruses.

Monoclonal antibodies may also hold promise for immune therapy. Cesar Milstein and Georges Kohler developed a means of producing large amounts of pure antibodies. First they isolated malignant lymphocytes, whose uncontrolled cell divisions yielded a large population of descendants just like themselves (clones). Then the researchers developed a population of antibody-producing B-cells by immunizing a mouse with a specific antigen. Later, B-cells were extracted from the mouse spleen and were fused with the malignant lymphocytes. Some of the hybrid cells and their progeny proliferated rapidly, as did the malignant parent, and produced quantities of the same type of antibodies as the parent B-cells. Clones of such hybrid cells can be maintained indefinitely and they continue to make antibody. Hence the name "monoclonal antibodies." All of these antibodies are identical, and all are derived from the same parent cell.

Monoclonal antibodies are already being used in passive immunization against malaria, flu viruses, and hepatitis B. They also are candidates for cancer therapy. By radioactively labeling monoclonal antibodies that are specific for certain types of cancer, it is possible to use scanning machines and home in on the exact location of cancer in the body. Such scans indicate whether cancer is present, where it is located in body tissues, and how large the growth is.

Monoclonal antibodies might also help overcome one of the major drawbacks to drug treatments of cancer. Such treatments have serious side effects because the drugs used are highly toxic and cannot discriminate between normal cells and cancerous ones. A current goal is to hook up drug molecules with a monoclonal antibody. As Milstein and Kohler speculate, "Once again the antibodies might be expected to home in on the cancer cells—only this time they would be dragging along with them a depth charge of monumental proportions." This prospect is one example of targeted drug therapy.

Allergy. Sometimes the immune system can damage the body instead of protecting it. An allergy is an altered secondary immune response to a normally harmless substance. It can actually cause tissue injury. Some antibody-mediated allergic reactions occur explosively, in minutes; others are delayed. About fifteen percent of the human population has a genetic predisposition to become sensitized to dust, pollen, insect venom or secretions, drugs, certain foods, and other seemingly innocuous things. These people produce unusually large amounts of a particular class of antibody, IgE, which gives rise to many of the symptoms of immediate allergic reactions.

Emotional state, physical conditions (outside temperature and air pressure, for instance), and infections can trigger or complicate reactions to dust and other antigen-behaving substances. With each recurring exposure to the antigen, molecules of IgE antibodies are produced and become attached to mediator cells of the immune system. Mediator cells release histamine, serotonin, prostaglandins, and other chemicals. Histamine causes increased capillary permeability and mucous secretions. Serotonin constricts smooth muscle. Prostaglandins and other factors cause platelet clumping. Together, these chemicals initiate a local inflammatory response. In asthma and hay fever, the resulting symptoms include a drippy nose, sneezing, congestion, and labored breathing.

In a few hypersensitive individuals, mediator cells release chemicals in copious amounts, and the inflammatory response can be explosive and life-threatening.

There can be massive constriction of air passages leading to the lungs. Circulatory shock can occur when plasma escapes rapidly, from capillaries made too permeable. That is why people who are hypersensitive to, say, wasp or bee venom can die within minutes following a secondary immune response to a single sting.

Therapy for allergy sufferers includes reliance on "blocking" antibodies. Once the allergy-producing substance has been identified, it can be injected periodically into the body in increasing amounts. The injections provoke production of another class of antibody (IgG), so that circulating antibodies are available to bind with and inactivate the substance before it interacts with IgE.

Autoimmune Disease. One of the most puzzling immune disorders is autoimmune disease, in which the body mobilizes its forces against certain of its own tissues. What causes such self-destructive responses? There are several possibilities. For instance, self-markers on the surface of body cells might become altered through mutation or when drugs and pollutants bind to them. Viral infections, too, might alter cellular machinery so that protein components of self-markers are changed. There might also be genetic predisposition to some autoimmune diseases, an unfortunate promise that may be fulfilled under certain environmental conditions.

For example, insulin-dependent diabetes mellitus is a variation of the more common disorder, diabetes mellitus. Individuals produce an antibody that reacts with insulin- and glucagon-releasing cells in pancreatic islets. Certain histocompatibility alleles are known to occur as much as ten times more frequently in persons who are afflicted with the disease. At some point, these persons may contract a viral or bacterial infection. The invaders may end up attacking the pancreas along with other tissues—and white blood cells would track them down there. (Recent studies show a correlation between the abrupt appearance of this type of diabetes and the higher incidence of infectious diseases in fall and winter.) White blood cells might become sensitized to the defectively marked islet cells and unleash their weapons against them.

A primary immune response occurs after the first injection of a vaccine. A secondary immune response occurs after a second injection ("booster shot"), which stimulates antibody production to levels that will impart resistance to the disease.

Passive immunity can be conferred on people who have been exposed to some infectious bacterial diseases (for example, diphtheria, tetanus, and botulism). These people receive injections of antibodies, which have been donated by individuals who have recovered from the disease, or which have been obtained from horses that have been immunized and that have been producing the required antibodies. Because the person's own lymphocytes are not producing the antibodies, the effects are not lasting; true immunity does not occur. However, the injections can help the individual through the immediate attack.

The Basis of Self-Recognition

When does the body acquire its capacity to distinguish self from nonself? In some way, its perception is established during embryonic development. Suppose that cells from one mouse strain are injected into a mouse embryo of another strain while it is developing in the mother's uterus. We know that the adult body perceives as foreign *any* material from a different strain, a different individual, even an organ from a different individual, and sets out to destroy it. Yet foreign cells injected into a mouse embryo are not perceived as foreign—they become recognized as self! How do we know this? When such mice have been allowed to mature, tissues from the same foreign strain have been surgically transplanted into them. The transplants have taken hold.

In mice, as in all mammals, particular DNA regions specify gene products that influence what the immune response will be to many antigens, how well the body will resist many diseases, and whether the body will reject tissue transplants. The DNA regions contain a number of split genes, called the **major histocompatibility complex** (MHC). The genes control surface recognition factors present on all nucleated cells. Foreign cells are assembled according to different DNA instructions, so they have different surface markers. T-cells can recognize the differences and destroy the nonself invaders.

But the genetic basis of self is only part of the story, as the mouse transplant experiment makes clear. Another part is when and how the T-cells learn what "self" is supposed to be. Studies suggest it is during embryonic development in the thymus that T-cells learn which surface markers to accept and which to reject. And changes in the thymus microenvironment might cause adjustments in what, exactly, is learned. Unraveling these genetic and molecular puzzles has clinical applications, for the answers may reveal why the body rejects transplants.

The body will normally tolerate tissue and organ transplants between identical twins (who have identical sets of DNA). But not everyone has an identical twin available (and willing) to donate replacements if one's own parts should break down. Given the nature of sexual reproduction, many different allelic combinations are possible in the MHC region that governs tissue rejection. As a result, the odds are about a thousand-to-one against transplants between unrelated individuals taking hold.

One goal of current research is to improve the odds. In the meantime, T-cell populations of organ recipients are bombarded with drugs and x-rays, which kill the transplant-fighting T-cells. Unfortunately, other kinds of cells are killed along with them. This stop-gap measure also has the alarming effect of severely compromising the body's ability to mount counterattacks against other kinds of invaders.

Case Study: The Silent, Unseen Struggles

The last part of this chapter has been dealing with major topics of widespread interest. Let's now conclude it with a case study of how the immune system helps *you* survive attack. Suppose it's a warm spring day and you are walking barefoot across the lawn to class. Abruptly you stop: you stepped on a staple that had been lying prong-upward. The next morning the punctured area is red, tender, and slightly swollen, even though you had pulled out the staple at once. Later on, the swelling begins to subside. Within a few more days your foot is back to normal, and you have completely forgotten the incident.

All that time, though, your body had been struggling against an unseen foe. You had inadvertently stepped on the place where a diseased bird had fallen the night before, and had lain until a scavenging animal carried it off. Your foot picked up some bacteria that had parted company from their feathered host. As long as the bacteria remained outside your body, they were harmless. But the staple prongs had carried several thousand bacterial cells into the moist warm flesh beneath your skin. Here they found conditions suitable for growth. And grow they did—they soon doubled in number and were on their way to doubling again. Left alone, they would have threatened your life.

There was nothing vicious in their attack. The bacteria were simply responding to available resources, as all forms of life do. But they were also releasing metabolic by-products that interfered with your own cell functioning. Eventually those substances would begin interfering with your tissue and organ activity.

Yet even as the staple penetrated your foot, events were set in motion that would mobilize your body's defense systems. Around the wound, some blood had escaped from ruptured capillaries, and it now pooled and clotted. Complement molecules in the blood became activated, and some of the fragments they formed released various chemicals from nearby cells. These chemicals began diffusing through the surrounding tissue. Some of the chemicals acted on precapillary sphincters, causing them to dilate and allow more blood to reach the injured site. And some of the fragments acted as cues for phagocytic white blood cells.

Usually most of your phagocytes remain in the bloodstream. But once complement stimulated them, their behavior changed. They attached themselves to capillary walls and crawled along, amoebalike, until they reached an epithelial junction. Then they slipped out into the tissue. There they crept about between cells and fibers, following the concentration gradient of complement fragments. Like bloodhounds on the trail, they moved in the direction of higher concentration.

Specifically avoiding your own cells, these phagocytes now began engulfing any particle not having a surface marker that meant, "Leave me alone—I'm *self!*" Dirt, rust, bits of broken host cells, bacteria—all were engulfed indiscriminately.

If bacteria had not entered the wound, or if they had been of a type that couldn't multiply rapidly in the tissue, then phagocytosis and inflammation would have cleaned things up. As it was, the bacterial multiplications were outpacing these nonspecific immune responses. It was time for the body's more discriminatory defenders: the lymphocyte lines and their products.

If this had been the first time your body encountered the bacterial species, few lymphocytes would have been around to respond to it. Your body would have had to make a primary immune response—it would have to wait for days while its B-lymphocytes divided enough times to produce enough antibody to control the invasion. But during your childhood, your body did fight off the same type of bacterium, and it still carries vestiges of the struggle: memory lymphocytes. When the bacteria showed up again, they encountered a lymphocyte trap ready to spring: they activated a secondary immune response.

As the inflammation progressed, lymphocytes were among the white blood cells creeping out of the bloodstream. Most were specific for other types of antigens and did not take part in the battle. But each specific memory lymphocyte entering the area encountered its target, bound a few antigens to its surface, and became activated. It moved into lymph vessels with its foreign cargo, tumbling along until it reached a lymph node and was filtered from the fluid. For the next few days, memory cells with bound antigens steadily accumulated in the node. They divided several times a day, so that their numbers and products increased rapidly.

For the first two days the bacteria appeared to be winning, for they were reproducing faster than phagocytic cells, antibody, and complement were destroying them. But by the third day, antibody production reached its peak and the tide of battle turned. For two weeks or more, antibody production will continue in your body until every last bacterium is destroyed. When it finally shuts down, the newly formed memory lymphocytes will go on circulating, prepared for some future struggle.

Readings

Bellanti, J. 1978. *Immunology II.* Second edition. Philadelphia: Saunders. Comprehensive coverage of basic principles, immune response mechanisms, and clinical applications.

Benditt, E. 1977. "The Origin of Atherosclerosis." *Scientific American* 236(2):74–86. Survey article on research into the causes of coronary disease.

Cooper, E. 1982. *General Immunology.* New York: Permagon Press. Contains an extensive discussion of the evolution of the immune response.

Ganong, W. 1979. *Review of Medical Physiology.* Ninth edition. Los Altos, California: Lange Medical Publications. Excellent, authoritative reference book. Section VI on circulation is recommended for the serious student reader. Paperback.

Golub, E. 1981. *The Cellular Basis of the Immune Response.* Second edition. Sunderland, Massachusetts: Sinauer Associates. A readable account of cellular immunology. Paperback.

Hickman, C., et al. 1979. *Integrated Principles of Zoology.* Sixth edition. St. Louis: Mosby. Good introduction to invertebrate and vertebrate circulation systems.

Hood, L., I. Weissman, and W. Wood. 1978. *Immunology.* Menlo Park, California: Benjamin/Cummings. Advanced overview of the molecular and cellular bases of the immune response. Paperback.

Krahenbuhl, J., and J. Remington. 1978. "Belligerent Blood Cells: Immunotherapy and Cancer." *Human Nature* 1(1): 52–59. Well-written article on immunotherapy as one treatment for cancer.

Leder, P. 1982. "The Genetics of Antibody Diversity." *Scientific American* 246(5):102–115. Describes how a few hundred units of split genes can be shuffled and recombined to make billions of different antibodies.

Nisonoff, A. *Introduction to Molecular Immunology.* Sunderland, Massachusetts: Sinauer Associates. Covers immunochemistry, and is complementary to Golub's text.

Vander, A., J. Sherman, and D. Luciano. 1980. *Human Physiology.* Third edition. New York: McGraw-Hill. One of the clearest expositions of circulation and of the body's defense systems.

Zucker, M. 1980. "The Functioning of Blood Platelets." *Scientific American* 246(6):86–103. Everything you ever wanted to know about platelets, as of the summer of 1980.

Review Questions

1. What are some of the functions of blood?

2. Describe the cellular components of blood. Describe the plasma portion of blood.

3. Can you define the functions of the following:
   a. heart
   b. cardiovascular system
   c. lymph vascular system

4. Distinguish between the following:
   a. open and closed circulation
   b. systemic and pulmonary circulation
   c. lymph vascular system and lymphoid organs
   d. systole and diastole

5. Describe the cardiac cycle in a four-chambered heart.

6. Can you identify the cardiac muscle fibers of the cardiac conduction system and describe how they work?

7. Explain how arteries, arterioles, and capillaries help regulate blood flow to different body regions.

8. State the main function of blood capillaries. What forces drive substances out of and into capillaries in capillary beds?

9. State the main function of venules and veins. What forces work together in returning venous blood to the heart?

10. Sponges aside, all animals have defenses against attack on normal cell functioning. Define the cells and products that constitute the vertebrate immune system of defense against such attacks.

11. Define inflammation. What happens during an inflammatory response?

12. Define antibody, antigen, and memory lymphocyte.

13. What is an immunization? A vaccine?

14. How do the main targets and outcomes of nonspecific and specific immune responses differ?

15. What is the immunosurveillance theory?

16. Define allergy and autoimmune disease.

25

RESPIRATION

OXYGEN ACQUISITION: SOME ENVIRONMENTAL CONSIDERATIONS

In most animals, the energy stored in food becomes available through aerobic respiration, the oxygen-demanding metabolic pathway described in Chapter Eight. Aquatic animals obtain oxygen that is dissolved in the surrounding water; land animals obtain oxygen from the air. In both cases, the oxygen must first diffuse across the body surface before it can reach individual cells.

Not much oxygen is dissolved in water (the concentration is at least twenty times less than it is in air). Also, oxygen takes longer to diffuse through water, which is more dense and viscous than air. The diffusion rates are enough to supply oxygen to sponges, cnidarians, and many aquatic worms. These animals do not have massive bodies or high metabolic rates, so their oxygen demands are not great.

Large, highly active aquatic animals require more oxygen. Among these animals, you will find special structures for oxygen acquisition. For example, a **gill** is an outward extension (evagination) of the body surface that increases the area available for oxygen uptake. Some gills are simple bumps or flaps on the body; others are more complex. Fish gills are composed of thin filaments covered with a thin

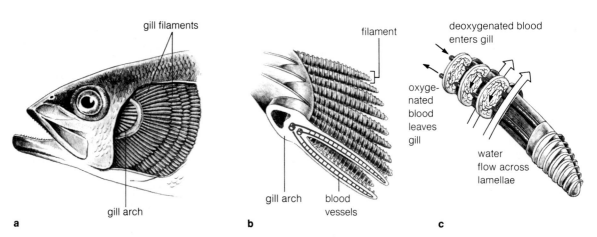

gill filaments

gill arch

a

filament

gill arch   blood vessels

b

deoxygenated blood enters gill

oxygenated blood leaves gill

water flow across lamellae

c

Figure 25.1 Fish gills. (**a**) Location of gills beneath the bony, protective lid (operculum), which has been removed for this sketch to show the chamber below. (**b,c**) Each gill has an outgoing and an incoming blood vessel. Along their length, capillary beds are arranged in thin membrane folds (lamellae). In these capillary beds, direction of water flow (large arrows) is opposite the direction of blood flow (small arrows). (After C. P. Hickman, Jr. et al., *Integrated Principles of Zoology*, 1979)

epithelial layer that is folded again and again into platelike lamellae. Blood capillaries thread through each lamella, where they pick up oxygen diffusing in from the water (Figure 25.1).

Like all gases, oxygen diffuses from regions of high concentration to regions of lower concentration. Within fish gills, blood in capillaries contains less oxygen than does the surrounding water. Basically, water moves past the capillaries in a direction opposite to the bloodstream (Figure 25.1). The mechanism is an example of **countercurrent flow**, and it enormously increases oxygen uptake. Water passing over the gill first encounters the domain of a vessel that is about to transport oxygen-poor blood deep into the body. Oxygen concentration in the water is greater than it is in this blood, so oxygen diffuses inward. Just before this same water moves completely past the gill, it passes over the domain of a vessel carrying blood from deep in the body—and this blood has even less oxygen than the (by now) oxygen-poor water. Hence oxygen still diffuses inward, down this second concentration gradient.

Fish gills are the most efficient oxygen-extracting structures for life in water. Nevertheless, given the low concentrations of dissolved oxygen, even the most efficiently adapted fish must devote up to twenty percent of its store of metabolic energy to obtain the oxygen needed in aerobic metabolism! (You use up only one or two percent for the same task.)

So far, we have been talking about oxygen acquisition. But keep in mind that the use of oxygen in aerobic respiration leads to carbon dioxide formation. This gas (and others) must be transported out of the body even as oxygen moves in.

The diffusion of any gas to and from the environment requires a *wet* surface in which gas molecules can dissolve. This applies to both sides of the surface. Diffusion also requires a *thin* surface layer. Wet, thin surfaces are not problems for animals submerged in water. But what happens in animals that live on land? How can gases move to and from a dry external environment? In animals that long ago made the transition to land, infoldings (invaginations) of the body surface developed into tubes and chambers that house thin, moist membranes for gas exchange.

For example, consider the oxygen-acquisition adaptation of land-dwelling insects, centipedes, and some spiders. These animals have **tracheas**: chitin-lined air tubes leading inward from the body surface (Figure 25.2). Each trachea branches into many finer tubes. The smallest tubes are air capillaries, a single micrometer in diameter. Each terminates directly on the plasma membrane of individual cells. The

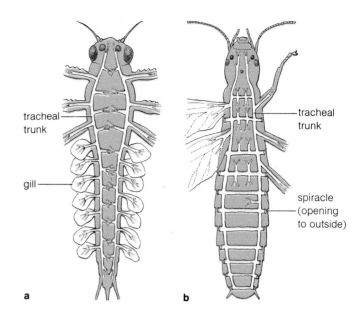

Figure 25.2 Tissue adaptations allowing for gas exchange in arthropods. (**a**) Many aquatic insects have closed tracheal systems, which extend into lateral body wall extensions that serve as gills. (**b**) In land arthropods, tracheal systems open to the outside through tubes in each abdominal and thoracic segment. (After Gardiner, *Biology of Invertebrates*, McGraw-Hill, 1972)

air capillaries contain fluid at the ends. Hence incoming oxygen can dissolve in the fluid and diffuse directly into cells. In some insects, a lidlike structure spans the tracheal opening to the outside and prevents evaporative water loss. The tracheal tubes are a complete internal system of gas transport and exchange; for insects, at least, no assistance is necessary from a circulation system. Sometimes, though, body movements provide assistance. If you have ever wondered why bees out foraging sometimes stop and move their abdomens in and out like telescopes, they are using body movements to speed up oxygen flow into the tracheal system and carbon dioxide from it.

In land vertebrates, membranes for gas exchange occur internally in **lungs**, which are chambers that receive air transported to them by tubular organs. You will read about the evolution of lungs in general in Chapter Thirty-Four. Mammalian lungs, which will be the focus of this chapter, are subdivided into millions of microscopically small pockets for air. The pockets are **alveoli** (singular, alveolus). Alveoli are lined with moist epithelium, and they are inter-meshed with blood capillaries. Gas exchange occurs down concentration gradients between alveoli and the capillaries, and the bloodstream carries gases to and from all body tissues.

A body surface that takes part in gas exchange between the external and internal environments must be thin, and moist on both surfaces, so that diffusion can occur.

When moisture retention is not a problem (which it is not for water-dwelling animals), gas exchange generally is enhanced by evagination (outfolded body surface region, as in gill filaments).

When moisture retention is a problem (as it can be for land-dwelling animals), gas exchange generally is enhanced by invagination (infolded body surface region, such as internal air tubes and lungs).

RESPIRATION: AN OVERVIEW

Oxygen acquisition and carbon dioxide elimination for the body as a whole is called **respiration**. The following events are necessary in respiration:

---

1. Ventilation, a bulk flow of air into and out from the lungs and a delivery of new air to alveoli.

2. Gas exchange by diffusion between alveolar air and blood in the lung capillaries.

3. Gas transport in the bloodstream.

4. Gas exchange between blood and interstitial fluid.

5. Gas exchange between interstitial fluid and individual cells.

In all mammals, the first two events occur within the same type of **respiratory system**. Organs of this system include the nose, nasal cavity, pharynx, larynx, trachea, bronchial tree, and lungs. The main functions of this system are air movement and gas exchange. However, respiratory organs serve additional functions. Some filter potentially harmful particles from air and help control air temperature and water content. Others assist in producing the sounds used in speech. Here we will consider these respiratory organs as they occur in the human body.

HUMAN RESPIRATORY SYSTEM

Respiratory Organs

Figure 25.3 shows the parts of the human respiratory system. Normally, air enters through the nose, although some also enters and leaves the mouth. Air travels through two narrow channels called **nasal cavities**. Hairs at the entrance of the channels, and cilia on their epithelial linings, filter out dust and other foreign particles. Numerous blood vessels embedded in the lining help warm incoming air, and mucous secretions moisten air before it flows into the lungs.

From the nasal cavity, air moves into the **pharynx**, the throat cavity behind the mouth. The pharynx connects with two tubes: the **larynx** (which leads to the lungs) and the esophagus (which leads to the stomach). The pharynx consists of muscles and cartilage, bound together by elastic connective tissue. One cartilage structure is attached to and supports the **epiglottis**, a flaplike structure that points upward and allows air to enter the larynx during breathing. When solid or liquid food is being swallowed, muscular contractions that force food back into the pharynx also raise the larynx against the base of the tongue. The epiglottis is thereupon pressed down, so that it partly covers the opening into the larynx and helps prevent food from moving down the wrong tube.

The larynx contains two **true vocal cords**: thickened folds of the larynx wall have muscles and elastic fibers used in producing the sounds of speech. When you are breathing normally, the space between the vocal cords remains open. This space is called the **glottis** (Figure 25.4). Air forced through the glottis gives rise to sound waves. The stronger the air pressure on the vocal cords, the louder the sound produced. The greater the muscle tension on the cords, the higher the sound.

During inhalation, air from the larynx moves into a flexible windpipe, or **trachea**. The trachea branches into two mucus-lined airways called **bronchi** (singular, bronchus). Each bronchus enters one of the paired lungs. Bronchi are the main branches of the **bronchial tree**, the increasingly subdivided air tubes that extend from the trachea to alveoli. The smallest tubes are the **bronchioles** and **alveolar ducts**. The lungs themselves are soft, spongelike sacs. The heart is positioned between them, and they are enclosed in a space defined by the thoracic cavity wall and the diaphragm (Figures 20.11 and 25.3).

The lungs contain more than 300 million alveoli. The total alveolar surface is enormous. If alveolar epithelium were stretched out as a continuous layer, it would cover

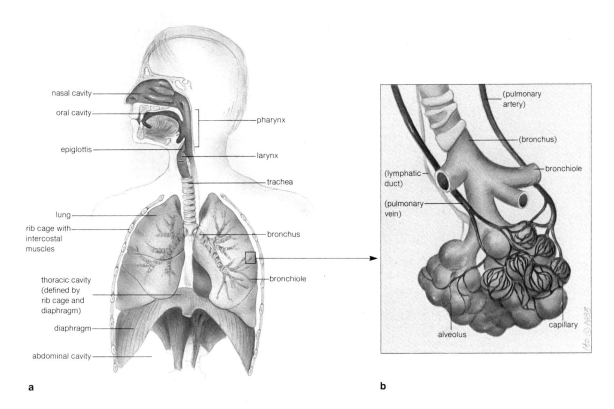

a

b

Figure 25.3 Human respiratory system (**a**). In this sketch, the paired lobes of the lung are shown in position, next to the heart. Lungs are located in the thoracic cavity, which is separated from the abdominal cavity by a muscular partition called a diaphragm. (**b**) Close-up of alveoli and lung capillaries. (After Avery, Wang, and Taeusch, Jr., ''The Lung of the Newborn Infant,'' *Scientific American,* April 1973. Copyright © 1973 by Scientific American, Inc. All rights reserved.)

a singles tennis court! As you will read shortly, gas exchange with the external environment occurs only across alveoli.

The mammalian respiratory system consists of an air-conducting zone (extending from the nasal cavities to the ends of bronchioles and alveolar ducts) and a gas exchange zone (which consists of alveoli and adjacent blood capillaries).

Relation Between the Lungs and the Pleural Sac

The lungs are not attached directly to the chest cavity wall. Rather, each lung is positioned within a thin-layered sac of epithelial and loose connective tissue, called the **pleural sac.** By analogy, imagine pushing a closed fist completely

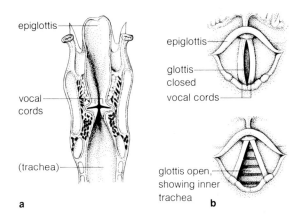

a

b

Figure 25.4 Where the sounds necessary for speech originate. (**a**) Front view of the larynx, showing the location of the vocal cords. (**b**) The two vocal cords as viewed from above when the glottis, or space between them, is closed and opened. (From J. Sobotta, *Atlas of Human Anatomy*)

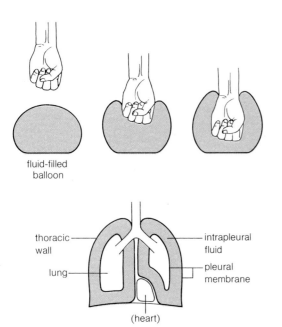

fluid-filled balloon

thoracic wall

lung

intrapleural fluid

pleural membrane

(heart)

Figure 25.5 Position of the lungs and pleural sac relative to the chest (thoracic) cavity. By analogy, when you push a closed fist into a fluid-filled balloon, the balloon completely surrounds the fist except at your arm. A lung is analogous to the fist; the balloon, to the pleural sac. Here, the volume of intrapleural fluid is enormously exaggerated for clarity. (From Vander et al., *Human Physiology*, third edition. ©1980 McGraw-Hill. Used with permission.)

into a large, fluid-filled balloon (Figure 25.5). Your fist is like a lung, and the balloon is like the pleural sac. The balloon completely surrounds your fist except at your arm (which is analogous to the main bronchial tube). In the body, the part of the pleural sac facing outward (the parietal pleura) adheres to the chest cavity wall. The part facing inward (the pulmonary pleura) is firmly attached to the lungs. All that really separates the parietal and pulmonary pleura is an extremely narrow space, filled with fluid that escapes from capillaries and is constantly being reabsorbed through lymph networks. (You would have to push a balloon completely back on itself to achieve the same intimate association.)

The pressure of the intrapleural fluid is always lower than the air pressure in the lungs. Even so, the pressure difference between this fluid and that in the alveoli varies during breathing. The changes lead directly to changes in lung size during breathing, in ways that will now be described.

VENTILATION

In the respiratory system just described, oxygen-rich air moves inward and air with high carbon dioxide concentrations moves outward through the same branched tubes. The term **inhalation** (or inspiration) refers to air movement into the bronchial tree and alveoli. **Exhalation** (or expiration) refers to the reverse movement of air.

Rhythmic changes in pressure gradients between the lungs and the atmosphere cause the reversible air movements of ventilation. The changes result from alterations in the volume of the chest cavity itself. Coordinated movements of the diaphragm, intercostal muscles (which move the ribs), as well as abdominal and neck muscles bring about these alterations in the volume of the chest cavity.

Inhalation and Exhalation

Right before inhalation, muscles that figure in ventilation are relaxed, and intrapleural pressure is below the alveolar air pressure. Inhalation begins with contractions of the diaphragm and intercostal muscles. The diaphragm moves downward and flattens; the rib cage moves outward and upward (Figures 25.6 and 25.7). As the rib cage moves away from the lungs, intrapleural pressure drops abruptly. There is now enough of a difference between the intrapleural space and alveoli to pull the lungs outward. Lung tissue stretches accordingly, and alveoli enlarge—which leads to a drop in air pressure within them. Air is sucked in through the nose and rushes down through the trachea, to the region of lower pressure.

At the start of exhalation, the muscular contractions that brought about expansion of the chest cavity (and lungs) have ceased. The muscles relax and the stretched tissues recoil to their resting position. The volume of the chest cavity and lungs decreases sharply, compressing the air in alveoli, thus increasing the pressure on that air. With this increase in alveolar pressure, air is forced out from the lungs and air tubes.

During exhalation, lungs do not collapse completely; considerable air remains inside. In fact, each breath of "new" air becomes mixed with the equivalent of seven breaths of "old" air in the lungs. (When the volume of each breath increases, as it does during strenuous exercise, the fraction of "new-to-old" air is greater than one to seven.) Thus it is not only metabolic activity that determines the amount of oxygen and carbon dioxide in the blood. It is also the rate and depth of breathing—hence the quantity of new air in the lungs.

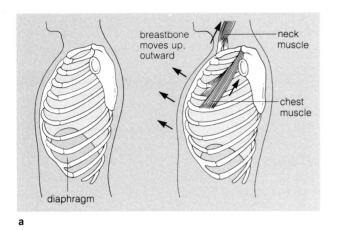

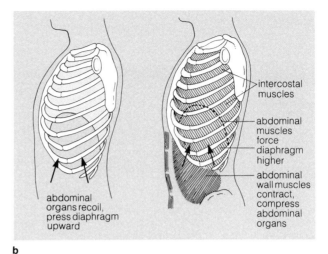

a

b

Figure 25.6 Effect of breathing on the shape of the thoracic cavity. (**a**) At the end of normal inhalation (left), and at the end of maximal inhalation (right) as aided by contraction of neck and chest muscles. (**b**) At the end of normal exhalation (left), as brought about by recoil of the thoracic wall and abdominal organs; and at the end of maximal exhalation (right), as aided by contractions of the abdominal wall and intercostal muscles at the back of the rib cage.

Controls Over Breathing

During ventilation, muscle contraction and relaxation normally proceed in a rhythmic manner. Where do the rhythmic contractions originate?

Diaphragm and intercostal muscles do not contract spontaneously. They are composed of skeletal muscle fibers, which can contract only under stimulation by the nervous system (Chapter Twenty-One). *Phrenic nerves* lead from the spinal cord to muscles of the diaphragm. *Intercostal nerves* lead from the spinal cord to the intercostal muscles. When these nerves (or the spinal regions where they originate) are destroyed, respiratory muscles become totally paralyzed and death can follow. (For example, poliovirus can attack motor nerves in the cervical region of the spinal cord, the result being muscle paralysis in the chest, intercostal, diaphragm, and upper abdominal regions. "Artificial lung" chambers are necessary to prevent death.)

Activities of phrenic and intercostal nerves are governed by the medulla, which is part of the brainstem. Some neurons in the medulla send out a steadily increasing number of excitatory signals calling for contraction of the diaphragm and intercostal muscles. More and more motor nerves are activated, and the contractile force increases with their recruitment. Then other neurons in the medulla inhibit the signals, so that there is a pause in contraction. The muscles relax, elastic tissue recoils—then the excitatory signals resume.

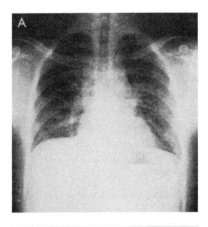

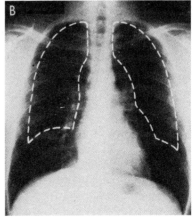

Figure 25.7 X-rays of the chest in full exhalation (A) and full inhalation (B). The dashed white line indicates the outline of the lungs in full exhalation. (From J. H. Comroe Jr., *Physiology of Respiration*, second edition, copyright 1974 by Year Book Medical Publishers, Inc., Chicago)

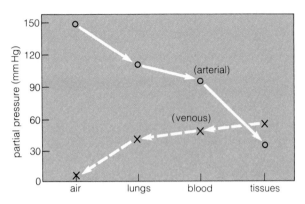

Figure 25.8 Summary of partial pressures for oxygen (solid lines) and for carbon dioxide (dashed lines) in air, lungs, blood, and tissues. This graph shows that both gases diffuse down gradients of decreasing partial pressure. (From J. M. Kinney, Transport of carbon dioxide in blood. *Anesthesiology*, 21:615, 1960)

The rate and depth of breathing are governed by a **respiratory center** in the brainstem. This center receives signals coming in from the lungs, blood vessels, and other brain regions. For instance, chemoreceptors in arterial walls detect changes in carbon dioxide levels in the blood. Chemoreceptors located within the brainstem itself detect carbon dioxide and hydrogen ions in the cerebrospinal fluid. When increases are sensed, nerve signals flow out from the brainstem to muscle fibers in the diaphragm and intercostal muscles. The contraction rate and strength of both muscle regions increase. Breathing becomes faster and deeper, which enhances the movement of carbon dioxide out of the body.

The skeletal muscles used in ventilation contract only under stimulation by the nervous system. A respiratory center in the brainstem governs the rate and depth of breathing.

GAS EXCHANGE AND TRANSPORT

Gas Exchange in Alveoli

Each alveolus is like a tiny, empty bowl, its rim continuous with the walls of an alveolar duct. Each bowl is no more than a single layer of epithelial cells, surrounded by a thin basement membrane. A dense network of blood capillaries is present in the alveolar walls. Interstitial fluid in a thin layer of connective tissue is all that separates the alveoli

from capillaries. This layer is only two-tenths of a micrometer thick. Gas exchange occurs across alveolar epithelium, through the interstitial fluid, and on across blood capillary epithelium.

The air entering alveoli is really a mixture of gases, including oxygen, nitrogen, and carbon dioxide. Recall that the amount of pressure each gas exerts depends on its concentration (Chapter Five). About twenty-one percent of the air we breathe is oxygen. On the average, atmospheric pressure is 760mm Hg. Thus oxygen is said to exert a **partial pressure** of 760/21, or 160mm Hg. Similarly, carbon dioxide in air has a partial pressure of 0.3mm Hg. Figure 25.8 shows the partial pressure gradients that exist for oxygen and carbon dioxide throughout the human respiratory system. Passive diffusion alone is enough to move oxygen across the respiratory membranes and into the bloodstream; and it is enough to move carbon dioxide in the reverse direction, into the alveolar air space.

Driven by its partial pressure gradient, oxygen diffuses from alveolar air spaces, through interstitial fluid, and across capillary epithelium. Carbon dioxide, driven by its partial pressure gradient, diffuses in the reverse direction.

Gas Transport Between Lungs and Tissues

By itself, the flow of either oxygen or carbon dioxide down their partial pressure gradients would not be enough to move these gases to all cells throughout the body. However, oxygen transport is increased seventy times over by the participation of oxygen-carrying hemoglobin. The carbon dioxide transport is increased seventeen times over by a series of reversible reactions that convert this gas to more transportable forms.

Oxygen Transport. With each new breath, air that is low in carbon dioxide and rich in oxygen enters the lungs and flows down into alveoli. Within adjacent lung capillaries is blood that is low in oxygen and rich in carbon dioxide. Oxygen diffuses into the blood plasma, then into red blood cells. When it does, it rapidly forms a weak, reversible bond with hemoglobin. The structure of the hemoglobin molecule was described in Figures 3.20 and 3.21. Recall that each hemoglobin molecule can transport four oxygen molecules at a time. With its cargo in place, the molecule is called **oxyhemoglobin**. The amount of oxygen that actually combines with hemoglobin depends on the partial pressure of the gas. The higher the pressure, the more oxygen mole-

Figure 25.9 The atmosphere contains the same percentage of oxygen at high and low altitudes. However, the atmospheric pressure is lower at high altitudes, so the partial pressure exerted by its oxygen component is not as great. Hence less oxygen moves from the air into the body. People who are not adapted to high altitudes can have problems in the mountains. At 2,400 meters (about 8,000 feet) above sea level, they can experience hypoxia, or cellular oxygen deficiency. Hypoxia is characterized by faster breathing, faster heart rate, and anxiety. At 3,650 meters (about 12,000 feet), oxygen partial pressure is only 100mm Hg. Here, hypoxia symptoms include headaches, nausea, and lethargy. At 7,000 meters (23,000 feet), people can lose consciousness and die from oxygen deficiency.

David Steinberg

cules will be picked up (until the hemoglobin binding sites are saturated).

The bonds holding oxygen to hemoglobin are weak. As oxygen partial pressure falls, hemoglobin gives up oxygen to the blood plasma. Where blood concentrations of carbon dioxide are increased over that in the lungs, oxyhemoglobin tends to release even more oxygen. Where pH is decreased or temperature is increased, the same thing happens. With greater metabolic activity in a given tissue region, more carbon dioxide is produced, pH values decline, and local temperatures rise. That is why oxygen is released more readily in highly active tissues (such as muscles during periods of exercise).

Oxyhemoglobin gives up oxygen when carbon dioxide concentrations are high, temperature is elevated, and pH values are low. These conditions are characteristic of tissues showing increased metabolic activity.

Carbon Dioxide Transport. Compared with the surrounding tissues, blood flowing in capillaries has a low partial pressure for carbon dioxide. Thus carbon dioxide diffuses down its gradient, from the tissue and into the capillaries. From there, it is transported to the lungs in these forms:

Carbon dioxide molecules dissolved in blood plasma

Combined with hemoglobin (as carbaminohemoglobin, or $HbCO_2$)

Bicarbonate ions (HCO_3^-)

Most of the carbon dioxide is transported in the form of bicarbonate. Recall, from Chapter Six, that carbon dioxide combines with water to form carbonic acid, which then dissociates into bicarbonate and hydrogen ions:

$$CO_2 + H_2O \rightleftarrows H_2CO_3 \rightleftarrows HCO_3^- + H^+$$

The reaction proceeds slowly in blood plasma. However, much of the carbon dioxide diffuses into red blood cells, which house the enzyme carbonic anhydrase. With this enzyme, the reaction rate increases 250 times over. The rapid reactions have the effect of lowering the concentration of free carbon dioxide in the blood. Hence the concentration gradient for carbon dioxide diffusion from interstitial fluid to the blood is maintained in the capillaries.

Hemoglobin acts as a buffer for the hydrogen ions produced by the dissociation of carbonic acid. The bicarbonate ions tend to diffuse out of the red blood cells and move into the blood plasma. Eighty-one percent of the carbon dioxide in blood is transported as bicarbonate. Only about eight percent remains dissolved in plasma (as carbon dioxide). The remaining eleven percent travels attached to hemoglobin (as carbaminohemoglobin).

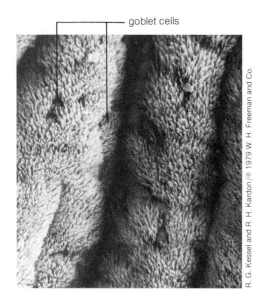

goblet cells

R. G. Kessel and R. H. Kardon/© 1979 W. H. Freeman and Co.

Figure 25.10 Ciliated epithelium of the human trachea, 1,310×.

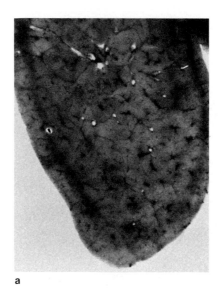

a

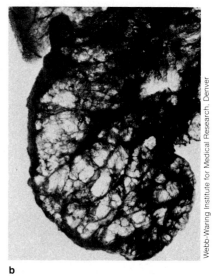

b

Webb-Waring Institute for Medical Research, Denver

Figure 25.11 (**a**) Normal appearance of human lung tissue and (**b**) appearance of a lung taken from a person who suffered emphysema.

Once blood returns to lung capillaries, the lower carbon dioxide concentration in alveoli allows the reactions to proceed in the reverse direction. Carbonic acid dissociates to form water and carbon dioxide. The hemoglobin shows greater affinity for oxygen than it does for carbon dioxide in this region, and it promptly releases its cargo. The carbon dioxide so released diffuses down its concentration gradient and is exhaled. The blood is now ready for another round trip through the systemic highways of the circulation system.

In summary, we can make the following points about the gas transport phases of respiration:

Oxygen transport between lungs and tissues is enhanced by participation of hemoglobin molecules, which combine with or release oxygen molecules as a function of carbon dioxide concentration, pH, and temperature.

Hemoglobin also helps maintain the oxygen partial pressure gradient by removing oxygen from blood plasma in lungs and releasing the oxygen in metabolizing tissues.

Carbon dioxide transportation is enhanced by reversible reactions that rapidly convert the gas to bicarbonate and hydrogen ions in tissues, then back to carbon dioxide in the lungs. The conversions help maintain the carbon dioxide gradients necessary to drive carbon dioxide into and out of the bloodstream.

CILIARY ACTION IN RESPIRATORY TRACTS

The airways extending from the trachea to the ends of bronchioles are lined with ciliated epithelium. Scattered between the hairlike cilia are mucus-secreting goblet cells (Figure 25.10). Inhaled particles become stuck against the mucus of the epithelium, and the upward-beating cilia sweep debris-laden mucus toward the mouth. This mucus can be swallowed or expelled from the mouth.

Ciliary action keeps the airways cleared. It also gets rid of numerous bacteria (which can be present in particles of airborne dust). It is one of the most important mechanisms for keeping the respiratory tract open. When something interferes with ciliary action, the consequences can be serious.

For example, Table 25.1 shows some of the effects of cigarette smoke on ciliary action. The noxious particles in smoke from one cigarette can prevent the cilia from beating for several hours. The particles also stimulate excessive mucous secretions, which can eventually clog the airways. "Smoker's cough" is one of the least serious consequences. Cigarette smoke can also destroy phagocytic cells that populate the respiratory epithelium. These cells help keep bacteria and debris out of the respiratory passages. A few of the eventual outcomes of prolonged exposure to noxious airborne substances are described in the *Commentary*.

COMMENTARY

When the Lungs Break Down

In urban environments, in certain occupations, even in the microenvironment surrounding a cigarette smoker, airborne particles and certain gases exist in abnormal amounts. They put an extra workload on the ciliated mucous membranes of respiratory passageways. These membranes are extremely sensitive to cigarette smoke, probably because of the chemical nature of the concentrated particles. Smoking and other forms of air pollution increase mucus secretion while interfering with ciliary movement in the passageways. As a result, mucus—and the particles it traps, which include bacteria—begins accumulating in the trachea and bronchi. Coughing sets in as the body reflexly attempts to clear away the mucus. If irritation continues, the coughing reflex persists. Coughing aggravates the condition because it further irritates the bronchial walls. Bronchial walls become inflamed and infected. Tissue is destroyed by bacterial activity or irritated by chemical agents. Cilia diminish in numbers. And mucus-producing cells increase as the body works to fight against the accumulating debris. All of this aggravation leads to the formation of fibrous scar tissue. Such are the characteristics of bronchitis.

A person suffering from an acute attack of bronchitis who is otherwise in good health responds to medical treatment. But what happens if the irritation persists—if, for example, a chain-smoker continues to smoke? As fibrous scar tissue begins to obstruct the respiratory passageways, bronchi become progressively clogged with more and more mucus. Air then becomes trapped in alveoli. As alveolar walls break down, the remaining alveoli enlarge and gas exchange with capillaries is impaired. Gases cannot be expelled efficiently from the lungs. The outcome is emphysema—the distension of lungs and loss of gas exchange efficiency to the extent that running, walking, even exhaling become difficult.

Why don't all cigarette smokers get emphysema? There is evidence that early environmental conditions—poor diet, chronic colds, other respiratory ailments—can create in some persons a predisposition to this disease later in life. In addition, many who suffer from emphysema have a hereditary deficiency in their ability to form antitrypsin, a substance that inhibits tissue-destroying enzymes produced by bacteria. These individuals may therefore be at a disadvantage in fighting off respiratory infections when they do strike. When such people have a smoking habit, their prospects unquestionably are grim. Part of the problem is that the potential threat seems exaggerated—what's so terrifying about coughing up mucus now and then? But emphysema is insidious. It can develop slowly, over twenty or thirty years; and few today seem to think much about what they will be doing twenty or thirty years hence, and about what shape their body will be in during their remaining years. By the time emphysema is detected, the damage to lung tissue is irreparable. The threat is not exaggerated: about 1,300,000 individuals in the United States alone now suffer from this disease, inflicting pain on themselves and stress on their families, who can do nothing to alleviate the condition.

Cigarette smoke is also known to contain compounds that can lead to lung cancer. These compounds, such as methylcholanthrene, are found in coal tar and cigarette smoke. It appears that they become chemically modified in the body, through the action of natural substances, into highly reactive intermediates that are the real carcinogens. In these forms they act on cells in lung tissues. Either they cause irreversible alterations in the way that the cellular DNA is expressed, or they alter the DNA itself. Whatever the case, cell division goes out of control.

The more cigarettes smoked each day, the longer that individuals inhale, the more deeply they inhale—all of these behaviors increase the susceptibility to a disease that is agonizing in its terminal stages. At least eighty percent of all lung cancer deaths are the legacy of cigarette smoking. It is a disease that only ten out of a hundred afflicted individuals will survive, with varying degrees of tissue damage and malfunctioning.

Table 25.1 To Smoke or Not to Smoke: Some Comparisons*	
Risks Associated With Smoking	Benefits of Quitting
Shortened Life Expectancy: Nonsmokers live an average of 8.3 years longer than those in mid-twenties who smoke two packs of cigarettes a day	Cumulative reduction of risk; after 10–15 years, ex-smokers approches life expectancy of nonsmokers
Chronic Bronchitis, Emphysema: Smokers have 4–25 times more risk of dying from these diseases than do nonsmokers	Greater chance of improving lung function and slowing down rate of deterioration
Lung Cancer: Cigarette smoking the major cause of lung cancer	After 10–15 years, risk approaches that of nonsmokers
Cancer of Mouth: 3–10 times greater risk among smokers	After 10–15 years, risk is reduced to that of nonsmokers
Cancer of Larynx: 2.9–17.7 times more frequent among smokers	After 10 years, risk is reduced to that of nonsmokers
Cancer of Esophagus: 2–9 times greater risk of dying from this form of cancer	Risk is proportional to amount smoked, so quitting should reduce risk
Cancer of Pancreas: 2–5 times greater risk of dying from pancreatic cancer	Risk is proportional to amount smoked, so quitting should reduce risk
Cancer of Bladder: 7–10 times greater risk for smokers	Risk decreases gradually over 7 years to that of nonsmokers
Coronary Heart Disease: Cigarette smoking a major contributing factor	Risk drops sharply after a year; after 10 years, risk reduced to that of nonsmokers
Effects on Offspring: Pregnant women who smoke have more stillbirths, and weight of liveborns averages less (hence babies are more vulnerable to disease, death)	When smoking stops before fourth month of pregnancy, risk of stillbirth and lower birthweight eliminated
Impaired Immune System Function: Increase in allergic responses, destruction of macrophages in respiratory tract	Avoidable by not smoking

*Based on data published in 1980 by the American Cancer Society, Inc.

Readings

American Cancer Society. 1980. *Dangers of Smoking; Benefits of Quitting and Relative Risks of Reduced Exposure.* Revised edition. New York: American Cancer Society, Inc. Up-to-date summary of scientific and medical studies on tobacco smoking and health.

Baker, P. 1969. "Human Adaptation to High Altitude." *Science* 163: 1149.

Ganong, W. 1979. *Review of Medical Physiology.* Ninth edition. Los Altos, California: Lange Publications. Advanced reading, but one of the most authoritative books on respiration.

Geise, A. 1973. *Cell Physiology.* Fourth edition. Philadelphia: Saunders.

Hickman, C., et al. 1979. *Integrated Principles of Zoology.* Sixth edition. St. Louis: Mosby.

Vander, A., J. Sherman, and D. Luciano. 1980. *Human Physiology: The Mechanisms of Body Function.* Third edition. New York: McGraw-Hill. Clear introduction to the respiration system and its functioning.

Wyman, R. 1977. "Neural Generation of the Breathing Mechanism." *Annual Review of Physiology* 39:417.

Review Questions

1. What is the main requirement for gas exchange in animals? What membrane adaptation enhances gas exchange in (a) water-dwelling animals and (b) land-dwelling animals?

2. Explain how a countercurrent flow mechanism works in a fish gill.

3. Define respiration. What five events are necessary in respiration?

4. Describe the two zones of the mammalian respiratory system. What organs occur in each zone?

5. By what mechanisms do carbon dioxide move out of your body and oxygen into it through the *same* system of branched tubes?

6. Which nerves are involved in controls over breathing, and how do they function? What governs the rate and depth of breathing?

7. What force drives oxygen from alveolar air spaces, through interstitial fluid, and across capillary epithelium? What force drives carbon dioxide in the reverse direction?

8. How does hemoglobin help maintain the oxygen partial pressure gradient during gas transport in the body? What reactions enhance the transport of carbon dioxide through the body?

Nutrition—here is a word that has to do with all those processes by which the body ingests, digests, and absorbs food. The word signals that you are about to begin one more educational trek through the animal gut. This time around, however, you will move beyond passive memorization of names for specialized tissues and organs. This time your main concern will be with *systems integration*—with how whole systems function together in meeting the metabolic needs of all cells in large, complex animals.

Consider the female bear in Figure 26.1 and the destination of that salmon in her mouth. Is it enough, really, to assume that the nutritional picture begins and ends in her gut? To reach the internal environment, nutrients must be reduced to small particles that can move across the gut cavity's lining. In the bear, as in all complex animals, a circulatory system then transports nutrients for distribution among cells in all tissue regions. Also, cellular *use* of the nutrients most often depends on being supplied with oxygen (for aerobic metabolism), and on being able to eliminate carbon dioxide wastes of metabolism. So "nutrition" in complex animals requires more than a system of food digestion and absorption. It also requires circulatory and respiratory systems that transport materials to and from individual cells (Figure 26.2).

In this chapter, you will first review the main components of digestive systems and their individual functions. Then you will see how the activities of three systems— digestive, circulatory, and respiratory—can be integrated through neural and hormonal signals. The main examples will be from an organism with which you are already more or less acquainted: yourself. Later, in Chapter Thirty-Four, you will read about how these interrelated systems might have evolved and how they have become specialized in different animal groups.

FEEDING STRATEGIES

A **digestive system** is some form of body cavity or tube where food is reduced to particles, then to molecules small enough to move into the internal environment.

An **incomplete digestive system** has only one opening. What goes in but cannot be digested goes out the same way. Consider the planarian, a type of flatworm (Figure 26.3). A muscular organ (pharynx) opens into a highly branched cavity that serves both digestive and circulatory functions. Food is partly digested and transported to cells even as residues are being sent back out through the pharynx.

26

DIGESTION AND ORGANIC METABOLISM

Figure 26.1 Digestion includes those interrelated processes by which food is ingested, prepared for absorption, and moved into the internal environment.

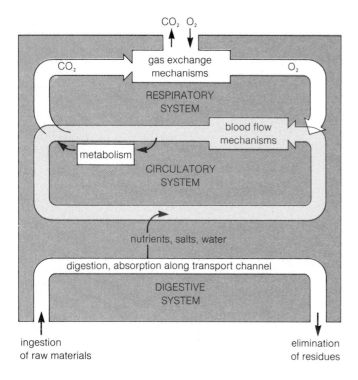

Figure 26.2 Interconnected systems for moving food into the internal environment and for assuring that cells can utilize the energy stored in food once it reaches them. The connections represented here are characteristic of most complex animals. Sensory receptors in each system channel information to the nervous system, which coordinates the interrelated activities. Hormonal controls are also at work among these systems.

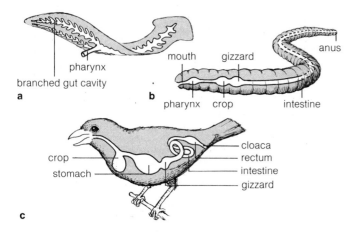

Figure 26.3 (a) Incomplete digestive system of the planarian, a flatworm. Its pharynx is a muscular tube that protrudes from the body during feeding. Complete digestive systems of animals ranging from earthworms (b) to birds (c) and humans have special food-processing regions and a one-way movement of material.

Given the two-way traffic, regions of this cavity cannot be specialized for different food processing, storage, and transport tasks.

Annelids, mollusks, arthropods, echinoderms, and chordates have **complete digestive systems**. Each has an internal tube with an opening at one end for taking in food and an opening at the other end for eliminating residues (Figure 26.3). Between the two openings, *food generally moves in one direction through organs specialized for transport, storage, and processing.* For instance, the crop is a food storage organ in the digestive system of earthworms and birds. A gizzard, which also occurs in these animals, is a muscular organ in which food is ground into smaller bits.

The specializations seen among animals with complete digestive systems can be correlated with the animal's feeding habits. These animals show *discontinuous feeding patterns.* Food supplies are not always available all the time. Perhaps predators or some other environmental pressure keeps the animal from eating steadily. Thus, for instance, grazing animals subject to predation have storage organs for food that is eaten rapidly and digested later, in comparative safety.

In some animals, the kind of food being eaten also requires longer processing time. Deer, cattle, sheep, goats—these so-called *ruminants* use plant cellulose as food. (Many animals, including humans, do not have the digestive equipment to tackle the tough cellulose fibers.) Ruminants have multiple stomachlike chambers. The first two chambers contain vast populations of microorganisms, some of which are symbiotic bacteria. The symbionts produce enzymes that can break down cellulose fibers along with other nutrients. When ruminants "chew their cud," they have regurgitated food from these two chambers and are grinding it up again in the mouth before swallowing it again. Gradually the food moves into two more stomachs and into the intestines for final digestion and absorption.

Regardless of the specializations that occur in the digestive systems of different species, in most cases those systems have three main functions:

Digestion: the mechanical and chemical reduction of ingested nutrients into particles, then into molecules small enough to move through epithelial cells and into the internal environment.

Absorption: the passage of digested nutrients from the gut lumen into the blood or lymph, which distribute them through the body.

Elimination: the expulsion of indigestible residues from the body.

Figure 26.4 Main components of the human digestive system.

(Far right: If you have ever wondered how far a stretched-out gastrointestinal tube extends, now you know. Photograph by Igaku-Shoin Ltd.)

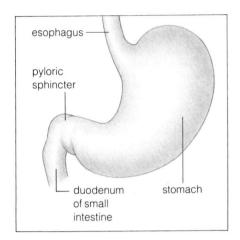

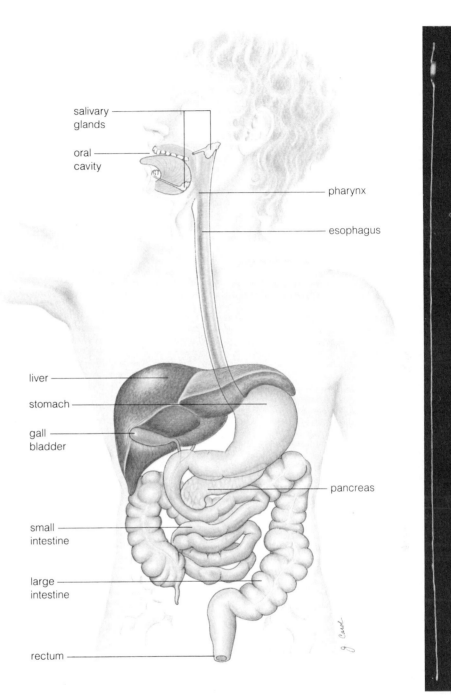

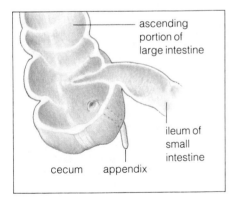

salivary glands

oral cavity

pharynx

esophagus

esophagus

pyloric sphincter

duodenum of small intestine

stomach

liver

stomach

gall bladder

pancreas

small intestine

large intestine

rectum

ascending portion of large intestine

ileum of small intestine

cecum appendix

HUMAN DIGESTIVE SYSTEM: AN OVERVIEW

Components of the Digestive System

Humans show discontinuous feeding patterns, and they dine on what must be called an eclectic array of foodstuffs. Accordingly, the human digestive system has regionally specialized organs. The organs are part of the same continuous tube, called the **gastrointestinal tract**. The tract is about 4.5 meters (fifteen feet) long in adults. Its organs are called the mouth, pharynx, esophagus, stomach, small intestine, large intestine (or colon), rectum, and anus (Figure 26.4). Glandular organs that play accessory roles in digestion and absorption include the salivary glands, liver, and pancreas.

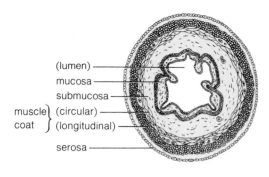

(lumen)
mucosa
submucosa
muscle coat — (circular)
(longitudinal)
serosa

Figure 26.5 Generalized sketch of the gastrointestinal tract walls, in cross-section. (From A.C. Guyton, *Textbook of Medical Physiology*, sixth edition, Philadelphia: W. B. Saunders Co., 1981. Reprinted with permission.)

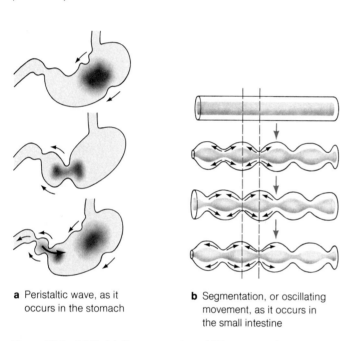

a Peristaltic wave, as it occurs in the stomach

b Segmentation, or oscillating movement, as it occurs in the small intestine

Figure 26.6 (**a**) Peristaltic movements and (**b**) segmentation movements that occur in the gastrointestinal tract. (From A. Vander et al., *Human Physiology*, third edition, © 1980 McGraw-Hill. Used by permission.)

General Structure of the Gastrointestinal Tract

Even with its regional specializations, the gastrointestinal tract has walls that are much the same along its entire length. As Figure 26.5 suggests, the innermost layer of the tubular wall is a mucous membrane, called the **mucosa**. In the stomach and intestine, the mucosa contains diverse secretory cells whose products serve digestive functions. Epithelial cells of the intestinal mucosa are specialized for the active and passive transport of nutrients into the inter-

nal environment, in ways that will be described later. The mucosa is surrounded by the **submucosa**, a connective tissue layer in which blood and lymph vessels are meshed. Next is a **muscle layer**, which has two sublayers of smooth muscle arranged in longitudinal and circular directions relative to the tube axis. The thin outermost layer of the tube is the **serosa**, which connects the tube to the abdominal wall (Figure 26.5).

Gastrointestinal Motility

Coordinated contractions in the muscle layer force food material through the gastrointestinal tract. One kind of movement is called **peristalsis**. In peristalsis, rings of circular muscles contract behind a mass of food material, and the mechanical pressure propels the material forward. As it moves, the mass expands the tube wall, the expansion stimulates peristalsis, and so on down the tract (Figure 26.6).

Peristalsis causes mixing movements in the stomach. Following a meal, peristaltic waves move down the stomach walls about three times a minute. At first the waves are like weak ripples, but they become fast and powerful enough to agitate the stomach contents. Food thereby becomes mixed with enzymes and other agents of digestion.

In the small intestine, rings of smooth muscle in the intestinal wall repeatedly contract and relax. They create an oscillating (back-and-forth) movement in the same place. This movement, called **segmentation**, constantly mixes the contents of the lumen and forces it against the absorptive surface of the intestinal wall (Figure 26.6).

The *direction* of movement through the gastrointestinal tract is partly controlled by the coordinated constriction of **sphincters**. These rings of smooth or skeletal muscle are located at the beginning and end of certain organs. For example, the *pyloric sphincter* is located between the stomach and small intestine, where it serves as a gate for food passing through. When the sphincter is open, material can be moved forward. When muscle contractions close the sphincter, material is prevented from moving forward or from backing up through the tract.

CONTROL OF GASTROINTESTINAL MOVEMENTS AND SECRETIONS

The gastrointestinal tract is innervated in much the same way throughout its length. One network of nerve tissue lies in the submucosa. Another lies between the longitudinal and circular muscles of the muscle layer. The networks

Table 26.1 Functions of Primary and Accessory Organs of Digestion

Organ	Secretions	Main Functions
Mouth	—	Mechanically breaks down food
Salivary glands (accessory organs)	Water	Moistens food
	Mucus	Lubricates and binds food into bolus
	Salivary amylase	Starts breakdown of starch, glycogen
	Bicarbonate	Buffering action neutralizes acidic food in mouth
Stomach		Stores, mixes, dissolves food; regulates emptying of chyme into small intestine
Secretory cells in stomach mucosa	Hydrochloric acid	Dissolves food particles; kills many microorganisms
	Pepsinogen	In activated form (pepsin), splits apart peptide bonds in protein chains
	Mucus	Lubricates and protects stomach lining
	Gastrin	Stimulates hydrochloric acid, pepsinogen secretions
Small intestine		Digestion and absorption of most nutrients; mixes and propels chyme forward
Secretory cells in intestinal mucosa*	Assorted enzymes	Break down all major food molecules
	Mucus	Lubricates chyme
	Gastrin	Stimulates hydrochloric acid secretion
	Secretin	Stimulates pancreatic bicarbonate secretion
	Cholecystokinin	Stimulates gallbladder contraction, pancreatic enzyme secretions, and stomach emptying
	Gastric-inhibitory peptide	Inhibits stomach acid secretion and motility
Pancreas (accessory organ)	Assorted enzymes (e.g., lipase)	Break down all major food molecules
	Bicarbonate	Buffering action neutralizes hydrochloric acid entering small intestine from stomach
Liver (accessory organ)	Bile salts	Hydration of emulsified fat droplets
	Bicarbonate	Buffering action neutralizes hydrochloric acid entering small intestine from stomach
Gallbladder (accessory organ)	—	Stores and concentrates bile from liver
Large intestine (colon)		Stores, concentrates undigested matter by absorbing water and salts; mixes and propels material forward
Secretory cells in intestinal mucosa	Mucus	Lubricates undigested residues
Rectum	—	Distension triggers expulsion reflex that rids body of undigested residues

*Most enzymes are embedded in plasma membrane facing the lumen; some released into lumen when cells shed and disintegrate.

receive information from chemoreceptors (which respond to the composition of material in the lumen) and mechanoreceptors (which respond to distension of the walls).

Intestinal walls have dual innervation from the autonomic nervous system. Generally, sympathetic and parasympathetic nerves work antagonistically in controlling the rate and strength of smooth muscle contractions. Signals from parasympathetic nerves usually increase activity in the tract. Signals from sympathetic nerves cause contraction of some sphincters; they take part in controls over the rate at which materials move forward.

Many different hormones help regulate digestion and absorption. Among the best understood are gastrin, secretin, cholecystokinin, and gastrin-inhibitory peptide (or GIP). Table 26.1 lists their sources and their functions.

STRUCTURE AND FUNCTION OF GASTROINTESTINAL ORGANS

Mouth and Salivary Glands

As Table 26.1 indicates, mechanical reduction of food begins in the **mouth** (oral cavity), as does polysaccharide digestion. Most animals have mouths, but humans and other mammals are the only ones that *chew* food in the mouth. Adult humans normally have thirty-two teeth (sixteen in the upper and sixteen in the lower jawbone). Each **tooth** consists of an enamel coat (hardened calcium deposits), dentine (a thick bonelike layer), and an inner pulp (which houses nerves and blood vessels). In the back of the mouth are flat-surfaced *molars*, which grind food. In the front we have chisel-shaped *incisors,* useful in biting off chunks of food. In between we have cone-shaped *cuspids,* for grasping and tearing food.

While the teeth and tongue are mechanically reducing food in the mouth, they are also mixing it with **saliva**, a fluid secreted from several **salivary glands**. The ducts of these exocrine glands empty into the oral cavity. (By running the tip of your tongue along the floor of the mouth and behind your upper molars, you can locate tiny flaps where ducts from three major pairs of salivary glands occur.)

Saliva contains **salivary amylase**, an enzyme that takes part in the initial hydrolysis of starch and glycogen. **Mucin**, a glycoprotein that lubricates food, is another component of the fluid. Saliva also contains bicarbonate ions (HCO_3^-), which act as buffers in keeping salivary pH between 6.5 and 7.5 even when acidic foods are in the mouth. This is the optimum pH range for the action of salivary amylase. The mucus component of saliva binds bits of food together into a softened ball, or *bolus.*

Pharynx and Esophagus

Once food is processed into a bolus, voluntary muscle contractions move the tongue up toward the roof of the mouth. The movement forces the bolus into the pharynx; it begins the process called swallowing. In humans, the **pharynx** is a muscular tube that is continuous with the **esophagus**, which leads to the stomach. The pharynx is also continuous with the trachea, which leads to the lungs. As you read in Chapter Twenty-Five, reflex action normally closes off the trachea and inhibits breathing for the brief time that food is in the pharynx. Neither the pharynx nor the esophagus contribute to mechanical or chemical digestion. Peristaltic movements in their walls simply propel food downward.

Stomach

The **stomach** is a muscular, distensible sac that has two main functions. First, the stomach stores and mixes food received from the esophagus. Second, the stomach helps regulate the rate of food movement into the small intestine.

Components of Gastric Fluid. Cells of the stomach mucosa secrete several substances, which together constitute the gastric fluid. The main exocrine secretions are hydrochloric acid, mucus, and pepsinogen. The main endocrine secretion is gastrin. The stomach mucosa produces as much as two liters of gastric fluid each day.

Hydrochloric acid (HCl) dissolves bits of food, thereby forming a solution called *chyme.* Hydrochloric acid, recall, dissociates into hydrogen ions and chloride ions. The resulting H^+ concentration in the lumen can be three million times greater than it is in arterial blood! The highly acidic environment changes the three-dimensional structure of ingested proteins by altering their ionized groups. It cannot break apart peptide bonds; it can only "soften up" the proteins by exposing these bonds to the proper enzymes. Hydrochloric acid serves another function, in that it kills most of the microorganisms entering the body in food material.

Another stomach secretion is **pepsinogen**, an enzyme precursor. When the stomach environment is highly acidic, pepsinogen is converted to several active enzymes. These enzymes are collectively called **pepsins**. Pepsins can break peptide bonds in proteins, thereby creating peptide fragments. (Proteins are also broken down into peptide fragments in the small intestine by two pancreatic enzymes, *trypsin* and *chymotrypsin.* The fragments are then digested to free amino acids by *peptidases,* secreted by the pancreas and the intestinal mucosa.)

When the stomach becomes distended with food, mechanoreceptors in the stomach walls trigger nerve reflexes, which act directly on cells that secrete hydrochloric acid. Also, when incoming proteins decrease stomach acidity (by acting as buffers for hydrogen ions), gastrin-secreting cells become active. Gastrin has a strong stimulatory effect on cells that secrete hydrochloric acid. A negative feedback loop is at work here, in that the presence of protein stimulates the secretion of substances that lead to its degradation:

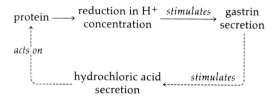

Hydrochloric acid secretions can be stimulated even when protein is *not* present in the stomach. Caffeine, found in coffee, tea, chocolate, and cola drinks, stimulates gastrin-secreting cells and thereby contributes to stomach acidity.

Sometimes a region of the stomach mucosa becomes aggravated by digestive action of the gastric fluid. The aggravated region is one form of a **peptic ulcer**. In some poorly understood way, the production rate of gastric fluid increases to intolerable levels, or normal control mechanisms that protect the mucosa are blocked. When the mu-

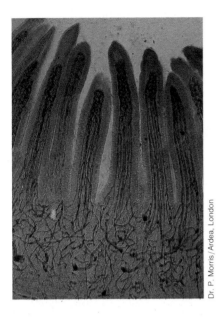

Dr. P. Morris/Ardea, London

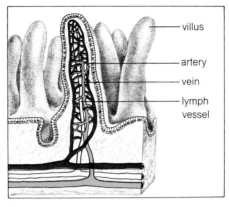

villus

artery

vein

lymph
vessel

Figure 26.7 The relationship between
each villus (a fingerlike projection of the
intestinal mucosa) and the bloodstream.

cosa breaks down, hydrogen ions diffuse into the mucosa itself, triggering the release of histamine from damaged cells. The histamine in turn triggers vasodilation, increased capillary permeability, and then release of more hydrogen ions. Thus a positive feedback loop is set up and leads to tissue damage.

Stomach Emptying. Chyme is mixed by peristaltic waves in the stomach. The waves begin near the esophagus and build up force as they reach the pyloric sphincter, at the other end of the stomach. The sphincter normally is relaxed, but strong contractions cause it to close. Most of the chyme sloshes back, but some moves into the duodenum, the first part of the small intestine (Figure 26.6a).

Three factors control how fast the stomach empties into the small intestine. *First,* distension of the stomach following a meal activates mechanoreceptors in the stomach wall. The larger the meal, the more these mechanoreceptors trigger reflex arcs that control the force of contraction. *Second,* the volume, osmotic pressure, acid content, and particularly the fat content of chyme in the duodenum helps control stomach emptying. These factors trigger the release of intestinal hormones such as GIP. The hormones have an inhibitory effect on reflexes involved in stomach motility. *Third,* emotional state can inhibit motility by signals that decrease parasympathetic and increase sympathetic output. For example, depression and fear tend to suppress normal stomach emptying reflexes.

Small Intestine

Digestion and absorption of most nutrients occur in the **small intestine**. This part of the gastrointestinal tract is divided into three zones: the *duodenum, jejunum,* and *ilium.*

By the time the chyme reaches the midpoint of the jejunum, most proteins, fats, and carbohydrates have been broken down completely to amino acids, fatty acids, monoglycerides, and monosaccharides. These are the only organic molecules that are small enough to move across the epithelial cells of the intestinal mucosa. The intestinal mucosa is densely outfolded into absorptive structures called **villi** (singular, villus), as shown in Figure 26.7. Villi look vaguely like tiny tongues. In themselves, these structures greatly increase the surface area available for interactions with the contents of the lumen. In addition, epithelial cells of each villus have a surface crown of **microvilli**: threadlike projections of the plasma membrane that further increase the surface area available for absorption (Figure 26.8).

Beneath its one-cell-thick epithelium, each villus houses blood and lymph vessels (Figure 26.7). Even while segmentation movements are occurring in the small intestine, each villus moves independently of the others through contractions of its own tiny network of smooth muscle fibers. In this way, microvilli come into contact with more small molecules that can be absorbed. Once small molecules move across the epithelial cells, they travel one of two routes. Amino acids, glucose, and water molecules are

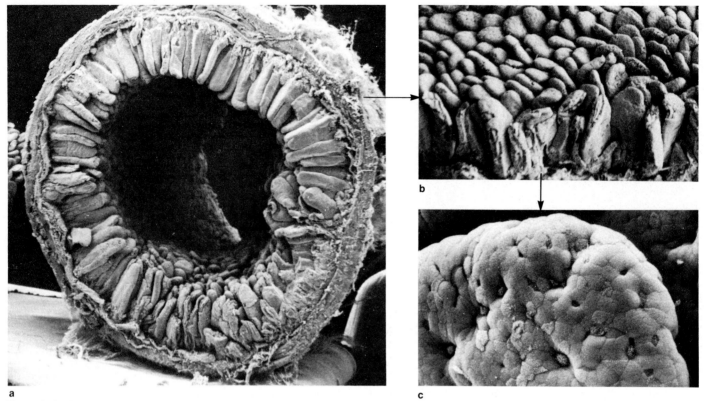

Figure 26.8 Location of microvilli-crowned cells in the mammalian intestine. Microvilli enhance cellular absorption and secretion. They are most profuse on absorptive cell surfaces. (**b**) Interstitial villi. ×50. (**c**) Single villus. Notice the surface boundaries of individual cells. ×725. (R. G. Kessel and R. H. Kardon, © 1979 W. H. Freeman and Co.)

actively transported into blood capillaries. Fats form again from fatty acids and monoglycerides inside the epithelial cells, then diffuse out and enter lymph vessels. These vessels, recall, eventually drain into the bloodstream.

Epithelial cells of intestinal villi show specialized transport functions: A cotransport mechanism simultaneously moves monosaccharides and sodium ions into these cells, across the membrane surface facing the lumen. (Free fatty acids and monoglycerides can diffuse across the epithelial cells, because they are soluble in the lipid bilayer of the plasma membrane.)

Besides organic molecules, the small intestine absorbs considerable water and dissolved mineral ions. Most of the solutes are sodium and chloride ions. Each day, about nine liters of fluid enter the small intestine from the stomach, liver, and pancreas. Of that, all but five percent is absorbed across the intestinal mucosa. Initially, water diffuses freely down its concentration gradient, established as a result of the mediated transport of solutes. Water absorption has the effect of increasing the solute concentrations in the lumen—so that diffusible solutes remaining move down their concentration gradients, into the internal environment.

Role of the Pancreas in Digestion. A duct leading from two organs—the pancreas and liver—empties into the duodenum. Under hormonal and neural signals, exocrine cells in the **pancreas** secrete enzymes into this duct (Figure 26.9). The enzymes degrade carbohydrates, fats, proteins, and nucleic acids. The pancreas also secretes bicarbonate, which helps neutralize highly acidic chyme in the small intestine. Without such neutralization, pancreatic enzymes could not function.

There are other patches of pancreatic cells (the islets of Langerhans), which do not secrete digestive enzymes.

Instead, they secrete the hormones insulin and glucagon, which are central in feedback controls over metabolism.

Role of the Liver in Digestion. The **liver** is the largest gland in the vertebrate body. One of its digestive functions is the secretion of **bile**, a solution containing bile salts, bile pigments, and lecithin. Bile is released into bile ducts, which join together and eventually connect with the pancreatic duct that empties into the duodenum. Between meals, bile is stored and concentrated in the **gallbladder**, a small sac that branches off the bile duct.

Bile salts are important in fat digestion and absorption. Fats, recall, are insoluble in water. Most of the fats you eat are in the form of triglyceride molecules, which clump together as large fat globules in liquid chyme. Pancreatic lipase can only split the triglycerides at the surface of each globule. Also, the products of lipase action (free fatty acids and monoglycerides) are nearly insoluble in water. Bile salts enhance fat breakdown and absorption in two ways. First, they emulsify the fat globules. Second, they help hydrate fat particles, and thereby enhance fat transport through the liquid environment.

A **bile salt** molecule has a hydrophobic cholesterol ring to which a hydrophilic side chain is attached. In the small intestine, segmentation movements mechanically break up the fat globules into droplets. When they do, the hydrophobic parts of bile salt molecules dissolve right into the droplets of fat. But the hydrophilic parts stick out from the droplets and interact with water—which prevents fat molecules from clumping together again. The fat droplets are thus suspended in liquid chyme, forming an emulsion. Being only about a micrometer in diameter, each droplet is more accessible to pancreatic lipase.

Following their emulsifying effects, bile salts combine with the breakdown products of lipase action and form micelles. A **micelle** is a hydrated fat aggregate only three to ten nanometers across. Micelle formation provides a means of transporting fats through the liquid environment until they encounter absorptive cells of the intestinal mucosa. There, fatty acids and monoglycerides diffuse out of the micelles and passively move down their concentration gradients, across the plasma membranes of mucosal cells. In those cells, the two lipid components are recombined into triglycerides within the membranes of the endoplasmic reticulum (ER). Vesicles form from ER membranes and transport the triglycerides to the cell surface. There, vesicles fuse with the plasma membrane, dumping their contents into interstitial fluid. The triglycerides are then picked up by lymph capillaries.

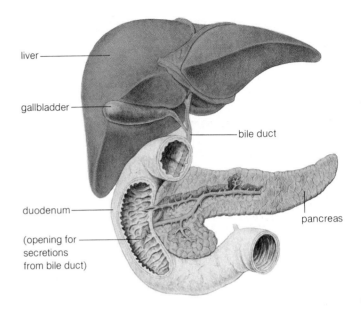

liver

gallbladder

bile duct

duodenum

(opening for secretions from bile duct)

pancreas

Figure 26.9 Location of ducts from the liver, gallbladder, and pancreas that carry secretions to the duodenum of the small intestine.

Large Intestine

Once most of the food is absorbed from the intestinal lumen, segmentation movements give way to peristaltic waves. The waves begin at the duodenum, then slowly force any remaining chyme into the **large intestine**, or **colon**. In a given day, only about 500 milliliters of chyme pass into this part of the gastrointestinal tract. The main function of the colon is the storage and concentration of *feces,* a mixture of undigested material, water, and bacteria. The concentration of this material occurs as epithelial cells of the colon actively transports sodium ions into the internal environment; water absorption follows passively as a result.

The colon is about 1.2 meters long. It ascends upward in the right side of the abdominal cavity, cuts across to the other side, then descends down the left side. The descending colon ends as an S-shaped (sigmoid) portion. The sigmoid colon empties into a small tube called the **rectum**. Distension of the rectal walls triggers reflex actions by which material is expelled from the body. This reflex can be overridden by nerves under voluntary control. The nerves cause contraction of a skeletal muscle sphincter of the **anus**, the terminal opening of the gastrointestinal tract.

Table 26.2 Major Enzymes of Digestion

Enzyme	Source	Where Active	Substrate	Main Breakdown Products*
Carbohydrate digestion:				
Salivary amylase	salivary glands	mouth	polysaccharides	disaccharides
Pancreatic amylase	pancreas	small intestine	polysaccharides	disaccharides
Disaccharidases	pancreas	small intestine	disaccharides	monosaccharides (e.g., glucose)
Protein digestion:				
Pepsins	stomach mucosa	stomach	proteins	peptide fragments
Trypsin and chymotrypsin	pancreas	small intestine	proteins and polypeptides	peptide fragments
Carboxypeptidase	pancreas	small intestine	peptide fragments	amino acids
Aminopeptidase	intestinal mucosa	small intestine	peptide fragments	amino acids
Fat digestion:				
Lipase	pancreas	small intestine	triglycerides	free fatty acids, monoglycerides
Nucleic acid digestion:				
Pancreatic nucleases	pancreas	small intestine	DNA, RNA	nucleotides
Intestinal nucleases	intestinal mucosa	small intestine	nucleotides	nucleotide bases, monosaccharides

*White part of table identifies breakdown products small enough to be absorbed into the internal environment.

The small intestine does not lead into the start of the colon. Rather, the sphincter between the two organs is located about a fourth of the way up the ascending colon. As Figure 26.4 indicates, the portion of the colon below the sphincter forms a blind pouch (the cecum). A small, narrow projection from the cecum is known as the **appendix**. Although the appendix has no known digestive functions, it does contain lymphatic tissue, which suggests a role in body defense. The appendix can become inflamed and infected, a condition called *appendicitis.* If ignored, an infected and inflamed appendix can rupture. Then, the bacteria normally inhabiting the colon can spread into the abdominal cavity and cause serious infections.

Enzymes of Digestion: A Summary

Now that you have completed this tour of the gastrointestinal tract, you may find it helpful to scan Table 26.2. This table summarizes the locations of carbohydrate, protein,

fat, and nucleic acid digestion, the enzymes responsible, and the breakdown products at each stage. It should be readily apparent, from this summary, that the small intestine is the major site of digestion and absorption.

HUMAN NUTRITIONAL REQUIREMENTS

Energy Needs

The energy and materials needed in body maintenance and growth comes from food of certain types, and this food must be obtained in certain minimum amounts. As for all organisms, our energy needs are measured in kilocalories (Chapter Six). How many kilocalories a human requires varies with size, age, degree of activity, and physiological state. An adult male of average size, who engages in normal activities, needs about 2,700 kilocalories each day. The "average" adult female needs about 2,000. Children in their mid-teens need 2,400 to 2,800 kilocalories.

Carbohydrates and Lipids

In the United States, the average carbohydrate intake is between 250 and 800 grams a day. Much of our food energy is derived from carbohydrates that are mostly in the form of starch and, to a lesser extent, sugars (such as sucrose and lactose). Glycogen, a storage polysaccharide in animal tissue, breaks down rapidly to glucose when the animal is killed for its meat. In the small intestine, incoming carbohydrates are broken down to glucose. Either glucose is used at once in cellular metabolism, or it is converted to glycogen and stored in the liver. Controls over the conversions from glucose and glycogen, and back again, help maintain blood glucose levels at about one milligram per milliliter.

Dietary intake of lipids ranges from about 25 to 160 grams a day. Most of our dietary lipids are in the form of triglycerides. Cholesterol represents a small part of the total lipid intake; however, the liver has the ability to synthesize cholesterol. This type of lipid occurs only in animal tissue (such as muscle, bone marrow, liver tissue, eggs, and milk). As you read in Chapter Twenty-Four, improper packaging and transport of cholesterol in the bloodstream has been implicated in heart diseases.

Proteins

The minimum daily requirement for protein probably ranges between 0.214 and 0.227 gram for every 454 grams (1 pound) of body weight. To this, another 0.28 gram can be added as a safety factor against individual differences. This translates to about 43 grams (about $1\frac{1}{2}$ ounces) of "pure" protein each day for an average adult male, and about 35 grams for an average female.

Of the twenty common amino acids necessary in building proteins, several are called **essential amino acids**. Our cells cannot build these molecules; they must be obtained from the diet. These amino acids are phenylalanine (and/or tyrosine), isoleucine, leucine, lysine, threonine, tryptophan, cysteine (and/or methionine), and valine.

In addition, our cells can build the other "nonessential" amino acids only if the total amino acid intake is adequate. They can convert the "nonessential" ones, but they can't make them from nothing. It takes an amino acid of one sort to make another amino acid. To build one, a cell has to tear another down.

Given the pervasive role of proteins in body structure and functioning, it is easy to see that protein deficiency is serious. It is most distressing among young children, for rapid brain growth and development occur early in life.

Table 26.3 Comparison of the Efficiency of Some Single Protein Sources in Meeting Minimum Daily Requirements				
Source	Protein Content (%)	Net Protein Utilization (NPU)	Amount Needed to Satisfy Minimum Daily Requirement	
			(Grams)	(Ounces)
Eggs	11	97	403	14.1
Milk	4	82	1,311	45.9***
Fish*	22	80	244	8.5
Cheese*	27	70	227	7.2
Meat*	25	68	253	8.8
Soybean flour	45	60	158**	5.5**
Soybeans	34	60	210**	7.3**
Kidney beans	23	40	468**	16.4**
Corn	10	50	860**	30.0**

*Average values.
**Dry weight values.
***Equivalent of 6 cups. The figure is somewhat misleading, for most of the volume of milk is water. Milk is actually a rich source of high-quality protein.

Unless enough protein is taken in just before and just after birth, irreversible mental retardation occurs. Even mild protein starvation can retard growth and affect mental and physical performance.

But quantity alone is not enough. *Cells must receive certain minimal proportions of all essential amino acids at the same time before they can assemble their own proteins.* Suppose the kind of protein you eat today has seven of the eight essential amino acids, in adequate amounts—but has only half the required lysine. Even if you eat 43 grams of that protein, you will not meet your daily protein needs. You must eat twice as much to get enough lysine.

To compare proteins from different sources, nutritionists use a measure called **net protein utilization** (NPU). NPU values range from 100 (all essential amino acids present, in ideal proportions) to 0 (one or more amino acids absent, which makes the protein useless when eaten alone). Balancing the diet with different proteins can make up for such deficiencies.

For much of the world, cereal grains are the main foods. As Table 26.3 suggests, cereal grains such as corn are low in protein content and NPU value. In contrast, beans are high in protein. Although NPU values for beans are no

COMMENTARY

Human Nutrition and Gastrointestinal Disorders

The United States harbors one of the best-fed populations in the world. Yet digestive disorders among its individuals are on the increase. Aside from child deliveries and tonsillectomies, about a third of all surgeries performed in the United States have to do with correcting problems of the gastrointestinal tract.

Along with affluence, it appears we have picked up some bad eating habits. We skip meals, eat too much and too fast when we do sit down at the table, and generally give our gastrointestinal tracts erratic workouts. Worse yet, our diet tends to be rich in refined sugar, cholesterol, and salt—and low in bulk. (Here, bulk means the volume of fiber and other undigested food materials that cannot be decreased by absorption.) The problem with too little bulk in the diet comes from the longer transit time of feces through the colon. This material has irritating and even potentially carcinogenic effects. The longer the material is in contact with the colon walls, the more damage it can do. Thus, the faster the colon contents are cleared out, the better. Increased bulk produces increased pressure on the colon walls, which stimulates expulsion of the material from the body.

Diseases such as appendicitis and cancer of the colon are practically nonexistent in rural Africa and India, where the inhabitants cannot afford to eat much more than whole grains. Whole grains happen to be high in fiber content. When individuals from these rural areas move to urban centers of the more affluent nations, they tend to become more susceptible to appendicitis and colon cancer. This suggests that diet is a key factor here. In addition, what we eat is known to affect the distribution and diversity of bacterial populations living in the gut. Do these changes somehow contribute to gastrointestinal disorders? That is not known.

Certainly the emotional stress associated with living in complex societies seems to compound the nutritional problem. Urban populations seem to be more susceptible to the irritable colon syndrome (once called colitis). Its symptoms include abdominal pain, diarrhea (excretion of watery feces), and constipation. Diarrhea can be brought on by emotional stress. There seems to be a genetic predisposition to some kinds of ulcers—inflammations of the stomach, the lower end of the esophagus, and the duodenum. But emotional stress apparently is a contributing factor in the development of some ulcers.

Where does this leave us? Short of surgery, there may not be much we can do about many inherited structural disorders of the gastrointestinal tract. Learning to handle stress is one way that we can ease up on the tract, though, and certainly learning how to eat properly is another.

Yet what is "eating properly"? In 1979 the United States Surgeon General released a report representing a medical consensus on how to promote health and avoid such afflictions as high blood pressure, heart disorders, cancer of the colon, and bad teeth. The report advised us to eat "less saturated fat and cholesterol; less salt; less sugar, relatively more complex carbohydrates such as whole grains, cereals, fruits, and vegetables; and relatively more fish, poultry, legumes (for example, peas, beans and peanuts); and less red meat."

The controversies over what constitutes proper nutrition rage on. In the meantime, it might not be a bad idea to think about your own eating habits and how moderation in some things might help you hedge your bets. Put the question to yourself: Do you look upon a bowl of bran cereal with the same passion as you look upon, say, french fries and ice cream, prime rib and chocolate mousse? Now put the same question to your colon.

higher than those for cereal grains, beans are deficient in *different* amino acids. When beans are eaten *with* grain, the one food enhances the other—and raises the overall NPU value.

Vitamins and Minerals

The catch-all category **vitamins** refers to more than a dozen accessory substances that are required, in small amounts, for normal metabolic activity. Most plant cells are able to synthesize all of these substances. In general, animal cells have lost the ability to do so, hence animals must obtain vitamins from food. Human cells need at least thirteen different vitamins (Table 26.4).

In addition to vitamins, all cells require inorganic materials known as **minerals**. (Some of these minerals are called *trace elements* because they are needed only in extremely small amounts.) Most cells require both calcium and magnesium in a host of enzyme-mediated reactions. All cells need phosphorus for phosphorylation. They need sodium and potassium for maintaining osmotic balances and for muscle and nerve functioning. They need potassium during protein synthesis. All cells require iron in building cytochromes. Red blood cells require still more iron in producing hemoglobin (Table 26.5).

The most reasonable way to supply cells with essential vitamins and minerals is to eat a well-balanced assortment of foods that contain carbohydrates, fats, and proteins of the right sorts. A diet of about 32–42 grams of protein, 250–500 grams of carbohydrates, and 66–83 grams of fat should also assure you of getting enough of these accessory substances. In recent years, there have been claims that massive doses of certain vitamins and minerals are spectacularly beneficial. To date, there is no clear evidence that vitamin intake exceeding the recommended daily allowances leads to better health. To the contrary, excessive vitamin doses are often merely wasted.

Individuals who take in large amounts of vitamin C don't realize that the body simply will not hold more vitamin C than it needs for normal functioning. Vitamin C is not fat-soluble and tends to be excreted. Direct chemical analysis shows that any amount above the recommended daily allowance ends up in the urine almost immediately after it is absorbed from the gut. Abnormal intake of at least two other vitamins—A and D—can cause serious disorders. The reason is that, like all fat-soluble vitamins, vitamins A and D can accumulate in the body (Table 26.4). *Both shortages and massive excess of vitamins and minerals can disturb the delicate balances that characterize physiological health.*

ORGANIC METABOLISM

So far, we have looked at the routes by which food molecules enter the internal environment. We have also looked at the types and proportions of organic molecules necessary for an adequate diet. Once these molecules are inside the body, some are used as building blocks for structural components of cells. Others are funneled into energy-releasing pathways that yield the ATP energy necessary in the metabolic reactions underlying cell activities. Figure 26.10 summarizes the main routes by which organic molecules enter and leave the body.

Figure 26.10 also shows the main routes by which organic molecules are shuffled and reshuffled once they are inside. With few exceptions (such as DNA), most organic molecules in the body are continually being broken down, with their component parts picked up and used again in new molecules. At the molecular level, your body undergoes massive and sometimes rapid turnovers! Such molecular interconversions figure in the dynamic adjustments between supply and demand.

The Vertebrate Liver

As Figure 26.10 suggests, the liver plays a central role in the interconversions associated with organic metabolism. The liver is active in carbohydrate, fat, and protein metabolism. It helps regulate the organic components of blood, and is a detoxifier for blood. It is in the liver that most hormones are finally inactivated, then sent to the kidneys for excretion from the body.

Most lipids are absorbed into the lymphatics of the small intestine, then carried to the general systemic circulation, and thereby reach the liver. Here, in the liver, some lipids are deposited, stored, or broken down into compounds such as acetyl-CoA. Acetyl-CoA, recall, is used in such metabolic pathways as the all-important Krebs cycle. Other nutrients are absorbed across the intestinal wall and transported directly by capillaries to the hepatic portal vein, which leads to the capillary bed in the liver. In the liver, excess glucose is stored as glycogen. Here, too, excess amino acids are converted to forms that can be sent through the Krebs cycle as an alternate energy source. Amino acid conversions in the liver form ammonia (NH_3), which is potentially toxic to cells. The liver immediately converts the ammonia to urea, a much less toxic waste product that can be expelled, by way of the kidneys, from the body. Table 26.6 summarizes some of the liver's functions.

Table 26.4　Vitamins Necessary for Normal Cell Functioning

Vitamin	RDA* (milligrams)	Dietary Sources	Major Body Functions	Possible Outcomes of Deficiency	Possible Outcomes of Excess
Water-Soluble					
Vitamin B$_1$ (thiamine)	1.5	Pork, organ meats, whole grains, legumes	Coenzyme (thiamine pyrophosphate) in the removal of carbon dioxide	Beriberi (peripheral nerve changes, edema, heart failure)	None reported
Vitamin B$_2$ (riboflavin)	1.8	Widely distributed in foods	Constituent of two flavin nucleotide coenzymes involved in energy metabolism (FAD and FMN)	Reddened lips, cracks at corner of mouth (cheilosis), lesions of eye	None reported
Niacin	20	Liver, lean meats, grains, legumes (can be formed from tryptophan)	Constituent of two coenzymes involved in oxidation-reduction reactions (NAD$^+$ and NADP$^+$)	Pellagra (skin and gastrointestinal lesions, nervous, mental disorders)	Flushing, burning and tingling around neck, face, and hands
Vitamin B$_6$ (pyridoxine)	2	Meats, vegetables, whole grain cereals	Coenzyme (pyridoxal phosphate) involved in amino acid metabolism	Irritability, convulsions, muscular twitching, kidney stones	None reported
Pantothenic acid	5–10	Widely distributed in foods	Constituent of coenzyme A, which plays a central role in energy metabolism	Fatigue, sleep disturbances, impaired coordination, nausea (rare in humans)	None reported
Folacin (folic acid)	0.4	Legumes, green vegetables, whole wheat products	Coenzyme (reduced form) in carbon transfer in nucleic acid and amino acid metabolism	Anemia, gastrointestinal disturbances, diarrhea, red tongue	None reported
Vitamin B$_{12}$	0.003	Muscle meats, eggs, dairy products	Coenzyme in carbon transfer in nucleic acid metabolism	Pernicious anemia, neurological disorders	None reported
Biotin	Not established. Usual diet provides 0.15–0.3	Legumes, vegetables, meats	Coenzyme in fat synthesis, amino acid metabolism, glycogen formation	Fatigue, depression, nausea, dermatitis, muscular pains	None reported
Choline	Not established. Usual diet provides 500–900	All foods containing phospholipids (egg yolk, liver, grains, legumes)	Constituent of phospholipids. Precursor of putative neurotransmitter acetylcholine	None reported for humans	None reported
Vitamin C (ascorbic acid)	45	Citrus fruits, tomatoes, green peppers, salad greens	Maintains intercellular matrix of cartilage, bone, and dentine. Important in collagen synthesis	Scurvy (degeneration of skin, teeth, blood vessels, epithelial hemorrhages)	Relatively nontoxic. Possibility of kidney stones
Fat-Soluble					
Vitamin A (retinol)	1	Provitamin A in green vegetables. Retinol in milk, butter, cheese, margarine	Constituent of rhodopsin (visual pigment). Maintenance of epithelial tissues	Xerophthalmia (keratinization of ocular tissue), night blindness, permanent blindness	Headache, vomiting, peeling of skin, anorexia, swelling of long bones
Vitamin D	0.01	Cod liver oil, eggs, dairy products, margarine	Promotes bone growth, mineralization. Increases calcium absorption	Rickets (bone deformities) in children. Osteomalacia in adults	Vomiting, diarrhea, weight loss, kidney damage
Vitamin E (tocopherol)	15	Seeds, green leafy vegetables, margarines	Functions as an antioxidant to prevent cell membrane damage	Possibly anemia; never observed in humans	Relatively nontoxic
Vitamin K (phylloquinone)	0.03	Green leafy vegetables. Small amount in cereals, fruits, and meats	Important in blood clotting (involved in formation of active prothrombin)	Deficiencies associated with severe bleeding, internal hemorrhages	Synthetic forms at high doses may cause jaundice

*Recommended daily allowance, for an adult male in good health.
From "The Requirements of Human Nutrition," by Nevin S. Scrimshaw and Vernon R. Young. Copyright © 1976 by Scientific American, Inc. All rights reserved.

Table 26.5 Minerals Necessary for Normal Cell Functioning

Mineral	Amount in Adult Body (grams)	RDA* (milligrams)	Dietary Sources	Major Body Functions	Possible Outcomes of Deficiency	Possible Outcomes of Excess
Calcium	1,500	800	Milk, cheese, dark-green vegetables, dried legumes	Bone and tooth formation Blood clotting Nerve transmission	Stunted growth Rickets, osteoporosis Convulsions	Not reported for humans
Phosphorus	860	800	Milk, cheese, meat, poultry, grains	Bone and tooth formation Acid-base balance, ATP formation, etc.	Weakness, demineralization of bone, loss of calcium	Erosion of jaw (fossy jaw)
Sulfur	300	(Provided by sulfur amino acids)	Sulfur amino acids (methionine and cystine) in dietary proteins	Constituent of active tissue compounds, cartilage and tendon	Related to intake and deficiency of sulfur amino acids	Excess sulfur amino acid intake leads to poor growth
Potassium	180	2,500	Meats, milk, many fruits	Acid-base balance Body water balance Nerve function	Muscular weakness Paralysis	Muscular weakness Death
Chlorine	74	2,000	Common salt	Formation of gastric juice Acid-base balance	Muscle cramps Mental apathy Reduced appetite	Vomiting
Sodium	64	2,500	Common salt	Acid-base balance Body water balance Nerve function	Muscle cramps Mental apathy Reduced appetite	High blood pressure
Magnesium	25	350	Whole grains, green leafy vegetables	Activates enzymes. Involved in protein synthesis	Growth failure. Behavioral disturbances Weakness, spasms	Diarrhea
Iron	4.5	10	Eggs, lean meats, legumes, whole grains, green leafy vegetables	Constituent of hemoglobin and enzymes involved in energy metabolism	Iron-deficiency anemia (weakness, reduced resistance to infection)	Siderosis Cirrhosis of liver
Fluorine	2.6	2	Drinking water, tea, seafood	May be important in maintenance of bone structure	Higher frequency of tooth decay	Mottling of teeth. Increased bone density. Neurological disturbances
Zinc	2	15	Widely distributed in foods	Constituent of enzymes involved in digestion	Growth failure Small sex glands	Fever, nausea, vomiting, diarrhea
Copper	0.1	2	Meats, drinking water	Constituent of enzymes associated with iron metabolism	Anemia, bone changes (rare in humans)	
Iodine	0.011	0.14	Marine fish and shellfish, dairy products	Constituent of thyroid hormones	Goiter (enlarged thyroid)	Very high intakes depress thyroid activity
Cobalt	0.0015	(Required as vitamin B_{12})	Organ and muscle meats, milk	Constituent of vitamin B_{12}	None reported for humans	Industrial exposure: dermatitis and diseases of red blood cells

*Recommended daily allowance, for an adult male in good health.
From "The Requirements of Human Nutrition," by Nevin S. Scrimshaw and Vernon R. Young. Copyright © 1976 by Scientific American, Inc. All rights reserved.

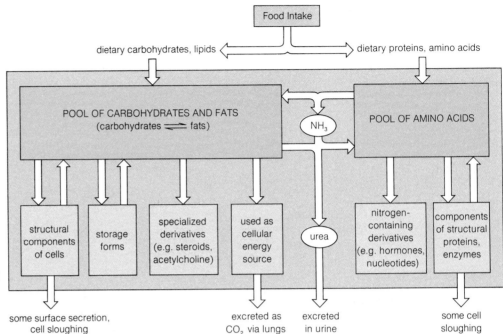

Figure 26.10 Summary of major pathways of organic metabolism. Ammonia (NH_3) and urea formation occur in the liver, during amino acid conversions. Carbohydrates and fats are continually being broken down and resynthesized. (Modified from A. Vander et al., *Human Physiology*, third edition, © McGraw-Hill. Used by permission.)

Absorptive and Post-Absorptive States

In terms of the total nutritional picture, there are two functional states of organic metabolism:

absorptive state	*ingested organic molecules enter the bloodstream from the gastrointestinal tract*
post-absorptive state	*gastrointestinal tract is not supplying nutrients; the body draws from its internal pools of organic molecules*

During the absorptive state, the body builds up its pools of organic molecules. Excess carbohydrates and other dietary molecules are transformed mostly into fats, which are stored in adipose tissue. Some also is converted to glycogen in the liver and in muscle tissue. Glucose is used as the primary energy source for this metabolic activity; there is no net breakdown of protein in muscle or other tissues.

During the post-absorptive state, there is a notable shift in activities. A key factor in this shift is the need to provide brain cells with glucose, the only nutrient they can use for energy. When glucose is being absorbed, its concentrations in the bloodstream are readily maintained. During the post-absorptive state, the body works to maintain blood glucose concentrations in the following ways. *First,* glycogen stores (particularly in the liver) are rapidly mobil-

ized to liberate glucose. *Second,* body proteins and, to a lesser extent, fats are broken down to provide amino acids and glycerol for synthesis of more glucose in the liver.

These aspects of organic metabolism are under homeostatic controls that have two primary functions:

---

1. During the absorptive state, controls enhance the movement of glucose into cells, where it can be used for energy and where the excess can be stored.

2. During the post-absorptive state, controls maintain a glucose supply for brain cells (which depend on it) and for cells that require glucose as an alternate energy source.

Both endocrine and neural controls govern the absorptive and post-absorptive states. The most important control agents are hormones that are secreted by pancreatic cell clusters (islets of Langerhans). These clusters include alpha and beta cell types, which function antagonistically. *Beta cells* secrete **insulin**, a hormone that enhances glucose uptake into cells. *Alpha cells* secrete **glucagon**, a hormone that prods liver cells into converting glycogen into glucose.

The picture just outlined seems simple enough, yet the mechanisms by which these events are carried out are truly complex, as the following case study suggests.

Table 26.6	Some Activities That Depend on Liver Functioning

1. Carbohydrate metabolism
2. Control over some aspects of plasma protein synthesis
3. Assembly and disassembly of certain proteins
4. Urea formation from nitrogen-containing wastes
5. Assembly and storage of some fats
6. Fat digestion (bile is formed by the liver)
7. Inactivation of many chemicals (such as hormones)
8. Detoxification of many poisons
9. Degradation of worn-out red blood cells
10. Immune response (removal of some foreign particles)
11. Red blood cell formation (liver absorbs, stores factors needed for red blood cell maturation in embryo)

Case Study: Feasting, Fasting, and Systems Integration

Suppose, this morning, you are vacationing in the mountains and decide on impulse to follow a forested trail. You fail to notice the wooden trail marker that bears the intriguing name, "Fat Man's Misery." As you walk down the tree-lined corridor, you are enjoying one of the benefits of discontinuous feeding. Having stocked your gastrointestinal tract with breakfast, your cells are assured of ongoing nourishment; you do not have to forage constantly amongst the ferns as, say, a nematode must do. Food partly digested in your stomach has already entered the small intestine. There, it is broken down farther by enzymes secreted from the pancreas and intestinal mucosa. Right now, amino acids, simple sugars, and fatty acids are moving across the intestinal wall, then into the bloodstream.

With the sudden surge of nutrients, glucose molecules are entering the bloodstream faster than your cells can use them. The level of blood glucose begins to rise slightly. However, your body has a homeostatic program for converting glucose into storage form when it is flooding in, then releasing some of the stores when glucose is scarce.

With the rise in blood glucose, pancreatic cell clusters are called into action. Insulin secretions rise—which prods cells into quickly using or storing the incoming glucose (Figure 26.11). Glucagon secretions dwindle—which slows the liver's conversion of glycogen reservoirs into glucose.

Insulin enters your bloodstream and travels to cells throughout your body. When insulin reaches target cells, it increases plasma membrane transport of glucose. So more glucose enters liver, fat, and muscle cells where it is used at once or stored. Increased glucose uptake, glucose metabo-

lism, and storage of the excess—these cellular activities proceed as you hike.

Even though you are no longer feeding your body, your brain cells have not lessened their high demands for glucose. Neither have your muscle cells, which are getting a strenuous workout. Little by little, blood glucose levels drop. Now endocrine activities shift in the pancreas. With less glucose binding to them, beta cells decrease their insulin secretion. With less glucose to inhibit them, alpha cells step up glucagon secretions. When glucagon reaches your liver, it causes the conversion of glycogen back to glucose—which is returned to your blood. This completes a feedback loop: blood glucose levels remain balanced.

But the best-laid balance of internal conditions can go astray when external conditions change. In your case, the "miserable" part of the trail has now begun. You find yourself scrambling up steep inclines, squeezing along narrow ledges, climbing higher and higher. Suddenly you stop, surprised, in great pain. You forgot to reckon with the lower oxygen pressure in the mountains, and your leg muscles cramped. Your body has already detected the need for producing more oxygen-carrying red blood cells at this altitude. However, it will take days before enough additional red blood cells accumulate. In the meantime, your muscle cells are not being supplied with enough oxygen for your strenuous climbs. They have switched to the anaerobic pathway of glycolysis and lactate fermentation. The end product, recall, is lactate—which is toxic to your cells if allowed to accumulate. The sudden lactate buildup has impaired muscle functioning.

Again, systems interact and work to return your body to a homeostatic state. Receptors in your arterial walls detect the reduction in oxygen pressure and an accompanying increase in hydrogen ion concentrations in the cerebrospinal fluid. Nerve impulses course toward the respiratory center in the medulla. The result: increased activity in the diaphragm and other muscles associated with inflating and deflating your lungs. You breathe faster now, and more deeply. Gradually muscle cells are purged of lactate and replenished with oxygen. Gradually lactate is carted off to the liver. In the liver, lactate is converted to glucose—which is returned to the blood.

On checking the sun's position, you see it's well past noon. And guess what: you forgot about lunch. When you start the long walk back, the drop in blood glucose levels triggers new homeostatic mechanisms. Under hypothalamic commands, your adrenal medulla begins secreting epinephrine and norepinephrine. Its main targets: the liver, adipose tissue, and muscles. In liver, glycogen synthesis stops. In muscles, glucose uptake is blocked. In fat cells, fats are

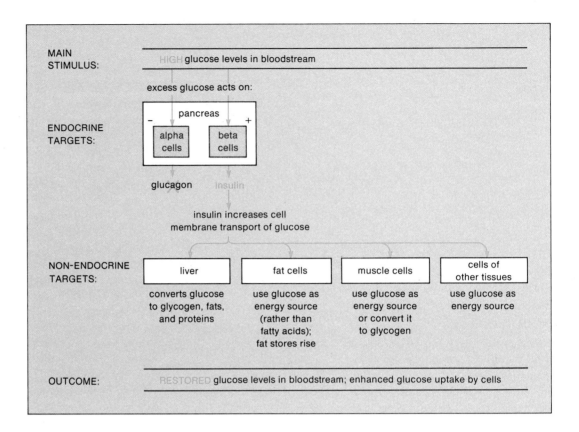

MAIN STIMULUS: HIGH glucose levels in bloodstream

excess glucose acts on:

ENDOCRINE TARGETS:

pancreas

− | +

alpha cells | beta cells

glucagon | insulin

insulin increases cell membrane transport of glucose

NON-ENDOCRINE TARGETS:

liver	fat cells	muscle cells	cells of other tissues
converts glucose to glycogen, fats, and proteins	use glucose as energy source (rather than fatty acids); fat stores rise	use glucose as energy source or convert it to glycogen	use glucose as energy source

OUTCOME: RESTORED glucose levels in bloodstream; enhanced glucose uptake by cells

Figure 26.11 Main metabolic routes and endocrine commands during times of feasting.

converted to fatty acids, which are routed to the liver, muscles, and other tissues as alternative energy sources (Figure 26.12). For every fatty acid molecule sent down metabolic pathways in those tissues, several glucose molecules are held in reserve for the brain.

You do get back to the start of the trail by sundown. However, your body had enough stored energy to sustain you for many more days, so the situation was never really desperate. The balance of blood sugar, glycogen, and fat is constantly monitored and controlled by the liver and hormones. Glucose levels only drop beyond the set point to stimulate glycogen conversion and fat conversion, and vice versa. It takes several days of fasting before blood sugar levels are markedly reduced.

Even after several days of fasting, your energy supplies would not have run out. Another hypothalamic command would have prodded your anterior pituitary into secreting adrenocorticotropic hormone (ACTH). In turn, ACTH would have prodded adrenal cortex cells into secreting glucocorticoid hormones, which have a potent effect on the synthesis of carbohydrates from proteins. Slowly, in mus-

cles and other tissues, your body's proteins would have been disassembled. Amino acids from these structural tissues would have been used in the liver as an alternative energy source—and once more your brain would have been kept active. As extreme as this last pathway might be, it would be a small price to pay for keeping your brain functional enough to figure out how to take in more nutrients, and bring the body back to a homeostatic state.

Readings

Clemente, C. 1981. *Anatomy: A Regional Atlas of the Human Body.* Second edition. Baltimore: Urban and Schwartzenberg. Stunning, detailed illustrations of human anatomy. Drawings of the gastrointestinal tract are among the best available.

Ganong, W. 1979. *Review of Medical Physiology.* Ninth edition. Los Altos, California: Lange Medical Publications. Excellent, although advanced reading on gastrointestinal functioning.

Hamilton, W. 1982. *Nutrition: Concepts and Controversies.* Menlo Park: West. Information on digestion, nutrition, diet, and health; evaluates fads and erroneous ideas about nutrition in light of current research.

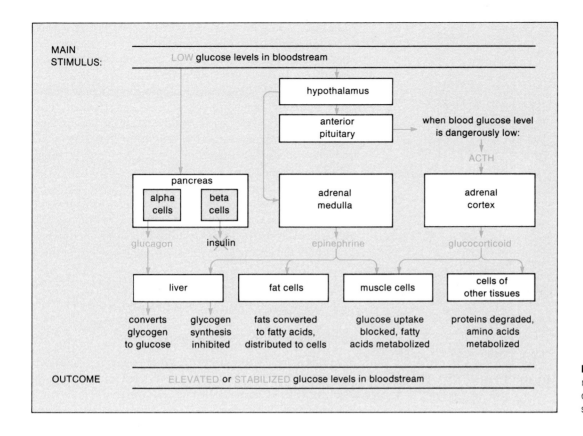

MAIN STIMULUS:

LOW glucose levels in bloodstream

hypothalamus

anterior pituitary

when blood glucose level is dangerously low:

ACTH

pancreas
- alpha cells
- beta cells

adrenal medulla

adrenal cortex

glucagon   insulin   epinephrine   glucocorticoid

liver   fat cells   muscle cells   cells of other tissues

converts glycogen to glucose | glycogen synthesis inhibited | fats converted to fatty acids, distributed to cells | glucose uptake blocked, fatty acids metabolized | proteins degraded, amino acids metabolized

OUTCOME

ELEVATED or STABILIZED glucose levels in bloodstream

Figure 26.12 Main metabolic routes and endocrine commands during times of fasting (and starvation).

Kessel, R., and R. Kardon. 1979. *Tissues and Organs: A Text-Atlas of Scanning Electron Microscopy.* San Francisco: Freeman. Outstanding, unique micrographs, accompanied by well-written descriptions of major tissues and organs.

Kretchmer, N., and W. van B. Robertson. 1978. *Human Nutrition.* San Francisco: Freeman. Excellent collection of articles from *Scientific American* that consider nutrition at the cellular level and the global level. Paperback.

Vander, A., J. Sherman, and D. Luciano. 1980. *Human Physiology: The Mechanisms of Body Function.* Third edition. New York: McGraw-Hill. Perhaps the most accurate, authoritative introduction to human organ systems and their function.

Review Questions

1. Study Figure 26.2. Then, on your own, diagram the connections between metabolism and the digestive, circulatory, and respiratory systems.

2. Explain the difference between digestion, absorption, and assimilation.

3. What are the main functions of the stomach? The small intestine? The large intestine?

4. In what ways are food materials mixed and propelled through the gastrointestinal tract?

5. Name three hormones at work in the digestive tract. What are their targets and their functions?

6. Which enzymes are involved in the breakdown of (a) polysaccharides, (b) proteins, and (c) fats? Name four kinds of breakdown products that are actually small enough to be absorbed across the intestinal mucosa and into the internal environment.

7. A glass of milk contains lactose, protein, butterfat, vitamins, and minerals. Explain what happens to each component when it passes through your digestive tract.

8. Describe some of the reasons why each of the following is nutritionally important: carbohydrates, fats, proteins, vitamins, and minerals.

9. Describe some of the functions of the liver.

10. What are the roles of insulin and glucagon in organic metabolism? When blood glucose levels are high, glucagon secretions are (enhanced/inhibited). When blood glucose levels are low, insulin secretions are (enhanced/inhibited).

27

REGULATION OF BODY TEMPERATURE AND BODY FLUIDS

Everett C. Johnson

Figure 27.1 Keeping the warm-blooded body warmer on cold winter nights in a West German zoo. In complex animals, diverse behavioral adjustments supplement built-in adaptations in maintaining the homeostatic state.

Your body is a tightly knit coalition of some 75 trillion cells, which generally function in ways that help maintain the internal environment. For example, cells of your circulatory, respiratory, nervous, and endocrine systems interact and help keep blood levels of oxygen and carbon dioxide within some tolerable range. Keeping cells well stocked with oxygen and cleared of carbon dioxide are no doubt vital functions, but they are not the only ones that keep your body homeostatically humming. What happens to those cells when you sit under the hot sun too long or can't get warm on a cold winter night? What happens when you eat a whole bag of potato chips, and salt loads increase in your bloodstream? In this chapter, we will look at homeostatic mechanisms whereby the body adjusts to shifts in temperature and in the character of its extracellular fluid.

CONTROL OF BODY TEMPERATURE

Temperature Range Suitable for Life

If you have ever stepped into a tub of water that is far too hot, you can admire the thermal endurance of Yellowstone National Park's thermophilic bacteria, which thrive in 92°C hot springs. (That is over 207°F.) Conversely, if you have ever suffered frostbitten toes, you can admire the fishes and assorted invertebrates that thrive in arctic waters, where the temperature is about −1.8°C. (That is low enough to freeze body fluids, without such adaptations as circulating glycoproteins that act like antifreeze in the blood.)

The organisms just mentioned are exceptional, in that they live at the fringes of environments suitable for most forms of life. More typically, the organic compounds on which life is based remain functional only within the range between 0°C and 40°C. Consider how temperature affects enzyme activity. Each type of enzyme is fully operational within a rather narrow temperature range. When temperatures climb above 40°C, protein denaturation usually begins and enzyme function starts to deteriorate (Chapter Five). For every ten-degree drop in temperature, the rate of enzyme activity drops by at least half. Given all the links between enzyme-mediated reactions, it is easy to imagine how the body's metabolic balance can be skewed when temperatures exceed or fall below the proper range.

As Table 27.1 suggests, temperatures of the surface waters of open oceans correspond to the range suitable for active life. Also, because of water's temperature-stabilizing properties (Chapter Five), ocean environments normally do not undergo sudden temperature changes. In contrast, air temperatures on land can be lethally high or low. Air has a much lower specific heat capacity than water, and it rapidly heats up under incoming solar radiation. Air rapidly loses heat to space. Thus air temperatures can shift enormously even in the same location, depending on the weather, the time of day, and the season.

What we have, then, are different temperature conditions in different environments:

1. Stable temperatures within the range suitable for life (0°C–40°C).

2. Temperatures that fluctuate within this range.

3. Temperatures that extend beyond this range.

It follows that all animals either live in places where they do not have to contend with temperature extremes, or they have the means to maintain *internal* body temperature (hence metabolic activity) when faced with extremes.

Heat Production and Heat Loss

Heat is a by-product of almost all energy transformations, including metabolism and muscle contraction. As long as an animal is alive, it continually produces heat and loses heat to the surroundings. At the same time, the environment is gaining and losing heat also. *The combined effects of these heat gains and heat losses dictate body temperature.*

Heat is exchanged between animals and the environment in complex ways. The main processes are conduction, convection, radiation, and evaporation. In *conduction,* heat energy is transferred from high- to low-temperature regions as a result of collisions between adjacent molecules, not by any mass movement. In *convection,* heat next to the body's surface undergoes mass transport by air or water currents. *Radiation* of infrared wavelengths is another process figuring in heat exchange. These wavelengths come from the sun; they can be radiated from objects (such as the body) when outside air temperature is lower. In *evaporation,* heat energy is released to the air when water escapes from body surfaces (such as skin).

When the rate of heat production equals that of heat loss, the body is said to be in **heat balance**. When the two are out of balance, body temperature will be affected.

Heat loss and heat production must be balanced if any given body temperature is to be maintained.

An animal passively loses most of its metabolically derived heat through conduction, convection, and radiation.

But what happens when the environmental temperature equals or exceeds body temperature? Then heat energy moves from the environment into the animal. A land animal might get rid of the excess through evaporation (for example, by sweating or panting). A marine animal, obviously, cannot.

For the overwhelming majority of animals, body temperature is dictated by heat gain from the environment. These animals are called **ectothermic** ("heat from outside"). Ectotherms are not highly active, and what little metabolic heat they do produce is conducted at once to the surroundings. Thus the body temperature of an ectotherm corresponds, more or less, to the environmental temperature.

A few animal groups are **endothermic** ("heat from within"). In these groups, a relatively constant body temperature is maintained by controls over metabolic activity (which is high, compared with ectotherms) and by controls over heat-conserving mechanisms. Some birds and mammals are continuous endotherms. Large, fast-swimming fishes such as tuna are partly endothermic; so are large reptiles. (For instance, female boa constrictors coil around their fertilized eggs, and through muscular contractions they generate the heat necessary for incubation.) Some insects, including beetles, moths, and bumblebees, are endothermic during flight, foraging, and other times of increased activity. Although these animals are capable of endothermic heat production, they do not maintain precisely the same body temperature at all times. These "sometime endotherms" are said to be **heterothermic**. Most birds and mammals are heterotherms.

Thermal Regulation in Ectotherms

From the preceding descriptions, you might think that ectotherms are completely at the mercy of their environment.

Table 27.1	Temperatures Favorable for Metabolism, Compared With Ranges of Environmental Temperatures	
Temperatures generally favorable for metabolism:	0°C to 40°C	(32°F to 104°F)
Air temperatures above land surfaces:	−70°C to +85°C	(−94°F to +185°F)
Surface temperatures of open oceans:	−2°C to +30°C	(+28.4°F to +86°F)

However, this is not entirely true. For example, these animals can compensate somewhat for naturally occurring temperature changes, a response called **acclimation**. The response has a genetic basis, in that these animals have backup sets of enzymes with different ranges of temperature sensitivities. With the backup systems, metabolic rates can be adjusted somewhat to gradual temperature changes. Ectotherms also compensate behaviorally for temperature changes. They have receptors that allow them to detect thermal gradients, and they move to regions that help assure the maintenance of a particular body temperature.

Complex behavioral responses are also seen among ectothermic reptiles, which are subject to rapid temperature changes in their land habitats. These animals control body temperature by changing their locations and by adjusting body posture. They bask in the sun, orienting themselves with respect to the sun's overhead position. They absorb radiated heat that was absorbed earlier in the day by a rock; they move in and out of shade when internal temperatures go up and down. At night, temperatures drop and their metabolic rates drop accordingly. The drop in metabolism is often enough to render these animals immobile. Before then, reptiles tuck themselves into crevices and under rocks (where they are not as vulnerable to predators).

Ectotherms show some degree of thermal regulation as a result of metabolic and behavioral responses to temperature change.

Thermal Regulation in Birds and Mammals

Even though ectotherms show some capacity for thermal regulation, their activities and their distribution are still limited to a large extent by outside temperatures. Birds, mammals, and a few animals of other groups have moved beyond this environmental restraint. *Within their nervous systems are control mechanisms that maintain body temperature according to a set point.*

For example, the human **core temperature** (temperature inside the body) averages 37°C (98.6°F) when recorded orally. This core temperature usually does not rise or fall more than a few degrees past its normal range, even when environmental temperature shifts. Suppose, for some peculiar reason, you find yourself stripped of all clothing in the dry air of a desert. Even if the air temperature drops as low as 13°C during the night, then skyrockets to 60°C the following day, your core temperature would remain nearly constant assuming you had sufficient food and water.

In humans and other mammals, the hypothalamus is the center of temperature control. Body temperature is regulated almost entirely by feedback mechanisms that operate through this part of the central nervous system (Figure 27.2). Thermoreceptors send information about temperature along nerves leading into the central nervous system. These thermoreceptors are located not only in skin but also throughout the body.

In birds and mammals, the hypothalamus governs thermal regulation.

Skin thermoreceptors provide early warning signals about shifts in environmental temperature.

Core thermoreceptors—including some in the spinal cord and hypothalamus—detect shifts in internal temperature.

The hypothalamus monitors core temperature minute by minute. When circulating blood temperature rises above or falls below normal, hypothalamic signals lead to altered metabolic rates and behavioral responses. More adjustments are made when receptors for blood temperature signal a return to normal body temperature. Figure 27.2 summarizes the main feedback relationships involved.

What sort of tissue responses does the hypothalamus evoke? As an example, consider the hypothalamic-directed responses to a sudden drop in temperature. Hypothalamic stimulation of the adrenal medulla leads to epinephrine secretion. This hormone helps mobilize energy stores that will be used to increase the metabolic rate. Norepinephrine acts directly on fat cells, mobilizing free fatty acids that can support the increased metabolic activity. When temperature remains low, the hypothalamus responds with signals sent, via the anterior pituitary, to the thyroid gland. The thyroid releases thyroxin, a hormone that stimulates increased metabolic activity (hence heat production) in most body cells.

Hypothalamic signals also lead to muscle contraction. Because muscles represent almost half the total body weight in mammals, considerable heat is released when they contract. More heat can be produced when muscles are made to contract very frequently, an activity called the **shivering response**. Still more heat can be produced behaviorally, through foot stomping, hand clapping, and other modes of conscious exercise. While these activities proceed, changes in the vasoconstriction of arterioles direct blood away from the body surface and into deeper tissue regions. This response cuts down the amount of heat carried to the skin and, from there, away from the body's surface. Mammals typically have a fat layer under the skin, and a hairy coat

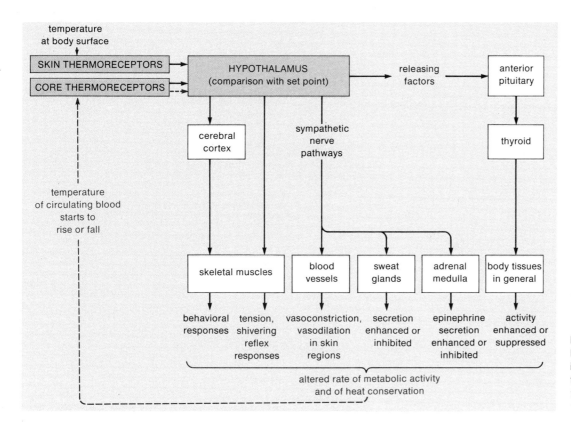

temperature
at body surface

SKIN THERMORECEPTORS

CORE THERMORECEPTORS

temperature
of circulating blood
starts to
rise or fall

HYPOTHALAMUS
(comparison with set point)

releasing
factors

anterior
pituitary

cerebral
cortex

sympathetic
nerve
pathways

thyroid

skeletal muscles

blood
vessels

sweat
glands

adrenal
medulla

body tissues
in general

behavioral
responses

tension,
shivering
reflex
responses

vasoconstriction,
vasodilation
in skin
regions

secretion
enhanced or
inhibited

epinephrine
secretion
enhanced or
inhibited

activity
enhanced or
suppressed

altered rate of metabolic activity
and of heat conservation

Figure 27.2 Summary of main homeostatic feedback relationships in controlling human body temperature. The dashed line completes the feedback loop. (After Vander, 1975, and Strand, 1978)

(fur)—two adaptations that also help hold heat close to the body. Also, muscles at the base of hairs cause fur to fluff, thereby forming a thermal blanket of air that holds heat near the body surface.

CONTROL OF EXTRACELLULAR FLUID

Water and Solute Balance

Cell functioning depends on stable chemical conditions in *extracellular fluid,* which in most animals is partitioned into blood and interstitial fluid. This stability requires constant monitoring of the amounts and concentrations of water and different dissolved substances, including mineral ions.

Water and solutes appear in the body as by-products of metabolism. (For example, water is produced during aerobic metabolism. Kangaroo rats, which live in hot deserts, derive ninety percent of their water from metabolism and only ten percent from foodstuffs.) Water and solutes are also absorbed daily across the epithelial lining of diges-

tive systems (and, in animals that live in fresh water, of gills). Usually, an environmental source of water contains some amount of dissolved salts. This is true of seas, freshwater lakes, ponds, streams, plant tissues, and animal tissues. Thus any "water" moving into the body from the outside is going to have some effect on the character of the extracellular fluid.

Water and solutes of extracellular fluid are derived from the external environment and from internal metabolic activities.

In complex animals, water and solutes also leave the body in several ways. First, sweat glands secrete a solution of water, salts, and some urea (a nitrogen-containing waste product associated with amino acid metabolism). Second, water leaves the lungs during exhalation. Third, water evaporates from the surface epithelial cells of skin when internal temperature increases. Fourth, water and many diverse solutes leave by way of the gastrointestinal tract. Finally, water, salts, and urea leave by way of an organ

Falling Overboard and the Odds for Survival

In 1912, the ocean liner *Titanic* set out from Europe on her maiden voyage to America. In that same year, a huge chunk of the leading edge of a Greenland glacier broke off and began floating out to sea. Late at night on April 14, off the coast of Newfoundland, the iceberg and the *Titanic* made their ill-fated rendezvous. The *Titanic* was considered unsinkable; four of the watertight compartments making up its hull could be ripped apart and the ship would remain afloat. The iceberg ripped through five. Lifeboats and survival drills had been neglected, and only about a fourth of the 2,000 people on board managed to scramble into the lifeboats that could be launched. What happened to the rest of the passengers? Within two hours, rescue ships were on the scene—yet 1,513 bodies were recovered from a calm sea. All were wearing life jackets. None had drowned. Every one of those individuals had died from hypothermia—from a drop in body core temperature below tolerance levels.

The following are responses at the body temperatures indicated:

36°–34°C (about 95°F)	Shivering response, increase in respiration. Increase in metabolic heat output. Constriction of peripheral blood vessels, so that blood is routed to deeper regions.
33°–32°C (about 91°F)	Shivering response stops. Metabolic heat output drops. Dizziness and nausea set in.
31°–30°C (about 86°F)	Capacity for voluntary motion is lost. Eye and tendon reflexes inhibited. Consciousness is lost. Cardiac muscle action becomes irregular.
26°–24°C (about 77°F)	Ventricular fibrillation sets in. Death follows.

system that helps maintain the extracellular fluid over time, through adjustments that *balance* the amount of water and solutes leaving with the amount being brought in. The urinary system of mammals specializes in this task. Similar systems occur in other animal groups as well (Chapter Thirty-Four).

A urinary system helps maintain the volume and composition of extracellular fluid by balancing the amount of water and salts leaving the body with the amount entering.

Normally, water loss from the body equals water gain. (See, for example, Table 27.2.) This balancing act is all the more remarkable because of the physiological variables involved. When temperatures soar, the hypothalamus triggers sweat production. The amount of physical activity varies during the day and, correspondingly, so do the by-products of metabolism. Some water is lost steadily by

evaporation from skin and lungs. Some small amount of water is lost in feces. Two mechanisms make adjustments that are proportional to the effect of all these variables. One is a thirst mechanism, and the other is a homeostatic control mechanism over water loss via the kidneys. You will read about these mechanisms later in the chapter.

What about salt balance? In mammals, regulation is primarily the responsibility of organs called kidneys. Through kidney functioning, the extracellular volume and concentration of water and salts are maintained with extraordinary precision.

Mammalian Urinary System

The **mammalian urinary system** consists of two kidneys, two ureters, a urinary bladder, and a urethra. **Kidneys** occur in pairs in the lower back region, one to a side (Figure 27.3). In humans, each kidney is a dark red organ,

Table 27.2	Normal Balance Between Water Gain and Water Loss in Kangaroo Rats and in Humans				
Organism		Water Gain (milliliters)		Water Loss (milliliters)	
Kangaroo rat* (measured over four weeks)	Ingested in solids: Ingested as liquids: Metabolically derived:	6.0 0 54.0 60.0	Urine: Feces: Evaporation:	13.5 2.6 43.9 60.0	
Adult human** (measured on daily basis)	Ingested in solids: Ingested as liquids: Metabolically derived:	1200 1000 350 2550	Urine: Feces: Evaporation:	1500 100 950 2550	

*Data from K. Schmidt-Nielsen, *Animal Physiology*, 1975.
**Data from A. Vander et al., *Human Physiology*, 1980.

about the size of a fist. Beneath its connective tissue coat is the kidney *cortex*, a rindlike layer in which initial functional links are made with the bloodstream. The cortex lies over an inner layer, the kidney *medulla*. The inner layer is filled with collecting ducts that empty into a central cavity, the *renal pelvis*. (The word "renal" comes from the Latin *renes*, meaning kidney.)

The walls of the renal pelvis converge with a tube, the **ureter**, which empties into a fluid storage organ called the **urinary bladder**. Two ureters (one from each kidney) empty into the bladder. Fluids then leave the bladder through a single tube, the **urethra**. The urethra opens to the outside at the end of the penis (in males) or just above the vaginal orifice (in females). Figure 27.3 shows how these parts are arranged in the human urinary system.

Every twenty-four hours, about 180 liters (190 quarts) of fluid filters from the blood through tubules in the paired human kidneys. On the average, only 1.5 liters actually leave the body through the urethra. The rest of the filtered fluid is taken back (reabsorbed) into the bloodstream. The fluid destined for discharge is called **urine**. It consists of water, salts, nitrogen-containing wastes (mainly urea), and substances the body cannot metabolize. These substances include excess vitamins and drugs such as penicillin.

Urine is a cell-free filtrate of blood to which some solutes are added and from which other solutes are removed.

As you have probably noticed, the human way of life would be somewhat hampered by an incessant dribbling of urine. Built-in controls exist over urine discharge. As a urinary bladder fills, tension increases in its strong, smooth-muscled walls. The increased tension triggers a reflex relaxation of sphincter muscles located at the upper ends of the urethra. At the same time, it triggers a coordinated contraction of the bladder walls. The contractions force fluid through the urethra. This response, called **urination**, is basically involuntary. However, the reflex discharge of fluid can be consciously inhibited by neural commands. This capacity for control emerges during early childhood development, when the cerebral cortex is developed enough to monitor signals from stretch receptors located in bladder walls. Despite the urgent promptings of some parents who don't know better, this maturation does not occur until children are about two years old.

Kidney Function

The basic functional unit of the kidney is a tubular structure called the **nephron**. In the human kidney, more than a million nephrons lie side by side, perpendicular to the surface. Blood from renal arteries makes its first functional contact with nephrons in the kidney cortex. Here, the nephron walls balloon outward and form a cup around a set of blood capillaries (Figure 27.3c). The capillary cluster is called a **glomerulus**. The nephron cup is known as **Bowman's capsule**.

The nephron is not open at its cupped beginning. Rather, Bowman's capsule is like a tennis ball that has been punched in on one side. From this capsule, the nephron walls become highly coiled. This part of the nephron is called the **proximal tubule**. From here, the tubular walls plunge down into the medulla, form a sharp loop, then shoot back up. The entire hairpin structure is the **loop of Henle**. At the end of the loop, the nephron becomes highly coiled again. This coiled part of the nephron is the **distal tubule**. The nephron finally straightens out and merges into a collecting duct (as do many neighboring nephrons). Collecting ducts join with even larger ducts, which eventually empty into the renal pelvis.

Blood travels from the renal artery, into arterioles, then into the glomerular capillaries. These capillaries do not then merge into veins. Rather, they merge into arterioles—which divide into a *second* set of blood capillaries, known as the **peritubular capillaries**. In nephrons that are positioned almost entirely in the cortex, peritubular capillaries thread profusely around the proximal tubule, the loop of Henle, and the distal tubule. From there, the peritubular capillaries merge into veins that lead away from the kidney.

The nephron and its associated capillaries form a functional unit in which three processes occur:

1. *Glomerular filtration:* a bulk flow of essentially protein-free plasma from glomerulus capillaries into Bowman's capsule.

2. *Tubular reabsorption:* passive transport of water, active and passive transport of solutes out of the nephron and into peritubular capillaries.

3. *Tubular secretion:* active and passive transport of solutes (especially hydrogen and potassium ions) from peritubular capillaries into the nephron.

In **filtration**, all the components of blood except blood cells and most proteins can move across the one-cell-thick capillary epithelium, then across the one-cell-thick capsule epithelium, and into Bowman's capsule. From there, the filtrate passes into the nephron tubule. At any given time, about one-fifth of the water and other noncellular components of blood are filtered. Active transport is not involved; filtration is an entirely passive event. What, then, causes the movement? Hydrostatic pressure in the glomerulus (created by heart contractions) is greater in capillaries than the fluid pressure in the tubule. The pressure drives out a certain amount of fluid and solutes from the blood. The proteins being left behind in the bloodstream do create an osmotic pressure gradient in the opposite direction. Even so, water and solute flow out of the glomerular capillaries is about a hundred times greater than it is in the systemic circulation. Thus, *the relatively high pressure difference across the glomerulus is the reason why kidneys can filter an astonishing volume of fluid each day.*

During **reabsorption**, about ninety-nine percent of the water and most of the solutes that entered the nephron are returned to the bloodstream. As the filtrate flows along the nephron, selective reabsorption rapidly alters its composition. For instance, sodium ions are actively transported across the proximal tubule walls and into interstitial fluid. Chloride ions, being oppositely charged, are attracted by the positively charged sodium ions and passively follow them in the same direction. On the average, seventy-five percent of the sodium and chloride present in the filtrate leaves the proximal tubule. The outward solute movement sets up an osmotic gradient, and water passively moves out. The solutes and water flow into capillaries surrounding the

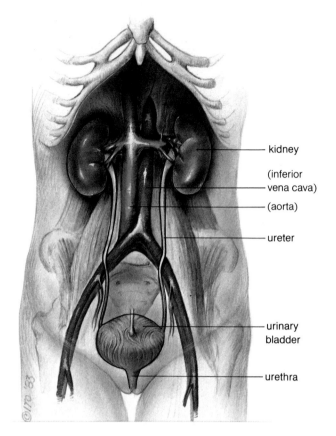

a Human urinary system

kidney

(inferior vena cava)

(aorta)

ureter

urinary bladder

urethra

tubule. Thus, *although water reabsorption into capillaries is a bulk flow process, water is reabsorbed only because solutes are reabsorbed first.*

Some substances appear in urine in greater amounts than were filtered into the nephron. They are actively transported from the peritubular capillaries into the nephron tubule, an event known as **tubular secretion**. These substances include potassium and hydrogen ions, penicillin and other drugs, and some toxic substances (such as pesticides). They include many metabolic wastes, such as uric acid (from nucleic acid breakdown), creatinine (released during ATP formation in muscle cells), and assorted products of hemoglobin breakdown.

Filtration, reabsorption, and secretion in the nephron/capillary unit of the kidney determines the ultimate composition and volume of urine. Hence they influence how much water and solutes the body conserves.

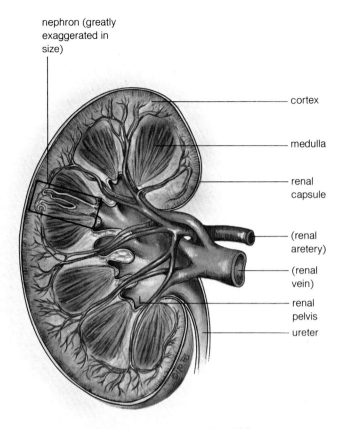

nephron (greatly exaggerated in size)

cortex

medulla

renal capsule

(renal aretery)

(renal vein)

renal pelvis

ureter

b Kidney, as if sliced lengthwise down the middle

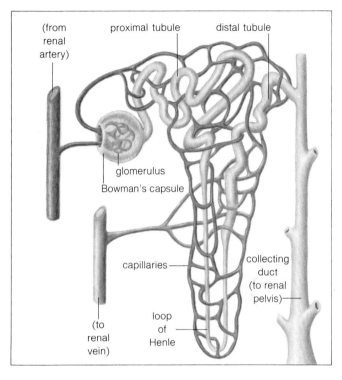

(from renal artery)

proximal tubule

distal tubule

glomerulus

Bowman's capsule

capillaries

collecting duct (to renal pelvis)

(to renal vein)

loop of Henle

c

Controls Over Fluid Volume and Composition

The volume and composition of extracellular fluid are under homeostatic control. Through these controls, adjustments are possible when changes in diet, muscular activity, and metabolic activity alter body fluid volume and composition.

Any increase or decrease in water volume automatically affects solute concentrations. The more water there is, the less concentrated salts become. Thus homeostatic controls over water intake and output can regulate solute levels. Two interrelated mechanisms are at work here. One is hormonal action that influences the amount of water excreted in urine; the other is a thirst mechanism that influences water intake. The hypothalamus helps govern both.

The hypothalamus contains a nerve cell cluster that is sensitive to concentrations of sodium and some other solutes in blood. When solute concentrations rise (or when blood volume drops), these cells become excited. Hypothalamic signals then travel to the posterior pituitary and

Figure 27.3 (**a**) Human urinary system. (**b**) One of the human kidneys, the organ concerned with regulating the amount and concentration of water and salt in extracellular fluid. (**c**) The nephron and associated capillaries—the functional unit within the kidney. The type of nephron depicted is positioned almost entirely within the kidney cortex, with only the hairpin turn of the loop of Henle extending into the medulla. In other nephrons, the proximal and distal tubules and most of the capillaries are located in the cortex, but the loop of Henle and a parallel capillary descend deep into the medulla.

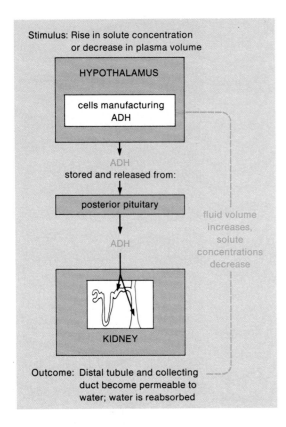

Figure 27.4 Homeostatic control over extracellular fluid volume. The hormone ADH acts on the nephron's distal convoluted tubule and the collecting duct walls, making them permeable to water. Water moves into the interstitial fluid and is reabsorbed into the bloodstream. Thus blood volume increases. The change is detected through the associated decrease in solute concentrations. Here, the blue dashed line completes the feedback loop.

trigger the release of **antidiuretic hormone**, or ADH. ("Diuresis" is a Greek word meaning urination; hence "antidiuretic" signifies that the hormone "opposes" urination. You can still urinate; the hormone only affects how much water is present in the urine.) ADH is the main hormonal agent that controls water loss, hence the volume of extracellular fluid (Figure 27.4).

When ADH is released from the posterior pituitary, it is picked up by the bloodstream and transported to the kidneys. There, ADH acts on cells of the distal tubules and collecting ducts, making them more permeable to water. With increased ADH secretion, more water is reabsorbed. As a result, urine volume decreases and its salt concentra-

tion increases. When ADH secretion is decreased, water reabsorption decreases. Hence urine volume increases and the fluid volume leaving the body is more dilute. Figures 27.4 and 27.5 illustrate these processes.

Also within the mammalian hypothalamus is a thirst center. This nerve cell cluster is stimulated at the same time that solute-concentration receptors call for ADH release. When these receptors detect a rise in solute levels (a drop in water volume), thirst center cells are stimulated into sending signals that initiate water-seeking behavior.

Aldosterone, a hormone produced and secreted by the adrenal glands, has major influence over sodium reabsorption. The kidneys themselves help control aldosterone secretion. Specialized cells lining arterioles in the kidneys produce and secrete the enzyme *renin*. This enzyme acts on a plasma protein that is produced in the liver and is always circulating, in inactive form, in the bloodstream. Renin catalyzes the removal of a polypeptide from this protein, and the fragment undergoes conversions into the hormone *angiotensin*. Angiotensin is a powerful stimulator of aldosterone secretion.

What stimulates the kidneys into secreting renin in the first place? The inputs are not fully understood. A drop in sodium levels and extracellular volume leads to a lowering of blood pressure. Baroreceptors in arterioles detect the drop in blood pressure and signal the central nervous system; from there, sympathetic nerves carry signals to the renin-secreting cells of the kidneys.

Stimulation of these cells leads to activation of the renin-angiotensin system, and aldosterone is secreted. Aldosterone acts on distal tubules and collecting ducts in the kidneys. It increases the rate of sodium reabsorption by enhancing the activity of sodium-potassium pumps found in the membranes of cells making up the tube walls.

In this manner, the renin-angiotensin system helps control sodium concentrations in the extracellular environment and, indirectly, blood pressure. Angiotensin contributes in another way to maintaining blood pressure, in that it also acts as a vasoconstrictor of arterioles. (Vasoconstriction, recall, increases arterial pressure.)

Still other factors are at work in controlling solute and water levels in the extracellular environment. For our purposes, however, the point to remember is this:

Extracellular volume and composition are regulated by hormonal action (which affects the amount of water and solutes excreted in urine) and by a thirst mechanism (which affects voluntary water intake).

COMMENTARY

Kidney Failure, Bypass Measures, and Transplants

Sometimes, kidneys no longer can perform their filtration, reabsorption, and secretion tasks. For example, atherosclerosis of blood vessels associated with the nephron can impair kidney function. As another example, salts may aggregate into "stones." Such stones can become lodged in the kidney (and ureter, bladder, or urethra), where they can alter or block urine discharge. In the United States alone, an estimated 3 million individuals suffer from some kidney disorder. And these disorders occur in all age groups.

When kidneys malfunction, plasma solute levels are disturbed. Substances such as potassium can accumulate in the bloodstream. The buildup may lead to nausea, fatigue, loss of memory and, in advanced cases, death. A kidney dialysis machine can be employed to restore the proper solute balance. It is sometimes called an artificial kidney, not because it resembles the natural organ but because its end result is the same. Concentrations of substances can be regulated by their selective addition to and removal from the bloodstream, as it is by way of the natural kidney.

The artificial kidney is based on dialysis: the separation of substances across a membrane between solutions of differing concentrations. In hemodialysis, a patient is plugged into the machine by tubes leading from an artery or vein. Blood is then pumped through narrow, coiled cellophane tubes. (Cellophane has pores of the same diameter as glomerular capillaries.) The cellophane tubes are located in a warm-water bath. The bath contains a precisely balanced mix of salts, glucose, acetate, amino acids, and other substances that set up the proper gradients with the blood flowing past. Thus, substances at too high a concentration in the patient's blood will diffuse into the dialysis fluid. On the average, hemodialysis takes about five hours. The machine does not approach the natural kidney's efficiency, and blood must circulate over and over again through the tubes. Afflicted people must be treated with the machine three times a week.

For temporary disorders, the artificial kidney is used as a bypass measure until normal kidney function resumes. For chronic kidney disease, it must be used for the remainder of the person's life, or until a functional kidney is transplanted. With treatment and with controlled diet, many are able to resume normal activity. Kidney dialysis, however, is controversial. Even after it had appeared in hospitals, hundreds died because they could not afford the treatment costs, which were then about 30,000 dollars a year. The costs are still a staggering 20,000 dollars annually, although Medicare will now pick up the tab, at taxpayers' expense. The catch is that the machines themselves are expensive to build, to maintain, and (with soaring hospital costs) to operate. Hospitals are equipped to handle only 1,000 of the 10,000 or so individuals who become stricken by kidney failure each year. Who selects the chosen few? Hospital committees—a mix of physicians, citizens, and clergy—and their task is not an enviable one.

An alternative approach is the transplantation of a living kidney into a patient. Although the surgery itself is expensive, it is far less than the costs of year after year of hemodialysis. There are problems here, too. Giving up a kidney is something that many healthy people are reluctant to do; donors are scarce. More than half the kidneys that are donated come from individuals who have died as a result of accidents. Imagine yourself in the position of a severely afflicted individual, in the ethical dilemma of waiting and half-hoping for someone else's death. Then, too, about a third of all kidney transplants induce an immune response and are rejected.

Is either the treatment or the transplantation really worth the cost? Would you ask the question if you yourself became one of the stricken—and would your answer be the same?

Figure 27.5 Urinary concentration and dilution in birds and mammals. By adjusting water content, the kidney maintains the body's total solute concentration within a narrow range. It does so even when there are large variations in fluid intake or water loss by other means (such as evaporation).

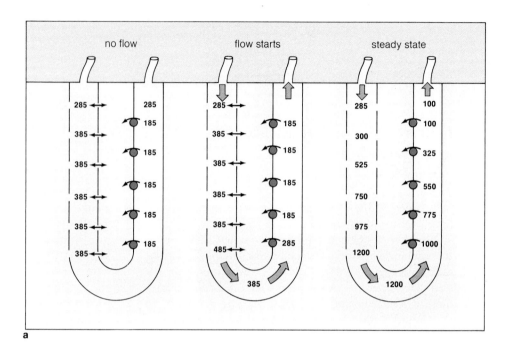

When the body's water content is high, walls of the collecting ducts in the kidney are impermeable to water, so the excess leaves the body in dilute urine. When water content is low, the hormone ADH makes the walls of the collecting ducts permeable to water. The water moves osmotically into the surrounding interstitial fluid, then back to the general circulation. When water is reclaimed, of course, the salts left behind in the ducts thereby become more concentrated in the urine.

What actually lets water leave the collecting ducts when the duct walls are made permeable? In brief, an osmotic gradient exists in the surrounding interstitial fluid. The gradient starts at the kidney cortex and extends to the base of the medulla, where solutes are most concentrated. The collecting ducts are positioned in such a way that they plunge down through the gradient. The steeper the gradient, the more water can be reclaimed (and the more concentrated urine becomes).

The concentration gradient in the kidney medulla is established partly through a process called *countercurrent multiplication*. The word *countercurrent*, recall, simply refers to a flow in opposing directions through a pair of interacting channels. This kind of flow exists between the descending and ascending limbs of the loop of Henle (the part of the kidney nephron shaped like a hairpin). The word *multiplication* refers to a cumulative transfer of solutes from the ascending limb to the descending limb as fluid moves through them both.

An analysis of this transfer is shown in (**a**). The descending limb is permeable to water and sodium chloride (NaCl). The ascending limb is impermeable to both—but it contains pumps that can actively transport sodium chloride into the interstitial fluid. Suppose that fluid entering the descending limb has a solute concentration of 285 mosm, the same as that of the surrounding interstitial fluid. (The abbreviation *mosm* stands for *milliosmoles*, a unit used in measuring the sum of the concentrations of solutes in a liter of solution). First imagine what would happen in the absence of flow: Sodium chloride would be actively transported out of the ascending limb, thereby *decreasing* the solute concentration in the second half of the

loop. The expelled sodium chloride would diffuse through the interstitial fluid and into the first half of the loop, thereby *increasing* the solute concentration in those two regions.

Now imagine what would happen if flow starts through the nephron: The more concentrated fluid in the descending limb would move around the bend. The pumps would reduce the incoming salt concentrations in the ascending limb—but their action simultaneously would raise the salt concentrations in the interstitial fluid and the descending limb. In a kidney, flow does not stop and start but is continuous; urine flow and the sodium chloride pump together maintain a 200-mosm difference between the two limbs of the nephron. Thus the solute concentration progressively increases from 285 to 1200 mosm from the cortex to the medulla, in both the interstitial fluid and the descending limb.

As shown in (**b**), ADH acting on the collecting ducts allows the urine to lose water to the increasingly salty interstitial fluid, and urine as concentrated as 1200 mosm is produced. In the absence of ADH, the dilute urine produced in the ascending limb of the nephron loses some solute by active reabsorption in distal tubules. But otherwise it moves relatively unchanged through the collecting ducts. Urine as dilute as 65 mosm can leave the kidneys.

One more point can be made here. The interstitial fluid bathes not only the nephron and collecting ducts; it also bathes the peritubular capillaries, which include a special branch around the loop of Henle. The walls of these capillaries are permeable to water and salts, so blood in these capillaries quickly comes to equilibrium with the concentrated surroundings. If high solute concentrations were to remain in the blood, solutes would be carried away and the osmotic gradient in the kidney medulla would soon disappear. However, a *countercurrent exchange* mechanism occurs here. As the capillaries loop back toward the cortex, solutes diffuse out of them, following the gradient into increasingly dilute regions of the interstitial fluid. The effect of this exchange is shown in (**b**).

Thus three processes maintain the osmotic gradient necessary for the concentration of urine:

1. Countercurrent multiplication at the loop of Henle
2. Adjustments in urine concentration at the collecting ducts
3. Countercurrent exchange at the peritubular capillaries

(Modified by William Harvey, Temple University, from Gottschalk and Lassiter, 1980)

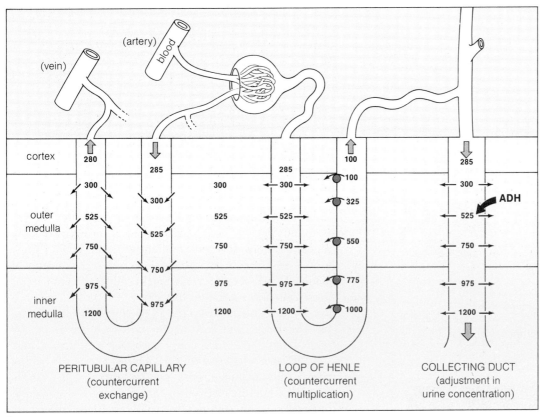

cortex

outer medulla

inner medulla

PERITUBULAR CAPILLARY
(countercurrent exchange)

LOOP OF HENLE
(countercurrent multiplication)

ADH

COLLECTING DUCT
(adjustment in urine concentration)

b

(**a**) Simplified picture of countercurrent multiplication in the loop of Henle. Numbers indicate total solute concentration in milliosmoles. Fluid in the descending limb is in osmotic equilibrium with the surrounding interstitial fluid. Blue circles on the ascending limb represent sodium chloride pumps, which are active transport systems. (**b**) Urine concentration in the loop of Henle.

Readings

Bartholomew, G. 1977. "Body Temperature and Energy Metabolism." In *Animal Physiology: Principles and Adaptations* by M. Gordon et al. Third edition. New York: Macmillan. Excellent introduction to thermal regulation in animals.

Merrill, J. 1961. "The Artificial Kidney." *Scientific American* 205(1): 56–64.

Prosser, C. 1973. *Comparative Animal Physiology*. Third edition. Philadelphia: Saunders.

Smith, H. 1961. *From Fish to Philosopher*. New York: Doubleday. Available in paperback.

Vander, A., J. Sherman, and D. Luciano. 1980. "Regulation of Water and Electrolyte Balance." In *Human Physiology: Mechanisms of Body Function*. Third edition. New York: McGraw-Hill. Excellent introduction to renal functioning.

Review Questions

1. Define ectotherm and endotherm. In endotherms, what controls help balance the amount of heat lost and heat gained?

2. In your own body, where are thermoreceptors and the main center of temperature control located?

3. All animals have mechanisms for maintaining body fluid concentration and composition. In your own body, which organs cooperate in these tasks? How does a nephron in your kidney resemble an earthworm nephridium?

4. Describe what happens during (a) filtration, (b) reabsorption, and (c) secretion in the kidney's nephron/capillary unit. What do these three processes influence?

5. Most exchanges between blood capillaries and nephrons are obligatory, but the final urine concentration is under complete homeostatic control. What two interrelated mechanisms act as the controls?

With a full-throated croak that only a female of its kind could find seductive, a male frog proclaims the onset of warm spring rains, of ponds, of sex in the night. By August the summer sun will have parched the earth, and his pond dominion will be gone. But tonight is the hour of the frog! Through the dark, a female moves toward the irresistibly vocal male. They meet, they dally; he clamps his forelegs about her swollen abdomen and gives it a prolonged squeeze. Out streams a ribbon of thousands of eggs. While eggs are being released, the male expels a milky cloud of swimming sperm. Each egg accepts and joins with a single sperm. Not long afterward, the sperm nucleus and egg nucleus fuse. With this event a zygote is formed, and fertilization is completed.

28

PRINCIPLES OF REPRODUCTION AND DEVELOPMENT

For the leopard frog *Rana pipiens,* a drama now begins to unfold that has been reenacted each spring, with only minor variations, for many millions of years. Within a few hours after fertilization, the single-celled zygote begins to divide into two, then four, then eight cells, and many more. These cells form a multicelled embryo. The frog embryo does not increase in size during this cleavage. Instead, the cells become smaller and smaller with each successive division. After twenty-one hours, there is a ball of tiny cells.

And now cells embark on a course of migrations, shape changes, and interactions that will lead to a specific embryonic shape. On the embryo surface, a dimple forms where some cells begin sinking inward. From these migrating cells, internal tissue layers will arise. A groove forms along one side of the surface, and the embryo elongates in the direction of the groove. The groove deepens, then the edges fold over and seal, forming a hollow tube. From the tube, a nervous system will form. Now eyes begin to form on the developing head. Within the trunk, a heart is forming and will soon beat rhythmically. Fins take shape; a mouth forms. These developments, appearing as they do at different points in time, speak of a process going on in *all* the cells that were so recently developed from a single zygote. They are becoming different from one another in appearance and in function!

Within twelve days after fertilization, the embryo has become transformed into a tadpole, a larval stage that can swim on its own. For the first time it feeds itself—and it begins to grow. For many months the larva grows until, in response to hormonal cues, it enters a new developmental stage. Its body now changes into the adult form. Legs grow from the body. The tail becomes shorter and shorter, then disappears. The small mouth, once suitable for feeding on algae, develops jaws that accommodate insects and worms. Eventually a full-fledged frog leaves the water for life on land. If it is lucky it will avoid hungry predators, bacterial

Hans Pfletschinger

Figure 28.1 A male frog clasping the female in a behavior called amplexus. As the female releases eggs into the surrounding water, the male releases sperm over the eggs.

attacks, and other threats through the many months ahead. With another spring it may find a pond, swollen with the warm waters of the new season's rains, and the hour of the frog will be upon us again.

Watching the promise of the zygote unfold into the reality of the adult, it is difficult not to view development as one of life's greatest mysteries. *How does a simple-looking zygote become transformed into all the specialized cells and structures of the adult body of a complex animal?* Chapter Fourteen surveyed the kinds of gene regulation studies that may help reveal the answers to this question. Here, we will turn to the actual transformations that occur from the time of reproduction to the emergence of the adult form.

THE BEGINNING: REPRODUCTIVE MODES

Chapter Nine described the cellular basis of **sexual reproduction**, which requires the fusion of the nuclei of two (or more) gametes to produce a new individual. It also described the cellular basis of **asexual reproduction**, whereby gametes are not required in the production of offspring. Here we will look at some of the structural, behavioral, and ecological adaptations associated with both kinds of reproductive modes.

Asexual Reproduction

Asexual reproduction occurs among some of the structurally simple invertebrates. The modes of asexual reproduction are fission and budding. In animal **fission**, the entire body of the parent divides into two roughly equivalent parts, with each part then growing into a whole individual. The division plane can be transverse or longitudinal. For example, some flatworms reproduce through transverse fission.

Hydra and some other cnidarians rely on **budding**, whereby the new individual develops as an outgrowth of the parent body. The bud from the parent body begins differentiating into a separate set of organs, then breaks away. *Hydra* reproduces through external budding from the parent body surface. Freshwater sponges produce internal buds called *gemmules*. Each gemmule develops into a separate individual when the parent body disintegrates.

As intriguing as fission and budding may be, neither reproductive mode promotes genetic variability. The offspring are clones (genetically identical copies of the parents). Cloning is advantageous only so long as the parents are highly adapted to the surroundings, and only so long

as the surroundings remain stable. When stability prevails, asexual reproduction is what you might call biologically inexpensive, for progeny can be produced without much energy outlay.

But most animals live in changing and unpredictable environments. Not surprisingly, most of them—and this includes cnidarians, sea stars, crabs, and lizards—depend on sex as the basic mode of reproduction.

Sexual Reproduction

Most commonly, sexual reproduction in animals is accomplished through fusion of gametes from a male parent and a female parent. However, sex is not always as straightforward as the male-frog-meets-female-frog example opening this chapter. **Parthenogenesis** refers to the cleavage and subsequent differentiation of an *unfertilized* egg into an adult. Every so often, between times of sexual reproduction, beetles and aphids produce fatherless offspring. For these arthropods, a sperm is not the only stimulus that can prod an egg into developing. Changes in pH, temperature, salinity, even mechanical stimulation of the egg can trigger parthenogenesis. They can do so not only in insects but also in rotifers, frogs, salamanders, turkeys and, in one experiment, rabbits. (Weak, sterile female rabbits were produced, but they were rabbits nevertheless.)

Or consider the earthworm and the parasitic tapeworm. Each of these animals has *both* male and female reproductive organs. Each produces both sperm and eggs. They are **hermaphrodites**. Two earthworms lie head to tail and exchange sperm, thereby cross-fertilizing each other. Parasitic tapeworms can fertilize themselves. One need not look askance at tapeworms, when one realizes that these animals can end up living all by themselves somewhere in tissues of a host animal. Given the bountiful supply of resources and the protected habitat, hermaphrodism does have its advantages for the lone parasite.

Animal reproductive strategies range from asexual processes, through development of unfertilized eggs into adults, through self-fertilization, to sexual reproduction between separate male and female forms.

Some Strategic Problems in Having Separate Sexes

Complete separation into male and female sexes imposes its own biologically expensive demands. After all, how is

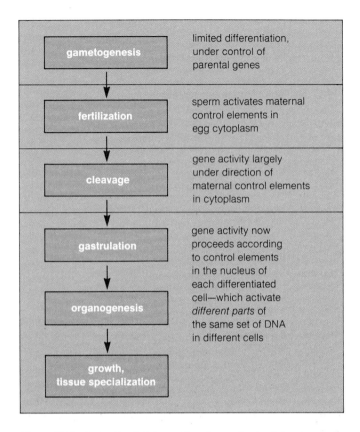

gametogenesis	limited differentiation, under control of parental genes
fertilization	sperm activates maternal control elements in egg cytoplasm
cleavage	gene activity largely under direction of maternal control elements in cytoplasm
gastrulation	gene activity now proceeds according to control elements in the nucleus of each differentiated cell—which activate *different parts* of the same set of DNA in different cells
organogenesis	
growth, tissue specialization	

Figure 28.2 Generalized picture of the stages of animal development. The same general pattern of gene activity applies to the development of complex, sexually reproducing plants. (Plant cells don't undergo gastrulation, and organ formation, growth, and tissue specialization continue through the plant life cycle.)

fertilization to be accomplished? All sorts of structural and behavioral adaptations surround the task of getting sperm from one individual to the egg of another.

In behavioral terms, male and female reproductive cycles must be *synchronous,* so that mature gametes are released at the same time. Synchrony requires complex hormonal control mechanisms and sensory receptors that detect such stimuli as lengthening days and other environmental cues. There must be some means by which males and females recognize each other as being of the same species, so energy outlays are necessary for constructing such structural signals as bright feathers and for performing courtship routines.

In structural terms, getting sperm and egg together is not too complicated among some water-dwelling animals such as sea urchins and frogs. Their gametes are simply released into the water, and the motile sperm can bump into an egg. Such *external* fertilization would be somewhat chancy if only one sperm and one egg were constructed and released each season. So there are more energy outlays, for the production of large numbers of sperm and eggs—outlays that enhance the probability of one gamete contacting another in the water.

In contrast, nearly all land-dwelling animals and even some aquatic forms depend on *internal* fertilization. Obviously, sperm released on dry land do not stand much of a chance of swimming over to an egg. Males of these animal species have ducts associated with reproductive organs called **testes**, which assure that sperm can be stored and nourished in a hospitable setting, then transferred via the duct to the female body. Thus many male animals have a **penis**, a copulatory organ at the end of the sperm duct. From this male organ, sperm are ejected into the female's **vagina**, a specialized duct between the outside world and the **ovary** (an organ where female gametes mature). Reptiles, birds, mammals—all have reproductive structures that enhance the probability of successful internal fertilization, and that protect sperm and eggs from harsh external conditions. Examples of these structures are described in Chapters Twenty-Nine and Thirty-Four.

Another problem to consider: how is the fertilized egg to be nourished? All animal eggs contain **yolk** (protein, lipids, and other nutritive substances), but some eggs contain more yolk than others. For example, sea urchin eggs are released from the parent's body and develop to a feeding stage within forty hours after fertilization. They do not require much yolk, and sea urchin eggs contain little of it. In contrast, bird eggs are mostly yolk; the cytoplasm and nucleus look like a thin cap on top of the yolk. Bird eggs are released from the mother's body but require more developmental time than do sea urchin eggs. Human eggs have very little yolk—but then, they are retained in the mother's body. The developing embryo quickly attaches to the mother's body and receives nourishment directly from her tissues.

The point of these limited examples is that tremendous diversity exists in reproductive and developmental strategies. However, some patterns are widespread through the animal kingdom, and these patterns will serve as the framework for the discussions to follow.

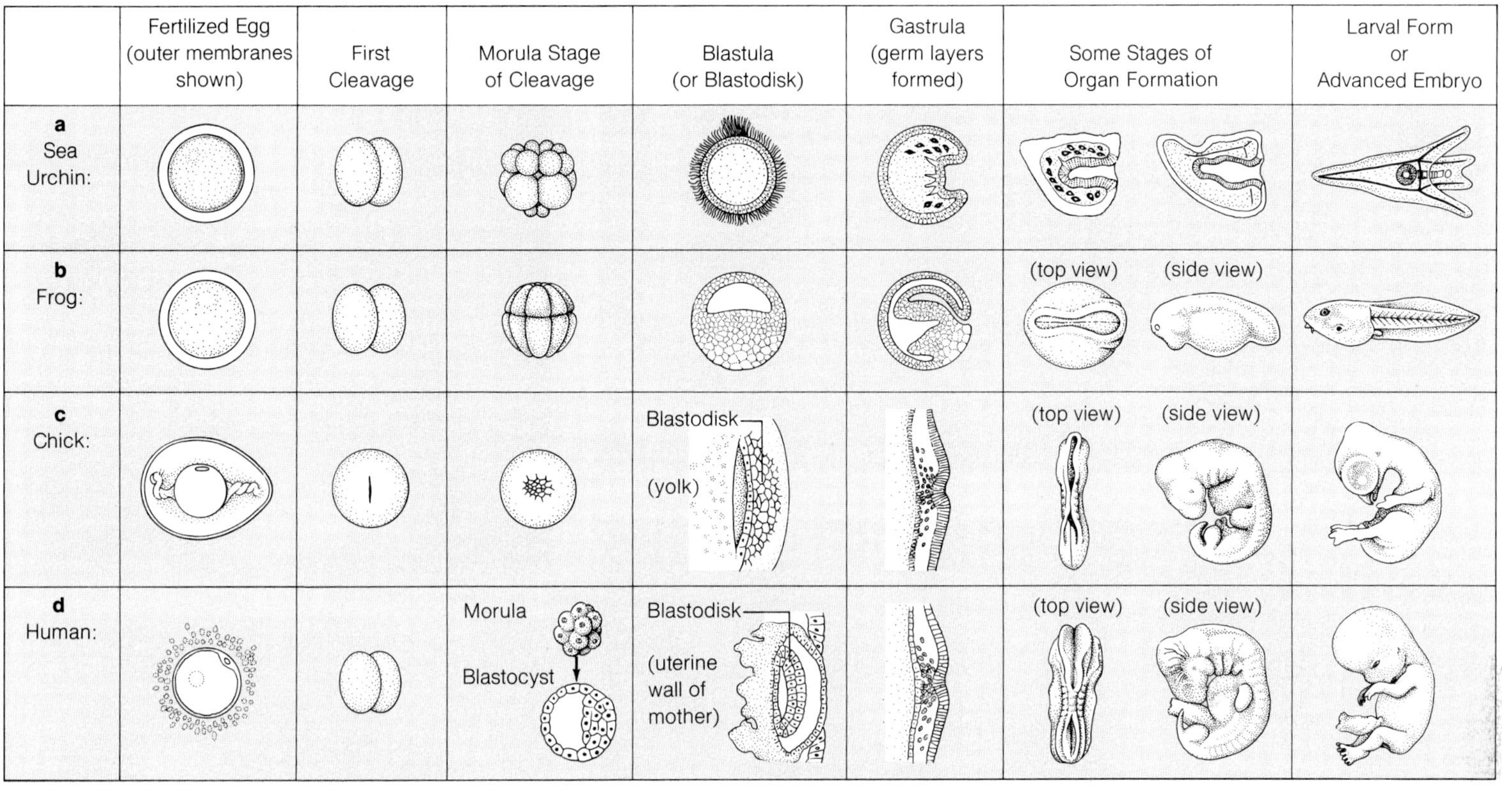

	Fertilized Egg (outer membranes shown)	First Cleavage	Morula Stage of Cleavage	Blastula (or Blastodisk)	Gastrula (germ layers formed)	Some Stages of Organ Formation		Larval Form or Advanced Embryo
a Sea Urchin:								
b Frog:						(top view)	(side view)	
c Chick:				Blastodisk (yolk)		(top view)	(side view)	
d Human:			Morula Blastocyst	Blastodisk (uterine wall of mother)		(top view)	(side view)	

Figure 28.3 Comparison of embryonic development in four different animals. The drawings are not to the same scale; however, they show the developmental patterns that are common to all four types. For clarity, the membranes surrounding the embryo are not shown from cleavage onward. Blastula and gastrula stages are shown in cross-section; they are described in more detail in this chapter and the next for frogs, birds, and humans. (Adapted from R. G. Ham and M. J. Veomett, *Mechanisms of Development*, C. V. Mosby Co., 1980)

STAGES OF EARLY EMBRYONIC DEVELOPMENT

Figures 28.2 and 28.3 show the stages through which development commonly proceeds. In the broadest sense, **gametogenesis** (gamete formation) is the first stage of animal development. During this time, sperm and egg form and mature within the parent reproductive system (Chapter Nine). Sperm get decked out with a motile structure that will help move their DNA to an egg. In contrast, rich stores of substances become assembled in localized regions of the egg cytoplasm.

The second developmental stage is triggered by sperm penetration into an egg. This stage, called **fertilization**, is completed when sperm and egg nuclei fuse. In **cleavage**, the third stage of animal development, the fertilized egg undergoes mitotic cell divisions that form the early embryo.

Gastrulation is the fourth stage of animal development. An elaborate process of cell migrations leads to the formation of two or more primary *germ layers*: regionally positioned layers of cells that will give rise to all organs of the animal body. In many species, the body axis of the embryo is established during gastrulation.

Once germ layers have formed, cell differentiation and changes in form produce all major organs. This is **organogenesis**, the fifth developmental stage. **Growth and tissue specialization**, the stage when organs acquire their specialized structural and chemical properties, continues past the time of birth.

a

b

c

d

Where do all of these developmental stages take place? The location varies, depending on the species. *Oviparous* animals release eggs into the environment; embryonic development and birth proceed apart from the mother's body. Some oviparous animals show protective behavior toward the more or less vulnerable eggs, and others do not (Figure 28.4). *Viviparous* animals retain the fertilized egg inside the body and nourish it directly from maternal tissues until giving birth. Most mammals are viviparous. In between are animals—some fishes, lizards, and a few snakes—that are *ovoviviparous.* Although the egg develops within and is hatched live from the mother's body, the sole nourishment comes from the yolk.

Egg Formation and the Onset of Gene Control

Figure 28.3 compared a few embryos at different stages of development. Let's look at the central events of these stages, especially as they occur in frog embryos (Figure 28.5).

Early developmental stages are not under the direct control of genes in the embryonic cell nucleus. Rather, they are governed by control elements that were already present in the egg cytoplasm before fertilization. What is the genetic nature of messages harbored in the egg? Some information has been gathered from studies of different animal groups. During gamete formation in the female frog, the immature egg cell (oocyte) increases many thousands of times in vol-

Wisniewski / ZEFA

Jean-Paul Ferrero / Ardea, London

g

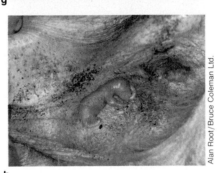

Jack Dermid

Alan Root / Bruce Coleman Ltd.

f

h

Figure 28.4 Examples of diversity in egg development. (**a**) Copperheads are among the few ovoviviparous snakes. Eggs develop in the mother's body but derive all nourishment from yolk. Here, liveborn copperheads are still contained in the relics of egg sacs. (**b**) Alligators are oviparous. Eggs with large yolk reserves are released from and develop outside the mother's body. The mother is highly protective of both the eggs and the offspring.(**c**) Snails also are oviparous but are not doting parents. The eggs are left unprotected.

(**d**) Monotremes, including the duckbilled platypus, are unique among mammals. The females are oviparous, in that they lay eggs that develop outside the body. Yet the females secrete milk (as do other mammals), which nourishes the juvenile form. (**e**) Birds show oviparity: Eggs with large yolk reserves are released from and develop outside the body. The hatchlings depend on parental feeding and protection.

The opossum (**f**) and kangaroo (**g**), both marsupials, are viviparous. However, their young emerge in somewhat unfinished form and undergo further fetal development in a pouch on the ventral surface of the mother's body, where they are nourished from mammary nipples. (**h**) Young kangaroo in pouch.

ume (Chapter Nine). Ribosomes, Golgi complexes, and endoplasmic reticulum required in protein synthesis are being stockpiled, as are mitochondria that will rapidly produce the ATP used to drive the synthesis reactions.

Even while the oocyte is growing, tremendous amounts of RNA are being transcribed from the maternal DNA. At least, a large pool of RNA transcripts can be detected at this time in the oocytes of some species (Chapter Fourteen). Many transcripts are translated at once into proteins such as histones, which will be used in DNA replication during the first embryonic divisions. Other transcripts become attached to ribosomes in different cytoplasmic regions, and there they remain inactive. These RNA transcripts are **maternal messages** that are activated at fertilization. Apparently, maternal messages direct the initial events of development.

The distribution of all these substances in the oocyte is not random. When the oocyte undergoes meiosis (Chapter Nine), the nucleus moves to one end of the cell and other cell components become arranged at the other. This positioning of the nucleus establishes **polarity** in the oocyte and, later, in the mature egg. The term means that there is

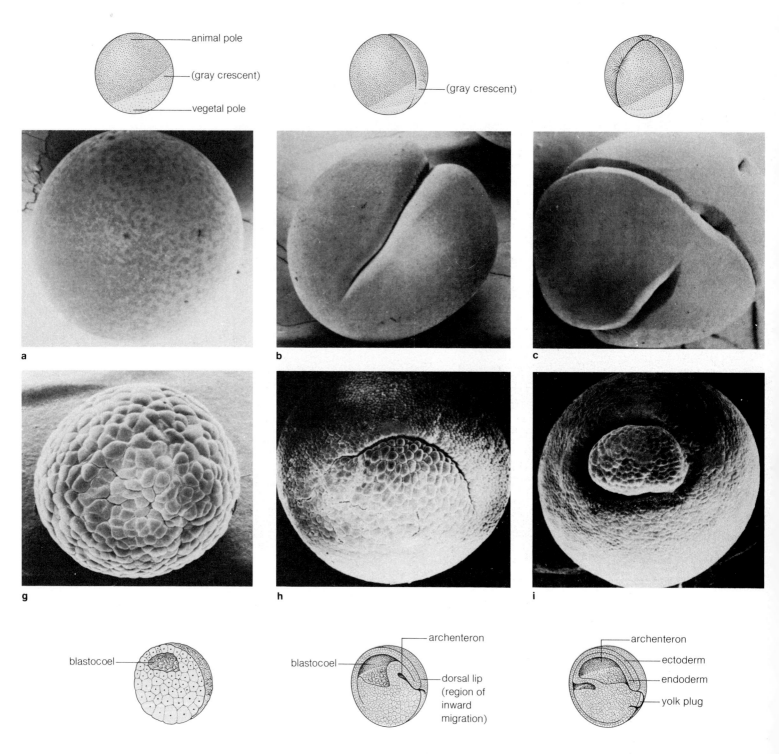

Figure 28.5 Early embryonic development of a frog. For these scanning electron micrographs, the jellylike layer surrounding the egg has been removed. (**a**) Within about an hour after fertilization, a region of differentiated surface cytoplasm (gray crescent) appears opposite the site where the sperm penetrated the egg. (**b-g**) Cleavage leads to a blastula, a ball of cells in which a cavity (blastocoel) has appeared. (**h,i**) Major cell movements and

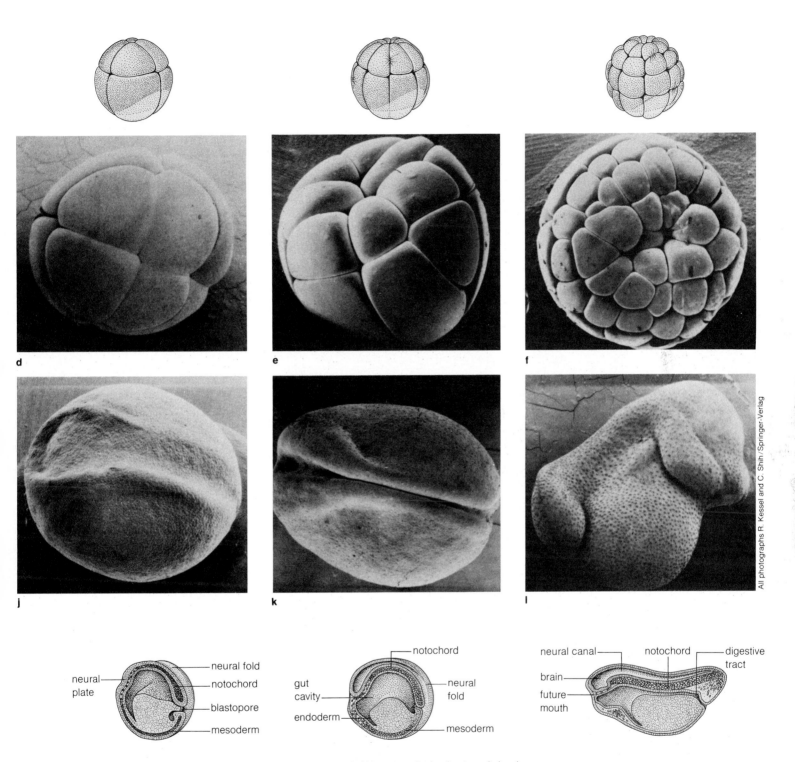

neural fold
neural plate
notochord
blastopore
mesoderm

notochord
gut cavity
endoderm
neural fold
mesoderm

neural canal
brain
future mouth
notochord
digestive tract

rearrangements occur during gastrulation. Tissue layers form; a primitive gut cavity (archenteron) develops. **(j,k)** Neural developments now take place, and a coelom, the fluid-filled body cavity in which vital organs will be suspended, appears. **(l)** Differentiation proceeds, moving the embryo on its way to becoming a functional larval form.

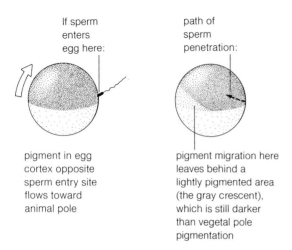

Figure 28.6 Gray crescent formation in the eggs of some amphibians.

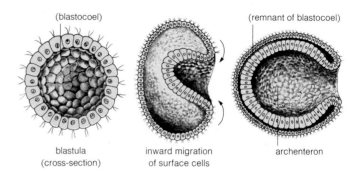

Figure 28.7 Inward migration of surface cells during gastrulation in *Amphioxus*. (After C. Hickman, Jr. et al., *Integrated Principles of Zoology*, 1979)

unequal distribution of cell components with respect to the two poles and the axis between them. The pole closest to the nucleus is the *animal pole*. Opposite is the *vegetal pole*, where substances such as yolk accumulate. All animal eggs show some form of polarity.

Polarization is the unequal distribution of structures and substances in the oocyte (and mature egg), including RNA transcripts of the maternal DNA. This unequal distribution is the initial determinant in the structural patterning of the embryo.

Visible Changes in Amphibian Eggs at Fertilization

Sperm penetration into the egg triggers fertilization. It sets in motion morphological and chemical activity within the egg cytoplasm. You can observe indirect signs of this activity in amphibian eggs. These eggs contain dark pigment granules in the egg cortex (which includes the plasma membrane and the cytoplasm just beneath it). In these eggs, pigment is concentrated more at the animal pole, which thereby appears darker than the vegetal pole. When a sperm penetrates the egg, elements of the cytoplasmic lattice (Chapter Four) cause pigment granules to flow toward the animal pole, then rotate with respect to the more yolky internal cytoplasm. The outcome is a **gray crescent,**

an area of intermediate pigmentation near the equator on the side of the egg opposite the sperm penetration site (Figure 28.6). In these eggs, the gray crescent is a visible marker of the site where the body axis will be established and where gastrulation will begin.

Cleavage: Carving Up Cytoplasmic Controls

Cleavage is a period of embryonic cell division without growth in size. The division products occupy the same volume as the original zygote. Most genes in the nucleus are known to be inactive during cleavage. Yet there are differences in cell activity at this stage. Some cells become flattened, some are rearranged; communication is established between them. Microvilli and ridges appear, with their number and shape depending on the cell's location in the embryo. As you will read shortly, we do not know what causes such differences in cell activity during cleavage. Whatever hypothesis is advanced will have to account for this apparent fact:

The destiny of cell lineages is in part established according to which sector of the egg cytoplasm is inherited by the first embryonic cells formed during cleavage.

The amount of yolk present in the eggs of different animal species influences cleavage patterns. When little yolk is present (as in mammalian eggs), cleavage planes pass completely through the egg, and all the newly divided cells are about the same size. Amphibian eggs are about one-half to three-fourths yolk, which is concentrated near the vegetal pole. Cleavage is more rapid at the opposite pole, as Figures 28.5d through 28.5f suggest. The eggs of reptiles, birds, and most fish have so much yolk that cleavage is "incomplete." It is restricted to the tiny, caplike region at the animal pole, near the egg surface (Figure 28.3c).

In early cleavage, the newly divided cells are spherical and form a solid mass of cells. Together they look more or less like a mulberry. At this stage, the embryo is a **morula** (Latin for mulberry). As cleavage proceeds, though, cell-to-cell adhesion increases and a true epithelium forms. In most animals, the epithelium is in the form of a hollow sphere, called a **blastula**. (The cavity it creates is the *blastocoel*.) In animals with abundantly yolky eggs, the epithelium has no room to form a sphere. In such eggs, the epithelium is in the form of a **blastodisk**: two flattened layers with a thin blastocoel between (Figure 28.3c).

In mammalian eggs, the outermost morula cells eventually form a surface epithelium. The epithelial layer will give rise to embryonic membranes, which will attach the embryo to the mother's uterus and which will mediate the entry of nutrients derived from her tissues. The mass of inner cells will give rise to the embryo itself. By late cleavage, a cavity appears inside the morula. Fluid moves inside the cavity and lifts the inner cell mass away from the surface layer on all but one side (Figure 28.3d). At this stage, the mammalian embryo is known as a **blastocyst**. In the next chapter, you will read more about the fate of the blastocyst during the course of human embryonic development.

Gastrulation: When Embryonic Controls Take Over

At the end of cleavage, the pace of cell division slows. Now cells and cell groups begin movements that dramatically change the structure of the embryo, even though there is little (if any) growth in size. Concentric tissue layers and the main body axis are established. Following cleavage, gene activity in the individual cells transcends the controls exerted by the maternal system. Transcription and translation proceed according to control elements in the nucleus of each cell, and different DNA regions are activated. Many new kinds of proteins, not present in the unfertilized egg, can now be detected in different cells. This stage of active cell movement and the onset of variable gene activity is known as **gastrulation**. The embryonic structure produced is the **gastrula**.

To understand this activity, think about the structural organization of animals. With few exceptions, most ingest food into a gut cavity; they have an internal layer of cells, tissues, and organs that function in digestion and absorption. All animals have a surface tissue layer that protects internal parts, and that has specialized areas for sensing and responding to environmental conditions. Except for sponges, jellyfishes, and their kin, all animals have a layer of tissues in between the other two. Here are tissues of many internal organ systems, such as those concerned with movement, support, and blood circulation. The three tissue layers are arranged concentrically and are referred to in this way:

endoderm	*inner layer; gives rise to lung epithelium, inner lining of gut, and accessory glands*
mesoderm	*intermediate layer; gives rise to muscle, the organs of circulation, reproduction, and excretion, most of the internal skeleton, and connective tissue layers of the gut and the body covering*
ectoderm	*surface layer; gives rise to nervous system and outer layer of body covering*

During gastrulation, the ball or disk of cells produced through cleavages is transformed into the three-layered organization typical of most animals. Commonly, groups of surface cells migrate to the interior, where some form the lining of an internal cavity. This cavity, the **archenteron**, will develop into the gastrointestinal tract. Figures 28.5 and 28.7 show how the archenteron forms in frogs and in *Amphioxus* (a marine invertebrate). Some inward-migrating cells are destined to become endodermal regions; others, mesodermal regions.

Organ Formation

Figure 28.8 shows the profound changes in a chick embryo during the first five days after fertilization. The details are not meant to be memorized. Rather, they are intended only to illustrate the magnitude of progressive developmental changes that lead to organ formation. The mechanisms by which organs actually form are not fully understood. In the remainder of this chapter, we will consider a few experiments and studies that tell us something about what is going on.

MORPHOGENESIS AND GROWTH

It is one thing to ask how a bone cell becomes different from a muscle cell or red blood cell. It is another thing to ask how one bone becomes different from all other bones. Consider that all the bones in your hand and arm are practically identical in molecular composition—yet they differ in size, shape, and arrangement. How do such differences arise in different clusters of cells, all of which are committed to making bone? The main processes involved are cell division, cell enlargement, changes in cell shape, local cell movements, differential growth in local body regions, and controlled cell death. These processes are the basis of **morphogenesis**: the growth, shaping, and arrangement of body parts according to predefined patterns. The extent, direction, and rate of morphogenesis depend on genetic as well as environmental controls. These controls are so interwoven that no one has yet detailed what goes on even in a single cell type that takes part in morphogenesis!

Growth Patterns

During embryonic development, overall growth requires an increase in cell number and cell size. These increases are influenced by genetic and environmental factors, such as diet. They are also governed by hormones. In vertebrates, hormones released from the pituitary, thyroid, adrenal glands, and gonads stimulate division in target cell populations. For example, thyroid hormones and growth hormone interact and stimulate normal growth and maturation in most body regions. As another example, when the diet is rich in carbohydrates, the pancreatic hormone insulin has an overall effect on growth. Insulin stimulates protein formation by triggering amino acid transport into cells. Hormonal secretions and the cell products or activities that they trigger interact through negative feedback mechanisms. These mechanisms control the onset, maintenance, and cessation of growth.

Aside from overall growth in body size, the embryo also shows *differential growth*, whereby some tissues enlarge more than others. This process changes the shape and proportion of particular organs and body parts (see, for example, Figure 28.9). Differential growth results partly from interactions among adjacent cells. For example, with increased cell density in a given region, some cells are physically pressed right against others; their growth slows, or becomes channeled along some body axis.

Cell Movements and Changes in Cell Shape

During morphogenesis, cells and entire tissues migrate from one site to another in the embryo. Three types of morphogenetic movements are (1) active cellular migration, (2) the folding of sheets of cells, and (3) movement of organs.

In active cell migration, individual cells move about on pseudopods. These are the threadlike cytoplasmic "feet" that are put out from the main cell body (Figures 4.1 and 4.21). Microtubules and microfilaments just beneath the cell surface membrane are the basis of these movements. Embryonic cells migrate over prescribed pathways, reaching a prescribed destination and establishing contact with cells already there. Think about how accurate those movements must be. For example, precursors of those billions of nerve cells in your brain migrated about and established functional connections with one another even before you were born!

How do embryonic cells know where to move? For one thing, the cells may show chemotaxis: movement in response to chemical gradients. In the embryonic environment, these gradients are created through the local release of certain chemicals from target tissues. For another thing, cells move along the surfaces of other cells and through the extracellular matrix. They move in response to adhesive cues, migrating from regions of weak adhesion to regions of stronger adhesion. These interactions may show marked specificity. For example, pigment cells move along the blood vessels but not nerve cell processes; and Schwann cells migrate along nerve cell processes but not blood vessels.

Another morphogenetic movement is the inward or outward folding of epithelial sheets. The inward migration of cells during gastrulation is an example of this kind of movement (Figure 28.7). The foldings give rise to tissue layers, body cavities, and evaginations of the body surface. Such folding movements are an outcome of coordinated changes in the shape of local cell populations. For example, in a newt embryo, the neural plate forms when the exposed cell surface area shrinks in some places and expands in others (Figure 28.10). Shrinkage occurs when individual neural plate cells lengthen. Circles of microfilaments in these cells contract, like a drawstring, and cause the cells to lengthen.

One more kind of morphogenetic movement involves whole organs. For example, in the human male, the reproductive organs called testes migrate from their original location (near the kidneys) down into the scrotum (a pouch suspended from the front of the abdominal cavity).

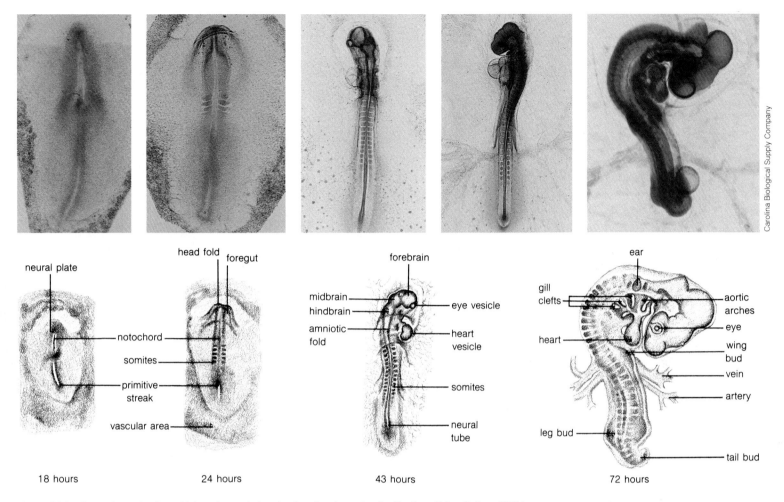

Figure 28.8 Organ formation in a chick embryo, during the first five days after fertilization. (After Patten, 1971)

Pattern Formation

Pattern formation, or cell differentiation in space, also controls the positioning of particular tissues at particular sites in the embryo. Two processes of pattern formation are called ooplasmic localization and embryonic induction.

Through **ooplasmic localization**, cells at particular sites in the embryo differentiate in a prescribed fashion because of the specific maternal messages they acquired when the zygote was carved up during cleavage. These messages become segregated in different cytoplasmic regions of the immature oocyte or they undergo segregation right after fertilization. The cells that ultimately contain one or another set of these messages differentiate into one or another cell type according to the cytoplasmic instructions.

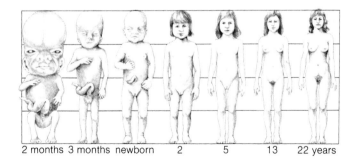

Figure 28.9 Diagram of changes in the proportions of the human body during prenatal and postnatal growth. Stages are shown to the same total height. (From L. B. Arey: *Developmental Anatomy,* Philadelphia: W. B. Saunders Co., 1965. Reprinted by permission.)

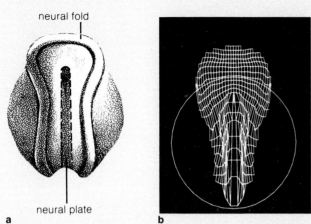

neural fold

neural plate

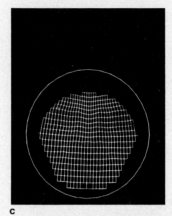

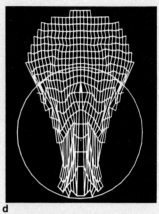

a b c d

Figure 28.10 Computer simulations of forces at work shaping the development of a neural plate in the California newt embryo (**a**). Tissue-shaping is depicted as a distortion of a geometric grid placed over the embryo. (**b**) Computation of two forces—nonuniform shrinkage, and elongation at the neural plate midline—produces a grid that corresponds almost exactly with the actual shape of the neural plate, except for foreshortening. (**c**) Computation of shrinkage alone produces a grid that doesn't have the keyhole shape characteristic of neural plates. (**d**) Computation of elongation alone produces an overlarge keyhole shape. Thus both shrinkage and cell elongation help shape the neural plate. (a from R. Gordon and A. Jacobson, "The Shaping of Tissues in Embryos," *Scientific American*, June 1978. Copyright © 1978 by Scientific American, Inc. All rights reserved. b–d courtesy Richard Gordon)

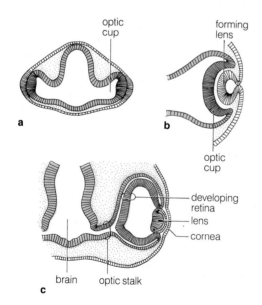

optic cup

forming lens

optic cup

developing retina
lens
cornea

brain   optic stalk

a b c

Figure 28.11 Cross-sectional view of the way the retina of a frog's eye develops as an outgrowth of the brain, and the lens develops as an ingrowth of the ectoderm. (After John W. Saunders, Jr., *Patterns and Principles of Animal Development.* Copyright © 1970 by John W. Saunders, Jr., Macmillan Publishing Co., Inc.)

Through **embryonic induction**, one body part differentiates in response to signals that it receives from an adjacent body part. These signals are thought to be chemical, but their precise nature has yet to be determined.

As an example of embryonic induction, we can consider how tissues come together in space to form a functional eye. During development, the retina of the eye originates from the side wall of the forebrain. The retina must come to be positioned in a precise way with respect to the lens, which focuses light onto the retina. The lens, though, originates from the epidermis of the head (Figure 28.11). At the start of this century, Hans Spemann studied pattern formation of the eye. He used a salamander embryo in which eye lenses were still unformed, but in which optic cups had started to grow out of the forebrain. He surgically removed one of the optic cups. Then he placed it just under the ectoderm of the belly region.

A lens never did develop where it was supposed to, on the side of the head now deprived of an optic cup. But belly epidermal cells that had come in contact with the transplanted optic cup differentiated and formed a lens—which fit perfectly into the transplanted part! Spemann concluded that a lens does not develop independently of a retina. Rather, it is caused (induced) to form wherever the optic cup makes contact with ectoderm cells.

Another example of embryonic induction was provided by Hilde Mangold, one of Spemann's students. For her experiments, Mangold used a dark-pigmented species and a light-pigmented species of salamander embryos. From the light embryo, she cut out a region known as the *dorsal lip*, a site of inward cell migration during gastrulation (Figure 28.6h). She inserted this tissue block into the fluid-filled blastocoel of the dark embryo, across from its own dorsal lip. Gastrulation proceeded at both sites. The outcome was Siamese twin salamander embryos, each with its own set of organs (Figure 28.12).

Almost all of the organs of the twin embryo were dark-pigmented. This meant that the extra set of organs had developed from the host, *not* from the transplanted tissue. The transplanted tissue block had induced some of the host cells into developing in ways that they otherwise would not have done.

In many species, it is likely that some tissues form largely as a result of ooplasmic localization. In others, tissues form largely as a result of embryonic induction. However, it is probably safe to say that the spatial formation of most tissues in most species depends on a combination of the two processes.

The coordinated development of body parts in specific regions depends on some combination of (1) the influence of cytoplasmic substances that become localized in the unfertilized egg, and (2) inductive interactions between cells at later stages of development.

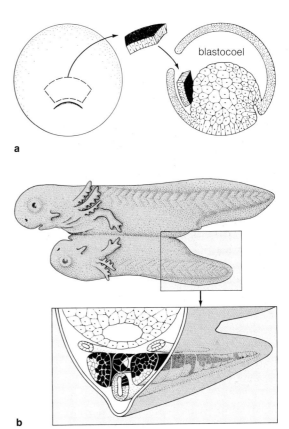

Figure 28.12 Mangold's experiment illustrating embryonic induction in the salamander. (**a**) A tissue block from the dorsal lip region of a dark-pigmented species was transplanted into the blastocoel of a light-pigmented species. (**b**) Self-differentiation and induction by the graft (shown in black) led to the development of Siamese twin embryos, in which most of the organs were derived from the donor species. (From Willier, Weiss, and Hamburger, *Analysis of Development*, Philadelphia: W. B. Saunders Co., 1955. Reprinted by permission.)

Controlled Cell Death

One more morphogenetic process is **controlled cell death**. This process eliminates tissues and cells that are necessary only for short periods in the embryo or the adult. The folding of parts, the hollowing out of tubes, the shaping of bones, the separation of one part from another, the opening of eyes, mouth, nostrils, and ears—all involve plans of cell death.

Perhaps you've noticed that kittens and puppies are born with their eyes sealed shut. From the time their eyes form until just after birth, the eyelids are an unbroken layer of skin. But just after birth, certain cells stretching in a thin line across each eyelid respond to some internal signal and die on cue. As the dead cells degenerate, a slit forms in the skin, and the upper and lower lids part company.

What controls are at work in such prescribed patterns of cell death? We will consider this question later, in the broader context of aging and death—two events built into the life cycle of all animals. Here, the important point is this:

Embryonic morphogenesis involves morphogenetic cell movement and tissue folding, morphogenetic cell death, differential growth, and pattern formation.

METAMORPHOSIS

After being born or hatched, some animals develop directly into the adult form. For them, the development of new tissues and organs slows down with increasing age. Some changes do occur, but they are never again as rapid and profound as those at cleavage, gastrulation, and organ formation. Such *direct development* into the adult form is characteristic of reptiles, birds, and mammals.

Other animal groups proceed through *indirect development* into the adult form. The individual enters the world as a **larva**: a sexually immature, free-living and free-feeding animal that grows and develops into the sexually mature adult form. Morphogenesis is triggered again at some point after the animal has been born or hatched. This process of reactivated development is called **metamorphosis**.

Typically, animals that release small and relatively yolkless eggs into water have long larval stages. Animals that lay large, yolky eggs in water tend to have a short larval stage or none at all. In other animals, such as grasshoppers and caterpillars, the transformation occurs gradually in the land environment. Metamorphosis for these animals involves a series of stages in which the larva grows, then *molts* (sheds its too-small skin or cuticle), then grows again. The adult moth is formed by transformations that occur during the post-larval stage called the pupa. Most of the larval tissues undergo cell death, and new adult structures (such as wings) develop from new groups of organ-specific cells. In grasshoppers, the larval form (nymph) is quite similar in appearance to the adult. Here, many larval tissues are used in the development of the adult. Figure 28.13 compares the tissue reorganization that occurs in grasshoppers and moths.

CELL DIFFERENTIATION

During the development of complex animals, cell populations with stable differences in phenotype arise from an initial population of cells that all have the same phenotype and the same developmental potential. This process is what we call **cell differentiation**.

For example, at the start of development, vertebrate ectoderm is "equipotential," which means that all of the cells have the potential to differentiate into any one of the cell types that ectoderm normally produces. Ultimately the ectoderm gives rise to cell types as diverse as neurons, retinal rods and cones, skin glands, lens epithelium, and olfactory epithelium. And *any* cell of the ectoderm at the gastrula stage has the ability to differentiate into any one of these specialized cell types.

What underlies such major differentiation? In general, development seems to be a conservative process, one that does not involve massive deletions or rearrangements in the hereditary material of each cell. Rather, it appears to involve differential gene activity in different cells.

During development, controls keep some cells undifferentiated and prod others down particular pathways. These controls regulate spatial development, in that they lead to regionally differentiated cell populations. They operate over time, such that the pace of development can vary within and between cell populations. There are dozens or hundreds of fully differentiated cell types in an adult animal. (For example, nerve cells are completely differentiated before birth. If these cells are later destroyed, no other cells take their place or assume their function.) An animal also has populations of stem cells, which can self-replicate, differentiate, or both. Such populations are the basis of ongoing cell replacements in skin, blood, the gut mucosa, and hair, to give a few examples.

Cell replacement reaches an extreme in **regeneration**. The word refers to the capacity of an injured animal to replace missing fragments or parts of its body. For example, sometimes predators tear away arms from sea stars and crabs, or tails from lizards. Each of these animals can grow replacements. Regeneration requires cell growth, differentiation, movements, and interactions. It probably involves the same kinds of interactions that occur during normal embryonic development.

Sometimes the part can even reconstitute the whole. Cells or body parts separated by surgery or injury from the body can develop into an entire animal. A detached sea star arm, for example, can serve as "parent" to a whole new sea star. The capacity of a separated cell or body part to reconstitute the whole organism is called **regulation**.

Animals show great variation in their capacity for regulation. Some can replace any missing part; theirs is a *regulative* pattern of development. In other animals, most parts are so irrevocably differentiated that they cannot grow into or be transformed into other parts. Theirs is a *mosaic pattern* of development.

Vertebrate embryos are highly regulative. For example, in one study a fertilized egg was removed from a black Alaska rabbit. After first cleavage, one of the two newly divided cells was destroyed. Cleavage continued, and the embryo was transplanted into a white chinchilla rabbit. A normal black rabbit developed from one-half of the implanted egg (Figure 28.13). The capacity for regulation is also observed when a human embryo is split into two

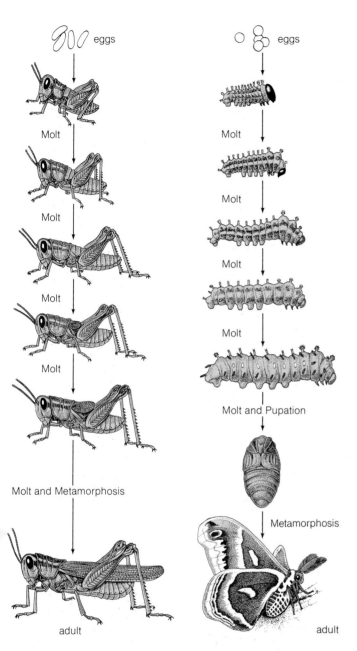

Figure 28.13 Metamorphosis of two insects, the grasshopper (*Melanoplus*) and the giant silkworm moth (cecropia). (From Willier, Weiss, and Hamburger, *Analysis of Development*, Philadelphia: W. B. Saunders Co., 1955. Reprinted by permission.)

Figure 28.14 Chinchilla rabbit foster mother and four black Alaska rabbits, each of which arose from one-half of an implanted black Alaska egg. Why do you suppose the experimenters used a foster mother of a different species? (F. Seidel, *Roux' Archives of Developmental Biology*, 1960, *152*:43–130)

equal parts. The result is not two half-embryos but **identical twins**: two complete, normal individuals. (In contrast, non-identical twins occur when two different eggs are fertilized at the same time by two different sperm.)

Embryos of sea squirts (a chordate), mollusks, and annelids (such as earthworms) are mostly mosaic in their developmental patterns. For example, when two cells are removed from the sea squirt embryo at the eight-cell stage of cleavage, the embryo still develops into a tadpole—but muscles never do develop in the tadpole tail. The early embryonic cells are already so differentiated that one cannot compensate for the absence of another. Many experimental studies of differentiation in animal development have provided the following insights:

1. In general, each differentiated cell contains a complete set of DNA, hence it contains *all* the genes necessary to produce a complete individual.

2. It follows that differentiated cells must be selectively expressing *different parts* of the same set of genes.

3. *Which* genes are expressed in a given cell depends on the nature of cytoplasmic changes induced by the environment and by interactions with other cells.

4. In *regulative* patterns of development, genes that were shut down in differentiated cells can become activated again when missing body parts must be replaced.

5. In *mosaic* patterns of development, more genes have been shut down by the time the egg matures than in regulative development, and those genes cannot be activated again.

AGING AND DEATH

Normal cells of all complex eukaryotes have limits on their life span—prescribed limits characteristic of their species. Following growth and differentiation, these cells begin to deteriorate. There is a gradual loss of efficiency in cellular functions, which culminates sooner or later in the death of the individual. The overall process of predictable cellular deterioration is called **aging**. It is built into the life cycle of all organisms in which differentiated cells show considerable specialization.

For instance, more than two decades ago, Paul Moorhead and Leonard Hayflick cultured normal embryonic cells from humans. They discovered that all the cell lines proceeded to divide about fifty times—and then the entire population died off. Furthermore, Hayflick took some of the cultured cells and froze them for a period of years. Afterward, he allowed them to thaw. The cells proceeded to complete the cycle of fifty doublings—whereupon they all died *on schedule*.

According to one hypothesis, aging is partly the result of an accumulation of environmental insults, which cause either structural changes or gene mutations in chromosomes. Over time, such mutations would indeed hamper a cell's ability to produce the enzymes and other proteins it requires for proper functioning. Yet this assumption does not explain the fact that, regardless of induced damage, *different* cell types in the same organism have very different and entirely predictable life spans! Aging, in other words, cannot be explained entirely in terms of random environmental "hits."

Consider the process of controlled cell death, which occurs in many morphogenetic events. Often, cell death is a response to a signal from a nearby developing structure. But there may be a long interval between receipt of a death warrant and cellular execution. In one experiment, John Saunders isolated two blocks of apparently similar cells from an embryo. One block came from a region where cell death normally occurs, the other came from a region where it does not. Both cell blocks were cultured on a nutrient-rich medium. For days, both flourished. Then, at precisely the moment it was scheduled to die in the embryo, the predoomed block of cells suddenly died! The other block continued to thrive.

One more important example should be given here. Originally, hands and feet of developing vertebrates are shaped like paddles. In many species such as our own, skin cells between the lobes of the "paddle" die on cue, leaving separate fingers and toes. In other species such as ducks, cell death normally does not occur in the paddles; that is

COMMENTARY

Death in the Open

Lewis Thomas

(Printed by permission from the New England Journal of Medicine, *January 11, 1973, 288:92–93)*

Everything in the world dies, but we only know about it as a kind of abstraction. If you stand in a meadow, at the edge of a hillside, and look around carefully, almost everything you can catch sight of is in the process of dying, and most things will be dead long before you are. If it were not for the constant renewal and replacement going on before your eyes, the whole place would turn to stone and sand under your feet.

There are some creatures that do not seem to die at all; they simply vanish totally into their own progeny. Single cells do this. The cell becomes two, then four, and so on, and after a while the last trace is gone. It cannot be seen as death; barring mutation, the descendants are simply the first cell, living all over again. The cycles of the slime mold have episodes that seem as conclusive as death, but the withered slug, with its stalk and fruiting body, is plainly the transient tissue of a developing organism; the free-swimming amoebocytes use this mode collectively in order to produce more of themselves.

There are said to be a billion billion insects on the earth at any moment, most of them with very short life expectancies by our standards. Someone has estimated that there are 25 million assorted insects hanging in the air over every temperate square mile, in a column extending upward for thousands of feet, drifting through the layers of atmosphere like plankton. They are dying steadily, some by being eaten, some just dropping in their tracks, tons of them around the earth, disintegrating as they die, invisibly.

Who ever sees dead birds, in anything like the huge numbers stipulated by the certainty of the death of all birds? A dead bird is an incongruity, more startling than an unexpected live bird, sure evidence to the human mind that something has gone wrong. Birds do their dying off somewhere, behind things, under things, never on the wing.

Animals seem to have an instinct for performing death alone, hidden. Even the largest, most conspicuous ones find ways to conceal themselves in time. If an elephant missteps and dies in an open place, the herd will not leave him there; the others will pick him up and carry the body from place to place, finally putting it down in some inexplicably suitable location. When elephants encounter the skeleton of an elephant in the open, they methodically take up each of the bones and distribute them, in a ponderous ceremony, over neighboring acres.

It is a natural marvel. All of the life of the earth dies, all of the time, in the same volume as the new life that dazzles us each morning, each spring. All we see of this is the odd stump, the fly struggling on the porch floor of the summer house in October, the fragment on the highway. I have lived all my life with an embarrassment of squirrels in my backyard, they are all over the place, all year long, and I have never seen, anywhere, a dead squirrel.

I suppose it is just as well. If the earth were otherwise, and all the dying were done in the open, with the dead there to be looked at, we would never have it out of our minds. We can forget about it much of the time, or think of it as an accident to be avoided, somehow. But it does make the process of dying seem more exceptional than it really is, and harder to engage in at the times when we must ourselves engage.

In our way, we conform as best we can to the rest of nature. The obituary pages tell us of the news that we are dying away, while the birth announcements in finer print, off at the side of the page, inform us of our replacements, but we get no grasp from this of the enormity of the scale. There are 4 billion of us on the earth, and all 4 billion must be dead, on a schedule, within this lifetime. The vast mortality, involving something over

50 million each year, takes place in relative secrecy. We can only really know of the deaths in our households, among our friends. These, detached in our minds from all the rest, we take to be unnatural events, anomalies, outrages. We speak of our own dead in low voices; struck down, we say, as though visible death can occur only for cause, by disease or violence, avoidably. We send off for flowers, grieve, make ceremonies, scatter bones, unaware of the rest of the 4 billion on the same schedule. All of that immense mass of flesh and bone and consciousness will disappear by absorption into the earth, without recognition by the transient survivors.

Less than half a century from now, our replacements will have more than doubled in numbers. It is hard to see how we can continue to keep the secret, with such multitudes doing the dying. We will have to give up the notion that death is a catastrophe, or detestable, or avoidable, or even strange. We will need to learn more about the cycling of life in the rest of the system, and about our connection to the process. Everything that comes alive seems to be in trade for everything that dies, cell for cell. There might be some comfort in the recognition of synchrony, in the information that we all go down together, in the best of company.

why ducks have webbed feet instead of toes. Now, in some mice and some humans, a certain gene mutation blocks cell death; and hands and feet remain webbed. Experiments in which skin was grafted from normal mice to mutant mice showed that the mutation does not affect the ability of inner parts of hands and feet to *generate* the death signal. Rather, it changes the capacity of skin cells to *respond* to the signal. All other events of controlled cell death in all other parts of the developing body proceed on cue. Apparently the gene controls the response to one signal required for morphogenesis.

On the basis of such investigations, we can only speculate that aging and death may be coded in large part in DNA, like all other events of development and differentiation—and that signals from the cytoplasm of cells nearby or some distance away in the differentiated body activate those messages, telling one another that it is time to die. And we can only speculate that we might learn to come to terms with the inevitability of the prospect, accepting it as a natural process in the development and differentiation of an immense number of organisms on earth.

Readings

Balinsky, B. 1981. *An Introduction to Embryology*. Fifth edition. Philadelphia: Saunders.

Gordon, R., and A. Jacobson. 1978. "The Shaping of Tissues in Embryos." *Scientific American* 238(6): 106–113. Interesting discussion of computer simulations of forces shaping embryonic morphogenesis.

Patten, B. M. 1971. *Early Embryology of the Chick*. Fifth edition. New York: McGraw-Hill.

Saunders, J. 1982. *Developmental Biology: Patterns, Problems, Principles*. New York: Macmillan. Excellent introduction to embryology.

Review Questions

1. What are some of the differences between asexual and sexual reproduction? Describe some forms of asexual reproduction. What are some adaptations associated with external and internal fertilization of sexually reproducing animals?

2. Describe what goes on during each of these developmental stages: fertilization, cleavage, gastrulation, organ formation.

3. How does the yolk of animal eggs influence cleavage patterns?

4. Distinguish among endoderm, mesoderm, and ectoderm.

5. Define morphogenesis. Describe some of the cell movements and changes in cell shape involved in morphogenesis.

6. Define two processes of pattern formation. Can you describe an experiment that gave insight into how tissues differentiate and become positioned in specific regions of the embryo?

7. Define indirect and direct development. Give some examples of animals that follow each developmental strategy.

8. During the development of duck embryos and human embryos, the ends of the leg buds differentiate into paddlelike appendages. In ducks, the paddles develop into webbed feet. In humans, the paddles develop separate toes. What morphogenetic process might give rise to the separate digits in humans?

9. Define cell differentiation. What is the difference between regulative and mosaic patterns of development?

In the preceding chapter, we looked at some general principles of animal reproduction and development. Here, we will focus on humans as a way of presenting an integrated picture of the structure and function of reproductive organs, gametogenesis, and the progressive developmental events from fertilization to birth. As part of this picture, we will also look at some of the mechanisms controlling reproduction.

DEFINITION OF PRIMARY REPRODUCTIVE ORGANS

Primary reproductive organs, or **gonads**, produce gametes and secrete important sex hormones. They are assisted in these two functions by **accessory reproductive organs**: glands as well as ducts through which gametes are transported. The sex hormones secreted by gonads influence the development of many physical traits, called *secondary sexual traits*. Such traits are distinctly associated with maleness and femaleness, but are not directly involved in reproduction. They include the amount and distribution of body fat, hair, and skeletal muscle.

Gonads and accessory reproductive organs are already formed at birth. However, they do not begin to reach their full size and they do not start to become reproductively functional until the onset of puberty (about age ten to fourteen). During puberty, the body becomes sexually developed enough that conception is possible.

29

HUMAN REPRODUCTION AND DEVELOPMENT

MALE REPRODUCTIVE SYSTEM

Male Reproductive Tract

Table 29.1 lists the organs and accessory glands of the male reproductive tract. Their arrangement relative to one another is shown in Figure 29.1. A male has two gonads, called **testes** (singular, testis). Testes are contained in the *scrotum*, a pouch suspended from the front portion of the abdominal cavity. The two functional components of a testis are seminiferous ("seed-bearing") tubules and interstitial cells. About 125 meters of tightly coiled *seminiferous tubules* are packed into each testis. These tubes are sperm production sites. *Interstitial cells*, which surround the tubules, produce and secrete sex hormones. The most influential of these hormones is testosterone. The accessory organs and glands of the reproductive tract function in sperm maturation, conduction, and motility.

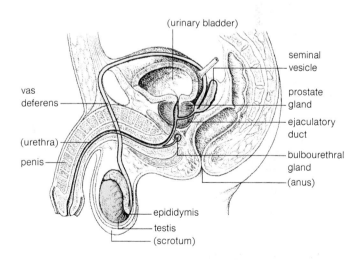

Figure 29.1 Human male reproductive tract, lateral view.

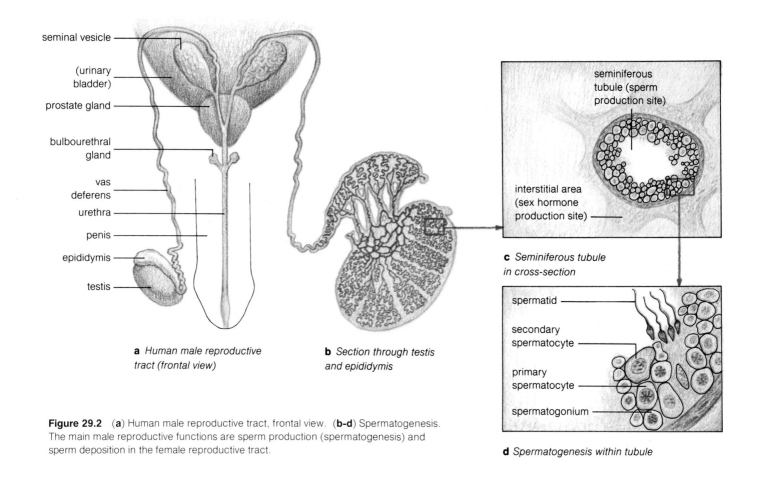

seminal vesicle

(urinary bladder)

prostate gland

bulbourethral gland

vas deferens

urethra

penis

epididymis

testis

a *Human male reproductive tract (frontal view)*

b *Section through testis and epididymis*

seminiferous tubule (sperm production site)

interstitial area (sex hormone production site)

c *Seminiferous tubule in cross-section*

spermatid

secondary spermatocyte

primary spermatocyte

spermatogonium

d *Spermatogenesis within tubule*

Figure 29.2 (**a**) Human male reproductive tract, frontal view. (**b-d**) Spermatogenesis. The main male reproductive functions are sperm production (spermatogenesis) and sperm deposition in the female reproductive tract.

Table 29.1	Organs and Accessory Glands of the Male Reproductive Tract
Organs:	
Testis (two)	Sperm production, sex hormone production
Epididymis (two)	Sperm maturation site, some sperm storage
Vas deferens (two)	Storage, conduction of sperm
Ejaculatory ducts	Conduction of sperm
Penis	Organ of sexual intercourse
Accessory Glands:	
Seminal vesicles	Secretions make up portion of seminal fluid*
Prostate gland	Same as above
Bulbourethral glands	Same as above

*Seminal fluid enhances sperm motility in various ways.

Spermatogenesis

Mammals generally reproduce on a seasonal basis, and spermatogenesis (Chapter Nine) generally coincides with the reproductive season. The human male is an exception. In a normal human male, several hundred million sperm can be produced, every day, from about age fourteen onward. It takes about seventy-two days for a primary spermatocyte to develop into a fully mature sperm. Within the seminiferous tubules, millions of cells are in different developmental stages, and sperm are maturing all the time.

Figure 29.2 shows a seminiferous tubule in cross-section. Undifferentiated cells (spermatogonia) are the only ones in contact with the basement membrane of the tubule. Ongoing mitotic divisions physically force some spermatogonia toward the lumen. These displaced cells grow larger (into primary spermatocytes), which divide into secondary spermatocytes and then spermatids. The spermatids later undergo final transformation into mature sperm.

A mature **sperm** consists of a head, midpiece, and tail (Figure 29.3). DNA is densely packed in the head region. The *acrosome,* a cap over most of the head, contains lytic enzymes that function in egg penetration. The midpiece is richly endowed with mitochondria, which provide the energy necessary for motility. In the tail are contractile filaments whose action produces whiplike movements. Sperm can move one to four millimeters a second in a suitable medium.

Sperm Movement Through the Reproductive Tract

Sperm leaving the seminiferous tubules move into the **epididymis**, one of two long, coiled ducts. Sperm are initially stored in this duct, and here they complete maturation and develop their motility. Sperm also are stored in the **vas deferens**, one of two thick-walled ducts that are continuous with the epididymides. Strong, peristaltic contractions of smooth muscles in the duct walls propel sperm forward through the reproductive tract.

The two vas deferens open into an **ejaculatory duct**, which begins at the prostate gland and empties into the urethra (a duct that also functions in urination). Two **seminal vesicles** also open into the ejaculatory duct. The seminal vesicles secrete nutrients (that sperm can take up) and mucus. A **prostate gland** secretes thin, alkaline fluid into the ejaculatory duct. (This fluid probably helps neutralize acidic secretions of the female vagina, which are about pH 3.5–4. When pH increases to about 6, sperm motility and fertility are enhanced.) Just below the prostate, two **bulbourethral glands** secrete mucus-rich fluid into the urethra during sexual arousal. The urethra is located inside a copulatory organ (the penis) and empties to the outside.

Sperm become mixed with the fluids secreted from the prostate, seminal vesicles, and bulbourethral glands. This fluid, which is ejaculated from the body during sexual activity, is called **semen**. Semen is a fluid medium that nourishes sperm and enhances their motility. It also contains prostaglandins that stimulate uterine contractions in the female. Such contractions possibly help propel sperm in the female reproductive tract.

Sperm can live for several weeks in the vas deferens. Once sperm are ejaculated into the female reproductive tract, they can live for twenty-four to seventy-two hours. The average ejaculate has 400 million sperm.

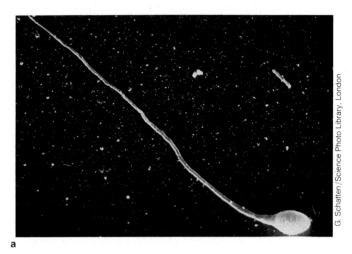

a

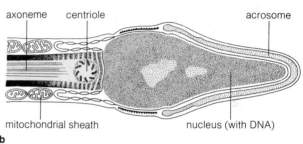

b

Figure 29.3 (**a**) Micrograph of a human sperm. The sketch (**b**) shows the head region in cross-section, and in profile. The head is rounded (as in the micrograph) in frontal view. (Redrawn from H. Pedersen and D. W. Fawcett in E.S.E. Hafez (ed.), *Human Semen and Fertility Regulation in Men,* C. V. Mosby Co., 1976)

Hormonal Control in the Male

Three hormones directly or indirectly control male reproductive functioning. One is **testosterone**, produced by interstitial cells in the testes. The other two are **follicle-stimulating hormone** (FSH) and **luteinizing hormone** (LH). As Chapter Twenty-Two indicated, these two gonadotropins are produced by the anterior pituitary. (FSH and LH were first named for their effects in females, but their molecular structure is exactly the same in males.)

Testosterone has multiple functions. First, it acts with the other two hormones in stimulating spermatogenesis. Second, testosterone is necessary for the growth, form, and function of all parts of the male reproductive tract. Third, testosterone promotes the normal development and maintenance of sexual behavior. (Aggressive behavior is also clearly dependent on testosterone.) Fourth, masculine secondary sexual traits are testosterone-dependent. (For ex-

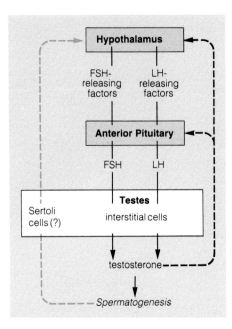

Figure 29.4 Hormonal control of gonadal function in human males. The black dashed line indicates that increased testosterone secretions inhibit LH secretions by the pituitary. The blue dashed line indicates that an inhibitory chemical signal (possibly arising from Sertoli cells, which occur with interstitial cells in seminiferous tubules) influences the hypothalamus and pituitary to limit FSH secretions.

Table 29.2	Female Reproductive Organs
Ovaries	Egg production, sex hormone production
Oviducts	Conduction of egg from ovary to uterus
Uterus	Chamber in which new individual develops
Cervix	Secretes mucus that enhances sperm movement into uterus and (after fertilization) reduces the embryo's risk of bacterial infection
Vagina	Organ of sexual intercourse; birth canal

ample, testosterone stimulates beard growth and pubic hair growth. It stimulates enlargement of the larynx, which causes the voice to deepen.)

FSH and LH stimulate testosterone secretion as well as spermatogenesis. Both of these hormones are under control of the hypothalamus. As Figure 29.4 suggests, negative feedback mechanisms link the hypothalamus, anterior pituitary, and interstitial cells in controlling gonadal function.

FEMALE REPRODUCTIVE SYSTEM

Female Reproductive Tract

Table 29.2 lists the components of the female reproductive tract. Female gonads are a pair of **ovaries**. In these organs, oocytes develop into mature ova (Figures 29.5 and 29.6). The ovaries also produce estrogen and progesterone. Accessory reproductive organs include the oviducts (or fallopian tubes), uterus, vagina, external genitalia, and mammary glands (breasts, which function in lactation).

The **oviducts** are passageways that channel ova into the uterus. These ducts are not directly connected with the ovaries. Rather, at one end they extend toward the ovaries with ciliated, fingerlike projections. An ovum is released into the pelvic cavity, and ciliary action at the oviduct entrance sweeps it into the tube.

The **uterus** houses the embryo during pregnancy. Strong contractions of the uterine walls expel the fetus from the mother's body at birth. The **cervix** is the opening between the uterus and vagina. Its mucous secretions enhance sperm movement and (after fertilization) help protect the developing embryo from bacterial attack by acting as a thick blockade to the uterus. The **vagina** receives sperm from the male. It also functions as part of the birth canal and acts as a channel to the outside for uterine secretions and menstrual flow, as will be described shortly. The external genitalia, or **vulva**, include organs for sexual stimulation (such as the clitoris). They also include organs lined with adipose tissue, which cushions the external parts.

Menstrual Cycle: An Overview

Unlike males, human females have a cyclic, intermittent reproductive capacity. In most mammalian females, the cyclic reproductive pattern is called the **estrous cycle**. During estrus, the female comes into "heat" (becomes sexually receptive to the male) only at specific times of year. Also during estrus, hormones stimulate the maturation and release of ova, and they prime the uterine lining for fertilization.

In humans and other primates, the cyclic reproductive capacity in females is called the **menstrual cycle**. Here, too, the reproductive tract and the ova maturing within it are primed for fertilization. Unlike estrus, though, there is no correspondence between heat and the time of fertility. All female primates have the potential to be physically and behaviorally receptive to the male's overtures at any time. Also unlike estrus, the hormone-primed uterine lining is sloughed off at the end of each cycle. Menstrual cycles be-

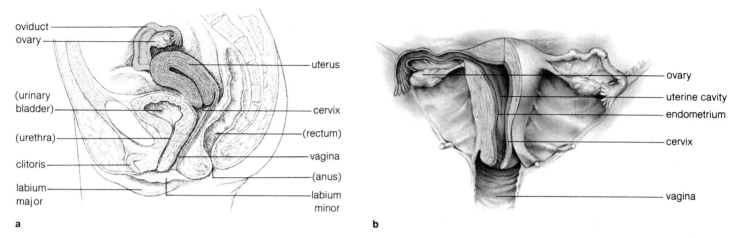

oviduct
ovary
uterus
(urinary bladder)
cervix
(urethra)
(rectum)
clitoris
vagina
labium major
(anus)
labium minor

a
b

ovary
uterine cavity
endometrium
cervix
vagina

Figure 29.5 Human female reproductive tract, lateral view (**a**), and frontal view of the uterus (**b**).

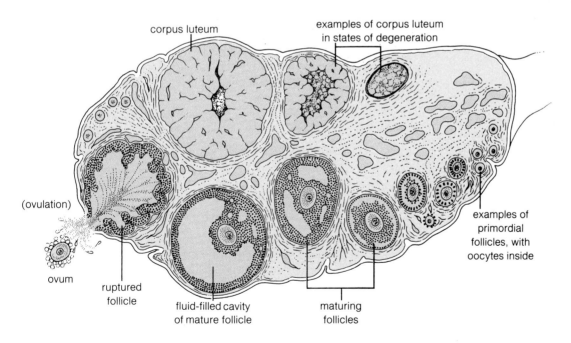

corpus luteum
examples of corpus luteum in states of degeneration
(ovulation)
examples of primordial follicles, with oocytes inside
ovum
ruptured follicle
fluid-filled cavity of mature follicle
maturing follicles

Figure 29.6 A human ovary, drawn as if sliced lengthwise through its midsection. Events in the ovarian cycle proceed from the growth and maturation of primordial follicles, through ovulation (rupturing of a mature follicle, with a concurrent release of an ovum), through the formation and maintenance (or degeneration) of an endocrine element called the corpus luteum. The positions of these structures in the ovary are varied for illustrative purposes only The maturation of an oocyte occurs at the *same* site, from the beginning of the cycle to ovulation.

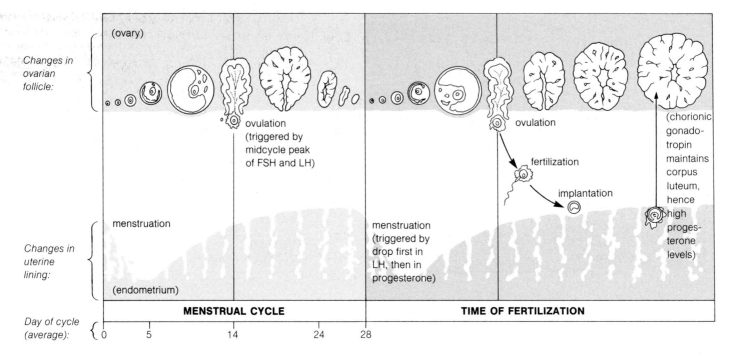

ovulation
(triggered by
midcycle peak
of FSH and LH)

ovulation

fertilization

implantation

(chorionic
gonado-
tropin
maintains
corpus
luteum,
hence
high
proges-
terone
levels)

Changes in
ovarian
follicle:

(ovary)

menstruation

Changes in
uterine
lining:

(endometrium)

menstruation
(triggered by
drop first in
LH, then in
progesterone)

MENSTRUAL CYCLE

TIME OF FERTILIZATION

Day of cycle
(average):

0   5   14   24   28

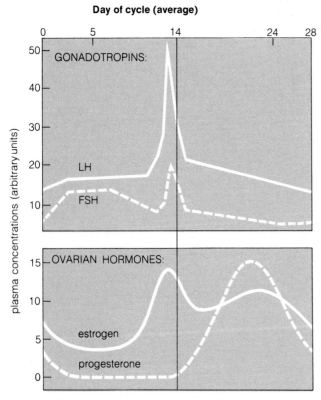

Day of cycle (average)

Figure 29.7 Correlation among gonadotropins, ovarian hormones, follicle development, ovulation, and changes in uterine function during the human menstrual cycle.

gin at about age thirteen and continue until *menopause* (in the late forties or early fifties).

On the average, it takes about twenty-eight days to complete one turn of the menstrual cycle. During this time span, changes take place within the ovary and in the **endometrium** (the uterine lining). The changes are controlled by hormonal feedback mechanisms that link together the hypothalamus, anterior pituitary, and ovaries. The following hormones are involved:

Ovarian hormones:	estrogen
	progesterone
Gonadotropins:	FSH
(released from pituitary)	LH

Let's look first at how these mechanisms influence ovarian function. Then we will look at the concurrent changes in the endometrium.

Ovarian Function

Follicle Maturation and Development. As Figure 29.6 suggests, an ovary contains many cell clusters called **primordial follicles**. About 400,000 primordial follicles are already present in the ovaries at birth; no others will be acquired later in life. Each follicle consists of an immature oocyte surrounded by a single layer of flattened cells, which can secrete estrogen and progesterone. Each oocyte is in an arrested stage of meiosis. But only about 400 will be stimulated—usually one at a time, on a monthly basis—to developing into mature ova. The rest do not receive stimulatory signals and they degenerate.

Apparently, some flattened cells of the follicle secrete an inhibitory substance that keeps the follicle in the immature state. However, at the onset of the menstrual cycle, FSH and LH blood concentrations rise. The increase stimulates mitotic divisions in the flat follicle cells. Under the combined influence of estrogen and FSH, the follicle cells proliferate, and they acquire membrane surface receptors for LH. The blood estrogen levels continue to rise.

At about midpoint of the menstrual cycle, estrogen levels have so increased that the hypothalamus stimulates the anterior pituitary into releasing a brief, rapid outpouring of LH. Within thirty-six to forty-eight hours, the **midcycle surge of LH** has triggered the following events:

1. Oocyte meiosis resumes, the outcome being a mature ovum.

2. Follicle cells decrease their estrogen secretions somewhat and step up progesterone secretions.

3. The follicle ruptures, and the mature ovum is released from the ovary. This event is called **ovulation**.

4. The ruptured follicle rapidly differentiates into a **corpus luteum**, a glandular structure that secretes elevated amounts of progesterone and some estrogen for a fixed time period.

How does LH actually cause ovulation? That is not known. However, some evidence suggests that LH stimulates production of enzymes that can dissolve the thin membranes between the follicle and the surroundings. These membranes are most exposed where the follicle bulges from the surface of the ovary.

The corpus luteum formed from the ruptured follicle can persist for about twelve days if fertilization does not follow ovulation. During that time, the high blood concentrations of estrogen register in the hypothalamus. The hypothalamus sends inhibitory signals to the anterior pituitary, which shuts down its LH and FSH secretions in response. Estrogen levels dwindle, hence a new follicle is prevented from developing until the menstrual cycle is completed. Also, the high blood concentrations of progesterone act on the hypothalamus, which sends out inhibitory signals that help prevent another LH surge.

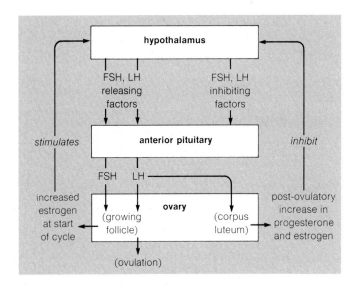

Figure 29.8 Feedback loops between the hypothalamus, anterior pituitary, and ovary during the menstrual cycle.

The hypothalamus apparently has two control centers related to the menstrual cycle. During the first half of the cycle, the rising estrogen levels in the blood have a positive feedback effect on one center. (This center initiates FSH and LH secretions, which stimulate the follicle into secreting estrogen, which stimulates more FSH and LH secretions, and so on.)

During the second half of the cycle, secretions from the corpus luteum (formed from the ruptured follicle) add to the blood levels of estrogen and greatly increase progesterone levels. The hormone concentrations are now so high that they have a negative feedback effect on another hypothalamic center. (They lead to a decrease in FSH and LH secretions, which led to the high estrogen and progesterone levels in the first place.)

When fertilization does not occur within the prescribed time frame, the corpus luteum starts to degenerate during the last days of the menstrual cycle. Prostaglandins in some way issue its death warrant, possibly in conjunction with a substance that binds to LH receptors on the gland's surface and blocks LH uptake. With disintegration of the corpus luteum, blood levels of estrogen and progesterone fall rapidly. The inhibitory effect of these two hormones on the hypothalamus and pituitary are thereby removed. FSH secretions rise, another follicle in the ovary is stimulated into developing—and the cycle begins anew.

Figure 29.7 summarizes the effects of changing hormone levels on both the follicle and the endometrium. Figure 29.8 summarizes the hormonal feedback controls underlying these changes.

Uterine Function

The changing estrogen and progesterone levels just described cause profound changes in the uterus. Estrogen stimulates the growth of endometrium and uterine smooth muscle. Progesterone acts on the thickened endometrium in several ways. Under its influence, blood vessels proliferate; glycogen and enzymes are stockpiled in endometrial glands and connective tissues. In such ways, the uterus is prepared for implantation.

At the time of ovulation, estrogen alone influences mucous secretions by the cervix. Now the mucus is thin, clear, and abundant. Mucus having these characteristics is an ideal medium through which sperm can travel. Just after ovulation, progesterone secretions from the corpus luteum act on the cervix. The mucus becomes thick and sticky, and serves as a physical barrier against bacteria that might enter the vagina and endanger a newly conceived embryo.

In the absence of fertilization, and with the disintegration of the corpus luteum, blood levels of progesterone and estrogen fall. Without its hormonal support, the highly developed endometrium starts disintegrating also. Endometrial blood vessels constrict and tissues, deprived of oxygen and nutrients, die off. Endometrial arterioles now

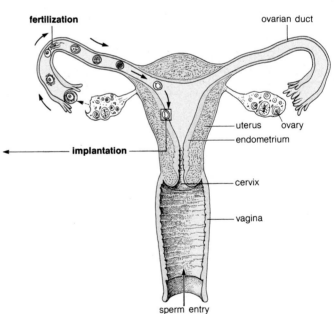

Figure 29.9 A current view of developmental events, from the time of implantation (about eight days after fertilization in the oviduct) to about the end of the first month, as described in the text. The various stages are not drawn to scale relative to one another, the point being simply to show the developmental fate of the inner cell mass.

dilate, and the increased blood flow ruptures the walls of weakened capillaries. Menstrual flow consists of blood and sloughed endometrial tissues. The flow moves out of the body through the vagina, and its appearance marks the first day of a new menstrual cycle. It will continue for three to six days, until rising estrogen levels stimulate the repair and growth of the endometrium.

SEXUAL UNION AND FERTILIZATION

A mature ovum can make its acquaintance with sperm during sexual union, or **coitus**. Sperm are ejaculated from the penis. The human **penis** contains three cylinders of spongy tissue, arranged around the urethra. At the tip of the penis, the ventral cylinder terminates as a mushroom-shaped structure called the *glans penis.* This structure contains abundant mechanoreceptors which, when stimulated by friction, are responsible for nerve signals that the brain interprets as pleasurable sensations. During normal activity, blood vessels leading into the three cylinders are constricted, and the penis is limp. During early sexual excitation, blood flows into the cylinders faster than it flows out. Blood collects in the spongy tissue, and the organ lengthens and hardens. These changes, which can occur within seconds of sexual excitation, facilitate penetration into the vagina.

During coitus, pelvic thrusts stimulate the penis, as well as the vaginal walls and clitoral region of the female body. The mechanical stimulation triggers rhythmic muscular contractions that force the contents of seminal vesicles and the prostate into the male urethra. The contractions, which are involuntary, expel semen into the vagina. (During ejaculation, a sphincter closes off the bladder. As a result, sperm cannot enter the bladder and urine cannot be excreted from it.) The involuntary muscular contractions, ejaculation, and associated sensations of release, warmth, and relaxation constitute the event called *orgasm.*

Female orgasm involves similar physical events, including an intense vaginal awareness, a series of involuntary uterine and vaginal contractions, and sensations of relaxation and warmth. A male or female may or may not reach this state of excitation during coitus.

If sperm ejaculation into the vagina coincides with ovulation—if it occurs between approximately three days before ovulation and about three days afterward—fertilization can result. Within thirty minutes after ejaculation from the penis, muscle contractions have moved sperm into the oviduct, where fertilization usually takes place (Figure 29.11).

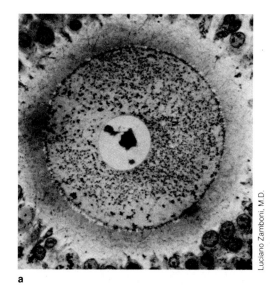

a

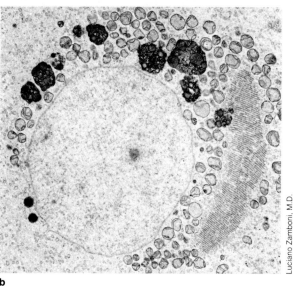

b

Figure 29.10 (**a**) Human ovum, surrounded by follicle cells in an ovary. 800×. (**b**) A closer look at the egg nucleus, showing the profusion of cytoplasmic organelles positioned near the nuclear envelope. This metabolic machinery is already in place by the time that a sperm nucleus fuses with the egg nucleus.

Of the several hundred million sperm entering the vagina, only a few thousand complete the journey, and only one succeeds in penetrating the ovum. Its success marks the onset of **pregnancy**—a sequence of events from fertilization, through implantation, embryonic growth, and birth.

FROM FERTILIZATION TO BIRTH

Early Embryonic Development

Implantation and Formation of Embryonic Membranes.
Figure 29.11 highlights some of the events that occur within the first month of development. For the first three or four days, the fertilized egg travels down the oviduct. It picks up nutrients from maternal secretions and undergoes its first cleavages. By the time it reaches the uterus, the egg is transformed into a solid cluster of cells known as a **morula**. The morula develops into a blastocyst, in the manner described in Chapter Twenty-Eight. The **blastocyst** consists of an inner cell mass, and a surface cell layer called the *trophoblast*.

About eight days after conception, the blastocyst contacts and adheres to the uterine wall. The trophoblast secretes enzymes that destroy some of the uterine lining, and the blastocyst burrows inside. As it does, enzyme action also causes maternal blood vessels to rupture. The entry site heals over, leaving the blastocyst inside a pool of the mother's blood.

Slender projections (villi) now grow out from the trophoblast and establish the first nutritional links between the embryo and the mother. These links are enough to nurture the embryo for the first few weeks. As it enlarges, however, more support structures are necessary. These structures arise from membranes that develop from the embryo itself. The embryonic membranes function in nutrition, respiration, and excretion. They are called the chorion, amnion, yolk sac, and allantois.

The **chorion** (derived from the trophoblast) develops into a membranous sac that completely surrounds the embryo and the three other embryonic membranes (Figure 29.9). Besides being a nutritional link with the mother, the chorion secretes a hormone (chorionic gonadotropin). This hormone is much like LH in its effect. It helps maintain the corpus luteum — hence the endometrium.

The **amnion** is a membranous, fluid-filled sac that initially forms from an opening that appears in the inner cell mass about two weeks after fertilization. Eventually it completely surrounds the embryo. The amniotic fluid is like a miniature aquarium that keeps the embryo from drying out. Later, it also acts like a fluid shock absorber. (The "water" that flows freely from the vagina just before childbirth is amniotic fluid, released when the amnion ruptures.)

The **yolk sac** also appears during the second week. This membranous sac starts out as a budlike outgrowth of the embryonic gut. Portions of the membrane help form the embryonic digestive tube. The yolk also functions in blood cell formation during early developmental stages.

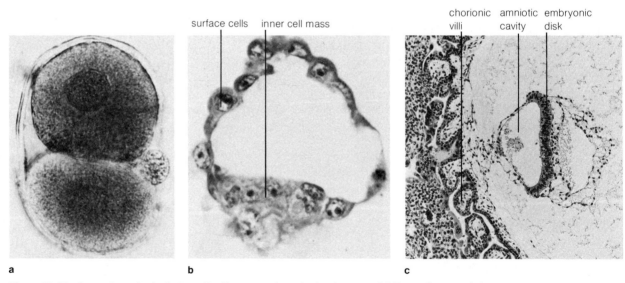

Figure 29.11 Some stages in the first month of human embryonic development. (**a**) Two-cell stage of cleavage, between two and three days after fertilization. (**b**) Blastocyst in cross-section, after four to six days. (**c**) Embryo in cross-section after about sixteen days. (The Carnegie Institution of Washington and Ronan O'Rahilly, M.D., Director of the Carnegie Collection)

During the third week, the **allantois** forms as an outgrowth of the embryonic gut. This membranous sac fuses with some chorionic tissue that by now forms a connecting stalk between the embryo and the mother. Together, the trophoblast, chorionic tissue, part of the yolk sac, and allantois tissue constitute the **placenta**. The placenta is an organ that mediates interchanges between the embryo and the mother. As it grows, it becomes richly endowed with embryonic blood vessels. The blood vessels extend into maternal lacunae (blood-filled spaces in the uterine lining). Here, the embryo absorbs oxygen and nutrients and gives off wastes that are disposed of through the mother's lungs and kidneys. Later on, the stalk portion of the allantois persists as the *umbilical cord*. The embryonic blood vessels in the cord function in gas exchange until the time of birth.

Differentiation and Organ Formation. By the time the placenta is forming, the inner cell mass has begun to differentiate along the same general course described earlier for all complex animals. Prior to gastrulation, the embryo consists simply of two flat layers of cells, the *embryonic disk* (Figure 29.11c). During the second week, the onset of gastrulation is marked by the appearance of a groove on the upper surface of the embryo. The groove is the site where surface cells migrate inward to form the mesoderm. When gastrulation is completed, the remaining surface tissue is ectoderm, which gives rise to the nervous system and skin. Inside, the endoderm forms the inner lining of the respiratory and digestive systems; and the mesoderm develops into such internal organs as the heart, muscles, and bone. By the end of the first month, the embryo has grown 500 times (Figure 29.12). This rapid growth spurt gives way to two months of relatively slow development for the main organs. This three-month period is the **first trimester** (Figure 29.13).

By the beginning of the **second trimester**, all major organs have formed. The embryo soon resembles an adult in miniature—it is about 7.5 centimeters (three inches) long. Through the **third trimester** the individual grows a great deal, but few new parts form. That is why the term *embryo* usually is reserved for the first trimester of human life, when body parts are being formed. During the remaining time inside the uterus, the developing individual is called a **fetus** (Figure 29.14).

Not until the middle of the third trimester is the fetus developed enough to survive on its own if born prematurely or if removed surgically from the uterus. By the seventh month, fetal development appears to be relatively complete, but fewer than ten percent of infants born at this stage survive, even with the best medical care. In most cases they

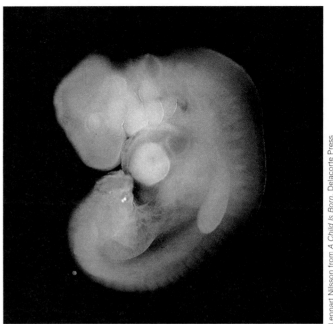

a

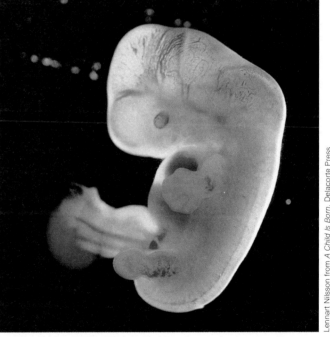

b

Figure 29.12 (**a**) Embryo at four weeks, about seven millimeters (0.3 inch) long. Notice the tail and the gill arches, which vaguely resemble a double chin. These features emerge during embryonic development of all vertebrates. Arm and leg buds are also visible now. (**b**) Embryo at end of five weeks, about twelve millimeters long. The head starts to enlarge and the trunk starts to straighten. Finger rays appear. The umbilical cord has developed.

are not yet able to breathe normally or maintain a normal core temperature. By the ninth month, survival chances increase to about ninety-five percent.

Case Study: Mother as Protector, Provider, Potential Threat

Many safeguards have been built into the female reproductive system. The placenta, for example, is a highly selective filter. It screens substances present in the maternal bloodstream and thereby prevents many noxious substances from gaining access to the embryo or fetus. Also, if the mother's diet is in some way deficient, the placenta often can take up nutrients at the expense of the mother's own body. Such safeguards are effective, but only to a point. From conception to birth, the developing individual is at the mercy of the mother's diet, her health habits, and her life-style.

Some Nutritional Considerations. During pregnancy, a balanced diet that provides enough carbohydrates, amino acids, and fats or oils normally provides all necessary vitamins and minerals in amounts sufficient for normal development. One of the most common fallacies of Western culture is that if you pop a vitamin pill into your mouth every day, the rest will take care of itself. Particularly with respect to pregnancy, nothing could be further from the truth. While the mother's vitamin needs are definitely increased, the developing fetus is more resistant than she is to vitamin and mineral deficiencies because the placenta preferentially absorbs vitamins and minerals from the mother's blood. In cases where the diet is marginal, the money spent on vitamin pills and other food supplements would usually do the fetus more good if spent on wholesome, protein-rich food.

A few years ago, it was fashionable for a pregnant woman to keep her total weight gain to ten or fifteen pounds. It is now clear that a woman who limits her weight gain to this level does so at the expense of her child. Especially during the last trimester, restricted food intake leads to restricted fetal development and an underweight newborn. Significantly underweight infants face more post-delivery complications than do infants of normal weight. They also face a much higher incidence of mental retardation and other handicaps later in life. In most cases, a pregnant woman apparently should manage her diet to assure a total weight gain of between twenty and twenty-five pounds.

Lennart Nilsson from *A Child Is Born*, Delacorte Press

Figure 29.13 The fetus at nine weeks, floating in fluid inside the amniotic sac. (Here, the chorion, which covers the amniotic sac, has been opened and pulled aside.)

As birth approaches, the growing fetus places more and more demands on the mother for essential nutrients. During the last phase of pregnancy, the mother's diet profoundly shapes the course of development. Poor nutrition affects all organs, but it is most damaging to the brain. The human brain undergoes its greatest growth in the weeks just before and just after delivery. Normal brain growth is assured only if there are adequate amounts and kinds of amino acids for building brain proteins.

Prospects for the newborn are also affected by the mother's long-term nutritional status. Generally, the better her nutrition has been (from before her own birth), the larger and healthier her infant is likely to be. In developing countries, the effects of marginal or inadequate nutrition persist for more than a generation. Recent studies in Asia show that children of malnourished women are less capable of using food efficiently. Also, when female children mature, they in turn tend to be small and to have smaller, less well-developed infants even if their own diet is improved. Studies in Japan suggest that long-term improvements in diet are necessary to diminish the effects of malnutrition.

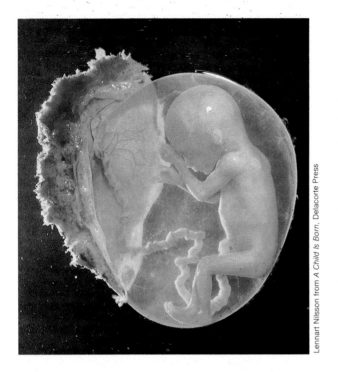

Figure 29.14 The four-month-old fetus: an adult in miniature (sixteen centimeters, or 6.4 inches, long).

Figure 29.15 Fetus at eighteen weeks, about eighteen centimeters (a little more than seven inches) long. The sucking reflex begins during the earliest fetal stage, as soon as nerves establish functional connections with developing muscles. Legs kick, arms wave, fingers make grasping motions—all reflexes that will be vital skills in the world outside the uterus.

Risk of Infections. Throughout pregnancy, antibodies are transferred across the placenta, and the developing individual has some protection from all but the most severe bacterial infections. But certain viral diseases can have their effects if they are contracted during the first six weeks after fertilization. That is the critical time of organ formation. The mother must maintain her body in the best of health and avoid becoming exposed to persons with viral infections.

For instance, if the mother contracts German measles during this period, there is a fifty percent chance that her embryo will become severely malformed. If the measles virus is contracted when ears are being formed, her infant can be born deaf. (With vaccination, German measles can be avoided. Also, the probability of damage diminishes after the first six weeks. The same disease, contracted during the fourth month or thereafter, has no discernible effect on the fetus.)

Effects of Drugs on Development. During the first trimester, the embryo is sensitive to drugs—to new, manufactured agents against which natural selection has not had the opportunity to build up defenses. The most shocking example of drug effects came during the first two years after the tranquilizer *thalidomide* was introduced on the market in Europe. Women using this drug during the first trimester gave birth to infants with missing or severely deformed arms and legs. As soon as the deformities were traced to thalidomide, the drug was withdrawn from the market. But there is evidence suggesting that various other tranquilizers as well as sedatives and barbiturates still in use might cause similar, although less severe, damage.

Even though certain drugs cause embryonic malformations only during the first trimester, the embryo does not become impervious to drugs in the maternal bloodstream at any stage. Many drugs pass freely across the placenta

COMMENTARY

In Vitro Fertilization

(The following is condensed from an article by Gina Kolata in Science, *201:698–699,*
25 August 1978. Copyright 1978 by the American Association for the Advancement of Science)*

Louise Brown, the first baby ever to be conceived in a petri dish, was born in England in July 1978. The technique for external conception (in vitro fertilization) is conceptually straightforward. Needed are ripe ova ready to be fertilized, sperm, a medium in which to mix the two, and a medium in which to support initial embryonic development. To obtain the ripe ova, the woman is given a hormone that causes her ovaries to prepare eggs for release. Then, thirty-three to thirty-four hours later, it is time to try recovering the eggs. If a few extra hours elapse, the eggs will have been released from the ovary and will be unrecoverable. The woman is put under general anesthesia for removal of the preovulatory eggs. A small incision is made in her abdomen and a laparoscope inserted. A laparoscope is a long metal tube containing a light and an optical system, and can be used to view ovaries directly. Preovulatory eggs, which look like bulges on the ovarian surface, are removed by suction.

Before laparoscopy, the woman's husband donates a sperm sample, which is washed and diluted in order to simulate conditions in the oviducts. The sperm are put in salt solution. Within a few fours, they undergo chemical changes that prepare them for fertilization. Sperm-containing droplets are then placed in a petri dish partly filled with inert oil. The oil keeps the droplets intact and confines the ova (which are added to one of these droplets) in a small volume, together with the sperm.

A few hours after sperm and ovum are combined, fertilization occurs. About twelve hours later, the embryo is transferred to a solution that supports embryonic development. Some time between two and four days after fertilization, the developing embryo is inserted into the woman's uterus. The embryo is drawn into a fine tube, the tube is inserted into the uterus, and the embryo is expelled. If all goes well, the embryo may implant.

With all this laboratory involvement in what is usually a natural process of conception and implantation, many have questioned whether the resulting babies will be normal. The geneticist Joseph Schulman says that "There are no data to support the fears that in vitro fertilization will lead to abnormal babies. But more research is clearly desirable." A substantial amount of work has been done with other animals, and there is no evidence that in vitro fertilization leads to genetic or morphological abnormalities in the offspring of any species. According to Schulman, preimplantation animal embryos are surprisingly resistant to manipulation. "You can remove cells from embryos, you can take two embryos and fuse them, or you can freeze embryos. Yet the resulting offspring are reported to be normal."

Even supposing there were an increased risk of abnormalities, Schulman says, the decision to have a child should be left to the prospective parents. This is common medical practice. For example, if a couple has a child with a genetic disease, there is often one chance in four that subsequent children will also have the disease. Yet no one tells such couples that they cannot have children.

*Louise Brown no longer remains the only baby conceived outside the human body. The technique has already been repeated, and the babies conceived in petri dishes appear to be normal in all respects.

and have the same kind of effect on the fetus as on the woman who takes them. For example, infants born to heroin addicts are themselves addicted. Fetal alcohol syndrome (FAS) is a constellation of deformities that are thought to result from excessive use of alcohol by the mother during pregnancy. It is true that certain medicines and drugs may be necessary in certain cases. However, the decision to use them at any time during pregnancy should be made by a skilled physician.

Effects of Smoking on Development. Cigarette smoking is known to have an adverse effect on fetal growth and development. A woman who smokes every day throughout pregnancy has smaller infants. They are smaller even when her weight and nutritional status and all other variables are identical with those of pregnant women who do not smoke. Often it has been stated that such infants are normal in all other ways. However, consider the results from a recent study in the British Isles. In England, Scotland, and Wales, records were kept for seven years on all infants born during one particular week. Those infants born to women who smoked were indeed smaller. They also had a thirty percent greater incidence of death shortly after delivery and a fifty percent greater incidence of heart abnormalities. More startling, at age seven, such children had an average "reading age" nearly half a year behind that of children born to women who were nonsmokers.

In this last study, the critical period was shown to be the last half of pregnancy. Children born to women who had stopped smoking by the middle of the second trimester were indistinguishable from those born to women who had never smoked. Although the mechanisms by which smoking exerts its effects on the fetus are not known, its demonstrated effects are further evidence that the placenta—marvelous structure that it is—cannot prevent all the assaults on the fetus that the human mind can dream up.

CONTROL OF HUMAN FERTILITY

Some Ethical Considerations

Few processes are more inspiring than the transformation of a single fertilized egg into an intricately detailed, coordinated adult—and few processes evoke more profound questions. *When does development begin?* As you have read, many key aspects of development have already emerged before the union of sperm and egg. This answer leads to

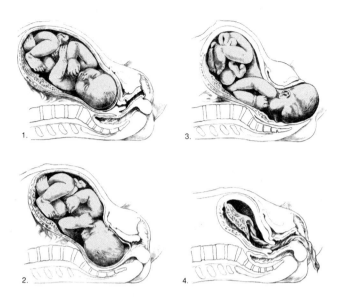

Figure 29.16 Movement of a full-term fetus from the uterus during childbirth. The last frame shows expulsion of the afterbirth (placenta).

a more basic question: *When does life begin?* During her lifetime, a human female can produce as many as four hundred eggs—and all those eggs are alive. During one ejaculation, a human male can produce a quarter of a billion sperm—and all of those sperm are alive. Even before sperm and egg merge by chance and establish the genetic constitution of a new individual, they are as much alive as any other form of life. It is scarcely tenable, then, to suggest that "life begins" when they fuse. *Life began billions of years ago; and each sperm and egg, each zygote and mature individual, is only a fleeting stage in the continuation of that beginning.*

This fact cannot diminish the meaning of conception, for it is no small thing to entrust a new individual with the gift of life, wrapped in the unique threads of our species and handed down through an immense sweep of time. Who among us can witness the birth of a living creature and not know the force of the life process? For an instant, the past and future converge as we sense the links between the newborn and unseen predecessors.

How can we reconcile the compelling moment of individual birth with our growing awareness of too many births in the biosphere? At the time this book is being written, an average of 2.2 infants are being born each second—132 each minute, 7,920 each hour. By the time you go to bed tonight, there will be 190,080 more humans on earth than there were last night at that hour. Within a week, the number will reach 1,330,560—about as many people as there are now in the entire state of Massachusetts. *Within one week.*

Our astounding birth rate has outstripped our resources, and each year millions face the horrors of starvation. Living as we do in one of the most productive lands on earth, few of us can know what it means to give birth to a child, to give it the gift of life, and have no food to keep it alive. Few of us can know what it means to a mother thirty years old, with eight children and with the knowledge that they face poverty and starvation. From a photograph in a magazine her dying children look out at us and, uncomprehending, we turn the page.

Living as they do with such realities, people over much of the world have practiced abortion, often by the most primitive and dangerous methods imaginable. Long before birth control became a global issue, individuals resorted to infanticide. Such practices mean the deliberate termination of life. Just as surely, indifference to rampant population growth means the deliberate termination of life. Many believe it is wrong to deny life to an unborn embryo. Just as many believe it is no solution to withhold compassion from those who have no alternative but to resign themselves to starving to death.

A related problem is the lack of enough educational programs concerning fertility control, as well as a disinclination to practice what *is* known about those controls. Each year in the United States we have about 100,000 shotgun marriages, about 200,000 unwed teenage mothers, and perhaps 1,500,000 abortions. This is a legacy of confusion arising from a sexual revolution that has swept through our society down to the primary school level. On the one hand, many parents promote increasingly early boy–girl relationships. On the other hand, they close their eyes to the possibility of premarital intercourse and unplanned pregnancy. Advice is often condensed to a terse, "Don't do it. But if you do it, be careful!"

More than 500 million years of sexual evolution have fostered a powerful motivation to engage in sex. Overlaid on that motivation are a few centuries of moral sanctions that demand suppression of the compelling sex drive, and a global population growth rate gone out of control. How will we reconcile our biological past and the need for a stabilized cultural present? Whether human fertility is to be controlled—and how it is to be controlled—are two of the most volatile issues of this decade. We will return to this issue in Chapter Thirty-Six, in the context of principles governing the growth and stability of all populations. Here, we can briefly consider some of the possible control options.

Possible Means of Birth Control

At present, notions about birth control fall into three categories:

1. Fertility control (*physical, chemical, surgical, or behavioral interventions that disrupt reproductive function or affect gamete survival*)

2. Implantation control (*physical or chemical interference with the blastocyst's ability to become lodged in the uterine wall*)

3. Abortion (*prevention of embryonic development after implantation has occurred*)

Let's consider some behavioral interventions first. The most effective method of preventing conception in the first place is complete **abstention**: no sexual intercourse whatsoever. It is unrealistic to expect many people to practice it. A modified form of abstention is the **rhythm method**, whereby intercourse is avoided during the woman's fertile period. The fertile period begins a few days before and ends a few days after ovulation. It is identified and tracked either by keeping records of the length of the woman's menstrual cycle or by taking her temperature each morning when she wakes up. (Just before the fertile period, there is a one-half to one-degree rise in core temperature.) However, ovulation can be irregular, and miscalculations are frequent. Also, sperm deposited in the vaginal tract a few days prior to ovulation can survive until ovulation. The method *is* inexpensive (it costs nothing after you buy the thermometer) and it doesn't require fittings and periodic checkups by a doctor. But its practitioners do run a substantial risk of becoming pregnant (see Table 29.3).

Withdrawal is the removal of the penis from the vagina prior to ejaculation. It is a truly ancient contraceptive method dating at least from biblical times. Withdrawal requires extraordinary willpower. Even if the mind manages to conquer the body, the method may fail anyway: fluid released from the penis just before ejaculation may contain viable sperm.

The practice of **douching**, or rinsing out the vagina with a chemical right after intercourse, is almost useless. Sperm can move past the cervix and out of reach of the douche within ninety seconds after ejaculation. No panicky flight to the medicine chest and frenzied rinsing is that rapid.

Other methods use physical or chemical barriers that prevent sperm from entering the uterus and moving to the ovarian ducts. **Spermicidal foam** or **spermicidal jelly** is packaged in an applicator. The applicator is inserted and emptied into the vagina just before intercourse. The product is toxic to sperm, yet is not always reliable when used without another device, such as a diaphragm or condom. A **diaphragm** is a flexible, dome-shaped device that is inserted into the vagina and positioned over the cervix before intercourse. A diaphragm is relatively effective when it is used with foam or jelly, when it has been fitted by a doctor, when it is inserted correctly with each use, and when foam or jelly is reapplied with each sexual contact.

Condoms are thin, tight-fitting sheaths of rubber or animal skin that are worn over the penis during intercourse. They are about eighty-five to ninety-three percent reliable. Condoms do have an advantage, in that they help prevent venereal disease. But they can only be put on over an erect penis, which calls for interruption of activity at a time when rational behavior might not seem as interesting as immediate fulfillment. Also, condoms can tear and leak, which renders them useless.

Another method of fertility control is hormonal intervention in the reproductive cycle. Most widely used is **the Pill**. The Pill is an oral contraceptive of synthetic estrogens and progesterones. The synthetic hormones suppress the normal release of gonadotropins from the pituitary, and thereby prevent the cyclic maturation and release of ova. The Pill is a prescription drug. Formulations vary and are selected to match the individual patient's needs. That is why it is not wise for a woman to borrow the Pill from someone else.

If the woman doesn't forget to take her daily dosage, the Pill is one of the most reliable methods of controlling fertility. There is no interruption of the sexual act, and the program is easy to follow. Often the Pill corrects erratic menstrual cycles and decreases the associated cramping. For a small number of users, the Pill is not without potential side effects. In the first month or so of use, it may cause nausea, weight gain, tissue swelling, and minor headaches. Its continued use may lead to blood clotting in the veins of a few women (3 out of 10,000) predisposed to this disorder. There have been some cases of elevated blood pressure and abnormalities in fat metabolism (which might be linked to a growing number of gallbladder disorders). Proponents of the Pill argue that for most women, the known risks associated with its use are far lower than the risks associated with pregnancy.

Hormonal control of male fertility is a more difficult matter. The hormonal methods for suppressing female fertility are based on the cyclic nature of the woman's reproductive capacity. Sperm production in males is not cyclic, and it is under a more diffuse kind of hormonal

Table 29.3	Effectiveness of Some Contraceptive Methods
Method Used	Number of Pregnancies Per 100 Women Per Year
None	115*
Douching	31
Rhythm method	13–24
Spermicidal jelly or foam alone	20
Withdrawal	18
Condom alone	14
Diaphragm with foam or jelly	3–17
IUD	5
The Pill	1
The Pill used correctly	0
Vasectomy	0
Tubal ligation	0

*This figure includes women who become pregnant more than once a year, following miscarriage or childbirth.

Data from D. Luciano et al., 1978, *Human Function and Structure* and other sources.

control. Various medications have been developed, but they are still experimental. It will probably be several years before they become available, and their potential effectiveness is currently in doubt.

Surgical intervention in the reproductive tract includes **vasectomy** in males. A tiny incision is made in the scrotum so that each vas deferens can be severed and tied off. The simple operation can be performed in twenty minutes in a doctor's office, with only a local anesthetic. After vasectomy, sperm cannot leave the epididymides, and therefore will not be present in seminal fluid. (Sperm can be present in duct regions below the surgical cuts, however, and they can be present in ejaculate for several weeks after the operation.) So far there is no firm evidence that vasectomy disrupts the male hormone system, and surveys suggest there is no noticeable difference in sexual activity. Although vasectomies can be reversed, half of the men who have undergone surgery will have already developed antibodies against sperm and there may be a higher incidence of infertility among them.

For females, surgical intervention includes **tubal ligation**. Here, the oviducts are cauterized or cut and tied off. Tubal ligation is more complex than vasectomy and is usually performed in a hospital. A small number of women who have had the operation suffer recurring bouts of pain and inflammation of tissues in the pelvic region where the surgery was performed. For women who later change their minds, the operation can be reversed, although major surgery is required and success is not always assured.

The **intrauterine device**, or **IUD**, is used to prevent implantation. A doctor must insert this small plastic or metal device into the uterus. With this foreign object in place, a fertilized egg cannot remain implanted in the uterine wall. In cases where implantation does occur, the IUD stimulates processes that dislodge the embryo. The IUD is relatively inexpensive. Once inserted, it requires not much further thought unless it is accidentally expelled from the uterus. With newer designs, such as the Copper-T, expulsions are rare.

Some complications are associated with the IUD. Typically, menstrual flow increases markedly. Usually the increase is inconvenient only, but in a few cases there are increased possibilities of anemia or hemorrhage. Some research indicates that the IUD can perforate the uterus, causing life-threatening hemorrhage and providing entry for bacteria into body tissues. With the potential for such complications, supervision by a doctor is necessary. A checkup every six months is advised to verify that the device is in place and functioning properly.

Once conception and implantation are realities, the only way of terminating a pregnancy is **abortion**, whereby the implanted embryo is dislodged and removed from the uterus. (In *miscarriages,* the embryo is dislodged and expelled spontaneously.) Until recently, abortions were generally forbidden by law in the United States, unless the pregnancy endangered the mother's life. Supreme Court rulings in the past decade held that the State does not have the power to forbid abortions during the early stages of pregnancy (typically up to five months). The outcome has been legalization of abortion in this country. Moving the large number of backroom operations to modern medical facilities at least reduces the frequency of dangerous, traumatic, and often fatal attempts to abort embryos, either by pregnant women themselves or by quacks. Newer methods have made it relatively rapid, painless, and free of complications when performed during the first trimester. Abortions in the second and third trimesters will probably remain extremely controversial unless the mother's life is clearly threatened. For both medical and humanitarian reasons, however, it is generally agreed in this country that an acceptable route to birth control is not through abortion but through control of conception in the first place.

Readings

Balinsky, B. 1981. *An Introduction to Embryology.* Fifth edition. Philadelphia: Saunders. A superior reference text.

Greep, R. (editor). 1980. *Reproductive Physiology III* (volume 22 of the *International Review of Physiology*). Baltimore: University Park Press. Distills recent concepts and discoveries in reproductive physiology. The article "Ovarian Follicular and Luteal Physiology" by C. Channing et al. is especially informative.

Nilsson, L., et al. 1977. *A Child Is Born.* New York: Delacourt Press/Seymour Lawrence. Extraordinary photographs of embryonic development.

Saunders, J. 1982. *Developmental Biology: Patterns, Problems, Principles.* New York: Macmillan.

Vander, A., J. Sherman, D. Luciano. 1980. *Human Physiology: The Mechanisms of Body Function.* Third edition. New York: McGraw-Hill. These authors consistently produce authoritative books on human physiology. The material on human reproductive physiology is very well done.

Review Questions

1. Study Table 29.1. Then list the main organs of the human male reproductive tract and identify their functions.

2. What are the accessory glands of the male reproductive tract? What are their functions?

3. Describe spermatogenesis and the route by which sperm leave the seminiferous tubules, then the body.

4. Which three hormones have profound influence over male reproductive functioning? Can you diagram how negative feedback mechanisms link the hypothalamus, anterior pituitary, and interstitial cells in controlling this functioning?

5. Study Table 29.2. Then list the main organs of the female reproductive tract and their functions.

6. Trace the events by which an oocyte matures into an ova.

7. What is the menstrual cycle? Which four hormones have profound influence on this cycle? Can you diagram the feedback loops between the hypothalamus, anterior pituitary, and ovary that govern these hormonal secretions? (Review Figure 29.9).

8. List the four events that are triggered by the surge of LH at the midpoint of the menstrual cycle.

9. What changes occur in the endometrium during the menstrual cycle?

10. Distinguish between (a) morula and blastocyst, and (b) embryo and fetus.

11. Define these embryonic membranes: amnion, yolk sac, allantois, and placenta. From what tissue does each arise, and what is its function?

UNIT SIX

EVOLUTION

30

INDIVIDUALS, POPULATIONS, AND EVOLUTION

Where would the mallard duck be now if its destiny had been placed in the hands of that seventeenth-century cataloger of life, Carl von Linné? There, awaiting classification, was a bird with emerald-green head feathers and with wings displaying metallic blue patches. There, in the same ponds and marshes, was a drab little brown-feathered duck bearing no obvious resemblance to the more resplendent waterfowl. Thus did von Linné, on the basis of appearance alone, pronounce the male and female mallard duck as separate species. (It goes without saying that the male and female duck, paying no attention whatsoever to his pronouncement, continued to produce more ducks.)

You may be thinking that it is somewhat unfair to von Linné to dredge up one of his erroneous deductions. But put yourself in his shoes and suppose you had come across the male and female mallard duck for the first time. How would you go about classifying them? The point is, anybody armed with the notion of rigid species slots would encounter some problems. Recall, from Chapter Two, that studies of organismic diversity were once funneled through the concept that species do not change. The approach was *typological*: an individual was selected as being the perfect

Gary Zahm

Figure 30.1 Population of snow geese at their wintering ground in New Mexico. Although these birds all look the same, there is considerable variation in genotypes from one individual to the next. Such variation is the raw material for evolution.

type for the species, based on a rather arbitrary choice of what "perfect" physical features were. Then individual specimens were compared against the standard to determine if they were the same kind of thing. Small variations among similar individuals were viewed as imperfect renditions of the perfect, static species plan. Dramatic variations in physical appearance were often viewed as evidence in itself of different species.

Today, this somewhat rigid approach has been set aside. *Far from being unimportant, variation within populations is now seen to be the raw material for evolution.*

VARIATION: WHAT IT IS, HOW IT ARISES

Sources of Variation. You know from earlier units that variation exists at many levels. For example, at the molecular level, one amino acid substitution gives rise to the abnormal hemoglobin S (HbS) associated with sickle-cell anemia. At the cytological level, nondisjunction at meiosis can lead to two copies of chromosome 21 in a human gamete. And fusion of this gamete with a normal one can lead to a variant trisomic 21 individual ($2n + 1$) showing Down's syndrome. Also at the cytological level, genetic recombination (through crossing over and independent assortment of chromosomes at meiosis) followed by sexual fusion can lead to phenotypic variation. Table 12.1 summarized the different sources of variation. Here, it is enough to keep in mind that they fall in these broad categories:

    Gene mutation
    Chromosome mutation
    Genetic recombination

Until now, we have considered the effects of these events mostly in terms of the individual. We are now ready to extend this picture to the level of populations.

Discontinuous and Continuous Variation. A population can be defined as a group of individuals of the same species, occupying a given area at a given time. Within any natural population, individuals show variation in phenotypes. As you read in Chapter Ten, some of this variation is *discontinuous*, in that the phenotypes fall into one or another of a few clearly distinguishable classes. Thus Mendel's pea plants showed discontinuous variation in flower color (white *or* purple, with no shades in between). However, most phenotypic variation is *continuous*, with small differences in some trait occurring over a more or less continuous range.

Individuals in a population sample can be measured in order to determine the distribution of values for a given trait. For example, Figure 30.2 shows the result of measurements for the frequency of different heights among a group of Army recruits. Commonly, charting the data from such measurements produces a bell-shaped curve of the sort shown in Figure 30.3. (The arrangement of individuals in the photograph of Figure 30.2 gives a rough approximation of this kind of curve.) Measurements of this sort can be taken over time, and the data can be compared to determine whether the frequency of a given value of a trait has remained the same or is shifting with time. As you will see, such documentation is important in population studies.

If there were no variation of the sort just described, then all phenotypes would be identical, so would the under-

(number of individuals)
1 0 0 1 5 7 7 22 25 26 27 17 11 17 4 4 1

(height, inches)
58 59 60 61 62 63 64 65 66 67 68 69 70 71 72 73 74

Figure 30.2 An example of continuous variation in a population sample: height distribution in a group of 175 United States Army recruits about the turn of the century.

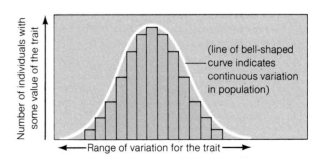

(line of bell-shaped curve indicates continuous variation in population)

Number of individuals with some value of the trait

Range of variation for the trait

Figure 30.3 Generalized bell-shaped curve typical of populations showing continuous variation in some trait.

Hardy-Weinberg Rule:

$$p + q = 1$$

where p is the frequency of one allele at a given gene locus, and q is the frequency of the alternative allele.

Assumptions: There is no mutation, the population is large and is isolated from other populations, mating is random, and all genotypes are equally viable and fertile.

Prediction: The allele frequencies *and* the genotypic frequencies will be stable through infinite generations.

Figure 30.4 Hardy-Weinberg equilibrium. To prove the validity of the Hardy-Weinberg rule stated above, let's follow the course of two alleles, *A* and *a*, through succeeding generations.

For all members of the population, the gene locus must be occupied by either *A* or *a*. In mathematical terms, the frequencies of *A* and *a* must add up to 1. For example, if *A* occupies half of all the gene loci and *a* occupies the other half, then $0.5 + 0.5 = 1$. If *A* occupies ninety percent of all the gene loci, then *a* must occupy the remaining ten percent ($0.9 + 0.1 = 1$). No matter what the proportions of alleles *A* and *a*,

$$p + q = 1$$

You know that during sexual reproduction of diploid organisms, the two alleles at a gene locus segregate and end up in separate gametes. Thus p is also the proportion of gametes carrying the *A* allele, and q the proportion carrying the *a* allele. To find the expected frequencies of the three possible genotypes (*AA, Aa,* and *aa*) in the population, we can construct a Punnett square:

	p Ⓐ	q ⓐ
p Ⓐ	*AA* (p^2)	*Aa* (pq)
q ⓐ	*Aa* (pq)	*aa* (q^2)

Because the frequency of genotypes must add up to 1,

$$p^2 + 2pq + q^2 = 1$$

To see how these calculations can be applied, let's follow the allele frequencies for a population of 1,000 diploid individuals made up of the following genotypes:

450 *AA*
500 *Aa*
50 *aa*
1,000 individuals (or 2,000 alleles)

Theoretically, of every 1,000 gametes produced, the frequency of *A* will be $450 + \frac{1}{2}(500) = 700$, or $p = 0.7$. The frequency of *a* will be $\frac{1}{2}(500) + 50 = 300$, or $q = 0.3$. Notice that

$$p + q = 0.7 + 0.3 = 1$$

After one round of random mating, the frequencies of the three genotypes possible in the next generation will be as follows:

$$AA = p^2 \quad = 0.7 \times 0.7 = 0.49$$
$$Aa = 2pq = 2 \times 0.7 \times 0.3 = 0.42$$
$$aa = q^2 \quad = 0.3 \times 0.3 = 0.09$$

and

$$p^2 + 2pq + q^2 = 0.49 + 0.42 + 0.09 = 1$$

Notice that the allele frequencies have not changed:

$$A = \frac{2 \times 490 + 420}{2{,}000 \text{ alleles}} = \frac{1{,}400}{2{,}000} = 0.7 = p$$

$$a = \frac{2 \times 90 + 420}{2{,}000 \text{ alleles}} = \frac{600}{2{,}000} = 0.3 = q$$

The genotypic frequencies have changed initially. However, given that the distribution of genotypes fits the equation $p^2 + 2pq + q^2$, the genotypic frequencies will be stable over succeeding generations. You can verify this by calculating the most probable allele frequencies for gametes produced by the second-generation individuals:

F_1 Genotypes: 0.49 *AA* 0.42 *Aa* 0.09 *aa*

Gametes: Ⓐ Ⓐ Ⓐ ⓐ ⓐ ⓐ

0.49 + 0.21 0.21 + 0.09

0.7 *A* 0.3 *a*

which is back where we started from. Because the allele frequencies are exactly the same as those of the original gametes, they will yield the same frequencies of genotypes as in the second generation.

You could go on with the calculations until you ran out of paper, or patience. As long as the population adheres to the conditions stated in the boxed inset for the Hardy-Weinberg rule, you would end up with the same results. When the frequencies of different alleles and different genotypes remain constant through successive generations, the population is in Hardy-Weinberg equilibrium; it is not evolving.

lying genotypes, and populations never would evolve. *Evolution can occur only when there is preexisting variation in a population.* The forces acting on that variation, and the consequences of their action, are the subjects of this chapter.

THE HARDY-WEINBERG BASELINE FOR MEASURING CHANGE

The sum total of all the genes of a given population has traditionally been called a gene pool. For populations of sexually reproducing individuals, it is more accurate to think of it as a pool of alleles. (*Alleles,* recall, are alternative forms of a gene at a given locus.) When you take the whole population into account, you find that for any one locus, some alleles occur more often than others. Thus it is possible to think of variation in terms of **allele frequencies**: the relative abundance of different alleles carried by the individuals in that population.

Early in this century, the mathematician G. Hardy and the physician W. Weinberg independently came up with a simple rule that can be used as a baseline against which changes in allele frequencies can be measured. They predicted the following:

In the absence of disturbing factors, the frequencies of different alleles and genotypes in a population will remain stable indefinitely.

This prediction is based on a mathematical formula called the **Hardy-Weinberg rule**, which is given in Figure 30.4. The prediction applies to an idealized population of sexually reproducing organisms that is not evolving. The assumption is that evolution cannot occur under the following conditions:

1. No mutation

2. Large population size

3. Isolation from other populations of the same species (existing members stay put, new members not added)

4. Equal viability and fertility of all genotypes (no selection)

Figure 30.4 gives an example of the genetic results when all of these conditions are met. The example shows that the frequencies of two alleles (*A* and *a*) can stay the same over succeeding generations. The alleles might be shuffled around (through chromosomal crossing over, inde-

pendent assortment, and random mating), but their *frequencies* in the overall population do not change. Neither do the relative frequencies of the three possible genotypes (*AA*, *Aa*, and *aa*) change over the long term. Such stability of allelic and genotypic ratios is called **genetic equilibrium**.

Genetic equilibrium implies a static state that rarely exists in natural populations. Why, then, do we mention it at all? The reason is that genetic equilibrium is useful as a reference point, signifying zero evolution. *Hence the degree to which deviations are measured from this reference point can serve as a measure of the rates of evolutionary change.*

FACTORS BRINGING ABOUT CHANGE

When a population is evolving, its allele frequencies are changing through successive generations as a result of one or more of the following factors:

1. Mutation. A heritable change in the kind, structure, sequence, or number of the component parts of DNA.

2. Genetic drift. A random fluctuation in allele frequencies over time, due to chance occurrence alone.

3. Gene flow. A change in allele frequencies due to immigration (new individuals enter the population) or emigration (some individuals leave).

4. Natural selection. Differential survival and reproduction of genotypes within a population.

Of these factors, natural selection is by far the most important. Gene flow is second only to natural selection in bringing about change. Genetic drift has a negligible effect, except in those cases where population size is small. Mutations occur only rarely, and their effect on rates of evolution in a given population is generally small.

You may have noticed that genetic recombination (resulting from crossing over and from independent assortment of chromosomes at meiosis) is not listed as a factor that causes evolution. Recombination does contribute to phenotypic variation, and other forces (such as selective agents) can act on that variation. However, recombination in itself does not *change* the underlying allele frequencies, as the Hardy-Weinberg example in Figure 30.4 makes clear.

Let's now take a look at the effects of mutation, genetic drift, and gene flow before exploring in detail the effects of natural selection.

Effects of Mutation

Mutation is the original source of genotypic variation, and mutations have been accumulating for billions of years. In any population, mutations arise very infrequently, *but inevitably,* by chance. These spontaneous events can bring about small changes in allele frequencies.

A mutation has no intrinsic value. Its effect, large or small, is determined by how it changes the structure, function, or behavior of the individual under prevailing conditions. For example, a certain gene codes for a protein used in cartilage formation. Cartilage is a key component of many biosynthetic programs followed in normal animal development. A mutation at this gene locus can lead to such deformities as blocked nostrils, narrowed tracheal passageways, thickened ribs, and loss of elasticity in lung tissue. Here, the new allele produced by mutation is expressed in the context of an intricate developmental program, and it can have lethally disruptive effects. As another example, a gene mutation can lead to an altered enzyme that functions at a higher temperature than normal. If the individual happens to end up in an environment where temperatures are higher than those typically encountered by its species, enzyme function will not be diminished. Here, the mutation is advantageous in the new environmental context but not in the old one.

Even though mutations are neither good nor bad in themselves, most mutations are harmful, even lethal. The reason is that a new allele represents a departure from alleles that have withstood the test of time. Overall, the structural, functional, and behavioral traits of an organism already allow it to function well in a particular context. A drastic change is likely to derange things rather than enhance them. Quite probably, all but a very small fraction of the rare mutations that do arise in a population prove to be harmful or lethal.

The rare new alleles that do appear in a given population are neither harmful nor beneficial in themselves; their effects depend on the contexts in which their gene products are expressed.

Of course, just because a new allele is not beneficial does not mean that it cannot be passed from one generation to the next. It could be that its effects are masked by its allelic partner. It could also be that the mutation makes no difference whatsoever in a given environmental context, so that there might be no selection for *or* against the mutation. And it could also be that the new allele is closely linked in the chromosome to highly adaptive genes. Thus it could ride on the coattails of the adaptive genes through meiosis, sexual fusion, and environmental tests.

Mutations and Sexual Reproduction: Over evolutionary time, the DNA in many sexually reproducing species has increased in amount, perhaps by such events as gene duplication (Chapter Twelve). With the increase, of course, came an increased potential for mutation. Mutations began to accumulate—and most mutations are harmful. That may be the reason why sexual reproduction, once it had emerged, turned out to be irreversible.

Consider that its practitioners benefit from gene complementation—a backup set of genes. If a harmful mutation appears in one DNA strand, the allele on the other might cover its function. If the environment changes, a variant allele might permit survival under new conditions. *Without this backup set of genes, the "hidden" stores of potentially harmful alleles would be expressed.* In this view, the basic advantage of sexual reproduction is that it helps keep mutation loads in check; its advantage in giving rise to genetic recombinants (upon which selective agents can act) came into play later.

Genetic Drift

Sometimes evolution occurs by genetic drift—the chance increase or decrease in the relative abundance of different alleles. Genetic drift can be at work in both large and small populations, but only in small populations does it have an important effect (Figure 30.5).

For example, suppose that over several generations in a small population, none of the bearers of an allele designated *A* reproduces—simply as a result of chance mating, illnesses, and early deaths. Assuming that genetic drift is the only force operating at the time, the *A* allele can be completely lost, leaving an alternative fixed in the population.

By analogy, there are two outcomes when you toss a coin, each with equal probability of occurring. When the coin is tossed ten times, it could by chance end up tails eight times, or two times, or one, rather than the expected 1:1 ratio (half heads, half tails). However, the laws of probability tell you that when the coin is tossed, say, a thousand times, there is greater chance of approaching the expected ratio. Now consider a large population subjected to no other evolutionary force than genetic drift. In such populations, there is more probability that allele frequencies will not change much over the long term simply because of the proportionally greater chances of survival and reproduction of all genotypes.

One more point can be made here. Some alleles in a population may not be the "best" possible alternatives in contributing to survival and reproduction. Through genetic drift, they may have become established just because other alternatives were lost by chance. Suppose that in a small population of blue parakeets and green parakeets, the allele governing blue feather color is lost as a result of genetic drift, and all parakeets of the next generation are green. This change in feather color has arisen not because one color is more advantageous than the other, but because chance events led to a change in genotypes (hence phenotypes).

Genetic drift is evolution by chance. It refers to an increase or decrease in the relative abundance of different alleles through successive generations, simply by chance.

Founder Effect. Sometimes a small number of dispersed individuals manage to establish a new population. Simply by chance, the allele frequencies at many gene loci are likely to be different in these individuals from what they were in the original population, and the new assortment will dictate the genotypic character of the new population. This extreme case of genetic drift is called the **founder effect**. The founder effect may be important in the colonization of oceanic islands and other isolated locations (such as landlocked, glacier-fed lakes that are "seeded" with a few trout by fishermen).

Bottlenecks. Genetic drift can also occur when populations go through **bottlenecks**, whereby population size is drastically reduced because of unfavorable conditions. Even though the population may eventually recover, genetic drift during the bottleneck can alter the relative abundance of alleles. For example, just before the turn of the century, hunters almost destroyed the population of northern elephant seals. Only twenty seals survived. Since that time, the population has increased to more than 30,000. Intriguingly, electrophoresis studies have shown that there is no allelic variation whatsoever at twenty-four gene loci that have been studied. The lack of variation is unique, compared to seal populations that have not gone through comparable bottlenecks. It suggests that a number of alleles were lost during the bottleneck.

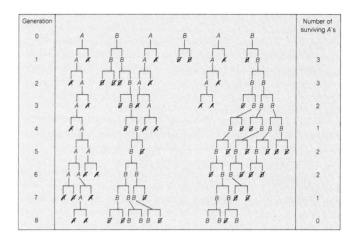

Figure 30.5 Example of genetic drift. Each individual of genotypes A and B produces two identical offspring in each generation. Half the offspring die before reproductive age (population size remains constant), but which ones die is random and does not depend on genotype. The relative abundance of genotypes fluctuates randomly until A no longer is represented and B becomes fixed in the population. (Which individuals were to die in this example was determined by tossing a coin.) (From D. Futuyma, *Evolutionary Biology*, Sinauer, 1979)

Gene Flow

Probably very few populations are completely isolated from other populations of the same species. Individuals migrate among populations, pollen grains drift or are transported from one to another, and currents carry sperm of marine organisms from one to another.

As a specific example, baboons in Africa generally live in troops. Each troop represents a separate allele pool. Commonly, some of the males wander off or are driven from one troop. They may join with another troop some distance away. Assuming that migrant males encounter receptive females in the new population, and assuming they have offspring, the pool of alleles changes, just as it changes in the troop the baboons left behind.

For many plant and animal species, most of the offspring, spores, or gametes end up close to the parent. (For example, in 1951, R. Colwell released and then tracked radioactively labeled pollen grains from a species of pine. Most of the pollen was dispersed downwind, only ten to twenty feet from the source. The amount dispersed then dropped off quickly farther from the source.) When such dispersal patterns continue over generations, populations with somewhat distinct genotypes can become established in the same region. At the same time, winds, insects, birds, and other dispersal agents might carry some offspring, spores, or gametes beyond the typical dispersal range. A small but probably significant amount of gene flow thereby occurs, the result being a homogenizing effect on the genotypic character of neighboring populations of the same species. Thus gene flow is thought to be a main factor in decreasing the variation between populations—variation that might arise through genetic drift, mutation, and selection.

Gene flow among populations is based on the physical dispersal of alleles, and tends to decrease divergence that might arise through other evolutionary factors.

In a few cases, long-distance migration can also occur, as it does for human populations. Generally, though, dispersal past a certain range can put offspring in an environment to which their particular genotypes are not well adapted, so survival is not necessarily assured.

Natural Selection

The simple fact that individuals vary in genotype and phenotype means that they are likely to be equipped in different ways to deal with environmental challenges. Some will be more suitable, in certain contexts, for surviving and reproducing. If their phenotypic differences are genetically based, then alleles associated with the advantageous phenotypes will tend to increase in frequency in the population.

The formal statement of this concept is called the theory of natural selection. It was first formulated in the nineteenth century by Charles Darwin and Alfred Wallace, as you read in Chapter Two. Here we will take a closer look at the logic of this theory.

Darwin, recall, was fascinated with the variation that exists in populations. Much of the variation had to be heritable, for it could be passed on from one generation to the next. At the same time, Darwin knew from his studies of artificial selection that the variation was not necessarily static. For example, selective breeding could lead to exuberantly diverse breeds of pigeons, as shown in Figure 2.8. In the case of pigeons, at least, humans obviously were doing the selecting—but what could be the basis of selection in *natural* populations?

In arriving at the answer, Darwin correlated his observations of inheritance with certain observable characteristics of populations and the environment. First, he knew that all populations have enormous reproductive potential. If all individuals that are born were themselves to reproduce, then population size would burgeon. (The reason is that, with each increase in the number of reproducing members, the potential reproductive base enlarges.) Yet Darwin also knew that populations generally do not undergo berserk expansions. Finally, he knew that food supplies and other resources do not increase explosively; in most environments, resources more or less remain within certain limits. Therefore, when population size outstrips the resources necessary to sustain it, there must be *competition* for the resources that are available.

From these and other observations, Darwin put together a theory of natural selection which, because of its importance, will be restated here:

1. In any population, more offspring tend to be produced than can survive to reproductive age.

2. Members of the population vary in form and behavior. Much of the variation is heritable.

3. Some varieties of heritable traits are more *adaptive* than others: they improve chances of surviving and reproducing under prevailing environmental conditions.

4. Because bearers of adaptive traits have a greater chance of reproducing, their offspring tend to make up an increasingly greater proportion of the reproductive base for each new generation. This tendency is called *differential reproduction*.

5. *"Differential reproduction"* is *natural selection*. Adaptive forms of traits show up (are selected for) with increased frequency in a population, because their bearers contribute proportionally more offspring to succeeding generations.

It is important to understand that natural selection is no longer in the realm of pure theory. It has been documented through studies of many plants, animals, and microorganisms. In the following section, we will consider a few examples of natural selection in specific populations.

EXAMPLES OF NATURAL SELECTION

There are three modes of natural selection, as Figure 30.6 and the following list indicate:

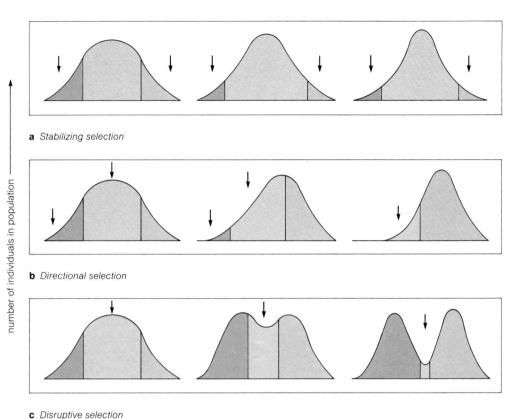

number of individuals in population

a *Stabilizing selection*

b *Directional selection*

c *Disruptive selection*

time

Figure 30.6 Three modes of natural selection. The blue-shaded and brown-shaded portions of the range of variation encompass individuals that are extreme phenotypes; the tan-shaded region is the range of the most common forms. (**a**) In stabilizing selection, conditions favor the most common forms. The downward-pointing arrows signify that variants are being selected against. (**b**) In directional selection, the phenotypic character of the population shifts as a whole in a consistent direction. (**c**) In disruptive selection, two or more extreme variants are favored and become increasingly represented in the population.

1. *Stabilizing selection* decreases the frequency of alleles that give rise to extreme forms of a trait, such that intermediate forms already well adapted to prevailing conditions are favored.

2. *Directional selection* moves the frequency distribution of alleles in a steady, consistent direction. The phenotypic character of the population shifts as a whole, either in response to directional change in the environment or as an adaptive response to a new environment.

3. *Disruptive selection* increases the frequency of two or more alleles that give rise to extreme forms of a trait, such that intermediate forms are selected against.

Stabilizing selection tends to counter the effects of mutation, genetic drift, and gene flow by favoring the most common forms of a trait. In contrast, directional selection

tends to favor one form at either extreme in the range of variation. Disruptive selection tends to foster an increase in the frequency of alleles at both extremes, the outcome being **dimorphism** (two forms of a trait) or **polymorphism** (three or more forms).

Stabilizing Selection

Human Birth Weight. On the average, human infants have a birth weight of about 7 pounds (3.2 kilograms). When birth weight is very low or very high relative to this value, there is much greater chance that the infant will not survive (Figure 30.8). The shape of the survival curve in this figure suggests that stabilizing selection is favoring individuals of birth weights between $7\frac{1}{2}$ and 8 pounds, and is working against those at either extreme. Studies in widely different populations have yielded remarkably similar data for birth weight and mortality.

Figure 30.7 Two hundred and fifty million years of stabilizing selection? (**a**) Body casting of a horseshoe crab made that long ago—imprints that could well be made by a modern-day horseshoe crab (**b**), here shown mating and perpetuating the general species form. (a, Peabody Museum of Natural History, Yale University)

a   b

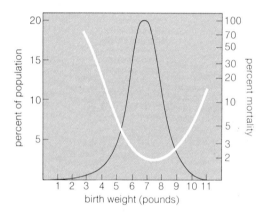

Figure 30.8 Birth weight distribution for 13,730 infants (black curve). The white line is the curve of early mortality in relation to birth weight. The optimum birth weight is between $7\frac{1}{2}$ and 8 pounds. (M. Karns, L. Penrose, *Annals of Eugenics*, 1951)

Horseshoe Crabs. Plowing across the sand in shallow waters off the northeast Atlantic coast is a dark-brown horseshoe crab (*Limulus polyphemus*). Its distinctive, somewhat flattened shape (Figure 30.7) is well suited for pushing through mud and sand as the animal scavenges for food, and for affording protection from predators.

Apparently horseshoe crabs are extremely well adapted to such environments. The fossil record indicates that for more than 250 million years, the form of horseshoe crabs has remained essentially the same, in essentially the same kind of environment. This kind of organism probably represents a balanced system of the best working combination of traits in a relatively stable environmental context. Presumably stabilizing selection has been at work here, eliminating variant individuals so that little structural change has occurred through evolutionary time.

Directional Selection

The Peppered Moth. Directional selection has occurred in populations of the peppered moth (*Biston betularia*), which is widely distributed in England. Before the mid-1800s, a speckled light-gray form of the moth (Figure 30.9) was prevalent. A dark-gray form also existed at that time but was extremely rare; at most it represented one percent of the population. Between 1848 and 1898, however, the dark form increased in frequency. Near one industrial city, it came to represent about ninety-eight percent of the population.

Today we know that a single gene locus, designated C, governs the wing and body color of these moths. The light-gray form is homozygous recessive (cc); the dark form is homozygous dominant or heterozygous. Thus the trait has a heritable basis and can be subject to selection.

In the 1930s, the geneticist E. Ford suggested that natural selection was causing the increased frequency of the dark form in industrial areas. Ford knew that before the industrial revolution, light-gray, speckled lichens grew profusely on trees. He also knew that the peppered moth is active at night but rests during the day on trees—where it is vulnerable to bird predators. Light-gray speckled moths

Table 30.1 Marked *Biston betularia* Moths Recaptured After Release in a Polluted Area and a Nonpolluted Area				
Area	Light-Gray Moths		Dark-Gray Moths	
	Number Released	Number Recaptured	Number Released	Number Recaptured
Near Birmingham (pollution high)	64	16 (25%)	154	82 (53%)
Near Dorset (pollution low)	393	54 (13.7%)	406	19 (4.7%)

Data after H. B. Kettlewell.

a

b

Figure 30.9 An example of variation that is subject to directional selection in changing environments. (**a**) The light- and dark-colored forms of the peppered moth are resting on a lichen-covered tree trunk. (**b**) This is how they appear on a soot-covered tree trunk, which was darkened by industrial air pollution.

resting on the lichens would be well camouflaged from the birds, whereas the dark moths would be most conspicuous (Figure 30.9a).

Ford reasoned that with the rise in industry, soot and other pollutants from smokestacks started killing the lichens and darkening the tree surfaces. In this new environmental context, the previously rare dark form blended with the blackened trees—and the light-gray form was no longer camouflaged. Hence the dark form began surviving and reproducing at a greater rate than its light-colored kin, and a change in allele frequencies resulted.

In the 1950s, H. Kettlewell used the *mark-release-recapture* method to test Ford's hypothesis. He bred both kinds of moths in captivity, then marked hundreds of them so that they could be identified as members of his experimental populations. He then released hundreds of the light and dark moths in two areas, one near the heavily industrialized area around Birmingham, and the other in the unpolluted area of Dorset. As many moths as possible were recaptured during the days that followed. Table 30.1 shows the results. More dark moths were recaptured in the polluted area—and more light moths were recaptured in the pollution-free area. By stationing watchers in blinds, Kettlewell also found by direct observations that birds captured light moths more easily around Birmingham—and dark moths more easily around Dorset.

About a hundred different species of moths have been undergoing the same kind of directional selection in response to pollution in industrial regions. However, as a result of strict pollution controls (which went into effect in 1952), lichens are now reestablished and tree surfaces are largely free of soot. As could be predicted by selection theory, the frequency of the dark forms is now declining in the moth populations.

Pesticide Resistance. Insect populations that develop resistance to insecticides provide other examples of directional selection. With the first application of an insecticide, most of the existing insects that it is designed to kill are indeed killed. But some individuals in the population may survive because of physiological differences that enable them to resist the insecticide's chemical effects. If the resistance has a genetic basis, it is a trait that can be passed on. Through differential survival and reproduction, the next generation will contain more of the resistant individuals.

Increasing numbers of resistant insects often lead to heavier and more frequent applications of the insecticide—

Figure 30.10 Effect of disruptive selection on females of African swallow-tail butterfly populations. Disruptive selection is apparently favoring several different female morphs.

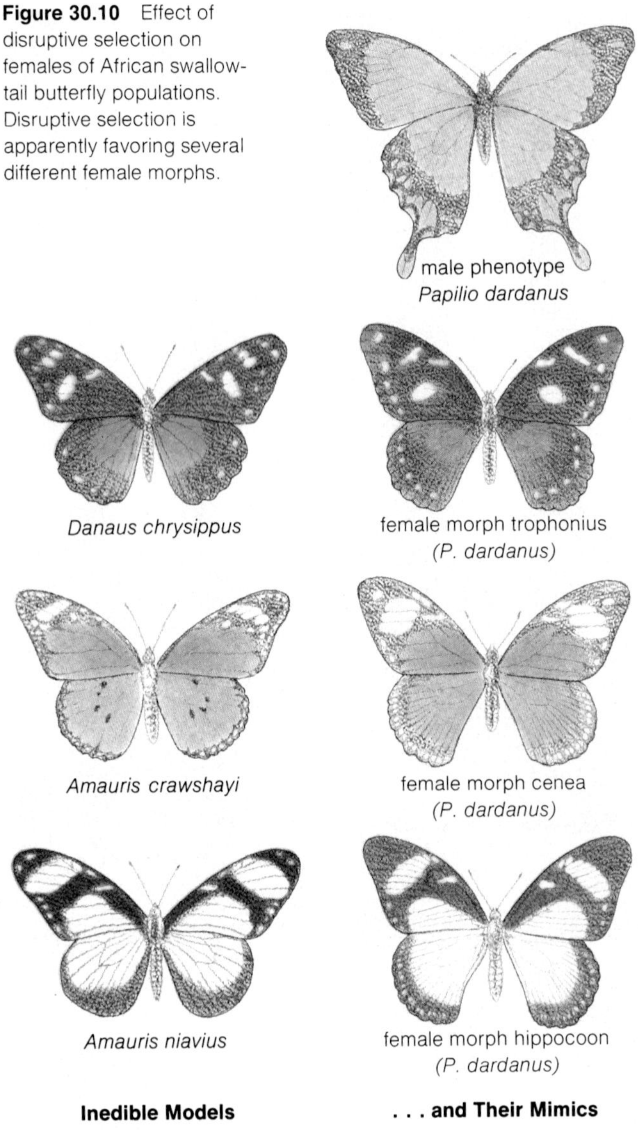

male phenotype
Papilio dardanus

Danaus chrysippus

female morph trophonius
(*P. dardanus*)

Amauris crawshayi

female morph cenea
(*P. dardanus*)

Amauris niavius

female morph hippocoon
(*P. dardanus*)

Inedible Models   **. . . and Their Mimics**

which acts as a selective agent that favors the resistant individuals even more. Gradually the genotypic structure of the population shifts in a consistent direction—toward more resistant phenotypes.

Disruptive Selection

Disruptive selection occurs in populations of the African swallowtail butterfly (*Papilio dardanus*). In this case, selection is associated with **mimicry**, whereby one species bears deceptive resemblance in color, form, or behavior to another species that has a selective advantage. The first species

is the mimic, the second is the model. For instance, if a model has warning coloration that identifies it as inedible to potential predators, then a tasty species that mimics it will have a better chance of being left alone.

All the males of *P. dardanus* populations have the same kind of yellow and black wings, which have "tails" at the tips. In most of tropical Africa, the *P. dardanus* females are conspicuously different in appearance from the males—and from one another. The different wing patterns and coloration of each female morph happen to mimic those of inedible species present in its distribution range (Figure 30.10). In regions where models are absent, so are the mimicking females. Bird predators are apparently the selective agents promoting polymorphism in these populations.

Unlike the females, *P. dardanus* males are not mimics of anything. Presumably, it is more advantageous to look only like themselves and not like males of other species during the breeding season, even if they are conspicuous to predators. The likely advantage is that females are more sexually receptive to males that have unambiguous form and coloration (and, hence, greater reproductive potential). The fact that all of the female morphs continue to recognize and accept the same males apparently counterbalances the effect of disruptive selection and keeps the population from diverging into separate species.

Sexual Selection

Some of the most dramatic examples of selection are found among animals that show **sexual dimorphism**. This term refers to differences in external appearance and behavior between males and females. Such differences are especially striking in birds and mammals (Figure 30.11).

Often, the males are larger, more conspicuous in color and patterning, and more aggressive. Of course, such traits do make the males of prey species more visible to predators, and the males of predatory species more visible to their prey. This means that in some respects, the traits are probably selected against. At the same time, the traits increase the chances of reproductive success because their bearers have a competitive advantage over others in securing a mate. Such **sexual selection** can be based on any trait that gives the individual a preferential advantage in mating and producing offspring.

For example, northern sea lions mate only on small rock outcroppings in the seas. Males that fight for and hold possession of the rocks have mating privileges with anywhere from ten to twenty females. The males that lose the battles do not mate at all and therefore contribute nothing to the allele pool of the next generation. The outcome of

Figure 30.11 Examples of sexual dimorphism in (**a**) the northern sea lions, (**b**) mallard ducks, (**c**) African lions, and (**d**) North American grouse.

sexual selection is clear: males can weigh in at 1,000 kilograms, which is about twice as heavy as the females (Figure 30.11a). As another example, the males of several species of North American grouse have a dazzling appearance, compared with the females, and they engage in striking behavioral displays (Figure 30.11e). The males establish small mating territories, called leks. There they fight one another, and the females are attracted by the fracas. They tend to mate with the most dazzling and aggressive males (the ones that manage to occupy the center of the lek).

Selection and Balanced Polymorphism

Selection pressures can so favor one allele that the allele completely supplants all others at the gene locus. Thus the same form of a trait eventually appears among all individuals of the population. Often, though, two or more alleles can persist at the same time. And they can persist at a frequency that is greater than can be accounted for by newly arising mutations alone. Populations in which two or more forms of a trait persist at some intermediate frequency are said to show **balanced polymorphism** at that gene locus.

Sickle-cell polymorphism is one of the best-studied examples of this condition. In West and Central Africa, the HbS allele associated with sickle-cell anemia is maintained at a high frequency relative to the normal HbA allele. Of a given population, HbS/HbS homozygotes make up about 2.5 percent and the heterozygotes (HbS/HbA) make up nearly 30 percent at birth. You may find this high frequency of the allele surprising. After all, HbS/HbS homozygotes often die in their teens and early twenties, and generally die before age forty-five. The abnormal hemoglobin arising from the mutant allele puts them at a disadvantage. Whenever the blood oxygen level is lower than normal (as it can be during overexertion or respiratory illness), HbS molecules crystallize and distort red blood cells into sickle shapes. Sickled cells cannot transport normal amounts of oxygen; they also clump up in capillaries. The clinical consequences can be severe, as Figure 10.13 indicated.

Why, you might ask, doesn't selection remove the HbS allele from the populations? The reason, again, is that variant alleles are not "good" or "bad" in themselves. *Their survival value must be weighed in context of the environment in which they are being expressed.*

Wherever sickle-cell polymorphism persists, malaria is rampant. About half of all cases of malaria are caused by *Plasmodium falciparum.* As described in Chapter Thirty-Two, this parasitic protistan uses only one kind of mosquito (*Anopheles*) to transmit its sporozoites to the human bloodstream. Such mosquitoes live only in the tropics and subtropics; hence malaria and sickle-cell polymorphism persist mostly in those parts of the world.

Many studies suggest that the sickle-cell polymorphism is maintained through (1) *differential mortality* and (2) *differential fertility* between the normal and the heterozygous members of the populations. (The frequency of the HbS/HbS homozygote is so low that its effect can be ignored here.) Let's look first at the nature of the HbS/HbA survival advantage.

When malarial infection is not a factor, the HbA/HbA homozygote has an eighty-five percent greater probability of surviving to reproductive age than does the heterozygote. However, the picture changes when malaria is considered. In 1954, A. Allison reported experimental evidence that heterozygotes have greater resistance to malaria and are more likely to survive severe infections. Allison infected fifteen HbA/HbA and fifteen HbS/HbA volunteers with *P. falciparum.* Malarial parasites were subsequently detected in the blood of fourteen of the normal homozygotes. In contrast, all but two of the heterozygotes were free of

infection. In another study, severe or fatal infections were found to be twice as high in HbA/HbA children.

We can imagine how differential fertility can occur as well. The heterozygous women have a lower incidence of spontaneous abortions, which may be the reason for their higher rate of fertility in relation to HbA/HbA women. Malarial infection can damage the placenta and thereby damage or destroy the fetus. Yet its effects are believed to be less severe in heterozygotes for the reasons given in the preceding paragraph, and this could account for the difference in birth rates.

Thus, in regions where malaria persists, sickle-cell polymorphism is maintained at high frequency largely through two counterbalancing selective forces:

1. When there is *no* malarial infection involved, selection favors the HbA/HbA homozygote (whose capacity to produce hemoglobin A is not diminished and who has a far greater chance of survival than the heterozygote).

2. When there *is* malarial infection, selection favors the HbS/HbA heterozygote (who has a far greater chance of surviving malaria).

EVOLUTION OF SPECIES

Defining a Species

Now that we have looked at the forces acting on variation within populations, we are ready to consider how those forces can bring about the evolution of species. For sexual organisms, a **species** can be defined as one or more populations whose members are able to interbreed under natural conditions and produce fertile offspring, and who are reproductively isolated from other species. Because of reproductive isolation, different species have independently evolving pools of alleles.

How do species originate? Within a population, shifts in allele frequencies can move the whole population in one direction or another; they can also lead to balanced polymorphism. No matter how diverse the members become, though, they remain members of the *same* species as long as they continue to interbreed successfully and share a common pool of alleles.

However, barriers can arise between parts of the population, forming local breeding units (demes). The barriers may be enough to create two or more pools of alleles where there had been only one before. Over time, the absence of gene flow and the action of selection, genetic drift, and mutation can lead to divergence. The term **divergence** refers to a build-up of differences in allele frequencies between reproductively isolated populations. When divergence becomes so great that successful interbreeding no longer occurs under natural conditions, the populations are said to be separate species.

Except in some special cases, which will be described shortly, it is impossible to identify the exact moment at which speciation occurs. As is the case for any gradual process (such as the development of an infant into an adult), species do not spring forth suddenly, at a single moment in time. Figure 30.12 depicts the generally gradual nature of speciation.

There is a related problem in identifying when true speciation has come about. Reproductively isolated populations must undergo enough divergence that interbreeding cannot occur, even if the opportunity presents itself again. But if the populations *are* isolated, how can we know for sure that enough divergence has indeed occurred? Consider that lions and tigers normally are reproductively isolated, they certainly look different, and we call them separate species. Yet when they are brought together under the atypical conditions of captivity, they can interbreed and produce hybrid offspring. Have we arbitrarily assigned the species status to these isolates before they are, in fact, separate species?

Finally, how do we assign fossils to one species or another? Certainly we have no idea of whether a now-fossilized individual was able to interbreed with individuals of similar morphology that lived in the same distribution range. Thus we have different interpretations of what was really going on among the earliest populations of hominids that lived in the same territories but that were morphologically varied. (Hominids are any primate in the human family. *Homo sapiens* is the only living representative.) It may be that biochemical tests will shed light on such ambiguities in the fossil record. Until then, morphological similarities and differences are the main handle we have on interpreting speciation in extinct populations.

The point of this discussion is that assigning the species status to some organism might not always reflect reality. Keep this qualification in mind when you use the following definition, which is probably the most satisfactory one developed to date:

For sexual organisms, a <u>species</u> **is one or more populations whose members interbreed under natural conditions and produce fertile offspring, and who are reproductively isolated from other species.**

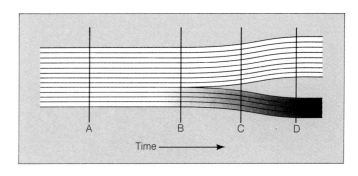

Figure 30.12 Divergence leading to speciation. Because evolution is gradual here, we cannot say at any one point in time that there are now two species rather than one. Each vertical line represents a different population. In A, there is only one species. In D, there are two. In B and C, divergence has begun but is far from complete. (From F. Ayala, J. Valentine, *Evolving*, 1979, Benjamin/Cummings)

Reproductive Isolating Mechanisms

Any aspect of structure, function, or behavior that prevents interbreeding is a **reproductive isolating mechanism**. As you will now discover, the mechanisms fall into two categories. First, isolation can occur prior to the zygote stage of development, such that hybrid zygotes never do form. Second, isolation can occur even if zygotes form, in that the hybrid offspring are sterile or die before reaching sexual maturity. (Such conditions can arise in the first hybrid generation or the one after that.) As you will see, all isolating mechanisms serve the same function: they prevent allele exchange between populations.

A reproductive isolating mechanism is some aspect of structure, behavior, or functioning that can prevent successful interbreeding (hence gene flow) between demes or populations.

Mechanical Isolation: Differences in the structure or functioning of reproductive organs may prevent individuals of different populations from producing hybrid zygotes. For example, a stigma of one plant species can be so different in size, shape, or length that a pollen tube of another plant species cannot reach the ovary. Another example of mechanical isolation can be observed in two species of sage in southern California. As Figure 30.13 shows, the species differ in the size and arrangement of floral parts—and in the size of their pollinators. Because of these differences, the pollinator of one species is usually incapable of coming into contact with the pollen of the other sage species.

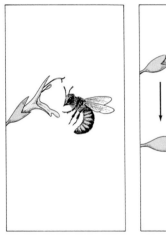 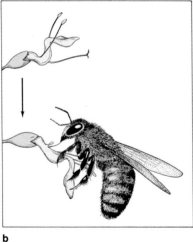

a   b

Figure 30.13 Mechanical isolation between two species of sage (*Salvia mellifera* and *S. apiana*). The first species (**a**) has a small floral landing platform for its small or medium-size pollinators. The second species (**b**) has a large landing platform and long stamens, which extend some distance away from the nectary. Even though small bees can land on this larger platform, they can do so without brushing against the pollen-bearing stamens. It takes larger pollinators to do this. Hence the small pollinators of *S. mellifera* are mostly incapable of spreading pollen to flowers of *S. apiana*; and the large pollinator of *S. apiana* cannot land on and cross-pollinate *S. mellifera*. The plants and their pollinators are all drawn to the same scale. (After V. Grant, *Organismic Evolution*, 1977, W. H. Freeman and Co.)

Gamete Isolation: Incompatibilities between the sperm of one species and the egg (or female reproductive system) of another can prevent fertilization. This is true of marine animals that rely on external fertilization. For example, even when eggs and sperm of two different species of sea urchin are released at the same time and in the same place, there rarely is any attraction between gametes of different species. In many cases, biochemical substances released from the female attract sperm to the proper species of egg. Gamete isolation also occurs among flowering plant species, which rely on complementarity between the stigma and the pollen grain surface (Chapter Eighteen).

Temporal Isolation: The timing of sexual reproduction can act as an isolating mechanism. For most animals and flowering plants, mating or pollination is a seasonal event; in some cases, the receptive period lasts for less than a day. Even when two species are closely related, they can be isolated from each other if the timing of reproduction does

not overlap. An extreme example is provided by two closely related species of cicadas. The reproductive stage of one of these insect species emerges every thirteen years, the other every seventeen years. The possibility of meeting in time occurs once every 221 years.

Behavioral Isolation: Behavioral isolation occurs among many animal groups. It is one of the strongest mechanisms at work among related species that live in the same territory. For instance, complex courtship rituals often precede mating. Perhaps squawks, head-bobbing, wing-spreading, and dancing are interwoven into a stereotyped pattern. Such behavior might stimulate a female of one bird species —but it probably would not even be recognized as an overture by a female of a related species. The effectiveness of behavioral isolation is evident in the results of Francisco Ayala's study of closely related *Drosophila* species (Table 30.2).

Hybrid Inviability and Infertility: Even when fertilization does occur between gametes of two different species, there can be incompatibilities between the developing embryo and the maternal organism. Because of these incompatibilities, the embryo can die. In some cases, hybrid offspring are born but they commonly are weaker in structure, physiology, or behavior than normal offspring of either species. Hence they will not have as much chance of surviving. In other cases, hybrid offspring are vigorous but sterile. For example, a cross between a female horse and a male donkey produces a mule. A mule is a hybrid that is fully functional *except* in its reproductive capacity.

Finally, even if a first-generation hybrid manages to survive and reproduce, there can be hybrid breakdown in the next generation because the offspring are typically very weak. For instance, crosses between two species of evening primrose give rise to a partially fertile first generation. However, the second-generation plants are slow-growing dwarfs, susceptible to disease and totally sterile.

Modes of Speciation

Allopatric Speciation: Sometimes physical barriers come to exist between parts of the same population and prevent the intermingling of their offspring. **Allopatric speciation** can occur when geographic separation prevents gene flow and thereby sets the stage for reproductive isolation. The term allopatric is derived from the Greek *allos* ("different") and the Latin *patria* ("native land").

Geographic separation can occur within a relatively short span of time, as when a few individuals are dispersed far beyond the normal distribution range for the population. It also can occur quite suddenly, as when a population of crawling insects is split by a change in a river's course. This sometimes happens during major floods or earthquakes. If the individuals so separated cannot fly, swim, or float, they are as effectively barred from interbreeding as if mountains stood between them.

Geographic separation can also occur because of long-term changes in the earth's crust. Entire continents have been colliding and drifting apart for hundreds of millions of years; mountain ranges have been thrust upward from the seafloor and parts of dry land have become totally submerged. As you will read in the next chapter, these massive environmental disruptions apparently led to allopatric speciation on a spectacular scale.

Parapatric Speciation: In **parapatric speciation**, populations that are side by side undergo genetic divergence. (Parapatric means "side by side with the native land.") In contrast to the allopatric route, reproductive isolation develops in spite of some gene flow between populations. This can happen under two conditions. First, the genotypes of each population must be selectively favored, such that "foreign" alleles are eliminated before they can spread through the distribution range. Second, gene flow cannot be large enough to overwhelm the selective forces maintaining the distinction between the populations.

Sympatric Speciation: The word sympatric means "same native land." **Sympatric speciation** arises from the divergence of populations within the same distribution range. At first it may seem odd that local breeding units within "cruising range" of one another can become reproductively isolated in the first place. Yet reproductive isolation without geographic separation does occur, particularly among flowering plants.

Sympatric speciation can occur through *polyploidy,* whereby the original chromosome number is multiplied in a particular zygote. This mechanism has been important in plant evolution: about forty percent of all flowering plants are polyploid. The reason for its widespread occurrence is that plants often are self-fertilizing, and most can reproduce asexually by vegetative propagation. Because the polyploid individual need not wait for a sexual partner with a comparably multiplied chromosome number, speciation is instantaneous. That one polyploid can give rise to a whole population just like itself.

Table 30.2 Behavioral Isolation Between Three Closely Related *Drosophila* Species				
Contact Limited to the Following Combinations:				
Females	Males	Number of Females	Number of Matings	Percent Matings
D. serrata	*D. serrata*	3,841	3,466	90.2
D. serrata	*D. birchii*	1,246	9	0.7
D. serrata	*D. dominicana*	395	5	1.3
D. birchii	*D. birchii*	2,458	1,891	76.9
D. birchii	*D. serrata*	699	7	1.0
D. birchii	*D. dominicana*	250	1	0.4
D. dominicana	*D. dominicana*	43	40	93.0
D. dominicana	*D. serrata*	163	0	0.0
D. dominicana	*D. birchii*	537	20	3.7

Data from F. Ayala. 1965. "Evolution of Fitness in Experimental Populations of *Drosophila serrata.*" *Science* 150:903–905.

Polyploidy combined with successful *hybridization* can also produce a new species. Usually, interspecific hybrids are sterile because they inherit chromosomes that differ in number or kind from their different parents; hence the "homologues" probably cannot pair during meiosis. However, if the interspecific hybrid undergoes polyploidy, then the *duplicates* can pair with the originals, meiosis can proceed, and viable gametes can form. Wheat is an example of a successful polyploid hybrid (Chapter Eleven).

MACROEVOLUTION

So far, we have looked at changes within populations of a species. What changes bring about the developments that distinguish the major groups of organisms within classification schemes, the so-called higher taxa? What gives rise to the clusters of related yet distinct species called genera? How can families, orders, classes, and phyla (or divisions) develop? These questions carry us past the small-scale changes within populations, for the events that shape the character of higher taxa must be considered in the immense framework of geologic time. Our focus now will be on **macroevolution**—the large-scale rates, trends, and patterns of change above the species level.

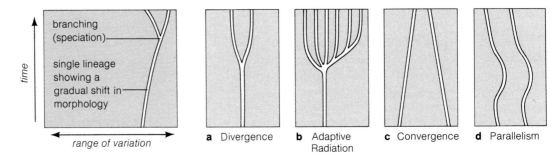

Figure 30.15 Four patterns of macroevolution: (**a**) divergence, (**b**) adaptive radiation, (**c**) convergence, and (**d**) parallelism.

A Time Scale for Macroevolution

Evolutionary time began with one or a few forms, not much different from some of the existing prokaryotes. As you will read in the next chapter, these forms originated more than $3\frac{1}{2}$ billion years ago. From this ancient beginning, countless branchings have given rise to all the diverse organisms that have ever appeared on earth.

In itself, the notion that forms as simple as bacteria could evolve into forms as complex as ourselves might elicit disbelief. Part of the problem is that we are used to thinking in terms of minutes, hours, days, and years, certainly never much beyond centuries. Besides, until recently there was no way to judge the true age of the earth, hence the span of time in which evolution might have taken place. There *were* signs of change through time. There were gradual changes in the fossil record, with simple forms in deep (older) rock formations and increasingly complex forms in the more recent formations. There were also some major discontinuities in this record that could be used as relative time boundaries. Thus the **geologic time scale** initially was no more than a progression of four broad eras, each with a distinct array of fossil organisms that had no absolute dates assigned to them:

Proterozoic	*very first life*
Paleozoic	*ancient life*
Mesozoic	*between-ancient-and-modern life*
Cenozoic	*modern life*

Within the past three decades, however, we have been able to assign fairly firm time boundaries to these geologic intervals by using radioactive dating methods. These methods are based on comparing the known, invariant decay rates of such radioactive isotopes as uranium, thorium, potassium, and strontium to the measured amounts of these isotopes and decay products in different kinds of rocks (Figure 30.14). The methods have been used on an enormous number of rock samples, taken from all over the earth. As a result of this work, the broad eras of the geologic time scale have been assigned the time boundaries shown in Figure 30.16.

Rates and Patterns of Change

An evolutionary tree of life can be constructed by plotting the degree of morphologic change in the fossil record against increments of geologic time. Figure 30.15 shows the kinds of "branches" that can occur in such trees. Each branch is a single line of descent, or **lineage**. The angle of each branch indicates the rate of morphologic change in a given time period. Shallow angles mean rapid change, and steeper angles mean gradual change.

Analysis of many such trees shows that four patterns of change have been common among independent lineages:

Divergence
Adaptive radiation
Convergent evolution
Parallel evolution

Divergence, as you have seen, is a branching of one lineage into two, and it can lead to speciation. Sometimes a lineage branches two or more times into lineages that radiate away

Era	Period	Epoch	Age (millions of years)
Cenozoic	Quaternary	Recent	0.01
		Pleistocene	2.5
	Tertiary	Pliocene	7
		Miocene	25
		Oligocene	38
		Eocene	54
		Paleocene	65
Mesozoic	Cretaceous	Late	100
		Early	135
	Jurassic		195
	Triassic		240
Paleozoic	Permian		285
	Carboniferous		375
	Devonian		420
	Silurian		450
	Ordovician		520
	Cambrian		570
Proterozoic (Precambrian)	*oxygen (O₂) abundant*		2,300
	oldest dated rocks; oldest definite fossils known		3,800
	approximate origin of the earth		4,600

Figure 30.16 Geologic time scale, with dates based on radioactive isotopes from rocks of each era.

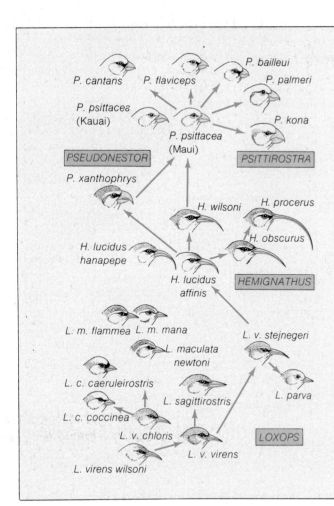

Figure 30.17 Adaptive radiation of Hawaiian honeycreepers.

The Hawaiian Islands are a volcanic archipelago, which began arising from the ocean floor less than 10 million years ago. Somewhere between then and now, insect-eating honeycreepers migrated to those isolated islands and founded a successful lineage. Every so often, some birds must have migrated to different parts of the archipelago, where they established separate populations. Being reproductively isolated from the parent stock, and being subject to different selection pressures and opportunities, these isolates underwent divergence. Some diverged into separate species.

At some point, individuals of different species were dispersed among the islands. Although there were now separate species, the birds still were not that different in overall morphology and feeding habits. Competition for resources presumably led to a partitioning of the environment. Such partitioning would represent an adaptive zone, with varied selection pressures and opportunities. Gradually there were shifts in morphology, particularly in beak shape—which reflects shifts in feeding habits.

For example, an early lineage underwent adaptive radiation and evolved into species classed as the genus *Loxops*. These species have thin, small beaks that are used to probe for insects hidden in bark and leaf buds. Another lineage radiated into a new adaptive zone characterized by an unexploited food resource—nectar. The genus *Hemignathus* arose, with its curve-beaked members adapted to feeding from the nectaries of diverse species of plants. Still another lineage evolved into the insect-eating genus *Psittirostra*; its members have thick, short, strong beaks that can chisel wood and expose the tunnels of boring insects. (From W. Bock, *Evolution*, 1970, *24*:704–722)

from one another. This pattern is called **adaptive radiation**. It indicates that diverging lineages have been able to partition the existing environment or to invade vacant environments where different modes of life are possible. Each potential mode of life is called an *adaptive zone.*

Adaptive radiation can occur under three conditions. *First,* there must be diversity within and between lineages, such that they can respond to the different opportunities and selection pressures of an adaptive zone. *Second,* the opportunities must be within reach. For example, until some insects had already developed wings, there could be no taking advantage of the opportunities associated with flight (rapid dispersal, freedom from landlocked competition). Adaptive traits must already exist, and by chance alone will they be adaptive also to a new mode of life. *Third,* there must be less competition or predation in the adaptive zone than there was in the old zone. Success for

the pioneers is chancy enough without a concurrent reduction in competition and predation pressures. (The reason is that pressures are usually severe during the initial invasion and during the fine-tuning of existing adaptations to the new way of life.) Figure 30.17 shows an example of adaptive radiation.

What about the other two patterns of macroevolution? In **convergent evolution**, morphologically distinct lineages that were only distantly related evolve in such ways that they end up resembling each other. Usually, convergent evolution indicates that the lineages have become adapted to the same kind of environment and have similar modes of living. In **parallel evolution**, independent lineages that resemble one another evolve in similar ways at about the same rate, the outcome being that resemblances between them persist. Such lineages probably have responded to similar shifts in environmental conditions.

Given the patterns just described, you can imagine how difficult it can be to interpret some resemblances between lineages. Many structures are **homologous**: their resemblance to one another is an outcome of the same evolutionary beginning from a common ancestor. Modifications on the common plan developed as lineages diverged into *different* adaptive zones. For example, the wings of birds and bats are homologous (Figure 2.3), having evolved from the forelimbs of a common reptilian ancestor. In contrast to homologous structures, many structures are **analogous**. They occur between independent lineages that have undergone convergent evolution into *similar* adaptive zones. For example, winged insects are not related to birds and bats. The insect wing is not a modified forelimb; it is a modified flap of the cuticle surrounding the insect body segments. The analogy is an outcome of convergent evolution, not of remote common ancestry.

EVOLUTIONARY TRENDS

In the evolutionary view, all existing species share one or at most a few common ancestors that marked the origin of life. Diversity is the outcome of countless branchings since that origin, some $3\frac{1}{2}$ billion years ago. Within this tremendous sweep of time, the pace of evolution has varied. For example, *Ginkgo biloba* is a species of tree that has persisted with no detectable change for more than 100 million years. In contrast, the hominid species that lived a mere 6 million years ago were considerably different from the one existing today. The first presumed members of the human family (the australopithecines) were only about three feet tall. Compared to you, they had small brains, low foreheads, and elongated apelike faces.

Taken as a whole, the fossil record shows immense periods of stability in form—*and* periods of rapid change in form. How can such a record be interpreted? Do species evolve most rapidly when they are first branching from ancestral lineages? Or does most of the evolution occur gradually, after speciation has occurred? The question is by no means settled, but we can briefly consider some of the models being proposed.

Phyletic Evolution

Figure 30.18 illustrates two ways of interpreting the history of life. At one extreme, all evolution is said to occur gradually within lineages. Change within an established lineage is called **phyletic evolution**. Titanotheres provide us with an example of phyletic evolution. These hoofed mammals

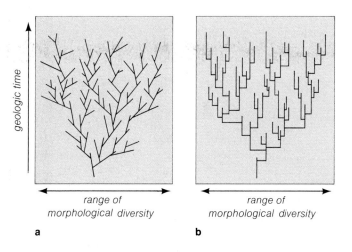

Figure 30.18 Extreme representations of two models of evolution. (**a**) The gradualistic model, whereby evolution occurs mostly within an established lineage. (**b**) The punctuational model, whereby evolution occurs mostly at the time of speciation, and lineages thereafter remain fairly stable in form (as indicated by the vertical lines).

arose during the Early Eocene and endured for about 28 million years. During that long stretch of time, there was a gradual change in such traits as horn size as early genera gave way to new ones (Figure 30.19).

According to the **gradualistic model**, phyletic evolution is the dominant trend in the history of life. Speciation itself is seen to account for only a small amount of large-scale change.

Quantum Evolution

Gradual evolutionary trends within established lineages are well documented. However, a more pervasive pattern is the sudden introduction of new lineages at a given time level. What is rare or missing are intermediate forms at the branch points. What could account for these so-called "gaps" in the fossil record? Let's briefly follow one line of thought that has led to a plausible explanation.

In 1944, George Simpson proposed that most higher taxa originate by **quantum evolution**: the rapid crossing of adaptive thresholds. The transition to a newly opened adaptive zone is an unstable, inadaptive phase. Because selection pressures are most intense during this phase, there is rapid movement into the adaptive zone. Thereafter, the rate of evolution slows since selection now favors the adapted forms.

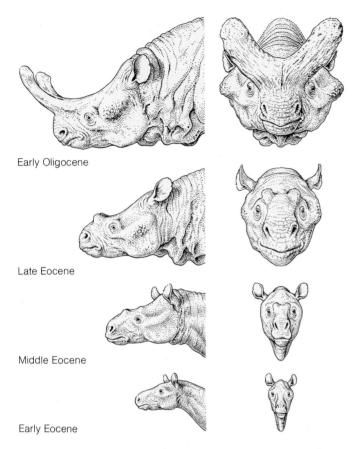

Early Oligocene

Late Eocene

Middle Eocene

Early Eocene

Figure 30.19 Example of phyletic evolution in the hoofed mammals titanotheres. Between the Early Eocene *Eotitanops* and the Early Oligocene *Brontotherium*, small, bony protuberances evolved into relatively large, blunt horns. The representatives shown are from separate genera at different time levels. (From S. Stanley, *Evolution*, 1974, *28*:447–457)

According to the **punctuational model**, quantum evolution occurs during the time of rapid speciation among small, isolated populations. This model might explain the relatively abrupt appearance of new, well-developed lineages in the fossil record. Consider that all known fossils represent only a tiny fraction of all the organisms that have ever lived. Discovery of representatives of any population depends partly on the population size and distribution. Small populations might have been already well adapted to some restricted environmental pocket, and the chance of finding fossil evidence of their existence would be extremely low. But suppose such a population suddenly had an opportunity for adaptive radiation as a result of an abrupt climatic or geologic change. Suppose variant forms in the population had the potential to move into new adaptive zones. Then the stage would have been set for the rapid multiplication of species. During the brief, unstable phase, selection pressures would have been severe, and transitional forms never would increase in numbers. Only the most adaptive forms would reproduce and come to be abundantly represented in the fossil record.

The punctuational model does not exclude the role of phyletic evolution; rather it implies that *most* of the major transitions occur through quantum evolution. In this respect, the model fits well with geologic evidence. As you will read in the next chapter, long periods of gradual evolution correspond to long periods of stability in the geologic record. And the many abrupt appearances of well-developed lineages do correspond to specific episodes of abrupt environmental change—and the opening of new adaptive zones.

Mosaic Evolution

One of the intriguing aspects of evolution is that the different body parts characteristic of an organism may not evolve at the same rates. Highly unequal rates of change in a type of organism are known as **mosaic evolution**. G. de Beer coined the term during his study of *Archaeopteryx*, a link between reptiles and birds. Figure 30.20 shows a skeleton and a restoration of a member of this transitional lineage. In teeth and tail, *Archaeopteryx* resembled small, two-legged dinosaurs. Yet it also resembled true birds in having feathers and wings, apparently used in gliding.

Mosaic evolution typically involves a particular trait, or **key character**. For example, the feather was a key character that permitted the evolution of birds from reptilian stock.

Evolution is largely restricted to a key character and to a few of the characters related to it. If you look at fossils of the highly diverse vertebrates, you will be struck by the basically conservative nature of evolution. For example, in overall skeletal structure, a bat is like a bird, a bird is like a reptile, a reptile is like an amphibian, and an amphibian is like a fish. Such fidelity in overall structure must have a genetic basis, for wholesale remodeling would have drastic repercussions on gene interactions that shape the development of a given type of organism. Major reconstructions do occur, but they occur gradually.

Extinction

The millions of different kinds of organisms alive today are a mere fraction of all that have gone before. **Extinction**, the disappearance of an entire taxon, is one of the major trends in evolution. Often a single group disappears. In addition, periods of mass extinction seem to have punctuated geologic time. The boundaries that define the major epochs of the geologic time scale were established on the basis of apparent times of mass extinctions in the seas, on land, or both. You will read about these extinctions next.

Regardless of whether conditions change slowly or rapidly, groups can become extinct if they do not have the potential for adapting to the new circumstances or for migrating elsewhere. The absence of genetic diversity, a narrow distribution range, and small population size can place a group on the brink of extinction should conditions change.

Readings

Ayala, F., and J. Valentine. 1979. *Evolving.* Menlo Park, California: Benjamin/Cummings. Short introduction to evolutionary theory. Excellent writing, interesting examples, and well-chosen illustrations.

Cavalli-Sforza, L., and W. Bodmer. 1971. *The Genetics of Human Populations.* San Francisco: Freeman. Objective look at problems of racial differentiation; clear discussion of sickle-cell polymorphism.

Futuyma, D. 1979. *Evolutionary Biology.* Sunderland, Massachusetts: Sinauer. Excellent synthesis of modern evolutionary thought. Futuyma writes beautifully and cuts through much of the confusion surrounding the development of concepts in this rapidly changing field.

Grant, V. 1981. *Plant Speciation.* Second edition. New York: Columbia University Press. Good discussion of speciation in plants.

Review Questions

1. What is the typological approach to categorizing species? In what fundamental way does the population concept differ from this approach?

2. Define these terms: individual, population, and species.

3. What is genotypic and phenotypic variation? Describe evolution in terms of frequency distributions for a given trait, and in terms of the underlying allele frequencies.

4. What is the Hardy-Weinberg baseline against which changes in allele frequencies may be measured? What is Hardy-Weinberg equilibrium?

5. Changes in allele frequencies may be brought about by mutation, genetic drift, gene flow, and selection pressure. Define these occurrences, then describe the way each one can send allele frequencies out of equilibrium.

6. What implications might the neutral effect of genetic drift hold for an earlier concept of "survival of the fittest?" As part of your answer, define polymorphism and explain how different phenotypes can persist indefinitely in the *same* population.

Figure 30.20 *Archaeopteryx*, a link between reptiles and birds and an example of mosaic evolution. The photograph above shows a restoration based on the fossil shown below.

7. Natural selection is no longer in the realm of pure theory. Can you recount the ongoing sagas of the peppered moth and the pesticide-resistant pests to explain why it is now considered an operating principle in biology?

8. Define stabilizing, directional, and disruptive forms of selection and give a brief example of each.

9. Before labeling a particular genotype as being advantageous or disadvantageous, what must you first consider?

10. Give two examples of isolating mechanisms, and outline what they accomplish.

11. What is the difference between allopatric and sympatric speciation? Which do you suppose occurs most often in plants?

31

ORIGINS AND THE EVOLUTION OF LIFE

By the close of the nineteenth century, "the fixity of species" was crumbling as a scientific concept. By the middle of the twentieth, "the fixity of continents" met a similar fate. Not only was life seen to be an ever changing drama, the drama itself was now seen to be unfolding on an outrageously restless stage. It was not just that the earth's crust has been buckling upward and eroding downward through time. It was not just that huge continents have been alternately drained and drowned. It was that the whole crust has been divided into vast plates, which have been moving on top of a plastic mantle and carrying the continents with them!

As unsettling as this knowledge of our planet may be, its implications are exhilarating. Here we are, living at a time when a cohesive theory is emerging—*a theory that the evolution of life is linked, from its very beginning, to the physical and chemical evolution of the earth.* Evidence in support of this theory comes from far-ranging studies of the evolution of stars, the solar system, and the earth. It comes from centuries of research into the earth's changing landscapes, oceans, climates, and fossil patterns. We encourage you at the outset to explore and evaluate this evidence for yourself by continuing with the readings listed at the chapter's end. Much of this evidence is well established; some is prelimi-

Figure 31.1 Representation of the primordial earth, about 4 billion years ago. Within another 500 million years, living cells would be present on the surface. (During its formation, the moon presumably was closer to the earth. Here it looms on the horizon, not yet fully condensed through gravitational compression.)

nary and perhaps not completely accurate in all of its details. Yet there is no denying that enough is there to show us that the coevolution of the earth and life is a drama of epic proportions.

ORIGIN OF LIFE

The Early Earth and Its Atmosphere

Billions of years ago titanic stellar explosions ripped through our galaxy, and from the remnants of those explosions, our solar system was born. It began 4.6 billion years ago as a dense cloud of dust and gas that extended trillions of miles in space. When that immense cloud became cool enough, it began to contract under its own gravitational attraction. As countless bits of matter gravitated toward one another, the cloud collapsed into a dense, flattened disk that spun through space. Gravitational pressure became more intense in the center of the disk. Temperatures there became extreme enough to drive the fusion between nuclei of colliding atoms of hydrogen and, to a lesser extent, helium. Thermonuclear chain reactions began that would feed themselves for many billions of years; the sun was born a luminous star.

Chesley Bonestell

Farther out from the center of the swirling disk, the earth and other planets were also forming through accretion and gravitational compression. At first the earth was a cold, homogeneous mass. However, through contraction and radioactive heating, its core grew increasingly dense—and hot. By 3.8 billion years ago, the earth was hurtling through space as a thin-crusted inferno (Figure 31.1).

Long before life appeared in this forbidding place, gases trapped beneath the thin crust or formed during reactions in the earth's molten interior were being forced to the outside. These emissions were the start of an early atmosphere. Although more than twenty percent of the air we breathe today is oxygen, there probably was very little of this gas on the early earth. More likely, the early atmosphere resembled those of Venus and Mars. Planetary probes have shown that oxygen accounts for less than one percent of the atmospheres of our two sister planets. Consider also that the molecules on which life is based (sugars, amino acids, nucleotides) cannot accumulate on their own in the presence of free oxygen (which readily combines with them and fixes them as oxides). In living cells, these molecules are protected against oxidation. Without such protection, living systems never could have arisen—unless the atmosphere was once oxygen-free.

Models of the early atmosphere differ in their details. But there is agreement that it contained large amounts of carbon dioxide and nitrogen, and very little free oxygen. What about water vapor? Certainly a tremendous amount of water would have been released during hydrolysis of minerals present in the earth's crust. Volcanic eruptions would have produced high-enough temperatures to drive the reactions. But as fast as water vapor condensed in the atmosphere, it would have evaporated in the intense heat blanketing the rumbling crust. Most likely, liquid water accumulated only after the surface cooled enough for it to rain. When the rains began, so began the stripping of mineral salts from the parched rocks, and salt-laden waters collected wherever basins had formed in the crust.

If the early earth had settled into an orbit closer to the sun, its surface would have remained so hot that water vapor never would have condensed in liquid form. If its orbit had been more distant, the surface would have become so cold that any water formed would have been locked up as ice. And if the earth had not become as large as it did, it would not have had enough gravitational mass to retain the atmosphere with its water vapor. Because of its size and its distance from the sun, the earth would retain liquid water on its surface.

If you could go back 3.5 billion years in time, you would find yourself in a world quite different from the one

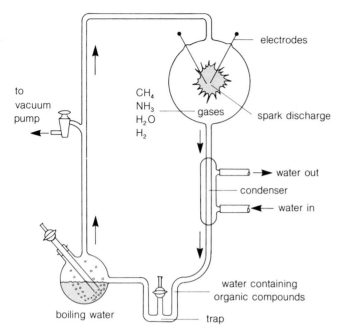

Figure 31.2 Stanley Miller's apparatus used in studying the synthesis of organic compounds under conditions believed to have been present on the early earth.

that exists today. Stretching to the horizons were volcanic islands, mud flats, and vast, shallow seas. This is the world in which living systems emerged.

Yet exactly where and when did life originate? There is no fossil record of the event. Most of the rocks from that period have been melted, solidified, and remelted many times over because of ongoing movements in the earth's mantle and crust. Some are buried far below more recently formed rocks, where they have been subjected to heat and compression. Thus any clues they might have held about the event would be altered beyond recognition.

Even though there is no direct evidence of the origin of life on earth, it is still possible to gain insight into the manner in which it occurred. To see how this can be done, we can start with the following questions:

1. What were physical and chemical conditions like at the time of origin?

2. Based on known physical, chemical, and evolutionary laws, could life have originated spontaneously under those conditions?

3. Can we postulate a sequence of events by which the first living systems developed?

4. Can we devise experiments to test whether that sequence could indeed have taken place?

Spontaneous Assembly of Organic Compounds

To begin with, the oldest earth rocks known are 3.8 billion years old. Samples taken from meteorites, the earth's moon, and Mars are all between 4.5 and 4.6 billion years old. They all contain the elements found in biological molecules, so we can assume that the earth and its atmosphere contained the materials necessary for the synthesis of organic compounds during the time span that preceded the origin of life.

What about energy sources to drive the synthesis reactions? Lightning, hot volcanic ash, even shock waves have enough energy to drive the assembly of carbon-containing compounds. We know this from the pioneering experiments of Stanley Miller, Harold Urey, and many other chemists. In 1953, for example, Miller set up a reaction chamber containing a mixture of hydrogen, methane, ammonia, and water (Figure 31.2). For a week he kept the mixture recirculating. All the while, he bombarded it with a continuous spark discharge to simulate lightning as an energy source. By the week's end, he found organic molecules had formed, including many kinds of amino acids.

Such experiments have been repeated many times, with variations in elements, gas mixtures, and energy sources. The results invariably show that all the building blocks in living systems—including lipids, carbohydrates, amino acids, and nucleotides—can form under abiotic conditions. In addition, when inorganic phosphate is present in the starting mixture, ATP will form. That molecule is an energy carrier used by all living systems.

Speculations on the First Self-Replicating Systems

Given the 300 million years available for it to happen, a tremendous amount of organic material probably accumulated in the shallow waters of the earth. What sequence of events led from this organic "soup" to self-reproducing systems? At the molecular level, reproduction requires the assembly of all those proteins found in the parent system (Figure 9.1). As you know, such assembly in existing cells involves a complex, linear relationship between nucleic acids and amino acids. How did this relationship evolve? There is no universally accepted hypothesis, although researchers are giving us some interesting experimental results to think about.

Templates for Protein Synthesis. To give you a sense of the kind of work going on, let's look briefly at an idea that the first templates for protein synthesis existed at the bottom of the primordial soup, in the mud of tidal flats and estuaries. G. Cairns-Smith has analyzed microscopic crystals of different clays in which metal ions (such as those of iron and zinc) are embedded. When such crystals grow through accretion, their latticelike organization is repeated again and again, right down to the small imperfections caused by the random inclusions of different metal ions. Now, if you have ever baked meat in a clay or metal pot, you know that bits of protein stick tenaciously to both kinds of heated surfaces. Cairns-Smith and J. Bernal suggest that naturally occurring clay crystals might have served as the original templates for the assembly of free amino acids into protein chains. In the absence of such a template, the assembly reactions would have proceeded entirely through chance encounters of amino acids during their diffusion through the water. With adsorption onto templates, there would have been greater probability of the reactions taking place.

Suppose that certain amino acids brought together on a clay template formed proteins that had weak catalytic activity. Perhaps some of these primordial enzymes hastened the peptide linkages between amino acids. In such ways, some clay templates would have selective advantages over others. *There would have been chemical competition between different types of clay templates for the amino acids available—and selection for the first macromolecules.*

Suppose now that nucleotides were also attracted to the clay surface or to amino acids adsorbed onto it. Intriguingly, most existing enzymes are assisted by coenzymes—*some of which closely resemble or are exactly the same in structure as RNA nucleotides.* The sugar-phosphate bonds of such coenzymes could have provided energy for the reactions occurring on the templates.

Such a preliminary association of amino acids and nucleotides could have been the foundation for the first self-replicating systems. To explore this idea, biologists including Sol Speigelman have been experimenting with viral RNA in cell-free systems. They have found that mutations and selection within these simple systems can indeed lead to increasing complexity in the encoded chemical information. Thus the first RNA-protein relationships could have become increasingly complex, and at some point, RNA could have taken over the role as template for chemical information. RNA templates and their diverse protein products could have become linked in self-replication, with some proteins serving as replication enzymes, others as activators of replication, and still others as enhancers of the speed and accuracy of replication. *Chemical cooperation of this sort would have played as much of a role as competition in the evolution of the first self-replicating systems.*

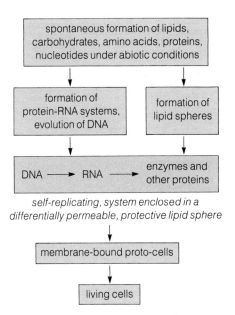

Figure 31.3 One hypothetical sequence of events that might have led to the first self-replicating systems and, later, living cells.

The longer and more complex the RNA templates and their products became, the more possibility there would have been for errors in assembly. At some point there would have been selection for more than an information-encoding and information-processing template. There would have been selection also for information *storage.* DNA, the nucleic acid so similar in structure to RNA, appeared as a double-stranded molecule that assured fidelity in self-replication (Figure 31.3).

What we have been describing here is one hypothetical sequence of events. Whatever their exact nature, they may not have been random, chance events. *It appears likely that they were inevitable outcomes of the probabilities inherent in the chemical and physical conditions present on the early earth.* To reinforce this point, we can ask a question about the "handedness" of the amino acids. Amino acids can exist as stereoisomers, which are like mirror images of two hands. Thus one form is called lefthanded, the other righthanded. In almost all living things, amino acids are in the lefthanded form. Was this chemical choice a result of chance? Some recent work by James Lawless suggests that it was not. Lawless began by studying meteorites. Samples from meteorites contain disorganized arrays of both lefthanded and righthanded amino acids. Yet Lawless discovered that when such disorganized mixtures are exposed to clay crystals, the clay attracts *only* the lefthanded forms.

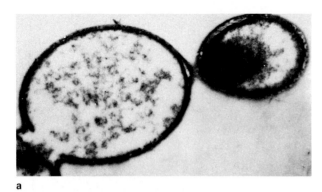

a

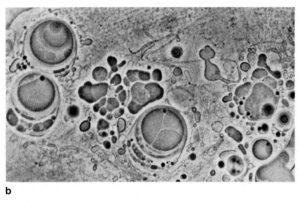

b

Figure 31.4 (**a**) Microspheres of protein chains, as they appear in water solutions. 11,000×. (**b**) Liposomes with multiple internal compartments made from simple, straight-chain lipids. (a from Sidney Fox, Institute for Molecular and Cellular Evolution, University of Miami; b from W. Hargreaves and D. Deamer)

Models for the First Plasma Membranes. All living cells have a differentially permeable plasma membrane. We do not know when membranes emerged in the sequence leading from chemical to organic evolution. What we do know is that metabolism means chemical control—and chemical control is possible only with chemical isolation from the random ebb and flow of materials in the environment. If we assert that chemical evolution led to a metabolic system, then we must show that molecular boundaries for a protein-nucleic acid system can arise spontaneously. Here again, experiments suggest some chemical probabilities.

For example, Sidney Fox and his coworkers heated amino acids under dry conditions, which produced a number of long polypeptide chains. The chains were placed in hot water solutions, then allowed to cool. Upon cooling, the polypeptides assembled into small, stable spheres, or **microspheres** (Figure 31.4). The microspheres selectively accumulated certain substances in greater concentrations than were found on the outside. In addition, the micro-

spheres tended to incorporate lipids that were present in the solution. The outcome was the formation of a lipid-protein film around each droplet.

William Hargreaves and David Deamer have proposed that lipids must have been important in the origin and evolution of biological membranes. Although existing membrane lipids are structurally complex, these workers have experimentally produced membranes from simple lipids having only single hydrocarbon tails and water-soluble heads. These lipids formed **liposomes** (microscopic, closed bags of water) with the following properties:

1. Self assembly into spheres

2. Formation of aqueous compartments within the spheres

3. Ion impermeability, water permeability

4. Fluidity and elasticity (self-repair)

All of these properties are characteristic of biological membrane lipids and contribute to membrane function.

What these and other experiments are indicating is that membranes as well as the self-replicating systems that they enclose probably arose through spontaneous but inevitable chemical events. If lipids were present in the primordial soup, they inevitably formed vesicles, for that is their thermodynamically favored state. Early self-replicating systems could have produced more complex lipids and thereby would have increased membrane stability. Whatever the sequence of chemical events, the first living cells that did appear on earth were probably little more than membrane-bound sacs containing the protein-nucleic acid template system.

THE AGE OF PROKARYOTES

Before 3.7 billion years ago, the earth's crust was exceedingly unstable. Even when rigid continental masses did form, they were fringed with mobile, volcanically active zones. By that time, however, there were volcanic islands rising above the primal seas. And it may have been in shallow waters around these islands that life arose. Some fossil cells have been discovered in sedimentary rocks that were deposited in tidal mud flats next to ancient volcanic formations. These fossils are tentatively dated at 3.5 billion years—and they were already well developed in structure (Figure 31.5).

In form and habitat, the first known cells were like the simple anaerobic prokaryotes that now live in mud

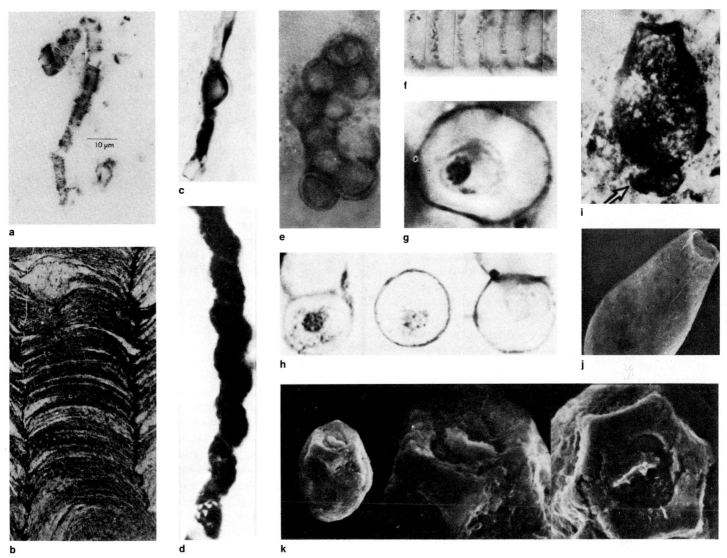

Figure 31.5 A sampling of the oldest known fossils. (**a**) From Western Australia, a filamentous form having cross walls; it is thought to be 3.5 billion years old. The filament diameter is about five micrometers, the same as that of modern cyanobacteria. (**b**) Limestone stromatolite from Rhodesia, about 3.1 billion years old. The stacked organic (dark) and inorganic (light) layering is almost identical with that laid down by modern communities of photosynthetic microbes. (**c**) Fossil cell from South Africa, about 2.25 billion years old; it is similar to modern cyanobacteria. (**d**) From Central Australia, a spiral form 900 million years old. (**e**) Colonial cells found in stromatolites in the USSR, about 650 million years old. (**f**) Filamentous form, about 650 million years old. (**g**) Presumed eukaryotic cell from Central Australia, about 900 million years old; the granules and spots may be remnants of organelles. (**h**) Fossil eukaryotes containing cytoplasmic remnants, about 900 million years old. (**i**) Eukaryotic cells 750 million years old. (**j, k**) Notice the well-developed mouth of these eukaryotes, 750 million years old. (a, Stanley M. Awramik; b-k, J. W. Schopf)

flats, bogs, and pond bottoms. Probably those early cells were heterotrophs, obtaining energy by consuming organic molecules that had accumulated spontaneously in the environment. The nucleotides such as ATP would have been the most accessible energy source available. Most likely, metabolic systems became more and more efficient at using the existing ATP, then later developed the means of producing ATP themselves.

Today, the most common anaerobic pathway for producing ATP is fermentation, and it probably was the first to evolve. (In fermentation, recall, hydrogen atoms and electrons are juggled among intermediates of sugar breakdown but are not transferred anywhere else. Thus considerable energy is still present in the breakdown products of sugars being used as energy sources.)

In one group, fermentation was supplemented by another pathway. High-energy electrons were transferred away from fermentation products to inorganic electron acceptors in the environment. These transfers generated ATP by the pathways of anaerobic respiration. (Today, *Desulfovibrio* and related bacteria use these pathways. *Desulfovibrio* produces ATP by fermenting sugars—*and by* reducing sulfate in the surroundings to sulfide.)

Electron transport chains used in such transfers were a key character in the evolution of autotrophs ("self-feeders") —including the first photosynthetic cells.

In the first stage of photosynthesis, sunlight energy drives the electron transfers leading to ATP formation. In the second stage, hydrogen ions are used to reduce carbon dioxide in reactions that produce energy-rich carbohydrates. Initially, the hydrogen must have been obtained from hydrogen sulfide, organic compounds, and hydrogen gas. Later, some cells developed the means to release hydrogen from water molecules. Water, being so abundant on the earth's surface, represented an unlimited source of hydrogen. Populations of photosynthetic cells now had the energy source, the carbon dioxide, and the hydrogen to explode in size. Of course, as they released hydrogen from water, they also released tremendous amounts of oxygen.

Over time, oxygen accumulated in the atmosphere. And its accumulation had two irreversible consequences for the origin and evolution of life. First, an oxygen-rich atmosphere meant that life no longer could arise spontaneously; oxygen now prevented further nonbiological synthesis of organic compounds. Second, an oxygen-rich environment was an adaptive zone of global dimensions. Some prokaryotic survived in a few oxygen-free habitats. Many other lines became extinct. And a few met the new challenge.

We can speculate that when oxygen started becoming a selective force, some cells were able to adapt metabolically in ways that rendered the oxygen harmless. In one such adaptation, oxygen was used as a dump for electrons from transport chains. Hydrogen joined with the oxygen to form water, the toxic element was removed—and aerobic respiration emerged.

Aerobic respiration proved to be highly efficient at generating ATP. It was a key character in the evolution of larger and structurally complex cells; it was pivotal in the evolution and diversification of eukaryotes.

THE RISE OF EUKARYOTES

Divergence Into Three Primordial Lineages

In reconstructing the past, biologists also search through the records built into living cells. For example, they compare the similarities and differences in the nucleotide sequences of DNA and RNA from diverse cell types. In so doing, they have discovered differences suggesting that the forerunners of eukaryotes arose simultaneously with the forerunners of existing prokaryotes. Today, research is pointing to the existence of three primoridal lineages that arose from a common ancestor:

Eubacteria	*True bacteria; includes photosynthesizers such as cyanobacteria*
Archaebacteria	*Includes methane-producing bacteria; strict anaerobes*
Urkaryote	*Long-since-vanished ancestor of eukaryotes*

When eukaryotic cells are compared with existing bacteria, a puzzle emerges. In some biochemical aspects, eukaryotes are like eubacteria; in others, they are like archaebacteria. In still other respects, particularly in amino acid sequences of functionally analogous proteins, eukaryotes are like neither one. These and other findings suggest that even before complex prokaryotic cells had evolved, there was divergence into a third line of descent—the urkaryotes, ancestral to all nucleated cells. All three branches underwent adaptive radiation during the Age of Prokaryotes, which endured from 3.5 billion to about 750 million years ago.

Symbiosis in the Evolution of Eukaryotes

In structural terms, the simplest eukaryotes are the soft-bodied protistans known as amoebas. Because these forms do not have hard parts, they usually disappear quickly when they die. Assuming that the ancestors of eukaryotes were no more complex than the simplest of these forms, it is not likely that fossil evidence of them will ever be found. Yet there must have been a long history of evolution leading to eukaryotes; 570 million years ago there were highly complex forms that already had well-developed shells, spines, and armored plates.

Yet what were the actual routes by which a form not much more complex than bacteria became eukaryotic— with internal organelles such as mitochondria, and with external structures such as spines? Lynn Margulis and others propose a symbiotic origin for eukaryotes. The word **symbiosis** means "living together." It refers to interactions in which one species serves as host to another species (the guest). Symbiotic relationships abound in the living world.

Origin of Mitochondria. Suppose that urkaryotes included predatory, amoebalike forms that were only weakly tolerant of free oxygen. Suppose some of these predators ingested aerobic bacteria that happened to resist digestion. Oxygen released by their respiring prey could have poisoned most of the predators. Yet some cells might have been more tolerant of the gas. If that were the case, the two species could benefit from continued association. The guest species would find itself in a protected environment, one with energy-rich remnants of the anaerobic host's fermentation activities. The guest cells would divide independently and come to be distributed in the cytoplasm of the host daughter cells. Over time, the guest species would lose its genetic independence, given that the host could perform many functions for it. And the host species would develop increased metabolic efficiency as a result of the guest's capacity for aerobic respiration. The host would have extra energy that could be channeled into growth in size and into more activity. It would have extra energy for constructing additional structures, such as hard body parts. Within the increasingly complex host cells would be mitochondria—the vestiges of symbiotic bacteria that are now the basis of aerobic metabolism in eukaryotes.

This scenario is not as farfetched as it might seem. Such partnerships can be observed today between cells of entirely different species, as Figure 31.6 suggests. More to the point, aerobic bacteria that serve as models for such a scenario are uncannily like mitochondria in their size, structure, and biochemistry (see page 222).

Origin of Chloroplasts. After urkaryotes developed the means for aerobic metabolism, some also gained a new kind of symbiont. By ingesting photosynthetic prokaryotes, these ancestral forms added photosynthesis to their metabolic repertoire.

In their metabolism, chloroplasts are like eubacteria. In their DNA they are also like eubacteria. A chloroplast has its own complement of DNA, separate from that of the cell in which it is located. A chloroplast has an ability to replicate its own DNA and parts of itself—in partial independence of the nuclear division of the cell!

If symbiosis were the route by which some urkaryotes acquired the capacity for photosynthesis, it may have been

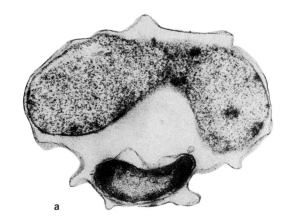

a

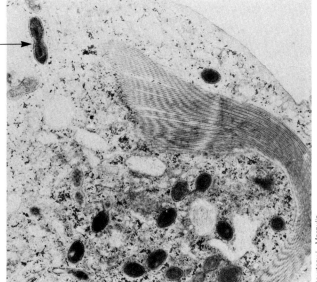

b

Figure 31.6 Symbiosis in existing prokaryotic and eukaryotic cells. (**a**) A predatory bacterium (small, dark oval) called *Bdellovibrio*, which has ended up living in the space between the cell wall and plasma membrane of a larger bacterium. (**b**) Symbiotic bacteria (small, dark ovals) living in *Pyrsonympha*, a protistan that dwells in the termite hindgut. The bacteria are the same size as mitochondria, they are distributed in the cytoplasm as mitochondria are, and they probably oxidize glycolytic products as mitochondria do. The arrow points to a bacterium that is dividing inside the cytoplasm (as mitochondria do). (a, H. Stolp)

Courtesy L. Margulis

followed by different ancestral lines. Today, the simplest photosynthetic eukaryotes resemble one another only in the fact that they are photosynthetic. They resemble different species of eubacteria. Their chloroplasts are not the same. They have different body forms and different life styles. Their accessory pigments also vary, so they differ in color (some are red, some are brown, green, and yellow).

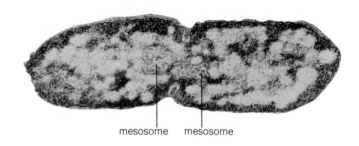

Figure 31.7 Mesosomes in a bacterium that lives in the gut of a rat. These two mesosomes, each an infolding of the plasma membrane that surrounds the DNA, have formed prior to cell division. (David Chase)

mesosome   mesosome

Origin of the Nucleus

Given that nuclear and cytoplasmic machinery function in such highly integrated and coordinated ways, it seems unlikely that the nucleus emerged full-blown, through symbiosis. Rather, the nucleus may have evolved from infoldings of the plasma membrane that came to enclose the DNA.

We have an example of such infoldings in some existing bacteria. Recall that in most bacteria, replicated DNA simply becomes attached to the plasma membrane, which grows and thereby separates the two molecules during cell division (Chapter Nine). In some bacteria, though, the plasma membrane folds elaborately around the replicated DNA in structures called **mesosomes** (Figure 31.7). Mesosomes retain their attachment to the plasma membrane. But it is possible that at some point, structures similar to mesosomes separated permanently from the outer membrane and became the forerunners of the nuclear envelope.

EUKARYOTES OF THE PRECAMBRIAN

Whatever their origins, full-fledged eukaryotes were established by 1.3 billion years ago. Fossils of green algae date from that time. Rock formations in Australia, dated at 900 million years, have yielded fossils of fifty-six species of green and red algae, fungi, and plant spores.

For the next 200 million years, the earth apparently underwent major changes as a result of **plate tectonic processes**—the large-scale movement of crustal plates (Figure 31.8). No fossils have been recovered for this period, which was the time of origin for multicelled plants and animals. Floating and sedentary forms of multicelled green algae were already well developed by 700 million years ago. Fossils have been recovered of multicelled animals, or **metazoans**, that are more than 600 million years old. The

animals were mostly soft-bodied, and they included cnidarians, corals, worms, echinoderms, and possibly mollusks. Their complexity suggests that a great deal of evolution preceded their appearance in the fossil record (Figure 31.9). It was not until the dawn of the Cambrian, about 570 million years ago, that animals with mineralized skeletons abounded. Such skeletons remain well preserved through time, and animal fossils thereafter became common throughout the world.

LIFE DURING THE PALEOZOIC

What we call the Paleozoic Era consisted of six distinct epochs in earth history:

Cambrian	Silurian	Carboniferous
Ordovician	Devonian	Permian

But if there was one feature that characterized the entire Paleozoic, it was the number of massive inundations of continents and retreats by shallow seas.

The Cambrian. By the Late Cambrian, plants, fungi, and animals had radiated through extensive marine environments. At that time, polar regions of the earth's crust were completely submerged. Two major continents, **Gondwana** and **Laurentia**, were positioned at low tropical latitudes. Shallow seas covered the low-lying platforms of these continents and of smaller land masses (Figure 31.10). Not far below the water's surface were layers of mud, sand, and more mud. This was the golden age of trilobites: mud-crawling, mud-burrowing crustaceans that eventually were 600 genera strong. Figure 31.9c shows a representative trilobite; like all its relatives, it scavenged for food on the sea floor. Other crustaceans and algae also flourished in the shallow seas. There is evidence that soft-bodied orga-

Figure 31.8 Plate tectonic theory. (**a**) The earth's surface is broken up into rigid plates. Today these plates are drifting toward or away from each other in the direction of the arrows. Boundaries between plates are marked by recurring earthquakes and volcanic activity.

(**b**) Seafloor spreading and continental drift. Plate tectonics is based on observations that the seafloor is slowly spreading away from sites called oceanic ridges, and on measured displacements of the continents relative to these ridges. Thermal convection in the mantle is proposed as the mechanism underlying these movements. More heat is seen as being generated deep beneath oceanic ridges than elsewhere. The hotter material slowly wells up, then spreads out laterally beneath the crust (much like hot air rising from a stove, then spreading out beneath the ceiling). Oceanic ridges are places where the material has ruptured the crust. As the cooler material moves away from the ridges, it acts like a conveyor belt, carrying older oceanic crust along with it. Thus plates grow and spread away at oceanic ridges. As the plates push against a continental margin, they are thrust beneath it, which causes the crumpling and upheaval by which most mountain ranges have formed.

a

b

a

b

c

National Museum of Natural History

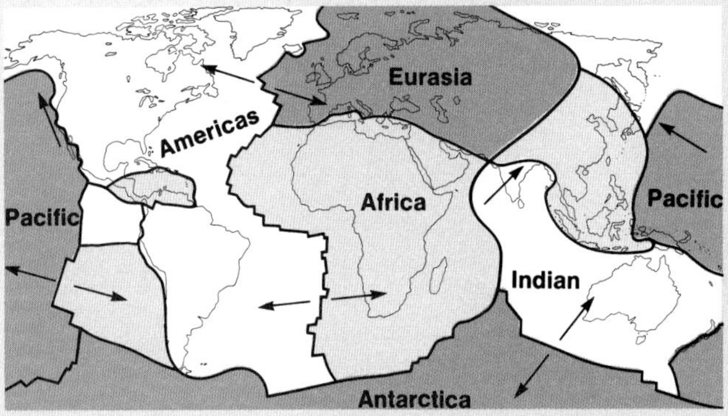

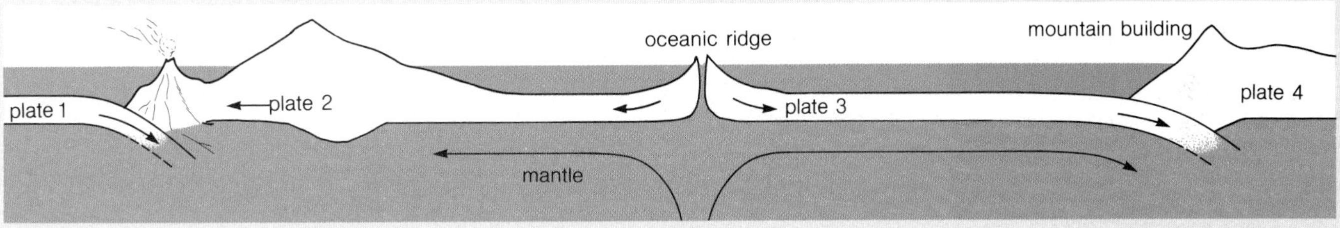

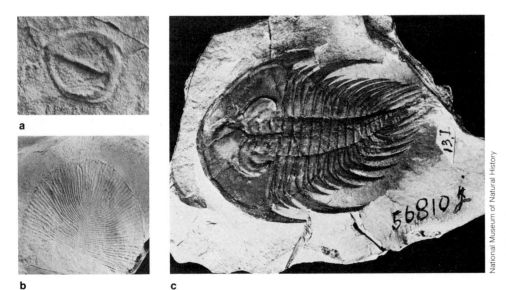

Figure 31.9 (**a, b**) Metazoan fossils, 600 million years old, from South Australia. (**c**) Fossil trilobite from the dawn of the Cambrian. These fossils abound in North America.

Figure 31.10 A correlation between geologic evolution and the evolution of life. The light blue areas on the maps designate known regions of shallow seas.

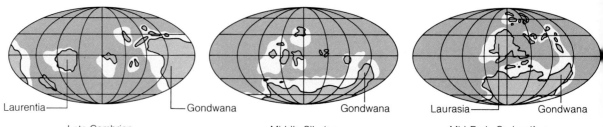

Laurentia —   — Gondwana
Late Cambrian
540 million years ago

                    Gondwana
Middle Silurian
430 million years ago

Laurasia —   — Gondwana
Mid-Early Carboniferous
360–340 million years ago

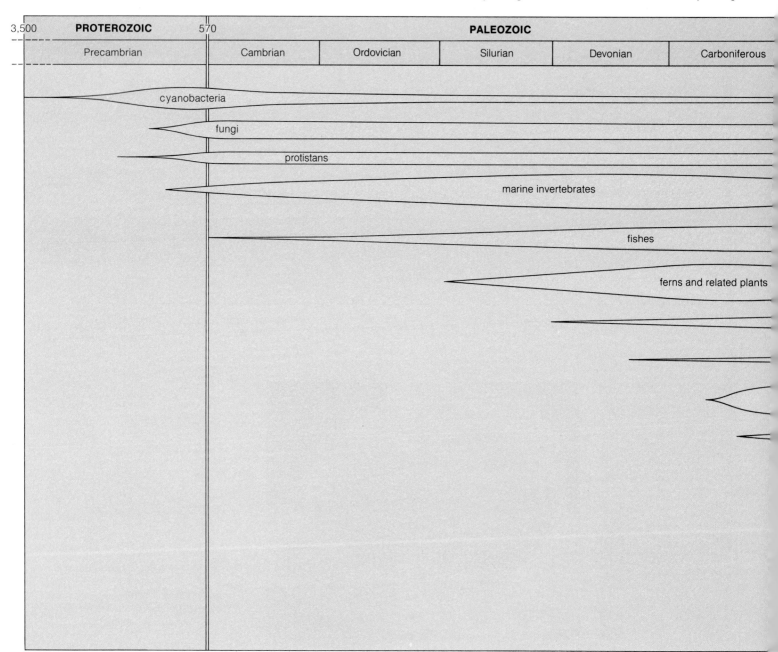

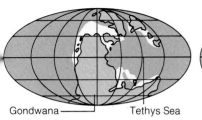 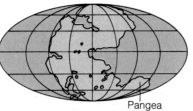 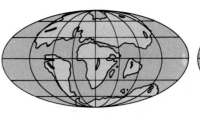 

Gondwana —— Tethys Sea   Pangea

Early Late Permian   Triassic into Jurassic   40–25 million years ago   Present
260–250 million years ago   240–195 million years ago

	240	**MESOZOIC**		65	**CENOZOIC**	
Permian	Triassic	Jurassic	Cretaceous	Tertiary	Quaternary

land invertebrates

gymnosperms

amphibians

reptiles

marine reptiles

mammals

flowering plants

birds

marine mammals

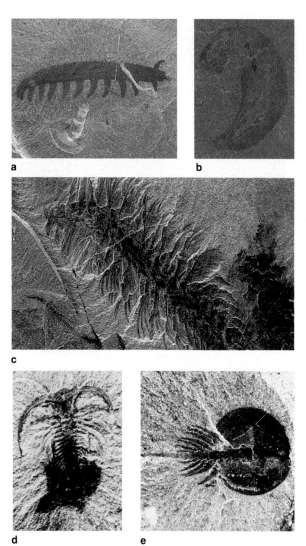

Figure 31.11 Middle Cambrian soft-bodied animals (**a-c**) and arthropods (**d-e**) from the Burgess Shale in British Columbia. The soft-bodied animals are remarkably well preserved. They might have died in relatively still, poorly oxygenated water, and scavengers did not reach them before they were buried gently in the sands. (All photos from National Museum of Natural History)

nisms actually outnumbered the crustaceans during the Cambrian, but they are seen only rarely in the fossil record (Figure 31.11).

The Ordovician. During the 60-million-year span known as the Ordovician, the crustal plate bearing Gondwana crunched its way southward until the supercontinent straddled the South Pole (Figure 31.10). The seas continued their transgressions of the land, and by the Late Ordovician, the

inundations were the most widespread ever recorded. As vast marine environments opened up, there were extensive radiations into adaptive zones. Trilobites continued to evolve, but they were outpaced in numbers by brachiopods (lampshells) and ectoprocts (moss animals). During the mid-Ordovician, the mollusks called cephalopods appeared in abundance and rapidly radiated into ten Orders. The eyes and brain regions of these animals underwent major evolution, which reflects a trend toward the more active life style typical of predators. Today their descendants include the meat-eating squids, octopods, and nautili.

What about the vertebrates? Even before this time, heavily armored, jawless fishes must have been evolving. From the few fossilized armored plates they left behind in Late Cambrian and Ordovician formations, we suspect that the ancestors of vertebrates resembled the jawless fishes of later times. There are no traces of internal skeletons; they may have had skeletons of cartilage, as some primitive fish do today.

Toward the end of the Ordovician, storms of mountain building were brewing as plate movements put Laurentia on a collision course with a smaller land mass to the east. Volcanic outpourings along the eastern edge of Laurentia created immense ancestral mountains as the plates closed in. These crunched-together land masses would part company millions of years later, and eventually would form what we call Europe and North America.

The Silurian. Silurian times were marked by major reorganization of the earth's crust. Gondwana plowed northward, even as land masses were being jostled about in the mid-latitudes. This was the beginning of the **Tethys Sea**, a vast marine environment in which organic reef building would flourish from Permian through Eocene times. Reefs feature warm, shallow, agitated (hence oxygenated) waters, as well as strong light penetration. They are perhaps the most promising of all habitats for the diversification of marine life.

The promise was not fulfilled among all groups. The Silurian was a time of near-extinction for the trilobites and the nautili. But it was also a time of major evolution for the armor-plated fishes, for by now the vertebrate jaw had developed. The jaw was modified from several gill arches, which were anterior, riblike bars that supported a respiratory system (Figure 25.1). The upper jaw became fused with the head plate and thereby became a rigid, efficient structure for feeding. The jaw was a key character that would enable vertebrate fishes to undergo rapid radiations during the Devonian, when unoccupied adaptive zones opened up.

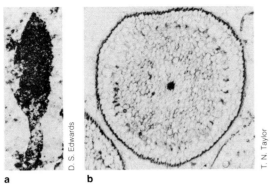

Figure 31.12 (**a**) Spore capsule of a stalked plant similar to the modern bryophyte *Pellia*. This fossil, from South Wales, dates from the Late Silurian. 12×. (**b**) Cross-section of the stem of *Rhynia*, plants from the Early Devonian. The stem extended from a delicate rhizome, which anchored the plant and absorbed nutrients from wet soil. At the center was a primitive water-conducting tube.

Figure 31.13 Reconstruction of the lobe-finned fish.

Even while animal groups were undergoing explosive diversification, a relatively inconspicuous event was taking place that would have major impact on the evolution of life. In the Late Silurian, small stalked plants no taller than your little finger were evolving in wet mud (Figure 31.12).

The Devonian. As the Silurian gave way to the Devonian some 400 million years ago, Laurentia gradually collided with the land mass to the east, forming the supercontinent **Laurasia**. Even as the marine environment between them disappeared, there was a dramatic increase in dry land area. Plants that were adapted to surviving near the land's edge now began their tentative forays onto the land itself. From Rhynie, Scotland, come fossils of Devonian plants called (appropriately) *Rhyniophyta*. These plants had leafless, aerial stems extending from horizontal rhizomes; they had rudimentary water-conducting tissue (Figure 31.12). Lycopods also appeared in tropical land environments during the Devonian, as did fernlike plants, woody trees, and possibly the earliest seed-bearing plants.

When the continents collided, many groups of fishes became extinct. Others, including the bony fishes, were at the threshold of a major adaptive radiation. These fishes had bony skeletons and paired fins. Their armor plates were reduced in size to thin, lightweight scales; their musculature was well developed. These were adaptations that permitted increased speed and maneuverability. Among the bony fishes were two groups—the lungfishes and lobe-finned fishes—that would adapt well to the dry environment.

By Devonian times, lungs were probably present in jawed fishes. They apparently originated long before then as pocketlike outgrowths of the pharynx, the advantage being an increase in the moist epithelium available for gas exchange. Although lungs at first must have supplemented the gas exchange taking place in gills, they became a key character on land. Perhaps out of necessity, lobe-finned fishes began relying more on lungs and less on gills when changes in the earth's crust left them trapped in the mud of freshwater pools and disappearing tidal flats. Perhaps out of necessity, the lobe-finned fishes began using their muscular fins to "walk" from pool to muddy pool (Figure 31.13). By the Late Devonian, they apparently gave rise to the first amphibians.

Labyrinthodont was a transitional form. In the words of Roger Batten, it looked like something a committee put together. It had a fishlike head and tail, and lobed fins with joints in them. But it was an air-breathing amphibian. Forty million years after the pioneering forays of plants, the vertebrate invasion of land was under way.

The Carboniferous. From the beginning to the end of the Carboniferous, land masses were submerged and drained no less than fifty times. Besides these major inundations, there were ever-changing sea levels in between. Imagine the conditions along the flat, low coastlines. Entire groups of marine invertebrates that lived in nearshore waters underwent wholesale extinctions. Immense swamp forests with large, scaly-barked trees became established; over time the seas moved in and buried them in sediments and debris; they became reestablished as the seas moved out—and then they were submerged again. The organic mess left behind has since compacted into the world's coal deposits.

But some groups survived, for adaptations had appeared among them that allowed movement onto higher (and drier) land. The gymnosperms were one such group. These seed-bearing plants were not restricted to the water's edge. They could complete their reproductive cycles without free-standing water (Chapter Thirty-Three). The reptiles were another group of survivors. These animals, which arose from primitive amphibians, could break away from an aquatic existence because of shelled eggs and internal fertilization. These adaptations meant that embryonic development could proceed within the eggshell, a moist and (compared to the outside) dependable setting. The Carboniferous also saw the first great radiations of insects.

The Permian. As magnificently adapted as many species were to the alternating conditions of the Carboniferous, many of their adaptations would not be of much use when the environment changed in an entirely new direction. And change it did, for as the Carboniferous gave way to the Permian, collisions of crustal plates began to crush all land masses together into one vast, unstable supercontinent, called **Pangea** (Figure 31.10).

An immense world ocean lapped both sides of Pangea; no other land masses intervened. The changes in the distribution of water, land area, and land elevation brought pronounced differentiation in world temperature and climate. To the north, arid lowlands and humid uplands emerged. To the south, near the pole, glaciers built up and ice sheets spread over the land that had become positioned there. As the shallow seas were drained from the immense continent, some forms of life radiated into the vacant land environment. And everywhere in the shrinking seas: massive extinctions. Fully half of all known marine species disappeared from the earth at this time. Trilobites, which had endured through the entire Paleozoic Era, were among them.

MESOZOIC: AGE OF THE DINOSAURS

After the great Permian marine extinctions, the survivors in the seas had 165 million years in which to diversify. On land, the character of the living community changed profoundly. By Jurassic times, the climate was warm and humid over widespread regions. Mountains had emerged, along with plains and vast lagoons. In these new settings, gymnosperms and reptiles had the competitive edge. Some groups

a

d

of reptiles became readapted to life in water, others came to develop means to take to the air (Figure 30.20). The ones remaining on land diversified in the most spectacular ways and were unchallenged for the next 125 million years—the golden age of dinosaurs (Figure 31.14).

Their ultimate replacements, though you might never have believed it at the time, would be descendants of the little ratlike mammals scurrying through the shrubbery of the Jurassic. Mammals evolved from the therapsids, a group of mammal-like reptiles that flourished during the Permian. At least some of the early mammals were predators. But they were also food for certain predatory dinosaurs, so they were probably clinging precariously to their place in the community. But cling they did, only to explode into the

biotic vacuum left by their predators at the end of the Cretaceous. At that time, all dinosaurs disappeared suddenly from the earth.

On the evolutionary time scale, the term "sudden" is applied more to events that occur over thousands or hundreds of thousands of years. For most of the dinosaurs, "sudden" extinction may have been over in six bad months. Sixty-five million years ago, an extraterrestrial body—perhaps an asteroid—is thought to have collided with the earth. This idea, first proposed by Luis and Walter Alvarez, is based on the discovery of a peculiar layer of sediments all over the globe. The sediments are one centimeter thick. Their elemental composition resembles that of meteorites, and they are 65 million years old. Calculations indicate

Figure 31.14 (**a**)Triassic thecodont reptiles capable of running on two legs. Such reptiles are thought to be ancestors of dinosaurs and birds. During the age of dinosaurs, some forms took to the air; (**b**) shown here, one pterosaur with wingspans of 12 meters (40 feet). Other forms became adapted to water and became large, swimming predators. Some long-necked plesiosaurs (**c**) reached 15 meters (50 feet) from head to tail. These forms became extinct when vast inland seas dried up. On land, dinosaur diversity reached its peak. Herbivores and carnivores ranged in size from the size of gophers to behemoths three stories high and half a block long (**d**). By this time, flowering plants were coming into dominance, as suggested by the right half of the painting.

Figure 31.15 The view northward across Crater Lake in Oregon, a collapsed volcanic cone aligned with Cascade volcanoes reaching into Washington—and all paralleling the Pacific Coast. These formations are testimony to the violent upheavals of the Cenozoic, when the continents began to take on their current configurations.

Jack Carey

that the asteroid must have been 3.3 kilometers in diameter. The impact of such a body against the earth's crust would have been equivalent to 10 million times the energy released during the 1980 Mount Saint Helens eruption.

Such an impact would have thrown up a cloud of dust that would have remained in the atmosphere for six months. For three of those months, visibility would have been no greater than that on a moonlit night. There would not have been enough light for photosynthesis; delicate food chains in the oceans and on land would have collapsed. Indeed, fossil evidence shows that phytoplankton, the microscopic photosynthetic cells making up the "pastures of the seas," abruptly disappeared 65 million years ago. If the asteroid struck the ocean basin, water as well as dust would have been thrown up into the atmosphere. Heat radiating from the earth could not have escaped through the thick, foglike cover, and air temperature would have risen dramatically. Organisms tend to be more sensitive to warming than to cooling. And apparently there were far more extinctions at this time in tropical latitudes than in northern ones.

The small, ratlike mammals of the Cretaceous could have crawled into holes and burrows to escape the heat; animals such as dinosaurs could not. Again, fossil evidence suggests that all animals larger than your average German shepherd disappeared at that time. How did the tiny mammals find food? In the words of Brian Toon, "One dead dinosaur could keep a lot of mice alive for a long time."

CENOZOIC: THRESHOLD TO THE PRESENT

It was the best of times, the worst of times; it was the dawn of the Cenozoic and the continents were truly on the move. Major reorganization was now going on among all the crustal plates. Unbelievable amounts of lava began pouring through immense faults and fissures that penetrated to the basement of the earth's crust. Fragmentation occurred along the coasts; severe volcanism and uplifting produced mountains along the margins of massive rifts and along zones where some plates were thrust under others. This was the time of formation for the Alps, the Andes, and Himalayas, the Sierra Nevadas, and the Cascade Range paralleling North America's western coast (Figure 31.15).

Correlated with this redistribution of the land was the onset of widespread extinction of some groups and expansions of others. In much of the world, shifts in climate led to the emergence of vast, semiarid, cooler grasslands in mid-Cenozoic times. Into these settings, plant-eating mammals and their predators radiated (Figure 31.16).

As the climate continued to change, the vast tropical forests dating from the preceding epoch began to be fragmented into a patchwork of new environments. Many of their inhabitants were forced into new life-styles in mountain highlands, in deserts, in the plains. One such evicted form was destined to give rise to the human species, an event to be described in Chapter Thirty-Five.

Figure 31.16 Reconstruction of North American mammals of the Eocene (**a**) and Pliocene (**b**).

PERSPECTIVE

All living things are composed of molecules made of the same chemical elements—primarily carbon, hydrogen, nitrogen, and oxygen. These elements were present, in one form or another, in the crust and atmosphere of the primordial earth. It has been demonstrated that these elements can combine spontaneously into carbohydrates, lipids, proteins, nucleic acids, even ATP—into the stuff of life—given the right chemical environment and a source of activation energy. It has been demonstrated that, given a particular set of physical and chemical conditions, such macromolecules can form differentially permeable structures much like simple cell membranes. Even now, research is shedding light on how such structures might have evolved chemically into the first organized, self-reproducing systems—into the first cells.

Whatever the details of such chemical evolution might have been, we suspect from fossil signposts that it flowed to the threshold of biological evolution and, eventually, to the explosive diversification of life.

And so today you are sharing the earth with at least 2 million species. They, and you, share allegiance to the same principles of energy flow and chemical interactions. They, and you, share the same molecular and cellular heritage. All these things speak of the underlying unity of life. They also speak eloquently of its subsequent diversity. For if the

environments of the first living things had never changed, if there never had been different abiotic and biotic horizons waiting the vanguard of inadvertent explorers, perhaps the world today would hold little more than testimony to life's unity. Perhaps there would be little more than cells of the sort preserved in ancient rocks—cells matted against rocks or suspended in the seas, quietly soaking up nutrients.

But the record of earth history tells us that environments *have* changed. It tells us that populations either have been equipped to adapt to those changes or have perished. The record also suggests that just as the diversity of life has been a product of evolution, so has it been an evolutionary force of the first magnitude. "Diversity" not only means adaptations to some combination of temperature, chemical balance, available water, light, dark, and living space. "Diversity" means adaptations to different kinds of predators, different prey, different competitors after the same resource, different behavior, coloration, and patterning that help assure reproductive success.

Thus all existing species can be viewed as the evolutionary products of interactions with the environment and one another. These interactions are the focus of paleoecology; they are the focus of modern ecology. And this brings us to a concept of profound importance. By the fact of their continuing existence, all species now on earth can claim adaptive success. However, success is assured only as long as there is responsiveness to the environment, and only as long as there is responsiveness among organisms making their home together. Both the environment and the community of life change, shifting as imperceptibly as shifting winds over centuries, or abruptly obliterating all trace of forms that have gone before.

And therein lies the story of evolution, the story of chemical competition and cooperation leading to the first self-reproducing forms of life, of dinosaurs, of continents on the move. Therein lies the story of simple strategies unchanged since the dawn of life, and of the complex human strategy—as yet unresolved—that can hold a world together or rip it apart. Yet must we predict gloomily that such unresolved activity on our part will end this magnificent story for all time? We doubt it. For if the record of earth history tells us anything at all, it is that life in one form or another has survived disruptions of the most cataclysmic sort. That life can evolve tenaciously through tests of flood and fire suggests it has every chance of evolving around and past our transgressions, too. *Viva Vida!*

Readings

Alvarez, L., W. Alvarez, F. Asaro, and H. Michel. 1980. "Extraterrestrial Cause for the Cretaceous-Tertiary Extinction." *Science* 208: 1095–1107.

Bambach, R., C. Scotese, and A. Ziegler. 1980. "Before Pangea: The Geographies of the Paleozoic World." *American Scientist* 68(1):26–38. Excellent summary article, complete with color-coded maps of the changing configurations of continents.

Cox, A. 1973. *Plate Tectonics and Geomagnetic Reversals.* San Francisco: Freeman. Overview of the evolution of plate tectonic theory.

Dott, R., and R. Batten. 1981. *Evolution of the Earth.* Third edition. New York: McGraw-Hill. Findings from diverse lines of research are distilled into a stunning picture of earth and life history. We enthusiastically recommend this book for your personal library.

Eigen, M., W. Gardiner, P. Schuster, and R. Winkler-Oswatitch. 1981. "The Origin of Genetic Information." *Scientific American* 244(4): 88–118. Describes experiments that indicate the chemical nature of the first self-replicating protein–RNA template systems.

Groves, D., J. Dunlop, and R. Buick. 1981. "An Early Habitat of Life." *Scientific American* 245(4):64–73. Evidence of ancient microbes.

Hargreaves, W., and D. Deamer. 1978. "Origin and Early Evolution of Bilayer Membranes." In *Light-Transducing Membranes* (D. Deamer, editor). New York: Academic Press.

Margulis, L. 1982. *Early Life.* Boston: Science Books International. Easy to read introduction to the origin and evolution of prokaryotes and eukaryotes. Paperback.

Schopf, J. 1975. "The Age of Microscopic Life." *Endeavor* 34(122): 51–58.

Stebbins, G. 1982. *Darwin to DNA, Molecules to Humanity.* San Francisco: Freeman. Excellent overview of evolutionary theory and of experiments at reconstructing the physical and chemical conditions leading to the origin of life. Paperback.

Woese, C. 1981. "Archaebacteria." *Scientific American* 244(6):98–125. Presents evidence of three primordial kingdoms of bacteria.

Review Questions

1. What three physical characteristics of the primordial earth were favorable for the origin of life?

2. What three conditions must have been met if life originated as a product of chemical evolution?

3. The early earth apparently had a "nonoxidizing atmosphere." What effect would such an atmosphere have had on the spontaneous assembly of complex organic molecules? (What effect does our present "oxidizing atmosphere" have?) What kinds of energy sources could have driven the formation of macromolecules of life?

4. How do experiments suggest that cell-like membranous spheres could have evolved? Why does it seem likely that metabolism cannot proceed without boundary layers such as cell membranes?

5. Even if cell-like membranous spheres could have evolved, how could the first *living* cells have originated? For your answer, think about the lifeless molecules called enzymes, nucleic acids, and nucleotides. Assuming these molecules became concentrated in membrane-like spheres, what might have happened?

6. Describe a radioactive element and how it breaks down spontaneously (decays) at its own unique rate. How are such elements used to date rocks?

7. Can you distinguish among the Eubacteria, Archaebacteria, and Urkaryote lineages?

8. What modern-day organisms did the earliest forms of life resemble? Given atmospheric and geologic conditions, what must have been their main energy-acquiring strategies?

9. What kind of existing evidence lends support to the idea of symbiotic origins of mitochondria?

10. How does plate tectonic theory help explain why different assemblages of organisms characterize the main geologic eras?

11. By the late Cambrian, major land masses were covered largely by shallow seas. What kinds of organisms evolved in this environment? By the Ordovician, even low-lying land was submerged. What kinds of organisms radiated into the vacant marine environment? What structural and behavioral traits must already have existed in Silurian times, before the geologic upheavals that created vast land environments in which such traits would prove adaptive?

12. What sort of organisms evolved during the Carboniferous, when land masses were submerged and drained no less than fifty times?

13. In the evolutionary story, what two kinds of interactions have given rise to all existing species?

DIVERSITY: EVOLUTIONARY FORCE, EVOLUTIONARY PRODUCT

32

VIRUSES, BACTERIA, AND PROTISTANS

Bacteria and protistans are found almost everywhere, including many places where humans would really rather not be. They live in near-boiling hot springs, Antarctic snows, parched deserts, the ocean depths, and your gut. Usually they are so small that they are hidden from the unaided eye. For instance, a handful of rich, moist soil may contain billions of microscopic bacteria. Even though we are not often conscious of their presence, we and all other complex organisms would disappear from the earth without them. Many of these microorganisms play extremely important roles, including food production, oxygen production, and the cycling of nutrients through the biosphere.

This chapter begins with some characteristics of bacteria. It includes a description of viruses, which many consider to be degenerate forms of bacteria that evolved long ago. The latter part of the chapter deals with the puzzling single-celled protistans. These eukaryotes are thought to mirror the ancient forms that gave rise to multicelled plants, fungi, and animals.

BACTERIA

Characteristics of Bacteria

There are only about 15,000 known species of bacteria, but they are the most abundant of all organisms. They are also the only prokaryotes—single cells that do not have diverse internal organelles, particularly a nucleus. Some bacteria seem to be multicelled filaments or masses, but they are linked only because the walls of adjacent cells fail to separate after cell reproduction. True multicellularity occurs only among eukaryotes.

Bacterial Form and Structure. Most bacterial species have a distinct form, although variations in the environment can introduce changes in those forms. The following terms refer to the three most common bacterial shapes: coccus (plural, cocci), rods, and spirals, as depicted in Figure 32.1. Some individual rods are so long that they look like filaments. Some spiral forms have only a few twists; others twist so many times that they are shaped like a helix. Both rods and cocci may remain attached following cell division, forming chains of various lengths.

All bacterial cells have the following components: plasma membrane, numerous ribosomes scattered through the cytoplasm, and a closed loop of double-stranded DNA. Sometimes the DNA is clustered in one region (the nucleoid), but it is never enclosed in a nuclear envelope, as it is in eukaryotes. Many bacteria also have one or more motile structures, or bacterial flagella (Chapter Four).

cocci (singular, coccus)
spherical

rods
cylindrical

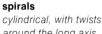

spirals
cylindrical, with twists around the long axis

Figure 32.1 The three most common shapes that occur among bacteria.

Most (but not all) bacteria have a cell wall, which sometimes is enclosed in a polysaccharide or polypeptide capsule. Eubacterial cell walls are composed of **peptidoglycan**, a substance that never occurs in eukaryotes. Peptidoglycan consists of sugars and amino acids, linked into a repeating structure that forms one or more layers of the cell wall.

Bacteria are classified in part by the way that they react to a violet staining procedure, named after the European microbiologist Hans Gram. Bacterial cells are first stained with a purple dye (called crystal violet), then washed with alcohol or acetone. **Gram-positive bacteria** retain the purple dye. **Gram-negative bacteria** lose the color when they are so washed; however, they take up a red dye that makes them appear pink. Apparently, the stain allows us to distinguish between bacteria that have two different types of cell walls. The distinction is clinically important: the cell walls of gram-negative bacteria apparently impart resistance to antibiotics.

Metabolism. Bacteria originated in relatively inhospitable places, which few other organisms could call home (Chapter Thirty-One). In some of these environments, there is an absence of air. Bacteria living in these places are typically obligate anaerobes (they cannot grow in the presence of oxygen). In other environments, oxygen is present some of the time but not all of the time. Here we find facultative anaerobes (which use anaerobic pathways of metabolism when oxygen is not present, and aerobic pathways when it is).

Most bacteria are heterotrophs: they cannot derive their energy from inorganic material, and instead use energy-rich organic compounds produced by other organisms. The majority of bacterial heterotrophs are **decomposers**. Along with fungi, they contribute to the decay and recycling of organic compounds in soil. Some bacterial heterotrophs are **parasites**. They use organic compounds that are incorporated in living organisms. The disease-causing (pathogenic) bacteria are among these parasitic forms. As you will read in Chapter Thirty-Seven, parasitism is an extreme form of symbiosis. At the other extreme are beneficial symbionts such as *Rhizobium*, a heterotrophic bacterium that lives in root tissues of legumes and enhances nitrogen availability for those plants as a consequence of its metabolic activities.

Bacteria that are autotrophs—"self-feeders"—either use sunlight energy or the energy of inorganic compounds in building their own complex organic materials. The chemosynthetic forms include the methanogenic bacteria. The photosynthetic forms include green bacteria, purple bacteria, and cyanobacteria (Figure 32.2).

heterocyst

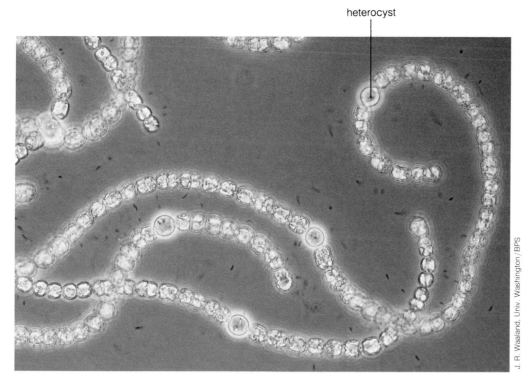

J. R. Waaland, Univ. Washington / BPS

Figure 32.2 One species of the cyanobacteria *Anabaena*. Individual cells remain attached following cell division. The resulting filaments become coated in a mucilaginous sheath, formed from cellular secretions. Nitrogen-fixing cells (heterocysts) of *Anabaena* form under anaerobic conditions.

Table 32.1	Some Representatives of Archaebacteria and Eubacteria
Archaebacteria	
Methanogens	*Methanobacteria, Halobacteria*
Thermoacidophiles	*Sulfobolus, Thermoplasma*
Eubacteria*	
Photosynthetic Bacteria:	
Cyanobacteria	*Anabaena, Oscillatoria*
Green bacteria	*Chlorobium*
Purple bacteria	*Rhodospirillum*
Spirochaetes	*Spirochaeta, Treponema*
Gram-Negative Bacteria	*Escherichia, Proteus, Pseudomonas, Rhizobium, Desulfobrio, Neisseria*
Gram-Positive Bacteria	*Streptococcus, Staphylococcus, Lactobacillus, Bacillus, Clostridium*
Actinomycetes	*Actinomyces*
Rickettsias	*Rickettsiae, Chlamydia*
Mycoplasmas	*Mycoplasma*

*There are many more groups than this. We include only those with genera mentioned in this book. For a complete listing, see *Bergey's Manual of Determinative Bacteriology,* eighth edition.

Sensory Reception and Response. As simple as they appear to be, bacteria show diverse responses to stimuli. Some bacterial cells move toward or away from regions of greatest light intensity (phototaxis). These cells also are attracted to and repelled by different substances, and they move toward or away from the region of greatest concentration (chemotaxis). *Escherichia coli* is one such form. We know that *E. coli* has twelve sugar-binding chemoreceptors located between the bacterial cell wall and the plasma membrane. On the plasma membrane itself are at least eight chemoreceptors for noxious substances. In some unknown way, chemical information from these receptors stimulates particular movements of the bacterial flagella.

E. coli uses flagella to swim rapidly in gentle, curved runs that are punctuated by short tumbles. After a tumble, the cell starts a new run in whatever direction it happens to be pointing. In favorable settings, there are more curved runs and fewer tumbles, so the cell circles more or less in the same place. In noxious settings, tumbles are more frequent and they tend to point the cell elsewhere.

Finally, consider one kind of spiral bacterium that lives in the iron-rich waters of a Massachusetts swamp. About twenty grains of magnetite (Fe_2O_3) accumulate at one end of its body, opposite the motile structure. As the bacterium swims, the magnet directs it downward—which is where food sources are most concentrated.

As you can see, bacteria are not nearly as complex as the eukaryotic cell—yet they do show diversity in structure and behavior. With this point in mind, let's now look at the two major groups that were introduced in the preceding chapter: the Archaebacteria and Eubacteria. Table 32.1 lists some representatives for each group.

Archaebacteria

The name **Archaebacteria** reflects a presumed evolutionary status as the oldest group of organisms on earth. In their metabolism, these bacteria are adapted to a limited range of extreme conditions that are thought to have prevailed on the early earth (Chapter Thirty-One).

Archaebacteria are distinctive in several respects. Their cell walls do not contain peptidoglycan, the hallmark of eubacteria. Their cell membranes are unusual in lipid composition, and they have distinctive transfer RNAs and RNA polymerases. In their biochemistry, these bacteria fall into two categories: the methanogens and thermoacidophiles.

The **methanogens** are typically found in swamps and marshes. They live in mud enriched with organic matter and in sludge (which contains fecal matter). There are a few forms that have taken up residence in the gut of some complex animals. The *Methanobacteria* subsist on such simple inorganic compounds as carbon dioxide, acetate, and methanol; typically they use electrons from hydrogen gas to convert these compounds to methane gas. The methane-producing bacteria are among the strictest anaerobes; contact with oxygen destroys them.

Related to the methane producers are the extreme halophiles, such as *Halobacterium*. They can be found in such settings as Utah's Great Salt Lake, where sodium chloride (NaCl) concentrations are very high. *Halobacterium* is mostly anaerobic; its habitat usually has low oxygen concentrations. However, in the presence of oxygen it can synthesize ATP with the aid of a carotenoid pigment called bacteriorhodopsin. This light-absorbing pigment is the basis of the simplest photophosphorylation system known.

The **thermoacidophiles** show remarkable resistance to acid concentrations and temperatures that are high enough to destroy most cells. *Sulfobolus,* a sulfur-oxidizing heterotroph, grows in hot springs and hot, acid soils. It tolerates a pH range from 1 to 5, and temperatures of 60°–85°C. Its enzymes and other proteins are resistant to denaturation. In addition, abundant saturated fats in the plasma membrane impart high-temperature stability to the membrane itself. (These fats are more strongly hydrophobic than the unsaturated forms that occur in most plasma membranes.)

Eubacteria

The term **eubacteria** reflects notions about what constitutes a "true" bacterium. These notions were developed before biochemical studies suggested that there are two major lineages of bacteria, not just one. Here we will consider just a few members of the eubacteria to give you an idea of their diversity.

Cyanobacteria.
The **cyanobacteria** are divided into 150 genera, within which are 2,000 known species. All of these photosynthetic bacteria have infoldings of the plasma membrane that are studded with light-trapping pigments. Depending on the array of pigments, each species appears blue, red-green, or almost black. Unlike other photosynthetic prokaryotes, the cyanobacteria have phycobilins and the *same* kind of chlorophyll found in plants (chlorophyll *a*).

Cyanobacteria live as single cells, colonies, or filaments. In many of the filamentous forms, both photosynthetic cells and nitrogen-fixing cells are present (Figure 32.2). The nitrogen-fixing cells reduce nitrogen gas to ammonium, which is converted to organic forms. Together with other nitrogen-fixing microbes, the cyanobacteria are a cornerstone of the biosphere. If deprived of their activities, the biosphere as we know it would probably collapse for lack of enough usable nitrogen compounds for protein synthesis.

Cyanobacteria live in freshwater, saltwater, and land environments. There are species in hot springs, salt lakes, permanent snowfields, and on desert rocks. Two factors underlie their adaptability to such a broad range of environments. First, cyanobacteria have simple requirements for energy and raw materials. Almost any place that has sunlight, carbon dioxide, some water, and simple mineral salts will permit their growth. Second, they reproduce by the simplest means possible. When conditions are favorable, they divide rapidly by bacterial fission. When conditions are unfavorable, some species form a thick wall or a gelatinlike coat that keeps them from drying out. Like prokaryotes generally, the cyanobacteria grow in good times and wait out the bad. It is a time-tested adaptation. Cyanobacteria were among the earliest forms of life on earth, and it is probable that they will be among the last.

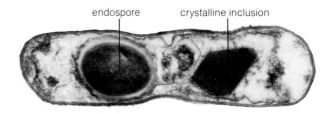

Figure 32.3 Endospore formation in *Bacillus thuringiensis*. The crystalline inclusion is of a kind that may be "harvested" and used as a natural insecticide for certain insect species. (David Vitale and George B. Chapman, Georgetown University)

Endospore-Forming Bacteria. Some eubacteria are able to form **endospores**: resistant structures that surround the hereditary material when nutrient concentrations drop or when temperatures are too high. Figure 32.3 shows an endospore. Once an endospore forms, the rest of the cell disintegrates.

During endospore formation in some bacilli, a crystalline protein is assembled inside the cell body (Figure 32.3). These bacilli happen to cause fatal diseases in certain insects. The protein is toxic to such crop destroyers as cabbage worms, tent caterpillars, gypsy moths, and silkworms. Some of these crystal-forming bacteria are being used commercially in biological control programs.

Endospore-forming bacteria also include species that cause diseases in animals, and some are particular problems for humans. Exposure to high temperatures for a few minutes is often enough to rid various foods and equipment of most actively growing bacteria. But if the environment is slightly alkaline, endospore-formers can live through several hours of boiling! That is why hospitals use **autoclaves**: steam pressure devices that raise the temperature above that of boiling water. At 121°C, ever bacterial endospores are destroyed after eighteen minutes in these moisture-saturated devices.

Clostridia are among the endospore-forming bacteria. They live primarily in soil and dust; a few live in water. Many take up residence in the animal gut, as you will read shortly. Sometimes these bacteria are accidentally carried into the internal environment of animals, and there they can cause serious disease. For example, puncture wounds, animal bites, and burns can allow *Clostridium tetani* to penetrate body tissues. If the tissues become necrotic (as happens when the injury is such that oxygen can no longer be delivered to them), these anaerobic bacteria can thrive and multiply. Unfortunately, a product of their metabolic activity is a neurotoxin that inhibits the enzyme acetylcholine esterase. In doing so, it prevents the release of the neuromuscular junction synapse, resulting in continued muscle contraction. The result is **tetanus**: prolonged, spastic paralysis of muscles that can lead to death. In the United States, children are routinely vaccinated with a modified, harmless form of the toxin. Booster injections are given every five to ten years after initial immunization. However, if several years have lapsed since the last injections, another booster may be recommended for individuals who are injured in ways that can allow *C. tetani* entry (for example, by stepping on a soil-covered nail or splinter).

Clostridium botulinum is an obligate anaerobe that lives in soil, in lake mud, and in decaying vegetation. Each year, many cattle and birds die after feeding on fermenting grains that house these bacteria. *C. botulinum* can produce a neurotoxin that is one of the most dangerous substances known. It has been estimated that only one milliliter of culture fluid could kill 2 million mice. Sometimes the bacterium can grow and produce toxin in food that has been improperly sterilized and packaged in an anaerobic environment (as in cans and jars). Ingestion of the food can lead to the form of poisoning called **botulism**. The toxin interferes with the release of acetylcholine from nerve endings and thereby prevents muscle contraction. Death can follow as a result of respiratory failure. Individuals who suspect that they have botulism can be given antitoxins; in serious cases, an artificial respirator can be used to prevent breathing failure.

Mycoplasmas. The **mycoplasmas** are the smallest known cells that are able to grow and reproduce without the aid of a living host. The sixty recognized species range in size from 0.12 to 0.25 micrometer in diameter. Unlike other prokaryotes, mycoplasmas do not have a cell wall (Figure 32.4). As might be expected, these "uncontained" cells vary considerably in shape, from extremely small spheres to noodlelike strands.

Mycoplasmas infect cattle, poultry, lambs, goats, sheep, swine, and humans. They can cause an atypical form of pneumonia among humans. Cells that resemble mycoplasmas apparently infect many plants. For example, one species alone is destroying numerous different species of palm trees in Florida.

Rickettsiae. The **Rickettsiae** are tiny bacteria of unknown affiliation. They are obligate parasitic bacteria that grow *inside* host cells. With only one exception (Q fever), rickettsial diseases are transmitted when an arthropod such as a tick bites an infected animal and then later bites an uninfected one.

Rickettsia rickettsii causes **Rocky Mountain spotted fever** which, if untreated, can lead to death. In humans, the disease is characterized by fever, severe headaches, and a rash of spots that usually emerge first on the palms of hands and the soles of feet. The arthropod vectors in this case are wood ticks and dog ticks. In the disease **typhus**, the vectors can be lice, ticks, mites, and fleas. Epidemic or louse-borne typhus is associated with highly crowded living conditions. It has reached epidemic proportions among troops during major wars, and is said to have forced Napoleon's retreat from Russia. During World War II and in Vietnam, one form or another of typhus occurred among troops.

Fifteen Thousand Species of Bacteria Can't Be All Bad

Whenever the activities of parasitic bacteria interfere with basic physiological processes, the outcome is serious disease. Among humans, examples are bacterial pneumonia, bubonic plague, cholera, tetanus, diphtheria, typhus, tuberculosis, and bacillary dysentary. Some parasitic forms are also agents of sexually transmitted diseases.

As if this were not enough, almost all plants are vulnerable to destructive bacterial diseases. For example, fire blight can destroy young apple and pear trees in a single growing season. Between 1930 and 1980, this bacterial disease wiped out the pear industry in all parts of the United States except a corner of the Northwest. Soft rots damage such food crops as potatoes, tomatoes, and onions. Non-woody plants are subject to bacterial wilts. Here, bacteria invade the xylem and destroy vessel walls. Their activities disrupt the movement of water and mineral ions through the vessels; the plant wilts, then dies.

It is tempting, after being reminded of some of the horrors of bacterial infections, to render all bacteria guilty by association. But the vast majority are not guilty of terrible deeds. Think about the bacteria that help cycle carbon, nitrogen, and other nutrients through the biosphere. Think about the forms that help produce the oxygen you breathe. What about the tremendous potential offered by genetically engineered bacteria? Even now, they are being used as commercial "factories" of vaccines, enzymes, hormones (such as insulin and growth hormone), many antibiotics (including neomycin and bacitracin), and interferon (the powerful antiviral substance in humans).

And can you imagine what the world would be like without bacteria to help dispose of human wastes? Modern wastewater treatment centers rely heavily on bacterial action to restore water to some semblance of its former self before it is dumped into the waterways (see Chapter Forty).

Also, consider that the insecticides and herbicides sprayed each year on crops must be disposed of after they have acted on their targets. Yet compounds such as some chlorinated hydrocarbons can linger in fields for more than a decade. They may accumulate to levels high enough to harm not only the insects and weeds but also the humans who eat the crops. Certain natural processes such as soil leaching help keep the levels of these compounds within tolerable limits. But bacteria with special enzymes are often involved in converting toxic compounds to harmless forms.

Finally, consider that bacterial populations in the gastrointestinal tract affect the well-being of their hosts. Among humans and other mammals, acid-tolerant bacteria (primarily *Lactobacillus* and *Streptococcus*) become well established in the intestinal contents within the first week after birth. The large intestine comes to house so many bacteria that it is, in effect, a high-powered fermentation tube. *Escherichia coli*, a facultative anaerobe, uses up oxygen present in the tube and thereby helps create benign conditions for its strictly anaerobic neighbors.

Some of these so-called enteric bacteria help emulsify dietary fats, and thereby promote the digestion and absorption of fats by the host. Bacteria synthesize vitamin K and some of the B vitamins. South Pacific islanders who subsist almost entirely on sweet potato tubers carry an anaerobic, nitrogen-fixing bacterium in the gut—which is fortunate for the islanders, because the high-carbohydrate tubers provide them with no nitrogen to speak of.

Cattle, sheep, deer, and other ruminants house a special community of bacteria. These animals have a large digestive organ, the **rumen**, in which tough cellulose fibers and other plant materials are digested. The rumen is an anaerobic setting, where temperatures are a constant 39°C. It supports cellulose decomposers of the genus *Clostridium*, starch decomposers such as *Streptococcus* and *Selenomonas*, and methane producers (*Methanobacterium*). Food entering the rumen becomes mixed with its microbial residents, some of which have enzymes that can hydrolyze cellulose into disaccharides and monosaccharides. The organic acids resulting from microbial fermentation of these and other sugars are the main source of energy for the animal host. Also, the enormous numbers of bacterial cells moving with partially digested plant material through the gastrointestinal tract undergo digestion, too. When they do, they provide the animal with most of its amino acids and vitamins.

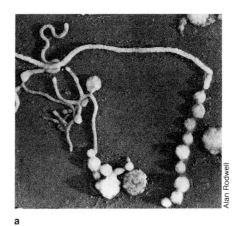

a

original cell wall   plasma membrane

b

Figure 32.4 (**a**) Mycoplasmas, and (**b**) a bacterium undergoing lysis. Three things point to an evolutionary link between mycoplasmas and bacteria. First, under certain conditions, cells resembling mycoplasmas can be made from bacteria. Most bacteria undergo lysis when their cell wall is degraded by an enzyme, which allows water to rush into the cell, expand it, and make it burst. But lysis can be prevented if the wall is removed in a concentrated sugar solution. (The sugar lowers the concentration of free water on the outside and prevents it from diffusing rapidly into the cell.) The organisms so stabilized end up looking rather like mycoplasmas. Second, although under certain conditions these naked bacteria may revert to their former clothed selves, some never do: they may go on growing like mycoplasmas. Third, the DNA composition of mycoplasmalike organisms closely resembles that of certain bacteria. (b, Dinah Abram)

For humans who ingest antibiotics to fight infections, there is a risk of disrupting the bacterial community present in the gastrointestinal tract. The antibiotics may arrest growth of some susceptible bacteria. With the destruction of the normal flora, antibiotic-resistant bacteria such as *Staphylococcus, Proteus,* and the yeast *Candida albicans* can flourish. Their activity and growth, however, can disrupt normal digestive functioning and lead to disease. It often takes some time for the normal bacterial community to displace them.

Table 32.2 Classification of Animal Viruses	
Category	Some Diseases Produced
DNA Viruses:	
Adenoviruses	*Respiratory infections; pinkeye; under some circumstances can cause malignant tumors in hamsters*
Parvoviruses	*Gastroenteritis (diarrhea, vomiting); implicated in hepatitis A in humans*
Papovaviruses	*Warts in humans, rabbits, dogs; cancer in mice, hamsters*
Herpesviruses	*Fever blisters; chickenpox; shingles; genital infections with neurological consequences; some induce cancer; one implicated in infectious mononucleosis*
Poxviruses	*Smallpox; cowpox; formation of fibromas (nodules or benign tumors)*
RNA Viruses:	
Entoviruses	*Diarrhea; polio; aseptic meningitis*
Rhinoviruses	*Common colds*
Togaviruses	*Yellow fever; German measles; equine encephalitis*
Influenzaviruses	*Influenzas*
Paramyxoviruses	*Mild respiratory disorders; Newcastle disease; measles*
Rhabdoviruses	*Rabies*
Arenaviruses	*Meningitis; hemorrhagic fevers*
Coronaviruses	*Upper respiratory disease*
Retroviruses	*Tumors (sarcomas); leukemia*
Reoviruses	*Mild respiratory disorders; severe diarrhea in humans, cattle, mice*

Data from W. Volk, *Essentials of Medical Microbiology*, 1979.

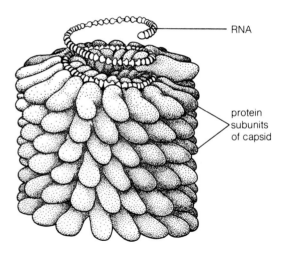

RNA

protein subunits of capsid

Figure 32.5 Structure of the tobacco mosaic virus. An entire rod-shaped virion (individual virus particle) is much longer than shown here.

VIRUSES

Characteristics of Viruses

Like the Rickettsias, **viruses** are obligate, intracellular parasites. Yet many biologists do not consider them to be alive. They do have their own nucleic acids (single- or double-stranded DNA or RNA). Some contain DNA or RNA polymerase. The nucleic acid is sheathed in a protective protein coat, or *viral capsid,* which ranges from 20 to 250 nanometers across. However, unlike all living cells, viruses are not capable of metabolism; they have no mechanisms for generating their own metabolic energy. Neither are they capable of replicating themselves. Viruses can be replicated only by subverting the biosynthetic machinery of a host cell, which then preferentially follows the instructions encoded in the

viral DNA or RNA. Because viruses can be perpetuated only inside the cells of another living organism, they probably developed at some point after cellular life originated. One hypothesis is that they are the noncellular remnants of ancient, parasitic forms of bacteria.

Even if viruses are not alive, their influence on the biosphere is staggering. They cause many plant and animal diseases, some of which reach epidemic proportions. One of the most thoroughly studied of these disease-causing agents is the **tobacco mosaic virus** (TMV), which causes severe damage to the leaves of tobacco plants. It is a rod-shaped RNA virus with a capsid composed of 2,200 identical protein units (Figure 32.5). The TMV was the first to be purified and crystallized, and when the needle-shaped crystals were subsequently dissolved in water, they infected healthy plants. Other well-studied viruses include the bacteriophages, which were described in Chapter Twelve.

Animal viruses are extremely destructive, as Table 32.2 suggests. For example, **influenzaviruses** (Figure 32.6) cause Asian flu, Hong Kong flu, and Spanish flu. These diseases can occur in *pandemic* form; they can occur as worldwide epidemics. They recur in ten- to forty-year cycles, and localized epidemics may occur every year in between. Between 1918 and 1920, more than 20 million people died under the attack of a Spanish flu virus. That happened not very long ago; your grandparents were alive then. The disease symptoms begin with sensations of chilling, followed by a sudden rise in body temperature to 100°–104°F. Muscles ache severely. The virus attacks the upper respiratory tract. Often, weakened respiratory tissues are susceptible to

COMMENTARY

Bacteria, Viruses, and Sexually Transmitted Diseases

(This Commentary was written on the basis of information supplied by the Centers for Disease Control, Atlanta, Georgia)

Sexually transmitted diseases (STDs) have reached epidemic proportions, even in countries with the highest medical standards. The disease agents, mostly bacterial and viral, are usually transmitted to uninfected persons during sexual intercourse. In the United States alone, 10 million young adults have reported that they have some form of STD; no one can estimate the number of unreported cases. The economics of this health problem are staggering. By conservative estimates, the cost of treatment is exceeding $2 billion a year. The social consequences are sobering. For example, of every twenty babies born in the United States, one will have a chlamydial infection. Of every 10,000 newborns, as many as three will contact systemic herpes; half may die early on, and a fourth of those surviving will suffer serious neurological defects. Each year, 1 million girls and adult women are stricken with pelvic inflammatory disease, a complication of chlamydial and gonococcal infections. Of these, more than 200,000 are hospitalized, more than 100,000 undergo pelvic surgery that results in permanent sterility, while 900 cannot recover and die. These and other sexually transmitted diseases are expected to increase at alarming proportions during this decade.

Gonorrhea. Gonorrhea ranks first among the reported communicable diseases in the United States. In 1979 alone, an estimated 1.6 to 2 million people became afflicted with the disease. Gonorrhea is caused by *Neisseria gonorrhoeae,* a bacterium that infects the epithelial cells of the genital tract (and the conjunctiva or pharynx if carried there). Males have a greater chance than females do of detecting the disease in early stages. Within a week, yellow pus is discharged from the urethra. Urination becomes more frequent and painful, because the urinary tract becomes inflamed. Females may or may not experience a burning sensation while urinating. There may or may not be a slight vaginal discharge—and even if there is, it is often is not considered abnormal. As a result, the

disease often goes untreated. The bacteria may spread into the oviducts, eventually leading to violent cramps, fever, vomiting, and often sterility.

Complications arising from gonorrheal infection can be avoided with prompt diagnosis and treatment. As a preventive measure, males who engage in sexual activity with more than one partner are being advised to wear condoms to help prevent the spread of infection. Part of the problem is that the initial stages of the disease are so uneventful that the dangers are masked. Also, it is a common belief that once cured of gonorrhea, a person is immune for life, which simply is not true.

Syphilis. Syphilis is caused by a motile spirochaete, *Treponema pallidum.* In its frequency, this reported communicable disease is exceeded only by cases of chickenpox and gonorrhea. Following sexual contact with an infected person, the bacterium penetrates exposed tissues and produces a chancre (localized ulceration), which teems with treponeme progeny. This primary lesion can occur anywhere between one to eight weeks following infection. By the time the chancre is visible, the treponemes have moved into the lymph vascular system and bloodstream. When the second stage of infection occurs, lesions can appear on mucous membranes, the eyes, bones, and in the central nervous system. After these early lesion stages, an infected person enters a latent stage. During latency, there are no outward symptoms and syphilis can be detected only by blood serum tests. The latent period can last many years. During that time, the immune system works against the bacterium; sometimes the body cures itself, but this is not the usual outcome.

If untreated, syphilis in its tertiary stage can produce lesions on the skin and internal organs, such as the liver, bones, and aorta. Scars form on organs; the walls of the aorta can be weakened. The treponemes also damage the brain and spinal cord in ways that lead to various forms of insanity and paralysis. Women who have been infected typically have miscarriages, stillbirths, or sickly, syphilitic offspring.

Chlamydial Infection. Chlamydial infection is one of the most prevalent sexually transmitted diseases. *Chlamydial trachomatis* is the causative agent. Like the rickettsiae, it is an intracellular parasite of unknown affiliation. Most often, it infects the genitals and urinary tract. Following infection, the parasites migrate to regional lymph nodes, which become enlarged and tender. The enlargement can obstruct lymph drainage and lead to pronounced tissue swelling in the area. The disease responds to tetracycline and sulfonamides. If untreated, it can lead to serious complications, such as pelvic inflammatory disease.

Genital Herpes. Genital herpes is an extremely contagious viral infection of the genitals. Usually, it occurs through intimate sexual contact with a partner who has active herpes lesions. It is transmitted when any part of a person's body comes in direct contact with active herpesviruses or sores that contain them. Mucous membranes (particularly of the mouth or genital area) are susceptible to invasion, as is broken or damaged skin. The virus probably is not acquired by nonsexual means; it does not survive for long away from the human body.

To the 5 million existing cases of genital herpes already reported by Americans, 300,000 are being added each year. Newborns are among these cases; they can develop the disease when they pass through an infected birth canal or are infected soon after birth.

There are many strains of herpesviruses, which are classed as types I and II. The type I strains infect primarily the lips, tongue, mouth, and eyes. The type II strains cause most of the genital infections. Disease symptoms occur two to ten days after exposure to the virus, although sometimes symptoms are mild or nonexistent. Among infected women, small, painful blisters appear on the vulva, cervix, urethra, or anal area. Among men, the blisters occur on the penis and around the anal area. Within three weeks, the sores crust over and heal without scarring. Once the first infection has occurred, sporadic reactivation can produce new, painful sores at or near the original site of infection. Recurrent infections may be triggered by sexual intercourse, emotional stress, menstruation, and other infections. At present there is no cure for genital herpes. However, a new antiviral drug (acyclovir) decreases the healing time and sometimes decreases the pain and the viral shedding.

Acquired Immune Deficiency Syndrome (AIDS). This syndrome arises from a weakening of natural, cell-mediated immunity, leaving the person extremely vulnerable to infections that might not otherwise be life-threatening. These so-called opportunistic infections include Kaposi's sarcoma (a rare type of cancer) and pneumocystosis (a rare lung infection caused by *Pneumocystis carinii*). Nearly all reported cases of AIDS have occurred among homosexual or bisexual males, intravenous drug abusers, Haitian immigrants to the United States, and some hemophiliacs who have received blood transfusions.

The cause (or causes) of AIDS has not been found. The fact that it occurs among hemophiliacs who have been given transfusions suggests that the causative agent is blood borne—a virus, perhaps. Between 1980 and 1983, the reported incidents of AIDS rose to twenty-six new cases a week—an increase of 900 percent. More than 400 people have died from the disease during this period. Public health officials consider AIDS to be one of the most potentially dangerous diseases of modern times; at present, there is no cure.

agents of pneumonia, a complication that accounts for a major part of the fatalities.

New strains of influenzaviruses arise periodically. There is growing evidence that pandemic strains do not arise through mutation, as was previously thought. Rather, new virulent strains appear to be recombinants of human viruses and animal viruses. Whatever the case, the World Health Organization has monitoring stations throughout the world. As soon as new strains are identified, researchers work rapidly to develop modified vaccines.

As another example, **Herpesviruses** are infectious agents that are widespread through the animal kingdom. Typically, these viruses produce latent infections that can recur sporadically over months or years, or that can be completely different from the original outbreak. This group of viruses is responsible for fever blisters or cold sores, chick-

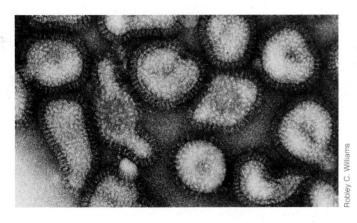

Figure 32.6 Virions of *Influenzavirus*, each a package of DNA enclosed in a protein capsid. 250,000×.

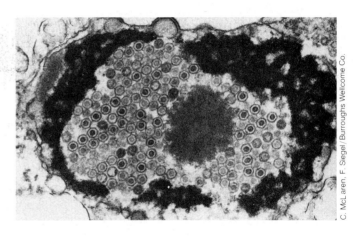

Figure 32.7 Virions of *Herpesvirus* in an infected cell.

enpox, and shingles. One *Herpesvirus* (Epstein-Barr virus) has been implicated in infectious mononucleosis, a disease that leads to marked increases in the number of circulating white blood cells. Symptoms include a severe sore throat, fever, enlarged lymph nodes, and overall weakness. Another *Herpesvirus* may be involved in certain forms of cancer. These pathogens are also responsible for genital herpes in more than 5 million Americans (see *Commentary*).

Herpesviruses have double-stranded DNA and a protein capsid. The capsid itself, about 100 nanometers across, acquires a membranous envelope as it buds from the host cell's nuclear envelope (Figure 32.8). A new cell is infected when the viral envelope fuses with the plasma membrane or when pinocytosis transports the virion into the cytoplasm.

Viroids

Are viruses the most stripped down of all disease agents? It appears not. **Viroids** are infectious nucleic acids that have no protein coat whatsoever. The known viroids are simply linear or closed circles of single-stranded RNA. Under natural conditions, the RNA molecule base-pairs back on itself like a hairpin, so that viroids look like tiny rods.

Viroids are mere snippets of genes, thousands of times smaller than the smallest virus. Yet they can wipe out huge fields of seed potatoes and groves of citrus or avocadoes. Thirty years ago, viroids almost destroyed the chrysanthemum industry in the United States. One viroid has destroyed more than 12 million coconut palms on Philippine plantations, with major economic consequences. There are suspicions that viroids may cause some forms of human cancer, as they are known to do in hamsters.

PROTISTANS

When we turn from prokaryotes to eukaryotes, we are talking about a new kind of cell. Even the single-celled eukaryotes are larger than bacteria, more complex in their internal structure, and more diverse in their behavior and life-styles. All of these single cells are known as **protistans**, but they have a hodgepodge of characteristics that puts many of them at the fringes of other kingdoms.

Some protistans are nonphotosynthetic, motile predators that ingest their food, and in this they resemble animals. In fact, they are known as protozoans (meaning "first animals"). Other protistans are photosynthesizers complete with chloroplasts, and in this they resemble multicelled plants. Still others resemble fungi in their life-style. Then there are forms such as *Euglena*, a motile, sometimes photosynthetic, sometimes predatory protistan (Figure 32.8). Except for their chloroplasts, *Euglena* and its relatives are virtually identical with a number of motile heterotrophic cells. Actually, if some species are raised in the dark, they rapidly change into forms having no chloroplasts at all. When the bleached-out individuals are later grown in sunlight, they never regain chloroplasts. From then on, they survive only if they can absorb a balanced diet of organic molecules from the environment.

How do we go about classifying little green animal-like cells? There is no clear answer. When it comes to single-celled eukaryotes, phylogenetic schemes are a little like fences that more or less follow the biochemical, morphological, and behavioral boundaries between organisms of different types. Currently, some protistans have to be viewed as fence straddlers. The idea may be frustrating to

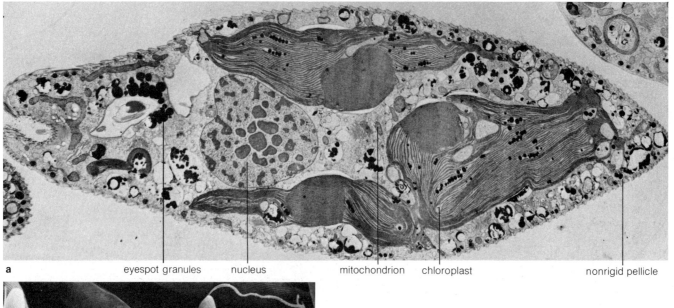

a	eyespot granules	nucleus	mitochondrion chloroplast	nonrigid pellicle

b

Figure 32.8 Anatomy of a single-celled protistan, *Euglena*. In (**a**), the profusion of internal organelles is evident. 5,200×. In (**b**), notice the flagellum; *Euglena* is a highly motile form. 1,700×. (a, P. L. Walne, J. H. Arnott, *Planta*, 1967, 77:325–354; b, C. Shih, R. G. Kessel, *Living Images*, © 1982 Jones and Bartlett Publishers, Inc., Boston)

those who would prefer a tidier picture than this. Yet it may give us a more accurate sense of the evolutionary experimentation that presumably occurred when prokaryotes first gave rise to eukaryotic cells. With this qualification in mind, let's turn to the generally recognized groups of protistans: the euglenids, chrysophytes and diatoms, dinoflagellates, and protozoans (Table 32.3).

Euglenids

There are 450 known species of **euglenids**: motile, photosynthetic cells that live in fresh water (preferably polluted). Euglenids have one, two, or three flagella projecting from a small cavity at one end of the cell. Like *Euglena,* shown in Figure 32.8, most of the cells are elongated and have a pellicle (an inner layer composed mostly of protein). Numerous chloroplasts and mitochondria are present in the cytoplasm. So is an **eyespot**, a photoreceptive organelle located near the base of the flagella (Figure 32.8a). Excitation of the carotenoid pigments in the eyespot is conducted along nervelike fibrils to the motile structures, which respond by propelling

the cell toward light (in dim waters) or away from it (when light intensity is high). Like most flagellated protistans, *Euglena* reproduces asexually, by longitudinal fission. Division occurs after the nucleus, eyespot, and motor apparatus have been replicated.

Chrysophytes and Diatoms

The 5,800 species of photosynthetic **chrysophytes** were once known as golden algae. They include flagellated, amoeboid, and nonmotile forms. Some have walls of cellulose, pectin, and often silicon; others have no walls at all. Some chrysophytes are single cells, others live in simple colonies. They all contain chlorophylls *a* and *c,* as well as a brown pigment (fucoxanthin) that may give them a golden color. Most reproduce asexually, but sexual reproduction is relatively common.

Today, chrysophytes exist mostly in fresh water. At one time they numbered in the billions. The Cretaceous fossils of one group make up tremendous chalk deposits in different parts of the world.

There are nearly 10,000 known species of **diatoms**: photosynthetic cells with thin, silica shells that fit together like a hatbox. On close inspection, it is apparent that the protective shell is intricately perforated (Figure 32.9), so the underlying plasma membrane remains in close contact with the environment.

Like golden algae, many diatoms occur as **phytoplankton**: communities of microscopic photosynthesizers that are suspended in water. Phytoplankton is the food-production base for marine and freshwater communities. (Despite their shells, both protistans are prey for other organisms.) The silica shells of diatoms do not dissolve readily, and enormous numbers accumulate on the seafloor. Immense deposits of these shells date from 70 to 10 million years ago and have since become part of continental land masses. They form fine, crumbly material called diatomaceous earth, which is used commercially in polishing, insulating, and filtering materials.

Dinoflagellates

The more than 1,000 species of **dinoflagellates** include forms encased in stiff cellulose plates, which have grooves between them. One groove circles the cell body and defines a channel for the movement of a ribbonlike flagellum. Another groove runs perpendicular to it and is a channel for another flagellum (Figure 32.10). When the two flagella beat in their respective channels, they make the cell spin like a top. These spinning species are known as "whirling whips."

Most dinoflagellates are photosynthetic, although a few colorless forms are heterotrophs. The photosynthetic forms contain chlorophylls *a* and *c*, but depending on the array of pigments, they may appear yellow-green, brown, or red. They occur as phytoplankton in marine and freshwater settings. Many dinoflagellates are bioluminescent (Figure 6.6). Other marine organisms that exhibit bioluminescence often do so because dinoflagellates are living symbiotically within them.

Periodically, red dinoflagellates such as *Gonyaulax* undergo explosive population growth. They actually color the seas red or brown. These so-called **red tides** are extremely devastating, for some of the dinoflagellates produce a powerful neurotoxin. Fish that feed on plankton are poisoned; sometimes hundreds of thousands are killed and wash up along coasts (Figure 32.11). Shellfish such as clams, oysters, and mussels are not affected by the neurotoxin. However, the poison builds up in their tissues, and humans eating the shellfish can be dangerously poisoned.

a

b

Figure 32.9 (**a**) Scanning electron micrograph of the magnificent glass house of a diatom. 580×. (**b**) Closer view of the glass shell, showing the intricate perforations. 2,340×. (b, C. Shih, R. G. Kessel, *Living Images*, © 1982 Jones and Bartlett Publishers, Inc. Boston)

Table 32.3   Summary of Protistan Groups
Euglenids
Chrysophytes and diatoms
Dinoflagellates

Protozoa:
  1. Flagellates (trypanosomes, trichosomes)
  2. Amoeboids (amoebas, foraminiferans, heliozoans, radiolarians)
  3. Sporozoans
  4. Ciliates

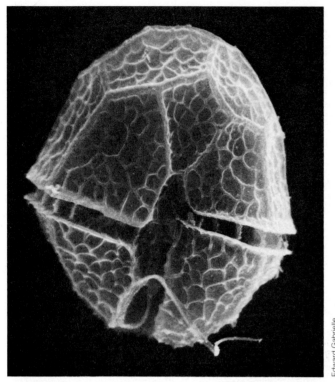

Figure 32.10 One of the "whirling whips"— dinoflagellates with two flagella that beat in opposing grooves in the armor-plated body. One flagellum is visible at the base; another beats in the groove running from left to right of this scanning electron micrograph.

Edward Gabrielle

Protozoa

Among the heterotrophic forms of dinoflagellates are walled cells that send out pseudopods, which are used in capturing prey. Among the dinoflagellates are forms that are photosynthetic *and* heterotrophic, as well as parasitic forms that absorb nutrients from hosts. These protistans may mirror evolutionary radiations that long ago gave rise to the similarly diverse protozoans. The **protozoa** include nonphotosynthetic, generally motile, single-celled forms. We can classify them as follows:

Mastigophora	*flagellate protozoans*
Rhizopoda	*amoeboid protozoans*
Sporozoa	*sporozoans*
Ciliophora	*ciliates*

Many thousands of protozoan species exist; of these, less than two dozen cause diseases in humans. However, the diseases that these few pathogens do cause are staggering in their extent. Perhaps as much as one-fourth of the entire human population is afflicted at a given time with a protozoan infection!

Flagellate Protozoans. For the most part, flagellate protozoans are parasites of invertebrates and vertebrates. Characteristically, these cells undergo longitudinal fission in the manner described for *Euglena.*

Figure 32.11 Portion of a fish kill that resulted from a dinoflagellate "bloom."

C. C. Lockwood

In this group are the leaf-shaped **trypanosomes**, which have a flagellum arising from the base of a small invagination at one end of the cell. During one stage of the life cycle, the flagellum is continuous with an undulating external membrane (Figure 32.12). Some trypanosomes develop in the salivary glands of insect vectors, which infect new hosts by biting. For instance, *Trypanosoma rhodesiens*, which causes African sleeping sickness, is transmitted from host to host by the tsetse fly. Other trypanosomes develop in the hindgut of insect vectors, leave in feces, and later penetrate the skin or mucous membranes of another host.

Also in this group are **trichosomes** of the sort shown in Figure 32.12. Among humans, *Trichomonas vaginalis* is a worldwide nuisance. It is transferred to new hosts through sexual intercourse. At any given time, as many as 20–40 percent of all women and 4–15 percent of all men are infected. Trichomonal infection can severely damage vaginal membranes if untreated. Among men, infection can occur in the urinary and reproductive tracts.

Amoeboid Protozoans. There are four groups of amoeboid protozoans: the amoebas, foraminiferans, heliozoans, and radiolarians. In all four groups, the adult forms have pseudopods, which are used in capturing prey or in locomotion. Except for the few parasitic species, food for the amoeboids consists of bacteria, algae, diatoms, other protozoans, and even small animals (such as nematodes).

The **amoebas** come with or without shells. The "naked" species, such as *Amoeba proteus* of biology laboratory fame, have a constantly changing shape (Figure 32.13). These protozoans can be found in fresh water, sea water, and soil. Most are microscopic, but some species are several millimeters long. Shelled amoebas inhibit fresh water, damp soil, and mosses. For them, pseudopods or much of the cell body can protrude through a large opening in the shell.

Like many other protistans, the freshwater species have organelles called **contractile vacuoles**. Because their surroundings have a lower concentration of solutes than is found in the cytoplasm, water continually flows down the gradient (into the cell). The excess moves into the vacuoles which, when extended, undergo contraction that expels water from the cell body.

Some amoeboid protozoans are parasites of humans. For instance, *Entameoba histolytica* occurs in the human gastrointestinal tract. This parasite causes amoebic dysentery, a disease characterized by fever, abdominal cramps, and severe diarrhea. *E. histolytica* proliferates in the gut during part of its life cycle. Then it develops into a thick-walled resting cell (a cyst). The cysts are excreted with feces. Without proper sewage treatment facilities, these cysts can contaminate food and water.

The elaborately shelled **foraminiferans** live mostly in the seas. Their hardened shells are often peppered with hundreds of thousands of tiny holes through which sticky,

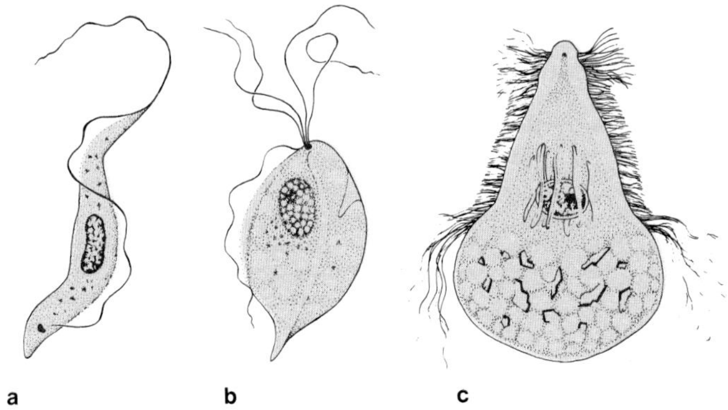

Figure 32.12 A few flagellate protozoans. (**a**) A leaf-shaped trypanosome, with its undulating membrane. (**b**) A trichomonad. These (generally) anaerobic parasites live in vertebrates and invertebrates. (**c**) *Trichonympha*, a flamboyant form that lives in the termite gut. (From Stanier, Adelberg, Ingraham, *The Microbial World*, fourth edition, © 1976. Reprinted by permission Prentice-Hall, Inc., Englewood Cliffs, N. J.)

a   b   c

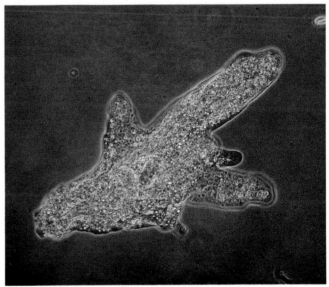

Biophoto Associates

Figure 32.13 *Amoeba proteus* under the light microscope.

Figure 32.14 Shells of some foraminiferans (the word means, loosely, "bearers of windows").

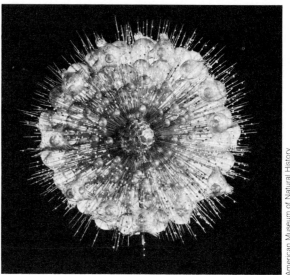

Figure 32.15 Glass model of *Trypanosphaera regina*, a colonial radiolarian that has a skeleton made of silicon.

threadlike pseudopods extend. Figure 32.14 shows some foraminiferan shells minus their inhabitants. Often the shells bear spines, which in some species are long enough that the shell can be seen with the naked eye.

The **heliozoans**, or "sun animals," have fine, needlelike pseudopods that radiate from the body like sun rays. Each pseudopod has a microtubular rod that can be shortened or lengthened by the removal or addition of tubulin subunits (Figure 4.23). These largely freshwater protozoans are floaters or bottom-dwellers. The cytoplasm forms an outer sphere around a denser core composed of denser cytoplasm and the bases of microtubular rods.

The **radiolarians** are perhaps the most beautiful of all protozoans. They are found mostly in marine plankton. In cytoplasmic structure they resemble the heliozoans, but most also have a skeleton of silicon. In addition, there are colonial radiolarians in which many individuals are cemented together (Figure 32.15). The abundant shells of both radiolarians and foraminiferans are a primary component of many ocean sediments.

Sporozoans. The **sporozoans** are a diverse assortment of parasites. They have in common the development of an infective, sporelike stage (sporozoites) during the life cycle. Like the amoeboids, different groups use pseudopods for feeding. Unlike the amoeboids, they move by gliding or by flexing the body wall. There are both asexual and sexual

stages to the life cycle, and often vectors such as insects transmit the parasites from one host to another.

Probably the most notorious sporozoans are the more than fifty species of *Plasmodium,* four of which cause the disease malaria in humans. The parasite requires an insect vector (mosquitoes) and an animal host (birds, mostly, and humans). In a bad year, 100 million people have been stricken with the disease. The *Plasmodium* life cycle is shown in Figure 32.16. This life cycle illustrates events that are common to most sporozoans:

1. Infection of the host

2. Asexual multiplication of the parasite in host tissues

3. Gamete development

4. Spore development, multiplication, and infection of a new host

Ciliate Protozoans. Nowhere in the microbial world is the potential of a single cell expressed more fully than among the **ciliate protozoans**. Some of these cells are covered with thousands of cilia, synchronized for swimming. Sometimes the cells bear hundreds of poison-charged, harpoonlike weapons that can be fired at prey and predator. Possessed of a voracious mouth, the ciliates prowl through or wait in ambush in woodland ponds, the intestinal contents of various organisms, and a variety of other habitats.

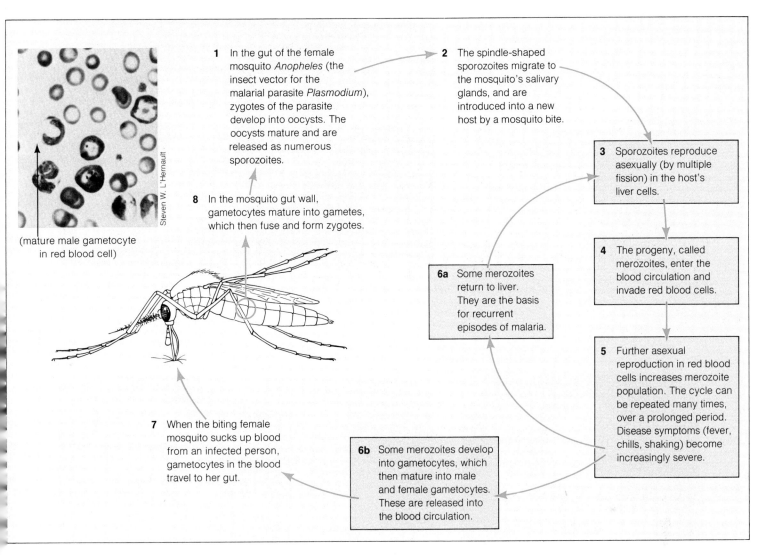

(mature male gametocyte in red blood cell)

1 In the gut of the female mosquito *Anopheles* (the insect vector for the malarial parasite *Plasmodium*), zygotes of the parasite develop into oocysts. The oocysts mature and are released as numerous sporozoites.

2 The spindle-shaped sporozoites migrate to the mosquito's salivary glands, and are introduced into a new host by a mosquito bite.

3 Sporozoites reproduce asexually (by multiple fission) in the host's liver cells.

4 The progeny, called merozoites, enter the blood circulation and invade red blood cells.

5 Further asexual reproduction in red blood cells increases merozoite population. The cycle can be repeated many times, over a prolonged period. Disease symptoms (fever, chills, shaking) become increasingly severe.

6a Some merozoites return to liver. They are the basis for recurrent episodes of malaria.

6b Some merozoites develop into gametocytes, which then mature into male and female gametocytes. These are released into the blood circulation.

7 When the biting female mosquito sucks up blood from an infected person, gametocytes in the blood travel to her gut.

8 In the mosquito gut wall, gametocytes mature into gametes, which then fuse and form zygotes.

Figure 32.16 Life cycle of the sporozoan *Plasmodium,* which causes the disease malaria. The life cycle unfolds in the human body and in an insect vector (the female mosquito *Anopheles*), which transfers the sporozoan to new hosts during bites. The events described in the gold-shaded boxes occur in the human body. (Illustration based on correspondence with Raul J. Cano)

Perhaps the most widely occurring ciliate is the predatory *Paramecium* (Figure 32.17). Like most ciliates, *Paramecium* has a gullet, a cavity that opens to the outside at the cell surface. Rows of specialized cilia beat food particles into the gullet. Once inside, the particles become enclosed in food vacuoles, where digestion takes place. Unused leftovers are carted off to a region known as the anal pore, which functions to eliminate wastes to the outside. Like the amoeboid protozoans, *Paramecium* relies on contractile vacuoles to keep from bursting under influxes of fresh water from its surroundings.

Paramecium is built for speed. Between 10,000 and 14,000 cilia project like tiny, flexible oars from the cell surface. Each orderly row of cilia beats in coordination with adjacent rows. So efficient is their coordination that the movements propel some species of *Paramecium* through their surroundings at a remarkable 1,000 micrometers per second.

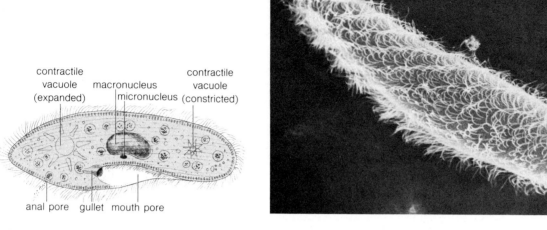

contractile
vacuole
(expanded)

macronucleus
micronucleus

contractile
vacuole
(constricted)

anal pore   gullet   mouth pore

Gary W. Grimes and Steven W. L'Hernault

Figure 32.17 Anatomy of *Paramecium,* a fast swimming, predatory ciliate.

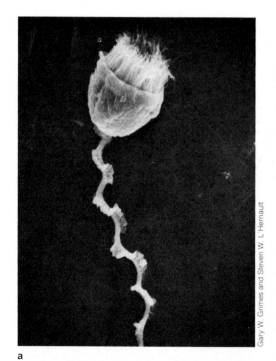

a

Gary W. Grimes and Steven W. L'Hernault

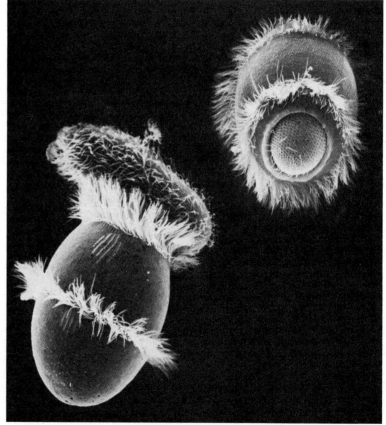

b

Gary W. Grimes and Steven W. L'Hernault

Figure 32.18 (**a**) *Vorticella,* a bottom-dwelling ciliate protozoan. (**b**) Mealtime for *Didinium,* a ciliate with a big mouth. Dinner in this case is another ciliate, the cucumber-shaped *Paramecium* poised at the mouth (left) and swallowed (upper right).

Ah, but that which works for one predatory ciliate also works for others. *Paramecium* itself is often outmaneuvered by another voracious ciliate, *Didinium* (Figure 32.18). When a didinium engulfs a paramecium, (which is typically the larger of the two cells), the engulfor seems to be all mouth. *Didinium* also has **trichocysts**—long contractile filaments anchored within the cell that are used to hold onto and paralyze its prey.

Both *Paramecium* and *Didinium* are free-swimming. Other ciliates crawl about or simply stay put. *Vorticella* normally rises stalklike from its holdfast on the floors of ponds, lakes, and streams. It gracefully turns its cilia-rimmed mouth into the currents flowing past—and carrying dinner to it (Figure 32.18). Although such ciliate protozoans are highly diverse in form, they hold one thing in common: they are the sharks of the microscopic world.

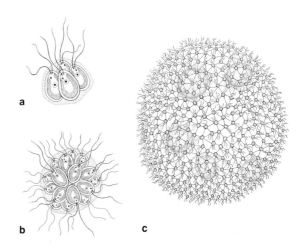

Figure 32.19 A few volvocines. (**a**) *Gonium*, (**b**) *Pandorina*, and (**c**) *Volvox*—all colonial forms that straddle the fence between protistans and plants. Compare this with Figure 6.1b. (Laszlo Meszoly in L. Margulis, *Early Life*, © 1982 Science Books International. Reprinted by permission of Jones and Bartlett Publishers, Inc. Boston)

ON THE ROAD TO MULTICELLULARITY

Among the bacteria and protistans are loose associations of cells—simple threads that form when cell walls fail to separate after division, and simple colonies in which cells are cemented together in a glasslike matrix that they themselves have secreted. When we think about enormously complex organisms such as redwoods and whales, it may be almost incomprehensible that simple associations, such as those seen among the microbes, gave rise to complex multicelled life. Yet the problem may be one of overlooking what must have been an immense evolutionary parade of intermediate forms.

Intriguingly, a photosynthetic bacterium called *Prochloron* contains chlorophyll *a*, chlorophyll *b*, and carotenoids—the exact same pigments found in land plants. *Prochloron* is thought to resemble the prokaryotic group that gave rise, symbiotically, to the chloroplasts of green algae. The simplest green alga is *Chlamydomonas*, a single cell with one chloroplast, one eyespot, and two flagella. Cells that closely resemble *Chlamydomonas* occur among the volvocines—colonial organisms that straddle the fence between protistans and plants. Put four, eight, sixteen, or thirty-two such cells together in a jellylike matrix, and you have one or another species of *Gonium* (Figure 32.19a). Put sixteen or thirty-two such cells together into an egg-shaped colony and you have the volvocine *Pandorina* (Figure 32.19b).

The peak of volvocine complexity is *Volvox*. Although this volvocine is thought to represent an evolutionary dead-end, it shows several intriguing developments. Depending on the species, *Volvox* is a single-layered, hollow sphere of 500 to 600,000 cells. It is differentiated into forward and rear poles; it rotates on the axis between poles when flagellar beating of its many cellular members propels it forward. Only a few cells reproduce. They divide and give rise to daughter colonies, which float inside the parent sphere. There comes a time when enzymes produced by the daughter colony dissolve the parent jellylike matrix, and the daughter colonies are released. In different *Volvox* species, we also see sexual differentiation. Some cells in some colonies produce eggs *and* sperm; cells in other colonies produce eggs *or* sperm. Among the most complex of these colonies, the reproductive cells have lost their flagella; other cells take care of movement. *Volvox*, then, straddles the line between colonial life and true **multicellularity**, with the interdependence and division of labor among specialized cells that the word implies.

Consider, now, a tiny pancake-shaped marine animal, *Trichoplax adhaerens*, which is a mere half a millimeter across. *Trichoplax* is little more than a flattened ball of ciliated cells (Figure 32.20). It has no right side, left side, front, or back; it simply moves any which way, amoebalike. It has a few more cilia on its top than on its bottom; but other than this, there is no cellular differentiation to speak of. However, think back on the discussion of animal embryonic development in Chapter Twenty-Eight. Most animal species have

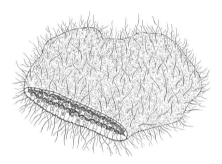

Figure 32.20 *Trichoplax adhaerens*, one of the simplest of all multicelled animals, being little more than a flattened ball of ciliated cells. (Laszlo Meszoly in L. Margulis, *Early Life*, © 1982 Science Books International. Reprinted by permission of Jones and Bartlett Publishers, Inc. Boston)

one thing in common: the development of a zygote into a blastula stage—into a hollow ball of cells. Given that blastula formation is so widespread among animals, it is probably a form of ancient origins. *Trichoplax* may be reminiscent of simple multicelled animals that made their entrance during the Proterozoic.

Still other living organisms provide us with clues about the first evolutionary roads toward multicellularity. Consider the mushroom. It is composed of no more than mats of threadlike cells—all pretty much identical, and cemented together at (typically) chitin-containing cell walls. Consider multicelled forms of green algae—straight or branched filaments a mere one cell thick, and simple sheets of cells. As you read in the last chapter, the tiny multicelled plants that first invaded the land were not much more complex than this.

Consider, finally, just one of your own multicelled systems—the calcium-containing bones of your endoskeleton. We can assume that controls over calcium intake must have existed in the earliest protistans. Calcium, after all, is required in microtubule assembly—and microtubules are required in such structures as pseudopods and mitotic spindles. Living organisms have proteins that preferentially bind and release calcium ions. In early protistans, such proteins could have latched onto calcium entering the cell from the environment; they could have been calcium storage centers. Such proteins could have become incorporated into cell surface layers—and into internal structures. In the increasingly elaborate shells and internal skeletons of protistans, we have hints of the origins of bones—of our own skeletal system, and our own calcium reservoirs.

Readings

Brock, T. 1979. *Biology of Microorganisms.* Third edition. Englewood Cliffs, New Jersey: Prentice-Hall. One of the best introductions to microbiology.

Diener, T. 1981. "Viroids." *Scientific American* 244(1):66–73. Good summary article on these smallest of all infectious particles.

Jurand, A., and G. Selman. 1969. *The Anatomy of Paramecium Aurelia.* New York: St. Martin's Press. A tribute to the astonishing complexity of a single cell.

Margulis, L. 1982. *Early Life.* Boston: Science Books International. An exceptional book, written for the general audience. Objective, compelling presentation of evidence for the early evolution of life. Paperback.

Noble, E., and G. Noble. 1982. *Parasitology: The Biology of Animal Parasites.* Fifth edition. Philadelphia: Lea and Febiger. One of the most authoritative references on parasitic protozoans.

Stanier, R., et al. 1976. *The Microbial World.* Fourth edition. Englewood Cliffs, New Jersey: Prentice-Hall. Excellent material on bacteria and protistans.

Wiesner, P., and W. Parra. 1982. "Sexually Transmitted Diseases: Meeting the 1990 Objectives—a Challenge for the 1980s." *Prevention* 97(5):409–416.

Woese, C. 1981. "Archaebacteria." *Scientific American.* 244(6):98–125. Summarizes evidence that points to separate origins for archaebacteria, eubacteria, and an ancestral line (urkaryotes) that gave rise to eukaryotes.

Review Questions

1. Can you describe the main characteristics that distinguish viruses from bacteria? Bacteria from protistans? Protistans from multicelled eukaryotes?

2. Identify and describe an example of the following types of bacteria: (1) disease-causing heterotroph, (2) symbiotic heterotroph, (3) chemosynthetic autotroph, and (4) photosynthetic autotroph.

3. Can you explain why some microbes are killed in the presence of oxygen, yet others are not? Why, also, do some microbes get along well whether oxygen is present or not?

4. Suppose you were working in a laboratory that uses cloned bacterial populations to manufacture insulin. Would you be more likely using Gram-positive or Gram-negative bacteria for your insulin factory?

5. Can you describe some of the bacteria and protistans that are beneficial to humans, and some that are harmful (or lethal)?

6. What kinds of protistans are photosynthetic? Predatory? Parasitic? Which move by means of pseudopodia?

7. Why is *Trichoplax* considered to be such an intriguing model for ideas about the emergence of multicellularity?

With this chapter, we cross the boundary between protistans and the kingdoms of multicelled fungi and plants. Traditionally, these two kingdoms have been considered the domains of botanists, although fungi are now considered to be as distinct from plants as they are from bacteria, protistans, and animals. In one important respect, though, fungi do resemble the simplest members of the plant kingdom: the haploid phase dominates the life cycle. We begin this chapter with the fungi so that we can start with the idea of haploid dominance. As you will see, there has been a distinct shift away from this strategy among increasingly complex plants—a shift toward diploid dominance that corresponds to a diversity of land habitats.

PART I. KINGDOM OF FUNGI

On the Fungal Way of Life

Fungi are heterotrophs; they cannot produce their own food. What they can do is decompose just about anything that has organic components—meat, fruit, vegetables, bread, cheddar cheese, clothing, paint, cardboard boxes, photographic film, even shoe leather. Most of these eclectic eaters are **saprobes**: they obtain nutrients from nonliving organic matter. Some are **parasites**, obtaining nutrients directly from organic matter that still belongs to a living host. In both cases, fungal cells secrete enzymes that promote digestion *outside* themselves, then nutrients are absorbed across the plasma membrane. For absorption to occur, of course, the substrate must be moist. Fungal growth cannot proceed in the absence of moisture, and the fungal life-style revolves around this restriction.

Together with heterotrophic bacteria, fungi are decomposers for the biosphere. Without them, the cycling of nutrients would largely cease. Even so, this activity on the grand scale is little consolation for humans whose leather shoes and cotton clothes fall apart under fungal attack in the tropics. It is little consolation for farmers and gardeners whose crops and garden plants are destroyed by one or another of 5,000 fungal species. As with bacteria, fungi tend to be evaluated in terms of their impact on human affairs. In this respect, they include many species that are highly beneficial, some that are mere nuisances, and others that are downright dangerous.

Fungal Body Plans

The multicelled fungal body, or **mycelium**, is a mesh of microscopic filaments that branch in any direction, spread-

33

FUNGI AND PLANTS

Figure 33.1 Plants and fungi in a forest setting.

© Pat O'Hara

ing over or within the organic matter used as food. Each filament is a **hypha** (plural, hyphae). It is a transparent, thin-walled tube that is often reinforced with chitin.

Each hypha is divided at irregular intervals by cross-walls, which form compartments that correspond to cells. Following nuclear division, primary cross-walls are laid down between daughter nuclei by inward growth from the hyphal walls. In some hyphae, the inward growth forms solid plates. In others, a central pore remains that allows cytoplasm and nuclei to migrate from compartment to compartment. Given the freedom of cytoplasmic and nuclear movement, a hypha is not "multicellular" in the usual sense of the word. Rather, it is a compartmented tube with a common, multinucleate cytoplasm.

If you happen to use edible mushrooms, you know that fungi are rather fragile. Even so, fungi are well represented in the fossil record. Isolated spores, reproductive structures, and vegetative filaments that date from the Precambrian have even been recovered (Chapter Thirty-One).

Overview of Reproductive Modes

Asexual reproduction dominates the fungal life cycle; typically it occurs several times in a single season. The asexual reproductive modes include the following:

1. Formation of **fungal spores** (reproductive cells that can each develop into a haploid mycelium)

2. Fragmentation of the mycelium (or a single hypha) into parts that grow into new individuals

3. Binary fission or budding

Many fungi also reproduce sexually, with two haploid gametes combining to produce a diploid zygote. In most species, the diploid zygote does not give rise to a multicelled diploid organism. Rather, the zygote usually divides at once by meiosis, and four haploid spores are formed. The spores undergo repeated mitotic divisions that form a haploid mycelium. Typically, part of the mycelium differentiates into gamete-producing reproductive structures. (Figure 33.2 depicts this sequence of events.)

Before considering some specific examples, one more point can be made about sex among the fungi. Sexual reproduction, as you know, requires the fusion of nuclei from compatible gametes. Some fungal species produce compatible male and female gametes on the same mycelium; they are self-fertilizing. Other species produce incompatible male and female gametes; they require outcrossing, in ways that will be described shortly.

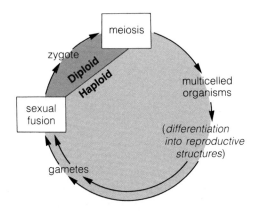

Figure 33.2 Generalized life cycle for fungi, showing how the haploid phase dominates. The diploid phase is most often limited to the zygote itself, which divides at once to form haploid cells. These cells in turn divide by mitosis and form the haploid, multicelled fungal body (mycelium).

Major Groups of Fungi

Today, 100,000 species of fungi have been cataloged; the actual number of existing species may be twice as high. Most species fall into four major **divisions**. (A division is equivalent to the phylum in animal classification schemes.)

Division	Common Name
Oomycota	*egg fungi*
Zygomycota	*zygospore-forming fungi*
Ascomycota	*sac fungi*
Basidiomycota	*club fungi*

Oomycota. This group contains fungi that have motile reproductive cells. (In most fungal groups, reproductive cells are immotile and dispersed by air currents.) Some of these so-called oomycetes have extensive mycelia. They are saprobes, for the most part, especially the aquatic species called water molds. Some, such as downy mildews, are plant parasites. One parasite, *Phytophthora infestans*, causes **late**

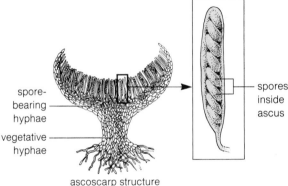

spore-
bearing
hyphae

vegetative
hyphae

ascoscarp structure

spores
inside
ascus

Victor Duran

Figure 33.3 Photograph of scarlet cup fungi, of the Division Ascomycota. The sketch shows the structure of one kind of ascocarp, composed of tightly interwoven hyphae. Saclike structures (asci) that bear spores occur within ascocarps, which can be cup-shaped, flask-shaped, or closed spheres. (Sketch from Rost, *Botany*, 1979)

blight (a disease that rots the vines of potatoes and tomatoes). The potato is native to cool, dry regions of the Peruvian Andes, where it was under cultivation almost 2,000 years ago. *P. infestans* was also native to the Peruvian regions, but it did not seriously threaten crops because local environmental conditions kept it in check. The potato was introduced to Europe in the sixteenth century. It became a major food crop. In Ireland it became *the* major food crop. During the growing season, Ireland has cool, moist nights and warm, humid days—quite unlike the climate of the Andes. Evidently, the fungus was not introduced at the same time as the potato. When it did gain entry, three conditions favored its explosive growth: the climate, the practice of planting uninterrupted fields (monocrop agriculture), and susceptible strains of potatoes (which were asexually propagated clones). The fungus simply went wild. Once a plant was stricken with late blight, its vines rotted within fourteen days. Between 1845 and 1860, a third of Ireland's population starved to death, or died in the outbreak of typhoid fever that followed as a secondary effect, or fled the country.

Zygomycota. This group of fungi is distinct because of its **zygospores**: diploid resting cells that develop from newly formed zygotes. For example, the bread mold *Rhizopus stolonifer* grows on baked goods exposed to moist air. Those black, cottonlike patches you sometimes see on moldy bread are myriad zygospores, which have formed after sexual fusion and zygote formation. The zygotes develop into a resting stage, complete with thick, black coats. Thus protected, they can lay dormant for several months. Under favorable conditions, they undergo meiosis to form haploid cells, which develop into new haploid mycelia.

Victor Duran

Figure 33.4 Edible morels, one of the ascomycetes.

Ascomycota. These fungi bear spores in saclike structures called **asci** (singular, ascus). The sacs are usually concentrated in an **ascocarp**, a rather complex reproductive structure of the sort shown in Figures 33.3 and 33.4.

Among the 30,000 sac fungi are most of the red, brown, and blue-green molds that cause food spoilage. One salmon-colored mold, *Neurospora crassa*, does considerable damage

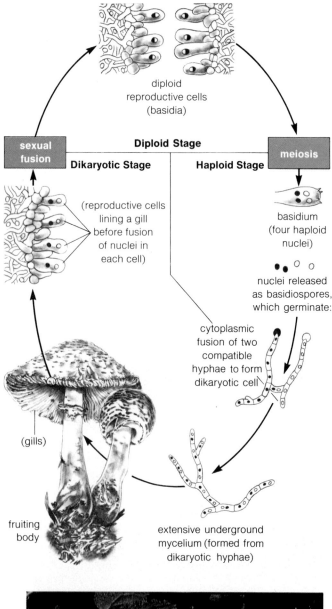

diploid
reproductive cells
(basidia)

Diploid Stage

sexual fusion

Dikaryotic Stage **Haploid Stage**

meiosis

(reproductive cells lining a gill before fusion of nuclei in each cell)

basidium
(four haploid
nuclei)

nuclei released
as basidiospores,
which germinate:

cytoplasmic fusion of two compatible hyphae to form dikaryotic cell

(gills)

fruiting
body

extensive underground
mycelium (formed from
dikaryotic hyphae)

Victor Duran

Figure 33.5 Life cycle of the common field mushroom. Notice the dikaryotic stage, in which hyphal cells contain two distinct nuclei.

but is also in the good graces of biologists, who use it in genetics studies (Chapter Ten). Sac fungi include the powdery mildews, which attack apples, grains, cherries, grapes, and other food crops. They include the fungal species that cause Dutch elm disease and chestnut blight. Among the more reputable members are the edible truffles and morels (Figure 33.4), whose fruiting bodies are prized by gourmets. Here also are many yeasts (*Saccharomyces*) that produce the ethanol used in brewing industries and the carbon dioxide used to raise bread for the baking industry. A few yeasts also produce human diseases. For example, *Trichophyton* lives amongst toes kept warm and moist inside shoes and causes the skin to peel and crack, a condition called athlete's foot.

Basidiomycota. The 25,000 or so species of club fungi range from saprobes to parasites and symbionts. They include edible mushrooms, extremely toxic ones (such as *Amanita*), shelf fungi, and puffballs. Figures 33.5 and 33.6 show representative species.

Club fungi are distinct from all others because they produce **basidiospores**. These are resting spores that develop on a club-shaped, spore-producing structure. When a basidiospore germinates, it produces a small, *primary mycelium* that is at first multinucleate. Cross-walls soon form within the individual hyphae, dividing the contents into single nucleated cells. Often a *secondary mycelium* forms when primary hyphae of two compatible mating types grow near each other and fuse. However, nuclear fusion does not immediately follow. The result is a "dikaryotic" hypha (with two nuclei per cell). Figure 33.6 depicts this sequence of events.

The dikaryotic hypha develops into an extensive mat, which is destined to become a long-lived network in soil. At some point in the life cycle, a dikaryotic, *tertiary mycelium* develops directly from the mat and forms an aboveground reproductive structure. This structure, the **basidiocarp**, is "the mushroom" of more familiar fungal species. (The mushroom is only the reproductive portion of the entire organism, which may be considerably larger.) Within a basidiocarp, the pairs of nuclei derived from the two different hyphae fuse at last (Figure 33.7). The fused diploid nuclei undergo meiosis at once, and spores are produced. Air currents disperse the spores, and the mushroom withers. As spores fall on moist ground and germinate, the cycle begins again.

Club fungi also include many rusts and smuts, which are major plant pathogens. For example, **wheat rust** currently destroys as much as ten percent of the annual wheat crop in the United States alone.

Figure 33.6 Basidiomycetes. (a) A coral fungus. (b) Shelf fungi, growing outward from a tree trunk. (c) Bird's nest fungi.

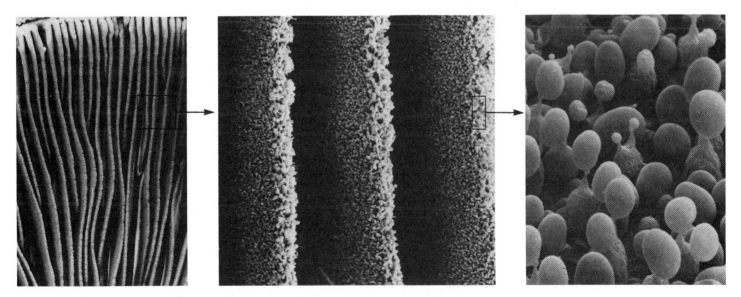

Figure 33.7 A closer look at the gills of a fruiting body from the common field mushroom. Notice the profusion of diploid reproductive cells (basidia). (C. Shih, R. G. Kessel, *Living Images*, © 1982 Science Books International. Reprinted by permission of Jones and Bartlett Publishers, Inc. Boston)

Figure 33.8 Two lichens: (**a**) *Cladonia rangiferina*, sometimes called reindeer "moss," and (**b**) *Usnea*, known as old man's beard, as it appears on tree limbs.

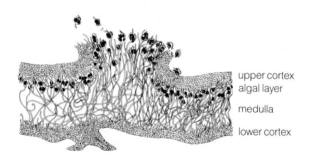

upper cortex
algal layer

medulla

lower cortex

Figure 33.9 Cross-section through a complex lichen, *Lobaria verrucosa*. Fungal hyphae with a gelatinlike coat form the upper, protective layer. Just below is a layer of algal cells, which are functionally connected with loosely interwoven, thin-walled hyphae. The lower layer attaches the lichen to the substrate. Notice the fragments containing both hyphae and algal cells; lichens reproduce asexually by such fragmentation. (From Raven, Everts, and Curtis, *Biology of Plants*, third edition, Worth Publishers, New York, 1981)

Mycorrhizal Mats and the Lichens

As you read in Chapter Seventeen, most complex land plants depend on symbiotic fungi that help them absorb mineral ions from soil. Pine trees, for instance, have hyphae of certain fungi that form dense mats (mycorrhizae) around and within their roots (Figure 17.5). The thick fungal mats help the trees absorb soil nutrients more rapidly than they otherwise would. The fungus benefits from the association by absorbing carbohydrates from root cells of its host.

Among the sac fungi (and, to some extent, club fungi) are species that are symbiotic with cyanobacteria and green algae. The associations are so intimate that the symbionts are referred to as a "composite organism," the **lichen**. Figure 33.8 shows two representatives of about 25,000 known lichen species.

In a lichen, fungal hyphae form a dense mat above and below the algal or bacterial cells. See, for example, Figure 33.9. In this arrangement, the fungus obtains photosynthetically derived food from the alga. The alga enjoys improved water conservation (water can be retained longer in the dense mat). It also benefits from mechanical protection (the mat keeps it from being blown away), better gas exchange (compare the anatomy of leaves, Chapter Sixteen), and less overlap between individual algal cells (as there would be in an algal crust).

Lichens have radiated into such diverse environments as open patches of forests, harsh deserts, tundras, regions of Antarctica, even bare rocks of isolated oceanic islands and mountain peaks.

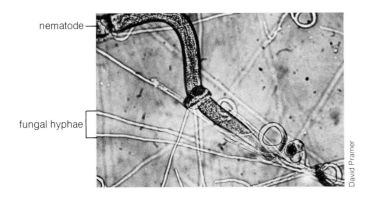

Figure 33.10 *Arthrobotrys dactyloides,* a predatory "imperfect" fungus with its dinner trapped. The fungal hyphae form nooselike rings that can swell rapidly with incoming water after the hyphal cell walls are stimulated (as when a nematode brushes past). Within a tenth of a second, the increased turgor pressure shrinks the "hole" in the noose and strangles the nematode. Hyphae grow into the animal body and release digestive enzymes.

Species of Unknown Affiliations

Fungi Imperfecti. In about 25,000 of the fungal species studied, a sexual phase is absent or as-yet undetected. Fungi that have no identifiable sexual phase in the life cycle are said to be "imperfect," although the name does imply a value judgment that is slightly absurd. These "imperfect" organisms include *Penicillium,* the source of the wonderfully fragrant, moldy cheeses called Roquefort and Camembert. *Penicillium* also produces the antibiotic penicillin, one of the few effective weapons against pneumonia, syphilis, gonorrhea, and other major diseases. Also in this group are efficient predators that capture small animals, which they then digest. Figure 33.10 shows one of fifty "imperfect" fungi that can ensnare a meal with hyphal nooses.

Slime Molds. Where the slime molds should be placed in classification schemes is controversial. They have funguslike and plantlike features; some strongly resemble amoeba-like protistans. Whatever their affinities, slime molds are studied more by mycologists than by anyone else, and that is why we will describe them here.

The vegetative body of a slime mold is a mass of cytoplasm, with no cell wall outside the plasma membrane. You can find these masses moving, amoebalike, on dead leaves and on moist rotting logs. They absorb nonliving organic matter or engulf bacteria and spore structures of other fungi. When slime molds reproduce, their spores have a rigid cell wall (as do the spores of the true fungi).

a

b

Figure 33.11 (**a**) One of the slime molds, *Physarum,* showing the vegetative body form. (**b**) Spore-bearing, or fruiting structures, of *Stemonitis splendens.*

Dictyostelium discoideum, described in Chapter Fourteen, is a cellular slime mold. At some point in its life cycle, many separate amoebas aggregate into a multicellular mass (a pseudoplasmodium). From this mass, a stalked fruiting structure arises and functions in spore dispersal (Figure 14.10).

Other slime molds are not composed of clustered cells; they are considered acellular. Each is a multinucleate cytoplasmic mass (plasmodium) that has increased in size from a single cell, without cell division. A plasmodium can stream out, veinlike, and back again as it feeds on microorganisms (Figure 33.11). Some grow into thin sheets measuring almost a meter across. Acellular slime molds also produce spore-bearing stalked masses. Spores released from these stalks are dispersed by air currents, an adaptive strategy that occurs among true fungi and among many species of plants.

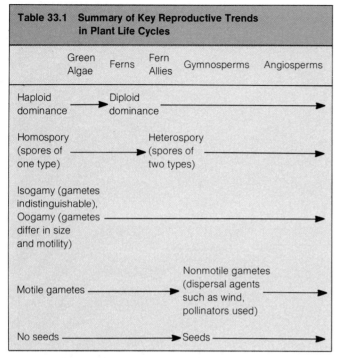

Table 33.1 Summary of Key Reproductive Trends in Plant Life Cycles

	Green Algae	Ferns	Fern Allies	Gymnosperms	Angiosperms
Haploid dominance → Diploid dominance					
Homospory (spores of one type) → Heterospory (spores of two types)					
Isogamy (gametes indistinguishable), Oogamy (gametes differ in size and motility)					
Motile gametes → Nonmotile gametes (dispersal agents such as wind, pollinators used)					
No seeds → Seeds					

(Table from James R. Estes, University of Oklahoma)

PART II. KINGDOM OF PLANTS

Evolutionary Trends Among Plants

Not much is understood about the ancient pedigrees of plants. At some unknown time, in the mud of tidal flats, lakes, ponds, or shallow seas, cells not much more complex than photosynthetic protistans founded the lineages that led to plants of the modern world. A little over 400 million years ago, some hopeful green stalks were already established in moist soil; they already had rudimentary water-conducting cells inside their leafless, aerial stems. In the tropical habitats of the Devonian, species having fernlike fronds, woody stems and, possibly, seeds made their entrance. Traditionally, the ancestors of these plants are thought to have evolved from aquatic cells that also gave rise to the green algae. Yet there is recent speculation that their ancestors were already multicellular, of entirely separate lineages, that evolved in soggy soil and mud.

There is no clear story line that can be developed for the evolution of plants. All we can do at present is identify some trends that apparently were important along the way, using existing species as our models. Foremost among these was the trend from nonvascular to vascular tissues. Certain

reproductive trends, of the sort outlined in Table 33.1, were also among the key factors that permitted adaptive radiations into the diverse environments that opened up during the past 400 million years.

From Nonvascular to Vascular Plants. No matter where they live, plants require water and sunlight energy for photosynthesis. The more the plant body increases in size and complexity, the more water uptake and sunlight absorption is required.

Aquatic plants have much of their weight supported by the surrounding water. The first land plants may not have needed support tissues. Perhaps those pioneers simply sprawled over moist soil, soaking up water from below and sunlight from above. However, as plants radiated into different zones, they were subject to different pressures and different opportunities. In response to drier conditions, they came to obtain water and nutrients through spreading root systems. In response to the more intense sunlight, plants grew taller and sent out the solar energy receptors called leaves. Supporting this expansion and differentiation were **vascular tissues**—xylem (which transports water and mineral ions through the plant body) and phloem (which transports sugars and other photosynthetically produced nutrients). Almost all land plants have vascular tissues.

From Haploid to Diploid Dominance. As Figure 33.12 shows, an alternation of haploid and diploid generations occurs among the aquatic green algae (one of the simplest of all plants) as well as the complex land plants. Generally, a diploid zygote undergoes meiosis and gives rise to haploid spores. Each spore develops into a **gametophyte**—a multi-celled structure that eventually bears haploid gametes. When two haploid gametes fuse, the diploid phase is restored in the resulting zygote.

The gametes produced are identical in some species (all are motile and of the same size). In other species, they are differentiated into motile sperm and immotile eggs. The two conditions, called *isogamy* and *oogamy*, occur among the simplest aquatic plants. In a watery medium, of course, motility is necessary if gametes are to get together.

Aquatic environments, as you know, are far less variable than land environments. There typically are few restrictions on growth and reproduction, and little of the life cycle is devoted to the diploid phase. In essence, the diploid zygote functions in producing more haploid spores in short order. In soils that tend to stay soggy, growth and reproduction are still not hampered much. However, dry land habitats are more challenging. The drier they are—seasonally or perpetually—the more pressure there is on

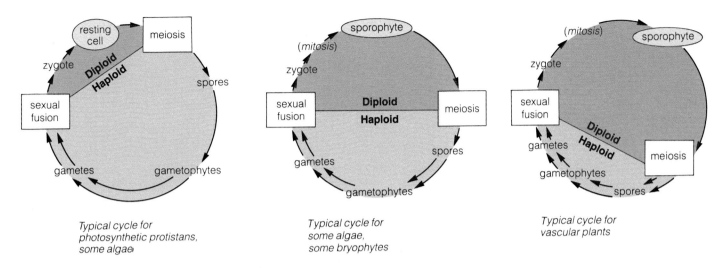

Typical cycle for
photosynthetic protistans,
some algae

Typical cycle for
some algae,
some bryophytes

Typical cycle for
vascular plants

Figure 33.12 Generalized plant life cycles, indicating the shift from haploid to diploid dominance. This shift corresponds with the evolution of more complex forms in land habitats. (From Mary Barkworth, Utah State University)

the plant. If it produces motile spores too soon (say, before the rains come), sperm might never have a sufficiently wet medium for travel to the eggs. Also, spores released in aquatic places do not usually drift far; on land, they can be blown and knocked about all over the place. Clearly there are pressures to hold onto the spores and nourish them until conditions are favorable for their independent survival. There are pressures to increase the number of spores produced (thereby increasing the odds that some, at least, will survive). There are pressures to produce spores that resist mechanical damage and drying out during their dispersal. Given the presence of outside agents that potentially can assist in dispersing the pollen that develops from spores, there is pressure to develop structures that can utilize or attract those agents. Here we are talking about wind, insects, and animals that can serve as pollinators.

Now, these tasks are more than a simple diploid zygote can handle. They require prolongation of the diploid phase of the life cycle; they require greater size and differentiation of the diploid body. Thus there has been a trend toward multicelled spore-producing bodies—the diploid **sporophytes** mentioned in Chapter Nine.

Homospory to Heterospory. The simplest sporophytes of vascular plants are **homosporous**: the spores they produce are all identical to one another (*homo-* means "same"). Others are **heterosporous**: they produce spores of two sorts (*hetero-,* "different"). Heterospory seems to have been the route by which the dominant group of vascular plants—the seed plants—arose.

All seed plants are heterosporous. They produce *megaspores* (which develop into female gametophytes) and *microspores* (which develop into male gametophytes). The female gametophytes mature while still attached to the parent plant. In this way, water and food required for early development are provided by the sporophyte—the stage that is well adapted for obtaining these resources on dry land. The immature male gametophytes, or **pollen grains**, are released from the parent plant and travel to the female by winds, insects, and the like. For the seed plants, the sperm are borne within the protective confines of the pollen grain.

More than any other factor, the development of pollen grains—which can reach female gametophytes *without* liquid water—would have allowed vascular plants to radiate from wet lowlands through drier settings.

From Unprotected Zygotes to Seeds. One more evolutionary development was central to survival on dry land. For vascular plants, the zygote that results from sexual fusion is an *embryo* sporophyte; it must embark on a course of repeated mitotic divisions and differentiation that leads to the multicelled adult form. Again, conditions on dry land are not as constant as they are in aquatic settings. There may be floods or drought; winds might not immediately deposit the embryo sporophyte in a spot suitable for germination and growth.

Table 33.2   Overview of Adaptations of Nonvascular Plants (Algae and Bryophytes)

Division (Phylum)	Some Representatives	Characteristic Habitat	Kinds of Tissue Differentiation
Rhodophyta (red algae)	*Porphyra, Nemalion*	Some freshwater; most marine; more abundant in warmer and tropical seas	Single-celled to branched filaments; some with filaments massed into stemlike and leaflike structures; no vascular (internal transport) tissue
Phaeophyta (brown algae)	*Fucus* (rockweed), kelps, *Sargassum*	Almost all marine, coastal waters especially; most abundant in colder seas	Branched filaments to complex parenchyma bodies; some with leaflike, stemlike (stipe), and anchoring (holdfast) structures; some with ducts for transporting photosynthetic products to different plant regions
Chlorophyta (green algae)	*Ulva* (sea lettuce), *Ulothrix, Spirogyra, Chlamydomonas*	Most freshwater; moist soils; many in shallow tropical seas	Single-celled filaments to simple sheetlike and siphonous forms; no vascular tissue
Bryophyta (bryophytes)	mosses, hornworts, liverworts	Most land; moist, humid sites; some arid sites; a few submerged aquatic sites	Threadlike anchoring structures (rhizoids); leaflike and stemlike structures, often branched; some with simple water- and food-conducting tissues; pores with guard cells in epidermis

*This classification scheme based on Weier et al., *Botany: An Introduction to Plant Biology*, Wiley, 1974.

At some point, tissues from the parent sporophyte developed into a protective coat around the embryo. The embryo sporophyte came to be dispersed as a **seed**: the embryo itself, surrounded by a protective outer coat that guards against damage and, often, containing food reserves.

The evolutionary trends among plants correspond to the potential inherent in the diversity of niches that opened up in land environments.

With this concept in mind, let's look briefly at the spectrum of plant diversity, particularly with respect to the environments in which different species exist. We will begin with the nonvascular plants known as algae and bryophytes. Table 33.2 summarizes the adaptations that occur among these groups.

Algae: Plants That Never Left the Water

Algae is a term that originally came into use to define simple aquatic "plants." It no longer has any formal significance in classification schemes. The organisms once grouped under the term are now recognized as belonging in three different kingdoms. Thus we have the following divisions (the equivalent of phyla):

Cyanobacteria (blue-green algae)	} Monera
Chrysophyta (golden algae, diatoms) Euglenophyta (photosynthetic flagellates Pyrrophyta (dinoflagellates)	} Protista
Rhodophyta (red algae) Phaeophyta (brown algae) Chlorophyta (green algae)	} Plantae

As you can see, the red, brown, and green algae remain in the plant kingdom. These three groups represent the peak of plant diversity in aquatic habitats (Figure 33.13).

Red Algae. The red algae (Rhodophyta) are distinct among algae because of the following combination of features. First, there are no motile cells at all in the life cycle. Second, accessory photosynthetic pigments called phycobilins are present. Third, thylakoids occur within the chloroplasts of red algae. Fourth, sexually reproducing red alga show oogamy: they have immotile sperm and specialized eggs.

Light-Harvesting Structures	Gas Exchange Mechanisms	Water Transport and Conservation Mechanisms	Main Reproductive Strategies
Chloroplasts; phycobilin pigments (trap blue-green light in deep water) plus chlorophylls; some species with radial or bilateral branches (nonoverlapping exposure to sunlight)	Diffusion of dissolved gases across individual cell membranes	Direct exchange with surrounding water, across individual cell membranes	Alternation of sexual fusion and meiosis; sexual reproduction based on oogamy (gametes different in appearance); also vegetative reproduction from plant body fragments or asexual spores
Chloroplasts; xanthophyll pigments plus chlorophylls; leaflike structures	↓	↓	Alternation of multicelled generations; sexual reproduction based on isogamy (gametes all identical in appearance), or oogamy; vegetative reproduction from plant body fragments or asexual spores
Well-organized arrays of chloroplasts with membrane stacks; chlorophylls dominant			Alternation of generations (some have resting spores); sexual reproduction based on isogamy to oogamy; also vegetative reproduction by fragments or spores
Well-organized arrays of chloroplasts with membrane stacks; leaflike structures show radial and bilateral symmetry	Diffusion of dissolved gases across individual cell membranes; some stomatal control	Direct exchange with moisture-laden air; absorption from moist substrate; simple water-conducting cells; waxy covering (cuticle) retards water loss	Alternation of generations; diploid plant body produces homospores (they produce only one type of spore); gametophyte is dominant generation with dependent sporophyte; vegetative reproduction mostly by asexual reproductive bodies (gemmae)

With the exception of a few freshwater forms, the 4,000 or so species of red algae live in habitats ranging from shallow intertidal zones to the basements of tropical reefs. Some live about 175 meters below the surface when water is clear enough for light penetration and photosynthesis. Most are attached to rocks or other algae; only a few species are free-floating.

Depending on the type and arrangement of their phycobilins, red algae range in color from green, to red, purple, and greenish-black. These accessory pigments contribute to photosynthesis in deeper waters. Chlorophyll functions most efficiently in light containing red wavelengths, which do not penetrate far below the surface of water. In submerged habitats, the available wavelengths are mostly blue-green, which accessory pigments in red algae can absorb. They pass some of the wavelength energy to nearby chlorophylls.

Patterns of sexual reproduction among red algae are complex and not yet well defined. In some species, the zygote immediately undergoes meiosis, and haploid spores are formed. The spores germinate and give rise to haploid gametophytes that are neither male nor female. Rather, each produces male and female sex organs as differentiated regions of the gametophyte. The nonmotile sperm produced are released into the surrounding water, and currents carry them to the egg-bearing organs. With the fusion of two gametes, a zygote forms and the cycle starts again.

Like most algae, the red algae also reproduce asexually. Fragments that break away from the parent plant can undergo vegetative growth into new individuals. Indeed, fragmentation is probably the most prevalent reproductive mode among algal groups.

Brown Algae. The brown algae (Phaeophyta) include about 1,500 olive-green and dark-brown species. Accessory pigments, particularly one of the xanthophylls, give them their distinct color. Many brown algae live along rocky coasts, attached to submerged rocks by *holdfasts* (differentiated cell masses at the base of the plants). Others, including the kelps, grow profusely offshore. The giant kelps sometimes grow 100 meters long, forming underwater forests that sway with the currents. Scuba divers avoid these strangely beautiful forests, for they can become entangled in the dense, waving plants. Some brown algae thrive in the open sea. *Sargassum* floats as immense, tangled masses through the Sargasso Sea, which lies between the Azores and the Bahamas. This brown alga in itself creates a unique habitat that helps support a community of marine animals.

a

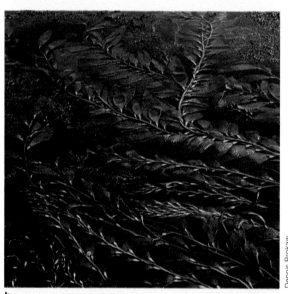

b

c

Figure 33.13 (**a**) A red alga; (**b**) kelp, a brown alga, as it appears on the water's surface; and (**c**) a representative green alga.

(vertical credits:) Douglas Faulkner · Dennis Brokaw · Hervé Chaumeton / Agence Nature

Many kelps have complex organization. In addition to a holdfast, some species have leaflike blades and a *stipe* (a stemlike structure). Sometimes hollow, gas-filled stipe regions called *floats* occur at regular intervals and help hold the plant body upright in water. Surrounded as they are by water, brown algae have no requirements for water-conducting tissues. However, some species have tubelike strands similar to phloem, which transport nutrients.

Brown algae have alternation of generations. Among simpler, filamentous species, the gametophyte and sporophyte may be much the same in outward appearance. In more developed species, the gametophyte is extremely reduced in size and a large, complex sporophyte dominates.

Green Algae.   There are at least 7,000 species of green algae (Chlorophyta). They are like complex land plants in terms of their photosynthetic pigments; all have chlorophylls *a* and *b,* carotenoids, and xanthophylls. Also like plants, they store excess carbohydrates as starch. Most green algae live in fresh water, but many species grow in salty (even brackish) water. If the substrate is wet enough, green algae can grow on snow, soil, patios, and tree trunks.

Green algae reproduce sexually and asexually. They are quite diverse in the details of their sexual reproductive modes. For example, isogamy occurs among some species of the single-celled *Chlamydomonas.* Although haploid cells of different mating types function as gametes, these cells are identical in size and structure. There never is a multicelled stage; *Chlamydomonas* simply alternates between haploid cells and diploid cells. Even among these simple green algae, though, are forms that rely on oogamy. Their gametes differ in size and motility, much like the motile male gametes (sperm) and larger, immotile female gametes (eggs) of animals. The gametes develop while attached to a gametophyte from the parent plant, and motile sperm reach the eggs by traveling through liquid water.

In more complex species of green algae, the diploid zygote grows through mitotic cell divisions, producing multicelled sporophytes. *Ulva,* or sea lettuce, is an example. As Figure 33.14 shows, it has a broad, leaflike *thallus* (a vegetative body with relatively little cell differentiation) in both the haploid and diploid phases of the life cycle.

For the most part, we can make the following generalizations about the green algae. Most often the haploid phase dominates the life cycle. The spores produced following meiosis are mostly the same; they are not differentiated into "male" and "female." There is variation in the types of gametes produced, with some species having isogamy and others, oogamy. Finally, the gametes are motile; they require liquid water for fertilization to occur.

The Bryophytes

Even before the Devonian, the first pioneers on land diverged into two lineages: the bryophytes and the vascular plants. Both lineages share features that must have been adaptive during the transition from water to land. First, a jacket layer surrounds the reproductive structures and keeps them from drying out. There are three kinds of reproductive structures:

Archegonium	*egg-producing cells or organ in the gametophyte*
Antheridium	*sperm-producing cells or organ in the gametophyte*
Sporangium	*spore-producing cells or organ in the sporophyte*

Second, some bryophytes and the vascular plants have a **cuticle**—a fatty protective layer that also helps prevent plant parts exposed to air from drying out. Where there is a cuticle, so also are there **stomata** (openings that help regulate gas movements into and from the plant body). Third, the embryo undergoes early development *within* the female gametophyte. Among algae, recall, the zygote is pretty much on its own.

   The **bryophytes** include about 16,000 species of mosses, liverworts, and hornworts (Figure 33.15). All are small plants, generally less than twenty centimeters long. All occur in habitats that are moist for at least part of the year; without liquid water, sperm cannot reach the egg-containing archegonia and sexual reproduction cannot occur.

   Unlike the vascular plants, the bryophytes do not have well-developed vascular tissues (xylem and phloem). Neither do they have true leaves, stems, and roots. What they do have are leaflike, stemlike, and rootlike structures. For

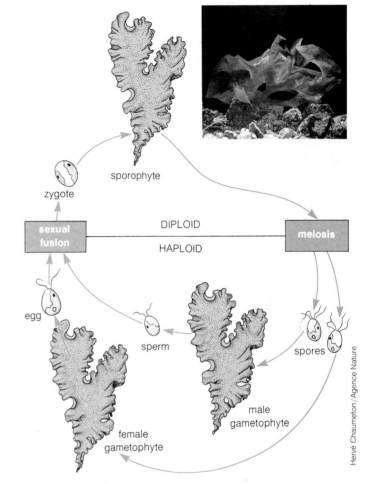

Figure 33.14 Life cycle of sea lettuce *(Ulva)*, one of the green algae.

Figure 33.15 (**a**) The moss and (**b**) the liverwort.

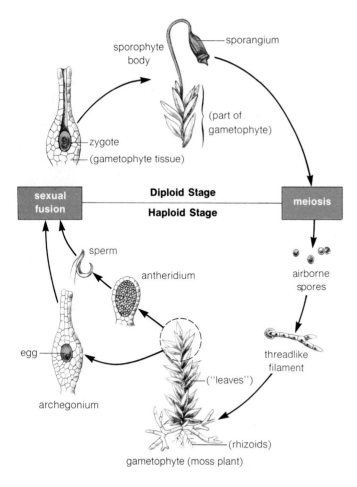

Figure 33.16 Moss life cycle. (As in the other plant life cycles, the various structures are not drawn to scale.) Notice how the sporophyte body remains attached to the gametophyte (moss plant) body.

Field Museum of Natural History

Figure 33.17 Vascular plants of the Carboniferous. Most of the tall, treelike forms shown here became extinct.

example, most have **rhizoids**: long, single cells or filaments that attach the gametophyte to the ground. Rhizoids are not true roots; water and mineral ions diffuse directly into parenchymal cells of the gametophyte and are not transported through the rhizoids.

Mosses are the most common bryophytes. Within the gametophyte of many moss genera is a central strand of undifferentiated, water-conducting cells. A few also contain living food-conducting cells arranged around the central strand.

When a moss spore germinates, it first produces a green, threadlike gametophyte that resembles filamentous green algae. The filament grows by mitosis to produce the familiar moss plant (Figure 33.16). The reproductive structures that develop on this haploid gametophyte can be male, female, or both. In most species, male and female reproductive structures occur on separate plants that are growing near each other.

When sexual fusion occurs, the resulting zygote divides mitotically to form a sporophyte. The sporophyte is carried on a stalk growing from the tip of the gametophyte body (Figure 33.16); it is *attached* to and dependent on the haploid plant.

Ferns and Their Allies: First of the Vascular Plants

The existing vascular plants are represented by the divisions listed in Table 33.3. Their ancestors appeared about 400 million years ago. Within a relatively short span of 50 million years, all major lines of vascular plants were established on land. Some forms that once dominated the landscape became extinct (Figure 33.17). But among existing vascular plants are lycopods, horsetails, and ferns—all of which bear strong resemblance to those ancient forms.

Lycopods. The lycopods (Lycophyta) were highly diverse 350 million years ago, when some forms were even tree-sized. The existing genus, *Lycopodium,* contains miniature descendants. Club mosses, which typically grow on forest floors, belong to this group. A *Lycopodium* sporophyte has roots and small, scalelike leaves that spiral around stems and branches. The sporophyte has conelike, spore-bearing structures called **strobili** (singular, strobilus). Figure 33.18 shows some of these structures. Spores dispersed from strobili germinate to form small, free-living gametophytes. Although most lycopods are homosporous, some have spores of different types. However, even the heterosporous species require ample water for their gametes to develop and for fertilization to occur.

Edward S. Ross

W. H. Hodge

Kratz/ZEFA

a b c

Figure 33.18 (**a**) *Lycopodium* sporophytes, showing the cone-like strobili in which spores are produced. (**b,c**) Horsetails *(Equisetum)* showing how strobili are carried on stems.

Horsetails. The horsetails (Sphenophyta) are relatively simple vascular plants. Their ancient relatives were highly diverse, and included treelike forms about fifteen meters tall. A single genus, *Equisetum*, survives. Plants of this genus often grow in vacant lots, along railroad tracks, and around ponds or lakes in parts of Eurasia and North America. Horsetail sporophytes typically have underground stems (rhizomes) and aerial branches arising at nodes. Scalelike leaves are arranged in whorls about a hollow, photosynthetic stem (Figure 33.18). Growing from some shoot tips or from side branches are spore-bearing strobili. Winds disperse the fragile horsetail spores, all of which are identical and which have only a few days to germinate on moist surfaces. Germinating spores give rise to haploid gametophytes. The horsetail gametophyte is a free-living plant about as small as a pinhead. It bears separate male and female reproductive structures in which sperm and eggs develop. Sperm must travel through free water (dew, raindrops) to reach the female structures.

Ferns. The ferns (Pterophyta) are another kind of primitive vascular plant with ancient origins. About 12,000 existing species have been identified. These plants have extensive rhizomes and well-developed leaves (Figure 33.19). Except for tropical tree ferns, their stems are horizontal to

Jean-Paul Ferrero/Ardea, London

Figure 33.19 Ferns in a temperate rain forest of Tasmania.

Table 33.3 Overview of Adaptations of Vascular Plants

Division* (Phylum)	Some Representatives	Characteristic Environment	Kinds of Tissue Differentiation
Ferns and Fern Allies (non-seed-bearing; depend on free water for fertilization)			
Lycophyta (lycopods or club mosses)	*Lycopodium, Selaginella*	Land; wet, shaded sites in tropics and subtropics; some arctic, desert	Sporophyte with true vascular system; roots, stems, leaves; stomata with guard cells in one or both leaf surfaces; vascular system makes possible a higher volume-to-surface ratio than in nonvascular plants. These features occur in all eight plant divisions listed here
Sphenophyta (sphenopsids)	*Equisetum* (horsetails), only living genus	Land; acid soil; sand dunes, swamps, moist woodlands, lake margins, railroad embankments	Sporophyte with true vascular system; extensive underground stem (rhizome) with roots and aerial shoots at nodes; aerial stems jointed, hollow, branched or unbranched
Pterophyta (ferns)	Sword ferns, lady ferns, *Cyathea* (tree ferns)	Land; some epiphytes (attached to but nonparasitic on other plants); most wet, humid sites	True vascular system; well-developed xylem and phloem; some with creeping rhizomes; columnlike stem in tree ferns
Gymnosperms ("naked-seed-bearing"; not dependent on free water for fertilization)			
Cycadophyta (cycads)	*Zamia*	Limited tropical, subtropical land regions	Well-developed, complex vascular system; stems short and bulbous, or columns; palmlike appearance; fernlike leaves; massive cones (reproductive structures bearing seeds)
Ginkgophyta (ginkgos)	*Ginkgo biloba* (only existing species)	Land; temperate regions	Well-developed, complex vascular system; tall, woody stem (trunk) with long side branches; fan-shaped, deciduous leaves, cones
Pinophyta (conifers)	pine, spruce, fir, juniper, hemlock, cypress, redwood, larch	Land; widespread through Northern and Southern hemispheres	Well-developed, complex vascular system; some shrubby, others impressively thick, tall-trunked trees; most with whorled or spiral branching; most evergreen, cones
Gnetophyta (gnetophytes)	*Gnetum, Ephedra, Welwitschia*	Land; warm-temperate regions; desert and mountain sand or rocky soil	Well-developed, complex vascular system; some shrubby, branched, with whorled leaves; *Welwitschia* short, bowl-shaped stem, two large, strap-shaped leaves, flowerlike reproductive structures
Angiosperms (flowering, seed-bearing; depend on pollinating agents; not dependent on free water for fertilization)			
Magnoliophyta Liliopsida (monocots)	Grasses, palms, lilies, orchids, onions, pineapple, bamboo	Almost all land zones; some aquatic	Well-developed, complex vascular system; floral structures; one seed leaf (cotyledon); floral parts generally in threes or multiples of threes; parallel-veined leaves common
Magnoliopsida (dicots)	Most temperate-zone fruit trees; roses, cabbages, melons, beans, potatoes	Almost all land zones; some aquatic	Two seed leaves; floral parts generally in fours, five, or multiples of these; net-veined leaves common

*This classification scheme based on Weier et al., *Botany: An Introduction to Plant Biology*, Wiley, 1974.

Light-Harvesting Structures	Gas Exchange Mechanisms	Water Transport and Conservation Mechanisms	Main Reproductive Strategies
Well-organized arrays of chloroplasts with membrane stacks; most with spirally arranged leaves; some with palisade layer of photosynthetic cells in leaves	Diffusion of dissolved gases across individual cell membranes; regulation through numerous stomata	Well-developed xylem and accessory cells; cuticle (retards water loss)	Alternation of generations; complex, dominant sporophyte independent of gametophyte; some homosporous (they produce only one type of spore), others heterosporous (produce spores of different types, which give rise to male or female gametophytes)
Well-organized chloroplast arrays; upright growth habit possible through pronounced stem thickening; whorled, scalelike leaves common but most photosynthesis in stems			Alternation of generations; complex, dominant sporophyte free-living (independent of gametophyte); homosporous
Well-organized chloroplast arrays; radially symmetrical leaves and stems common; epiphytes capture light above forest floor			Alternation of generations; sporophyte body initially develops on gametophyte (which later disintegrates); most homosporous
Well-organized chloroplast arrays; complex leaves, arranged in pattern that allows good sunlight exposure	Diffusion of dissolved gases across individual cell membranes; complex stomatal control	Well-developed xylem and accessory cells; cuticle; water storage in roots, stems	Alternation of generations; dominant, woody sporophyte body, heterosporous; well-developed, seed-bearing cones; pollen
			Alternation of generations; dominant, woody sporophyte body, heterosporous; well-developed, seed-bearing ''cones''; pollen
			Alternation of generations; dominant, woody sporophyte body (e.g., the pine tree); heterosporous, well-developed seed-bearing cones; pollen
Well-organized chloroplast arrays; in *Ephedra*, most photosynthesis in stems and branches (almost leafless)			Alternation of generations; dominant, woody sporophyte body, heterosporous; ''male'' and ''female'' diploid plants; bears small, naked seeds; pollen
Well-organized chloroplast arrays; complex leaves, arranged in patterns that allow good sunlight exposure	Diffusion of dissolved gases across individual cell membranes; complex stomatal control	Well-developed xylem and accessory cells; cuticle; water storage in roots, stems	Alternation of generations; dominant woody or herbaceous sporophyte body; diverse floral structures adapted to pollinating agents (wind, water, insects, birds, bats); all are heterosporous; seeds enclosed within ovary; fruits (ripened ovary) aid in seed dispersal by wind, water, animals

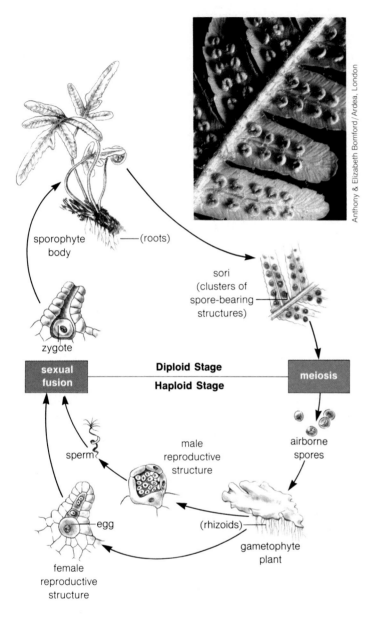

Figure 33.20 Fern life cycle. *Sori*, in which spores are produced, occur on the underside of the fern leaf.

Labels in figure:
sporophyte body — (roots)
sori (clusters of spore-bearing structures)
zygote
sexual fusion — **Diploid Stage** / **Haploid Stage** — **meiosis**
airborne spores
sperm
male reproductive structure
egg
(rhizoids)
gametophyte plant
female reproductive structure

Anthony & Elizabeth Bomford / Ardea, London

the ground's surface or just beneath it; only the leaves are aerial. The sporophyte is the conspicuous fern plant (Figure 33.19). Some species are homosporous; others are heterosporous. In both cases, the spores are dispersed through air. They germinate and develop into small, heart-shaped gametophytes, of the sort shown in Figure 33.20. Fusion of fern gametes eventually leads to a new diploid generation.

Lycopod, horsetail, and fern sporophytes have well-developed vascular systems; they are adapted for life on land. But they are largely limited to wet, humid habitats, because their short-lived gametophytes usually have no vascular tissue for water transport and conservation. Also, the male gametes must have liquid water if they are to reach the eggs that remain in archegonia. Thus the primitive vascular plants are the plant kingdom's equivalent to amphibians: for part of the life cycle they are, in essence, aquatic.

Gymnosperms: The Conifers and Their Kin

There are two divisions of seed plants: the gymnosperms and angiosperms. They take their name from the seed (the structure in which embryo sporophytes are dispersed). The word **gymnosperm** means "naked seed." It refers to the way that seeds of these plants are borne on surfaces of reproductive structures, without being protected by additional tissue layers (as they are in angiosperms). The gymnosperms include cycads, ginkgos, conifers, and gnetophytes.

Cycads. During the Mesozoic, cycads (Cycadophyta) flourished along with the dinosaurs. The surviving cycad genera are confined to the tropics and subtropics. At first glance you might mistake a cycad for a small palm tree (Figure 33.21). Despite having similar leaves and stems, palms and cycads are not closely related. (Palms have true flowers.) Cycads have massive spore-bearing structures called **cones**, some of which are shown in Figure 33.21c. Sharp spines on some cycad cones (along with spiny leaf tips) are probably adaptations that minimize seed predation. Seeds are sought after as food in areas where water (hence plant growth) is limited.

Ginkgos. The ginkgos (Ginkgophyta) are even more restricted in native distribution than the cycads. Only a single species (Figure 33.21) has survived, despite the success of this plant during the Mesozoic. It seems that several thousand years ago, this attractive tree species was extensively planted in cultivated grounds around Asian temples. But the small natural population from which these "domesticated" trees were derived must have become extinct. The near-extinction of this living fossil from the age of dinosaurs is puzzling, for ginkgos seem to be hardier than many trees. In cities, they are planted because they are attractive and because they are resistant to insects, disease, even air pollution. However, cultivated plants are propagated by humans and they grow under protected conditions. In the natural state, ginkgos may be less adaptive.

Figure 33.21 Two seed-bearing plants: the cycad (**a**) and the ginkgo (**b**). Cycad cones are shown in (**c**); the seeds of the ginkgo are shown in (**d**).

Gnetophytes. The division Gnetophyta contains about seventy species, which are divided into three orders: *Gnetum, Ephedra,* and *Welwitschia.* Of all vascular plants, the *Welwitschia* of southwestern Africa is probably the most unusual. Most of this seed-producing plant is underground; the only exposed part is a woody disk that bears the leaves. *Welwitschia* never produces more than two strap-shaped leaves, which split lengthwise repeatedly as the plant grows older. The outcome is a plant that appears to be a pile of straggly leaves (Figure 33.22).

Conifers. The most diverse and widely distributed gymnosperms are the conifers (the Pinophyta). They are cone-bearing woody trees and shrubs, with needlelike or scalelike leaves. The leaves of most conifers are retained for several years on the sporophyte. Some leaves are always present on the sporophytes of most species; that is why conifers are commonly called evergreens. Pine, spruce, fir, hemlock, juniper, and cypress are conifers; so is the redwood.

Conifer seeds develop on the surface of perhaps a hundred shelflike scales that are arranged into a cone (Figure 33.23). Each pine cone scale has two sporangia (spore-producing structures) on its upper surface. The sporangia of "male" cones bear microspores that develop into pollen grains. Sporangia of "female" cones bear megaspores that develop into immature female gametophytes.

Figure 33.22 *Welwitschia,* a seed-producing gnetophyte.

Conifer life cycles are diverse in the duration of events. Here we will look only at the pine life cycle (Figure 33.23). The pine tree is the sporophyte. Each spring, it produces perhaps millions of microspores, which develop into pollen grains. The pollen grains have projections that may help make them more buoyant in air (the projections may also help position the pollen grain once it arrives at the female

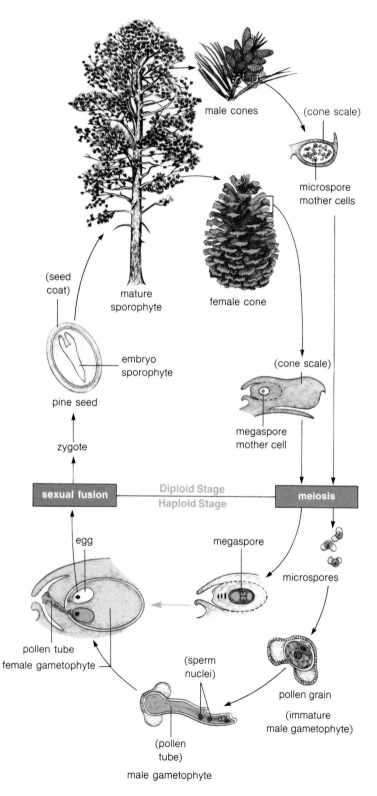

Figure 33.23 Pine life cycle.

cone). On these projections, pollen grains float through the air, sometimes as thick yellow clouds. With such extravagant discharges, some pollen grains are bound to land by chance on female cones, which they do. A sticky substance on the female cone scales holds them in place. Here they remain trapped, not too far away from the megasporangia. When the sticky fluid dries, it pulls pollen grains onto the megasporangium surface.

At least a year now passes between the time of pollination and fertilization. During this period, the pollen grain produces a pollen tube (a tubelike projection) that starts to grow through the megasporangium wall. Eventually, a cell of the pollen grains divides mitotically, and one of the cells produced goes on to form two sperm cells.

During this period, events are proceeding in the megasporangia that will lead to a female gametophyte. Within each megasporangium is a diploid "megaspore mother cell." This cell divides by meiosis to form four haploid megaspores. Three abort; the one remaining divides mitotically and gives rise to female gametophyte—an oval mass of cells within the sporangium walls. The megasporangium, tissue-layer cover, and female gametophyte constitute an **ovule**.

The gametophyte contains archegonia, each with a single egg. As soon as a sperm fertilizes an egg, the stage is set for development of the embryo sporophyte—the pine seed. The diploid zygote divides repeatedly by mitosis, initiating the formation of an embryo that becomes the next sporophyte generation. A seed coat forms. The female gametophyte tissue serves as food reserves for the embryo during germination.

Conifers were the dominant land plants during the Mesozoic. Their mechanisms of seed production, protection, and dispersal helped assure their radiation into many land habitats. Since then, their distribution has been gradually reduced. They are still the dominant plants in many habitats, especially in northern regions and at high altitudes (Figure 32.24). They are sources of lumber, paper, and other commercial and industrial products.

Angiosperms: The Flowering Plants

Angiosperm means a seed carried within a container—namely, within a mature ovary. This descriptive term applies to flowering plants (the Magnoliophyta). If numbers are indicative of adaptive success, then the flowering plants are indeed successful. There are about 250,000 known species, far more than any other division can claim. They are also the most diverse. They range in size from tiny duckweeds (about a millimeter long) to *Eucalyptus* trees more than 100 meters tall. Most are free-living, but saprobic and parasitic species also exist. Flowering plants have radiated into an enormous range of habitats, not only on dry land but also on wet land margins and in the water itself.

The many and diverse members of the division are grouped into two classes: the monocots and dicots (Chapter Sixteen). Figure 33.25 shows some representatives of both classes. There are at least 200,000 species of dicots, which include most of the familiar shrubs and trees (other than conifers), most of the herbs, the cacti, and water lilies. The monocots include grasses, palms, lilies, and orchids. The main crop plants supporting the human population are wheat, corn, rice, oats, rye, and barley—all monocots, and all domesticated grasses.

Many factors have contributed to the adaptive success of the flowering plants. As in other groups described in this chapter, the diploid sporophyte dominates the life cycle— a sporophyte well adapted for life on land and that retains and nourishes the gametophyte. Flowering plants are heterosporous, and they are oogamous. The gametophyte in turn retains and nourishes the immature eggs and sperm during their development. Flowering plants package their zygotes as fruits and seeds—packaging that assures protection and dispersal. Above all, they have a unique reproductive system involving flower formation (Chapter Eighteen). Their diverse floral structures have coevolved with pollinating vectors—insects, winds, animals of myriad sorts. With these vectors providing transport for them, flowering plants have been dispersed across the face of the earth.

Figure 33.24 Representative conifer: ponderosa pine high above Yosemite Valley.

a

b

Figure 33.25 Floral structure of the wild iris, a representative monocot (**a**); and *Hypericum*, a representative dicot (**b**).

PERSPECTIVE

How often, if we think of them at all, do we think of plants as little more than greenery in the scenery? How often do we look upon fungi as curious and/or nasty intruders into human affairs? Yet, without these organisms, without their initial invasion of the land and subsequent interactions, we could scarcely have even made it onto the environmental stage. Until they came to cloak the earth, inch by inch, continent by continent, there could be no other forms of life on the vacant land. Their evolution, while not smacking of the drama of, say, the rise and fall of dinosaurs, was remarkable nevertheless when we stop to consider the odds.

The vegetative bodies of plants are immobile. They cannot crawl, leap, run, or fly. Beginning with ancestral forms that could not have been more complex than simple green algae, a long series of mutations apparently led to plants having a few relatively inconspicuous traits. They had a few threadlike anchors to sink into muddy margins of pools and lagoons, a tiny chloroplast-filled stalk, a few scalelike projections that spread out stiffly beneath the sun.

Yet within those anchors, stalks, and scales, hollow tubes eventually appeared. These tubes were forerunners of highly adaptive transport systems that now run through roots, stems, and leaves. The diploid stage of some aquatic plant life cycles proved to have remarkable potential. Resistant as it was to adverse conditions, the diploid sporophyte generation gradually became more and more pronounced in the move to higher and drier land. Among some land plants, gametophytes came to be housed in the parent sporophyte body. The sporophyte transport system could nurture these gametophytes with water and dissolved nutrients. In some lines, seeds took over the dispersal function of spores.

Reproductive structures became attuned to seasons, to times of rain and winds. Most astonishing of all, some plants coevolved with insects and other animals. Their life cycles came to depend on animals to carry pollen grains to female reproductive structures, and to disperse seeds. Simultaneously, life cycles of the animal pollinators came to depend on specific plants for food. Over time, the fungi became part of life on land, as they have been in water—decomposers, recyclers of life-giving nutrients for the animals and plants with which they are linked in the web of life. Like plants, most fungi rely on wind, splashing rain, and insects for dispersal. Thus, without means of their own for spectacular motility, plants and fungi have moved over the barren plains, to the mountains, to land everywhere.

Readings

Bold, H., C. Alexopoulos, and T. Delevoryas. 1980. *Morphology of Plants and Fungi.* Fourth edition. New York: Harper & Row. Outstanding source book.

Christensen, C. 1972. *The Molds and Man.* Third edition. Minneapolis: University of Minnesota Press.

Raven, P., R. Evert, and H. Curtis. 1981. *Biology of Plants.* Third edition. New York: Worth. One of the most popular of all introductions to botany. Exquisite illustrations; there is nothing else like it.

Rost, T., et al. 1979. *Botany: A Brief Introduction to Plant Biology.* New York: Wiley. Abridged version of a classic (T. Weier et al., 1974, fifth edition; same publisher)

Stebbins, G., and G. Hill. March 1980. "Did Multicellular Plants Invade the Land?" *The American Naturalist* 115(3):342–353.

Taylor, T. 1981. *Paleobotany.* New York: McGraw-Hill. Everything you ever wanted to know about the ancestors of modern-day plants and fungi.

Volk, W. 1978. *Essentials of Medical Microbiology.* New York: Lippincott. Everything you ever wanted to know about fungi that cause diseases in humans.

Review Questions

1. Name the four main divisions of fungi and describe a representative for each.

2. What are three characteristic events in the asexual reproduction of a fungus?

3. Can you describe what kind of stage intervenes between the haploid and diploid stages in the life cycle of a common field mushroom?

4. What is the difference between a mycorrhizal mat and a lichen?

5. Distinguish between the spores and gametes of land plants. As part of your answer, define sporophyte and gametophyte. Which is haploid? Which is diploid?

6. Describe four major evolutionary trends that figured in the invasion of land by plants.

7. What are some similarities and differences between algae and bryophytes? Bryophytes and lycopods?

8. If both gymnosperms and flowering plants are seed-bearing, then how do they differ in reproductive modes?

9. Can you name the four divisions of nonvascular plants? The eight divisions of vascular plants?

It is the last scene of an epic Western film. The hero has finally tracked down the rustlers, saved the longhorns, fought off a mountain lion with his bare hands, narrowly escaped the lunge of a rattlesnake, and found the rancher's daughter (who had been kidnapped and hastily abandoned in the desert) by spotting the vultures circling in the sky above her. Now, with his faithful dog beside him, he waves goodbye to the girl, mounts his restless stallion, splashes across a shallow stream, and rides off into the golden west.

When you think back over the stories on which we are raised, it is easy to see how we acquire a stereotyped picture of what "animals" are. For example, you may have noticed that seven kinds of animals made their entrance and exit in the scene described above. But did you happen to notice also that they all were *vertebrates*—animals with backbones? The story is somewhat lopsided, for more than ninety-nine percent of all animals in the world are backboneless *invertebrates.* Undoubtedly just out of camera range were diverse worms, grasshoppers, spiders, scorpions, ticks, centipedes, millipedes, water fleas, mosquitoes, flies, beetles, butterflies, moths, aphids, snails, bees, and other spineless things. Long after we finished counting all the kinds and numbers of vertebrates alive today, we would still be counting the kinds and numbers of a staggering array of invertebrates.

In this chapter, we will consider some examples of these less conspicuous animals. Before we do, we will take a look at some general features that all animals have in common. Then, by using existing phyla as our models, we will piece together a picture of evolutionary trends toward diversity among several different groups. Our focus will be on key characters that eventually led to animals as complex and conspicuous as snakes, dogs, horses, longhorns, and ourselves.

34

ANIMAL DIVERSITY

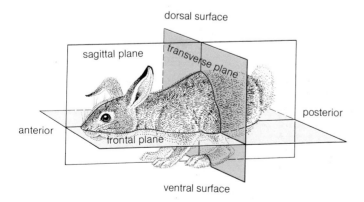

Figure 34.1 Planes of symmetry for bilateral animals. The frontal plane (blue shading) divides the bilateral body into dorsal and ventral halves. The sagittal plane divides the body into right and left halves. A transverse plane divides it into anterior (front) and posterior (rear) parts.

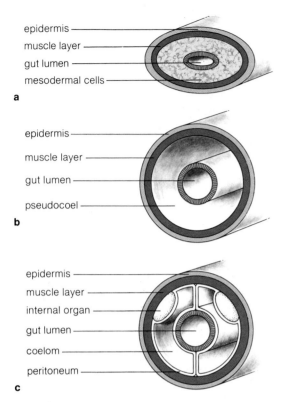

Figure 34.2 Body plans for bilateral animals. (**a**) Acoelomate, as occurs among the flatworms. (**b**) Pseudocoelomate, as occurs among the roundworms. (**c**) Coelomate, a plan that is elaborated upon among mollusks, annelids, arthropods, echinoderms, and chordates.

GENERAL CHARACTERISTICS OF ANIMALS

The animal kingdom encompasses the **metazoans**, which by definition have the following characteristics:

1. Animals are multicellular. Except for *Trichoplast* (Figure 32.20), animals have cells differentiated into tissues, and most have tissues aggregated into organs.

2. Animals are heterotrophs. Except for a few parasites that absorb small organic molecules directly from host tissues, animals ingest particles or chunks of food which are then broken down (digested) and absorbed.

3. Animals reproduce sexually; many also can reproduce asexually.

4. Animals go through progressive stages of embryonic development (Chapter Twenty-Eight).

5. Animals are motile during at least part of the life cycle.

Body Plans

Animals are further characterized according to four general features: body symmetry, body cavity (or lack of it), the presence or absence of segmentation, and cephalization.

Body Symmetry. The term *radial symmetry,* recall, refers to a body plan in which parts are more or less arranged like spokes of a bike wheel about a central axis. *Bilateral symmetry* refers to a body plan such as your own, which has right and left halves that are largely mirror-images of each other. Figure 34.1 indicates some of the planes of symmetry in bilateral animals.

Sponges, and jellyfish and their kin, are the only animals with "primary" radial symmetry: the trait has persisted from the time of their beginnings. Those sea stars you see in tide pools or aquariums have what is called "secondary" radial symmetry, for they actually evolved from bilateral ancestors. With few exceptions, all other existing animals have always been bilateral.

Body Cavity. Radial animals have few (if any) internal organs. The cnidarians do have a gut (an epithelium-lined cavity for digestion) with one permanent opening (the mouth). This body plan is called a *blind sac,* for what goes in and is not digested must be expelled through the same opening. Flatworms, which are bilateral animals, also have this blind-sac arrangement. All other bilateral animals have a *tube-within-a-tube* body plan. There are two permanent openings (mouth and anus), one at each end of the gut. Thus the gut is a continuous tube enclosed within the outer "tube" defined by the body wall.

In tube-within-a-tube animals, the gut either is embedded in a solid tissue of mesenchymal cells or suspended in a fluid-filled cavity. The word **coelom** generally means any fluid-filled cavity surrounding the gut. Often the coelom serves as a hydrostatic skeleton, assisting in body movements. During animal evolution, the coelom has also served as a chamber in which organs have undergone enlargement (increased in surface area) and have become more complex.

Flatworms have no such cavity between the gut and body wall; they are said to be **acoelomate**. The roundworms and a few other animals are **pseudocoelomate**. Their body cavity is derived from the blastocoel, a cavity that forms during the blastula stage of embryonic development. (See, for example, Figure 28.5.) In a pseudocoelomate, internal organs are freely suspended. All other bilateral animals are **coelomate**. They have a true coelom, which arises as a cavity within the mesoderm of a developing embryo. Mesodermal cells form a lining, the *peritoneum,* for the cavity. Although internal organs typically bulge into the coelom, they are positioned behind the peritoneum and are never freely suspended within it. Figure 34.2 illustrates the differences between the three body plans for bilateral animals.

Segmentation. Of all animal phyla, three are characterized by repeats of similar body units. This repetition of structural units is called **segmentation**. It occurs among the annelids, arthropods, and chordates. (It also occurs among one class of flatworms, the cestodes.) For example, your own body has repeats of nerves and vertebrae, as Chapter Twenty-One described. Segmentation has been important in animal evolution, for individual segments have been modified in ways that permit specialized functioning.

Cephalization. One of the greatest differences between radial and bilateral animals is **cephalization**. The word refers to differentiation of one end of the body into a head, in which nervous tissue and sensory organs are especially concentrated. Chapter Twenty-One included a detailed look at this feature, which represents one of the major trends in animal evolution.

Major Groups of Animals

Twenty-nine phyla of animals are recognized, although in terms of actual numbers of species, only nine are said to be major groups:

Porifera	Nematoda	Arthropoda
Cnidaria	Mollusca	Echinodermata
Platyhelminthes	Annelida	Chordata

The numbers range from 6,000 species of echinoderms (sea stars and their kin) to 923,000 species of arthropods (crustaceans, spiders, and insects). We will be looking at some characteristics of the nine major phyla, as outlined in Table 34.1. Our first subjects are the sponges—anatomically simple animals, but a cut above *Trichoplax.* As Figure 34.3 suggests, sponges are thought to be close to the evolutionary boundary between animals and the ancestral, protistanlike forms from which they arose.

SPONGES

Phylum Porifera consists of 10,000 species of sponges. Only 150 species occur in fresh water; the rest live in the seas. The adult sponge form is always *sessile* (it remains attached to one spot) and shows little obvious movement.

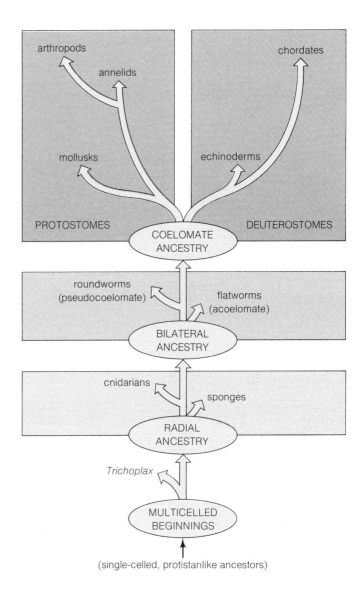

Figure 34.3 Presumed evolutionary relationships among the nine major animal phyla. All of these lineages were established by Cambrian times, which began some 570 million years ago.

Some sponges are no longer than your smallest fingernail, yet others are massive enough to fill a large kitchen sink. Most sponges have irregular shapes, although some are radial. The shapes are maintained by loose networks of a translucent protein fiber (spongin), or calcium-containing spikes (spicules), or both.

The simplest sponges look like small vases (Figure 34.4). A layer of flattened cells covers the outside, but unlike true epithelium, it has no basement membrane. The

Table 34.1 Overview of Characteristics of Major Animal Phyla

Phylum (and some representatives)	Characteristic Environment	Characteristic Life-Style of Adult Form	Integration	Support and Movement
Porifera (10,000)* sponges	Most marine, some freshwater	Filter feeders; attached to substrate	Some contractile cells, no true nervous system	Support elements (needlelike spicules and/or protein fibers); contractile cells
Cnidaria (9,000) hydras, sea anemones, jellyfishes, corals	Most marine, some freshwater	Predatory; some attached, some float or swim feebly; hydra somersault	Nerve nets; some have eyespots, statocysts (balance), sensory cells on tentacles	Muscle fibers in epithelium; some secrete hard external chamber material
Platyhelminthes (12,700) flatworms, flukes, tapeworms	Marine, freshwater, body fluids of host, moist land	Predatory or parasitic; free-living or dependent on animal host tissue	Central and peripheral nervous systems; cephalization, dorsal-ventral differentiation, bilateral symmetry in systems	Well-developed muscle layers; no skeletal system
Nematoda (10,000) roundworms	Marine, freshwater, body fluids of host, land (deserts to ice)	Predatory or parasitic; free-living or dependent on plant or animal host tissue	Same as above	Longitudinal muscle fibers in body wall; tough cuticle; hydrostatic skeleton
Mollusca (100,000) snails, slugs, clams; squids, octopuses	Marine, freshwater, some on land	Predatory or scavengers; some crawling; squid and octopus, water-jet propulsion	Same as above in many groups	Muscular mantle; muscular foot in many; external shell in some
Annelida (8,700) earthworms, leeches, polychaetes	Marine, freshwater, moist land	Scavengers, casual symbionts, or parasitic	Same as above	Longitudinal, circular muscles; some have parapodia (paddle-like appendages); hydrostatic skeleton
Arthropoda (923,000) crustaceans, spiders, insects	Marine, freshwater, land	Predatory (carnivores, herbivores) or scavengers; some casual symbionts or parasitic; diverse life-styles from burrowing to flying	Same as above	Muscle bundles in jointed appendages; exoskeleton
Echinodermata (6,000) sea stars, brittle stars, sea urchins, sea lilies, sea cucumbers	All marine	Predatory; some attached to substrate; others crawling	Central and peripheral nervous systems; nerve ring, dorsal-ventral differentiation, radial symmetry in systems	Endoskeleton of hard plates joined by muscles and connective tissue; tube feet for water-jet propulsion
Chordata (39,000) tunicates, lancelets, jawless fishes, jawed fishes, amphibians, reptiles, birds, mammals	Marine, freshwater, land	Predatory (carnivores, herbivores) or scavengers; few marine forms attached but most free-living; none strictly parasitic; highly diverse life-styles	Central and peripheral nervous systems; cephalization, dorsal-ventral differentiation, bilateral symmetry in systems	Antagonistic muscle system in many; axial, rodlike endoskeleton (notochord or vertebral column)

*Number in parentheses indicates approximate number of species.

**Monoecious means having male and female reproductive organs, or gonads, in the same individual; hermaphroditic.
  Dioecious means male and female reproductive organs in separate individuals.

Digestion	Gas Exchange	Circulation of Fluids	Water, Salt Regulation	Usual Reproduction
No digestive cavity; some cells transport food particles	Direct diffusion across cell membranes	External water circulation only	Some cells help regulate water flow	Asexual budding; sexual (monoecious or dioecious**)
Incomplete, saclike digestive tract (tentacles, mouth, gut)	Direct diffusion	No true circulatory system (gastrovascular cavity)	Direct diffusion	Asexual budding; monoecious or dioecious; simple gonads (reproductive organs)
Flatworms: incomplete, saclike digestive tract (mouth, gut); none in others	Direct diffusion	No true circulatory system (gastrovascular cavity)	Ciliated excretory cells (flame cells), excretory ducts	Monoecious; well-developed system of ducts, gonads, accessory organs
Complete straight digestive tract (mouth, gut, anus)	Direct diffusion (some internal parasites anaerobic)	No circulatory system	Bladderlike excretory organ (proto-nephridia)	Dioecious; well-developed reproductive system
Complete digestive tract	Usually gills	Closed blood-vascular system in some, open in others	Organ system with nephridia	Dioecious; well-developed reproductive system
Complete digestive tract	Capillaries in parapodia; some have gills (thin filaments with capillary networks)	Closed blood-vascular system (heart, blood vessels)	Organ system with kidneylike structures (nephridia)	Dioecious or monoecious; well-developed reproductive system
Complete digestive tract	System of gills, tracheae (finely branched tubes); some with book lungs (respiratory organs)	Open blood-vascular system (from heart, into tissues, to gills or book lungs, back to heart)	Malpighian tubules or secretory glands	Dioecious; well-developed reproductive system
Most have complete digestive tract; no anus in some	System of gills or respiratory "trees"; also exchange with water moving through tube feet	Closed radial, blood-vascular system	Water-vascular system	Dioecious; some asexual by self-division; gonads, large, simple ducts
Complete digestive tract	Gills in some; respiratory system of tracheae, bronchi, bronchioles, lungs in others	Closed blood-vascular system; some with lymphatic system	Organ system that may include kidneys, ducts, tubules, bladder	Dioecious; well-developed reproductive system

Figure 34.4 Representative sponges in their aquatic habitat.

Figure 34.6 A tubular sponge (*Verongia archeri*) of the West Indies, releasing sperm to the surrounding water.

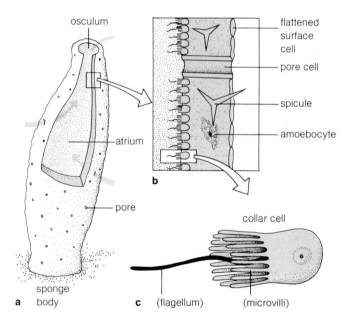

Figure 34.5 Anatomy of a simple sponge. (**a**) Gold arrows indicate the direction of water movement through the sponge body. (**b**) A cross-section through the body wall. (**c**) A sponge collar cell, showing the ring of microvilli in which nutrients are trapped.

interior is called the *atrium,* and the opening at the top is the *osculum.* In the body wall are many small, tubelike cells, with the lumen of each tube extending across the wall.

Sponges have no organs, not even a digestive cavity. What they do have are cells aggregated into **water-canal systems**. In essence, water moves through the tubelike cells and into the atrium, then out the osculum (Figure 34.5). Lining the atrium are *collar cells,* each with a flagellum surrounded by a ring of cytoplasmic projections (microvilli). The flagella do not beat in synchrony, but the sum total of their movements causes a large volume of water to move through the sponge body. For example, every day, the 2 million collar cells of some sponges pump more than twenty-two liters of water! The currents carry nutrients and oxygen to the collar cell microvilli, where they are absorbed, and they carry away metabolic wastes. The collar cells can also engulf larger particles, as can amoebalike cells (amoebocytes) that crawl about within the body wall. Both cell types pass on food to other cells in the body.

Sponges reproduce asexually by budding or by gemmule formation. A **gemmule** is an aggregate of amoebocytes and other cells, often enclosed in a hard covering. During harsh winter conditions, the parent sponge disintegrates and the gemmules are on their own. In spring, they develop into new sponges.

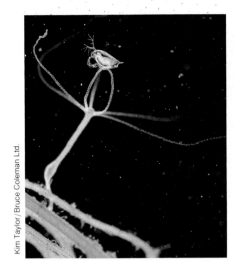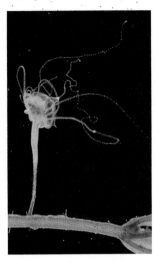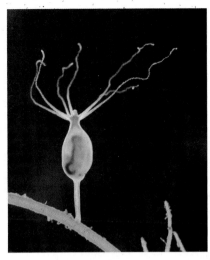

Figure 34.7 Dinnertime for *Hydra vulgaris*, here positioning a copepod with its tentacles, and then with a bulging gut. Compare these photographs with the anatomical sketch of hydras in Figure 21.11.

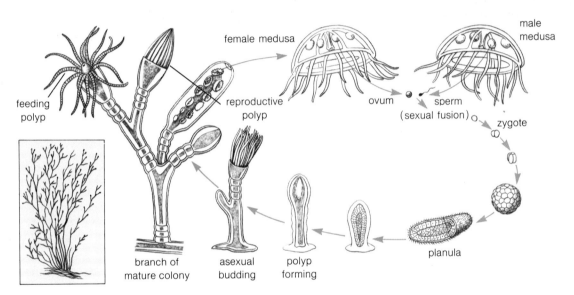

Figure 34.8 Life cycle of the hydra *Obelia*. The inset shows a mature colony, actual size. On its branches are feeding polyps and reproductive polyps, both formed by asexual budding. The medusa stage is free-swimming. Sexual fusion of gametes from male and female medusae leads to a zygote, which develops into a planula. The swimming or crawling planula settles on one end and develops into a polyp, which starts a new colony. (From T. Storer et al., *General Zoology*, sixth edition, © 1979 McGraw-Hill)

Sponges also reproduce sexually. In some species, male and female reproductive organs are present in the same individual; in others, they are present in different individuals. The sperm and eggs form by differentiation of collar cells and some amoebocytes. Sperm are released into the water, sometimes spectacularly (Figure 34.6), and travel to the eggs. The fertilized eggs either are released and develop on their own, or they develop to the larval stage inside the parent.

CNIDARIANS

Phylum Cnidaria includes 9,000 species of radial animals called jellyfishes, sea anemones, hydras, and corals. All but the hydras and a few other freshwater species live in shallow seawater, on rocky coasts, or on tropical reefs. All are carnivores, as the hydra in Figure 34.7 so aptly illustrates.

Figure 34.9 Sea nettle *(Chrysaora)*, one of the large cnidarians with abundant stinging nematocysts. The frilled structures are oral arms that assist in capturing and ingesting prey. Sea nettles are common along the Atlantic coast. Because of their painful stings, they are avoided by knowledgeable swimmers.

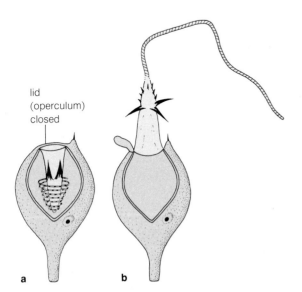

lid
(operculum)
closed

a   b

Figure 34.10 One nematocyst intact (**a**) and discharged (**b**), with the barbed stinging apparatus exploded outward.

From earlier chapters, you know that cnidarians are remarkably diverse. Yet the diversity is overlaid on a body plan that all cnidarians hold in common. These radial animals are shaped like an upside-down or rightside-up bell, with the rim of the "bell" being the diameter of the mouth. Sessile forms have upward-pointing mouths and are called **polyps**. Free-swimming forms have downward-pointing mouths and are called **medusae**.

A medusa stage develops during the life cycle of most cnidarians (Figure 34.8). Medusae produce eggs and sperm, which undergo sexual fusion to form a zygote. The zygote develops into a **planula**, a larval form composed of an undifferentiated cell mass and an outer layer of ciliated cells. At first a planula crawls or swims, then it settles on one end. A mouth forms at the other end, forming an entrance to a **gastrovascular cavity** (an internal space for digestion). Around the mouth, extensions from the body wall form a ring of **tentacles** that assist in capturing and ingesting food. The tentacled, sessile form is the polyp. Polyps can reproduce asexually by budding. Often, many such asexually produced individuals remain attached to the parent body, forming colonies (Figure 1.5).

In cnidarians, the body wall is differentiated into three layers: an epidermis, a gastrovascular cavity lining, and mesoglea in between. In some species, **mesoglea** is no more than a thin, acellular membrane; in others, it is a thick, jellylike mass of cells. The mesoglea of jellyfish makes up most of the body mass, hence the name (Figure 34.9).

The cnidarian epidermis contains specialized cells, including some concerned with sensory reception, neural integration, and muscular response (Figure 23.6). Especially in the epithelium of tentacles is another cell type, the *cnidocyte,* which occurs in all cnidarians. Within these cells is a capsule with a tiny lid or flap on the end that is at the body surface. The capsule houses a coiled, threadlike tube, which can be exploded outward from the body as a stinging or adhesive structure. The touch or chemical taste of prey (or predators) can trigger nerve impulses, which cause a change in the permeability of the capsule wall. Water rushes in, the lid opens, and hydrostatic pressure turns the tube inside out. The entire apparatus—capsule and all—explodes to the outside. One of the stinging structures is a **nematocyst**. As Figure 34.10 shows, it consists of a capsule and a threadlike tube that is decked out with barbs around the base. Many nematocysts can penetrate and deliver toxin into the body tissues of organisms that brush against the cnidarian body (Figure 34.9).

In sum, cnidarians have well-developed tissues, and they have tissues aggregated into organs (such as tentacles). They are the most complex of the radial animals.

FLATWORMS

The 12,700 species of flatworms (phylum Platyhelminthes) include free-living turbellarians, parasitic flukes, and parasitic tapeworms. All of these bilateral animals have flattened bodies, much like broad leaves and long ribbons. All have solid (acoelomate) bodies. Given their flat shapes, these worms have no need of respiratory or circulatory systems. They have only a blind-sac body pattern. Yet crammed into those flattened bodies is an array of organ systems concerned with such tasks as muscular movement, neural control, water regulation, and reproduction. Some of these systems are quite complex.

Turbellarians

Almost all turbellarians are aquatic, with the majority found in the sand and mud of shallow seas. Some, such as the planarian, live in freshwater lakes, streams, and ponds. A few species live in wet soil, hiding by day and feeding at night. These animals are mostly predators or scavengers of (living or dead) invertebrates such as tiny crustaceans, snails, and insects. Some enterprising species stab their prey with a stylet-hardened penis. Others wrap themselves around prey, smear it with slime, and proceed to dine. When they feed, a **pharynx** projects out the mouth. This muscular tube leads to the gastrovascular cavity (Figure 34.11).

A water-regulating system is characteristic of the group. It has two longitudinal canals, each with branching tubules and each emptying to the outside by way of a dorsal pore (Figure 34.12). A blind-ended **flame cell** (sometimes called a proto-nephridium) opens into each tubule. Inside the base of this cell is a tuft of cilia. Within the cell, beating cilia (which resemble a flame) drives fluids from the system to the outside. Because the flame cell system is most highly developed in freshwater species, biologists suspect that the system functions in expelling excess water that continually diffuses inward through the body wall.

These animals have complex sexual reproductive systems, complete with gonads, ducts, and accessory organs. They are monoecious (with male and female organs in the same individual), and sperm transfer is usually reciprocal. In addition, some turbellarians can reproduce asexually by fission.

Trematodes

The trematodes, or flukes, include parasites that live outside or inside their hosts. These worms have a thick cuticle that resists digestion by host enzymes. Adhesive organs occur

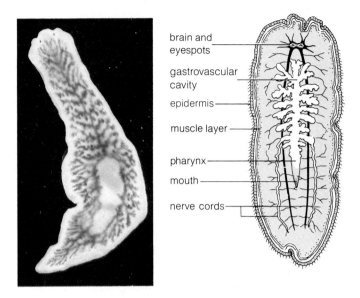

Figure 34.11 Bilateral arrangement of organ systems in the turbellarian body. (Photograph Kim Taylor/Bruce Coleman Ltd.)

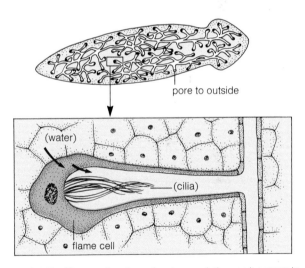

Figure 34.12 Flame cell system of water regulation, as it occurs in a planarian. (From Storer et al., *General Zoology*, sixth edition, © 1979 McGraw-Hill. Used with permission.)

around the mouth, which leads to a pharynx (a muscular tube leading to the gastrovascular cavity). Rather large reproductive organs occupy much of the body. The trematodes, it seems, are devoted to little more than eating and producing more of themselves.

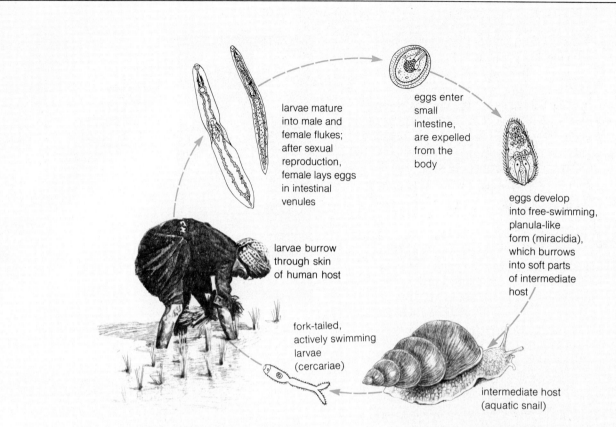

Figure 34.13 Life cycle of *Schistosoma japonicum*, a blood fluke of Southeast Asia.

The cycle begins when the female fluke lays masses of eggs on thin-walled venules of the small intestine. Secretions from the eggs weaken the walls and the blood vessels rupture, releasing the eggs into the intestinal lumen. From there, the eggs leave the human body. In countries where raw sewage is not treated or is used as fertilizer, the eggs hatch and develop into

free-swimming, ciliated forms (miracidia). These forms burrow into soft body parts of tiny aquatic snails. The snails are intermediate hosts in which miracidia develop into fork-tailed larvae. When larvae leave the snails, they actively swim about. When they encounter human skin, they become attached to it and release tissue-degrading enzymes. The larvae bore inward and migrate to the circulatory system, in which they mature. They end up at the intestinal venules, where sexual reproduction takes place and the cycle begins anew. (Data from Noble and Noble, 1982)

The blood flukes, *Schistosoma*, cause **schistosomiasis**, a disease of humans and other animals. At a given time, 200 million people are afflicted with this disease. An infected host typically makes a cellular immune response to masses of fluke eggs being produced within its body. Leukocytes and other cell types infiltrate and produce granular masses in tissues. The disease leads to deterioration and malfunctioning of the liver, spleen, bladder, and kidneys. Figure 34.13 shows the life cycle of one blood fluke that causes schistosomiasis.

Cestodes

The most specialized of all flatworms are the cestodes, or tapeworms. Different species of these parasites live inside the tissues of almost all vertebrates, including dogs, pigs, sheep, cattle, and humans.

The tapeworm has three parts. At the head end is a **scolex**, a small structure with suckers, hooks, or adhesive organs by which the worm attaches to its host. The body is a linear array of segments called **proglottids** (Figure 34.14).

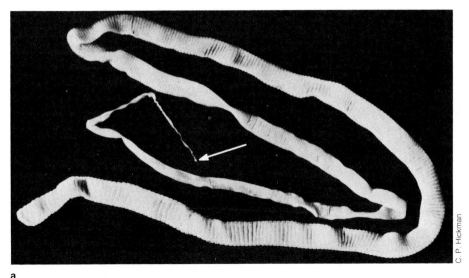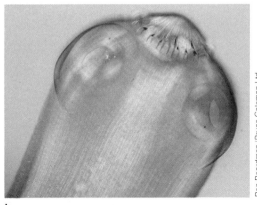

a   b

Figure 34.14 (**a**) Sheep tapeworm, showing the size of the scolex (white arrow) relative to the rest of the body. (**b**) Close-up of one tapeworm scolex.

With such repeating segments, the body reaches lengths of eighteen meters in some species. Between the scolex and the body is a **neck**, a short, narrowed region where new segments are added by growth and transverse constriction.

Although a nervous system and water-regulating system extend continuously through the series of proglottids, each proglottid has its own reproductive system. When two tapeworms get together, cross-fertilization occurs. Otherwise, self-fertilization can occur between proglottids of the same individual.

Flatworm Origins

The simplest flatworms bear striking resemblance to the planula stage of cnidarian life cycles. This resemblance inspired the planuloid theory of origins for bilateral animals, as described generally in Chapter Twenty-One. According to one scenario, long ago some mutant, planula-like forms kept on crawling instead of growing up to be a vase. For such forms, food and danger were encountered most often by the leading end. Hence directional movement fostered selection for nerve and sensory cell clustering at the head end (the advantage being faster sensing and response). The selective force of predation worked in other ways on body plans. For example, predators could attack crawlers from above but not very often from below. Hence dorsal-ventral

differentiation was encouraged. In addition, food and danger were found as often on one side of the forward-crawlers as the other—hence the emergence of bilateral symmetry. Such a shift from radial to bilateral symmetry could have led to paired organs of the sort seen in many flatworms. *And bilateral forms not much more complex than the flatworms apparently were ancestral to all existing bilateral animals.*

ROUNDWORMS

Phylogenetically, the roundworms (nematodes) are among the early offshoots of the first bilateral lineages. As the name implies, they have perfectly cylindrical shapes (Figure 34.15). Although they have many of the traits characteristic of bilateral animals, they also have radial arrays of structures about the mouth. It may be that early members of the phylum became sessile at first, and that the radial symmetry was superimposed as a secondary pattern.

Whatever its origins, the nematode body plan is an evolutionary success. The phylum boasts 10,000 species, which live in remarkably diverse settings. Many of these species are plant and animal parasites. Others are free-living forms found in deserts, snows, hot springs, and ocean depths. And are they abundant! A single rotting apple may contain 100,000 nematodes. An acre of rich farm soil may contain 100 billion nematodes in its top few inches.

Figure 34.15 A parasitic nematode, *Trichenella spiralis*, which lives in muscle tissue of rats, cats, dogs, hogs, and humans. This tiny nematode causes the disease trichinosis. Adult worms burrow into the lining of the small intestine. There, female worms produce larvae. The larvae travel the bloodstream to muscles, where they coil up and live in cysts for perhaps years. Because undercooked pork (and other flesh) can carry live larvae, it is prudent to cook meat thoroughly.

Most nematodes are microscopic. The body is long and slender, with longitudinal muscles in the body wall. It has a tough, collagen-containing cuticle, which offers protection and flexibility. The body plan is pseudocoelomate, with the fluid-filled cavity serving as a hydrostatic skeleton. The nematode body is adapted to getting about with undulating movements in wet environments.

Nematodes are remarkably resistant to environmental insults. They can survive high levels of acidity and alkalinity, terrible temperatures, and noxious compounds. Sometimes, when being prepared for microscopic examination, they live for hours in fixatives that would instantly kill other animals. Nematodes also are remarkably resistant to suffocation. When oxygen is present, they use it. When it is not, they switch to anaerobic pathways. We should be so blessed, especially during smog alerts. In fact, if the environment continues to be polluted in every way imaginable, we can be sure the nematodes will be among the last to suffer.

TWO MAIN LINES OF DIVERGENCE: PROTOSTOMES AND DEUTEROSTOMES

Shortly after the emergence of bilateral body plans, it appears that two key evolutionary roads opened up. The existing travelers of these roads are called **protostomes** and **deuterostomes**, and they include the following major phyla:

Protostomes	Deuterostomes
mollusks	echinoderms
annelids	chordates
arthropods	

Both types of animals have a tube-within-a-tube body plan, and all are coelomate. However, each follows its own patterns of early embryonic development. Among the most important of these patterns are the following.

First, recall that a single opening (blastopore) forms in the early embryo at the gastrula stage. In protostomes, this first opening becomes the mouth; the anus forms later. (Protostome means "first mouth.") In deuterostomes, the first opening becomes the anus and the second, the mouth.

Second, the fate of the first embryonic cells formed during cleavage is fixed in protostomes; each can follow only a prescribed developmental pathway. In contrast, the first embryonic cells of deuterostomes are not already committed to one course only. (For example, if the cells of a sea star embryo are separated at the four-cell stage, each can develop into a complete larva.)

Third, the cleavage pattern differs between the two types of animals. As you saw in Figure 28.5, cleavage in frog embryos occurs parallel and at right angles to the axis established by the animal and vegetal poles. The outcome is an array of cells each located directly above or below one another:

The pattern is said to be one of *radial cleavage,* and it is characteristic of deuterostomes. In almost all protostomes, cleavage proceeds obliquely relative to the polar axis. The outcome is a tiered array of cells, with each cell in one tier snuggled against two cells of adjacent tiers:

This pattern is called *spiral cleavage.*

Finally, the coelom itself arises in one of two ways. In protostomes, two masses of mesoderm on either side of the body *split*:

developing gut

The resulting cavities enlarge to form a coelom of the sort shown in Figure 34.2c. In deuterostomes, *pouches* form in the walls of the developing gut cavity (archenteron). The pouches separate to form the coelom:

MOLLUSKS

Some time during the Precambrian, marine animals much like the turbellarians may have given rise to the mollusks. (Many mollusks have a larval stage similar to that of marine turbellarians; some have a ladderlike nervous system that resembles the turbellarian system.) Apparently the mollusks first evolved in shallow, nearshore waters where food was abundant and habitats varied. Later, some forms radiated into deeper waters, others into freshwater and even brackish habitats. Only one evolutionary line led onto land; its living representatives are the familiar garden snails. Today the phylum Mollusca has more than 100,000 species. Here we will focus on just three of the seven classes within the phylum:

Class	Some Representatives
Gastropoda	*snails, slugs, whelks, conchs, abalones, nudibranchs, periwinkles*
Bivalvia	*mussels, clams, oysters, scallops*
Cephalopoda	*squids, octopods, nautili, cuttlefishes*

Figure 34.16 is a generalized body plan for mollusks. Typically the head has a **radula**: a tonguelike, rasping organ used in scraping algae and other material from substrates. Most mollusks move about on a **foot**: a muscular organ sometimes flattened on the ventral surface. Soft body parts and organs are called the **visceral mass**. The dorsal body wall is extended as a pair of folds, or **mantle**, that cloaks the visceral mass. Cells of the outer mantle surface secrete proteins and calcium carbonate, forming a hardened shell above the mantle.

Between the mantle and the visceral mass is the **mantle cavity**, which is vital in molluscan physiology. Gills (or lungs) open to this protected chamber, where gas exchange occurs. So do the digestive and reproductive systems. Often, tubular water-regulating systems (nephridia) also empty into the mantle cavity.

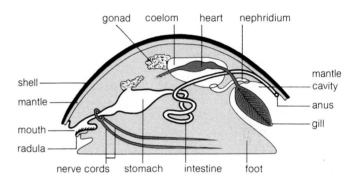

Figure 34.16 Hypothetical body plan of the animal ancestral to mollusks, such as the land snail shown above.

Gastropods

The largest and most widespread group of mollusks are the gastropods (the word means "belly-foot"). Gastropods alone undergo a strange internal realignment called **torsion**. During early development, the anus and the head are at opposite ends of the body. Through rapid, unequal growth of muscles, the anus and mantle cavity are moved and twisted to the front of the body:

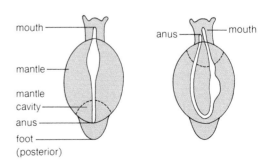

As you might imagine, this rearrangement must create something of a sanitation problem, what with wastes being dumped near the gills and mouth. Whatever selective advantage torsion offers is not understood. However, having the mantle cavity up front does provide a protected chamber into which the sensitive head end can be drawn during times of danger. The tough foot is drawn in behind it as a barrier to the outside.

Figure 34.17 A nudibranch, one of the soft-bodied gastropods that do not have a shell.

Most gastropods have coiled shells, such as those of land snails. Yet among the more spectacular gastropods are the nudibranchs, or sea slugs. Over time, this evolutionary line has lost not only the shell but also the mantle cavity and original gill (Figure 34.17). Nudibranchs are good swimmers, and some species have skin glands that produce foul-tasting sulfuric acid. In such ways these beautiful animals avoid predation.

Bivalves

Bivalves are largely **filter feeders**. Beating cilia in their gills produce currents that draw suspended food particles to gills, where they are trapped on mucus. Bivalves have two shells hinged together. Most often the shells are somewhat flattened, as is the foot. Bivalves do not have much of a head; some do not even have a foot. Yet the bivalve body plan originally was adapted for burrowing in soft mud and sand, with a muscular, forward-pointing foot doing the digging.

Deep-burrowing bivalves, such as the razor clams of the Atlantic coast, have **siphons**. These tubular extensions from the mantle serve as inhalant and exhalant channels for water flow. Typically, blood pressure or water pressure within the mantle cavity forces siphons to the surface of the sand. An exception is the giant geoduck of the Pacific Northwest; its siphon (and body) is too large to be retracted

Figure 34.18 Escape swimming among scallops. Scallops are among the few bivalves that can clap together their valves, an action that rapidly ejects water from the mantle. By using these water jets, scallops can swim away, clap at a time, from predators such as this sea star.

within its valves. The geoduck can burrow three meters below the surface, leaving only the tip of the siphon exposed.

Some bivalves, such as the shipworm, attach to substrates. Shipworms burrow into wood by opening and rocking their valves, and they use the excavated sawdust as one source of food. These bivalves cause considerable damage to wooden ship hulls and piers. A few bivalves, such as scallops, live on the surface of the seafloor (Figure 34.18). They have mucus-covered tentacles, which they extend into sediments. Food and other particles are carried by ciliary action to the stomach, where sorting occurs.

Cephalopods

Taken as a whole, the cephalopods have become adapted for swimming. For them, the molluscan foot has become modified into a crown of large tentacles or arms, which encircle the head. The visceral mass is at the rear of the body, as shown in Figure 34.19. Only the nautilus (Figure 1.6f) has retained a protective shell. In other cephalopods, the shell has become reduced or has disappeared entirely.

Most cephalopods swim by **water propulsion**. The mantle has become folded into a conelike envelope around the body. It is highly muscularized and innervated, and it can be contracted with great force. When the mantle cavity expands, water moves inward. Mantle contraction forces the water out in a powerful stream at one end that propels the body in the opposite direction.

Thus freed from a cumbersome shell and equipped with a jet-propulsive mantle, some cephalopods have become the most magnificent swimmers of the invertebrate world. Here we are referring to the squids, which are also the largest invertebrates. Some individuals measure eighteen meters (about sixty feet) from their dorsal surface to the tip of their tentacles. Giant sperm whales prey on these giant squid, which probably put up quite a fight. Large sucker scars observed on whale bodies suggest that there may be squids of monstrous dimensions in the deep oceans.

Compared with vertebrates, the squids and octopods are examples of parallel evolution. Both the vertebrates and these cephalopods had fast-swimming, predatory ancestors. Their ancestors developed increasingly refined systems of detecting, pursuing, and capturing prey in dimly lit waters. Predictably, like vertebrates, these cephalopods have acute vision and refined motor control. They also have developed many neural and sensory structures that parallel those found among vertebrates (Chapters Twenty-One and Twenty-Three).

The nervous systems of squids and octopods represent the peak of complexity among invertebrates. In terms of size and integrative capacity, their brains approach those of mammals.

Figure 34.19 The cuttlefish *Sepia*, a representative cephalopod. In these species, the dorsal wall projects as a shield over the tentacles, which ring the head end. In this rare photograph, a male and female are mating.

Douglas Faulkner

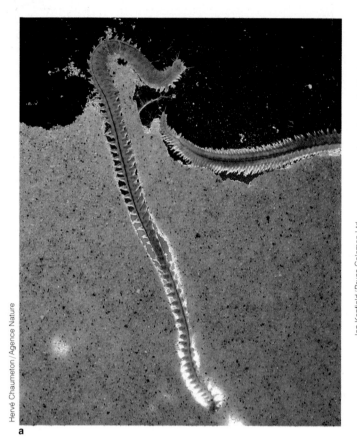

a

b

Figure 34.20 Polychaetes. (**a**) This photograph shows the inside of the burrow of a marine polychaete. (**b**) The spectacularly specialized head appendages of one tube-dwelling marine worm.

ANNELIDS

Another line leading away from the ancestral flatworms gave rise to the phylum Annelida, the segmented worms. The best known of its 9,000 species are the earthworms and leeches. Less familiar is the larger and far more exotic array of marine worms, the polychaetes.

Earthworms belong to the class called oligochaetes. They are mostly land-dwelling and freshwater scavengers that typically burrow in moist soil, mud, and silt. They feed largely on decomposing plant material and also use organic matter that is ingested as they form their burrows. In soft soil, the earthworm bores forward and enlarges its highly muscular pharynx, which pushes the soil aside. In compacted soil, it literally eats dirt in order to burrow. Every twenty-four hours, earthworms can ingest their own weight in soil. They not only aerate soil (which is beneficial to plants), they also carry subsoil to the surface, where the nutrients it contains are made available to other organisms.

Leeches live mostly in fresh water, and they are mostly nuisances. Many are bloodsucking predators; others are scavengers. They typically use a proboscis (an extensible tube for feeding) or a jaw with a muscular, pumping pharynx when they dine. They attach to a food source (such as a human) with two suckers, one at the head end and one at the other.

Far less obnoxious (to humans, at least) are the polychaetes, which include burrowing, crawling, and free-swimming forms (Figure 34.20). Some excavate vertical or U-shaped burrows in soft sand; others live in tubes made of secretions or of sand and shell fragments cemented together. Many polychaetes feed on small invertebrates, some feed on algae, and others use organic matter present in sediments. The predatory forms have jaws and a muscular pharynx, which can be everted into prey.

The annelids as a group show considerable segmentation. Partitions (septae) create the segments, which actually are individual coelomic chambers. In the body wall are longitudinal and circular muscles, which work antagonistically. The muscles operate against the forces exerted by fluid pressure within each coelomic chamber. In effect, these animals have multiple **hydrostatic skeletons**, such that different body regions can bend, shorten, and lengthen independently. How is anarchy among the segments avoided? A brain at the head end integrates sensory input for the whole worm. Leading away from the brain is a double nerve cord that travels the length of the body. In each segment are clusters of neurons that control local activity.

Annelids also feature chitin-containing bristles, called **setae**, which project in pairs from the sides of the body. Setae are short in burrowing annelids such as earthworms; they anchor the body during movement and thereby prevent backward slippage. Setae are longer in some aquatic forms and are used in swimming. Some annelids have these bristles embedded in **parapodia**: fleshy lobes that project from both sides of the body (Figure 34.20). Parapodia function primarily in respiration and locomotion.

Early in annelid evolution, a closed circulatory system developed. The circulating fluid—blood—provided a means of transporting materials through bodies more massive than those of flatworms. In the annelid system, forceful contractions in muscularized blood vessels ("hearts") keep blood circulating in one direction. As Figure 34.21 suggests, smaller vessels of the system carry blood to cells of the gut, nerve cord, and body wall.

Functionally linked to the closed circulatory system is a tubular system for regulating water and solute levels in the body. The basic unit of this system is a well-developed **nephridium** (Figure 34.22). Most body segments have their own nephridium, which removes wastes from the coelom as well as from blood.

Annelids, in short, have a body plan that reflects some important evolutionary trends. Compared with other groups we have described, their external segmentation and segmentally arranged muscles are the basis for more precise movements. The animals are coelomate, a pattern that allows internal organs to increase in size and complexity. They have a complete digestive system, which allows for regional specialization; they have a closed circulatory system functionally linked with nephridia (the worm's equivalent to the vertebrate kidneys). Some of these worms have paddle-shaped parapodia—a feature that apparently has been developed to a remarkable degree among the largest of all animal groups, the arthropods.

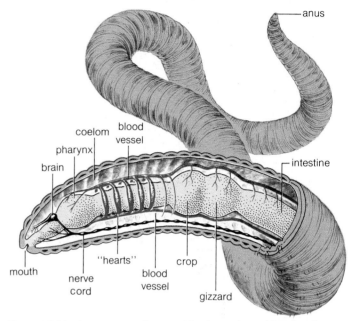

Figure 34.21 Arrangement of nerves, blood vessels, and the digestive system of an earthworm, all of which extend longitudinally through one coelomic chamber after another.

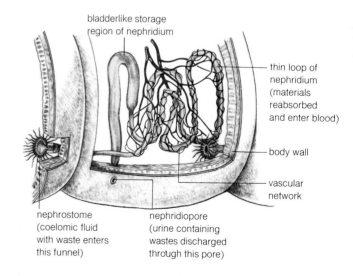

Figure 34.22 Earthworm system of salt and water regulation. The functional unit of the system is the nephridium. (After Hickman, 1979)

ARTHROPODS

At the peak of evolutionary diversity for protostomes are the arthropods, with 923,000 known species. Evidently, ancestral annelids or animals like them gave rise to four different arthropod groups. These groups are so distinct that each is now being considered a subphylum:

Subphylum	Representatives
Trilobita	*trilobites (described in Chapter Thirty-One; now extinct)*
Chelicerata	*horseshoe crabs, spiders, scorpions, ticks, mites*
Crustacea	*crustaceans (including copepods, crabs, lobsters, shrimps, barnacles)*
Uniramia	*centipedes, millipedes, insects*

a

Arthropod Adaptations

The arthropods are more widely distributed through more habitats than any other animal group. Most are herbivores, feeding on algae or land plants; others are carnivores, omnivores, and symbionts.

What adaptations have contributed to the success of these diverse animals? Perhaps the most important are these:

1. Hardened exoskeleton

2. Differentiation of segments

3. Jointed appendages

4. Highly specialized respiratory systems

5. Highly specialized sensory organs (Unit Five)

The Arthropod Exoskeleton.   Among annelids, the cuticle covering the body is thin and flexible enough to permit extensive bending. It is also thin enough to be pierced by predators. From the fossil record, we know that some early annelids developed thicker, hardened cuticles—a pattern that also continued among the arthropods and gave rise to an **exoskeleton** (external skeleton). The outer layers of the arthropod exoskeleton contain protein and chitin, a combination that is flexible, lightweight, and protective. In most crustaceans, the inner layers are impregnated with calcium salts, which reduce flexibility but help create "armor" plates. At first, arthropod exoskeletons were probably useful in defense against predators. They also turned out to be useful in other ways, when arthropods radiated into dry land en-

vironments. *The arthropod exoskeleton is a superb barrier to evaporative water loss, and it also provides support for an animal body deprived of water's buoyancy.*

Differentiation of Segments.   Arthropods as a group show a trend toward modification of body segments. Among more complex forms, some segments have become fused into larger body units, other segments have been lost. Still others have become highly differentiated in structure and function. Figure 34.23 shows the relatively undifferentiated segments of one arthropod (a centipede) and the highly modified segments of two of its relatives.

Each arthropod body segment is completely enclosed in its own plates or cylinders of cuticle. Between body segments, the cuticle remains thin and pliable, and functions as a hinge. Bundles of striated muscle attach to the inside of adjacent plates, forming the basis of a lever system of movement. Longitudinal muscles contracting on one side of the body cause bending toward that side. Dorsal muscles contracting cause the body to bend upward; ventral muscles have the opposite effect.

Jointed Appendages.   In arthropods, locomotion is accomplished not so much by body movements as by movements of appendages that function in walking, sensory probing, and food handling. These appendages may have been derived from soft parapodia of the sort that occur among some polychaetes. In arthropods, appendages are jointed (the word arthropod means "jointed foot"). They also are covered with cuticle, and muscles connect adjacent parts. In

b

c

many groups, the number of appendages used in movement has been reduced; with fewer legs to worry about, speed and maneuverability are enhanced.

Specialized Respiratory Systems. The larger marine arthropods extract oxygen from water, and they do so with gills: thin tissue flaps or tubes richly supplied with blood vessels (Chapter Twenty-Five). However, gills cannot function out of water; their filaments collapse and stick together. In ancestors of spiders and their kin, gills came to be enclosed in **book lungs**: pairs of pockets on the ventral surface of the abdomen in which gas exchange occurs. The wall of one pocket is folded repeatedly into leaflike layers in which blood circulates (Figure 34.24). Air enters the book lung through a spiracle (opening in the body wall) and circulates freely through the layers.

Book lungs are rather small organs that do not provide enough gas exchange for a highly active existence. In most arthropod stocks, another means of breathing developed. A series of branching tubes—**tracheae**—were used as routes for air flow in all directions through the body. These fine tubes became stiffened with chitin, which kept them from collapsing under the pressure of the body's weight. Although some spiders rely on tracheal breathing also, this adaptation reaches its peak of development among the insects. Here, tracheal tubes branch into ever smaller tubules, which terminate next to interior cells (see, for example, Figure 25.2). Hence each cell in the insect body has its own supply of fresh air. This means of oxygenation is the basis for the highest metabolic rates known. The rates are re-

Figure 34.23 Arthropod variations on a segmented theme. (**a**) Spiders have a cephalothorax (head and thorax segments fused together) and an abdomen. Most spiders are harmless to humans and as a group help keep insect pests in check. However, a bite from the brown recluse shown here can be severe to fatal; its venom is hemolytic. This North American spider lives under bark and rocks, and in and around buildings. It can be identified by the violin-shaped mark on its cephalothorax. (**b**) Some crustaceans such as this blue lobster have a head segment, more segments differentiated into a thorax, then more that form an abdomen. (**c**) Compare these diverse body plans with the less complex centipede. The one shown here, dining on a frog, is from Southeast Asia. Almost all of its body segments are identical, as they are in annelids.

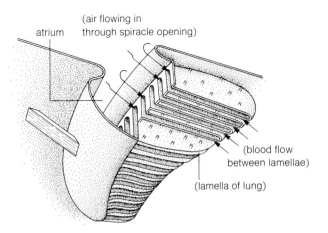

atrium

(air flowing in through spiracle opening)

(blood flow between lamellae)

(lamella of lung)

Figure 34.24 A book lung, a type of respiratory organ that occurs among spiders and scorpions.

Figure 34.25 Specialized appendages of a land crab (a crustacean).

Figure 34.26 The copepod *Calanoidea*, a tiny animal that is a component of food webs of the seas.

quired for the powerful, tiny muscles used in insect loco-motion, especially flight.

Chelicerates

Chelicerates originated in the shallow seas of the Early Paleozoic. Today only the horseshoe crabs still live in the water. The scorpions, spiders, ticks, mites, and other land-dwelling members of this subphylum are thought to be descendants of giant water scorpions. Some of these an-cestral forms were three meters long (fortunately for divers, they are now extinct). All existing chelicerates have a body divided into a cephalothorax and abdomen. The first pair of appendages are feeding structures (called chelicerae); the second pair serves varied functions (such as seizing prey). These are followed by four pairs of appendages used as legs. Unlike other arthropods, the chelicerates have no sensory antennas and no mandibles (jaws); they typically suck liquid food from prey.

The spiders especially rely on photoreception for de-tecting movements in the environment; they typically have eight eyes. Even with this formidable array of light-receptor organs, few spiders seem to be capable of actual image for-mation. Environmental stimuli are sensed more precisely by body hairs and bristles that detect air currents and move-ments, such as those generated by web-entangled insects.

Crustaceans

In terms of their departure from highly segmented ances-tors, some crustaceans have departed more than others. Typically, crustaceans have between sixteen and twenty segments, although some have more than sixty. Commonly, as in crabs, the segmentation is not readily apparent be-cause the dorsal cuticle of the head extends backward, cov-ering some or all of the body segments with a **carapace** (a shieldlike cover).

In crustaceans, the appendages on the thorax and abdo-men are used in swimming and crawling. Appendages on the head include two pairs of antennae, a pair of food-handling structures, and jaws (Figure 34.25).

The crustaceans include predatory, scavenging, para-sitic, and symbiotic forms. Lobsters and crayfish are among the more eclectic eaters and rarely eschew anything organic. Also in this group are small species such as copepods (Fig-ure 34.26), which are primary consumers of phytoplankton. These tiny animals are, in turn, food for fishes; they are a vital component of food webs of the seas.

Insects and Their Kin

Insects, centipedes, and millipedes are mostly land-dwelling arthropods. They are thought to have evolved from caterpillar-

Figure 34.27 Puzzling *Peripatus*, a member of the phylum Onychophora. The members of this phylum resemble both annelids and arthropods.

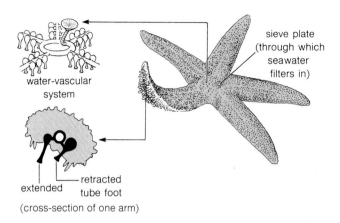

Figure 34.28 Water-vascular system of canals and tube feet, the basis of echinoderm locomotion.

like animals of the sort now grouped in a relatively obscure phylum called Onychophora (Figure 34.27). These animals look like peg-legged slugs, with tiny claws at the end of anywhere from fourteen to forty-three pairs of legs. Externally, the soft body has a thin, flexible cuticle; internally the animals resemble both annelids and arthropods.

Centipedes and millipedes bear closest resemblance to the onychophores. These leggy animals in turn are distant cousins of the insects. The insects alone have three pairs of legs. Typically the insect thorax has two pairs of wings.

Perhaps more than any other factor, the evolution of wings underlies the success of many insects. With flight, they can traverse large distances, thereby dispersing their populations far more rapidly than those of land-bound species. With flight, they can expand their range of available food sources. With flight, they can escape predation and swoop in on prey. Today there are almost 800,000 known species of insects living in almost all land habitats; a few are even found in aquatic settings.

ECHINODERMS

In evolutionary terms, the echinoderms are ancient travelers of the deuterostome road. "Echinoderm" means spiny-skinned, a reference to the bristling spines on some mem-

bers of this phylum. Echinoderms include sea urchins, sea stars, brittle stars, crinoids, and sea cucumbers.

Most members of this phylum go through a free-swimming, bilateral larval stage. Adults generally are radial. Some echinoderms, such as the sea stars, can move in any direction over a surface. Their unique mode of locomotion is based on constant circulation of seawater through canals and tube feet, which form a **water-vascular system**. As Figure 34.28 shows, each tube foot leads from short branches of radial canals. One end of the tube is a muscular bulb, the other bears a sucker. Contraction of the bulb wall forces water into the tube region, making it rigid and extended. Extension and retraction of many suckered tube feet is coordinated with contraction and relaxation of muscles in the tube foot walls. Neural activity governs the movement of body parts in specific directions.

How did echinoderms arise? During the Precambrian, when predators were increasing in size and complexity, the early flatworms were already embarked on a course of bilateral symmetry. In one of these evolutionary lines, the body wall became protected with mineralized plates, which served as armor. Heavy armor would have provided some insurance against being eaten. However, the increased weight also would have forced the animals to settle on the seafloor. Today their descendants are sessile or lumber slowly over sand and coral formations. Radial symmetry has been overlaid on a bilateral heritage (Figure 34.29).

a

b

c

d

Figure 34.29 Representative echinoderms. (**a**) Crinoid, with flowerlike arms. Both its mouth and anus are at the center of the tentacles, on the dorsal surface. (**b**) Cobalt sea star. Unlike most sea stars, which have five arms, this colorful species has six. (**c**) Brittle star, which moves with rapid, snakelike twists of its arms. (**d**) Sea urchin, with rounded body and bristling spines on the dorsal surface. (**e**) Sea cucumber, the only echinoderm with a long body that has tube feet running down the sides. Although this photograph does not really show the elongate body, it does show the radial pattern, so flamboyantly marked by rows of tube feet that converge at the posterior.

CHORDATES

If you were asked to identify the key character that figured in the early evolution of chordates, it would have to be the **notochord**. This rod of stiffened tissue typically extends the length of the body and serves as a skeletal axis. The notochord apparently was the forerunner of the vertebrate internal skeleton, or endoskeleton. The following animals have a notochord at some embryonic stage or throughout their lives:

Subphylum	Representatives
Urochordata	*tunicates*
Cephalochordata	*lancelets*
Vertebrata	*jawless fishes (lampreys, hagfishes), jawed fishes (sharks, rays, bony fishes), amphibians, reptiles, birds, mammals*

Kjell Sandved. Smithsonian Institution

e

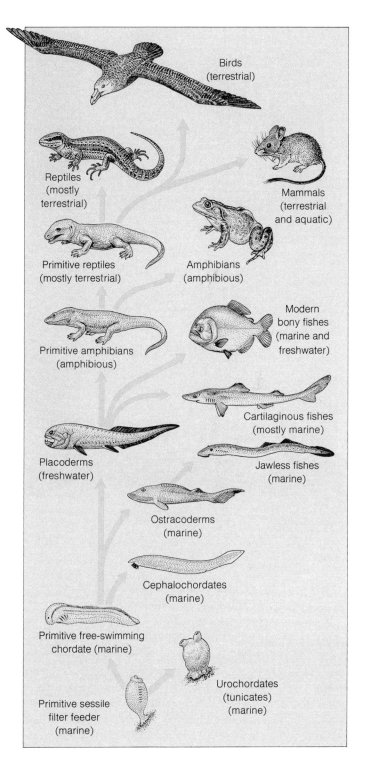

Figure 34.30 is one model of how these diverse animals might be phylogenetically related to one another. Some representative species are shown later in Figure 34.34, which also includes a brief description of the class to which they belong.

From Notochords to Backbones

Structurally, tunicates are the simplest of all living chordates. The larval forms look and swim like tadpoles. They are bilateral, with the notochord running the length of the body. After the swimming stage, tunicate larvae settle on their head and undergo drastic metamorphosis, whereby they lose the tail, notochord, and most of the brain. The adult animal develops in a tough outer covering, or "tunic" (Figure 34.31), hence the name.

Figure 34.30 A family tree for chordates. Placoderms (jawed fishes) are thought to have given rise to lines leading to cartilaginous fishes, bony fishes, and amphibians. (After Hickman, 1979)

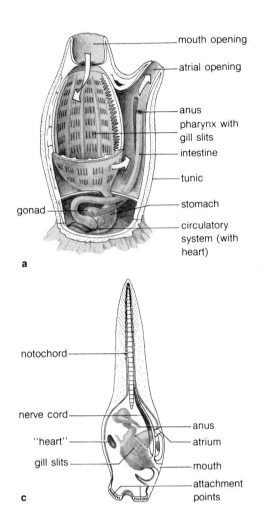

mouth opening
atrial opening
anus
pharynx with gill slits
intestine
tunic
stomach
circulatory system (with heart)
gonad

a

notochord
nerve cord
"heart"
gill slits
anus
atrium
mouth
attachment points

c

b

Douglas P. Wilson

Figure 34.31 Cutaway view (**a**) and photograph (**b**) of adult tunicates, or "sea squirts." The larval form is shown in (**c**), although it is not drawn to the same scale. (Drawings after W. D. Russell-Hunter, *A Biology of Higher Invertebrates.* Copyright © 1969 W. D. Russell-Hunter. Macmillan Publishing Co., Inc.)

Tunicates are filter feeders. Water drawn in through the mouth passes through a series of pores, or **gill slits**. Cilia lining the gill slits create the water currents, and a sheet of mucus captures food particles from the water flowing past. Filter feeding is efficient, as long as plenty of food floats past. Of course, if a larva becomes attached to a site where food does not flow past, it has blown its one chance. Adult tunicates cannot detach themselves and move on. Like other sessile animals, tunicates produce many offspring (which assures that at least some will attach to suitable sites and survive) and the larval forms have sensory structures (which improve the likelihood that at least some will locate suitable sites).

Some zoologists believe that the chordates originated with forms that resembled tunicates. They envision ancient

seas in which great numbers of larval chordates swam about. They envision variation in how fast the larvae became attached to substrates and metamorphosed into adults. Rare individuals may have failed to make the change at all, and thus retained the option of escaping from a bad spot. Today, living in seafloor sediments throughout the world are a few chordates that settle down yet retain the capacity to move on. They are the lancelets *(Amphioxus)*.

As Figure 34.32 shows, adult lancelets are fishlike; they have a bilateral body built for swimming. On locating what appears to be a suitable feeding site, lancelets burrow into sediments, leaving only the mouth exposed. Then they draw in water and extract food particles from it, much as adult tunicates do. If food does not float past, lancelets swim away in search of it.

If ancestral chordates did resemble the lancelets, there would have been important selection pressures associated with their roaming, searching life-style. Such a life-style would depend on a capacity to move effectively through tides and currents. Better swimming abilities would require stronger muscles—and stronger muscles would be useless without a stronger skeletal framework to pull against. During the Cambrian, free-swimming chordates did indeed develop strengthened yet flexible notochords. And through that development, the vertebrates apparently emerged.

Evolutionary Potential of Bones and Jaws

The first vertebrates were jawless fishes (agnathus, leading to placoderms; Figure 34.30). The reinforced notochords of their ancestors had become supplemented with a series of hard bones, called **vertebrae**. These bones were arranged in a vertical column that formed a backbone (Chapter Twenty-One). The vertebrae had three unique features. First, the shape provided firm attachment sites for muscles running in several directions from the backbone to the body wall. Second, the vertebrae fit next to each other with smooth joints, an arrangement that allowed flexing and bending. Third, the vertebrae were hollow and served as a protective shield for the nervous system.

In one evolutionary line, the brain region became protected by bony plates that eventually developed into **skulls**. Gradually, variations arose in the size, number, shape, and position of bones in both the skull and backbone. One of these variations had to do with a piece of bone that developed as a gill support but became attached to muscles controlling mouth movements (Figure 34.33). This **bony jaw** was the distinguishing characteristic of the first placoderms— jawed fishes that could tear off chunks of almost anything edible in sight.

Movable, bony jaws were surely a key character of far-reaching consequences. Among the predators equipped with this feeding apparatus, competition for prey probably intensified. There would have been selective advantage in being able to discern more food in the distance. Indeed, the evolution of these predators was marked by increasingly sensitive eyes, olfactory receptors, and pressure sensors for detecting movements in the water. These sensory structures were functionally linked with a brain and spinal cord that became more and more complex. *And this trend toward more specialized sensory organs and nervous systems among the jawed fishes prevailed through descendant forms that moved onto land.* This trend was the evolutionary legacy of all modern amphibians, reptiles, birds, and mammals.

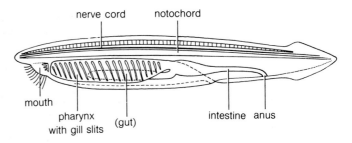

Figure 34.32 Cutaway view of a lancelet *(Amphioxus)*, showing the position of its nerve cord and flexible notochord. (After J. Young, *The Life of Vertebrates*, Oxford University Press, 1962)

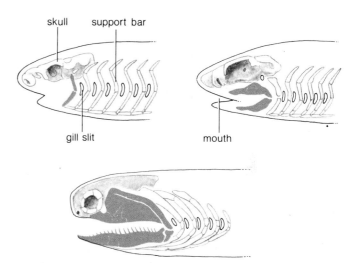

Figure 34.33 Suggested evolution of gill-supported structures, as found in jawless fishes, into the hinged vertebrate jaw. (After J. Young, *The Life of Vertebrates*, Oxford University Press, 1962)

Lungs and the Vertebrate Heart

Among early filter-feeding chordates, gills were devices mainly for feeding. Their role in respiration was secondary; most oxygen was obtained by simple diffusion into body tissues. By comparison, the jawless fishes required far more oxygen for their more active life-style, and gills became more important in providing it. Among the jawed fishes, gills became devoted entirely to oxygenating blood.

Because gills are located more or less externally, they quickly become nonfunctional when exposed to air. How, then, did some vertebrates begin moving onto land during the Devonian? Apparently, reliance on gills gave way to reliance on **lungs**. These already existing structures evolved as pockets of the foregut, providing more surface area for gas exchange. In some fishes, lungs evolved into a **swim bladder**: an organ that maintains body position and balance

Class Osteichthyes: bony fishes. All have mostly bony endoskeletons and overlapping rows of thin, flexible scales. Respiration is through a single gill with an operculum (lid) on both sides of the body. Many have a swim bladder. Bony fishes include ray-finned fishes (such as sturgeons) and teleosts (such as eels, salmon, minnows, catfish, rockfish, perch, tuna, and deep-sea luminescent fishes). Above, a soldier fish.

Class Chondrichthyes: sharks, rays, skates, and chimaeras. These carnivorous fishes have endoskeletons of cartilage. They have no swim bladder; five to seven gill slits occur in separate clefts along both sides of the pharynx. All are skilled swimmers with powerful jaws. They have small conelike scales or none at all. Some sharks, fifteen meters long, are among the largest living vertebrates. A blue-spotted reef ray (above) and a gray shark (right).

Class Amphibia: frogs, toads, newts, salamanders, and caecilians. Amphibians have a mostly bony endoskeleton and, most often, four legs (some have none). Respiration occurs through gills, lungs, skin, and pharyngeal regions. Amphibians have a three-chambered heart. Their smooth, moist, thin skin is vulnerable to drying out. Eggs must be laid in water or moist places. Above, a Blue-Ridge Spring salamander.

Class Aves: birds. Most have forelimbs modified for flight. They have a four-chambered heart and lungs with air sacs. They have feathers, leg scales, and horny beaks. Shelled eggs develop outside the body. Strong, lightweight bones are filled with air cavities (the endoskeleton of a frigate bird, with a seven-foot wingspan, weighs only four ounces). Here, an owl on the wing.

Class Mammalia: egg-laying mammals (Prototheria), pouched mammals (Metatheria), and placental mammals (Eutheria), all descendants of reptiles. Embryonic development is internal; liveborn are nourished by milk-secreting glands. Most mammals are covered with hair; whales are not, and reptilian scales persist on tails of beavers and rats. Adults have a permanent set of teeth (reptiles have successive sets). They have lungs, a four-chambered heart, and a well-developed cerebral cortex. Above, an arctic fox in its winter coat.

Class Reptilia: lizards, turtles, and snakes. Reptiles have a well-developed bony endoskeleton and dry, scaly skin that resists desiccation. Most depend entirely on lungs, with air being sucked in (not forced in by mouth muscles, as in amphibians). Almost all lay shelled eggs on land. Within the shell, the embryo floats in the "aquatic" world of the amniotic sac; it receives nutrients from a yolk sac; it uses the allantois, another membrane, as a surface for gas exchange. The shelled egg was a key character in the vertebrate invasion of land. Above, a green python native to New Guinea and Northeast Australia.

Figure 34.34 Representative vertebrates which, together with the tunicates and lancelets described earlier, are members of the phylum Chordata. The phylogenetic relationship of these varied groups is given in Appendix I.

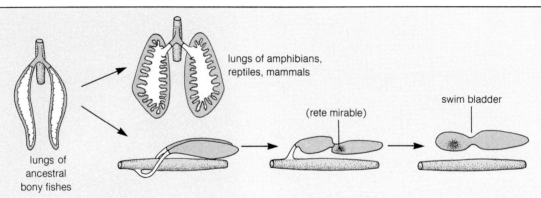

Figure 34.35 Evolution of the vertebrate lung and the swim bladder of bony fishes. Gold-shaded structure is the esophagus; pink-shaded parts are respiratory tissues.

Lungs, recall, originated as pockets of the foregut; they provided more surface area for gas exchange in oxygen-depleted environments. In some evolutionary lines, the lung sacs became positioned dorsally above the esophagus and became swim bladders (buoyancy devices that help keep fishes from sinking). Adjustments in gas volume can allow the fish to remain suspended indefinitely at different depths.

Less specialized fishes have a duct between the swim bladder and esophagus; they must replenish air in the bladder by surfacing and gulping air. Fishes adapted to deeper water have no such duct. The swim bladder has a dense mesh of blood vessels (rete mirable) in which arteries and veins run in opposite directions. Through a countercurrent flow mechanism, gas concentration within the bladder can be multiplied tremendously. The part of the bladder containing this meshwork is called the secretory region; another part of the bladder allows reabsorption of gases by body tissues.

in water, through adjustments in gas volume (Figure 34.35). In the moist, thin-walled swim bladder, air also gives up oxygen to the surrounding blood and tissues.

During this period of evolution, gills and air sacs received oxygen at the same time. In fishes, blood traveled from gills to a heart having a single atrium. The heart pumped blood to the rest of the body, then the blood moved sluggishly back to the heart (Figure 34.36). The earliest amphibian hearts were equipped with a second atrium, which received oxygen-rich blood directly from the lungs. The blood from both atria was forced into the same ventricle. Although the ventricle was undivided (as it is in modern amphibians), blood flow from one atrium tended not to mix with blood flow from the other. Thus oxygenated blood was sent to body tissues, and oxygen-poor blood flowed separately to the lungs.

This heart structure became modified in two separate lines of reptiles, one of which gave rise to birds and one to mammals. In all existing birds and mammals, a partition divides the ventricle into two chambers also. Blood flow is separated into systemic and pulmonary circulation (Chapter Twenty-Four). Thus, *what began as a single circulation system among primitive chordates became, in birds and mammals, a dual-circulation system.*

On the Vertebrate Nervous System

All chordates share another characteristic: a single, hollow **nerve cord** running dorsal to the digestive tract. Among the ancient jawless fishes, the nerve cord underwent modification into what would become the basic plan of the vertebrate nervous system—an enlarged brain at the head end, and paired cranial nerves, as described in Chapter Twenty-One. When amphibians moved onto land, they encountered diverse new stimuli. The brain underwent dramatic development, particularly in the hindbrain and midbrain regions concerned with processing signals related to hearing, balance, and vision.

The first true cerebral cortex emerged during the evolution of reptiles. Although this neural layering was small, it provided the foundation for more complex integration than existed among the amphibians. It was not until the rise of mammals that the cerebral cortex began to show its evolutionary potential (see Figure 34.37). Then the brain began its dramatic expansion into an immense mass of information-encoding and information-processing cells. Thus, like other developments we explored in this chapter, *the vertebrate brain is a result of evolutionary accretion—with new layerings on structures of more ancient origins.*

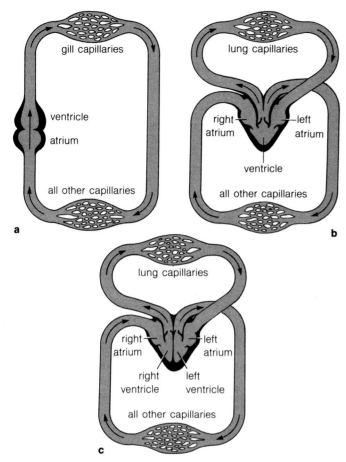

Figure 34.36 Relationship between the heart and blood vessels for (**a**) fishes, (**b**) amphibians, and (**c**) birds and mammals.

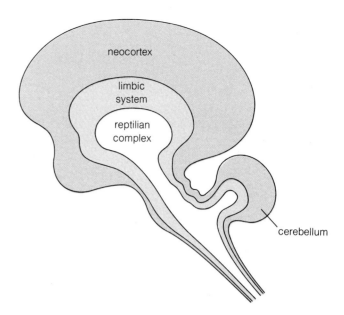

Figure 34.37 The hindbrain and midbrain represent the basic machinery of neural functioning. Paul MacLean sees three evolutionary layers driving this machinery. The most ancient, surrounding the midbrain, probably evolved several hundred million years ago. It is the reptilian, or *R complex*. Surrounding this is the *limbic system*, which evolved more than 150 million years ago. This layer is well-developed in mammals but not in reptiles. Tens of millions of years ago, the *neocortex* began its dramatic expansion in mammals. These three neural layerings are anatomically and physiologically distinct, and may represent a foundation for major behavioral differences between reptiles and mammals.

Readings

Barnes, R. 1980. *Invertebrate Zoology.* Fourth edition. Philadelphia: W. B. Saunders. Outstanding introduction to the invertebrates.

Hickman, C., et al. 1979. *Integrated Principles of Zoology.* Sixth edition. St. Louis: Mosby.

Romer, A., and T. Parsons. 1977. *The Vertebrate Body.* Fifth edition. Philadelphia: W. B. Saunders. Chapter 16 contains detailed pictures of vertebrate nervous systems. Excellent reference book.

Russell-Hunter, W. 1968. *A Biology of Lower Invertebrates.* New York: Macmillan. An excellent little paperback covering biological unity and diversity from coelenterates to mollusks.

Review Questions

1. In what ways are sponges unlike other animals? In what ways are they similar?

2. Can you put together a scenario based on the planuloid theory of origins for bilaterally symmetrical animals? How do you suppose this theory helps explain why you happen to have two eyes instead of one (like the mythical cyclops), two arms, two legs, two ears? Why one mouth instead of two? Why brain tissue concentrated in your head instead of strung out, noodlelike, through your elongate body?

3. In the anatomical sense, are flatworms more complex than sponges? Than jellyfish? Than earthworms?

4. Flatworms are thought to be living representatives of ancient organisms from which two main lines of animals diverged long ago. Name these two evolutionary lines, and state which of the existing animal phyla each includes. If this divergence did indeed occur, then are insects or echinoderms closer to you on the evolutionary tree?

5. Explain what role the following developments probably played in the evolution of larger and more complex forms of animals: coelom, circulatory system, segmentation, lungs.

6. Arthropods include insects, crustaceans, arachnids, and their kin. Describe the basic body plan that characterizes these diverse organisms. How might some of these features have helped some of their ancient aquatic ancestors radiate onto land?

7. Mollusks include forms ranging from small soft-bodied slugs to hard-shelled clams to giant squid that may be as long as a six-story building is tall. What body features do such diverse animals hold in common?

35

HUMAN ORIGINS AND EVOLUTION

Figure 35.1 Pygmy chimpanzee walking upright on a bough eighty feet above the ground. Its hands are thus freed to carry objects—in this case, fruits from the boongola tree.

Noel Badrian

In the preceding chapter, we covered a tremendous span of animal evolution. We pieced together a picture of adaptations leading to bilateral symmetry and segmentation, foretelling such structures as paddles, fins, and legs. We brought other adaptations into the picture: internal circulation systems for supplying ever-larger bodies with nutrients and for removing metabolic wastes, backbones for strength and flexibility, and complex nervous systems that meet the challenges of increasingly complex environments. In doing so, we watched the sprouting of the first metazoans and their subsequent growth over 2 billion years into the mammalian stem, one of many stems on the animal phylogenetic tree. It is here that we exist, one branch among a diverse array of other mammalian forms.

How did we arrive here? At present there is no universally accepted answer to this question. Tantalizing clues have been uncovered, but the fact remains that the clues are being interpreted in numerous ways. In this chapter, we will survey some of the discoveries and hypotheses about human origins from a biological point of view.

THE PRIMATE FAMILY

Primate Origins

According to one classification scheme, the order **Primates** has fifty-seven existing genera, which are divided into two suborders:

Prosimians	*tree shrews, tarsiers, lemurs, and kin*
Anthropoids	*New World monkeys (ceboids)*
	Old World monkeys (cercopithecoids)
	apes, humans (hominoids)

The primates in Figure 35.2 show some of the distinguishing limb and sensory adaptations that the members of all these genera hold in common. To understand the significance of these adaptations, we must return to the dawn of the Cenozoic, some 65 million years ago—the time of origin for the primates.

Like all placental mammals, the primates apparently arose from ancestral forms of the order Insectivora. Fossils of those mammals resemble the small, ground-dwelling tree shrews that live in Southeast Asia (Figure 35.3). As the name implies, the early insectivores ate insects; like shrews, they probably ate seeds, buds, eggs, and tiny animals as well. Shrews are night-time omnivores—highly active, and hungry (they eat the equivalent of their own weight nightly). They have a long snout and a well-developed olfactory

Bruce Coleman Ltd.

a

Larry Burrows / Aspect Picture Library, London

b

Figure 35.2 (**a**) The gibbon and (**b**) two tarsiers. These and other primates are characterized by bodies and limbs adapted for climbing, and by precise vision in a three-dimensional field.

sense, useful in snuffling out food and catching the scent of predators, which once included some of the smaller dinosaurs. With the widespread extinction of dinosaurs by the close of the Mesozoic, the shrewlike forms underwent large-scale adaptive radiations. Some lineages went underground and evolved into moles. Others took to the water and to the air; their descendants include otter shrews and bats. And one lineage took to the trees.

The forest canopy, with its abundance of fruits and insects, and its safety from ground-dwelling predators, was a promising adaptive zone. Yet with all of its advantages, life in the trees also was demanding. It must have been a visually complex world then, as it is now, with dense leaves, dappled sunlight, boughs swaying in the wind, darting insects and other prey, perhaps predatory birds. The mammalian snout would not have been much use in such a world, where air currents disperse the scent of food and predators. However, eyes that could discern color, shape, and movement in a three-dimensional field would have been enormously useful in leaping and moving among the branches. At the same time, four legs so useful in running would not have been as useful as limbs adapted for climbing.

The key characters of primate evolution were (1) body and limbs adapted for tree-climbing, and (2) eyes adapted for discerning color, shape, and movement in a three-dimensional field.

Owen Newman / Bruce Coleman Ltd

Figure 35.3 Common shrew *(Sorex)*.

General Characteristics of the Primates

The key characters just described were the basis of the following five developments that occurred among the primates:

1. *A capacity to move limbs and the head freely in different planes.* Primate arm and leg limbs can swivel freely in their sockets. By swinging the limbs up, down, sideways, backward, or forward, the body can be supported from any direction, not just from the flat ground. Also, primates show considerable head rotation, as the tarsiers in Figure 35.2 so aptly illustrate.

2. *Mobile digits capable of grasping.* Among monkeys, apes, and humans, four digits on each hand are complemented by an opposable thumb, which permits detailed manipulation and examination of objects. In humans alone, the thumb is long and powerful enough for strong yet precise gripping of objects.

3. *Upright vertebral column and body posture.* Early in primate evolution, the body's center of gravity shifted until it was well back over the hindlimbs. This development made upright sitting positions possible and freed the forelimbs for manipulation. The development required changes in the proportions and details of pelvic, leg, and foot bones as well as in the vertebral column. (Interpretation of these changes in fossils is central to attempts to reconstruct primate evolution.)

4. *Enhanced vision.* The early primates had forward-directed eyes, which means they had an overlapping visual field and, thereby, depth perception. Over time, the retina became increasingly good at detecting light of different intensities (dim to bright) and wavelengths (colors). The eyes themselves became larger and were able to detect more light and detail. As the eyes and their sockets enlarged, the greater reliance on vision was accompanied by a reduction in the snout (and the sense of smell). Gradually the position of the eyes shifted back into the skull and came to be protected by a bony ridge above that part of the brain.

5. *A nervous system that integrates and processes diverse stimuli, then coordinates precise, rapid, yet flexible movements in response.* Before walking, swinging, and leaping (especially!) can be undertaken high up in the forest canopy, the brain must assess myriad factors—distance, body weight, wind, the suitability of the destination, how to compensate quickly for miscalculations. The exquisite neural control characteristic of primates was perhaps an inevitable outgrowth of life in the trees.

EARLY HOMINIDS (PERHAPS) AND THEIR PREDECESSORS (MAYBE)

Ancient Apelike Forms

About 35 million years ago, in what is now a large, hot desert southwest of Cairo, Egypt, the land was cloaked with the lush vegetation of a tropical rain forest. Humid swamps lined the many rivers that ran through the forest and emptied into the Mediterranean Sea. This setting, now called the Fayum Depression, was home to the forerunners of monkeys and apes. All were small hominoids, adapted for life in the trees. Given the altogether nightmarish predatory reptiles that are known to have inhabited the swamps at the time, it is perhaps understandable why the first hominoids stayed mostly up in the trees.

One of the Fayum hominoids, *Aegyptopithecus*, lived 30 million years ago. As Figure 35.4 shows, it had a monkeylike skull but teeth that were more apelike. It was the size of a house cat, and it apparently was quadrupedal (four-legged) and arboreal. If not directly in the line of descent leading to apes and humans, *Aegyptopithecus* may resemble the transitional forms that did.

While these hominoids were evolving, major land masses were on the move as crustal plates began to assume their most recent positions (Chapter Thirty-One). At the start of the Miocene, some 25 million years ago, the redistribution of land masses led to pronounced shifts in climate. In what is now Africa, Europe, and elsewhere, there began a major cooling trend and a decline in rainfall that would culminate in the Pleistocene. Over time, the tropical and subtropical forests would gradually give way to grasslands. In the interim, there was a mosaic of forests and savannas.

The hominoids confronted with the changing environment are collectively called the **dryopithecines** (Figure 35.4). The first known fossils of these forms date from about 25 million years ago. Toward the end of the Miocene, the dryopithecines apparently underwent radiation into the new adaptive zones. Some of the later species were the size of modern gorillas, with brains almost as large as those of chimpanzees. They were reasonably adept at swinging through the trees.

By about 17 million years ago, the African crustal plate collided with the Eurasian plate. For the next 3 million years, hominoids evolved into a variety of forms, collectively called the **sivapithecines**. Among them were *Sivapithecus*, *Ramapithecus*, and *Gigantopithecus*. By 12 million years ago, The molars of the sivapithecines were larger than those of the dryopithecines, with thicker enamel. The Asian forms appear to be ancestral to the orangutan, but whether the

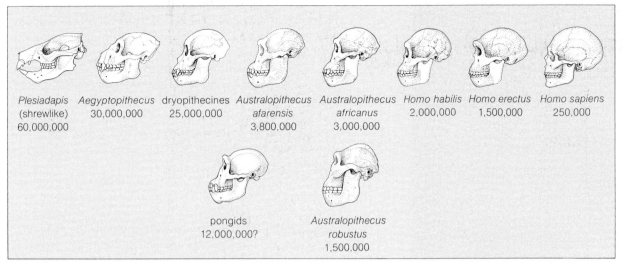

Figure 35.4 Comparison of the skull shapes and dentition of some anthropoids, living and extinct. (The skulls are not drawn to the same scale; for example, the *Aegyptopithecus* skull was no larger than that of a house cat.)

descendants of the Asian forms would include **hominids**—human forms—is not yet clear.

Paleontological and biochemical studies both suggest that some dryopithecine lines gave rise to modern apes. They also suggest that a major divergence occurred somewhere between 12 million and 6 million years ago—a divergence that marked the beginning of the hominid line. However, we have only a few tantalizing fragments dating from this period, including some recently unearthed fossils from Kenya that are thought to be 8 million years old. At this writing, the fossil hunters in the East African Rift Valley and elsewhere may soon change the current picture of early hominoid evolution.

Australopithecines

From about 3.8 to 1 million years ago, humanlike forms are known to have lived in Africa and Southeast Asia. The phylogenetic relationships among these forms are still topics of debate. However, there is general agreement that they all belong to the same genus, *Australopithecus.*

The **australopithecines** were neither ape nor human. The earliest fossils include Donald Johanson's discovery of a female, dubbed Lucy (Figure 35.5). These hominoids were between 3½ and 5 feet tall, and they weighed between 60 and 150 pounds. They were fully bipedal (two-legged), with essentially human bodies and ape-shaped heads. With a cranial capacity of 380 to 550 cubic centimeters, they had brains no larger than those of chimpanzees. Although small,

the early australopithecines were thick-boned and heavily muscled; their hands were a mosaic of ape and human characteristics.

Over time, it seems that some australopithecine lines developed into larger, heftier forms having more massive molars. The huge (and definitely nonhuman) molars suggest that these lines became highly specialized in feeding on coarse plant material. It is possible that earlier forms, as represented by Lucy, were ancestral to the first human forms *(Homo).* As Figure 35.6 suggests, there is no consensus on this point.

The First Humans

By at least 2 million years ago, members of the genus *Homo* were living in the same regions as the later australopithecines. The likely cranial capacity of the earliest known fossils was about 650 cubic centimeters—more than a chimpanzee's but only half the capacity of the average modern human brain (about 1,325 cubic centimeters). These hominids were using stones as tools. By about 1½ million years ago, there were forms with enough distinctive traits to be classified as a new species, *Homo erectus.* This species endured until about 300,000 years ago. Its members probably had an average cranial capacity of 1,000 cubic centimeters. Individuals were relatively tall (5 to 5½ feet), with the long, straight legs of skilled two-legged walkers. By 500,000 years ago, *H. erectus* cranial capacity was approximately that of modern humans.

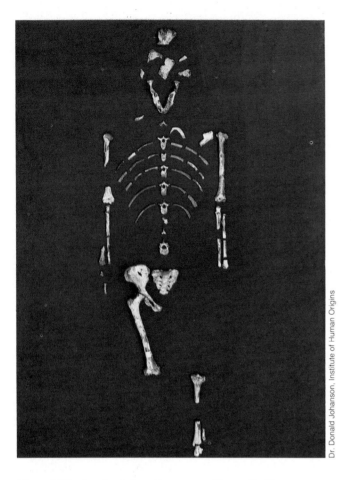

Figure 35.5 Fossil remains of Lucy, one of the earliest known australopithecines.

Some of these large-brained hominids are thought to have lived in bands of about twenty to fifty. Later populations were skilled at making and using tools for hunting and butchering large animals. Animal pelts were used, probably as clothing; fire was used in controlled ways. Although *H. erectus* often used caves for shelter, members of this species were also adept at building large, wooden huts—complete with stone hearths—near hunting sites. With such adaptations, *H. erectus* underwent adaptive radiations out of the tropics and into the more harsh environments of Europe and Asia.

The span between 400,000 and 250,000 years ago apparently was a transitional period in human evolution. Fossils recovered from England, Germany, and elsewhere are like those of *H. erectus* and modern humans. By that time, major evolutionary trends among the hominids were becoming restricted, at least in the physical sense. There was still some fine-tuning in brow ridges and other features. But the major trend continued to be one of enlargement in brain volume—almost surely a reflection of an increased reliance on culture.

This trend continued through the Neanderthalers, distinct populations of *Homo sapiens* that lived from at least 100,000 to as recently as 30,000 years ago. The trend continued through the era known as the Upper Paleolithic, which brought with it a plethora of tool types and a new means of dealing with the world. The hominids of this era were skilled toolmakers and artisans. Among them were the presumed ancestors of the one remaining hominid species: *Homo sapiens sapiens*, man the reasoner, self-proclaimed man the wise.

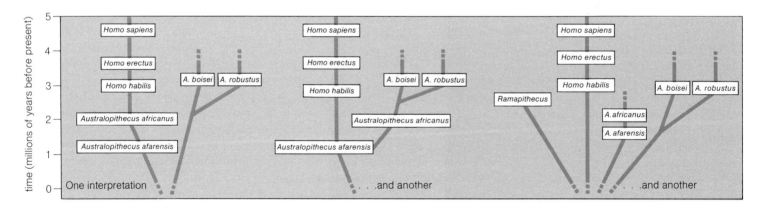

Figure 35.6 Three of the current interpretations of phylogenetic relationships among fossil hominids. *Homo sapiens* is the only living species. (After Cronin and coworkers, 1981)

COMMENTARY

A Biological Perspective on Human Origins

A summary of some ideas advanced by C. Owen Lovejoy in "The Origin of Man," Science, 23 January 1981

Humans are said to be unique among the hominoids by virtue of their extraordinary culture. Bernard Campbell defines culture as the sum total of behavior patterns of a social group of animals, passed between generations by observation, imitation, and instruction (in other words, by learning). Traditionally, the divergence of humans from other hominoids is said to be a direct consequence of three key characters: an upright stance; brain expansion; and the acquisition of culture (beginning with tool use) over the past 3 million years. All of these key characters are said to have evolved after the apelike dryopithecines were forced out of the dwindling Miocene forests for life in the open grasslands. A two-legged stance presumably heralded upright feeding behavior, which was favored because it allowed peering above the grasses for approaching predators and because it freed the hands for using handheld objects—weapons—when escape was impossible. Traditions of tool use thereupon developed, followed by expansion of brain regions concerned with processing information and selecting complex motor responses.

C. Owen Lovejoy argues persuasively that the key characters just described emerged later in human evolution—that they were *sequels* to behavioral adaptations that had already developed among the tree-dwelling forerunners to the hominoids.

For one thing, running away from predators is certainly slower with two legs than with four. In itself, bipedalism would have drastically reduced speed and agility, and therefore would have been a handicap, not an advantage. More likely, hominoids were already bipedal when they moved into the open savannas.

For another thing, savannas did not develop suddenly. During the cool, arid conditions and more pronounced seasons of the Late Miocene, mosaics of forests and grasslands persisted. The tree-dwelling hominoids would have had a better chance of survival by expanding

their feeding range to include the new habitats without giving up the old ones. In other words, bipedalism could have evolved even before hominoids permanently left the trees.

Recent scanning electron micrographs of fossil teeth support this view. The micrographs show what the earliest humanlike forms were not eating. They were not eating grass or seeds, and they weren't crunching bones. (To have done so would have left telltale pits and gouges in the teeth from dirt picked up by eating food on the ground.)

In addition, by the time we get to the distinctly humanlike forms (some 8 million years after the dryopithecines), there still is no evidence of increased cranial capacity. Fossils from this period include the female australopithecine dubbed Lucy. As Lovejoy (a professor of human anatomy and orthopedic surgery) has pointed out, the shape and size of Lucy's birth canal shows little if any selection for passage of an enlarged fetal cranium.

If bipedalism, acquisition of culture, and increased cranial capacity were not the foundation for human origins, what was? Consider that, for the Miocene hominoids, *invasion of newly opening environments could have occurred only through some combination of preexisting traits.* Lovejoy suggests that modifications of existing mammalian and primate reproductive strategies could have been the trigger.

Interpretations of newer fossil discoveries as well as studies of existing primate behavior support this idea. Among the groups of the order Primates, there is a trend toward longer life spans (see figure page 596). Correlated with this trend are longer periods of infant dependency, longer periods between pregnancies, and single births rather than litters. There is, in other words, increased parental investment in fewer offspring. Of course, the investment pays off *only* if the overall infant mortality rate is likewise reduced. Among the apes, such reduction is accomplished through strong social bonds, intense parenting, longer periods of learning, and application of intelligence.

Now, among primates, infants cling rather precariously to their mothers during foraging activities. Sometimes they fall off. In fact, Jane van Lawick-Goodall reports that falling from the mother is one of the primary causes of infant mortality among chimpanzees. Many actively foraging mammals other than primates get

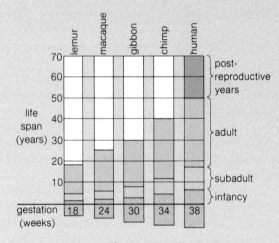

Trend toward longer life spans among primates.

around this problem by sequestering the offspring at a home base—a nest, a burrow, and the like. Suppose that the Miocene hominoids began to develop a kind of home base strategy, also. With the evolution of mosaic environments, more time would have been required to search for food. The increase in foraging time could have led to an increase in infant mortality—unless the females somehow began to limit their foraging range. They could have done this if the males began to increase *their* foraging range, for in this manner competition for food between the males and females would have been reduced—and the infants would have been safer from accidents and from predators.

Lovejoy carries this line of thought further. Suppose that males began provisioning for their female mates and offspring by collecting and carrying food back to the home base. (Some existing primates that form monogamous pair bonds do this.) By provisioning for their young, the males would have increased their reproductive rate—and infant survivorship would have been enhanced. Thus carrying significant amounts of food would have been selectively advantageous—and would have promoted bipedalism. Perhaps, then, the handheld objects that put the hominoids on their unique evolutionary roads were not weapons but food for the family.

Readings

Campbell, B. 1974. *Human Evolution.* Second edition. New York: Aldine. Excellent introduction to research, evidence, and theories about human origins and evolution by a leading anthropologist.

Cronin, J., N. Boaz, C. Stringer, and Y. Rak. 1981. "Tempo and Mode in Hominid Evolution." *Nature* 292:113–122. Good state-of-the-art summary.

Herbert, W. "Lucy's Uncommon Forebear." *Science News,* 1983.

Lovejoy, C. O. 1981. "The Origin of Man." *Science* 211:341–350. Provocative article; includes many more intriguing ideas than those highlighted in the *Commentary* of this chapter.

Miller, D. 1977. "Evolution of Primate Chromosomes." *Science* 198:1116–1124. Nice description of chromosome banding studies designed to shed light on phylogenetic relationships among the primates.

Rensberger, R. 1981. "Facing the Past." *Science 81* 2(8):41–50. Intriguing look at how artist reconstructions of early hominids can bias our perceptions of how "human" these forms really were. Shows how one of the leading illustrators does his reconstructions, starting from fossil bones and adding muscles, skin, and other details.

Review Questions

1. Two key characters in primate evolution were (1) body and limbs adapted for tree-climbing and (2) eyes adapted for discerning color, shape, and movement in a three-dimensional field. These key characters were the basis of which five developments?

2. Are you a hominoid, a hominid, or both?

3. Would you say the picture is fairly clear regarding early hominoid evolution? Would you say we now have a fairly good idea of how the early record of fossil hominids should be interpreted?

4. Traditionally, bipedalism, acquisition of culture, and increases in cranial capacity have been said to be the key characters that developed after the ancestors of hominids left the trees for life in open grasslands. Can you give some arguments for or against these propositions?

UNIT EIGHT

ECOLOGY AND BEHAVIOR

36

POPULATION ECOLOGY

The optimist proclaims that we live in the best of all possible worlds; and the pessimist fears this is true.—James Branch Cabell

Suppose this year the federal government passes legislation to limit the size of your family to three children. Suppose the new law also specifies that each father must be sterilized after the birth of the third child—and that if he refuses, he will be jailed for a few years and sterilized with or without his consent. *It would never happen here,* you might be thinking. For one thing, our democratic society would never tolerate such a forced invasion of privacy. For another thing, there is widespread perception that the quantity of life has a pronounced effect on its quality, and large families are not high on the priority list for the general population.

However, we belong to a nation that excels in food production, standards of hygiene, and medical care. Primarily for this reason, we are among the few in the world who have the luxury of a choice in family size. Most do not have the same luxury, and the individual right to reproduce is on a collision course with the rights of the overall population.

For example, each year in India, 9 million die—but 22 million are born. To a population now standing at well over 600 million, *13 million new members are added annually.* There are more people in India than in North and South America combined. Most of the people do not have enough food or adequate medical care, and living conditions are often appalling. Each *week* 100,000 more people enter the job market for nonexistent jobs.

Because of these circumstances, the Indian government has supported population control programs for more than two decades. The programs have not worked. Seventy percent of the people are illiterate and pertinent information must be conveyed by word of mouth. Also, sustained population control programs are hampered because eighty percent of the people live in remote agricultural villages that are not easy to reach. Finally, the villagers see that many die of disease and starvation. They believe that having more children will increase their own chance for survival. Without large families, they say, who will help a father tend fields? Who will go to the cities in the hope of earning money to send back home? How can a father otherwise know he will be survived by at least one son, who must, by Hindu tradition, conduct the last rites to assure that the soul of his dead father will rest in peace?

Clearly there is serious discrepancy between the way that Indian villagers see their world and what the greater world has actually come to be. Because of this discrepancy, twenty-five years from now the population may reach 1 billion. If that happens, India will be unable to increase crop production and break the cycle of poverty, disease, and starvation that plagues it. That is why, in desperation, the Indian federal government passed legislation in 1976 calling for compulsory sterilization. For them, the hypothe-

Norman Meyers / Bruce Coleman Ltd.

tical example opening this chapter briefly became reality, until public outrage became so great that the law was rescinded.

Is there a way out of such dilemmas? Should nations having surplus resources freely donate the excess to support the growing populations of undeveloped nations? Would the donations alleviate the problem, or would they fan greater increases in population size? Suppose the expanded populations came to depend on continuing support. What would happen if a series of annual droughts severely limited the agricultural productivity of the nations doing the donating?

Whether we are talking about humans or any other kind of organism, certain principles govern the growth and stability of populations. For us, social, economic, and political considerations may influence the short-term distribution of resources on which any human population depends. Over the long term, however, we must also reckon with the consequences of such actions, the inevitability of which can be predicted from known biological principles.

ECOLOGY DEFINED

The principles we are talking about were identified by ecologists, who (it has been said) study just about everything. The word *ecology* is based on the Greek *oikos*, meaning "house," and refers in general to the study of the home that one, some, many, or all organisms live in. The first ecological studies were primarily descriptive, resulting from observations of individuals, populations, and communities in different parts of the world. Gradually, mathematical models and theories were developed to explain how organisms interact with one another and their environment. With this descriptive and theoretical base, it became evident that organisms have been linked, on a global scale, through their interactions. The domain of ecologists came to extend from the individual to the biosphere.

Ecology is the study of the relations between organisms and the totality of the physical and biological factors affecting them or influenced by them. *The origin, mechanisms, and consequences of these ecological interactions represent the stage on which all evolutionary change is played out.* Mutations change the genotypic character of populations, and diverse phenotypes are the expressions of genetic change. Are the mutations harmful, helpful, or neutral? In other words, how do they affect the ability of the organism to survive and reproduce? The question has meaning only on the ecological stage, with its many and varied *tests* of phenotypes.

The "stage" in this analogy is not a flat expanse; it has multiple dimensions in space and time. It is a stage where populations, communities, ecosystems, and the biosphere form overlapping sets, each more inclusive than the one before. In this unit of the book we will consider each of these settings in turn:

1. The **population**: a group of individuals of the same species occupying a given area at a given time. We have already looked at the genetic basis for the evolution of populations. Here the focus will be on the ecological relationships that influence population size, structure, and distribution.

2. The **community**: all those populations that occupy a given area at a given time. We will be looking at the kinds of population interactions that shape community structure.

3. The **ecosystem**: a community and its physical environment. An ecosystem has living (biotic) and nonliving (abiotic) components. Soils, temperature, rainfall, even organic matter are examples of the abiotic component. The biotic component has three broad categories of organisms:

> **producers**: autotrophs (photosynthesizers and chemosynthesizers that use an environmental energy source to build complex organic molecules from simple inorganic precursors such as carbon dioxide and water)

> **consumers**: mostly animals and predatory protistans, both of which are heterotrophs (they cannot build complex organic molecules from inorganic matter and obtain them by ingesting other organisms)

> **decomposers**: mostly heterotrophic bacteria and fungi that obtain energy by breaking down organic remains or products of other organisms; their activities cycle simple compounds back to autotrophs

4. The **biosphere**: all the earth's living organisms that, through their interactions with the physical environment as a whole, maintain a system of energy use and materials cycling. This system runs on energy flowing into it (from the sun) and it gives up energy (primarily as low-grade heat) to space.

You should know at the outset that no one has yet identified all of the interlocking relationships in any one of these settings. However, the guiding principles that will be described help us understand the kinds of events that are taking place, and they may enable us to predict the consequences of those events.

POPULATION DENSITY AND DISTRIBUTION

Ecological Density

In selection theory, **fitness** is the genetically based ability of an organism to perpetuate itself under prevailing environmental conditions. As you will perceive by the end of this chapter, one of the most influential determinants of individual fitness is population size. In itself, "size" is a meaningless concept; it must be described in terms of the area or volume of space in which members of the population live. Some number of people live within the geographic area called Canada. Some number of moose live in a particular lake-forest system whose boundaries are defined by the wildlife biologist doing the counting. Some number of fish of a given species live in the volume of space called a pond. Some number of ragweed plants have sprouted in a newly plowed field. For these and other populations, the measured number of individuals in a defined area or volume of space is the **crude density**.

Crude density is no more than a head count, and it tells little about how individuals are actually spaced in the area under study. For example, not all of the space in a defined area may be used as a **habitat**: the place where the population (or organism) actually lives. Because of large or small differences in sunlight, temperature, nesting space, and so forth, parts of the area might be uninhabitable for that population, either seasonally or continually. Thus population density must also be measured in terms of the amount of space that is actually being occupied in a given area. That gives us the **ecological density** for the population.

Distribution in Space

Even when the amount of habitat is defined, we still don't know how the population is distributed within that space. Individuals might be clumped together, spread out rather uniformly, or dispersed randomly:

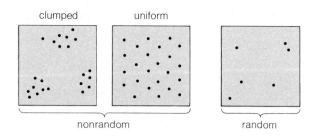

Clumping, a common spatial distribution, is a nonrandom response to the presence of other organisms (such as predators), and to temporal or spatial variation in resources within the habitat. It often is a consequence of reproductive patterns, as when offspring of intertidal organisms settle near one another and their parents. Uniform distribution is a regular spacing that can result from competition among individuals of the population. An example is the nearly uniform spacing of creosote bushes (*Larrea*) in scrub deserts, such as those of the American Southwest. The roots of this plant release substances that inhibit germination of other creosote plants within the ring defined by the root system. Random spacing can occur when environmental conditions are the same throughout the habitat and when members of the population neither repel nor attract one another. Spiders on the floors of forests may be an example of such random distribution.

Distribution Over Time

Population distribution also varies with time, in ways that often correspond to environmental rhythms. Few environments are so productive that they yield abundant resources all year long. For example, temperatures drop and food supplies dwindle during the winter in north temperate regions (such as parts of Canada and Europe), where many migratory birds reproduce. Whole populations move southward to winter feeding grounds in (for example) South America and Africa. With the return of spring, they make the return trip north, when their breeding grounds are warmer and have abundant new growth of plants and insect populations.

Crude density is a rough measure of the number of individuals of a population in a defined area.

Ecological density is a more precise measure, for it also defines the portion of space that the individuals really do occupy as their habitat within the defined area.

Ecological density can vary even when crude density remains constant, because the distribution of individuals usually changes in space and time.

POPULATION DYNAMICS

Parameters Affecting Population Size

Population density rises or falls with changes in one or more of the following parameters:

natality	*births*
mortality	*deaths*
immigration	*individuals from other areas join the population*
emigration	*individuals move out and take up residence elsewhere*

These four parameters determine changes in **population size**, or the rate of change in the number of individuals (N) at a given time:

$$\Delta N = (\text{births} + \text{immigration}) - (\text{death} + \text{emigration})$$

When the birth rate plus immigration is balanced over the long term by the death rate and emigration, population size is stabilized; there is said to be **zero population growth**.

Life Expectancy and Survivorship Curves

The term **life expectancy** refers to the average number of years left to be lived by an individual of a population. Expectations are rosier for some individuals than for others, depending on such factors as age. For example, a human infant twelve months old has a greater probability of surviving (hence a greater life expectancy) than one who is only six months old.

For many animal and plant populations, **life tables** have been constructed as age-specific summaries of births and deaths. Such tables give an idea of the expected life remaining to an individual (or group of individuals) on the basis of age. Life insurance companies use such tables to establish their insurance rates for humans in a particular age bracket; some brackets are riskier than others, and the premium rates are correspondingly higher (Table 36.1).

The data summarized in life tables can be used to construct **survivorship curves**, which show trends in mortality and survivorship. Such curves are obtained by plotting the number of individuals of a particular group still alive at each age increment. Survivorship curves of this sort have revealed three basic trends that affect population size:

Survivorship Curve	Trend
Type I	*low mortality early in life, most deaths in narrow time span at maturity*
Type II	*rate of mortality fairly constant at all age increments*
Type III	*high mortality early in life*

Figure 36.2 provides a general picture of these trends, along with a survivorship curve for an actual population.

Table 36.1 Life Table for the United States Population in 1979*

Age Interval	Age-Specific Mortality Rate	Number Living at Start of Age Interval	Number Dying During Age Interval	Average Number Still Alive During Age Interval	Total Years Lived by All Individuals of Population	Life Expectancy
00 to 01	0.0132	100,000	1,315	98,855	7,391,312	73.9
01 to 05	0.0025	98,685	250	394,159	7,292,457	73.9
05 to 10	0.0016	98,435	154	491,761	6,898,298	70.1
10 to 15	0.0016	98,281	157	491,074	6,406,537	65.2
15 to 20	0.0050	98,124	486	489,518	5,915,463	60.3
20 to 25	0.0065	97,638	639	486,613	5,425,945	55.6
25 to 30	0.0065	96,999	629	483,422	4,939,332	50.9
30 to 35	0.0068	96,370	657	480,279	4,455,910	46.2
35 to 40	0.0092	95,713	879	476,508	3,975,631	41.5
40 to 45	0.0140	94,834	1,332	471,059	3,499,123	36.9
45 to 50	0.0224	93,502	2,096	462,597	3,028,064	32.4
50 to 55	0.0355	91,406	3,245	449,422	2,565,467	28.1
55 to 60	0.0522	88,161	4,598	429,930	2,116,045	24.0
60 to 65	0.0798	83,563	6,669	401,912	1,686,115	20.2
65 to 70	0.1133	76,894	8,709	363,546	1,284,203	16.7
70 to 75	0.1678	68,185	11,441	313,229	920,657	13.5
75 to 80	0.2361	56,744	13,397	250,696	607,428	10.7
80 to 85	0.3476	43,347	15,068	178,455	356,732	8.2
85 and up	1.0000	28,279	28,279	178,277	178,277	6.3

From Statistical Resources Branch, Division of Vital Statistics, National Center for Health Statistics.
*Figures given are for every 100,000 born alive.

POPULATION GROWTH

Biotic Potential

The individuals of any population are physiologically equipped to produce a maximum possible number of new individuals. The implication of this so-called **biotic potential** is staggering. For example, assume that one man and woman produce the maximum number of children possible during the woman's reproductive years. Assume that all their grandchildren survive and do the same, as do their grandchildren. Theoretically, that one man and woman could thereby add 200,000 new individuals to the human population within a century. The biotic potential of fruit flies (Drosophila) is $3,368 \times 10^{52}$ in one year. These phenomenal increases would be the outcome of unrestricted growth, of the sort to be described next.

Exponential Growth

Population growth results when births and immigration exceed deaths and emigration. The difference between the two at any specified instant is the **rate of increase** (r) for the population.

Another way to express the rate of increase is to use the population's doubling time (how long it takes to double in size). Some bacteria double their numbers every thirty minutes; humans are now doubling their numbers every thirty-nine years. Regardless of the unit of time, in the absence of environmental constraints the pattern is always the same. What starts out as a gradual increase suddenly accelerates, and there is a burgeoning of numbers; this is the pattern of **exponential growth**.

Exponential growth can also be expressed by the following equation:

$$\frac{dN}{dt} = r_m N$$

which simply means this:

$$\begin{pmatrix} \text{rate of change} \\ \text{in numbers} \\ \text{per unit time} \end{pmatrix} = \begin{pmatrix} \text{maximum} \\ \text{rate of} \\ \text{increase} \end{pmatrix} \times \begin{pmatrix} \text{population} \\ \text{size} \end{pmatrix}$$

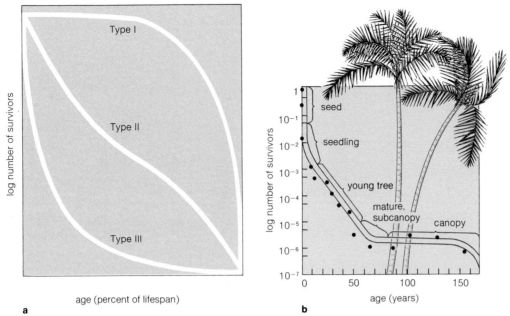

Figure 36.2 (**a**) Three generalized types of survivorship curves. For Type I populations, there is high survivorship until some age, then steep mortality. Type II populations show a fairly constant rate of change in mortality at all ages. Both types are characteristic of many lizards and mammals. For Type III populations, there is low survivorship early in life; many fish, marine invertebrates, some insects, and many plants follow this trend.

Many survivorship curves do not fall into any one of these categories but show trends intermediate between the different types. One example is a survivorship curve plotted for the palm tree *Euterpe globosa* (**b**). (Data from L. Van Valen, *Biotropica, 7*:260–269)

When a population is indeed presented with the best of all possible conditions, many new individuals can be born and initially nothing seems to be getting out of hand. With successive doubling periods, however, population size skyrockets. The reason is that the additions of new individuals *enlarge the potential reproductive base.* The next generation enlarges it more, and so on until the reproductive base is enormous.

We can see how this happens by putting a single bacterium in a culture flask with a complete supply of nutrients. In thirty minutes the bacterium divides in two; thirty minutes later the two divide into four. Assuming no cells die between divisions, the number doubles every thirty minutes. The larger the population base becomes, the more bacteria are around to fulfill the biotic potential. After only $9\frac{1}{2}$ hours (nineteen doublings), the population will be more than 500,000—and by 10 hours (twenty doublings), it will soar past 1 million. Such size increases can be plotted against increments of time. The result is a **J-shaped curve**, which is characteristic of populations undergoing exponential growth (Figure 36.3a).

For a slowly reproducing species such as a whale, it may take a hundred years for population size to double. Even so, after only twenty doublings (2,000 years), there would be a million whales derived from each original pair.

You may think that mortality alone would counter exponential growth. (After all, a whale does not live to be 2,000 years old; some members of a whale population are dying even as others are being born.) To test the effect of mortality on growth rate, let's start over with our bacterium in its nutrient-rich culture flask. This time, assume that twenty-five percent of the population dies between each doubling time. The death rate does slow things a bit, in that it takes almost two hours instead of thirty minutes to double population size. However, *only the time scale changes.* It now takes thirty hours instead of ten to arrive at a million bacteria—and we still have a J-shaped curve, as shown in Figure 36.3b.

As long as the birth rate remains even slightly above the death rate, a population has the potential to grow exponentially.

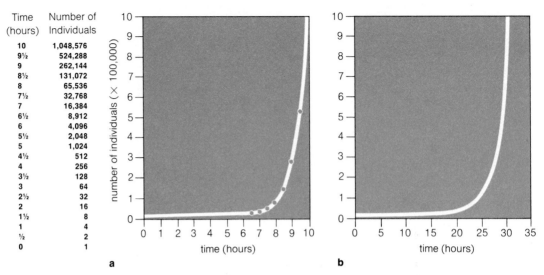

Time (hours)	Number of Individuals
10	1,048,576
9½	524,288
9	262,144
8½	131,072
8	65,536
7½	32,768
7	16,384
6½	8,912
6	4,096
5½	2,048
5	1,024
4½	512
4	256
3½	128
3	64
2½	32
2	16
1½	8
1	4
½	2
0	1

Figure 36.3 (**a**) Exponential growth for a bacterial population that is dividing by fission every half hour. (**b**) Exponential growth of the population when division occurs every half hour, but when twenty-five percent dies between divisions. Although deaths slow things down a bit, in themselves they are not enough to stop exponential growth.

Environmental Resistance to Growth

Obviously, there must be limits on population size that prevent berserk expressions of exponential growth. For example, chances are you know that when you take a walk through a forest you are not going to be trampled to death by a billion rabbits. Something about a natural system such as a forest keeps its populations in check; somehow birth rates are generally balanced with death rates.

However, identifying the nature of those limits is extremely difficult in a natural ecosystem because of the complex interactions going on within and among its populations. For that reason, let's go back to that (by now exhausted) bacterium in its culture flask, where we know we can control the variables. First we will feed it a balanced diet of glucose, minerals, and nitrogen; then we will allow it to reproduce for many generations. Initially the population goes through an exponential growth phase. Then growth tapers off, and for a while population size remains relatively stable. Then the population begins to decline—suddenly at first, followed by a more gradual pace until the entire population is dead.

What caused this pattern of growth and decline? For these organisms, glucose meant food and energy—but the culture dish held only so much glucose. We can deduce that, as the population expanded faster and faster, the glu-

cose was being used up faster and faster, also. When the supplies began dwindling, so did the basis for growth. When any essential resource is in short supply, it becomes a limiting factor for population growth.

What would have happened if we kept adding glucose to the culture dish? Although extra glucose would have been necessary for further growth, there would have been no extra supplies of nitrogen and other necessary nutrients. Some other resource would have become the limiting factor.

Nutrients are not the only potential limiting factors on population growth. If we were to supply that bacterial population with all necessary nutrients, it would not only decline following exponential growth, it would crash. In this case, the increased numbers would mean increased metabolic wastes which, in high enough concentrations, would drastically change the nature of the environment. Unless the tainted medium were removed every so often from the culture flask, the bacteria would poison themselves to death.

Taken together, all of the factors that limit increases in the size of a population are called the **environmental resistance** to growth. The collection of limiting factors can be enormous and their relative effects variable, as our hypothetical bacterial population made clear. For natural populations, the environmental resistance can fluctuate considerably over time. J. Liebig called such consequences the "law of the minimum." He perceived that nutrients can limit growth, but that growth (yield) would be limited by the relatively least abundant nutrient. This concept was later extended to other environmental conditions (such as climate and predators).

Factors that limit increases in the size of a population are collectively called the **environmental resistance** to growth. Change in any one factor can affect what the maximum increase will be.

Tolerance Limits

As the self-poisoned bacteria make clear, too much of something can be as harmful as too little. In 1913, V. Shelford formalized this idea as the "law of tolerance." Each organism has upper and lower limits of tolerance to environmental variation. When performance is measured and plotted against variation in some environmental factor, the result is a **tolerance curve**. Typically, tolerance curves are bell-shaped, with the peak range representing the region of optimal performance and the valleys at either end indicating the tolerance limits (Figure 36.4).

Carrying Capacity and Logistic Growth

For a given population, the environmental resistance defines the **carrying capacity** (K). The term refers to the maximum density of individuals that can be indefinitely sustained per unit area, under a given set of environmental conditions. When a population reaches its carrying capacity after undergoing exponential growth, a plot of the rate of increase shows that the growth curve flattens out (Figure 36.5). Overall, we end up with a sigmoid, or **S-shaped curve**. Such curves are characteristic of **logistic growth**, in which the rate of increase is at first exponential and then flattens out as the carrying capacity is reached.

Logistic growth can be expressed by the following equation:

$$\frac{dN}{dt} = r_m N \left(\frac{K - N}{K} \right)$$

or, more simply,

$$\begin{pmatrix} \text{rate of change} \\ \text{in numbers} \\ \text{per unit time} \end{pmatrix} = \begin{pmatrix} \text{maximum} \\ \text{rate of} \\ \text{increase} \end{pmatrix} \times N \begin{pmatrix} \text{portion of} \\ \text{unexploited} \\ \text{resource} \end{pmatrix}$$

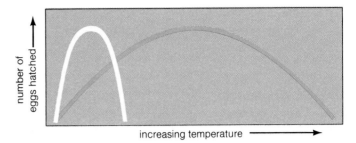

Figure 36.4 Tolerance curves for trout eggs (white line) and leopard frog eggs (blue line) exposed to increasing temperatures. Trout eggs develop between 0°C and 12°C, with peak development and hatching occurring at about 4°C. The frog eggs develop between 0°C and 30°C; for them, peak development and hatching occur at about 22°C.

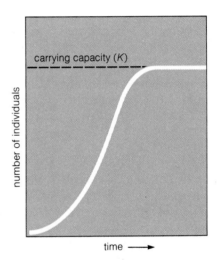

Figure 36.5 S-shaped curve characteristic of logistic growth. Following an exponential growth phase, the growth curve flattens out as the carrying capacity of the environment is reached.

In this case, a feedback relationship exists between population size and its rate of increase. When a population exceeds K, it declines in size. When the population declines below K it tends to increase in size.

In theory, populations tend to fluctuate around the carrying capacity. However, sometimes exponential growth is so dramatic that the population overshoots the carrying capacity, then crashes (for example, through starvation or disease). This happened in one of the Pribilof Islands of Alaska. In 1910, four male and twenty-two female reindeer were introduced on the island. Within thirty years, the population increased to two thousand. The vegetation on which the reindeer grazed almost disappeared, and in 1950 the herd size plummeted to eight members (Figure 36.6).

In logistic growth, the population increase is at first exponential, then it slows and levels off as the carrying capacity of the environment is reached.

REPRODUCTIVE RESPONSES TO GROWTH LIMITS

Fitness, again, is the genetically based ability of an organism to perpetuate itself under prevailing conditions. As you have seen, however, rampant perpetuation is not a long-running play on the ecological stage. The carrying capacity of different environments apparently has had profound influence on the evolution of reproductive patterns. Thus, the timing of reproduction, how often reproduction occurs in the life cycle, and the number of offspring produced at a time have become adapted to the carrying capacity.

Generally, there are two reproductive responses to growth limits, known as r-selection and K-selection. The term **r-selection** refers to selection that occurs under low population densities, and that favors those characteristics leading to rapid rates of increase (r). If we view life cycles in terms of the energy allocated to such tasks as growth, predator avoidance, resource acquisition, and reproduction, then r-selected individuals spend a large portion of their energy in reproductive efforts. When much of a habitat remains unexploited, the individuals that channel more energy into reproduction will ultimately leave more offspring than those putting energy into competitive ability or increased body size.

In environments subject to large-scale changes, it may be more advantageous to produce large numbers of small offspring (the reduced "investment" allows more to be produced). Most of the offspring succumb to environmental pressures, such as competition and predation (recall the Type III survivorship curve in Figure 36.2). But the ones that do survive develop rapidly, reproduce early, and thereby make up for the losses caused by environmentally induced mortality. Typically, such r-selected individuals have short life spans; relatively little of the total energy budget remains for parents to increase their own survival odds. The net effect of r-selection is to increase the rate at which the population can grow under low-density conditions. However,

Table 36.2	Traits Associated With r-Selection and K-Selection
r-Selected Populations	K-Selected Populations
1. Variable or unpredictable climatic conditions	1. Fairly constant or more predictable climatic conditions
2. Often catastrophic mortality, independent of population density	2. Mortality correlated with degree of population density (more competition, predation, etc., for dense populations)
3. Type III populations (high mortality early in life)	3. Types I and II populations (low mortality early in life, with rate of change in mortality mostly within narrow span at maturity or fairly constant at all age increments)
4. Short life spans, rapid development, single reproductive period	4. Longer life spans, slower development, repeated reproductive periods
5. Variable competition in a limited environment; adapted for rapid dispersal and colonization	5. Intense competition in a limited environment; not well adapted for dispersal
Overall characteristic:	*Overall characteristic:*
High productivity that can replace environmentally induced losses; recurring approaches toward and crashes below carrying capacity	Lower productivity but more efficiency and specialization in competing for resources; population size stabilizes around the carrying capacity

keep in mind that r is a property of populations, not individuals, and so is not acted upon *directly* by selective agents.

Many insect populations are r-selected. Weeds that colonize new habitats (such as plowed fields) are consummate r-strategists. They produce enormous numbers of small seeds, and the barest minimum of energy reserves are packaged inside the seed coats. As for all r-selected populations, the number of weeds that survive is usually well below the carrying capacity.

A different pattern occurs when populations hover near the carrying capacity. For example, in tropical regions, where climatic conditions are stable, individuals tend to spend proportionally less energy on reproduction and more on competing for available resources in efficient, specialized ways (see, for example, Figure 36.7). The term **K-selection**

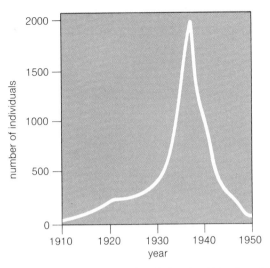

Figure 36.6 Rise and fall of a reindeer herd introduced on one of the Pribilof Islands, Alaska. Exponential growth led to an overshooting of the carrying capacity of the environment. Growth stopped abruptly, and the population size crashed to eight reindeer—eighteen less than were present in the starting population. (Data from V. Scheffer, *Science Monthly*, 1951, *73*:356–362)

refers to selection that occurs in populations near the carrying capacity. The populations tend to stabilize near *K*; there is a balance between births and deaths. Long-lived individuals that produce a few well-endowed young over the entire life span are favored. Among plants, seeds are endowed with energy reserves that help assure survival during early stages following germination. Among animals, parents typically care for and protect the young. An example is the elephant, which produces four or five large calves and makes a four-year parental investment in each one.

As with *r*-selection, selective agents cannot act on *K* directly. However, the carrying capacity may increase over time as a result of selection favoring better competitive abilities and efficiency of resource utilization by individuals.

Table 36.2 summarizes the overall differences between *r*-selection and *K*-selection. Keep in mind that they actually represent opposite ends of a continuum of reproductive strategies that occur in nature. Within any group of organisms, such as insects, there will be some species that are more *r*-selected than others. Similarly, within any area (such as a temperate forest), there will be a range of reproductive strategies among the species present, because each species responds to the environment in its unique manner.

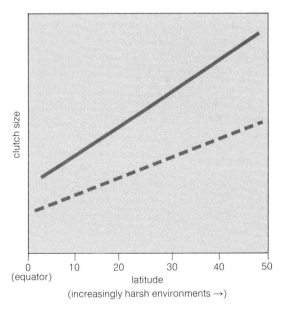

Figure 36.7 Relationship between latitude and clutch size in two families of birds. One family includes meadowlarks, blackbirds, and orioles (dashed line); the other, ruddy ducks and masked ducks (solid line). The dashed line is a plot of data gathered in North and South America. The solid line is a plot of data gathered throughout the world. (Data from M. Cody, *Evolution*, 1966, *20*:174–184)

FACTORS THAT REGULATE POPULATION GROWTH

Density-Dependent and Density-Independent Factors

Some of the mechanisms that regulate populations vary in relation to population density. They are **density-dependent mechanisms**, and they have an overall homeostatic effect. When the population size increases, the mechanisms cut it back by decreasing the birth rate, increasing the death rate, or promoting emigration. When population size decreases, the pressures ease up and growth proceeds.

For instance, when population size increases, the amount of food available for each individual declines. The decline in food may lead to impaired health, which may affect the reproductive rate. But when population size falls, the survivors have more food available, their health may improve, and their reproductive rate may rise.

Other mechanisms are not influenced by population density; they are **density-independent mechanisms**. For example, catastrophic changes in the weather can have enormous impact on survival and growth regardless of how large or small a population happens to be.

It appears that density-dependent and density-independent mechanisms interact in such complex ways that the effects of one often mask the effects of the other. For instance, whether a rabbit population tolerates a sudden freeze depends on whether its members have enough food and burrows. Food and burrow availability are density-dependent factors—yet here they interact with a density-independent change in temperature. Because it is so difficult to determine whether one or both mechanisms are operating, ecologists often classify the regulatory factors as being either extrinsic or intrinsic to the population itself.

Extrinsic Influences

External conditions (both abiotic and biotic) that affect populations are called **extrinsic factors**. They include temperature, rainfall, resource availability, and predation. We will explore these factors in detail in later chapters. Only a few examples will be included here to give you a general idea of the forces at work on population size and distribution.

Abiotic Conditions. The effects of abiotic conditions can be density-independent. For example, you could boil a culture flask full of bacteria and the entire population would drop dead no matter how many or how few there were. Such catastrophic events are not confined to culture flasks. They await natural populations whenever environmental variables rise above or fall below tolerance ranges characteristic of the species.

The effects of abiotic conditions can also be density-dependent. For example, during the continuous night of Antarctic winter, emperor penguins face winds that reach 140 kilometers (90 miles) per hour and $-60°C$ temperatures. They face the icy blasts in huddles of thousands of individuals. The large groups are effective in breaking the force of the wind and in keeping individuals far warmer than they would be in less dense groupings.

Competition Within Populations. Resource availability is an extrinsic influence that is density-dependent. (The more individuals there are in a given space, the fewer resources there are to go around.) It is the source of two types of **intraspecific competition** (contests between individuals of the population):

scramble competition	*All individuals have access to the resource and each scrambles to get it.*
contest competition	*The resource gets divided only among the individuals that compete successfully for it; unsuccessful individuals go without and, typically, die or are dispersed.*

During competition for limited resources, some fraction of the population generally fails to obtain them, and that fraction fails to survive or reproduce. Under scramble conditions, it may happen that all members get such a small portion that only a few can survive. The outcome may be a catastrophic swing in population density (Figure 36.8).

Under contest conditions, these kinds of swings are less likely to occur. The successful members carve out a supply of resources necessary for survival and reproduction; the unsuccessful are denied access to the resources. When the resource is food, deaths still occur, but they are limited to a small part of the population; overall, population density still remains relatively high. Territoriality and social dominance (Chapter Forty-One) are manifestations of contest competition.

Predation. Predators are one of the most powerful extrinsic influences on populations. When prey populations become increasingly dense, their members face a proportionally greater risk of being dispatched by predators. Theoretically, as the predator population increases (or decreases), the abundance of prey decreases (or increases). This is apparently as true of herbivores, or "plant predators," as it is of carnivores. Rabbits, for example, can keep the density of grass populations at depressed levels. Their impact was dramatically illustrated in the English countryside in the 1950s, when the rabbit population was nearly decimated by the disease myxomatosis. Shortly afterward, there was spectacular growth among the grasses and perennial weeds. The next chapter will provide more detailed examples of the effects of predation. For now, the point to remember is this:

Extrinsic factors are external conditions (abiotic and biotic) that act on the individuals of a population. Their effects may be influenced by population density or they may occur independently of density.

Intrinsic Influences

Intrinsic factors are properties of individuals that change as population density changes, and that in turn influence population size. These properties can be some aspect of structure, physiology, metabolism, and behavior of individuals.

For example, consider what happens when increases in population size lead to overcrowding. In 1971, K. Myers reported the results of experiments in which populations of wild rabbits were confined to variably sized spaces of their natural habitat. The rabbits confined to medium or large spaces showed no abnormalities; those confined to the smallest space were affected profoundly. Females showed increased aggressive and sexual activity, yet they did not ovulate at a normal rate and they produced fewer offspring. Autopsies showed that kidneys had become inflamed, adrenal glands had enlarged, and the liver and spleen had decreased in weight. Offspring of the stressed females were stunted overall and had abnormally small organs. They also had a poor survival rate.

Overcrowding also stresses vascular plant populations. Increased density can restrict leaf exposure to sunlight and root exposure to the dilute concentrations of nutrients in soil. Responses include adjustments in the size, shape, and number of roots and leaves.

Intrinsic factors are aspects of physiology, metabolism, and behavior of individuals that change when population density changes, and that in turn influence population size.

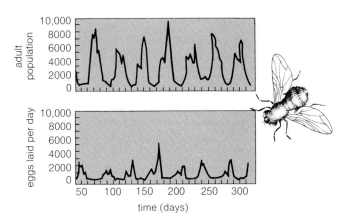

Figure 36.8 Effect of resource availability and scramble competition on population density for sheep blowflies *(Lucilia cuprina)*. In one laboratory experiment, A. Nicholson fed limited amounts of beef liver to fly larvae. He also fed unlimited amounts of sugar and water to adults that were part of the same experimental group.

When the adult population density was high, so many eggs were laid that the resulting larvae devoured all the food before completing their development, and they all died. Through natural mortality, the size of the existing adult population dwindled and fewer eggs were laid. Fewer eggs meant fewer larvae—and less competition among them. Now some larvae were able to mature into adults. For a while, population density declined because of the time lag between the survival of larvae and the development of egg-laying adults. The delay permitted an increasing number of larvae to survive—and the adult population soared again.

The outcome of this scramble competition was a drastic overshoot-undershoot oscillation in population size over time. (Data from A. J. Nicholson, *Cold Spring Harbor Symposium on Quantitative Biology*, 22:153–173)

HUMAN POPULATION GROWTH

So far we have touched on a few of the mechanisms that regulate the growth of natural populations. Thus you can see how populations grow explosively under certain combinations of short-term variables, only to decline in the long term as regulatory mechanisms reassert themselves. Let's see how this pattern applies to human population growth.

Doubling Time for the Human Population

In 1983, the human population reached nearly 4.7 billion. Even if this number represented a stabilized population level, we would have to contend with monumental problems. For example, in a given year, between 5 and 20 million people now die of starvation and malnutrition-related diseases. What makes future prospects especially chilling is that our population size is by no means static.

In 1983, Mexico's growth rate was 2.6 percent. At this rate, its population will double in twenty-seven years. Japan's growth rate was 0.7 percent; its population will double within a hundred years at this rate. The world average in 1983 was 1.8 percent. If this rate continues, world population will double within thirty-nine years. This means that by the year 2020—well within your lifetime—world population could be nearly 8 billion!

With the most intensive effort, we might be able to double food production over the next forty-one years to keep pace with growth. However, we would succeed in doing little more than maintaining marginal living conditions for most of the world. Under such conditions, deaths from starvation could be 10 to 40 million a year. For a while, it would be like the Red Queen's garden in Lewis Carroll's *Through the Looking Glass,* where one is forced to run as fast as one can to remain in the same place. However, what happens when resources other than food become limiting factors? What happens when the population doubles again to 16 billion? Can you brush this picture aside as being too far in the future to warrant your concern? It is no farther removed from you than your own sons and daughters; that world is their legacy.

Where We Began Sidestepping Controls

How did we get into this predicament in the first place? For most of our existence as a species, human population growth has been slow. In the past two centuries, there has been an astounding increase in the rate of population growth (Figure 36.9). Unfortunately, no special rules govern the growth of the human population over the long term. It is subject to much the same regulating factors that occur among populations of other large animals having relatively long life spans. Why, then, has our long-term growth rate increased so dramatically? There are three possible reasons:

1. We steadily developed the capacity to expand into new environments.

2. The carrying capacity of the environment was increased.

3. A series of limiting factors was removed.

Let's consider the first possibility. We know that by 50,000 years ago, the human species had radiated through much of the world. For most animal species, such extensive radiations would not have occurred as rapidly (Chapter Thirty). Humans were able to do so with the application of learning and memory—how to build fires, assemble shelters, create clothing and tools, plan a community hunt. Learned experiences were not confined to individuals but spread quickly from one human group to another because of language—our ability for cultural communication. (It took less than seven decades from the time we first ventured into the air until we landed on the moon.) Thus the human population expanded into new environments, and it did so in an extremely short time span compared with the radiations of other organisms.

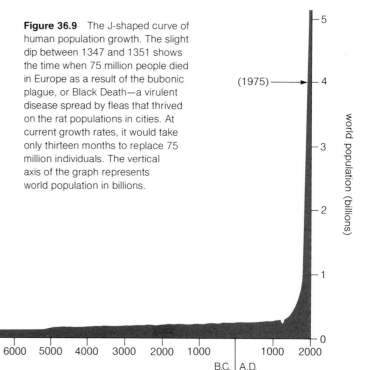

Figure 36.9 The J-shaped curve of human population growth. The slight dip between 1347 and 1351 shows the time when 75 million people died in Europe as a result of the bubonic plague, or Black Death—a virulent disease spread by fleas that thrived on the rat populations in cities. At current growth rates, it would take only thirteen months to replace 75 million individuals. The vertical axis of the graph represents world population in billions.

What about the second possibility? Since the human species first appeared, there have been profound changes in world climate. Climate has a major influence on the amounts and kinds of vegetation that will grow in a region, hence on the numbers and kinds of animals that vegetation supports. About 11,000 years ago, an overall warming of the earth apparently triggered a shift from the hunting way of life to agriculture—from risky, demanding moves after the game herds to a settled, more dependable basis for existence in more favorable settings. Even in its simplest form, agricultural management of food supplies bypassed the natural carrying capacity of the environment. Through the development of irrigation, metallurgy, social stratification (which provides a labor base) and, later, use of fertilizers and pesticides, the limits were expanded and were met again with a resurgence of human population growth. Thus, with the domestication of plants and animals, the carrying capacity has indeed risen abruptly for human populations.

What about the third possibility—the removal of limiting factors? The potential for growth inherent in the development of agriculture began to be realized with the suppression of contagious diseases. Until about 300 years ago, contagious diseases kept the death rate relatively high, and it counteracted the high birth rate. Contagious diseases are density-dependent factors, and they spread rapidly through crowded settlements and cities. Without proper hygiene and sewage disposal methods, and plagued with such disease carriers as fleas and rats, population size increased only slowly at first. Then plumbing and sewage treatment methods appeared. Bacteria and viruses were recognized as disease agents. Vaccines, antitoxins, and drugs such as antibiotics were developed. Thus one after another major limiting factor on human population growth has been largely pushed aside. Smallpox, plague, diphtheria, cholera, measles, malaria—many diseases have been brought under control in the developed countries. Concurrently, medical technology has been exported in a humanitarian effort to control disease in developing countries as well. With war, old age, and starvation the only major checks remaining, population growth has been sky-rocketing ever since.

Age Structure and Fertility Rates

Two important factors influence just how much we can expect our rate of increase to slow down. The first has to do with **age structure**: how individuals are distributed at each age level for a population. Figure 36.10 shows generalized examples of age structure diagrams. Let's look at the

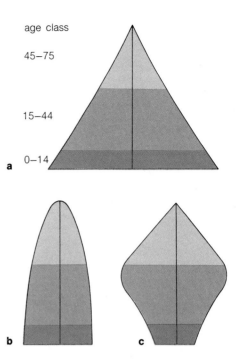

Figure 36.10 Generalized age structure diagrams for (**a**) a rapidly expanding population, (**b**) a slowly expanding population, and (**c**) a stable population.

meaning of these factors by placing individuals of a population into three categories—those before, during, and after reproductive age. We can use the ages 15 to 44 as the average range of childbearing years. Once we do this, we can create diagrams that readily show the prospects for population growth.

The age structure pyramid for a rapidly growing population has a broad base, as Figure 36.11 suggests. It is filled not only with reproductive-age men and women but with a large number of children who will move into that category during the next fifteen years. As Table 36.3 indicates, *more than a third of the world population now falls in the broad pre-reproductive base.* Such figures give an idea of the magnitude of the effort that would be needed to control birth rates on a global scale.

One other factor influencing the short-term picture of population growth is the **fertility rate**: how many infants are born to each woman during her reproductive years. Frequently, the general fertility rate is calculated on the basis of number of births each year per 1,000 women between ages 15 and 44. Today the average number of

Table 36.3	Percent of World Population Ready To Move Into Reproductive Age Bracket	
Country or Region	Population Under Age 15 (percent)	
Africa		
Northern Africa	43	
Western Africa	47	
Eastern Africa	45	45 (average)
Middle Africa	44	
Southern Africa	42	
Asia		
Southwest Asia	41	
Middle South Asia	41	36
Southeast Asia	39	
East Asia	31	
North America		
Canada	23	23
United States	23	
Latin America		
Central America	44	
Caribbean	36	39
Tropical South America	39	
Temperate South America (Argentina, Chile, Uruguay)	29	
Europe		
Northern Europe	20	
Western Europe	19	22
Eastern Europe	23	
Southern Europe	23	
USSR	25	
Oceania	29	
WORLD AVERAGE:	34	

Percentages from the 1983 World Population Data Sheet, Population Reference Bureau, Inc.

children in a family is 1.9 in industrialized countries and 5.2 in developing countries. A world average of 2.5 children per family is the estimated "replacement level" fertility rate that would bring us to zero population growth, given the mortality rate among children. But even assuming that a world average of 2.5 children is achieved and maintained, it would still be 70 to 100 years before the human population stops growing. Why? An immense number of existing children are yet to move into the reproductive age category.

The most that can be hoped for in the immediate future is to slow the growth rate and buy time to implement more effective measures. A simple way to slow things down would be to encourage delayed reproduction—childbearing in the early thirties as opposed to the mid-teens or early twenties. In Ireland, women customarily marry later in life. In China, the government has raised the age at which marriage is allowed; there are strong economic and social penalties for having more than two children, and rewards for having only one. Such cultural constraints tend to lower the number of children in each family. Figure 36.3 showed how delayed reproduction can slow down population growth rates. However, remember that as long as birth rates even slightly exceed death rates, populations experience exponential growth.

PERSPECTIVE

In this chapter, we began with the premise that all populations have the potential for exponential growth—growth at increasing rates to enormous numbers. We proceeded to analyze the nature of limiting factors that keep populations in check and thereby assure stability according to the imperatives of the environment. For the human population, as for all others, the biological implications of instability are staggering. Yet so are the social implications of achieving stability, of achieving and maintaining zero population growth.

For instance, consider that most members of an actively growing population fall in younger age brackets. Under conditions of constant growth, the age distribution means that there is a large work force. A large work force is capable of supporting older, nonproductive individuals with various welfare programs, such as social security, low-cost housing, and health care. With zero population growth, far more people will fall in the older age brackets. How, then, can goods and services be provided for nonproductive members if productive ones are asked to carry a greater and greater share of the burden? These are not abstract questions. Put them to yourself. How much are you willing to bear for the sake of your parents, your grandparents? How much will your children be able to bear for you?

We have arrived at a major turning point, not only in our biological evolution but also in our social evolution. The decisions awaiting us are among the most difficult we will ever have to make. Yet it is clear that they must be made, and soon.

All species face limits to growth. In one sense, we have proved ourselves different from the rest, for our unique ability to undergo cultural evolution has allowed us to

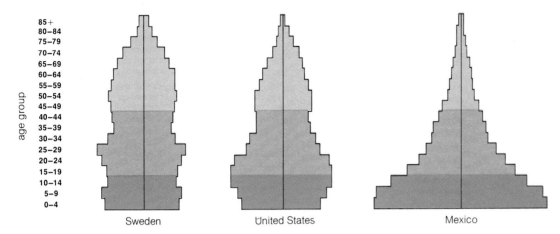

age group

85+
80–84
75–79
70–74
65–69
60–64
55–59
50–54
45–49
40–44
35–39
30–34
25–29
20–24
15–19
10–14
5–9
0–4

Sweden   United States   Mexico

Figure 36.11   Age structure diagrams for three countries in 1977. Dark green indicates the pre-reproductive base. Dark blue indicates reproductive years; light blue, the post-reproductive years. The portion of the population to the left of the vertical axis in each diagram represents males; the portion to the right represents females. Mexico has a very rapid rate of increase. In 1980, Sweden showed zero population growth. (After Miller, *Living in the Environment,* Wadsworth, 1982)

postpone the action of most of the factors limiting growth. But the key word here is *postpone.* No amount of cultural intervention can hold back the ultimate check of limited resources. We have repealed a number of the smaller laws of nature; in the process, we have become more vulnerable to those laws which cannot be repealed. Today there may be only two options available. Either we make a global effort to limit population growth in accordance with environmental carrying capacity, or we wait passively until the environment does it for us.

Readings

Barbor, M., J. Burk, and W. Pitts. 1980. *Terrestrial Plant Ecology.* Menlo Park, California: Benjamin/Cummings.

Begon, M., and M. Mortimer. 1981. *Population Ecology: A Unified Study of Plants and Animals.* Sunderland, Massachusetts: Sinauer Associates.

Environmental Fund. 1983. *World Population Estimates.* Washington, D.C.: The Environmental Fund.

Pianka, E. 1983. *Population Ecology.* Third edition. New York: Harper & Row.

Polgar, S. 1972. "Population History and Population Policies From an Anthropological Perspective." *Current Anthropology* 13(2):203–241. Analyzes often-ignored cultural barriers to programs for population control.

Price, P. 1975. *Insect Ecology.* New York: Wiley.

Scientific American. 1974. *The Human Population.* San Francisco: Freeman. Entire issue devoted to world population problems.

Smith, R. 1980. *Ecology and Field Biology.* Third edition. New York: Harper & Row. Probably the most accessible introductory book in the field. Profuse illustrations and examples, step-by-step explanation of principles and methodology.

Wilson, E., and W. Bossert. 1971. *A Primer of Population Biology.* Sunderland, Massachusetts: Sinauer Associates.

Review Questions

1. Why do populations that are not restricted in some way grow exponentially?

2. If the birth rate equals the death rate, what happens to the growth rate of a population? If the birth rate remains slightly higher than the death rate, what happens?

3. Explain the relationship between factors that limit population growth and the carrying capacity of the environment in which that population is found.

4. Distinguish between extrinsic and intrinsic limiting factors on population growth.

5. At present growth rates, how many years will elapse before the human population doubles in number?

6. How have human populations developed the means to expand steadily into new environments? How have humans increased the carrying capacity of their environments? How have they avoided some of the limiting factors on population growth– or is the avoidance illusory?

7. If a third of the world population is now below age fifteen, what effect will this age distribution have on the growth rate of the human population? What sorts of humane recommendations would you make that would encourage this age group to limit the number of children they plan to have?

37

COMMUNITY INTERACTIONS

Flying through the dense rain forest canopies of New Guinea is something that is not your typical pigeon. The natives call it *gara*. The *gara* is about as big as a turkey, with cobalt blue feathers and plumes on its head. It flaps so slowly and noisily that its flight has been likened to the sound of an idling truck. This New Guinea pigeon eats fruit, as do eight other sympatric species. Now, this rather enormous pigeon obviously requires more food energy than its smaller relatives do in order to maintain body weight. Could it be that *gara* populations eat so much that the other pigeon populations are severely limited in numbers or bordering on starvation? Not so. All of these related fruit-eating species have carved out a place for themselves in the same setting. The larger birds must perch on heavy branches when they feed. Fortunately for the smaller birds, fruit also hangs from thin branches that never would support the weight of a turkey-size pigeon. Hence part of the food supply that is not available to one species is utilized by others in the same forest, even in the same trees.

This example reminds us that populations rarely, if ever, exist by themselves. To understand how they are organized and how they function, we must also consider their place in the community. A **community** consists of all those populations of different species that are living together in a given area. This chapter will focus primarily on three kinds of community interactions:

1. *Interspecific competition* for limited resources

2. *Predation* of one species on another

3. *Coevolution* of two species over time

Studies of these interactions provide insight into how particular populations are performing in the community, as measured by their relative reproductive success.

HABITAT AND NICHE

A **habitat** is where an individual or population of a given species lives—its address, so to speak. The word does not refer to a geographic range. Rather, it generally refers to a "place" character, such as a vegetation zone, the height above ground in a forest canopy, or the depth in the mud at the bottom of a pond. For example, in the Sierra Nevada of California are four different chipmunk species, each occupying a different habitat (Figure 37.2). The four habitats occur at different altitudes, and each represents a distinct vegetation zone:

alpine habitat	*alpine chipmunk*
lodgepole pine habitat	*lodgepole chipmunk*
piñon pine/sagebrush habitat	*yellow pine chipmunk*
sagebrush habitat	*least chipmunk*

All such living spaces are characterized by a particular range of physical and chemical conditions, including light, temperature, humidity, and pH. Each species is anatomically, physiologically, and behaviorally adapted to respond to the conditions of its habitat. The species also is equipped to respond to a range of conditions imposed, directly or indirectly, by other organisms in the community (such as variations in prey size, numbers, and distribution).

The full range of abiotic and biotic conditions under which a species can live and reproduce is called its **fundamental niche**. Within this range, different conditions shift in large and small ways, creating an ever-changing mosaic to which the species responds. In fact, there is no way to determine what conditions are being imposed at any instant because the number of combinations is, for all practical purposes, infinite. In their studies, ecologists therefore must focus on only a few conditions at a time.

Niche conditions can be viewed as resource categories. The response of a species in one of these categories can be plotted in graph form, with one axis of the graph representing the resource gradient, and the other representing the

Figure 37.1 Confrontation between predator and prey. As a last resort, the baboon has turned back to face the leopard with threat behavior. The effect has momentarily stopped the predator's advance; under other circumstances it might have meant the difference between capture and escape. Here, in the open, the baboon has run out of alternatives.

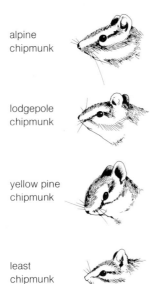

alpine
chipmunk

lodgepole
chipmunk

yellow pine
chipmunk

least
chipmunk

Figure 37.2 In the foreground, alpine tundra, with a stand of lodgepole pines in the distance. These are examples of two of the vegetational zones of the eastern slopes of the Sierra Nevada in California. Each zone is the habitat of a different species of chipmunk (*Eutamias*).

Clara Calhoun / Bruce Coleman Ltd.

measured activity of the species (its *resource utilization*) in relation to the gradient:

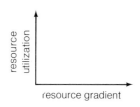

For example, prey size would be one resource category, and the number of individuals that capture prey of one size or another could be plotted relative to it:

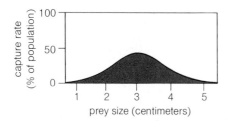

Here, a bell-shaped curve results and shows the distributional response of the species along the resource gradient.

Now, if a species were the only one in a habitat, we might imagine that it could make a full response in any given resource category. However, other species are present, and they can interfere with one another in ways that modify or prevent the full response. A species can be forced to retreat from part of its niche, either some of the time or all of the time. (For example, for one reason or another, blue-gray gnatcatchers do not feed much of the time on insects more than twelve centimeters long, and they do not feed very often at the base of oak trees. Figure 37.3 shows what may be the actual boundaries for the size of prey they do capture and for their foraging area.) The *actual* range of conditions under which a species exists is called its **realized niche**.

By way of analogy, *think of the realized niche as an ever changing cloud.* The cloud shrinks and expands along many axes, in large and small ways, depending on where the cloud happens to be in relation to other niches.

Habitats are points in the landscape (such as height above ground or a vegetation zone) at which a species is distributed.

A species responds to the physical conditions of its habitat and to the conditions imposed by the activities of other species present.

The full range of variable conditions under which a species can function (assuming no interference from other species) is its fundamental niche.

The actual range of conditions under which a species exists is its realized niche.

TYPES OF COMMUNITY INTERACTIONS

Even the simplest communities are composed of dozens or hundreds of species, and a staggering number of interactions can be influencing the realized niche at any time. Some interactions, such as prey capture, can be obvious enough to field observers. Others are indirect and often distant, and they usually become apparent only after prolonged, detailed analyses. Through many studies, however, certain patterns have been identified.

Recurring interactions between two species are forms of **symbiosis**, a term coined in 1879 by Anton de Bary. Broadly speaking, symbiosis means "living together." Symbiotic interactions differ in three ways:

1. The degree (or closeness) of the association

2. How exclusive the relationship is

3. The extent to which one species is helped or harmed by the presence or activity of the other

In this last respect, the interactions can be positive, negative, or neutral (Table 37.1). Although specific examples of symbiotic interactions will be described throughout this unit of the book, it will be useful to start with general definitions of the different types.

Neutral interactions have no direct effect on either species. There are two kinds of positive interactions that benefit both species: protocooperation and mutualism. In **protocooperation**, the interaction is beneficial but not really essential; it is not obligatory. For instance, when honeybees find clover blooming profusely, they concentrate on collecting food from clover. When blossoms of that species fade, they turn to honeysuckle, apple blossoms, and other flowers. Similarly, if honeybees are not around, then bumblebees, butterflies, and moths may pollinate the clover. Positive benefits flow both ways between any two of the plant and animal species, but the interaction is not essential to the survival of either one.

Some interactions have positive effects on both species. In **mutualism**, positive benefits exist and are crucial to the survival of both species; the interaction is obligatory. An example of this kind of interaction will be described later.

Sometimes the interaction is positive for one species and neutral for the other. In **commensalism**, one species benefits from the interaction; the other does not garner direct benefits, but neither is it harmed. For instance, perhaps you maintain a yard with a large lawn. Robins benefit from your lawn-maintenance activities (lawns happen to be a wonderful habitat for earthworms, which are food for

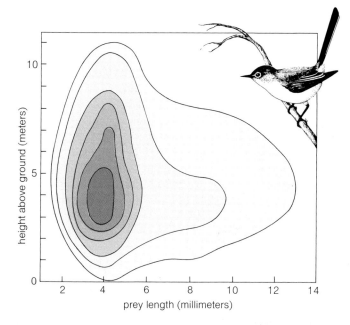

Figure 37.3 Plot of niche space in two dimensions for the blue-gray gnatcatcher, a small insect-eating bird of California's oak woodlands. The ecologist R. Root measured the length of the insects captured and the height at which the birds foraged in the trees. (Measurements were based on observed frequency of capture and analysis of stomach contents of the birds.) He then plotted the data along two axes of a graph. Here, the niche "center" (darkest shading) represents the maximum response levels in the resource categories. The contour lines around this center represent less effective response levels. The outermost contour line probably represents the boundary of the realized niche for the two dimensions studied. (After R. Root, 1967)

Table 37.1 Types of Symbiotic Interactions Between Two Species		
	Effect of Interaction*	
Type of Interaction	Species 1*	Species 2
Neutral	0	0
Protocooperation (nonobligatory)	+	+
Mutualism (obligatory)	+	+
Commensalism	+	0
Predation	+	−
Parasitism	+	−
Interspecific competition	−	−

* 0 indicates no direct effect on population growth,
+ indicates positive effect, − indicates negative effect.
After P. Burkholder, 1952. *American Scientist*, 40:601–631

robins). It is not impossible for robins to live without your gardening activities, but foraging is easier because of them. At the same time, the robin's worm-gathering activities don't really affect you one way or the other.

Sometimes the interaction is positive for one species and negative for the other. In **predation**, the population that does the dining garners positive effects, whereas the population serving as dinner does not. **Parasitism** is another form of positive-negative interaction. Often it is viewed as a weak form of predation, for tissues of a host organism are ingested by the parasite. In most parasitic interactions, though, the victim either survives or takes a relatively long time dying. (If it did not, the parasite would be quickly selected against.)

Finally, there are symbiotic interactions that can have a negative effect on both species. **Interspecific competition** (or competition between species) falls in this category.

INTERSPECIFIC COMPETITION

When different species in a community have some requirement or activity in common, their fundamental niches overlap. In some resource categories (such as atmospheric oxygen, used in aerobic respiration), supplies are unlimited and therefore the niche overlaps present no problems. In other categories, however, supplies can be limited and the species may end up competing for them. The greater the potential for resource overlap, the greater the potential for competition.

Interspecific competition (between species) usually is not as intense as *intraspecific* competition (within a population of a species). Why is this so? Consider that the activity of each individual using a resource depletes or limits it to some extent, and therefore affects the ability of others to use the resource. Because requirements are much the same for all members of the population, intraspecific competition can be fierce when resources are in short supply. Although requirements for different species might be similar, they cannot be identical, so competition is usually less intense.

The Concept of Competitive Exclusion

How similar can niches be before competition becomes intense enough for exclusion to occur—in other words, to force one species out of the niche space? In the 1920s, models were developed to explain what happens when two species compete intensely for the same limited resource. These models indicated that a large enough population in-

crease by one species would have a negative effect on the other, and would drive it to extinction. (The difference in the rate of increase would be the outcome of some structural, physical, or behavioral difference between the two species, a difference that would give one the competitive edge.)

In the 1930s, G. Gause tested this idea by growing two species of *Paramecium* together, in the same culture. Because the two species require similar food, Gause reasoned that there would be strong competition between them. His experiments, summarized in Figure 37.4, suggested that the mathematical models were correct. Gause reported his evidence for the concept that complete competitors cannot coexist, an idea now called **competitive exclusion**.

The competitive exclusion hypothesis is based on experiments indicating that when two species compete intensely for the same resource, one will be deprived of that resource because of the more effective competitive ability of the other.

Field Evidence of Competitive Exclusion

Although competitive exclusion has been demonstrated under laboratory conditions, it is not so easy to detect in natural communities. There, competition can be occurring so gradually that it is not apparent. Also, it may be that competition is only one of many interactions that are forcing one species out of a particular niche. In long-standing communities, there may be no evidence at all of competitive exclusion, simply because the losers are no longer around.

Even so, some field evidence does lend support to the concept. For example, at one time a species of giant tortoise lived on Abingdon Island of the Galápagos Archipelago. In 1962, there was no trace of living tortoises—although remains of individuals were found that could not have died more than a few years earlier. Their extinction was the outcome of competition with goats, which fishermen introduced to the island in 1957—and which completely consumed the only plants that the tortoises used as food. This is an example of *exploitative competition,* in which two (or more) species require the same limited resource and have equal access to it.

There is also field evidence of *interference competition,* in which one species denies another species access to a limited resource, usually by aggressive behavior. For example, the fundamental niche of the least chipmunk mentioned earlier *could* extend from sagebrush deserts to the alpine zone of the Sierra Nevada. However, aggressive behavior of the yellow pine chipmunks in the vegetational zone above it

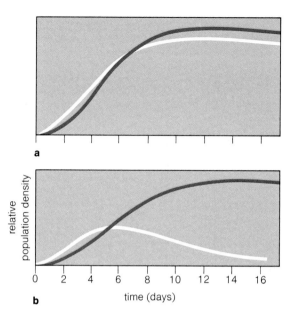

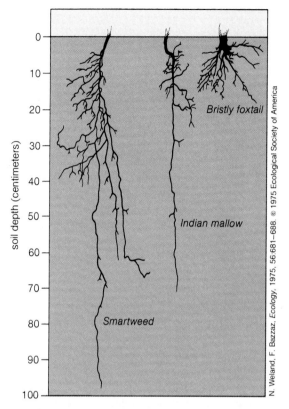

Figure 37.4 Increase in population size for two *Paramecium* species when grown in separate cultures (**a**), and when grown together (**b**). Of the two species, *P. caudatum* (white graph line) was larger in body size and slower growing. Both species thrived in the absence of interspecific competition. The *P. caudatum* population became extinct when grown with *P. aurelia,* represented by the red graph line. (After G. Gause, 1934)

N. Weiland, F. Bazzaz, Ecology, 1975, 56:681–688. © 1975 Ecological Society of America

Figure 37.5 Partitioning of a resource (soil, with its nutrients and water) by three annual plant species that became established in a field plowed one year before.

restricts that species to sagebrush habitats. Similarly, alpine chipmunks in the highest vegetational zone vigorously defend their habitat against intrusions by chipmunks below it. Both alpine and yellow pine chipmunks face seasonal shortages of food, to the extent that they store supplies for the winter. For them, an extremely limited food supply may be a source of competitive behavior.

Although such evidence is intriguing, the role of competition in the day-to-day ecology of a species is not really understood. Some ecologists doubt its significance; others readily accept it.

Coexistence in Resource Categories

Resource utilization curves for different species can overlap. In some cases of overlapping, it may be that competition is absent or weak, with the activity of each species concentrated within a narrow range of the total resource gradient. The distribution of three such species might look like this:

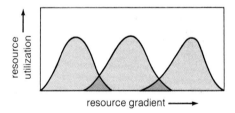

where the shaded areas represent overlap. However, in natural communities, competition is spread over a number of resource gradients, not just one. Coexistence may be possible if competition for some resource is low, even though competition for others is intense. (Conversely, low competition from several species along different resource gradients may have an additive effect, leading to the exclusion of a species that simply cannot fit into the community.)

Coexistence may also be possible through **resource partitioning**, whereby two or more species share resources in different ways, in different areas, or at different times.

N. Weland and F. Bazzaz studied resource partitioning in a field that had been abandoned a year after being plowed. Three annual plant species moved in. Like all land plants, each required sunlight, water, and mineral ions from the soil. Each met those requirements without interfering with the others by exploiting different areas of the habitat space (Figure 37.5). Bristly foxtail grasses became established in soil that held varying amounts of water. With their shallow, fibrous root systems the foxtails could rapidly absorb water after rains and could recover rapidly from droughts. Mallow plants occupied different areas of the soil. With their taproot systems, these plants could exploit soil depths that remained moist early in the growing season but that were less moist later on. The third plant species, smartwood, has a taproot system that branched not only in the topsoil but also in continuously moist soil below the rooting zone of the other two species.

Dogs of the same or different species partition their daytime activities to avoid direct competition. These animals establish *territories:* areas defined not by any particular behavior (such as defense) but by the degree to which they are used exclusively by the occupants. Often the "territories" are no more than networks of paths and places where activities occur, such that some territories overlap extensively in space. Scent marking, a form of olfactory signaling, allows coexistence without confrontation. Paul Leyhausen speculated that "a fresh mark means 'section closed,' an older mark means 'proceed with caution,' and a very old mark means 'go on, but before you use this please put your own mark so that the next one knows exactly what to do.'" In effect, the scent marks are traffic signals that partition activities in time.

Coexistence of two or more species that compete in the same resource category can occur when each specializes within a narrow range of the resource gradient.

Coexistence may also occur through resource partitioning, whereby species share the same resource in different ways, in different areas, or at different times.

PREDATION

Of all community interactions, predation is perhaps the most riveting of our attention (as well as the prey's). Dramatic examples abound, including the confrontation

Figure 37.6 Correlation between the lynx population (dashed line) and the snowshoe hare population (solid line) in Canada over a ninety-year period. These data are derived not from field observations but from counts of the pelts that trappers sold to Hudsons Bay Co. The curves have been taken to be a general example of the way that predation can control the populations of both predator and prey. (Data from D. MacLulich, University of Toronto Studies, Biology Series 43, 1937)

This figure is a good test of how willing you are to accept conclusions without questioning their scientific basis. (Remember the discussion of scientific methods in Chapter Two?) For example, what other extrinsic and intrinsic control factors could have been influencing the population levels? Were there also fluctuations in climate over this time span? Were some winters more rigorous, thereby imposing a higher death rate on one or both populations? Although this is called a simple predator-prey system, weren't the hares preying on the vegetation, which may have been overbrowsed in some years but not in others? What about owls, martens, and foxes—which also prey on hares? What if some years there were fewer trappers because of such very real variables as Indian uprisings? What about fluctuating demands for furs by the fashion industry? What if some years there was more lynx trapping than hare trapping, or vice vera?

between the leopard and baboon shown in Figure 37.1. Less dramatic are the interactions between herbivores (such as goats) and plants, also considered a form of predation. In all such cases, the relationship is the same: one living organism is the diner, the other is dinner.

Some mathematical models predict that predator-prey interactions lead to oscillations in population growth. One of the first models, developed by A. Lotka and V. Volterra, suggested that as a predator population increases, the population of its prey decreases, whereupon the responses are reversed and an oscillation in the interaction is produced. The abundance of the two populations over time can be depicted in this general way:

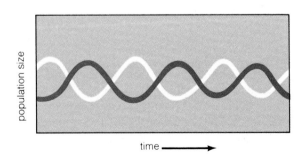

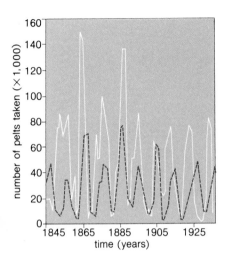

where the white graph line represents the population of prey and the red line, that of the predator. As this graph suggests, when the prey density increases, the number of predators increases. More predators mean more predation, hence fewer prey. The prey population size declines, as does the predator population, whereupon the cycle begins again.

Cyclic oscillations of this sort have been documented in a few simple predator-prey systems. For example, one long-term study points to a correlation between population sizes of the Canadian lynx and the snowshoe hare (Figure 37.6). There is indeed a correspondence between the rise and fall of these predator and prey populations, but the assumption that predation alone causes the oscillation is too simplistic.

For one thing, when prey population density is at its peak, predators are not usually numerous enough to bring about an immediate decline of the huge hordes of hares. *A numerical response to increased prey density requires time for more predators to move into areas where prey are abundant, or time for an increase in the predator population.* More abundant food can promote survival, more rapid development, even fertility, but there is a lag time between the birth of potential predators and the point at which they are mature enough to take prey. Thus increased predation can make a major contribution to the decline of the prey population, but it probably cannot trigger the decline. What does?

Figure 37.7 Snowshoe hare browsing on an early successional shrub. At the peak of the ten-year hare cycle, such plants are overbrowsed. The new shoots they put out have high concentrations of toxins, which severely stress the hares. These conditions may last long enough to cause a crash in the hare population.

There is some evidence that recurring wildfires, floods, and insect outbreaks have indirect bearing on the hare-lynx cycles. Such environmental disturbances can destroy mature forest canopies and thereby create favorable conditions for different plant species that are adapted to moving in and becoming established in exposed settings. These species flourish until the species characteristic of the mature forest system become reestablished and gradually succeed them (Chapter Thirty-Eight). Now, these so-called early successional species provide ideal forage for the hares; in fact, the peaks in hare population densities correspond to the occurrence of this type of vegetation cover. However, the early successional shrubs and trees include alders, poplar, black spruce, and birch species. These plants produce toxins, which become particularly concentrated in new, adventitious shoots. During winter, the hares preferentially feed on other plant parts with no ill effects. When population density is high, though, the hares destroy the harmless parts of their winter forage, and they are forced to begin feeding on the toxic shoots. Experiments show that hares ingesting high concentrations of the plant toxins rapidly lose weight and become severely stressed. Thus it may be that the cyclic oscillations in population density are more of a consequence of hares preying on plants than of lynx preying on hares. It may be an outcome of built-in chemical defenses of early successional, disturbance-tolerant plants—defenses against potentially devastating increases in the numbers of hares (Figure 37.7).

COEVOLUTION

The term **coevolution** refers to the joint evolution of two (or more) species that are interacting in some close ecological fashion. When one species evolves, the other also evolves to some extent because the change affects selection pressures operating between the two. For example, predators and prey exert continual selection pressure on each other. When some new, heritable means of defense spreads through the prey population, predators that specialize on those prey must be equipped to counter the defense if they are to eat. Examples of the coevolutionary outcomes of predator-prey systems will be described next, beginning with warning coloration and mimicry (Figure 37.8).

Ecologically interacting species can coevolve through reciprocal selection pressures.

a

Figure 37.8 Mimicry. Many animals—especially those bite-sized morsels, the insects—avoid being eaten by having a bad taste, obnoxious secretion, or painful bite or sting. Among predators, knowledge of these traits is not inherited. Each young predator learns about them the hard way, by often unpleasant trials.

Among many prey species, dangerous or unpalatable individuals are easily recognized and remembered. If this were not the case, many individuals would be lost as inexperienced predators learned their lessons. Thus repugnant species tend to have distinctive, memorable appearances—bright colors (such as red, which bird predators see so well), and bold markings (such as stripes, bands, and spots). These flamboyant species make no effort to conceal themselves. Sometimes they even deliberately flash colors with an uplift of the body or the wings. Their coloration and patterning are called "aposematic" (apo-, meaning "away," and sematic, meaning "signal").

In the natural world, each of the hundreds of dangerous or unpalatable species does not have a distinct warning signal, for too many signals would tax the learning capacity of predators. Instead there are whole groups of related species having almost identical aposematic appearances. Thus, many species benefit from a single taste trial. In turn, many less related and even totally unrelated species avoid predation by mimicking the appearance and behavior of the repugnant or dangerous model species.

Some mimics are as unpalatable as their models; they are called Müllerian mimics (after Fritz Müller, who named the phenomenon). Others may be quite edible yet are still avoided; they are called Batesian mimics (after Henry Bates, who discovered this class of mimics). Most mimicry series comprise both of these types.

There are other types of mimicry. In aggressive mimicry, parasites or predators bear resemblances to their hosts or prey. In speed mimicry, sluggish, easy-to-catch prey species resemble fast-running or fast-flying species that predators have given up trying to catch. (This might well be termed "frustration" mimicry.)

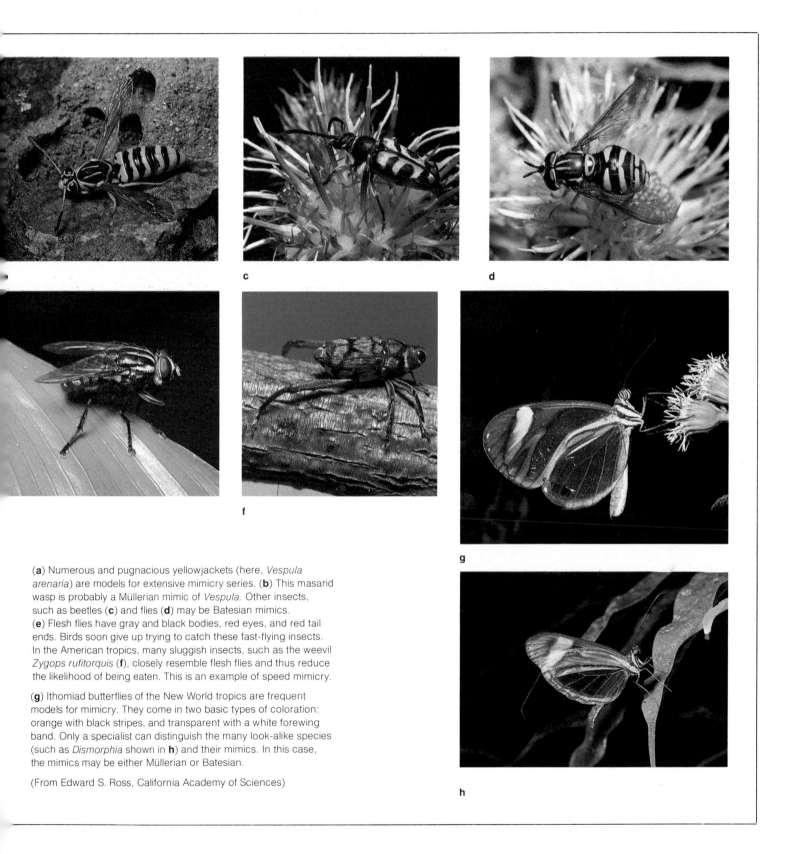

(a) Numerous and pugnacious yellowjackets (here, *Vespula arenaria*) are models for extensive mimicry series. (b) This masarid wasp is probably a Müllerian mimic of *Vespula*. Other insects, such as beetles (c) and flies (d) may be Batesian mimics. (e) Flesh flies have gray and black bodies, red eyes, and red tail ends. Birds soon give up trying to catch these fast-flying insects. In the American tropics, many sluggish insects, such as the weevil *Zygops rufitorquis* (f), closely resemble flesh flies and thus reduce the likelihood of being eaten. This is an example of speed mimicry.

(g) Ithomiad butterflies of the New World tropics are frequent models for mimicry. They come in two basic types of coloration: orange with black stripes, and transparent with a white forewing band. Only a specialist can distinguish the many look-alike species (such as *Dismorphia* shown in h) and their mimics. In this case, the mimics may be either Müllerian or Batesian.

(From Edward S. Ross, California Academy of Sciences)

Figure 37.9 Camouflage among the rocks. Find the plants (*Lithops*) that have the form, patterning, and color of stones.

W. M. Laetsch

Warning Coloration and Mimicry

One evolutionary outcome of predation is the existence of many prey species that are bad-tasting, toxic, or able to sting or otherwise inflict pain on their attackers. Often, toxic prey species are decked out with conspicuous colors and bold patterns that serve warning to potential predators. Inexperienced predators might attack a black-and-white striped skunk, a bright orange monarch butterfly, or a yellow-banded wasp. As a result of the experience, they quickly learn to associate the colors and patterning with pain or digestive upsets.

Other prey species that are not equipped with such defenses can still sport warning colors or patterns that *resemble* those of distasteful, toxic, or dangerous species. The resemblance of an edible species to a relatively inedible one is called **mimicry** (Figure 37.8).

Camouflage

Among the most remarkable evolutionary outcomes of predation are the ways in which many species of prey (and predators) are able to "hide" in the open. **Camouflage** refers to adaptations in form, patterning, color, or behavior that enable an organism to blend with its surroundings, the better to escape detection.

For example, *Lithops* is a desert plant that resembles small rocks in shape and color (Figure 37.9). Only during the brief rainy season, when other vegetation and water are more plentiful for herbivores, do these "living rocks" put forth bright-colored flowers that draw the attention of pollinators. Figure 37.10 shows other examples of camouflage as it occurs among prey animals. Camouflage, of course, is not the exclusive domain of prey. Predators that rely on stealth also blend well with their backgrounds. To give a few examples, consider the effectiveness of polar bears against snow, tigers against tall-stalked and golden grasses, and pastel spiders against pastel flower petals (Figure 37.10).

Moment-of-Truth Defenses

Camouflage allows some prey to escape detection, but what alternatives are available for those that do not? When cornered, some prey species defend themselves with display behavior that may startle or intimidate a predator (Figures 37.1 and 37.11a). Such behavior can create momentary confusion, and a moment may be all that it takes for the prey to escape. When attacked, the bombardier beetle raises its abdomen and sprays a noxious chemical at its predator. It is an effective adaptation in some cases. However, grasshopper mice have a behavioral counteradaptation. These mice pick up the beetle, shove its tail end into the earth, and munch the head end.

Chemical Defenses

The bombardier beetle just mentioned is an example of a prey species that releases chemicals to repel or otherwise deter a potential attacker. Among many plants and animals, chemicals serve as warning odors, repellants, alarm substances, and outright poisons. Earwigs, grasshoppers, skunks, and plants called skunk cabbages can produce awful odors. The foliage and seeds of some plants contain tannins, which taste bitter and which decrease the digestibility of the plant material. The tissues of other plants incorporate terpenes, which can be toxic. Nibbling on a buttercup (*Ranunculus*) leads to highly irritated mucous membranes in the mouth.

Some pheromones serve as alarm substances among prey fish that travel in schools and that have neither spines nor other built-in defenses. (Unlike hormones, which have internal targets, a **pheromone** is an exocrine gland secretion with some target outside the animal body. Pheromones can trigger behavioral changes in other animals of the same species by acting as alarm substances, trail markers, sex attractants, and the like.) The pheromones, released when the skin is broken (as during an attack) trigger a flight response in neighboring fish. Even a trace of the chemical will throw the school into panicked flight.

Predation and Seed Dispersal

In an intriguing countermove against predation, many flowering plants have come to exploit predators as resources.

Figure 37.10 The fine art of camouflage, as developed in predator-prey interactions. (**a**) One katydid species "hides" in the open from bird predators by looking like leaves—even down to blemishes and chewed-up parts. (**b**) Caterpillars of some moth species tend to look like bird droppings because of their coloration and the body positions that they assume. (**c**) By lurking motionless against its like-colored background, the yellow crab spider is essentially invisible to prey. (**d**) What bird??? With the approach of a potential predator, the American bittern stretches its reed-colored neck and thrusts its beak upward—and even sways gently, like the surrounding reeds in a soft wind.

Figure 37.11 Moment-of-truth defensive behavior. (**a**) A cornered short-eared owl spreads its wings in a startling display that must have worked against some of its predators some of the time; it is part of the behavioral repertoire of the species. (**b**) As a last resort, some beetles spray noxious chemicals at their attackers, which works some of the time but not all of the time. (**c**) Grasshopper mice plunge the chemical-secreting tail end into the ground and feast on the head end.

The predators are utilized as dispersal agents for the new generation (seeds). Think of the logistics of such a tactic. The seeds must not be advertised as food until they are developmentally primed for dispersal. When ovules finally mature into seeds, they must be packaged in ways that will attract (or become attached to) predators. Once ingested, seeds must be able to withstand the mechanical and chemical insults of the predator's digestive tract, such that the plant embryos emerge intact from the animal body.

Among many flowering plant species, developing ovules are sequestered in well-camouflaged, green ovaries (unripe fruit tissues) that blend with the surrounding foliage. When mature, fruits typically attract predators with fragrances or bright colors. The embryos themselves are encased in hard seed coats that resist digestion once inside the animal gut. In fact, such seeds often do not germinate *until* the seed coat is "softened up" by digestive enzymes. Fruits, of course, appear only during one stage of the plant life cycle. The fruit-eating predators must be opportunistic, using fruit some of the time and other food resources at other times.

Energy Outlays for Predation

As prey species have become more diverse in their ways of avoiding the negative effects of predation, predators have become more diverse in their prey-acquisition activities. To a large extent, however, the diverse predation strategies can be described in terms of energy outlays for the search, pursuit, capture, and handling of prey.

Predators generally focus on prey that are large enough or numerous enough to make the hunt and/or the capture worth the energy outlay. For instance, tiny shrimplike forms called krill are prey for such behemoths as the blue whale. If you put twelve elephants together, they collectively would be about as massive as one blue whale. However, a krill population consists of many hundreds of thousands of small marine animals that collectively represent a large enough mass to be worth the energy outlay in their capture.

In contrast, the killer whale gets by with a dozen or two seals, penguins, and dolphins—which are certainly larger than krill but trickier to find, pursue, and catch. They represent a larger energy return that may or may not equal the larger energy investment required, depending on the hunting skill of the individual.

Mutualism

In contrast to predator-prey systems, some species have coevolved structurally, physiologically, or behaviorally to the extent that each is important to the survival of the other. Such systems are mutualistic, with positive benefits flowing in both directions.

Mycorrhiza, the intimate association between plant root hairs and fungal mycelia, is a mutualistic relationship (Chapter Sixteen). Other examples of mutualism come from pollinators that specialize on certain species of flowering plants. Consider the yucca moth (Figure 37.12), which obtains pollen only from the yucca plant; even its larval form dines only on yucca seeds. The yucca plant depends exclusively on this one moth pollinator. Hence the moth's private energy source, available throughout its lifetime,

a

b

c

Figure 37.12 Mutualism in the high desert of Colorado. There are several species of yucca plants (**a**), but each has coevolved exclusively with only one kind of yucca moth species (**b**). The adult stage of the moth life cycle coincides with the blossoming of yucca flowers. Using mouthparts that have become modified for the task, the female moth gathers up the somewhat sticky pollen and rolls it into a ball. Then she flies to another flower and, after piercing the ovary wall, lays her eggs among the ovules. She crawls out the style and shoves the ball of pollen into the opening of the stigma. When the larvae emerge (**c**), they eat a small portion of the yucca seeds. Then they gnaw their way out of the ovary to continue the life cycle. The seeds remaining are enough to give rise to a new yucca generation. So refined is this mutual dependency that the moth and larva can obtain food from no other plant, and the flower can be pollinated by no other agent.

helps assure reproductive success. At the same time, the moth helps assure reproductive success for the plant: the pollen is carried exactly where it must go instead of being randomly spread about by a less picky pollinator that visits assorted plant species.

Parasitism

Parasite-Host Relationships. True parasites obtain nourishment from living organisms but typically do not kill their hosts outright. Rather, the coevolved host may be weakened and may die from secondary infections. An example of this is schistosomiasis, a disease caused by the parasitic worms called blood flukes (Chapter Thirty-Four). More typically, a parasite causes death only when it ends up in a novel host that has no coevolved defenses against it.

Not all parasites obtain nourishment directly from the tissues of a host. In *social parasitism,* one species depends on the social behavior of another to complete its life cycle. For example, consider the North American brown-headed cowbird, which never does build a nest, incubate its eggs, or care for its offspring. Instead it removes one egg from the nest of another bird and lays one egg as a "replacement." Some birds recognize the foreign egg and shove it from the nest. Others, including the Kirtland warbler, do not. They hatch the egg and raise the young cowbird. Being larger and more aggressive than the warbler nestlings, the young cowbird usually pushes nestmates out of the nest or snaps up most of the food, such that others can starve to death.

You might be thinking that parasitism is a one-way street. Yet here again, positive benefits sometimes flow in two directions. Being predisposed to snap at anything that moves, the aggressive parasitic cowbird snaps at botflies. Botflies have larvae that burrow into nestlings, feed on

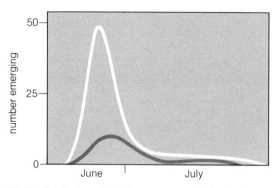

Figure 37.13 Qualitative effect of cocoon parasitoid activity on sawfly emergence. The red line represents emergence when attack by parasitoids is prevented; the white line represents emergence after parasitoid attack. Notice that most attacks occurred on the would-be early emergers, which did not burrow as deeply into the forest litter. (Data from P. Price and H. Tripp, *Canadian Entomology*, 1972, 104:1003–1016)

bird tissues, then pupate at the bottom of the nest. The botfly thus kills a lot of nestlings—at least those in nests where cowbirds are *not* being raised. Where there is a young cowbird, so also is there an absence or near-absence of botflies. Thus, even with the awful behavior of the parasite, more host offspring survive than they would in cowbird-free nests.

Parasitoid-Host Relationships. In contrast to parasites, some insect larvae are *parasitoids,* which kill their host by completely consuming its soft tissues by the time they metamorphose into adults. What sort of defenses evolve against attacks of parasitoids? One example was described by Peter Price, who studied the effects of parasitoid larvae on jackpine sawfly larvae. The sawfly larvae emerge in trees, then drop to the forest floor, where they burrow into the leaf litter and spin their cocoons. The number of sawflies that emerge from cocoons depends on how many sawfly larvae are parasitized. The parasitoids tend to locate cocoons that are nearest the surface of the litter. The adults from these cocoons are the first to emerge, compared with those from more deeply buried cocoons (Figure 37.13).

In their activity, the parasitoids are exerting selection pressure on the sawfly population, with the advantage bestowed on the late-emerging (and deep-burrowing) sawflies. In turn, the prey population is exerting selection pressure on the parasitoids, with the advantage bestowed on those individuals having a more robust build that enables them to burrow deeper, after the deeper burrowing fly larvae. As Price points out, the host stays ahead in this coevolutionary contest. Each time it burrows deeper, the parasitoid search time becomes greater, fewer parasitoid eggs are laid, and the parasitoid population is held in check.

Readings

Barbour, M., et al. 1980. *Terrestrial Plant Ecology*. Menlo Park, California: Benjamin/Cummings.

Bryant, J. 1981. "Hare Trigger." *Natural History* 90(11):46–52. Describes toxins, produced by heavily browsed plants, that may play a critical role in the cyclic oscillations of snowshoe hare population densities.

Price, P. 1975. *Insect Ecology*. New York: Wiley. Excellent examples of coevolved parasitoid-host interactions.

Ricklefs, R. 1979. *Ecology*. Second edition. New York: Chiron Press. Somewhat advanced reading; packed with interesting examples.

Root, R. 1967. "The Niche Exploitation Pattern of the Blue-Gray Gnatcatcher." *Ecological Monographs* 37:317–350.

Review Questions

1. Define habitat. Why do you suppose it might be difficult to define "the human habitat"?

2. What is the difference between a fundamental niche and a realized niche? As part of your answer, use an analogy of a warlike nation whose goal is world dominion.

3. Give an example of each of the three kinds of basic interactions that exist between populations.

4. Define interspecific competition. Explain how this form of behavior is incorporated into the concept of competitive exclusion.

5. Why is it difficult to observe competitive exclusion in the natural world, as opposed to observations of simple two-species interactions (such as bacteria) in a laboratory?

6. How might two species that compete in the same resource category coexist? Can you think of some possible examples besides the ones used in this chapter?

7. Define symbiosis. Protocooperation, mutualism, commensalism, parasitism, and interspecific competition are all forms of symbiosis. Explain how they differ from one another. In which category would you place beef-eating humans and beef cattle? Humans and dairy cattle?

8. Can you explain why predation alone may not account for the long-term oscillations in population growth of the Canadian lynx and snowshoe hare?

9. Define coevolution. How might two species coevolve to the extent that they enter a commensal relationship?

10. What is the difference between camouflage and mimicry? Can you give some examples of mimicry among insects? Camouflage among insects?

11. What is the difference between a parasite and a parasitoid? What sort of coevolutionary defenses do host species have against parasitoids?

If you have done much traveling, you know firsthand that the regions of the earth's surface are remarkably diverse. In climate, topography, and vegetation cover, deserts differ from one another and from mountains, which differ from foothills and tundra, which differ from flat or rolling plains. Oceans, lakes, ponds, rivers, and estuaries differ in species composition and physical features. Yet despite the diversity, each such region functions as a *system,* in much the same way as the others. With only rare exceptions, the systems run on energy from the sun. Solar energy flows into each one by way of autotrophs, "self-feeders" that convert the energy to forms that are used in building organic compounds from simple inorganic substances. The autotrophs represent the *energy fixation base* for the entire system. Energy stored in the food they produce is transferred through some array of heterotrophs—the predators and decomposers—before being dissipated in the surroundings.

The autotrophs also represent the *nutrient concentration base* for the system. During growth, their tissues must necessarily be constructed of macronutrients and micronutrients absorbed from the surrounding air, soil, or water (Chapter Seventeen). These nutrients are transferred to and among the heterotrophic consumers, which include bacteria

38

ECOSYSTEMS

David Steinberg

Figure 38.1 Sign of the times in the African savanna, where natural ecosystems are undergoing large-scale disruptions, adjustments, and change.

Table 38.1 Trophic Levels in Ecosystems		
Trophic Level	Energy Source	Examples
Photosynthesizers (primary producers)	Sunlight energy	Photosynthetic bacteria and protistans; plants
Chemosynthesizers (primary producers)	Oxidation of inorganic substances	Nitrifying bacteria
Herbivores (primary consumers)	Primary producers	Plant-eating mollusks, deer, grasshoppers
Primary carnivores	Herbivores	Spiders, lynx
Secondary carnivores	Primary carnivores	Red-tailed hawks, killer whales
Omnivores	Primary producers and consumers, carnivores	Humans
Decomposers	Organic remains and products of all other organisms	Heterotrophic bacteria, fungi, litter-feeding invertebrates

and fungi that decompose organic matter and thereby help release nutrients that can be cycled back to the producers.

What we have just described in broad outline is the ecosystem. An **ecosystem** is a region of the physical environment, together with all of its organisms that secure, use, and transfer energy as well as material resources among them. It is important to understand that even though ecosystems might appear to be isolated, few are actually independent of others. The intrusion of human tourist activities in the ecosystems of Africa is only one example (Figure 38.1); other disruptions will be described in this chapter.

An ecosystem is a region of the physical environment and its array of organisms that secure, use, and transfer energy and materials among themselves.

Autotrophic organisms such as photosynthetic plants and protistans are the energy fixation base and nutrient concentration base for ecosystems.

ORGANIZATION OF ECOSYSTEMS

Trophic Levels

Ecosystems are organized in part according to how different species acquire energy. All those species that obtain energy primarily from a common source constitute a **trophic level**. For example, the photosynthetic protistans and aquatic plants growing in an estuary represent one trophic level; all obtain their energy from the sun. Many species (such as humans) actually obtain energy from more than one source and thereby straddle two or more trophic levels. However, the categories given in Table 38.1 are useful as a starting point in describing the feeding relationships.

Food Webs

The general sequence of who eats whom is sometimes called a **food chain**. However, the term implies a simple, isolated relationship, which seldom occurs in ecosystems. More typically, the same food resource is part of more than one chain, especially when that resource is at one of the low trophic levels. Thus there are interconnected networks of feeding relationships that take the form of **food webs**, of the sort shown in Figure 38.2.

For example, imagine a fisherman netting some fish that were feeding on algae near the ocean's surface. Come lunchtime, he cooks some of his catch. Should he later lose his footing on the deck and fall into the water, where other carnivores lurk, the "chain" might be portrayed as:

$$\text{algae} \rightarrow \text{fish} \rightarrow \text{fisherman} \rightarrow \text{shark}$$

Yet this chain would be an oversimplification of feeding relationships, for it would exclude any number of alternatives. Most likely, crustaceans were also grazing on the algae. Small squids and assorted medium-sized fishes might have been feeding on the crustaceans; some larger fishes were probably feeding on smaller ones. Sharks may have been moving in to feed on the large and medium-sized fishes. The fisherman might have cooked his fish in wine and herbs. Thus he would have shifted back and forth between herbivore and carnivore—and would have been even more omnivorous in consuming the alcoholic product of decomposers (yeasts whose fermentation activities yield wine from crushed grapes).

A food web is a network of crossing, interlinked food chains, encompassing primary producers and an array of consumers and decomposers.

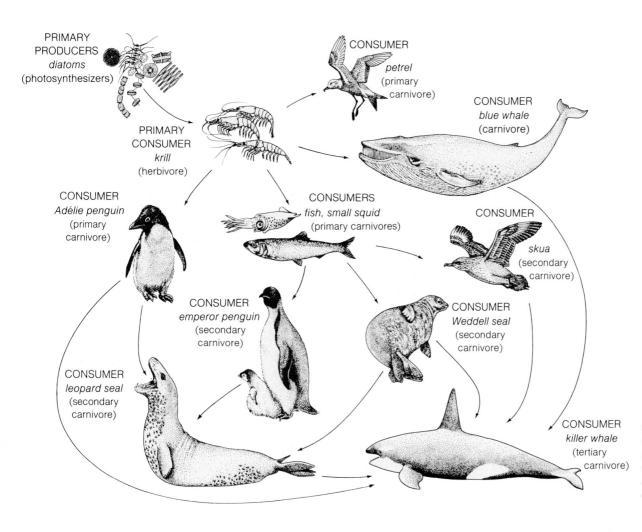

PRIMARY PRODUCERS
diatoms
(photosynthesizers)

PRIMARY CONSUMER
krill
(herbivore)

CONSUMER
petrel
(primary carnivore)

CONSUMER
blue whale
(carnivore)

CONSUMER
Adélie penguin
(primary carnivore)

CONSUMERS
fish, small squid
(primary carnivores)

CONSUMER
skua
(secondary carnivore)

CONSUMER
emperor penguin
(secondary carnivore)

CONSUMER
Weddell seal
(secondary carnivore)

CONSUMER
leopard seal
(secondary carnivore)

CONSUMER
killer whale
(tertiary carnivore)

Figure 38.2 Simplified picture of a food web in the Antarctic; there are many more participants, including an array of decomposer organisms.

Case Study: Biological Concentration of DDT

Disturbances of food webs can have truly unexpected results. A classic example occurred in 1955, during a major campaign to eliminate malaria-transmitting mosquitoes from the island of Borneo (now a state of Indonesia). DDT is a chlorinated hydrocarbon compound that sends insects into convulsions, paralysis, and on to death. It has been instrumental in bringing many pests (including mosquitoes) more or less under control.

Now, DDT is a stable compound; it is nondegradable and insoluble in water. However, it is soluble in fat. It tends to accumulate in the fatty tissues of organisms. For this reason, DDT is a prime candidate for **biological concentration**: the increasing concentration of a nondegradable substance as it moves up through trophic levels. The DDT that becomes concentrated in tissues of herbivores (such as insects) becomes more concentrated in tissues of carnivores that eat quantities of the DDT-harboring herbivores. It does this at each trophic level.

In 1955, the World Health Organization initiated its DDT-spraying program in Borneo. That step was not taken lightly. Nine out of ten people there were afflicted with malaria, an epidemic by anybody's standards. The program worked, insofar as the mosquitoes transmitting this terrible disease were brought almost entirely under control. But DDT is a broad-spectrum insecticide; it kills nontarget as well as target species. Sure enough, the mosquitoes had company: flies and cockroaches that made a nuisance of themselves in the thatch-roofed houses on the island fell dead to the floor. At first there was much applause. Then the small lizards that also lived in the houses and preyed on flies and cockroaches found themselves presented with a veritable feast. Feast they did—and they died, too. So did the house cats that otherwise would have preyed on the lizards. With the house cats dead, the rat population of

Borneo was rid of its natural predator, and rats were soon overrunning the island. Now, the fleas on rats were carriers of still another disease, called the sylvatic plague, which can be transmitted to humans. Fortunately, the threat of this new epidemic was averted in time; someone got the inspired idea to parachute DDT-free cats into the remote parts of the island. But on top of everything else, some of the people of Borneo found themselves sitting under caved-in roofs. The thatch in their roofs was made of certain leaves that happen to be the food resource of a certain caterpillar. The DDT did not affect the caterpillar but it killed the wasps that were its natural predator. When the predator population collapsed, so did the roofs.

ENERGY FLOW THROUGH ECOSYSTEMS

Primary Productivity and Energy Storage

The rate at which energy becomes stored in organic compounds through photosynthesis is known as **primary productivity**. Most often it is expressed in terms of energy gained in a specified area over some specified time. (Typically, primary productivity is expressed in kilocalories per square meter per year.)

Of course, not all of the organic matter produced during photosynthesis accumulates in tissues. The primary producers use up much of it in pathways of energy metabolism, particularly aerobic respiration. The term *gross primary production* refers to the total amount of solar energy that actually flows into the ecosystem by way of photosynthesizers. *Net primary production* refers to the energy remaining after respiration; it is the energy inherent in **biomass** (organic matter that accumulates over time). Biomass typically is expressed as grams (dry weight) of organic matter per unit area. Changes in biomass can be determined by measuring weight gain during growth of the organisms involved.

Primary productivity is the rate at which energy becomes stored in organic compounds through photosynthesis.

Gross primary production is the total amount of solar energy converted to organic compounds during photosynthesis.

Net primary production is the energy remaining after aerobic respiration by autotrophs and stored over time as organic matter (biomass).

In a given ecosystem, net primary production is influenced by such variables as the availability of sunlight and nutrients, temperature, rainfall, predation, duration of the growing season, and the occurrence of fires. These variables influence not only the amount but also the distribution of net primary production. For example, the proportion of biomass allocated to the roots and shoots of land plants depends partly on the availability of water and nutrients. The harsher the environment in these respects, the greater the ratio of roots to shoots. The more favorable the environment, the more growth is put into photosynthetic parts (shoots), hence the greater the productivity.

Competition for sunlight is another variable that influences the distribution of net primary production in an ecosystem. Contrary to what you might expect, maximum productivity does not occur at the surface of a forest canopy or at the water's surface of aquatic ecosystems. In these zones, sunlight is the most intense—and light that is too intense actually inhibits photosynthesis in many species (Chapter Seven). Maximum productivity occurs at some zone below the surface. Below the zone of maximum primary production, energy fixation decreases because the accumulation of biomass (leaves or plankton) reduces light penetration.

Another variable that affects net primary production is age of the producer organisms. For example, when understory trees of a forest are becoming established, their annual primary production is high. The older and larger they get, the more production is channeled into maintenance of existing plant parts; little gross primary production is left for growth (increase in biomass).

Net primary production varies over time and in its spatial distribution. This is the variable energy base available for consumers in the ecosystem.

Major Pathways of Energy Flow

Figure 38.3 illustrates the general direction of energy flow through ecosystems. Of all the solar radiation reaching the earth, only a small fraction becomes converted into organic matter. This fraction becomes available to other members of the ecosystem in two forms: as living tissues of the producers and as *detritus* (organic wastes, dead tissues, and partially decayed organic matter).

A **grazing food web** begins with consumption of living plant tissues by herbivores, which are in turn consumed by some array of carnivores. Figure 38.2 is an example of this pathway of energy flow.

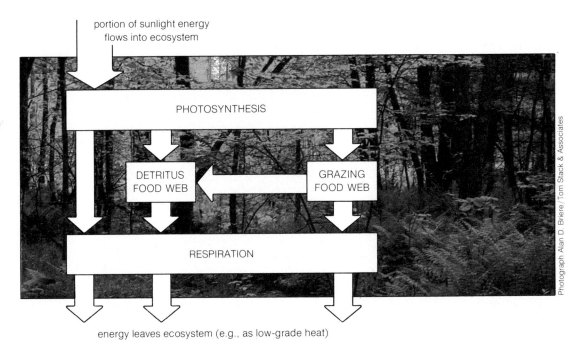

portion of sunlight energy
flows into ecosystem

PHOTOSYNTHESIS

DETRITUS
FOOD WEB

GRAZING
FOOD WEB

RESPIRATION

energy leaves ecosystem (e.g., as low-grade heat)

Photograph Alan D. Briere/Tom Stack & Associates

Figure 38.3 Generalized model of the main pathways of energy flow through an ecosystem. Photosynthesizers capture only a small fraction of solar energy reaching the earth. They use it in assembling organic matter, some of which is incorporated in plant tissues. In a grazing food web, herbivores feed on living plant parts, and carnivores feed on herbivores as well as on each other. In a detritus food web, decomposers feed on organic wastes, dead tissues, and partially decayed organic matter. All organisms of the ecosystem release energy to the surroundings (typically as low-grade heat) as a result of energy metabolism. Thus there is a one-way flow of energy into then out of the ecosystem.

With each transfer through a grazing food web, the amount of energy available for still another transfer is reduced by a magnitude of 10, on the average. In very general terms, of the 1,000 kilocalories of energy in plant tissues that are consumed by herbivores, 100 will be converted to herbivore tissues. Of the 100 kilocalories consumed by primary carnivores, only 10 will be converted to primary carnivore tissues. The secondary carnivores end up with only 1 kilocalorie for every 10 taken in.

Even though grazing food webs are the most obvious pathways of energy flow, they are not the most important ones except in some aquatic ecosystems. For example, even when cattle graze heavily on the plants of shortgrass prairies, they consume only about three percent of the net primary production available.

Far more important are the **detrital food webs**, in which decomposers consume organic waste products and dead or partly decomposed tissues. In land ecosystems, the partici-

pants include bacteria and fungi. They also include an assortment of invertebrates collectively called *detritus feeders.* Earthworms are in this category (Chapter Twenty-Six); so are millipedes and the larvae of flies and beetles. Feeding on the decomposers are microscopic consumers, including the abundant nematodes.

Energy flows into ecosystems from outside sources such as solar radiation.

Energy flows through ecosystems by way of grazing food webs (based on the living tissues of photosynthesizers) and detritus food webs (based on organic waste products and remains of photosynthesizers and consumers).

Energy leaves ecosystems as a result of metabolic activities (aerobic respiration, mostly) of each producer and consumer organism.

Figure 38.4 Annual energy flow (measured in kilocalories per square meter per year) for an aquatic ecosystem in Silver Springs, Florida.

The producers are mostly green aquatic plants. The carnivores are insects and small fish, and the top carnivores are larger fish. The energy source (sunlight) is available all year long.

Only 1.2 percent of the incoming solar energy is actually trapped in photosynthesis to generate new plant biomass. And more than 63 percent of the photosynthetic products is metabolized by the plants themselves to meet their own energy needs. Only 16 percent is harvested by herbivores, and the remainder is eventually decomposed by bacteria and fungi. Similarly, most of the herbivore energy is expended in metabolism and goes into the decomposer system; only 11.4 percent is consumed by carnivores. Once again, the carnivores burn up most of the energy they take in and only 5.5 percent is passed on to top carnivores. The decomposers cycle and recycle all the biomass received from all other trophic levels. Eventually all of the 5,060 kilocalories will appear as heat produced during metabolism. (Decomposers, too, are eventually decomposed.)

This diagram has been deliberately oversimplified. No community is completely isolated from all others. Organisms and materials are constantly dropping into the springs. There is a slow but steady loss of other organisms and materials that flow outward in the stream that leaves the community. (After H. T. Odum, "Trophic Structure and Productivity of Silver Springs," *Ecological Monographs,* 27:55– 112, 1957. Copyright 1957 by the Ecological Society of America)

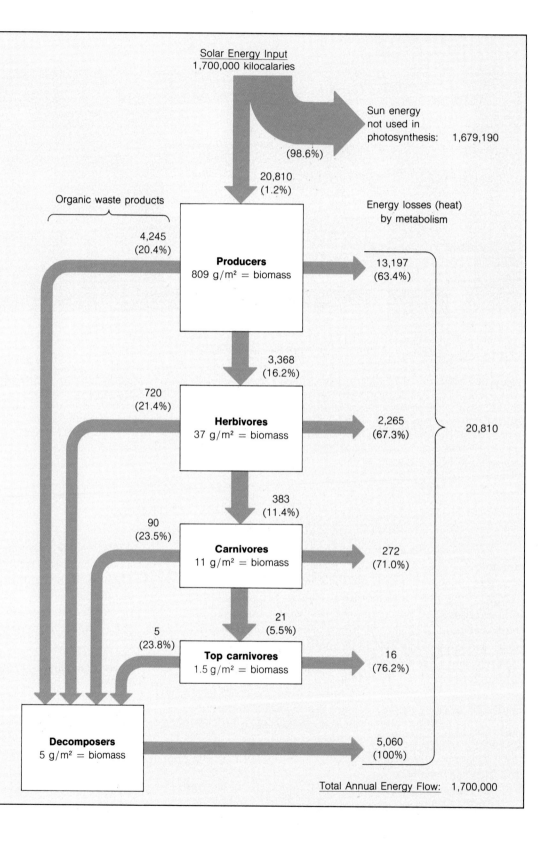

Solar Energy Input
1,700,000 kilocalaries

Sun energy not used in photosynthesis: 1,679,190

(98.6%)

20,810
(1.2%)

Organic waste products

Energy losses (heat) by metabolism

4,245
(20.4%)

Producers
809 g/m² = biomass

13,197
(63.4%)

3,368
(16.2%)

720
(21.4%)

Herbivores
37 g/m² = biomass

2,265
(67.3%)

20,810

383
(11.4%)

90
(23.5%)

Carnivores
11 g/m² = biomass

272
(71.0%)

21
(5.5%)

5
(23.8%)

Top carnivores
1.5 g/m² = biomass

16
(76.2%)

Decomposers
5 g/m² = biomass

5,060
(100%)

Total Annual Energy Flow: 1,700,000

Energy Budgets

Pyramid of Numbers. The energy entering and leaving an ecosystem can be measured to give a picture of how well the system is functioning over time, in terms of its production and energy utilization efficiency. With one approach, energy flow and the number of individuals in each trophic level are depicted as a pyramid. The shape of the pyramid roughly corresponds to actual counts made of all the individuals within a defined area. For example, we might have the following pyramid for a bluegrass field, where the base of the pyramid represents the food production base for additional trophic levels:

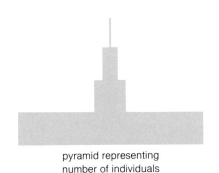

3 top carnivores
(birds, moles)

354,904 carnivores
(spiders, ants, beetles)

708,624 herbivores
(invertebrates)

5,842,424 producers
(grasses, weeds)

pyramid representing
number of individuals

Aside from the monumental patience required to count the organisms, a pyramid of numbers does not completely define the energy budget for an ecosystem. For one thing, it defines feeding relationships only at one moment—*and feeding relationships can change cyclically or permanently over time.* For another thing, a pyramid of numbers does not take into account that *the sizes of organisms being counted in each trophic level can vary.* A count in a redwood forest would yield a small number of large producers (the trees) which still manage to support a large number of herbivores and carnivores (insects). One deer would be counted as a single herbivore, as would a single insect—even though a deer eats far more than an insect ever would.

Pyramid of Biomass. Another approach is to weigh individuals in each trophic level instead of counting them. This would give us a pyramid of biomass (the total weight of all organisms in a given category). Weighing the organisms is better than making a simple head count and gives insight into the allocation of energy at each trophic level. In most

ecosystems on land, the pyramids of biomass have a large base of primary production, with ever smaller trophic levels perched on top. In contrast, in some aquatic ecosystems, the producers are tiny phytoplankton that grow and reproduce rapidly. Here, the pyramid of biomass can be upside-down, with the consumer biomass at any instant actually exceeding the producer biomass. The phytoplankton are consumed about as fast as they reproduce; it is just that the survivors (few as they may be) are reproducing at a phenomenal rate.

Ecosystem Analysis. Pyramids of biomass are deficient in an important respect, because not all organisms of the same biomass have the same impact on an ecosystem. (For instance, a mouse is much more active and consumes far more food than, say, a lizard of the same size and life expectancy.) Thus a picture of energy flow must be based on an **ecosystem analysis**: a determination of the actual amounts of energy that individuals take in, how much they burn up during metabolism, how much remains in their waste products, and how much they store in their body tissues. The inputs and outputs for each ecosystem category (such as a particular producer species, meteorological input, and leaching of nutrients from the soil) are calculated so that energy flow can be expressed per unit of land (or water) per unit time. Such calculation is difficult to do, but it has been done in a few studies. One example of the results is shown in Figure 38.4.

NUTRIENT CYCLING

A Model of Nutrient Flow

Figure 38.5 depicts a general model of nutrient flow through the components of an ecosystem. This model takes into account four factors:

1. Nutrient availability, which depends on replenishment of detritus

2. The decomposition rate for existing detritus

3. The amount of detritus and nutrients present in storage forms

4. Nutrient release from the storage reserves

The following case study will illustrate how these factors are interlinked in an actual ecosystem.

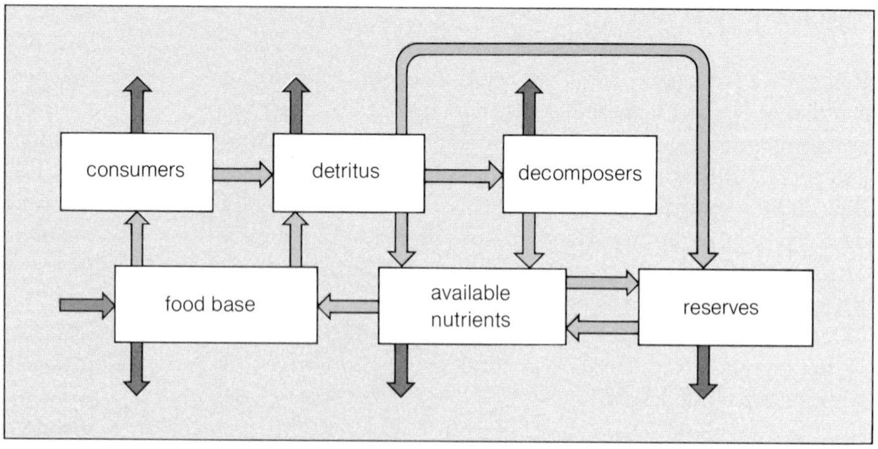

Figure 38.5 A generalized model of nutrient flow through ecosystems. Blue arrows indicate the direction of flow between components of the ecosystem. Gray arrows indicate the fraction of nutrients leaving (as a result of runoff, leaching from the soil, emigration of animals, and so forth). The green arrow indicates inputs (such as nutrients carried in by rainfall and immigration of animals).

Figure 38.6 A view of the arctic tundra ecosystem.

Lynn Erckmann, University of Washington /BPS

Case Study: Nutrient Recovery in the Arctic Tundra

Tundra is a word derived from the Finnish *tuntura*, meaning a treeless plain. Arctic tundra lies to the north, between the polar ice cap and the huge belts of coniferous forests in North America, Europe, and Asia. In Alaska, much of the tundra is flat, windswept, and desolate (Figure 38.6). Temperatures average 5°C (41°F) in midsummer, and −32°C (−26°F) in midwinter. The air is too cold to permit formation of much water vapor, so rainfall is sparse. Yet for three summer months, sunlight is nearly continuous. Then, plant growth is profuse, with flowering and seed ripening completed quickly.

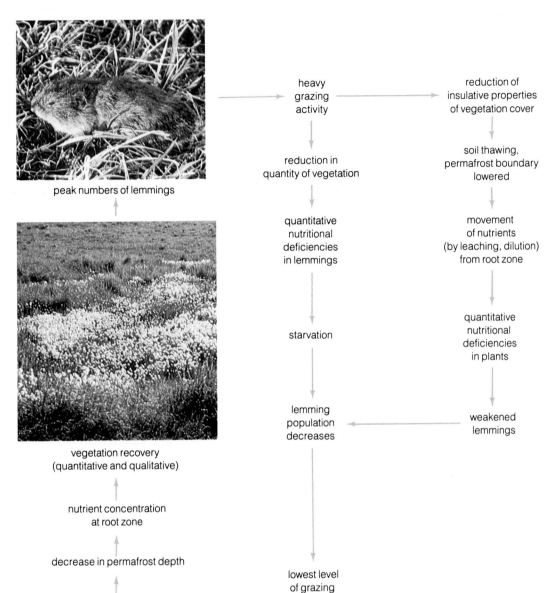

peak numbers of lemmings

vegetation recovery
(quantitative and qualitative)

nutrient concentration
at root zone

decrease in permafrost depth

vegetation cover build-up

heavy
grazing
activity

reduction in
quantity of vegetation

quantitative
nutritional
deficiencies
in lemmings

starvation

lemming
population
decreases

lowest level
of grazing
activity

reduction of
insulative properties
of vegetation cover

soil thawing,
permafrost boundary
lowered

movement
of nutrients
(by leaching, dilution)
from root zone

quantitative
nutritional
deficiencies
in plants

weakened
lemmings

Figure 38.7 Feedback relationships that influence nutrient cycling in the arctic tundra ecosystem. Interactions exist between the vegetation cover and the lemmings that graze on it. They exist also between the degree of grazing, the depth of permafrost (a frozen basement beneath the soil surface), and nutrient reserves. (After F. Pitelka and A. Schultz, 1964; photographs Roger K. Burnard)

Although the tundra is not completely covered with snow all year long, the brief summer thaw is not enough to warm much more than surface soil. Just beneath the surface is the **permafrost**, a permanently frozen layer more than 500 meters thick in this region. Permafrost forms an impenetrable basement beneath the flat terrain, hence drainage is inhibited. In combination with the low temperatures, permafrost has a major effect on nutrient cycling. Organic matter cannot completely decompose here. It is gradually becoming locked up in soggy masses (peat). At present, more than ninety-five percent of the carbon in the arctic is inaccessible to the tundra organisms. Less than two percent of the total carbon, nitrogen, and phosphorus is found in plants, mostly concentrated in underground plant parts.

In the arctic tundra, most of the plant biomass is confined to no more than ten different species. There is only one main herbivore: a small rodent called the brown lemming (Figure 38.7). What this herbivore lacks in size, it makes up for in sheer numbers. Feeding on roots of grasses and sedges, lemmings live in underground burrows. Although they consume quantities of vegetation, they also deposit droppings that fertilize the plants and thereby stimulate plant growth. Every three to five years, however, the lemming population density reaches high levels, and the population declines sharply.

In the 1960s, the ecologists Frank Pitelka and Arnold Schultz analyzed nutrient flow through the arctic tundra ecosystem. Their observations formed the basis of a **nutrient recovery hypothesis**. According to this hypothesis, cyclic variations in population size result from interactions between the vegetation cover and the herbivores grazing on it. Further, these variations are said to be mediated by factors of nutrient recovery and nutrient availability in the soil. Figure 38.7 shows how these factors affect the cycling of nutrients.

Nitrogen Cycling in Ecosystems

The Nitrogen Cycle. As the example of the arctic ecosystem suggested, nutrients usually are not abundantly available. Added to this, many nutrients are often in chemical forms that some species cannot use directly. For example, nitrogen is a necessary component of proteins, which are central to the structure and functioning of all living things. Gaseous nitrogen (N_2) makes up about eighty percent of the atmosphere, so it would seem to be abundant just about everywhere. However, N_2 molecules are held together by stable, triple covalent bonds ($N\equiv N$), and very few organisms have the metabolic equipment for tackling them. Some bacteria can.

In **nitrogen fixation**, certain soil bacteria assimilate nitrogen from the air. They attach electrons (and associated H^+ ions) to the nitrogen through a series of reduction reactions, thereby forming ammonia (NH_3) or ammonium (NH_4^+). They use these compounds in growth, maintenance, and reproduction. When the nitrogen-fixing microbes die, the compounds are released during decay processes. Other bacteria present in soil use the compounds as energy sources.

In **nitrification**, soil bacteria strip the ammonia or ammonium of electrons, and nitrite (NO_2^-) is released as a product of the reaction. Still other nitrifying bacteria then use nitrite for energy metabolism, which yields nitrate (NO_3^-) as a product.

When ammonia and nitrate dissolve in soil water, they can be taken up by plant roots and incorporated into organic compounds. These compounds are the only nitrogen source for animals, which feed directly or indirectly on plants. Later, in a process called **ammonification**, the nitrogenous wastes and remains of plants and animals are decomposed by some species of bacteria and fungi. The decomposers use the proteins and amino acids being released for their own growth, and they release the excess as ammonia or ammonium. Some of these nitrogen-containing by-products are also used by plants.

Nitrogen is usually the limiting nutrient for plant growth. Some plants, however, benefit from increased rates of nitrogen uptake because of their relationship with free-living or symbiotic microorganisms. Legumes (such as peas and beans) are an example of this dependency. They harbor symbiotic nitrogen fixers in their roots, supplying their guests with energy-rich sugar molecules in exchange for fixed nitrogen.

Taken together, nitrogen fixation, nitrification, and ammonification are the basis of an overall flow of nitrogen through ecosystems. The nitrogen is harnessed from the air by nitrogen-fixing bacteria, it moves through other microbes in the soil, through plants, animals, then back to the soil. Some of it then returns to the air by way of denitrification, a process to be described next. This overall sequence of events is known as the **nitrogen cycle** (Figure 38.8).

Denitrification. In itself, the continual production of ammonia by innumerable bacterial populations would seem to assure plants of plenty of nitrogen. Yet soil nitrogen is scarce. During crop harvests, of course, some nitrogen leaves the fields with the plants. Because nitrite, nitrate, and ammonia are soluble, some may run off in streams with rainwater. However, the major cause of nitrogen scarcity in wet soils is a bacterial process called **denitrification**: the reduction of nitrate or nitrite to N_2 and a small amount of nitrous oxide (N_2O). The overwhelming majority of bacteria that take part in this process are ordinary species that rely on aerobic respiration. Under some conditions, though, especially when soil is poorly aerated, they switch to anaerobic respiration. They use nitrate, nitrite, or nitrous

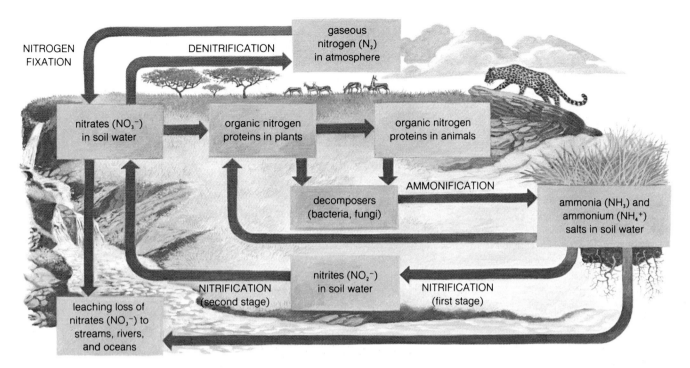

Figure 38.8 Simplified picture of the nitrogen cycle.

oxide instead of oxygen as the terminal electron acceptor (Chapter Eight).

Nitrogen Scarcity and Modern Agriculture. With any loss of fixed nitrogen, soil fertility (hence plant growth) is reduced. Farms in Europe and the North America have traditionally depended on crop rotation to restore the soil. For example, legumes are planted between plantings of wheat or sugar beet crops. This practice has helped maintain soils in stable and productive condition, in some cases for thousands of years.

Modern agriculture depends on nitrogen-rich fertilizers. With plant breeding, fertilization, and pest control, the crop yields per acre have doubled and even quadrupled over the past forty years. With intelligent management, it appears that soil can maintain such high yields indefinitely—as long as water and commercial nitrogen-containing fertilizers are available.

The catch, of course, is that we can't get something for nothing. Enormous amounts of energy are needed to produce fertilizer—not energy from the unending stream of sunlight, but energy from oil. As long as the supply of oil was viewed as unending, there was little concern about the energetic cost of fertilizer production. In many cases, we have been pouring more energy into the soil (in the form of fertilizer) than we are getting out of it (in the form of food). Unlike natural ecosystems, in which nutrients such as nitrogen are cycled, our agricultural systems exist only because of constant, massive infusions of energetically expensive fertilizers.

However, as any hungry person will tell you, food calories are more basic to survival than are gasoline calories or perhaps, even, than a car. As long as the human population continues to grow exponentially, farmers will be engaged in a constant race to supply food to as many individuals as possible (see *Commentary*). Soil enrichment with nitrogen-containing fertilizers is essential in the race, as it is now being run.

COMMENTARY

Resources and the Human Condition

There are now more than 4.7 billion humans on earth— each requiring a minimum daily intake of energy and nutrients, and collectively dependent upon an immense agricultural base of primary production. When ecologists study a natural ecosystem, they ask how well it is faring in terms of primary production and energy conversion efficiency. What sort of answers do we get when we ask the same question of the human "system" of energy and nutrient utilization?

The first answer is that the human system is not doing very well at all. Of the entire population, only 700 million have adequate diets. A unique problem associated with these well-fed few is obesity: energy intake exceeds body requirements and results in weight gain. Another 1 billion get enough energy but not enough protein. For the remaining 3 billion, the situation is desperate.

When caloric intake remains below the minimum requirement, starvation begins. The total number of deaths from starvation is impossible to estimate. Undoubtedly the annual figure reaches into the millions. Certainly it is greater than the toll of the greatest wars.

The High Cost of Protein Conversion

An adult male of average weight can meet his daily protein needs by eating about 1,000 grams (about 2 pounds) of dried corn. Of course, those of us in affluent countries don't think of corn when we hear the word protein. We think of meat. It is true that less than 257 grams (9 ounces) of meat are enough to satisfy daily protein needs. The problem with meat is the large energy investment needed to produce it.

For example, cattle are used as converters of "low-grade" plant protein into "high-grade" meat protein. Cattle and other ruminants can make the conversion largely because of the activity of cellulose-degrading microbes in their digestive tracts (Chapter Twenty-Six). The breakdown products are used in building fatty acids. Some of the fatty acids are used in assembling amino acids, which cattle cannot produce for themselves. Using plants as an amino acid source enables cattle to build proteins at a rapid rate.

Conversion costs depend somewhat on external factors. At one time, cattle were raised on the open range: semiarid land, at best only marginally suitable for raising crops. The raw materials (grasses) were not being used in other ways. Hence the conversion was profitable even though between 3,175 and 4,536 grams (7 and 10 pounds) of grasses were needed to produce only 454 grams (1 pound) of meat. That is a conversion cost of about 10 to 1.

In modern agriculture, cattle spend very little time grazing on the open range. They are confined to feedlots: pens in which they are fed high-quality grains to bring them to market size. The conversion cost is about the same as before: about 10 to 1. However, here we are talking about grains that can be used as a *direct* food source for humans. A tremendous amount of the grain produced each year in the United States becomes feed for cattle, pigs, chickens, and turkeys. Of the exported grain, much goes to developed countries where it is used as livestock feed.

To some, the answer is simple. Humans can subsist most efficiently on plant proteins. *When domestic cattle are inserted between the primary production base and human consumers, there is a 10-to-1 conversion loss in both calories and proteins.* Yet, can you honestly envision the entire United States giving up table meat? That simply will not happen, at least not in the foreseeable future. It will be more realistic to concentrate on working out alternatives to the ideal.

For example, consider that 454 grams of ground beef now cost about twice as much as the same amount of turkey. The cost difference stems from two things. Turkeys are more efficient than beef cattle at protein conversion; it takes less feed to produce the same amount of meat. Also, turkeys require less preparation to make them market-ready. More useful protein can be produced at lower cost, and the market price reflects it.

Consider also the potential of fish harvesting. Fish harvests represent only five percent or so of the world protein supply for humans. Yet more than half of what the world's oceans seem to be capable of supporting is now being harvested. Massive efforts to step up harvesting would seriously deplete fish populations, and it would not change the world protein picture very much as it did.

Fish farming may be another matter. For centuries, small-scale fishponds have been part of Asian agriculture. Human and livestock wastes are emptied into the ponds, which contain controlled numbers of fish species. Nutrients in the wastes fan the growth of microbes that are food for some fish; plants thriving in the enriched water are food for other fish that can grow to about 15,570 grams (35 pounds). Such ponds also can nurture disease-causing microbes, but development of proper waste treatment methods could eliminate the hazard. Efforts are under way to develop a cycle in which (1) grains are used to feed livestock, (2) the runoff from feedlots is used to stimulate plant growth in nearby ponds that incorporate waste treatment facilities, (3) the plants are consumed by selected kinds of fish, (4) pondwater is used in fertilizing grain fields, and (5) fish are harvested for food.

There may also be some shifts to more efficient use of plant proteins. Adults can meet their daily recommended allowances with only 210 grams of soybeans. When soybeans are processed into flour, the protein content jumps to forty-five percent. This means only 158 grams of dried flour per day is enough to meet protein needs. Efforts are also being made to breed plants for higher protein content. For instance, corn and rice are low in lysine, which limits their nutritional value. Varieties with higher lysine content are being developed by careful breeding and selection experiments. However, the high-lysine varieties demand even more nitrogen-rich fertilizers than are used now. Genetic engineering of plants may change this picture; work to incorporate nitrogen-fixing abilities into the hereditary systems of crop plants is under way.

Other alternatives include raising bacteria on petroleum or sewage sludge and harvesting edible by-products; they include mass culturing protein-rich algae. No matter how technologically or biologically feasible, such fundamentally different food sources will require monumental reeducation if well-fed people are to accept them as alternatives to T-bone steaks.

Other Variables

As valuable as they may be, research efforts in themselves are not enough to make the world food crisis disappear. The problem must be approached on many levels. At each level, simplistic programs have already been proposed. However, it is important to recognize that their implementation could create a whole new set of problems. To see why this is so, let's consider just four of these suggestions.

First suggestion: Improve crop production on existing land. The idea here is to (1) improve plant varieties for higher yields and (2) export modern agricultural practices and equipment to developing countries. This idea is the basis for the so-called green revolution.

However, high-yield crops require fertilizers, pesticides, and ample irrigation. The plain truth is that developing countries depend on subsistence farmers who cannot afford to take widespread advantage of the new crop strains. The ones who can afford to make the investment come to depend on industrialized producers of fertilizers and machinery. Of necessity, the costs of fertilizers and machinery are reflected in market food prices. Thus food becomes too expensive for the country's own population.

In the long term, even industrialized countries may have to reassess their agricultural practices. One reason is that energy sources available to drive mechanized farming are dwindling and becoming more expensive for everyone. A realistic alternative is to build agricultural systems around harnessing solar energy. Some devices are on the drawing boards now. For example, low-cost, solar-powered microcircuits may be able to harness heat energy from the sun and convert it to direct currents of electric energy.

Second suggestion: <u>Open up new areas for agriculture.</u> Almost 3.5 billion acres are now under cultivation. It has been proposed that another 7 or 8 billion acres be converted to agriculture. Aside from the environmental impact of such expansion, the best land available for agriculture is already being used for agriculture. What remains as arable land (able to support cultivation) is less desirable. In some heavily populated regions such as Asia, food problems are severe, yet more than eighty percent of the arable land is being intensively cultivated. Much of what remains is in tropical regions of Africa and South America. However, land that supports the rich tropical forests growing there simply will not support crops for more than a few years after clearing (Chapter Thirty-Nine). Desert areas are another possibility, assuming water and fertilizers can be brought in. Yet desert irrigation brings its own problems, such as salt buildup in the soil. (There is not enough rain to wash away salts that accumulate because of the rapid evaporation of irrigation water in hot climates.) Besides, where will the water come from? Water, too, is not an unlimited resource. Desalinizing ocean water (reducing its salt content) is not yet economically feasible for large-scale efforts. As long as desalinization processes are based on energy from petroleum, they will not help much in the short term.

The cost of opening up new lands must also be taken into account. There are costs of the land itself, clearing and building roads, and developing efficient transport and storage systems. Assuming each acre so cleared will support only one person, it might well cost about 30 billion dollars a year, every year, just to keep up with the current population growth rate.

Third suggestion: <u>Equalize food distribution.</u> This is the easy one—just make sure everybody gets an equal share. It is probably the most impractical suggestion of all, simply because we are dealing with human beings. In any nation with an agricultural surplus, farmers pay taxes on their land and buy seeds, fertilizers, and machinery. They expect a return for their labors in producing above and beyond what they personally need. They want to be paid for their crops. If a government wishes to give crops to other people, the goverment must directly or indirectly pay the farmers. In other words, it is the taxpayer who foots the bill. Each year sees a boost in energy costs and inflation, so it becomes more difficult to sell a program of international assistance to a hard-pressed general public. Lacking such programs, farmers often sell the surplus to whoever can pay the most—other industrialized nations, usually.

Fourth suggestion: <u>Stabilize or reduce world population.</u> Ours is a finite world with finite resources. It can support a large number of individuals at a bare subsistence level. It can, as it does now, support a small number in first-class accommodations while confining the rest to steerage. Alternatively, it could support a smaller number in dignity and modest comfort. To achieve this alternative, we must do more than stop; we must back up in terms of population growth.

We can dream of science pulling some new technological rabbit out of a hat. It is not a vain dream, for there probably are innumerable rabbits hidden among the folds and shadows. *However, any solution must be in accord with the supply of material resources and the principles of energy flow.*

So it is a numbers game we are playing, and the manner in which we choose to play will affect our own lives to some extent. More importantly, it will restrict the options of all those who follow. A question on the horizon is this: Who gets first-class or even second- and third-class tickets—and who gets left behind?

SUCCESSION

Succession Defined

Ecosystems of the tundra and elsewhere have more or less self-sustaining communities, each with an assortment of species organized in a trophic structure. Such communities do not arise full-blown in the environment. Whether we are talking about a totally raw environment devoid of life (such as a newly formed volcanic island) or a disturbed patch of a previously inhabited environment (such as an abandoned pasture), the composition and organization of species found there change over time. One community replaces another until a relatively stable, self-maintaining community is established. This self-sustaining assemblage of organisms is the *climax community*. The changes in species composition and trophic structure that lead to it are collectively called **succession**.

When the changes occur in an area previously devoid of life, they are known as *primary succession*. When they proceed in a disturbed area that was already inhabited, the sequential changes are known as *secondary succession*.

Opportunistic and Equilibrium Species

Succession begins with colonization of an uninhabited site by pioneer species—plants that can grow in many exposed areas where sunlight is intense, where there are wide swings in air temperature, and where soils or other substrates are poor in nutrients. Typically the pioneers are small and low-growing. They have short life cycles, and each year they produce abundant small seeds that can be dispersed quickly. As you know from Chapter Thirty-Six, these are characteristics of *r*-selected, **opportunistic species**.

Each year, pioneer plants start over from scratch, so to speak, in that they must sprout from seeds or send out new shoots from the withered plant body. This puts them at a disadvantage when plant species characteristic of later successional stages begin to emerge. These so-called **equilibrium species** are taller, more vigorous, and can begin seasonal growth before the pioneer plants. They store more biomass, produce relatively few seeds, and the seeds are well endowed with nutrients necessary for early growth. They are *K*-selected plants, specialized for life in a narrow range of environmental conditions (Chapter Thirty-Six). Gradually the equilibrium species crowd out the pioneers, the seeds of which become fugitives on the wind and water—destined, perhaps, for a new but ever temporary habitat.

Sometimes the opportunistic species bring on succession themselves. Through their growth above and below ground, they change local environmental conditions in ways that are more favorable for other types of plants. (They can, for example, shade the soil from intense sunlight, they can cut strong winds, and the growth of their roots can break up compact soil.) At other times, succession begins with any one of several species (or some assortment of them) able to colonize the site. The trick is getting there first, and thereby excluding or inhibiting colonization by others.

At some point, the climax community emerges. Barring disturbances, there now are only small-scale changes in species composition and trophic structure, and the community persists for a relatively long period. Figure 38.9 is an example of succession from the pioneer stage to a climax community.

Disturbances in Succession

Even with its array of exquisitely adapted species, a climax community does not perpetuate itself indefinitely. Even the natural communities that seem most stable can be a mosaic of successional patches as a result of major and minor disturbances. Winds, fires, insect infestations, and overgrazing all modify and shape the direction of succession. They can encourage proliferation of some species even while they eliminate others.

One response to disturbance is **cyclic replacement**. For example, the Sierra Nevada mountains of California contain isolated groves of sequoia trees. Some of the giant trees of this climax community are more than 4,000 years old, which certainly implies long-term stability in the region. Their longevity might seem odd, given that brush fires sweep through the community every so often. However, the disturbance caused by the fires actually helps maintain the climax configuration. Sequoia seeds germinate only in the absence of smaller, shade-tolerent plant species. If there is extensive litter on the forest floor, there cannot be any new sequoias. Modest fires eliminate the species of trees and shrubs that compete with the sequoias. Yet the fires do not damage the sequoias themselves. The mature trees have extraordinarily thick bark, which burns poorly and insulates the trees against modest heat damage.

a

c

b

d

Figure 38.9 Primary succession in the Glacier Bay region of Alaska (**a**), where changes in newly deglaciated regions have been carefully documented. A comparison of maps from 1794 onward shows that ice has been retreating at annual rates ranging from 3 meters (at the glacier's sides) to a phenomenal 600 meters at its tip over bays.
(**b**) When a glacier retreats, the constant flow of meltwater tends to leach the newly exposed soil of minerals, including nitrogen. The soil here was buried below ice less than ten years ago. (**c, d**) The first invaders of these nutrient-poor sites are the feathery seeds of mountain avens (*Dryas*), drifting over on the winds. Mountain avens is a pioneer species that benefits from the nitrogen-fixing activities of symbiotic microbes. It grows and spreads rapidly over glacial till.

(**e**) Within twenty years, young alders take hold. These deciduous shrubs also are symbiotic with nitrogen-fixing microbes. Young cottonwood and willows also emerge (**f**). Eventually the alders form dense thickets (**g**). As the thickets mature, cottonwood and hemlock trees grow rapidly, as do a few evergreen spruce trees.
(**h**) By eighty years, the spruce crowd out the mature alders. (**i**) In areas deglaciated for more than a century, dense forests of Sitka spruce and western hemlock dominate. By this time, nitrogen reserves are depleted, and much of the biomass is tied up in peat: excessively moist, compressed organic matter that resists decomposition and that forms a thick mat on the forest floor.

Many sequoia groves are protected as part of national and state park systems. Among other things, protection traditionally meant minimizing the incidence of fires—not only accidental fires from campsites and discarded cigarettes, but also natural fires touched off by lightning. Of course, when small, cyclic fires are prevented, litter builds up. Other species take hold that are susceptible to fire. Even though these species do not displace the mature sequoias, the sequoia seeds cannot germinate and give rise to the replacements necessary to maintain the climax community. The litter and undergrowth represent so much potential fuel that fires are hotter than they otherwise would be—hot enough to damage the giants. Thus the fire prevention efforts aimed at preserving the climax community actually could have the opposite effect.

Ecosystem stability often requires episodes of instability, which permits cyclic replacements of equilibrium species and thereby maintains the climax community over time.

e

Roger K. Burnard

f

Roger K. Burnard

g

E. R. Degginger

h

E. R. Degginger

i

Roger K. Burnard

Table 38.2 Effects of Introducing a Few Species into the United States

Species Introduced	Origin	Mode of Introduction	Outcome
Water hyacinth	South America	Intentionally introduced (1884)	Clogged waterways; shading out of other vegetation
Dutch elm disease The fungus *Cerastomella ulmi* (the disease agent)	Europe	Accidentally imported on infected elm timber used for veneers (1930)	Destruction of millions of elms; great disruption of forest ecology
Bark beetle (the disease carrier)		Accidentally imported on unbarked elm timber (1909)	
Chestnut blight fungus	Asia	Accidentally imported on nursery plants (1900)	Destruction of nearly all eastern American chestnuts; disruption of forest ecology
Argentine fire ant	Argentina	In coffee shipments from Brazil? (1891)	Crop damage; destruction of native ant communities
Camphor scale insect	Japan	Accidentally imported on nursery stock (1920s)	Damage to nearly 200 species of plants in Louisiana, Texas, and Alabama
Japanese beetle	Japan	Accidentally imported on irises or azaleas (1911)	Defoliation of more than 250 species of trees and other plants, including commercially important species such as citrus
Carp	Germany	Intentionally released (1887)	Displacement of native fish; uprooting of water plants with loss of waterfowl populations
Sea lamprey	North Atlantic Ocean	Through Welland Canal (1829)	Destruction of lake trout, lake whitefish, and suckers in Great Lakes
European starling	Europe	Released intentionally in New York City (1890)	Competition with native songbirds; crop damage; transmission of swine diseases; airport runway interference; noisy and messy in large flocks
House sparrow	England	Released intentionally (1853)	Crop damage; displacement of native songbirds; transmission of some diseases
European wild boar	Russia	Intentionally imported (1912); escaped captivity	Destruction of habitat by rooting; crop damage
Nutria (large rodent)	Argentina	Intentionally imported (1940); escaped captivity	Alteration of marsh ecology; damage to earth dams and levees; crop destruction

From David W. Ehrenfeld, *Biological Conservation*, 1970, Holt, Rinehart and Winston and *Conserving Life on Earth*, 1972, Oxford University Press

SPECIES INTRODUCTIONS

Succession normally occurs with some assortment of species that have existed for prolonged periods in a particular region. However, over the past two centuries, enormous numbers of species have been shuffled among different regions, even different continents. They have been moved about intentionally at times and inadvertently at other times by human travelers. Species that are introduced to a region often become part of the species composition of their new home. Just as often, species introductions can have disastrous effects.

For example, in the 1880s, the water hyacinth from South America was put on display for the New Orleans Cotton Exposition. Flower fanciers from Florida and Louisiana carried home clippings of the blue-flowered plants and set them out for ornamental display in ponds and streams. Unchecked by natural predators and nourished by the nutrient-rich waters of the region, the fast-growing hyacinths rapidly displaced many of the equilibrium species. In fact, they spread so rapidly that they choked off ponds and streams. Then they went to work on rivers and canals. They are still there, and they are still bringing river traffic to a halt.

Species introductions into established communities do not always lead to such wholesale replacements. Honeybees, mosquitofish, and ring-necked pheasant are examples of species that have been absorbed into existing community structures. Most of our foodstuffs, including apples, cabbages, wheat, oranges, cattle, and chickens, are the progeny of imports. But as Table 38.2 suggests, we cannot always say that nothing ever goes wrong, and that equilibrium species become reestablished.

Readings

Gosz, J., et al. 1978. "The Flow of Energy in a Forest Ecosystem." *Scientific American* 238(3):93–102. Classic study of the energetics of a forest ecosystem, part of the Hubbard Brook Experimental Forest in the White Mountains of New Hampshire. Quantitative analyses revealed how energy is partitioned among the components of the ecosystem.

Payne, W. 1983. "Bacterial Denitrification: Asset or Defect?" *Bioscience* 33(5):319–325. Good summarization of the global implications of denitrification.

Pitelka, F., and A. Schultz. 1964. "The Nutrient Recovery Hypothesis for Arctic Microtine Cycles." Part I by Pitelka, Part II by Schultz. In *Grazing in Terrestrial and Marine Environments* (D. Crisp, editor). Oxford: Blackwell.

Price, P. 1975. *Insect Ecology.* New York: Wiley. Advanced reading, but excellent examples of ecological interactions.

Smith, R. 1980. *Ecology and Field Biology.* Third edition. New York: Harper & Row. This is one of the clearest introductions to the topics described in this chapter. Particularly good descriptions of energy flow in ecosystems and of succession.

Review Questions

1. Define ecosystem. Autotrophs represent the energy fixation base and nutrient concentration base for ecosystems. Can you explain what these terms mean?

2. Define trophic level. Can you name and give examples of seven trophic levels in ecosystems? What is the energy source for each level?

3. Distinguish between a food chain and a food web. Can you imagine an extreme situation whereby you would be a participant in a food chain?

4. Explain the difference between primary productivity, gross primary production, and net primary production. If you were growing a vegetable garden, what variables might affect its net primary production?

5. There are two major pathways of energy flow through ecosystems: grazing food webs and detrital food webs. Can you characterize each? How does energy leave each one?

6. "Energy budget" refers to the energy entering and leaving an ecosystem in a given time span. Ecologists measure this energy flow as a way of determining how well the ecosystem is functioning in terms of production and energy utilization efficiency. What are some of the ways they do this?

7. Look at the generalized model of nutrient flow in Figure 38.5. For the town or city where you live, can you write in examples for each category (consumers, food base, reserves, and so forth)? Why or why not?

8. Define these terms: nitrogen fixation, nitrification, ammonification, and denitrification. Collectively, what do they represent?

9. After reading the Commentary in this chapter, would you agree with its premise that the agricultural base of primary production for the human population is not functioning well at all? Why or why not?

10. Define primary and secondary succession. What is an opportunistic species? An equilibrium species? In what ways can succession be disturbed, and are all such disturbances bad?

11. Can you think of some species introductions that have had a major impact on the area where you live? (For example, the Mediterranean fruit fly in regions of California and elsewhere.)

39

THE BIOSPHERE

At the northern edge of the Kalahari Desert, in the nation of Botswana, the longest river in southern Africa ends in an immense freshwater delta. Here, lush grasses, shrubs, and groves are the primary production base for a magnificent array of wildlife—birds, crocodiles, lions, buffaloes, elephants, elands, kudus, wildebeests, and many more. These large animals are hosts to bloodsucking mosquitoes and tsetse flies, which transmit the dread sleeping sickness to humans and cattle. By their very presence in the delta, these insects have kept humans and cattle out.

Now, it happens that cattle raising is Botswana's economic mainstay. Cattle need water and grazing land, which are becoming scarce. Pressure is on to open up the delta for the cattle industry by eradicating the tsetse fly and the mosquito. That means clearing the woodlands, burning off the brush, draining the swamps—and destroying the wildlife.

Why would people do such a thing? For profit, of course, but also to feed other people. Anyway, how can we demand that they *not* do such a thing? Would Californians so readily turn over the fields and vineyards of their fertile inland valleys to quails and rabbits, coyotes and hawks? Would Texans so readily set aside their open range for the preservation of prairie dogs and rattlesnakes? Would Nebraskans so readily donate their fields of waving grain to support

We are no more than sunlight dancing on the stream, and no less.

NASA

human populations in Africa so that the African wildlife can be left alone?

Questions such as these illustrate that the concerns of any particular group of people are often relative to what part of the world they happen to live in. They also illustrate that what might be a simple answer to one group might be no answer at all to another. Through their research, many ecologists have been extending public concerns beyond the immediate horizons, and today there is growing awareness of problems and interdependencies on a global scale. Through their explorations, astronauts have reinforced this awareness. Photographs from space show the earth to be isolated in darkness, beckoning, yet oddly vulnerable. What would be immense cloud systems from below appear as thin white traceries across oceans and continents, seen now as finite patches of blues and tans.

Within this thin wrapping of air, water, and surface land are constellations of organisms linked by the flow of energy on the stream of time. This is the home we live in, the biosphere; it is all we have.

COMPONENTS OF THE BIOSPHERE

The **biosphere** is a narrow zone that harbors life, no more than the waters of the earth, a fraction of its crust, and the lower region of the surrounding air. Its rocks, soils, and sediments are only the surface of the *lithosphere,* the outer portion of a crust that is divided into rigid plates and that extends to depths of 60 to 100 kilometers. Liquid and frozen water on or near the surface of the lithosphere is known as the *hydrosphere.* It includes the oceans and smaller bodies of water, the polar ice caps, and a small amount of airborne water. Enveloping the earth is the *atmosphere,* a region of gases, particulate matter, and water vapor. Most of the molecules making up the atmosphere are distributed within 50 kilometers above the earth's surface.

The biosphere is composed of myriad ecosystems, ranging in size from vast forests and stretches of tundra to the small systems that occur, for example, in a pond. Virtually all of the ecosystems are interlinked through movements of materials and energy that span the globe, in ways that will now be described.

GLOBAL PATTERNS OF CLIMATE

What determines whether a particular region at or near the earth's surface will be a desert, forest, coral reef, or other type of ecosystem? The main determinant is **climate**. The word refers to prevailing weather conditions, including temperature, humidity, wind velocity, degree of cloud cover, and rainfall. Climate itself is an outcome of many interacting factors. Here we will consider four of the most important:

1. Variations in the amount of incoming solar radiation
2. The earth's daily rotation and path around the sun
3. Distribution of continents and oceans
4. Altitude of land masses

These factors interact to produce the prevailing winds and ocean currents in different regions. In turn, the currents influence global weather patterns. Finally, weather affects the composition and character of soils and sediments (through erosion, for example), and these substrates influence the growth and distribution of primary producers, hence the nature of the ecosystem itself.

Mediating Effects of the Atmosphere

The atmosphere has profound effects on the amount and kind of solar radiation reaching the earth's surface. At the outermost layers of the atmosphere, oxygen and ozone (O_3) absorb nearly all of the ultraviolet wavelengths, which are potentially lethal to most forms of life (Figure 7.3). Of the wavelengths that do penetrate the atmosphere, about thirty-two percent is reflected back into space by clouds and particulate matter. Clouds, dust, and water vapor absorb another eighteen percent. Thus, one-half of the solar radiation penetrating the atmosphere is lost through reflection and absorption even before it reaches the earth's surface.

Light of visible wavelengths can penetrate the atmosphere easily enough. But after those wavelengths are absorbed, they are radiated from the earth's surface as infrared wavelengths (heat). The ozone layer of the upper atmosphere inhibits the escape of these longer wavelengths, hence the heat is temporarily held in. The effect is analogous to heat retention in a greenhouse, which allows penetration of sunlight rays but holds in the heat radiated from plants and the soil on the inside. *Thus heat indirectly derived from the sun warms the atmosphere.*

Air Currents

In global terms, the heating effect of solar radiation is not uniform. Light rays strike more directly on the equator than on polar regions (Figure 39.2). Air becomes heated more at the equator than at the poles. The warm equatorial air rises and spreads out, northward and southward. In the

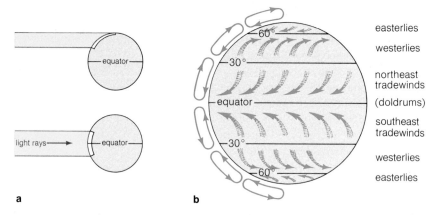

Figure 39.2 Formation of worldwide prevailing air currents. (**a**) Sunlight rays are almost perpendicular (hence more concentrated) at the equator than at the poles, where their angle of incidence spreads them out over a larger surface area. The unequal heating of polar and equatorial air causes air to circulate from the equator, toward the poles, then back to the equator.

(**b**) Because of a force created by the earth's rotation on its axis, this immense pattern of air circulation becomes divided into belts of prevailing east and west winds. Unequal heat retention by oceans and land masses contributes to the formation of these belts, which dictate global patterns of rainfall. In turn, the amount of rainfall helps dictate the distribution of major types of ecosystems throughout the world.

arctic regions the air becomes cooler, sinks downward, then moves back to the equator.

Two factors modify this immense pattern of air circulation. First, heat retention is not the same for land as it is for oceans (the land heats and cools more rapidly), and land masses are not distributed uniformly. These variations disrupt the basic pattern of air movements. Second, a force associated with the earth's rotation deflects air flow in the northern hemisphere to the right and, in the southern hemisphere, to the left. The outcome is worldwide belts of prevailing east and west air currents (Figure 39.2b).

These prevailing air currents help dictate the distribution of different types of ecosystems. At the equator, for example, hot air gives up moisture as it rises to cooler altitudes, and the rainfall supports luxuriant plant growth. The less moist air descends at about 30° latitudes; here, the earth's great deserts occur. The air again becomes warm, picks up moisture, and descends at 60° latitudes. Then the air rises and travels poleward. Almost no rainfall accompanies its descent in polar regions.

Ocean Currents

The earth's rotation, prevailing air currents, and variations in water temperature give rise to currents and surface drifts that tend to move parallel with the equator. Of course, land masses intervene and alter the movements of the world's great oceans, the Atlantic and Pacific. Dominating each ocean are two circular water movements, called **gyres**. In the northern hemisphere, currents in the gyre move clockwise; in the southern hemisphere, they move counterclockwise. An equatorial countercurrent separates the two gyres and carries water away from the western boundaries of the ocean basins (Figure 39.3).

Gyres move water warmed at the equator northward and southward. For example, the Gulf Stream flows north from the Caribbean and along the southeastern coast of the United States. From there it flows northeast across the Atlantic. Then it divides into the North Atlantic Drift and the Canary Current (Figure 39.3). Because of the Gulf Stream, the climate of Great Britain and Norway is wetter and milder than you might expect if air currents were the only consideration. The current spawns moisture-laden fog and clouds, which have a mediating effect on temperature and which lead to abundant rainfall.

Gyres also carry water cooled at the poles toward the equator, along the western coasts of Africa, North America, and South America. These cold currents transport deep, nutrient-rich waters to the surface. (This movement is known as upwelling and will be considered shortly.) The

Figure 39.3 Surface drifts and ocean currents in January. The solid arrows indicate warm water movements; dashed arrows indicate cold water movements. (After the U.S. Navy Oceanographic Department)

cold currents also have a mediating effect on climate, particularly in coastal regions, which they often shroud in fog. The mild, wet climate of the Pacific Northwest coast of America is largely a result of the California current. As the moisture move inland, it even cools the air over the hottest deserts. In such ways, *ocean currents influence the physical conditions characteristic of diverse ecosystems.*

Seasonal Variations in Climate

Through the year, climates change in the northern and southern hemispheres. Again, variations in the amount of incoming solar radiation contribute to climatic change.

Many biological rhythms correspond with the annual changes in light, temperature, and rainfall. In essence, biological rhythms permit the organism to anticipate and adjust to seasonal change. In *temperate* regions (which have moderate climates compared, say, to arctic regions), organisms respond more to seasonal changes in light and temperature than to other factors. In tropical regions, they respond more to changes in amounts of rainfall. Thus there are cycles of leafing out, flowering, fruiting, and leaf drop among many plants (Chapter Nineteen). There are cycles of breeding and migration among animals, including caribou, bison, and butterflies (Figure 39.4). In the seas, animals

including turtles, seals, and whales also migrate. Such movements correspond with seasonal bursts of primary production on land and in the seas.

What causes seasonal variations in climate? The circle of illumination that divides earth days and nights is always perpendicular to the sun. However, the earth's axis is tilted in relation to its annual path around the sun. In December, the North Pole is most tilted away from the sun. December means winter in the northern hemisphere. Temperatures are lower than at other times of year because days are shorter and incoming light rays are more spread out (Figure 39.5). In the southern hemisphere, Decembers are warmer. Temperatures are higher because days are longer and light rays are not as spread out. The situation is reversed for the two hemispheres in June. Notice, in Figure 39.5, that winter in the north polar regions is a time of near-perpetual darkness, and that daylight is nearly continuous in summer.

Regional Climates

Climate is influenced by more than general patterns of light, temperature, and rainfall. It is influenced also by the presence or absence of bodies of water, mountains, valleys, and vegetation cover.

Figure 39.4 Monarch butterflies, migrants that aggregate in trees of California coastal regions and central Mexico. Monarchs typically travel hundreds of miles south to these regions, which are cool and humid in winter; if they stayed in their breeding grounds, they would risk being killed by frost.

For example, mountain ranges parallel the west coasts of North and South America. Here, climatic variations are reflected in successive belts of vegetation that change with altitude. At the eastern base of the Rocky Mountains, the belt includes grasslands and shrubs adapted to dry, warm conditions. Above this is the montane belt, with deciduous and coniferous trees that are tolerant of more moisture and cooler temperatures. Above the montane forests is the subalpine belt, with conifers adapted to the rigors of a still cooler climate. The cold alpine belt above this cannot support trees; here, grasses and sedges dominate. On the highest peaks, with their cover of snow and ice, a vegetation cover is conspicuously absent.

Such changes in vegetation cover with altitude are due partly to the way that mountains modify patterns of rainfall. When prevailing winds reach a mountain range, the air rises, cools, and loses moisture (cool air holds less moisture than does warm air). Here, the abundant rainfall promotes plant growth. After flowing over mountain crests, the air descends. As it does, it becomes warmer, its moisture-holding capacity increases, and it picks up moisture. Thus, a so-called *rain shadow* exists on the eastern slopes of these mountains, in that arid or semiarid deserts are created by the lack of abundant rainfall. Rain shadows also exist in the mountain ranges of Europe, the Himalayas of Asia, and the Andes of South America.

Aquatic regions also are influenced by features that interrupt or channel air and water movements. These movements have profound effects on aquatic ecosystems, in ways that will be described shortly.

BIOGEOCHEMICAL CYCLES

Hydrologic Cycle

So far, we have considered some of the air and water movements that underlie prevailing weather conditions. Cold and warm ocean currents, clouds, winds, and rainfall are all part of a cycle, driven by solar radiation, that spans the biosphere. The waters of the earth move slowly and on a vast

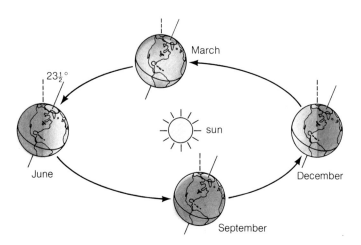

Figure 39.5 Annual variation in the amount of incoming solar radiation. Notice that the northern end of the earth's axis tilts toward the sun in June and away from it in December. Notice also the annual variation in the position of the equator relative to the boundary of illumination between day and night. Such variations in the intensity and duration of daylight lead to seasonal variations in temperature in different hemispheres and at the poles.

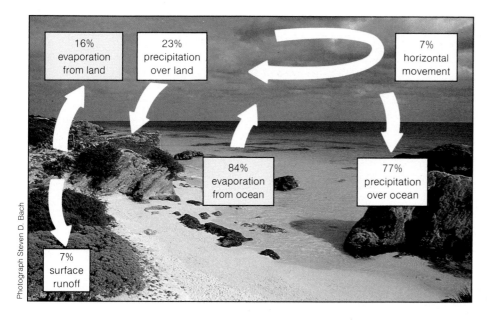

16%
evaporation
from land

23%
precipitation
over land

7%
horizontal
movement

84%
evaporation
from ocean

77%
precipitation
over ocean

7%
surface
runoff

Figure 39.6 Simplified picture of the hydrologic cycle. Percentages indicate the annual mean distribution of water.

scale through the atmosphere, on or through the uppermost layers of land masses, to the oceans, and back again. These global water movements represent the **hydrologic cycle**.

The global cycling of water, shown in Figure 39.6, is influenced by the following factors:

evaporation	*release of water as vapor into the atmosphere*
precipitation	*release of water from the atmosphere as rain or snow*
detention	*temporary storage of water on land or in oceans*
transportation	*movement of water on winds or as surface runoff*

Only a fraction of the water is present in the atmosphere as vapor, clouds, and ice crystals. The amount is greater over oceans than over land, for two reasons. More than ninety percent of all water is located in oceans, and the surface of open oceans places less restriction on evaporation. (For example, in a dense forest, the canopy keeps the air relatively cool and thereby restricts evaporative water loss.)

On the average, a water molecule does not stay aloft for more than about ten days. Thus the turnover rate is rapid for this part of the hydrologic cycle. Water released as precipitation is detained on land for no more than 10 to 120 days on the average, depending on the season and on where it falls. (The residence time is longer in dense coniferous forests than elsewhere, for example.) Some evaporates;

some is transported by rivers and the like to the sea. There, large-scale evaporation begins the cycle again.

Gaseous Cycles

The atmosphere and oceans also are reservoirs for many of the inorganic substances essential for life. Molecules such as oxygen, carbon dioxide, and nitrogen undergo movements known as gaseous cycles. The nitrogen cycle was described in the preceding chapter and illustrated in Figure 38.8. The cycling of oxygen and carbon dioxide is interrelated through the processes of photosynthesis and respiration (Figure 39.7).

On a global scale, photosynthesizers harness and use a tremendous amount of carbon dioxide. Billions of metric tons of carbon become incorporated into organic compounds. Both the photosynthesizers and the consumers that directly or indirectly feed on them release carbon dioxide during respiration. Overall, carbon dioxide fixation during photosynthesis and its release during respiration tend to be in equilibrium.

However, the turnover rate of carbon varies, depending on environmental conditions. In tropical forests, decomposition and carbon uptake are rapid, so not much carbon is found in the soil. In bogs and marshes, organic compounds are not broken down completely, and much accumulates in forms such as peat. In aquatic food webs, carbon can become

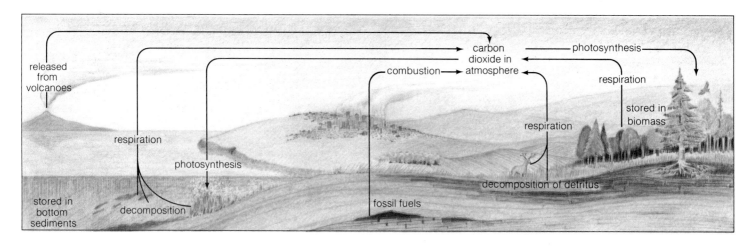

Figure 39.7 Simplified picture of the carbon cycle. Carbon dioxide in the atmosphere is harnessed during the second stage of photosynthesis. Compounds containing carbon and oxygen are assembled into tissues (living biomass). Oxygen is released to the atmosphere during photosynthesis; carbon dioxide is released during aerobic respiration. Conversions to carbon-containing inorganic compounds occur during decomposition. Carbon can also become locked up in peat, coal, oil, and gas, then subsequently released during the combustion of fossil fuels. Some carbon becomes locked up in the bottom sediments of oceans. New carbon enters the atmosphere during volcanic eruptions.

bound as carbonate in shells and other hard parts. When the shelled organisms die, they sink and become buried in bottom sediments of different depths. In deep oceans, carbon can remain buried for millions of years, until geologic movements bring them once more to the surface. Still other carbon is slowly converted to long-standing reserves of gas, petroleum, and coal deep in the earth. These reserves are used as fossil fuels.

With the burning of fossil fuels, carbon dioxide is rapidly reintroduced into the atmosphere. Through volcanic eruptions, carbon also is released from material deep in the lithosphere. About half the total carbon released in the atmosphere is destined for storage in two global sinks: the oceans and accumulated plant biomass. However, there is speculation that increased burning of fossil fuels and increases in volcanic eruptions can introduce too much carbon into the atmosphere, and thereby exceed the capacity of global sinks. Theoretically, increases in atmospheric carbon dioxide could create a worldwide "blanket" effect by causing more radiated heat to be held in. Global warming could lead to a rise in sea level (because of glacial melting), submergence of coasts, and expansion of the world's great desert regions, to name a few possible consequences. Only a few degrees increase may be all that is required for these events to occur.

Sedimentary Cycles

In sedimentary cycles, minerals move from land, to sediments in the seas, and back to the land. The earth's crust is the main storehouse for mineral nutrients that flow through sedimentary cycles.

For example, the phosphorus cycle begins with phosphate rock formations in the earth. Through weathering and other erosive forces, phosphorus is washed into rivers and streams, then moves to the oceans. There, largely on continental shelves, phosphorus builds up as insoluble deposits. Millions of years pass, and geological events lead to the uplifting and exposure of the seafloor. Many phosphate deposits occur in mountain ranges that parallel the coasts; large deposits are mined in Florida. (In the United States alone, 2 billion kilograms of phosphorus are mined annually for use in fertilizers.)

There is a biological component to the phosphorus cycle. All living things require phosphorus, which becomes incorporated in the nucleotides of DNA, RNA, ATP, and the like. Phosphorus is released from living tissues in detrital food webs. It may not remain for long in soil and water; photosynthetic organisms can take it up again and thereby recycle it through the ecosystem. We will return to the cycling of solid materials (page 670).

Figure 39.8 An example of a lake ecosystem in Canada.

AQUATIC ECOSYSTEMS

In global terms, there are two classes of aquatic ecosystems as defined by salinity:

freshwater ecosystems	*lentic (inland bodies of standing fresh water) and lotic (running fresh water)*
marine and estuarine ecosystems	*oceans, seas, estuaries, inland bodies of brackish water*

The productivity of both classes of aquatic ecosystems depends on light penetration, temperature, nutrient concentrations, underwater topography, water depth, and the direction and degree of water movement. These factors change daily and they change with seasonal variations in climate. In turn, the changes influence the nature and distribution of aquatic life.

Freshwater Ecosystems

A "typical" freshwater ecosystem is like a "typical" cell; there is no such thing. These ecosystems vary in size from small ponds to lakes that cover many thousands of square kilometers. Some are shallow enough to wade across; one is more than 1,700 meters deep. All have gradients in light penetration, temperature, and dissolved gases, but the gradients vary from one ecosystem to another, both daily and seasonally.

Figure 39.8 shows one kind of lake ecosystem. During winter, the deep waters are cold, low in oxygen, and high in carbon dioxide. With the lengthening of daylight in spring, the surface waters become warmer. The temperature stratification as well as the strong spring winds set up currents that mix the water from the surface to the bottom of the lake basin. This *spring overturn* mixes bottom nutrients, oxygen, and plankton throughout the lake and is accompanied by a burst in primary productivity.

As the spring sun warms the surface waters, they become less dense than the underlying waters. In summer, differences in temperature and density are greatest. These differences oppose the force of winds, and waters resist vertical mixing. Below the surface layer (where waters freely circulate), temperatures drop rapidly (1°C for each meter of depth). This midlayer of steeply declining temperature is the *thermocline*. The bottom layer is deep, cold, with gentle drops in temperature.

In autumn, air temperature drops and the surface layer becomes cooler. Then the thermocline narrows, and temperature becomes much the same through the lake. This is the *fall overturn:* nutrients, oxygen, and plankton are mixed once more throughout the lake basin, and there may be another burst in productivity before the coming of winter.

In terms of photosynthetic activity, lake ecosystems have three zones. The **littoral** includes all those areas where light penetrates to the lake bottom. Rooted plants characterize the littoral zone, as do abundant decomposers. Beyond this is the **limnetic** zone of open sunlit water, with suspended phytoplankton. The **profundal** zone includes those areas below the depth of light penetration. Anaerobic bacterial decomposers dominate here.

a

b

Figure 39.9 Hydrothermal vent ecosystems. In 1977, biologists discovered a distinct type of ecosystem deep in the Pacific Ocean, where sunlight never penetrates. John Corliss and his coworkers were exploring the Galápagos Rift, a volcanically active boundary between two of the earth's crustal plates. There, on the ocean floor, the near-freezing seawater seeps into fissures, becomes heated, and is spewed out through vents at temperatures exceeding 700°F.

This hydrothermal effluent deposits zinc, iron, and copper sulfides as well as calcium and magnesium sulfates, all leached from rocks as pressure forces the heated water upward. In marked contrast to most of the deep ocean floor, these nutrient-rich, warm "oases" support diverse marine communities. Chemosynthetic bacteria and other microbes use the inorganic deposits as energy sources. They are the primary producers in a food web that includes tube worms, clams, sea anemones, crabs, and fishes (**a**, **b**).

So far, other hydrothermal vent ecosystems have been discovered near Easter Island, off the northwestern United States, in the Gulf of California, and about 150 miles south of the tip of Baja California, Mexico. (a, Robert Hessler; b, Fred Grassle, Woods Hole Institution of Oceanography)

Lakes may be further classified in terms of nutrient concentration. *Eutrophic* lakes are rich in nutrients; *oligotrophic* lakes are nutrient-poor. Many lakes are undergoing human-caused eutrophication, with nutrients such as nitrogen and phosphates being added rapidly from agricultural runoff, sewage, and industrial wastes.

Marine and Estuarine Ecosystems

Marine environments cover seventy percent of the earth's surface. They include estuaries, mud flats, tidal marshes, tidal pools, rocky and sandy shores, and coral reefs, all of which are confined to coastal waters.

Open Oceans. Beyond the continental shelves is the vast province of the open oceans (Figures 39.9 and 39.10). In some places, it extends to depths of 7,000 meters. There are three zones of the open ocean:

---

1. *Epipelagic zone,* or photic zone. These are illuminated surface waters, extending downward for about 200 meters, in which photosynthesis can occur. There are sharp gradients of light, temperature, and salinity.

2. *Mesopelagic zone.* This "middle" region extends downward from 200 meters to 1,000 meters. Little light penetrates, and the temperature gradient is gradual. Many regions of this zone contain the greatest concentrations of nitrates and phosphates.

3. *Bathypelagic zone.* This is the zone of deepest waters and bottom sediments, devoid of sunlight. Temperatures are cold, and water pressure is great.

Compared with ecosystems on land, productivity is low in the open oceans. Distinct ecosystems are rare, because primary producers are rarely concentrated in one place. (One exception is described in Figure 39.9.) Photosynthetic activity is restricted to the upper surface waters, where phytoplankton often drift with ocean currents. Zooplankton (including copepods, planktonic arthropods, and shrimplike krill) graze on the suspended marine pastures. In turn, nektonic forms (small fishes, squids, and other carnivores) feed on the herbivores. In the open oceans, remains and wastes of all these organisms sink downward. They are potential sources of nutrients, but a permanent thermocline in deep water restricts their circulation to surface waters. Permanent thermal stratification is most pronounced in tropical waters. There, production is lowest of all, even though light is the most intense and temperatures are warm.

a

Figure 39.10 The ocean. The most productive regions of this vast province are coastal waters, where light penetration and vertical circulation of nutrients support photosynthetic activities. (**a**) Here, a California sea lion cavorts above kelp, eelgrass, and other photosynthesizers rooted just offshore.

Chuck Nicklin

b

Dennis Brokaw

Figure 39.11 New England salt marsh, with *Spartina* predominating.

E. R. Degginger

Temperate oceans are more productive because they do not have a permanent thermocline; there are spring (and, to some extent) fall overturns of nutrients.

Upwellings and Coastal Waters. Primary production of the oceans is greatest in shallow coastal waters and in regions of upwelling along the margins of continents. There, currents stir the water and keep nutrients circulating to the photosynthesizers.

Upwelling is an upward movement of deep water that carries nutrients to the surface zone. The movement is associated with reversals in prevailing coastal winds. These reversals occur primarily along the western coasts of Peru, southern California, northern and southwestern Africa, and the Antarctic. In winter, winds slam into the coastal regions, and the wind-driven water piles up. In summer, the coastal winds flow north and south, toward the equator. The force of the winds causes surface waters piled up along the coast to move away from the shore. When the surface water moves out, deep water moves in vertically to replace it.

For example, upwelling near Peru is coupled with the northward flow of the cold Humboldt Current (Figure 39.3). Together, these movements bring up tremendous amounts of nitrate and phosphates from below; they are the foundation for one of the world's richest fisheries. Periodically, prevailing wind direction shifts and warm equatorial waters displace the Humboldt Current. This condition, known as El Niño, prevents upwelling and productivity plummets.

Estuaries. In estuaries, fresh water from rivers and streams mixes with seawater. The waters become enriched with nutrients from surrounding tidal marshes of the sort shown in Figure 39.11. These marshes are flooded daily by incoming tides. Litter and wastes from the marsh plants, such as *Spartina*, are carried in with the water and enrich the estuarine nutrient base.

Estuary ecosystems have both planktonic and detrital food webs. In water, dinoflagellates and diatoms are major producers in these webs; aquatic plants, such as eelgrass, are also important. Estuaries serve as nurseries, where much of the animal life of the sea is born.

TERRESTRIAL ECOSYSTEMS

Effect of Soils

The distribution of different ecosystems on land depends primarily on differences in prevailing climates. It also depends on the composition of regional soils. **Soil** contains rock and organic matter in some state of decomposition. Depending on the degree of weathering, the rock component ranges from coarse-grained gravel to sand, silt, and fine-grained clay. Typically, soils are layered in this manner:

A horizon	*topsoil, with the greatest accumulation of organic matter (humus)*
B horizon	*subsoil (particles mixed with minerals leached from the topsoil)*
C horizon	*loose rock, extending to the layer of bedrock below*

Water and minerals are rapidly leached from soils with high gravel and sand content. Clay soils are so dense that they tend to hold water and keep out gaseous oxygen. Some anaerobic bacteria can do well in such saturated, oxygen-poor soils; plant roots generally cannot. However, the fine-grained clay particles have negative charges on their surface, and collectively they present a large surface

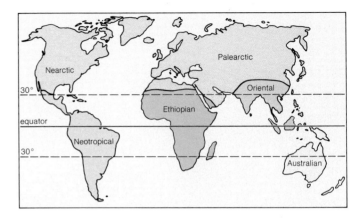

Figure 39.12 Major biogeographic realms, as first proposed by W. Sclater and Alfred Wallace in the 1800s. The scheme is still widely accepted.

area. Thus they can attract and hold an abundance of positively charged micronutrients, such as the potassium essential for plant growth. The most productive soil is loam, which is clay that has enough larger particles mixed in to prevent packing.

The Concept of Biomes

Ever since global explorations began in the sixteenth century (Chapter Two), biologists have recognized that huge tracts of grasslands, deserts, forests, and tundra exist. There have been numerous attempts to group all such ecosystems into simple classification schemes. For example, W. Sclater and then Alfred Wallace were the first to propose six **biogeographic realms**, which contain characteristic assemblages of animals and plants. Barriers such as oceans, mountain ranges, and deserts keep the species of each realm more or less isolated from the others by restricting their dispersal. (Thus the kangaroos of the Australian realm would not, on their own, be able to radiate elsewhere.) Figure 39.12 depicts this biogeographic scheme, which is still widely accepted.

Each such realm is actually a mosaic of climate and topography. Accordingly, each is further subdivided into broad regions, with distinct plant formations that support particular arrays of consumer organisms. The climax communities of these regions have a uniform, dominant type of plant, such as grasses. These broad, vegetational subdivisions of the biogeographic realms are known as **biomes**. As Figure 39.13 suggests, they include different types of deserts, shrublands, grasslands, forests, and tundra.

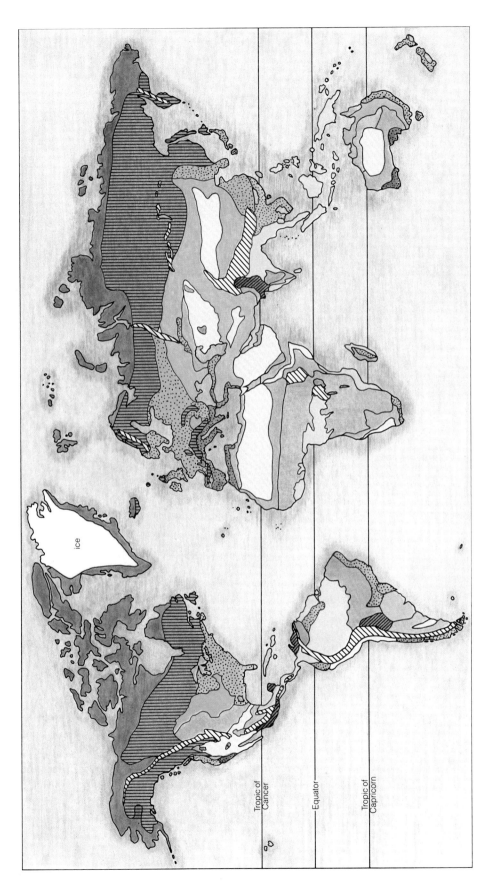

	tropical scrub forest
	tropical savanna, thorn forest
	semidesert, arid grassland
	mountains (complex zonation)

	chaparral/Mediterranean
	desert
	tropical rain forest, tropical evergreen forest
	tropical deciduous forest

	tundra
	boreal forest (taiga), montane coniferous forest
	temperate forest
	temperate grassland

Tropic of Cancer

Equator

Tropic of Capricorn

ice

Figure 39.13 Simplified picture of the world's major biomes. Arctic tundra and boreal forests are continuous over vast regions, and contain ecologically equivalent and taxonomically related species. Other biomes that are isolated but of the same type generally have ecologically equivalent but often taxonomically unrelated species. The overall pattern of biome distribution roughly corresponds with patterns of soil type distributions and climate.

a

b

Figure 39.14 (**a**) Warm desert near Tucson, Arizona. The vegetation cover includes creosote bushes, ocotillo, saguaro cacti, and prickly pear cacti. (**b**) Chaparral-covered hills east of San Diego, California.

Deserts

Where evaporation exceeds rainfall, there you will find deserts. Again, these climatic conditions are pronounced at latitudes 30° from the equator. Global air movements play a role here, as do mountain barriers that create rain shadows. The vegetational cover is minimal in deserts, compared with other biomes. When rain does fall, it falls in heavy, brief pulses. The unprotected soil erodes rapidly during violent windstorms and thunderstorms. Because of the low humidity, sunlight penetration through the atmosphere is high and the ground heats up rapidly. At night, the heat quickly radiates back to the air. Thus deserts typically are hot by day and cool by night.

Desert species are adapted to resisting or evading times of drought. For example, some plants persist mostly as

a

seeds, which sprout and flower at astonishing rates after the brief rains. Many animals sleep or remain in shade by day and are active by night. Functionally, deserts are regions of low net production, and detrital food webs dominate. Figure 39.14 is a desert in the American Southwest.

Shrublands

Shrublands occur in semiarid regions with cool, moist winters and long, hot, dry summers. Most of the rains fall during the winter, and temperatures typically fall below 15°C for one of the winter months. There is a burst of plant growth at the end of the wet season. Five regions of *Mediterranean-type shrublands* are concentrated mostly between 30° and 40° latitudes. The chaparral shrublands of California fall in this broad zone (Figure 39.14). Some of the

b

Figure 39.15 (a) Rolling shortgrass prairie; in the background, the Rocky Mountains. (b) A patch of natural tallgrass prairie.

cool, arid regions east of the Rocky Mountains are classified as cold deserts; they are also major shrublands dominated by sagebrush. *Successional shrublands* occur in transitional zones between grasslands and forests. If dense enough, they can persist for long periods. On wet ground (such as drainage channels and around lakes or ponds), shrub thickets often include alders, sumac, willows, dogwood shrubs, and blackberries.

In shrubland biomes, the most prevalent plants are generally well-branched, short, and woody. In Mediterranean-type shrublands, there is no understory or ground litter. The plants are highly flammable and produce abundant seeds. Many species actually depend on heat and scarring to prepare seeds for germination. For centuries, Mediterranean-type shrublands have been maintained by episodes of fire, which clears away old growth and contributes to the recycling of nutrients.

Grasslands

The world's great grasslands occur in South Africa, South America, and midcontinental regions of North America and the USSR. At one time, grasslands covered more than forty percent of the land; today, they have been largely cleared for agriculture. All grassland biomes share several characteristics. The land itself is flat or rolling; it is dry, with high rates of evaporation. Rainfall is between ten and thirty inches a year—enough to keep the regions from turning into deserts, but not enough to support heavy forest growth. Grazing and burrowing species are the dominant forms of animal life. In many grasslands, grazing and episodes of fire help maintain the climax communities by creating conditions necessary for renewed growth.

There are different types of grassland biomes. For example, *tallgrass prairie* of the sort shown in Figure 39.15 once ran north to south along the deciduous forests of North America. In some tallgrass regions, species of composites such as daisies actually outnumbered the species of grasses (leading to the suggestion that they ought to have been called daisyland instead). Legumes were also abundant; these nitrogen-fixing plants increased the net primary production for the region, compared with other grassland biomes. Most tallgrass prairie has been converted to agriculture.

Shortgrass prairie occurs where winds are strong, rainfall light and infrequent, and evaporation rapid. Figure 39.15 shows an example. Plant roots soak up the brief, seasonal rainfall on the surface, above the permanently dry subsoil.

Thase Daniel

a

Much of the shortgrass prairie of the American Midwest was overgrazed and plowed under for wheat, which requires more moisture than the region provides. Removal of the tight vegetation cover, drought, and strong prevailing winds combined to turn much of the plains into a Dust Bowl. John Steinbeck's *Grapes of Wrath* and James Michener's *Centennial* are two historical novels that speak eloquently of this disruption and its consequences.

Tropical grasslands include the broad belts of African savanna, described in Chapter One. In savanna regions of low rainfall, the main species are rapid-growing, tufted grasses. Where rainfall increases slightly, shrubs such as acacia grow in scattered patches. Savanna regions of high rainfall are mosaics of tall, coarse grasses, shrubs, and low trees, even of humid forests. Tropical grasslands also extend into Southeast Asia, where they are known as monsoon

Thase Daniel

Dona Hutchins

b

Figure 39.16 Tropical rain forest, showing aerial plants (including bromeliads) and vines in the canopy (**a**). Where light breaks through the canopy, exuberant new growth occurs (**b**).

grasslands. The dominant plant species are adapted to the hot, wet summers and cool to cold winters of this region.

Forests

There are three major types of forest biomes: coniferous, deciduous, and rain forests. The forests of all three biomes are stratified between the canopy and the forest floor, creating a stratification in light, temperature, and moisture. In all three, gross primary productivity is high. However, much of the production is allocated to maintaining the existing forest structure (as much as forty-five percent in coniferous forests). Nutrients accumulate in woody biomass and are locked away from short-term cycling. Minerals become available more from decaying roots and litter than from the soil.

Tropical Rain Forests. In most equatorial regions, rainfall is heavy (during at least one season), humidity is high, and the annual mean temperature is about 28°C. These are regions that include tropical rain forests (Figure 39.16). Here, vines clamber up toward the sun. Mosses, orchids, lichens, and bromeliads (plants related to the pineapple) grow on tree branches. They take up minerals dissolved in tiny pockets of water, minerals released during the decay of bits of leaves, insects, and litter. Entire communities of insects, spiders, and amphibians live, breed, and die in the small pools of water that collect in the leaves of these plants. Many insects, birds, and monkeys spend most of their lives at a single level in the stratified forest. In some cases, the kinds of organisms living in or on a single tree may exceed the kinds of organisms living in an entire forest to the north. Yet, with all of this diversity, a tropical rain forest is one of

Spring

Autumn

the worst places to grow crops. There is practically no organic debris; quantities of nutrients are tied up in the standing biomass. Decomposition is rapid in the hot, humid climate. Minerals released during decomposition are rapidly picked up by roots and mycorrhizae concentrated in the top

layers of soil; there is very little nutrient storage in the subsoil. Thus, when such forests are cleared for agriculture, most of the nutrients are permanently cleared away.

With *slash-and-burn agriculture*, forest biomass can be reduced to nutrient-rich ashes, then the ashes can be tilled

Summer

Winter

All photographs Thomas E. Hemmerly

Figure 39.17 The changing character of a temperate deciduous forest in spring, summer, autumn, and winter.

into the soil. Even then, heavy rains wash away most of the nutrients from the exposed clay soils. After a few years, cleared fields become infertile and usually are abandoned. Because nutrients are so depleted, successional replacement is extremely slow.

Deciduous Forests. In some parts of the world, a growing season characterized by moderate rainfall and mild temperatures alternates with a pronounced dry season. Deciduous forests are adapted to these conditions. Unlike the other two biomes, mineral cycling here is more pronounced. Conditions are favorable for decomposition, and the seasonal leaf drop assures abundant litter on the forest floor.

In many tropical regions, including parts of Southeast Asia, temperatures remain mild but precipitation dwindles for part of the year. These regions support *tropical seasonal forests*, which are dominated by deciduous and semideciduous species. Regions of North America, Europe, and eastern Asia support *temperate deciduous forests*, of the sort shown in Figure 39.17. These forests once covered much of the eastern United States. Depending on patterns of human settlement, they were cleared or cut over, often several times. Today the forests of the Southern Appalachian Mountains are the best example of this rapidly disappearing biome.

Coniferous Forests.   There are two major types of coniferous forests. One, the *montane coniferous forest*, occurs in the Sierra Nevadas, Cascades, and Rocky Mountains of the United States, in Europe, and in parts of Central America. At high elevations, winters are long and snow is heavy; yet summers are warm enough to promote the dense growth of coniferous trees, such as spruces, firs, and pines. At lower elevations, Douglas fir and ponderosa pine predominate. Figure 39.18 shows an example of a montane coniferous forest.

South of the tree line in northern regions of the world is an extensive zone known as the *boreal forest*, or *taiga* (Figure 39.18). For the most part, these coniferous forests occupy glaciated regions punctuated with cold lakes, bogs, and rivers. Winters are prolonged and extremely cold, with a fairly constant snow cover. As with the montane forests, however, the summer is warm enough to promote dense growth.

Food webs built around these conifers include insects that feed on the bark, buds, cones, leaves, and shoots of the trees. Decomposition is slower than in tropical and deciduous forests, because of the lower temperatures and the chemical composition of the (acid-rich) conifer leaves. Seed-eating squirrels and mice are prevalent. Larger herbivores, such as hare, beaver, moose, and deer, usually do not use the conifers as a primary food source. Instead they forage on low-growing vegetation and deciduous trees or shrubs that spring up around the region's many lakes, streams, bogs, and marshes ("taiga" is Russian for swamp forest). The forest is used primarily as protection against predators.

Is it this same recognition of sanctuary that draws us to a forest? It is interesting that at a time when grasslands were being tilled under, a conservation movement began in

a

Figure 39.18   (**a**) Boreal forest, or taiga and (**b**) the montane coniferous forest of Yosemite beneath the first snows of winter.

order to save the forests. The first bureau of conservation was the United States Forest Service. Partly as a result of its initial efforts, a third of the United States is still heavily forested. The Forest Service manages all wildlife, watersheds, recreation, and lumbering in the national forest system. Part of its program is based on *tree farming*: the replacement of climax communities with monoculture stands of fast-growing species. As simplification is permitted to occur, the forest systems become more vulnerable and must be protected like other crops—with widespread use of insecticides and fertilizers. There is also increased clear-cutting, given the demands for wood products. (The average American uses about 560 pounds of wood products such as paper each year.) Ninety percent of the national forests in the United States are potentially open to clear-cutting.

b

 *(credit, vertical text at right: Ansel Adams)*

Tundra

In Chapter Thirty-Eight, you read about nutrient cycling in the *arctic tundra,* a treeless plain that extends beyond the tree line of the far north. Another tundra biome exists, in the high mountain ranges at lower latitudes. This *alpine tundra* also is characterized by low temperature, low precipitation, and short growing seasons. Growth rates for the vegetation are low, as they are in the arctic tundra. However, alpine tundra ecosystems have no permafrost layer below the soil surface. The plant species often form cushions and mats that can withstand buffeting from the strong winds that sweep through the mountains. Because the growing season is so short in both ecosystems, net primary production is low.

The City As Ecosystem

The preceding photographs were not presented to make you gasp in wonder over the glories of nature. It was not out of indifference that we excluded pictures of a squirrel or wolf here, a rabbit or partridge there. Rather, the photographs are meant to convey that *the foundation of any ecosystem is its array of producer organisms.* This is where all webs of life begin.

For the past 11,000 years, a new kind of ecosystem has been evolving. It contains merging human communities called cities; when the surrounding urban areas are included, this kind of ecosystem is called a megalopolis (Figure 39.19). As with other ecosystems, such urban centers interact with the land, the waters, even the local climate.

Figure 39.19 The city as ecosystem.

However, urban centers have no producers. They have only consumers (humans, their pets, and scavengers such as rats, cockroaches, and pigeons). Compared to the human biomass, they have a negligible number of decomposers. Each day, hundreds of thousands of tons of resources are imported. Outside the urban sphere, other ecosystems must be converted to agriculture, mined for metals, and stripped of other resources. *Cities function as ecosystems only because they import energy and materials from someplace else, and export rather than recycle wastes.* What are some of the consequences of this one-way flow of energy into cities and the one-way flow of wastes from them? The next chapter will take a look.

Readings

Ricklefs, R. 1976. *The Economy of Nature*. Portland, Oregon: Chiron Press. Ricklefs is one of the poets of ecology.

Smith, R. 1980. *Ecology and Field Biology*. Third edition. New York: Harper & Row. Good introduction to the structure and functioning of the biosphere.

West, S. 1980. "Smokers, Red Worms, and Deep Sea Plumbing." *Science News* 117(2):28–30. An account of deep-sea exploration and discoveries in the Galápagos Rift.

Whittaker, R. 1975. *Communities and Ecosystems*. Second edition. New York: Macmillan.

Review Questions

1. Define the three main components of the biosphere.

2. Define climate. What four interacting factors influence climate? What does climate in turn influence?

3. How do prevailing air and ocean currents help dictate the distribution of different types of ecosystems?

4. Define rain shadow. How does a rain shadow affect ecosystems on both sides of a mountain range?

5. What is the difference between the littoral, limnetic, and profundal zones of a lake ecosystem? What kinds of lakes are eutrophic? Oligotrophic?

6. What are the three zones of the open ocean, and which shows the greatest productivity?

7. What is a thermocline? Are thermoclines most pronounced in temperate or tropical oceans?

8. Define upwelling, and give an example of a region where upwelling has a profound effect on primary production.

9. How does the composition of regional soils affect ecosystem distribution?

10. Distinguish between biogeographic realm and biome. In what type of biome region would you say you live?

11. How do climatic conditions affect the character of the following biomes: desert, shrublands, grasslands, tropical rain forests, deciduous forests, coniferous forests, and tundra?

The ecosystems described in the preceding chapter have had a long history of development. As a result of coevolutionary adjustments, energy is utilized and materials are cycled efficiently through them over the long term. Sometimes resources dwindle severely, as they do when snowshoe hares overbrowse in Canadian forests (Figure 37.7). Yet the plants fight back, so to speak, and the forest ecosystem more or less bounces back over the years. Sometimes toxins build up, as happened when oxygen first started accumulating in the Permian atmosphere. Yet gradually, some organisms were able to adapt to this photosynthetically produced "toxin" by using it as an electron acceptor in aerobic respiration. Sometimes, too, species introductions can lead to wholesale displacements of other species, as happened when water hyacinths underwent explosive growth in waterways of the American South.

Natural ecosystems, then, are not static—but they tend to recover from disruptions or adjust to them. If this is true, why is there such widespread concern over the disruptions that human populations are creating in ecosystems throughout the biosphere? *The answer is that natural disruptions are not of the same magnitude in time and space.* The changes we are introducing are global in dimension and they are occurring at an accelerated pace. As one indication of our effects, species are becoming extinct fifty times faster than they were even a century ago.

The demands of the human population are increasing at a phenomenal rate, one that parallels our J-shaped curve of population growth. At the same time, resource utilization is not exactly what you would call efficient. Energy resources are not being conserved. Also, the products of our existence are accumulating to levels that are high enough and harmful enough to be called pollutants. **Pollutants** can be any substances with which ecosystems have had no prior evolutionary experience, in terms of kinds or amounts.

We can reduce, collect, concentrate, bury, and burn wastes. We can spread them out through other ecosystems. Yet we are never completely rid of the pollutants we are generating. Consider that for the past four decades, 350 million gallons of sewage from metropolitan New York and New Jersey have been dumped each day off the shore of Long Island. There, being out of sight, it was easy to put out of mind. Then, in the summer of 1970, a dead sea of sewage unaccountably began moving back toward the land, bringing with it the specter of hepatitis, encephalitis, and other terrible diseases to the cities that created it.

What options are available to us? The following case studies will give you an idea of how limited the current options really are.

40

HUMAN IMPACT
ON THE BIOSPHERE

Case Study: Solid Wastes

Lisa is entering college in the fall. On the outskirts of Del Mar, the town where she lives, a plot of land has been set aside as a recycling center for newspapers, glass, and aluminum cans. Last week Lisa decided to take part in the recycling program. There was a brief period of adjustment: the members of her family had to begin stacking newspapers in the garage, putting glass jars and bottles in one container, and putting aluminum cans in another. By the weekend, Lisa was surprised at how much had accumulated; she had assumed it would take months to stack up. It took only a few minutes to take the wastes to the recycling center. However, along the way she became aware, for the first time, of how many trashcans lined the streets, waiting to be emptied. Two or three trashcans sat in front of each house. There are about 5,000 homes in town, she thought. That meant about 12,000 trashcans a week had to be emptied somewhere. In the surrounding metropolitan area, there are about 200,000 homes. Could it be—400,000 to 600,000 trashcans *each week?*

After Lisa deposited the wastes in collecting bins at the recycling center, she decided to take a run out to the county "sanitary landfill station" where the nonrecycled solid wastes end up. There she watched one trash-filled truck after another rumble through the gate, antlike in their line to the dumping ground. Mounds of refuse were being bulldozed down the sides of what had once been chaparral-covered canyons. There are only so many canyons; what will happen when they are all filled?

Lisa realized then that this same thing must be happening all over the nation. What could her isolated commitment possibly mean? How could one small action help turn such a tide of waste? Somebody ought to start a campaign for public awareness, she mused. But with college starting soon, how could she get involved? Somebody else would have to do it.

Which "somebody" is going to tackle the 4.5 billion metric tons of solid wastes that are dumped, burned, and buried each year in the United States? Who is going to decide where the landfills go next? Conversely, is recycling itself a workable alternative? Recycling is part of the answer, but it cannot be a hit-or-miss effort. For instance, in her drive to the recycling center, Lisa used up some gasoline—a nonrenewable energy source that ultimately must be figured as part of the energy cost of the program. Although the energy cost is lower than it would be to extract and use new raw materials, it is still significant—particularly when you multiply the energy cost by all the individuals driving separately to the center.

What it will take, in the long run, is a change in basic living habits. We have what is known as a "throwaway" mentality: use it once, discard it, buy another. For instance, between fifty and sixty-five percent of urban wastes are paper products—of which only nineteen percent is now being recycled. If half the paper being thrown away each year were recycled, we would do more than conserve trees. The energy it takes to produce an equivalent amount of new paper could be diverted to provide electricity to about 10 million homes. Or consider that about 60 billion beverage containers are sold annually in the United States. About 50 billion are nonreturnable cans and bottles, many of which are discarded in public places. These containers represent three-fourths of the litter picked up along highways—a time-consuming, energy-draining activity that costs thousands of barrels of petroleum (not to mention hundreds of millions of tax dollars) each year.

A transition from a throwaway life style to one based on conservation and reuse is economically feasible, and we have most of the technology needed to implement the change. The question becomes one of commitment. For instance, consumer pressure can be brought to bear on manufacturers by refusing to buy goods that are lavishly wrapped, excessively boxed, and designed for one-time use. Individuals can ask the local post office to turn off their daily flow of junk mail, a flow that represents an astounding amount of paper, time, and energy—and higher mail delivery rates for everyone. Individuals can work to see that local city and county governments develop large-scale resource recovery centers, of the sort depicted in Figure 40.1. In such systems, existing dumps and landfills would be urban "mines." From them, nearly one-quarter of our past and present solid wastes might be recoverable.

Case Study: Water Pollution

Over the next five years, forty thousand homes are scheduled to be built across the freeway from the small Arizona town in which Adán lives. After reading newspaper accounts of the development, Adán became concerned. There is no way existing public facilities (schools, roads, power plants, waste disposal systems) can absorb the demands of the increased population. For example, the present waste-water treatment facilities are operating at capacity, and there simply is not enough water in this part of the country to process more raw sewage before releasing it into the few existing waterways. Can more water be brought in? Even assuming someone will pay for it, where will the water come from?

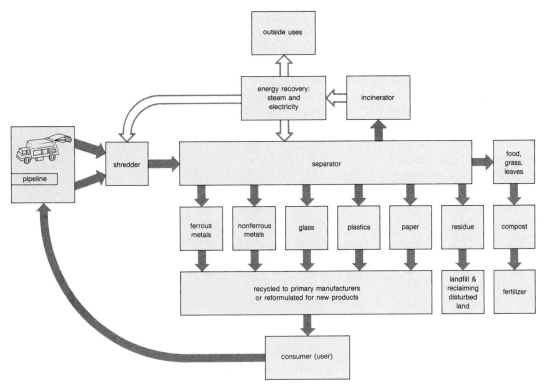

Figure 40.1 Generalized resource recovery system. Solid wastes are treated as urban "ore." Bulk items are sorted out, and the remainder is shredded and separated. Electromagnets could be used to extract steel and iron; air blowers could send plastic and paper to different recovery chambers. Mechanical screening, flotation, and centrifugal hurling could sort out metals, glass, and garbage.

Once sorted, metals could be returned to mills, smelters, and foundries; glass to various glass processing plants. Organic matter could go to compost centers, later to be used as fertilizers or soil conditioners, perhaps as fuel or animal feed. Wood could be used as fuel. Paper could be recycled or used as fuel. Even residues from incinerated materials (including particles removed from smoke to limit air pollution) could be processed into road or building material.

Miller, *Living in the Environment*, 1975

True, there is a tremendous amount of water in the world. Yet three of every four humans alive today do not have enough water or, if they do, the supplies are in some way contaminated. Water is not distributed equally everywhere. Most is ocean water and cannot be used for human consumption or agriculture because it is too salty. In fact, for every 1 million gallons of water, only about 6 gallons are readily available in a form that is usable to humans.

With each passing decade, more water is becoming useless or harmful. We have tapped into the hydrologic cycle and are using it, directly or indirectly, as a dumping ground for by-products of human existence. Thus water becomes unfit to drink (even to swim in) because it contains human sewage and animal wastes, which can encourage the growth of large populations of disease-causing microbes. Through agricultural runoff, water becomes polluted with sediments, pesticides, herbicides, and plant nutrients (such as nitrate and phosphate). Often the plant nutrients cause explosive growth of cyanobacteria in lakes and slow-moving rivers. When these bacteria die, the water can become putrid. Through industrial activity and power-generating plants, water becomes polluted with chemicals, radioactive material, and excess heat (thermal pollution).

Table 40.1 highlights some suggestions for reversing the trend toward unmanageable water pollution. To get an idea of how difficult the task will be, consider the problems inherent in **waste-water treatment** methods used today. About half the waste water in the United States is not being treated at all. The other half is more or less purified and restored while channeled through primary, secondary, and (sometimes) tertiary treatment centers before it is discharged into waterways and seas.

In *primary treatment*, mechanical screens and sedimentation tanks remove the coarse suspended solids from water, forming a sludge. Chemicals such as aluminum sulfate are added to accelerate the process. About thirty percent of all waste water goes only through primary treatment before the liquid (effluent) is discharged. Although the effluent is treated with chlorine to kill pathogenic microbes, chlorine alone does not get rid of them completely. Also, the chlorine reacts with some industrial chemicals, producing carcinogenic compounds in the water.

Secondary treatment depends on microbial action to degrade the sludge. In some cases, sludge is sprayed and trickled through large beds of exposed gravel in which monerans and protistans live. In other cases, sludge is aerated with pure oxygen to promote microbial activity. As it happens, the microbes themselves are vulnerable to pollution: toxic substances that enter the treatment centers can destroy them. Then, treatment activities must be shut down until new microbial populations are established. Because levels of pollutants are rising, the search is on to find chemicals that can degrade sludge as well as the microbes can.

Even after secondary treatment, the effluent still contains oxygen-demanding wastes, suspended solids, nitrates, phosphates, viruses, and dissolved salts such as heavy metals, pesticides, and radioactive isotopes. The water discharged from secondary treatment plants is typically used in irrigation and industry. After it has been held for a while in settling lagoons, it is often dumped into whatever local bodies of water are available.

Tertiary treatment adequately reduces the pollutant levels in effluent. Among the processes involved are advanced methods of precipitating suspended solids and phosphate compounds, absorption of dissolved organic compounds, reverse osmosis, stripping nitrogen from ammonia, and disinfecting the water through chlorination or ultrasonic energy vibrations. Tertiary treatment, however, is rarely used. It is largely in the experimental stage and is expensive.

What all this means is that most treatment centers are not properly treating existing levels of water pollution. What, then, is going on? A typical pattern is repeated thousands of times along our waterways. Water for drinking is removed *upstream* from a city, and wastes from industry and sewage treatment are discharged *downstream*. It takes no great leap of the imagination to see that pollution intensifies as rivers flow toward the oceans. In Louisiana, where the waters drained from the central states flow toward the Gulf of Mexico, pollution levels are high enough to be a real threat to public health. Water destined for drinking does get treated to remove pathogens — but the treatment does not remove poisonous heavy metals (such as mercury) that are dumped into the waterways by numerous factories upstream. You may find it illuminating to investigate where your own city's water supply comes from and where it has been.

Case Study: Air Pollution

Denise was about to throw up. The flight from Dallas to Chicago was so crowded that she had to sit in the "Smoking Allowed" section of the plane. The man sitting next to her lit up a cigar, and the blue smoke began to cling to her nostrils and clothing. The flight attendant asked the man to put out the cigar (cigarette smoke was okay, cigar smoke was not), but the strong odor prevailed all the way to Chicago. In the airport parking lot, Denise started up the engine of her badly tuned car and drove away, cursing all smokers for their outrageous insensitivity. Clouds of exhaust billowed from the tailpipe all the way home, although Denise was not aware of it. When she reached home she turned on all the lights and turned up the furnace, not thinking of the fuel being burned at the regional power plant, which was releasing smoke into the air as it worked to provide business, industry, and homes (including hers) with energy.

In a way, the finite space inside the airplane cabin is like the finite space of our atmosphere. Denise was acutely aware of the tobacco smoke because it had reached high concentrations in a short time. However, the same kind of thing is happening to the air around us. If you were to compare the earth with an apple from the supermarket, the atmosphere would be no thicker than the layer of shiny wax applied to it. Yet this thin, finite layer of air receives more than 700,000 metric tons of pollutants each day in the United States alone.

It is not just that pollutants make the air smell, or cut down visibility, or discolor buildings. Air pollutants can *corrode* buildings. They can ruin oranges, wilt lettuce, stunt the growth of peaches and corn, and damage leaves on conifers hundreds of kilometers away from their source. They can cause humans to suffer headaches, burning eyes, bronchitis, emphysema, and lung cancer. Even in rush-hour traffic, prolonged exposure to the fumes from vehicles can cause headaches, nausea, stomach cramps, and impaired coordination and vision. Air pollutants are diverse in their source and their chemical composition. Here we will focus on two of the most serious kinds.

Acid Deposition

Oxides of sulfur and nitrogen are among the most dangerous air pollutants. Coal-burning power plants, factories, and metal smelters are the main sources of sulfur dioxide emissions. Vehicles and fossil fuel power plants produce the nitrogen dioxides.

Depending on climatic conditions, some of these emissions can remain airborne for a time as tiny particles; others dissolve in water to form acidic vapor. When they come in contact with objects in the environment, they are said to be *dry acid depositions*. These airborne pollutants attack marble, metals, mortar, rubber, and plastic. They cause extensive crop damage near large cities. At times, droplets of sulfuric acid form in the mist air of downtown St. Louis,

Table 40.1 Major Water Pollutants: Sources, Effects, and Possible Controls

Pollutant	Main Sources	Effects	Possible Controls
Organic oxygen-demanding wastes	Human sewage, animal wastes, decaying plant life, industrial wastes	*Overload depletes dissolved oxygen in water; animal life destroyed or migrates away; plant life destroyed*	Provide secondary and tertiary waste-water treatment; minimize agricultural runoff
Plant nutrients	Agricultural runoff, detergents, industrial wastes, inadequate waste-water treatment	*Algal blooms and excessive aquatic plant growth upset ecological balances; eutrophication*	Agricultural runoff too widespread, diffuse for adequate control
Pathogenic bacteria and viruses	Presence of sewage and animal wastes in water	*Outbreaks of such diseases as typhoid, infectious hepatitis*	Provide secondary and tertiary waste-water treatment; minimize agricultural runoff
Inorganic chemicals and minerals	Mining, manufacturing, irrigation, oil fields	*Alters acidity, basicity, or salinity; also renders water toxic*	Remove through waste-water treatment; stop pollutants at source
Synthetic organic chemicals (plastics, pesticides, etc.)	At least 10,000 agricultural, manufacturing, and consumer uses	*Many are not biodegradable, chemical interactions in environment are poorly understood. Some poisonous*	Push for biodegradable materials; prevent entry into water supply at source
Fossil fuels (oil particularly)	Two-thirds from machinery, automobile wastes; pipeline breaks; offshore blowouts and seepage, supertanker accidents, spills, and wrecks; heating; transportation; industry; agriculture	*Varies with location, duration, and type of fossil fuel; potential disruption of ecosystems; economic, recreational, and aesthetic damage to coasts*	Strictly regulate oil drilling, transportation, storage; collect and reprocess engine oil and grease; develop means to contain spills
Sediments	Natural erosion, poor soil conservation practices in agriculture, mining, construction	*Major source of pollution (700 times more tonnage than solid sewage discharge), fills in waterways, reduces shellfish and fish populations*	Put already existing soil conservation practices to use

then dissolve holes in nylon stockings of women who step outside office buildings at lunchtime.

Between seventy and ninety percent of the sulfur and nitrogen dioxides end up in **acid rain**, a catchword for rain and snow that becomes as strongly acidic as lemon juice. In the atmosphere, these emissions react with water to form weak solutions of sulfuric acid and nitric acid. Winds can distribute these acids over great distances before they fall to the earth (Figure 40.2). They are said to be *wet acid depositions.*

Acid deposition originating in industrial regions of England and West Germany is damaging large tracts of forests in northern Europe. In Canada and the United States, acid deposition is damaging forests and crops. Through chemical reactions with the depositions, nutrients are being leached from soils. Because acidic snow melts quickly, the runoff accumulates rapidly, to high levels, in nearby bodies of water. Thus acid deposition is destroying aquatic life (such as trout and salmon) in lakes and streams. More than 300 lakes in the Adirondack Mountains of New York are now devoid of fish. Some Canadian biologists predict that 48,000 lakes in Ontario will be devoid of life within the next two decades. In addition, when bottom sediments become acidic enough, anaerobic bacteria can convert mercury deposits to methyl mercury. This compound is toxic enough to seriously damage the nervous system, lead to blindness, and cause crippling and mental retardation in newborns.

In 1983, a U.S. government task force finally confirmed that power plants, factories, and vehicles are indeed the main sources of acid depositions, and that these airborne pollutants are indeed damaging the environment. Ironically, local air pollution standards have in some cases contributed to the problem by calling for remarkably tall smokestacks on power plants and smelting plants. The idea is to dump the acid-laden smoke high enough in the atmosphere for winds to distribute it elsewhere—which winds readily do. The world's tallest smokestack, in Sudbury, Ontario, accounts all by itself for about one percent of the annual worldwide sulfur dioxide emissions. Canada, however, cannot be singled out in this issue. Canada is presently receiving more acid depositions from industrialized regions of the northeastern United States than it sends across its southern border. Prevailing winds do not stop at national boundaries; the problem is of global concern.

Industrial and Photochemical Smog

Climate, topography, and air pollutants can interact in ways that intensify the effects of local air pollution. For example, in a **thermal inversion**, a layer of dense, cool air becomes trapped beneath a layer of warm air. When that happens, pollutants cannot diffuse into the higher atmosphere or be dispersed by winds; they can accumulate to dangerous levels right above their sources. By intensifying a phenomenon known as smog, thermal inversions have been a contributing factor in some of the worst air pollution disasters.

There are two general types of smog (gray air and brown air), although both types occur in the same major cities. **Industrial smog** is gray air. It characteristically predominates in industrialized cities that have cold, wet winters, such as London, New York, Pittsburgh, and Chicago. Such cities burn considerable amounts of fossil fuel for heating, manufacturing, and producing electric power. The burning fuel releases two major classes of pollutants:

particulates	*airborne solid particles or liquid droplets (including dust, smoke, ashes, soot, asbestos, oil, and bits of heavy metals such as lead)*
oxides of sulfur	*in particular, sulfur dioxide and sulfur trioxide*

When winds and rain do not disperse these substances, they can reach lethal concentrations. For example, industrial smog was the source of London's 1952 air pollution disaster, in which 4,000 people died.

Photochemical smog is brown, it smells, and it is hazardous to living things. It occurs most often in cities with warm, dry climates and where the main source of air pollution is nitric oxide, produced in the internal combustion engine. Los Angeles, Denver, and Salt Lake City are ex-

Figure 40.2 Regions of the continental United States and Canada where acid deposition is pronounced. The darker the shaded areas, the more severe the acid deposition. (From Miller, 1982)

amples of brown air cities. Nitric oxide reacts with oxygen in the air to form nitrogen dioxide, the main source of the brownish haze. When exposed to sunlight, nitrogen dioxide can react with hydrocarbons (spilled or partially burned gasoline, most often) to form *photochemical oxidants.* These are among the main components of photochemical smog. Other components are ozone and PANS (short for *peroxyacylnitrates*), which are similar to tear gas. Traces of PAN compounds are enough to sting the eyes, irritate the lungs, and damage crops.

SOME ENERGY OPTIONS

Paralleling the J-shaped curve of human population growth is a steep rise in energy consumption. The rise is due to more than increased numbers of energy users. It is due also to excessive consumption and waste.

For example, in one of the most temperate of all climates, a major university constructed seven- and eight-story buildings having narrow, sealed windows. Windows cannot be opened to catch prevailing ocean breezes; neither the windows nor the buildings are designed or aligned to take advantage of the abundant sunlight for passive solar heating. Massive cooling and heating systems are used instead.

Extravagances of this sort may be curtailed sooner than might be expected, for current energy supplies are limited. When you hear talk of abundant energy supplies, keep in mind that there can be an enormous difference between the total and the net amount available. *Net energy* is that left over after subtracting the energy it takes to locate, extract, ship, store, and deliver energy to consumers.

Fossil Fuels

Fossil fuels are legacies from primary producers that lived hundreds of millions of years ago. Over time, immense coastal forests were submerged and the remains of countless populations of phytoplankton accumulated on ocean floors. They became buried and compressed in sediments; over time, these carbon-containing remains were transformed into coal, oil, and natural gas.

Fossil fuels have been used as energy sources for many generations. Yet more fossil fuel has been used up during the past three decades than in all of the preceding years combined. Even with stringent conservation efforts, known fossil fuel reserves may be depleted early in the next century.

In addition to petroleum reserves, there are vast deposits of oil shale in Colorado, Utah, and Wyoming. **Oil shale** is buried rock that contains kerogen, a hydrocarbon compound that can be converted to oil. The deposits in the western states probably contain more oil than does the entire Middle East. However, collecting, concentrating, heating, and converting kerogen to shale oil may cost so much that the net energy yield would be negligible, if not nonexistent. Also, the extraction process would disfigure the land, increase water and air pollution, and tax existing water supplies in regions already facing water shortages. Another problem is that a product of the extraction process is benzopyrene, a known carcinogen. Benzopyrene would be produced by the ton, even though there is no known way to use it or dispose of it safely. Finally, oil shale processing produces twelve percent more solid waste than the space the original rock formation occupied. (It is something like popping unpopped corn.) Where do the leftovers go? Some have suggested that controlled atomic blasts deep in the rock formations might distill the kerogen in place. It would take six blasts a day to meet ten percent of our current demands for energy. No one has determined what six blasts a day would do to the ecological and geological stability of the surrounding regions.

What about **coal**? One-fourth of the world's known coal reserves occur in the United States. In principle, the reserves are enough to meet the energy needs of the entire population for at least several centuries. The problem is that coal burning has been the largest single source of air pollution. Most coal reserves contain low-quality, high-sulfur material. Unless sulfur is removed from coal before it is burned or removed afterward (from the gases in smokestacks), this fuel burning produces high levels of sulfur oxides in the air.

In addition, coal mining carries its own risks. More than a billion dollars a year is being paid in benefits to coal miners afflicted with black-lung disease. Modern air-quality standards in mines minimize but do not eliminate this affliction, an outcome of breathing coal dust. Also, mine explosions, collapsed mine shafts, and the release of poisonous gases are still frequent.

Pressure is on to permit widespread **strip mining**. Some coal reserves are close enough to the surface to be gouged out of the earth. How many millions of acres should be opened to mining companies? Strip mining renders the land useless for agriculture until it is restored. However, who will pay for restoration, and will restoration be complete?

Nuclear Energy

As Hiroshima burned in 1945, the world recoiled in horror from the destructive potential of nuclear energy. Optimism soon replaced the horror as nuclear energy became publicized as an instrument of progress. That was the beginning of Operation Plowshare, a massive effort to harness the atom for peacetime use. Now, almost four decades later, nuclear-powered, electricity-generating stations dot the American landscape. Yet plans to extend reliance on nuclear energy have been delayed or canceled. Serious questions have been raised about the cost, efficiency, environmental impact, and safety of nuclear energy.

How much net energy does the nuclear power program produce? Current estimates are that nuclear enrichment (the conversion of uranium into a form that can be used as fuel) requires nearly three percent of all electricity used in the United States. (Nuclear power plants themselves produce only eight percent.) There are also mining, refining, transportation, and generator construction costs. By 1990, using nuclear energy to generate electricity may cost slightly more than using coal to do the same thing, even if the coal-burning plants are equipped with expensive pollution control devices.

What about safety? The amount of radioactivity escaping from a nuclear plant during normal operation is actually less than the amount released from a coal-burning plant of the same capacity. Also, nuclear plants do not add carbon dioxide to the atmosphere, as coal-burning plants do. What about possible accidents?

There is potential danger of a **meltdown**. As nuclear fuel breaks down, it releases considerable heat. Typically, water circulates under very high pressure over the fuel and absorbs the heat. This heated water produces the steam that drives electricity-generating turbines. Should a leak develop in the circulating water system, water levels around the fuel might plummet. The absence of water for only sixty seconds may be enough to start a meltdown. The nuclear fuel would heat rapidly, past its melting point. Melting fuel would pour to the floor of the generator, where it would contact the remaining water and instantly convert it to steam. Formation of enough steam could blow the system apart, and radioactive material could be spewed to the exterior.

All nuclear reactors have secondary cooling systems that can flood the reactor with water at once if the initial cooling water is lost. The chance of this happening is extremely small, but possible. The Three-Mile Island nuclear power plant in Pennsylvania came very close to a meltdown as a result of equipment failure and human error. Some critics believe that a meltdown was avoided by pure luck. Others believe that the incident proved the effectiveness of multiple backup safety systems in nuclear power plants. No meltdown occurred, and no lives were lost. However, the very fact that the incident occurred at all brought the issue home to individuals throughout the nation.

What of nuclear wastes? Nuclear fuel cannot be burned to harmless ashes, like coal. After about four years, the fuel elements of a reactor are spent. They still contain about a third of the useful uranium fuel, but they also contain hundreds of new radioactive isotopes produced during the operation of the reactor. Altogether, these wastes are an enormously radioactive, extremely dangerous collection of nasty materials. As they undergo radioactive decay, they produce tremendous heat. They are immediately plunged into water-filled pools and stored for several months at the power plant. The water cools the wastes and keeps radioactive material from escaping. At the end of the holding period, however, the remaining radioactivity of long-lived isotopes is lethal. The wastes must be transported in special equipment to centralized facilities. There they are held in temporary storage for another five years, at least. But the decay rates of some remaining isotopes means that they must be kept out of the environment for thousands of years. If an isotope of plutonium is not removed, they must be stored for *a quarter of a million years!*

No radioactive wastes have been put into permanent underground storage in the United States. Such storage will soon be initiated. Nuclear wastes will be mixed with molten glass, which will be cast into rods a foot in diameter and ten feet long. (One year's wastes from one nuclear plant may produce ten such rods.) The rods will be placed in steel cylinders and sealed. Eventually the cylinders will be inserted in holes of the same size that have been drilled in deep salt deposits. Salt deposits are typically found in regions that have been undisturbed (by earthquakes, for example) for millions of years. The very presence of salt beds is said to be indicative of long-term absence of underground water that could dissolve the wastes and move them about. Also, salt tends to flow slowly under pressure; it will reseal any cracks introduced during the drilling and storage activities. It is widely—but by no means uniformly—believed that wastes can thus be kept out of the way until they are no longer dangerous.

Another type of reactor is being considered for development. In theory, **breeder reactors** would consume a rare isotope of uranium and, as they did, they would convert a much greater amount of the common, unusable form of uranium to an isotope of plutonium. That isotope is usable as nuclear fuel. However, breeder reactors could not be cooled with water. In the design being most actively pursued, liquid metallic sodium would be used as the coolant. It is a highly dangerous, corrosive substance. The problems of containing the molten sodium and of maintaining the reactors in a functional state are horrendous. Also, even though conventional reactors cannot explode like atomic bombs, breeder reactors potentially could. Mishaps could cause the entire reactor to explode, spreading radioactive wastes equivalent to those produced by 1,000 Hiroshima-sized bombs over many square kilometers.

Plutonium, in the form produced and used in reactors, is one of the most toxic substances known. A speck the size of a pollen grain almost certainly will cause fatal lung cancer. It is also the stuff used in atomic bombs. Making a bomb from uranium requires a major scientific and industrial effort that can only be mounted by a country with substantial resources. By comparison, fashioning a bomb from plutonium is relatively simple. A small amount of plutonium in the hands of terrorists could be used for extortion; a somewhat larger amount could be used for mindless devastation. If we enter an era of breeder reactors, we will surely enter an era of plutonium economy in which all aspects of the nuclear power industry—processing plants, transport systems, reactors, and disposal sites—will require utmost security precautions.

A third type of nuclear power source that may become available is **fusion power**, in which hydrogen atoms are fused to form helium atoms, with considerable release of energy. The process is analogous to reactions that cause the heat energy of the sun. However, the problems associated with developing fusion power are so great that, without a major breakthrough, fusion power will not be developed within four decades (if ever).

In sum, nuclear reactors of the type now in use are probably safer than many of their critics proclaim, but far less safe than their advocates claim. The most negative aspects are that they have a low net energy yield, achieved at a much higher cost than initially expected. The supply of naturally occurring fuel will be quickly exhausted. Breeder reactors could get around the problem by producing plutonium. But then we must be willing to gamble on the possibility of not having major accidents, of not encountering sabotage or terrorist activities. Fusion, an ultimate possibility, is so far into the future that it cannot help us solve the energy problems of this century.

Wind Energy

In many regions, winds are strong and predictable enough to be a source of energy. For example, high prevailing winds sweep through the American Midwest, from the Dakotas to Texas. Wind energy is thus seen to be an attractive energy option. It would be an unlimited energy source, it would not generate pollution, and it certainly would be harmless in the hands of terrorists. It has been proposed that perhaps 300,000 turbine towers be used to harness the winds of the plains and thereby provide fully half of the present energy needs of the United States.

Many windmills presently being introduced in Europe are of a simple design that will disfigure the landscape far less than several other energy alternatives. Turbine towers would take up less land than, say, solar-energy generating plants. They would be far less disruptive than strip mining for coal. It is also possible that windmills constructed on existing electrical transmission towers could feed electrical output directly into regional utility lines. The possibility of harnessing the winds is economically and technologically feasible right now.

Solar Energy

A virtually limitless, free energy source is potentially available, as it has always been to life on earth. Solar energy ranks with wind energy as the most abundant, clean, and safe energy sources now being considered as alternatives to fossil fuels. Solar power plants would not release heat to the same extent as coal-burning and nuclear plants do. They would be nonpolluting. It has been estimated that if 39,000 square kilometers (15,000 square miles) of desert were set aside in Arizona and California for solar collectors that convert sunlight energy directly into electricity, the system could provide half the nation's annual energy needs, even decades from today.

However, such massive developments would have profound impact on desert ecosystems. Also, the *net* energy yield would be low and costs high—unless it becomes a question of how much we are willing to pay for a safe energy source. To date, research funds have come mainly from environmentally concerned groups and private citizens.

PERSPECTIVE

Molecules, cells, tissues, organs, organ systems, multicelled organisms, populations, communities, ecosystems, the biosphere. These are the architectural systems of life, assembled in increasingly complex ways over the past $3\frac{1}{2}$ billion years. We are latecomers to this immense biological building program. Yet, during the relatively short span of 50,000 years, we have been restructuring the stuff of life at all levels—from recombining DNA of different species to changing the nature of the thin, life-giving atmosphere.

It would be presumptuous to think we are the only organisms that have ever changed the nature of living systems. Even during Precambrian times, photosynthetic organisms were irrevocably changing the course of biological evolution by gradually enriching the atmosphere with oxygen. In the present as well as the past, competitive adaptations have assured the rise of some groups, whose dominance has assured the decline of others. Thus change is nothing new to this biological building program. What *is* new is the accelerated, potentially cataclysmic change being brought on by the human population. We now have the population size, the technology, and the cultural inclination to use up energy and modify the environment at frightening rates.

Where will rampant, accelerated change lead us? Will feedback controls begin to operate as they do, for example, when population growth exceeds the carrying capacity of the environment? In other words, will negative feedback controls come into play and keep things from getting too far out of hand?

Feedback control will not be enough, for it operates only when deviation already exists. Our explosive population growth and patterns of resource consumption are founded on an illusion of unlimited resources and a forgiving environment. A prolonged, global shortage of food or the passing of a critical threshold for some toxic pollutant in the atmosphere can come too fast to be corrected. At some point, such deviations may have too great an impact to be reversed.

What about feedforward mechanisms? Many organisms have early warning systems. For example, skin receptors sense a drop in outside air temperature. Each sends messages to the nervous system, which responds by triggering mechanisms that raise internal body temperature before the body itself becomes dangerously chilled. With feedforward control, corrective measures can begin before change in the external environment significantly alters the system.

Even feedforward controls are not enough for us, for they go into operation only when change is under way. Consider, by analogy, the DEW line—the Distant Early Warning system. This system is like a sensory receptor, one that detects intercontinental ballistic missiles that may be launched against North America. By the time this system detects what it is designed to detect, it may be far too late, not only for North America but for the entire biosphere.

It would be naïve to assume we can ever reverse who we are at this point in evolutionary time, to de-evolve ourselves culturally and biologically into becoming less complex in the hope of averting disaster. However, there is no reason to assume that we cannot avert disaster by using a third kind of control mechanism, one that is uniquely our own. We have the capacity to anticipate events *before* they happen. We are not locked into responding only after irreversible change has begun. We have the capacity to anticipate the future—it is the essence of our visions of utopia or of nightmarish hell. Thus we all have the capacity for adapting to a future which we can partly shape. We can, for example, learn to live with less. Far from being a return to primitive simplicity, it would be one of the most complex and intelligent behaviors of which we are capable.

Having that capacity and using it are not the same thing. We have already put the world of life on dangerous grounds because we have not yet mobilized ourselves as a species to work toward self-control. Our survival depends on predicting possible futures. It depends on designing and constructing ecosystems that are in harmony not only with what we define as basic human values but also with the biological models available to us. Human values can change; our expectations can and must be adapted to biological reality. *For the principles of energy flow and resource utilization, which govern the survival of all systems of life, do not change.* It is our biological and cultural imperative that we come to terms at last with these principles, and with what will be the long-term contribution of the human species to the unity and diversity of life.

Readings

Audubon (bimonthly). National Audubon Society. 1130 Fifth Avenue, New York, New York 10028.

BioScience (monthly). American Institute of Biological Sciences. 3900 Wisconsin Avenue NW, Washington, D.C. 20016. Official publication of AIBS; major coverage of environmental concerns.

Miller, G., Jr. 1982. *Living in the Environment: Concepts, Problems, and Alternatives.* Third edition. Belmont, California: Wadsworth. This is probably your best bet as an introduction to environmental science.

New Scientist (monthly). 128 Long Acre, London, W.C. 2, England. Excellent journal on general science.

Science (weekly). The American Association for the Advancement of Science. 1515 Massachusetts Avenue NW, Washington, D.C. 20036. Outstanding forum for American science. Probably the single best source for keeping up with research, and with what researchers are thinking in terms of applications and consequences of research.

Scientific American (monthly). 415 Madison Avenue, New York, New York 10017.

Review Questions

1. Under which conditions would an ecologically based system for handling solid wastes benefit the culture more than a recycling system?

2. What is the basic plan of a generalized resource recovery system?

3. What is meant by primary, secondary, and tertiary waste-water treatment?

4. Where do organic oxygen-demanding wastes come from, how do they affect organisms, and how can this type of pollutant be controlled?

5. Categorize the principal air pollutants, their sources, and the methods of controlling each.

6. How can energy overconsumption and waste be reduced by the average U.S. citizen?

7. What is a meltdown? Can a nuclear power plant explode like an atom bomb?

Prowling about on the seafloor is *Tritonia,* one of the predatory, sluglike animals called nudibranchs. Sometimes, when it is hunting for hydroids and sea anemones, *Tritonia* bumps into a sea star. Sea stars also are predators of many marine animals, including nudibranchs. *Tritonia,* however, can make a quick getaway. On contacting a sea star, it quickly pulls back its head, stretches its elongate body, and flattens its anterior and posterior regions into paddle-like shapes. Then *Tritonia* arches its body up and down, repeatedly, in strong swimming movements that propel it away from danger.

In 1971, Dennis Willows studied this escape response of *Tritonia.* He made recordings of the activity of single neurons in its brain and showed that they discharged with a patterned frequency and intensity that corresponded precisely to the observed pattern of swimming movements. Then Willows surgically removed the brain from the rest of the body, so that it could not receive any feedback from muscles or the peripheral nervous system. He subjected single neurons within that isolated brain to a short pulse of electrical stimulation. The stimulated neurons responded with a coordinated series of discharges—which were exactly the same as those made when the intact animal performed the escape response. *These results demonstrated that a specific pattern of behavior has its origin in neural circuits in the brain.*

All animals have the capacity to make coordinated neuromotor responses to changes in the internal and external environments. These responses are what we call animal behavior (Chapter Twenty-Three). Some behavioral responses are simple, others are extraordinarily complex. All are expressions of genetic, sensory, neural, and endocrine inputs. These inputs are truly diverse. To complicate matters, even predictable behavior, such as *Tritonia's* flight response, will not always be exactly the same all of the time. Some predictable responses can be modified in novel ways, as a result of learning experiences.

Identifying the foundations of behavior is one of the major challenges in biology. Yet even here, evolutionary theory is providing a clear intellectual path through the maze of behavioral diversity. As you will read in this chapter, it is being applied successfully to an impressive range of animal groups, from so-called simple invertebrates to the complex societies of birds and mammals, including humans. Before turning to examples of these applications, let us begin with a few of the basic terms that are commonly used in behavioral studies.

41

ANIMAL BEHAVIOR

Figure 41.1 What is the adaptive significance of animal behavior, such as the territorial display of a bird during the breeding season? This chapter considers some possibilities.

Innate Behavior

Even if *Tritonia* has never before bumped into a sea star, and even if it has never learned what to do by watching what other nudibranchs do during such encounters, it immediately performs an escape response. The units of neurons that trigger such unlearned responses are called **innate releasing mechanisms**. Exactly what calls the mechanisms into action? All animals have sensory receptors that detect environmental stimuli and relay information to the brain (Chapter Twenty-Three). An innate releasing mechanism is responsive to signals about a specific stimulus, known as its **releaser**. Detection of a releaser can lead to a **motor score**: a programmed sequence of neural signals that cause the animal to carry out a precisely structured pattern of actions.

The kind of unlearned response we have been describing is said to be instinctive, or **innate behavior**. It has a genetic foundation, in that genes control the development of the particular neural and muscular circuitry required for its performance, and it is performed even without prior experience with the key environmental stimulus. Escape behavior, feeding behavior, sexual behavior, and aggressive behavior are examples of responses that in some species are known to involve innate releasing mechanisms.

Categories of Learning

The word **learning** refers to an adaptive modification of behavior, arising from specific experiences in an animal's lifetime. Here we will briefly describe a few categories of learning as reference points for later discussion.

Associative Learning: In this form of behavior, an animal has a capacity to make a connection between a new stimulus and a familiar one. Ivan Pavlov, a physiologist who was interested in digestive juice secretion, provided a classic, controlled study of associative learning. Pavlov observed that his laboratory dogs salivated just after he placed a meat extract on their tongues. He interpreted this to be a simple reflex response. Then he found that if he rang a bell just before giving the dogs the extract, the dogs began salivating at the sound of the bell alone. Pavlov called this new response a *conditioned reflex*, for the dogs had come to associate the sound of the bell (a conditioned stimulus) with food (a reinforcing stimulus).

Instrumental conditioning is another form of associative learning. Here, a reinforcing stimulus (either reward or punishment) appears after a particular behavior is performed by chance. The animal learns by trial and error. For example, earthworms can do this in simple T-mazes (which have a base and two arms shaped like a "T"). They enter the maze at the base, and if they turn down one of its arms, they

encounter an irritating stimulus such as an electric shock. If they turn down the other arm, they encounter a moist, darkened chamber that approximates the earthworm habitat. After many trials and enough shocks, the "right" response becomes more frequent.

Extinction: In the forms of learning just defined, the behavior persists for as long as the reinforcement persists. However, if the reinforcing stimulus is withdrawn, the learned behavior may soon become extinguished. This, too, is a learning process; it is called extinction.

Latent Learning: This term refers to an ability to store information about features of the environment, information that is later used in guiding the animal through its environment. For example, a rat will learn to find its way through a complicated maze more quickly when it is first given a chance to explore, even without any reward when it happens to find the way out.

Insight Learning: It is only among some primates that insight learning has been adequately demonstrated. With this behavior, novel problems can be solved without trial-and-error practice. In a sense, insight learning is a trial-and-error process that goes on in the brain. It is a synthesis of accumulated experiences that can suggest what responses might be appropriate in new situations.

AN EVOLUTIONARY APPROACH TO BEHAVIOR

Genes, Environment, and the Development of Behavior

It is commonly held that innate behavior is genetically determined, whereas learned behavior is environmentally determined. However, few (if any) forms of animal behavior lend themselves to such a rigid distinction. Beginning with the first development stages of the animal embryo, genes and the environment interact in ways that contribute to phenotype. Behavior, too, is an expression of these interactions, as the following examples will make clear.

Housekeeping Behavior of Honeybees. Honeybees live together in hives, which are maintained by a complex division of labor among its members. One maintenance task is ridding the hive of pupae that have become infected by pathogenic bacteria. To carry out this task, a worker honeybee cuts off the wax cap of the sealed brood cell containing a diseased pupa, then carries the pupa out and drops it away from the hive. All worker bees do this instinctively, the very first time they detect the key behavioral releasers (probably the odors emanating from an infected pupa).

a

b

Figure 41.2 (a) Human imprinting objects. No one can tell these goslings that Konrad Lorenz is not Mother Goose. (b) An imprinted rooster wading out to meet the objects of his affections. During a critical period of the rooster's life, he was exposed to a mallard duck. Although sexual behavior patterns were not yet developing during that period, the imprinting object became fixed in the rooster's mind for life. Then, with the maturation of sexual behavior, the rooster sought out ducks, forsaking birds of his own kind, and lending further support to the finding that imprinting may be one of the reasons why birds of a feather do flock together.

Genes and the environment both contribute to the behavioral responses just described. Detection of a diseased pupa is possible only through specialized sensory receptors; the complex movements used to cut the wax cap from the brood cell and to cart away the contents are possible only with neural controls. The sensory and nerve cells required for the responses are the products of gene activity, which indirectly controlled the biochemical reactions needed to construct those cells (Chapter Fourteen). At the same time, the biochemical reactions themselves never would have proceeded without energy and raw materials obtained from the environment. (Here we are talking about nutrients present in the fertilized egg, as well as in food received from workers after the egg hatched.) Similarly, how well those sensory and neural cells operate (or whether they operate at all) is influenced by gene activity and environmental inputs. Thus, *genes and environmental factors play different yet complementary roles in the development of instinctive behavior.*

Like instinctive behavior, the learned behavior of honeybees requires genetic as well as environmental inputs. For example, honeybees can learn the location of a rich food source. Suppose you put a saucer of concentrated sugar water on a window ledge every day, between four and five o'clock in the afternoon. After a number of days, more and more bees arrive shortly before four, in anticipation of the

food. Suppose you now put an empty saucer on the ledge. The bees still show up, right on schedule. Their arrival even when the sugar water is *not* present demonstrates that information gained from personal experience has been stored and is being used to modify foraging behavior. Under natural conditions, worker bees learn the time of day when the blossoms of flowering plants open up. By visiting the plants only when nectar and pollen can be collected easily, they make economical use of available search time.

Information about when a particular food is available can be stored in the honeybee brain because of the neural architecture of that brain. Here again, the nervous system is an expression of genetic information. During embryonic development, this information shaped the development of specialized nerve cells that can encode, store, and transmit signals about information gained through experience. *Genes and the environment also play complementary roles in the development of learned behavior.*

Imprinting. Let us now consider a form of learned behavior called imprinting. In **imprinting,** the nervous system seems primed to acquire certain kinds of information during a specific learning situation, which usually occurs early in life. This time of learning is called the *sensitive period.* For example, within a few hours after being hatched, a duckling or gosling instinctively follows a moving object—normally, its mother when she waddles away from the nest to water. As a result of this following response, the young bird quickly forms a social attachment to the mother. If the young bird is a male, the identifying traits of females of his species are imprinted in his brain at this time. When he matures, the stored information influences his mating preferences.

The nature of imprinting was first researched fully by Konrad Lorenz. When Lorenz reared young greylag geese from eggs that had been taken from nesting parents, the hatchlings followed him when he moved away from their nest box during the sensitive period. Thereafter, the goslings were attached to him, not to any member of their own species. When the male goslings matured many months later, they ignored female greylags and courted Lorenz or other humans instead. Under such artificial conditions, the information that becomes stored in the brain can lead to sexual attachments between the male birds and, variously, human keepers, beachballs, or female birds of other species (Figure 41.2). In imprinting, as in all other forms of learning, *an information-storing capacity is required within the nervous system, which itself required a genetic foundation for its development.*

Language Learning. One more example will reinforce the point that learned behavior has genetic as well as environmental inputs. Different people speak English, Russian, Jivaro, Swahili, Navajo, Hindi, or some other language. The language learned depends on personal experience in particular environmental settings. For that reason, language is often said to be free from biological (genetic) influence. However, when specific regions of the cerebral cortex are damaged, the ability to acquire or use *any* language is lost. Destruction of one patch of this brain tissue renders a person incapable of uttering coherent sentences and of comprehending the written or spoken word. Obviously, then, language depends on the integrity of brain structure—which is genetically prescribed.

Consider also that a normal human acquires language effortlessly at a young age. At eighteen months, the average child has command of fifty *words*—not mere noises such as barks, whistles, and clunks. At twenty-four months, children use about 1,000 words, and the symbolic content of just about everything typically said to them seems to be understood. The fact that humans acquire language so soon and so rapidly suggests a neurological predisposition to do so. By comparison, it is difficult (if not impossible) to teach members of other species to communicate through language. Even our phylogenetically close relatives, the chimpanzee and the gorilla, cannot produce speech. To be sure, they can be taught the signs of American Sign Language,

which many deaf people use. Some researchers suggest that their primate charges acquire the capacity to use these signs in a grammatical fashion. Others say the primates merely are intelligent enough to string together signs by picking up subtle, unconsciously given cues from their trainers, the advantage being the rewards that a pleased trainer bestows when they do so. The issue is not yet resolved, but the point here is this: No one doubts the neural ability of a two-year-old human to master a language, but skepticism persists about what a much older, much more heroically trained nonhuman primate can do. The genetically based capacity for language learning seems to be unique to our species.

Evolution of Behavior

Whether we are talking about the instincts of a bee or the learning ability of a human, it is clear that genes are necessary for all forms of behavior. *Thus we can assume that some kinds of behavioral variation among the members of a population are due to genetic variation among individuals.*

Many studies support this assumption. For example, W. Rothenbuhler demonstrated that one behavioral difference among honeybees arises from different allelic combinations at one gene locus (designated *U*). Worker honeybees that do not uncap brood cells containing diseased pupae are homozygous dominant (*UU*) or heterozygous (*Uu*) at this locus. Only the ones that are homozygous recessive (*uu*) will uncap these cells. Now, a single gene seldom (if ever) controls only a single trait; many genes and their products interact to produce phenotype. However, this example does show that even a small genetic difference can have a pronounced effect on behavior.

Similarly, artificial selection experiments strongly support the assumption that genetic variation affects the development of behavior. In the 1940s, R. Tryon tested a population of rats for their ability to run through a maze having many blind alleys. The maze had only one exit, where a food reward was waiting. First Tryon counted the errors that each rat made after a number of learning trials. After experience with the maze, some rats evidently had learned the route to the exit, for they hurried through without entering many blind alleys. Other rats had much more difficulty and wandered into many dead ends first. Tryon permitted the "maze-bright" rats to interbreed. He also permitted the ones that made errors to interbreed. Rats with intermediate scores were dropped from the experiment. It turned out that the trained offspring of maze-bright rats learned to run the maze with significantly fewer errors than equally experienced "maze-dull" offspring. By repeating the artificial selection procedure over several generations, Tryon produced two distinct populations with respect to the maze-running ability (Figure 41.3). The rats did not differ with respect to other behavioral tasks. These results suggest that genes in some way affected the development of the ability to negotiate the maze.

No matter what the trait, artificial selection can be used to produce descendant populations of animals that differ from the original population. One can artificially produce a population of male crickets that almost never sing *or* that sing much more than most males from natural populations; fruit flies that tolerate very close contact with one another *or* that attack their neighbors; and dogs that are gentle companions for children *or* that are prone to maul humans on command.

Behavior has a genetic foundation, otherwise experimenters could not create such distinctive hereditary lines through selective breeding. This finding leads us to an important point. *If humans can exaggerate behavioral variants through artificial selection, there is reason to assume that natural selection could have the same result over evolutionary time.*

ECOLOGICAL ASPECTS OF BEHAVIOR

If natural selection has shaped the behavior of animals, then we should be able to observe behavioral adaptations to specific environments. Also, because selection pressures vary from one species to the next, we should be able to observe variation in behavioral responses to environmental challenges. This variation does indeed exist, as examples in the following section indicate.

Biological Clocks, Compasses, and Maps

Let's begin with an aspect of the environment that almost all animals deal with. Approximately every twenty-four hours, the earth completes one rotation about its long axis. This movement (a circadian rhythm) is the basis for alternating periods of daylight and darkness. However, the amount of daylight is not constant through the year, for the *length* of day changes as the earth completes its annual journey around the sun. For example, much of North America has short days and long nights in December, and long days and short nights in June. Changes in daylength affect prevailing climates, primary production, and other aspects of the animal's environment (Chapter Thirty-Eight).

Animals can detect these changes in daylength through neural and hormonal mechanisms called **biological clocks**. The clocks trigger physiological and behavioral adjustments to environmental change. (In birds and mammals, one such

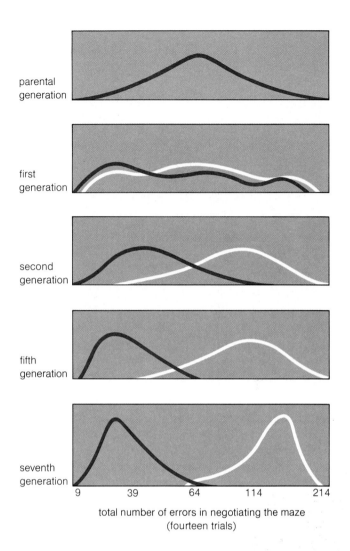

total number of errors in negotiating the maze
(fourteen trials)

Figure 41.3 Artificial selection for maze-running ability in laboratory rats. By repeatedly selecting the extremes of the population, R. Tryon gradually produced two rat populations with very different learning capacities with respect to maze-running. The red curve represents all individuals of "maze-bright" populations. The white curve represents all individuals of "maze-dull" populations.

clock is the pineal gland, which secretes the hormone melatonin. Melatonin output coordinates motor activity and metabolic rates. In some species, this hormone is related to an increase in gonad size associated with reproductive cycles. Light perception controls melatonin production by controlling the activity of an enzyme required for its synthesis. During the dark, enzyme activity is enhanced; during daylight, it is inhibited.)

Different species respond in different ways to their perception of environmental change. Some small insect-eating birds, including warblers, cannot live through the

a

b

Figure 41.4 Feeding behavior of predators. (**a**) A woodpecker finch of the Galápagos Islands uses a cactus spine in prying wood-boring insects from their tunnels. (**b**) Beneath the hot African sun, a black heron holds its wings over its head, like an umbrella. Minnows drawn to the shade of the umbrella are within range of the heron's bill.

winter in Canada and the northern United States, where temperatures can drop below freezing and food supplies (insects and the like) dwindle. Generally, the small birds that stay put (such as chickadees) are ones that can feed on plant matter. The warblers are one of many kinds of animals that undergo **migration**: a cyclic movement between two distant regions, at times of year that correspond to seasonal change. Warblers migrate and spend the winter in the subtropics or tropics. They return to nest in temperate regions during spring and summer, when temperatures are mild and food production is at its peak. The stay-put tactics of a chickadee and the migration of a warbler both have their pluses and minuses. The chickadee does not have to fly hundreds or thousands of miles twice a year; the warbler does not have to cope with the risk of starvation or freezing to death in winter. Given that warblers migrate and chickadees do not, these two kinds of birds differ in their ecology and, correspondingly, in behavioral attributes.

It is true that both chickadees and warblers show **homing behavior**: an ability to return to part of the environment that serves as a home base after moving (or being moved) some distance away from it. However, in warblers and other migratory species, homing behavior is developed to an extraordinary degree compared to chickadees. For example, once there was an attempt to move albatrosses from their home on Midway Island in the South Pacific, because the

birds were interfering with military planes landing and taking off. The birds were transported to potential homes as far away as Oregon and Washington. One albatross released in Washington refused to be displaced by the United States Armed Forces. It returned to Midway in a little over ten days, having averaged 317 miles a day for the 3,200-mile journey—a journey it had never before undertaken and most of it occurring away from landmarks, over the ocean!

Clearly albatrosses have a well-developed **map sense**: the ability of an animal to detect where it is relative to some destination. They also must have a **compass sense**: an ability to travel in a constant direction. These abilities are characteristic of migratory animals in general.

One such environmental cue is the apparent position of stars in the night sky. Studies of one night-flying migrant, the indigo bunting, show that the young birds become imprinted on the North Star. Through the night, apparent positions of other stars change relative to the North Star, which more or less stays put. Thus it can be used as a reliable compass point during fall and spring migrations.

Other migrants, such as day-flying starlings, use the sun as an environmental cue. However, this raises a question. What happens when a primary compass guide such as the sun is obscured by clouds? Some animals are known to have one or more back-up systems. For example, some have a **magnetic sense**, which enables the animals to use

Figure 41.5 Angler fish from the ocean depths. Like all angler fish, this species sports a prey-attracting lure on its head.

William H. Amos

Figure 41.6 Predator avoidance behavior by a snake caterpillar. This insect has altered the shape of its body in response to being poked. The anterior segments of the caterpillar let go of the vine and puff up like a snake head, which strikes at whatever touches it.

Lincoln P. Brower

variations in the earth's magnetic field as an environmental cue. In some experiments, the sun or stars were blocked from the view of a migratory bird. At the same time, the magnetic field around the bird was altered—and the bird altered its migratory orientation accordingly.

Predator and Prey Behavior

Chapter Thirty-Seven described some of the unique physical adaptations that enable animals to secure food and avoid being eaten. Behavior, too, is a deciding factor in contests between potential diners and dinners. Scorpions hunt burrowing cockroaches, which hide under sand. A twig-wielding finch teases insect larvae from tunnels in wood; a black heron forms an umbrella with its wings and the shade attracts tasty minnows (Figure 41.4).

Or consider the angler fish. Some species live on coral reefs and look like lumps of encrusted coral. So camouflaged, these fish can escape detection by enemies and prey alike. An angler fish remains motionless—except it twitches an appendage on its head that resembles a small minnow. The "lure" attracts small, predatory fishes. When they come within range, the angler fish lunges forward and sucks a meal into its gaping mouth. This form of behavior is called, appropriately, **aggressive mimicry**.

Predator avoidance behavior is equally impressive. Some night-flying moths are prey for bats (Chapter Twenty-Three). An echolocating bat attempts to detect and intercept a moth in midair. The moth, in turn, detects echolocating pulses with receptors that are sensitive to ultrasonic frequencies. The moth engages in evasive behavior, plunging straight down into (if it is lucky) the cover of foliage or looping wildly in directions that (if it is lucky) will avoid interception with the bat mouth.

Caterpillars of very large tropical moths employ a special behavioral response to predation. When fully grown, these caterpillars are nearly fifteen centimeters long. During the day, they remain motionless on vines. When poked sharply (as by a bird beak), the caterpillar drops part way from the vine and puffs up its anterior segments, so that it looks like a snake (Figure 41.6). The pseudosnake even strikes at whatever touches it. A small bird typically hesitates before continuing an attack. A reluctance to deal with snakes generally prolongs the bird's life, a response that the caterpillar exploits to its own advantage.

BEHAVIORAL ADAPTATION: WHO BENEFITS?

On Individual Selection

As the preceding examples illustrate, behavioral traits seem generally adaptive in that they help promote survival and reproduction. Yet who, exactly, benefits from behavioral adaptation? At one time, it was widely accepted that animals behave in ways that promote the survival of the species as a whole. Some animals were said to show **altruism** (self-sacrificing behavior), in that by helping others of their species, they gave up chances for their own reproduction. In this way they were unlike "genetically selfish" individuals, whose behavior promotes personal chances of reproduction.

In the mid-1960s, however, the evolutionary biologist G. Williams pointed out a flaw in this hypothesis. He asked a revealing question: What would happen in a population composed of self-sacrificing types if there was only one selfish genetic variant? A moment's thought leads to a key conclusion: *In the competition between bearers of "selfish" alleles and others with self-sacrificing tendencies, the selfish types would become more common over time.* The "for-the-good-of-the-species" types would fail to have as many surviving offspring, and their alleles would not occur as frequently in future generations. Through natural selection, the end result would be their complete replacement.

An example will illustrate this point. Norwegian lemmings disperse when population densities become extremely high, and many perish by accidental drowning, starvation, and predatory attack during their travels. The dispersals were once viewed as altruistic behavior: individuals committed suicide in order to prevent overpopulation. After all, an overlarge population would destroy the environment and risk extinction of the species as a whole. This view was given popular impetus by a nature film that showed masses of lemmings marching over a cliff and drowning in the water below.

There is an instructive cartoon that shows a legion of lemmings plunging into the water, presumably in the act of suicide. However, one member of the group has come equipped with an inflated inner tube about its waist. The point is, if lemming populations really were composed of animals programmed to commit suicide so that a few unrelated survivors could carry on the species, then individual selection would favor the mutant that avoided the ultimate sacrifice. That mutant would be one of the few left to exploit remaining resources, produce offspring, and leave copies of its "selfish" alleles in surviving "selfish" descendants. During the next population explosion, these animals would not be inclined to commit suicide. Over time, nonsuicidal types obviously would completely replace those with suicidal tendencies.

In sum, the current consensus among behavioral scientists is this: *In developing a working hypothesis to explain some behavioral trait, it may be more profitable to use Darwinian individual selection (not good-of-the-group selection) as the departure point.*

Case Study: Siblicide Among the Egrets

As soon as it was widely understood that natural selection favors reproductively selfish behavior, researchers began to reinterpret events that were once thought of as species-survival promoters. Consider the case of the baby great egrets. In this species, parents begin incubating as soon as the first egg is laid. Three eggs are deposited in the nest over several days, so the young do not hatch at the same time. As a result, there are notable size differences in a clutch of egrets. When food is in short supply, the older offspring attack the third member of the nest. They may even kill it by beating it to death, preventing it from eating, or forcing it out of the nest.

Now, if mutant parent egrets could rear more young by preventing siblicide, then individual selection would favor mutant types that did *not* incubate eggs until all three eggs were laid. This would make it harder for any one nestling to beat up another. However, synchronous incubation has not spread through the great egret population. Could it be, then, that sibling aggression *promotes* reproductive success of the parents? Perhaps the amount of food (fish) that parents can collect for their offspring varies. In poor fishing years, a parent that divided its catch among three equal-sized offspring might actually rear fewer to adulthood than a parent that fed only the most vigorous—which had disposed of the "runt of the litter." Under such conditions, sibling aggression might enhance the number of offspring likely to reach reproductive age.

To be useful, a hypothesis must be tested by examining predictions derived from it. One prediction is that under natural conditions, parent great egrets will not intervene in fights among siblings. If siblicide is in the best interests of the parents, then the parents should not waste energy trying to prevent it—and they do not. Even while the runt is being battered to death, adult great egrets stand to one side, ignoring the event.

Case Study: Courtship Behavior

Many animals engage in complex rituals prior to mating. For example, among albatrosses (indeed, among almost all

a

b

c

d

Figure 41.7 Courtship behavior of various species of albatross. (**a**) The male spreads his wings as part of a courtship ritual that also includes pointing his head harmlessly at the sky. These birds are at a future nest site in the male's territory. (**b-d**) After pair formation is well advanced, the birds begin to touch bills. This contact display precedes copulation.

birds), males claim a breeding area as their own territory, which they defend vigorously against intruders. From this location they announce ownership through vocalizations and visual displays. Unattached females are attracted to the males and may attempt to land within their territories. Initially, a male tends not to be terribly friendly; he may even attack the female as if she were a rival male. At best, his first responses are likely to be ambivalent. He makes an aggressive display, such as drawing back his head as if

to strike her; then he performs a courtship display (Figure 41.7). If the female persists in approaching him and is not driven away, the birds may form a pair bond. This attachment between male and female may last for only the breeding season or for a lifetime, depending on the species.

Among birds such as albatrosses, the pairing process usually takes some time. It includes a progression of display patterns by the male, by the female, and by both at the same time. Figure 41.7 illustrates one of these displays, called bill-clattering, in which both birds shake heads while touching beaks. Many days may pass, each with bouts of ritual movements, before the birds attempt to copulate.

What is the advantage of such prolonged, elaborate courtship? Traditionally, courtship has been viewed as a way of establishing friendly relations between a male and female, a necessary prelude to the cooperative ventures of copulation, nest-building, egg incubation, and feeding the young. Also, prolonged courtship supposedly helps synchronize reproductive cycles, for the eggs must be ready for fertilization when the male produces sperm. This view is not unreasonable, but it fails to explain the genetic advantage to individuals of prolonged courtship.

Why hasn't selection favored males that reserve hostility for male territorial invaders and are immediately receptive to females? Why hasn't selection favored females primed for fertilization when a territory owner is first approached? Skipping the prolonged courtship would allow more time and energy for raising the offspring.

Yet selection may be favoring courtship as a hedge against reproductive gain by one participant at the expense of the other. Suppose a female albatross approaches a male but has already mated elsewhere. If the male were to accept her, feed her, and care for her young, then a rival male would benefit and the helpful male would, genetically, gain nothing. Viewed in this light, an extended courtship could lower his risk by helping to assure the optimum reproductive state of his would-be partner. Similarly, we can speculate that if a female copulates at once with a male, he could abandon her after fertilizing the eggs and spread his genes among eggs of many more females. Certainly that would be genetically advantageous for the male, but the female would be left without help in raising the young. As it happens, the longer the courtship, the less advantageous it is for the male to fly the coop, so to speak. In species that have a limited breeding season, very few females are left unpaired by the time a male finally gets around to inseminating his partner.

Case Study: Competition for Females

Male animals typically produce enormous numbers of sperm, which are stripped-down gametes with little more than a DNA-containing head, midpiece, and tail. Female animals typically produce larger and more complex gametes (eggs), and they produce far fewer of them. Also, the females of many species become permanently unreceptive to males once they have received and stored enough sperm to fertilize their lifetime supply of eggs. From a genetic standpoint, then, females are generally a limited resource for mate-seeking males. We can therefore predict that competition

among males for potential mates should often be intense—and it is.

When two male animals fight, they are probably fighting over an immediate right to inseminate one or more females, or over material goods that can attract future mates to the territory. Fights over possession of a female occur among thousands of species, ranging from shrimps and beetles, fishes and frogs, to birds and mammals.

Consider the black-winged damselfly, a common insect around streams of the eastern United States. The females generally are dispersed in fields and at the edge of woodlands, where they hunt for insect prey. However, they lay eggs only on barely submerged aquatic plants. In most streams, good substrates are in short supply. Individual males compete for territories that contain submerged clusters of rootlets or cattail leaves. In the breeding season, males square off in flight over these territories. They dart at one another before flying in spiraling, whirling chases that can last as long as a half hour. Eventually one male retires, leaving the other in control of the area—hence with access to the receptive females laying eggs there. A good territory can attract ten or more females in one afternoon, enabling the resident male to benefit from disproportionate mating success.

Competition for females is especially pronounced when the females live in groups. For example, female elk band together, probably in defense against predators. As another example, only a few beaches are suitable birthing sites for female elephant seals, which tend to congregate there. Even when ecological pressures of this sort are absent, pockets of useful resources can attract more than one female. Females living in the same area represent ready-made harems. The availability of harems favors strongly competitive males. In many such species, the males tend to be larger than the females, and they are equipped with combative structures such as tusks. Male elephant seals (Figure 30.11a) use their massive bodies in jarring slams against one another; elks have antler-clashing battles when claiming or defending receptive females, which cluster in certain places at certain times of year. Such battles are dangerous and energy-draining for both contestants. However, the larger male is usually able to subdue or repel smaller opponents. He may end up inseminating dozens of females during the breeding season, while his defeated opponents secure few or no matings.

Case Study: Tactics of Defeated Males

Do males that are defeated in competition for females resign themselves gracefully to reproductive suicide? In many

Figure 41.8 Male and female Caspian terns, which cooperate in the care of their young. Male parental behavior occurs in most bird species, but overall is rare in the animal kingdom.

species they do not. Instead, they continue their attempts at breeding—but they do so in ways that get around their inferior fighting ability. Rather than directly challenging a stronger elk or elephant seal, the defeated males lurk at the edges of his territory. When the resident stag or bull is occupied by a dispute with another challenger, they may sneak into the harem and attempt quick copulation with a female, then scurry off before he returns. The same general kind of "sneaky" sexual behavior occurs among several species of insects and birds. Its occurrence is taken as evidence against the " for-the-good-of-the-species" hypothesis. If selection were going on for altruistic behavior, then defeated males would not be attempting to breed and thereby dilute the population's supply of genes from the more successfully competitive males.

The sneaky tactics of defeated males apparently have fostered mate-guarding behavior. For example, a territorial black-winged damselfly keeps close watch over the females as they lay eggs in his territory. Rival males approaching these females are usually attacked and driven off. In other damselfly species, the male physically grips the female with a set of claspers on the tip of his abdomen while she deposits the eggs, thereby assuring that an opponent will not replace him. Mate guarding also occurs in some birds and mammals.

Eggs of a female bank swallow can be fertilized only during a few days of the breeding season. Then, her pair-bonded mate accompanies her wherever she goes. If he is not in close attendance, other males harass the female and may force her to the ground, where they attempt copulation with her. Similarly, males of some baboon species keep a very close watch over a partner during her estrous period, particularly when she is most likely to ovulate.

ON "SELFISH" BEHAVIOR AND SOCIAL LIFE

Sexual territoriality, mate stealing, and mate guarding are all examples of the kind of "selfishness" that individual selection is expected to favor. Yet is there not another aspect of animal behavior that is "selfless"? What about the numerous cases of friendly behavior, cooperation, and out-and-out sacrifice that are especially pronounced in the complex societies of some species? Even here, we can interpret this behavior as selfishness in the sense of promoting transmission of an individual's genes in unconscious competition with other genetically different individuals. Let's consider a few examples to see why this is so.

Parenting as Genetically Selfish Behavior

Parenting is the most familiar form of self-sacrificing behavior. A breeding pair of Caspian terns is shown in Figure 41.8. These birds incubate their eggs, shelter the nestlings, bring them food, and accompany them for some time, even after they have begun to fly and feed partly on their own. Such parental activities take time and energy that the adults might spend in ways that would improve their own chance of living to reproduce another time. Even more dramatically, a parental tern will defend its brood against predators and thereby run the risk of being killed. In general, parents of many animal species incur such costs and dangers in helping their offspring.

However, if a parent can significantly improve the odds that some of its offspring will live to reproductive age, then its sacrifice could increase the frequency of the parental genes in the population. *Because of the genetic continuity between a parent and its offspring, it is possible for an individual to give up some of its own chances for future reproduction and still have its genes spread through the population.* What is critical is that the parent sacrifice for its *own* offspring, not those of another. Typically, parents are adept at recognizing their own, which they help, while ignoring or even attacking the offspring of others. For example, many terns and gulls nest at the same time in extraordinarily dense colonies. After eggs have hatched and the young have grown a bit, there may be hundreds or thousands of dependent chicks, all about the same age, in a relatively small area. Yet the adult birds have no trouble identifying their own chicks. They almost never feed the chicks of other parents. Indeed, they may even eat them if they catch them unprotected.

Individual Advantages of Group Living

Although family groups are a common form of animal "society," there are other, much larger clusters that are not composed of family members alone. How can we account for the formation of these groups? Whereas friendly behavior between parent and offspring can be explained in terms of shared genes and improved individual genetic success, the same explanation cannot apply to social interactions within a large herd of African antelope or a school of fish.

However, keep in mind that interactions in groups of nonrelatives generally are *not* friendly or cooperative in terms of requiring self-sacrifice for other group members. Selfish behavior of the most extreme sort occurs, as when an adult gull consumes the chick of another or when one male mates surreptitiously with the mate of another.

If not for the good of the species, then, why do selfish strangers gather together? In some cases, prey capture is more effective when it is a group effort, as Figure 41.9 suggests. For most social species, the main benefit of group living is protection from predators. Evidently, survival is sufficiently enhanced so that the advantages of sociality outweigh the assorted disadvantages. For example, musk oxen form a circle when wolves approach (Figure 41.9b). By doing so, they use one another to protect their (vulnerable) flanks while presenting their (formidable) horns.

Often, however, group living is simply a result of the so-called **dilution effect**. Being clustered in a large group, members of a prey species may swamp the feeding capacity of local predators and thereby reduce the odds that any one member will be among the unlucky ones eaten that day. For example, say that a certain number of birds along a stream bank can eat 1,000 mayflies an hour, and that 2,000 mayflies emerge. This means each insect runs one chance in two of being killed. But if 10,000 mayflies emerge at the same time, then the risk of death is only one in ten.

The dilution effect also works among groups of prey mammals, such as wildebeest and zebra of the African savanna. Many predators of the savanna are territorial, defending a feeding preserve. Thus the number of carnivores in an area is limited, and many more prey can cluster there than the local predators can consume. When attacked, wildebeest and zebra flee in a tight mass, twisting and turning as an integrated unit. Although this escape behavior seems to be a cooperative undertaking, it almost certainly results from the efforts of individual prey not to become separated from the herd. Isolated animals are easily tracked and safely killed. (Even a lion may hesitate before plunging into a mass of flying hooves.)

Considerable evidence also exists that members of a group jockey for the safest positions. For example, individuals on the outside of many schools of fish attempt, strongly, to move to the inside. Peripheral members are the most vulnerable to attackers slashing in from the outside. Individuals in gull colonies and flocks of feeding geese may fight for central locations within the group for similar reasons.

Cooperative Societies of Birds and Mammals

As the preceding examples suggest, there is a great deal of obviously selfish behavior in the animal kingdom. Yet there also appear to be friendly and helpful interactions, particularly among some species of birds and mammals. Members of baboon troops groom one another for hours, removing parasites and burrs. At some risk to themselves, the adult

Figure 41.9 (**a**) Porpoises engaging in social pursuit of schooling fish. Sociality sometimes exists because individuals can forage more effectively for prey when they do so as a group. (**b**) Defensive formation of musk oxen. Predation pressure can favor the evolution of social life when members of the group are safer than are solitary animals.

males may join forces and face an attacking predator while the smaller females and juveniles flee to safety. Adult wolves cooperate in hunting large, potentially dangerous prey such as moose. Much of the behavior in a wolf pack seems friendly, not selfish; in fact, the returning hunters often regurgitate food to pack members that remained at the den, protecting the wolf pups. Groups of Florida scrubjays cooperate in defending a breeding territory, repelling predators, and feeding the young.

Dominance Hierarchies. There is little doubt, then, that truly self-sacrificing behavior does occur. Before analyzing its evolutionary basis, however, we must point out that considerable aggression, tension, and exploitation of others occur even within the cooperative societies. In fact, competitive interactions lead to the formation of a **dominance hierarchy**, or social ranking of members of a group.

For example, among male baboons and scrubjays, one individual occupies the top, so-called "alpha" position in

Figure 41.10 Appeasement behavior among baboons. Notice the assured position of the dominant animal—and the abject stare and groveling posture of the subordinate one, who is intent on making little conciliatory smacking noises with its lips.

the hierarchy. An alpha male can preempt from all others a safe sleeping place, choice bits of food, or a receptive female. A second-ranking male can preempt all but the alpha male. The third-ranking member can preempt all but the two above him, and so on down the totem pole of dominance. Female baboons and female jays adhere to a similar ranking system, as do females of many other species of birds and mammals.

Subordinate members remain within their group and almost never actively challenge the more dominant ones. In fact, they apparently seek out the company of dominant members to groom them or simply to be near them. A dominant member may or may not tolerate their close presence, although it usually accepts appeasement gestures of the sort shown in Figures 41.10 and 41.11.

The Selfish Side of Subordinates.   In terms of individual selection theory, what could possibly be the genetic advantage of remaining subordinate in a group where the options of reproducing are so restricted? We can account for subordinate behavior with two hypotheses:

---

1. Even dominant members die or become injured, old, or feeble—and a patient subordinate may thereupon move up to a higher position in the social hierarchy.

2. Nonreproducing subordinate members have a similar genotype to close relatives in the group, and any helpful behavior on their part will still help perpetuate a particular assortment of genes.

Figure 41.11 A dominant male and female member of a wolf pack (**a**). Typically, the dominant male is the only pack member likely to breed successfully. (**b**) Subordinate members of the pack greet a dominant male.

Consider the first hypothesis. A young, small, or weak animal has three options, *First*, it could compete all out for dominance—and probably gain nothing. In fact, a challenge to a much stronger individual might lead to injury or death, and any future chance at reproduction would be lost. *Second*, the subordinate animal could strike out on its own, find a mate, and form a new breeding group. This, too, is a recipe for injury or early death. (For example, a wandering solitary baboon no doubt quickens the pulse of the first leopard that spots it. A young, isolated scrubjay is not likely to displace other groups of birds that occupy other suitable habitats.) *Third*, the subordinate animal simply could gain more by being patient. Being subordinate brings with it the benefits of group living, which provides better protection against predators and enhances the foraging range. Thus a subordinate member is likely to survive longer than it would on its own. Then, if a dominant animal dies or becomes vulnerable to challenges, a subordinate may move up in the hierarchy. In the long run, a patient subordinate may leave more descendants than an impatient one.

Now consider the second hypothesis. Even if a subordinate never actually succeeds in reproducing, it may still help pass on copies of some of its genes. *True altruism, even if it involves reproductive self-sacrifice, can be genetically advan-tageous if the beneficiaries of the sacrifice are relatives of the altruist.* Individuals share a certain proportion of genes not only with their offspring but also with their relatives. Two siblings will have about half the same genotype as the other, given that they have inherited some of the same genes from the same parents. Due to common descent, about one-fourth of the genotype of an uncle and nephew is the same. Similarly, about one-eighth of the genotype of cousins is the same. Thus an individual that bears genes leading to the development of helpful behavior can *indirectly* propagate those genes by helping preserve and produce more relatives.

In many animal societies, altruistic behavior is directed strictly to close relatives. For example, a communal flock of scrubjays is composed of a breeding pair and as many as six helpers-at-the-nest. The helpers almost always are older offspring of the pair. They help, feed, and protect younger brothers and sisters. They may never reproduce, yet the sacrificing individuals help perpetuate some "shared" genes when their siblings reproduce.

Suicide, Sterility, and Social Insects

What about animals that are permanently incapable of reproduction? What genetic advantage could be attributed

Figure 41.12 Life in a honeybee colony. (**a**) The only fertile female in the hive is the queen bee, shown here surrounded by her court of sterile worker daughters. These individuals feed her and relay her pheromone throughout the hive, regulating the activity of all of its members.

(**b**) Transfer of food from bee to bee, one of the helpful actions within honeybee society.

(**c**) Bee dance. The central bee is in the midst of a complex dance maneuver, which contains information about the direction and distance to a food source. Floral odors on the dancer's body are also useful to the recruits, which follow her movements before flying out in search of the food.

(**d**) Guard bees. Worker females assume a typical stance at the colony entrance. They are quick to repel intruders from the hive.

(**e**) The queen is much larger than the workers in part because her ovaries are fully developed (unlike those of her sterile daughters).

(**f**) Stingless drones are produced at certain times of the year. They do not work for the colony but instead attempt to mate with queens of other hives.

(**g**) Worker bees forage, feed larvae, guard the colony, construct honeycomb, and clean and maintain the nest. Between 30,000 and 50,000 are present in a colony. They live about six weeks in the spring and summer, and can survive about four months in an overwintering colony.

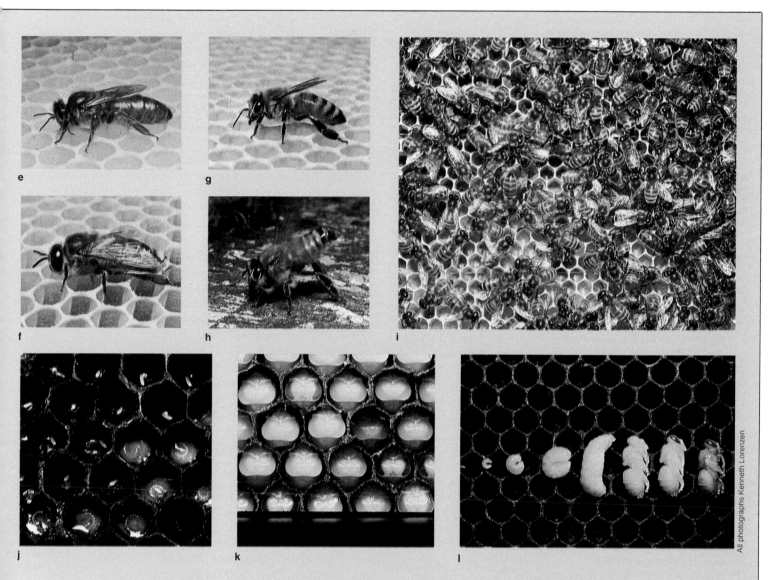

(**h**) Scent-fanning, another cooperative action by the worker. As air is fanned, it passes over the exposed scent gland of the bee. The pheromones released from the gland help other bees orient to the colony entrance.

(**i**) Worker bees constructing new honeycomb from wax secretions. Here, honey or pollen may be stored or new generations may be cared for from the egg stage to the emergence of the adult.

(**j**) The initial stages in the life cycle of a bee. The brood cell caps have been removed, revealing eggs and larvae of various ages. Larvae are fed by young worker bees.

(**k**) Worker pupae. Once again the cell caps have been removed, exposing pupae that will metamorphose into future workers.

(**l**) Complete sequence of developmental stages of a worker bee, from the egg (far left) to a six-day-old larva (fourth from left), to a twenty-one-day-old pupa about to become an adult (far right).

to their altruistic behavior in a group? Consider sterile helpers or workers, which are found among social insects such as honeybees. A honeybee colony is characterized by great sacrifices of the sterile workers (Figure 41.12). A single queen bee is the sole reproductively active female among tens of thousands of bees. Workers force feed her with food that they collect, groom her, and distribute her socially binding pheromones throughout the colony. They also feed one another, build honeycomb, attend to the queen's eggs, feed larvae, remove dead or diseased pupae, and guard the hive entrance. When a guard bee detects a nest parasite or predator (such as a raccoon), it attacks and stings the intruder. It also releases a chemical attractant that recruits still more defenders, which also attack and sting. Because the loss of a stinger and associated poison glands is fatal, these workers are animals that commit suicide! Suicidal behavior is regularly exhibited by worker ants, wasps, and soldier termites, as well as by worker bees.

How can suicidal behavior and sterility evolve, given that individuals having these traits fail to reproduce? Here, too, close relatives play a role. For example, at some stage a queen bee departs with about half of the work force and starts a new colony. Before she does, drone sons and future queen daughters are produced. All are fertile. One of these future queens inherits the remaining half of the work force, and remains at the hive. The drones leave the colony and may mate with new queens produced at other colonies. Thus worker bees help the queen mother rear one reproducing sister, and many workers stay with this new queen and help her after their mother leaves. They also help produce a number of potentially reproducing brothers. *When workers sacrifice their own reproductive chances, they increase the number of potentially reproducing siblings—which have a substantial proportion of particular genes in common with them.* This is true of social insects generally.

Sterility, then, can be explained in evolutionary terms as a mechanism that increases the representation of certain genes in certain populations. Modern analysts of worker castes now suggest that worker members do not exist to benefit the species as a whole. Rather, the focus is on how even extreme cooperation in social animals may have evolved through competition at the genetic level.

SELECTION THEORY AND THE EVOLUTION OF HUMAN BEHAVIOR

So far, we have considered examples of how the concept of individual selection can be used to explain animal behavior.

Can the concept also be applied to analysis of human behavior? Oddly, the question is controversial. Since Darwin's time, strong evidence has accumulated in support of the principle of biological evolution, and today there is widespread belief that we share an evolutionary heritage with all other forms of life. Yet there is still a prevailing belief that humans are so evolutionarily advanced that they are totally unique, even compared with our closest relatives in the animal kingdom.

To be sure, our cultural evolution has been so extraordinary that we are unique in many ways. But surely, beneath the elaborate and diverse layerings of culture, there still resides a biological core for human behavior. The human body contains genetic material, as do the bodies of all other living things; and that genetic material has profound influence on the course of our development as it does theirs. If experiments strongly support the hypothesis that behavioral development has a genetic basis and therefore is subject to individual selection, then an argument can be made that human behavior may also be ultimately explainable in these terms.

Think about some forms of behavior that occur in all societies. For example, smiling has an innate basis. It starts among newborns, even those born prematurely. Apparently, smiling helps establish strong emotional ties between infants and the adults who help assure their survival. As another example, beginning at four or five weeks after birth, all infants make strong visual contact with their mothers— even infants who were born blind. Here, too, the behavior apparently helps strengthen social bonds between the protector and the protected. Universally, humans express pleasure, anger, distress, surprise, and rage with the same kinds of facial movements. The meaning of all such behavioral expressions is universally recognized; they are all genetically based mechanisms that help promote survival and reproductive success in human social groups.

What about more complex behavioral traits—sexual jealousy, for example? This behavior is prevalent among human societies, although its expressed forms are remarkably diverse. Could sexual jealousy be a more embroidered version of the mate-guarding behavior described earlier in the chapter? We can speculate that over the course of human evolution, jealousy proved adaptive in minimizing the possibility of sexual promiscuity by a wife, which could be detrimental to a husband's reproductive success. For example, a male might end up raising a child who is not his own and who would not, therefore, enhance representation of his particular genes in the population. An abandoned female would have to raise the children without the emotional and economic support of the male who sired them. Thus the children to whom her (as well as his) genes were entrusted could be at a disadvantage, being deprived of his guidance and provisioning until reproductive age.

In some quarters, speculations of this sort are said to be scientifically irresponsible. Critics argue that human behavior cannot be explained in terms of genetic "selfishness." Some contend that if you were to ask people why they behaved in a particular way, no one would ever say "My genes made me do it." They contend that any behavior in any environmental context is an entirely learned response. Yet conscious awareness of the genetic contribution to some behavior is not a requirement for its expression. If it could talk, a baby egret battering its younger sibling to death wouldn't say "My genes made me do it" either; it simply has a genetically based capacity to behave in ways that help assure its own survival and, ultimately, its reproduction.

Notice the word *capacity*. Having a genetic basis for the development of some behavior does not mean that the trait is biologically determined, in the sense of being impossible to alter. There are no "genes for behavioral traits." There are only genes that code for enzymes and other products—and the synthesis and activity of those products is profoundly influenced by the environment. As pointed out repeatedly in this book, *change the environment, and the course of development can change.* Thus, whatever the extent of its genetic foundation, expression of behavior such as jealousy can also be modified, depending on the social environment. Control of the environment might well eliminate some of its effects, which many consider undesirable.

An evolutionary approach to human behavior may be under most attack by individuals who fear that what it reveals will be misused. They may think that to suggest a trait such as jealousy is adaptive (genetically advantageous) is to imply that it is desirable in moral or social terms. Yet there is a clear difference between trying to explain something (by reference to its possible evolutionary history) and trying to justify it. "Adaptive" does not mean "moral." It means *valuable in the transmission of an individual's genes.*

Research into the relationship between evolution, genes, and our behavioral capacity is in its infancy. Yet improved knowledge of ourselves could be used to help resolve many critical issues related to our biology as a species, including overpopulation, exploitation of the environment, and aggression among modern nations. It remains to be seen how quickly this knowledge will be gained, and whether it will actually be employed to alleviate negative aspects of the human condition. In the meantime, perhaps some readers will find that an appreciation of the natural world can be deepened through application of an evolutionary approach to one of its most diverse expressions— human behavior.

Readings

Alcock, J. 1983. *Animal Behavior: An Evolutionary Approach.* Third edition. Sunderland, Mass.: Sinauer Associates. Outstanding introduction to the many topics that make up the study of behavior; strong emphasis on evolutionary theory. Excellent choice of illustrations.

Dawkins, R. 1976. *The Selfish Gene.* New York: Oxford University Press. For a general audience; entertainingly written book.

Krebs, J., and N. Davies. 1981. *An Introduction to Behavioral Ecology.* Sunderland, Mass.: Sinauer Associates. Describes the evolved relations between behavior and environment.

von Frisch, K. 1953. *The Dancing Bees.* New York: Harcourt Brace Jovanovich. Classic on the natural history and behavior of honeybees.

Williams, G. 1966. *Adaptation and Natural Selection.* Princeton, New Jersey: Princeton University Press. Key book in the revolution in thinking about animal behavior in terms of individual selection.

Review Questions

1. Rephrase the statement "There is a gene for sexual imprinting by greylag geese". The reworded statement should avoid the implication that genes "make" behavioral traits in a one-to-one relationship.

2. What role does the environment play in the development of an instinct?

3. What contributions have behavior geneticists made to an understanding of the evolutionary basis of behavior?

4. Develop a hypothesis for the observation that male lions will kill the offspring of females they acquire when they chase away the males that had been the previous mates of these females. How would you test your hypothesis?

5. How can an animal be cooperative and still pass on more of its genes than a non-cooperative individual?

6. Is parental behavior always adaptive?

7. What is true altruism?

8. How can an individual propagate its genes even if it is sterile?

9. When is solitary living a "superior" mode of existence in evolutionary terms than complex social life?

10. If someone claims that human aggression is biologically adaptive (or genetically advantageous for individuals), does this mean that he or she believes there is no environmental component to the development of human aggression? Does it mean that he or she feels aggression is necessarily desirable in social terms?

APPENDIX I
BRIEF SYSTEM OF CLASSIFICATION

This classification scheme is a composite of several used in microbiology, botany, and zoology. There is no universally accepted scheme; although the major groupings are fairly well agreed upon, what to call them and, sometimes, where to place them in phylogenetic terms are not. (For example, microbiologists and botanists use the term "Division" and zoologists use "Phylum," which are equivalent categories.)

Also, the scheme given here is by no means all-encompassing. It simply covers some of the organisms mentioned in the text. Numbers refer to some pages on which representatives are described or discussed.

KINGDOM MONERA   Prokaryotes (single-celled, with no nucleus or other organelles; autotrophic and heterotrophic forms)   34, 504ff.

Subkingdom Archaebacteria. Methanogens,
    thermoacidophiles   506, 512, 522
Subkingdom Eubacteria. True bacteria; photosynthetic
    bacteria (such as cyanobacteria), spirochaetes, etc.   61, 507, 523, 527

KINGDOM PROTISTA*   Single-celled eukaryotes (with nucleus and other organelles; heterotrophs, some autotrophs)   34, 529ff.

Phylum Pyrrophyta. Dinoflagellates   531
Phylum Chrysophyta. Chrysophytes, Golden algae, diatoms   530
Phylum Euglenophyta. Euglenids (photosynthetic
    flagellates)   529, 530
Phylum Protozoa. Protozoans
    Subphylum Mastigophora. Flagellates
        (nonphotosynthetic)   531–532
    Subphylum Sarcodina. Amoebas   533
    Subphylum Sporozoa. Sporozoans   534
    Subphylum Ciliophora. Ciliates   534–535

KINGDOM FUNGI   Multicelled eukaryotes (heterotrophs; most rely on extracellular digestion and absorption of nutrients)   34, 539ff.

Division Oomycota. Egg-forming fungi   540
Division Zygomycota. Zygospore-forming fungi   541
Division Ascomycota. Sac fungi   541
Division Basidiomycota. Club fungi   106, 542–543
Division Deuteromycota. Fungi imperfecti   545
Division Myxomycota.** Acellular slime molds   545
Division Acrasiomycota.** Cellular slime molds   545

KINGDOM PLANTAE*   Mostly multicelled eukaryotes (photosynthetic autotrophs)   34, 546ff.

Division Rhodophyta. Red algae   61, 548, 549
Division Phaeophyta. Brown algae   548, 549
Division Chlorophyta. Green algae   233, 537, 550
Division Bryophyta. Mosses, liverworts   548, 551
Division Rhyniophyta. Early land plants (extinct)   513
Division Lycophyta. Club mosses   552, 554
Division Sphenophyta. Horsetails   553, 554
Division Pterophyta. Ferns   553, 554
Division Cycadophyta. Cycads   554, 556
Division Ginkgophyta. Ginkgo   554, 556
Division Gnetophyta. Gnetophytes   554, 557
Division Pinophyta. Gymnosperms   249, 265, 554, 557
Division Magnoliophyta. Angiosperms (flowering
    plants)   249ff., 276ff., 283
    Class Liliopsida. Monocots; grasses, orchids, lilies, etc.   249, 554, 559
    Class Magnoliopsida. Dicots; most of the common
        flowering plants not mentioned above   249, 554, 559

KINGDOM ANIMALIA   Multicelled eukaryotes (heterotrophs of varied sorts; herbivores, carnivores, parasites)   34, 561ff.

Phylum Porifera. Sponges   10, 562, 566
Phylum Cnidaria. Jellyfishes, hydroids, corals   328, 449, 564, 567
Phylum Ctenophora. Comb jellies
Phylum Platyhelminthes. Flatworms, flukes, tapeworms   410, 449, 564, 569
Phylum Nematoda. Roundworms   571
Phylum Rotifera. Rotifers   564
Phylum Mollusca. Gastropods, bivalves, cephalopods   361, 573
Phylum Annelida. Segmented worms   330, 367, 576
Phylum Arthropoda. Spiders, crustaceans, insects, etc.   7, 11, 330, 362, 578
Phylum Tardigrada. Water bears   86
Phylum Onchyophora. *Peripatus*   581
Phylum Echinodermata. Sea stars, sea lilies, sea
    urchins, etc.   10, 564, 581
Phylum Hemichordata. Acorn worms
Phylum Chordata   582ff.
    Subphylum Urochordata. Tunicates (sea squirts)   582, 583
    Subphylum Cephalochordata. Lancelets   582ff.
    Subphylum Vertebrata. Vertebrates   564, 582ff.
        Class Agnatha. Jawless fishes; lampreys, hagfishes   585
        Class Osteichthyes. Bony fishes; salmon,
            minnows, etc.   10, 585, 586
        Class Chondrichthyes. Cartilaginous fishes;
            sharks, rays   586
        Class Amphibia. Frogs, toads, newts, salamanders   5, 440, 453, 586
        Class Reptilia. Lizards, snakes, turtles, etc.   171, 444, 587, 588
        Class Aves. Birds   3, 32, 170, 587, 588
        Class Mammalia. Mammals
            Subclass Prototheria. Egg-laying mammals;
                anteater, duckbilled platypus   444
            Subclass Metatheria. Pouched mammals;
                opossum, kangaroo, etc.   445
            Subclass Eutheria. Placental mammals   587
                Order Insectivora. Insect-eating mammals;
                    moles, etc.
                Order Edentata. Toothless mammals; sloths,
                    armadillos
                Order Rodentia. Rats, squirrels, etc.
                Order Perissodactyla. Odd-toed ungulates;
                    horses, etc.   14, 15
                Order Artiodactyla. Even-toed ungulates;
                    hippopotamus, deer, cattle, etc.   14, 15
                Order Proboscidea. Elephants   18
                Order Lagomorpha. Rabbits, hares   456, 609
                Order Sirenia. Manatees, dugongs, sea cows
                Order Carnivora. Wolves, dogs, cats, bears,   16, 173,
                    seals, etc.   409, 489, 587
                Order Cetacea. Whales   61
                Order Chiroptera. Bats   354
                Order Primates. Monkeys, apes, humans, etc.   469, 590ff., 599, 615

*The use of *phylum* or *division* varies, depending on who is setting up the classification scheme.
**Unknown affiliation; sometimes placed in Kingdom Protista.

APPENDIX II
SOLUTIONS TO GENETICS PROBLEMS

Chapter Ten

1. a. *AB*
   b. *AB* and *aB*
   c. *Ab* and *ab*
   d. *AB, aB, Ab,* and *ab*

2. a. *AaBB* will occur in all the offspring.
   b. 25% *AABB*; 25% *AaBB*; 25% *AABb*; 25% *AaBb*.
   c. 25% *AaBb*; 25% *Aabb*; 25% *aaBb*; 25% *aabb*.
   d. $\frac{1}{16}$ *AABB* (6.25%)
      $\frac{1}{8}$ *AaBB* (12.5%)
      $\frac{1}{16}$ *aaBB* (6.25%)
      $\frac{1}{8}$ *AABb* (12.5%)
      $\frac{1}{4}$ *AaBb* (25 %)
      $\frac{1}{8}$ *aaBb* (12.5%)
      $\frac{1}{16}$ *AAbb* (6.25%)
      $\frac{1}{8}$ *Aabb* (12.5%)
      $\frac{1}{16}$ *aabb* (6.25%)

3. a. Yellow is recessive. Because the first-generation plants must be heterozygous and had a green phenotype, green must be dominant over the recessive yellow.
   b. $(\frac{3}{4})(135) = 101.25$ green in second generation.
      $(\frac{1}{4})(135) = 33.75$ yellow in second generation.
      Obviously one cannot have fractional offspring. However, in actual situations, the expected number will often turn out to be in fractional form. From a practical standpoint, geneticists would probably respond by asserting that about 101 green second-generation plants would be expected and about 34 yellow, although slight variation from these predictions would be common and expected.

4. a. Mother must be heterozygous for both genes; father is homozygous recessive for both genes. The first child is also homozygous recessive for both genes.
   b. The probability that the second child will not be able to roll the tongue and will have free earlobes is $\frac{1}{4}$ (25%).

5. a. *ABC*
   b. *ABc* and *aBc*
   c. *ABC, aBC, ABc,* and *aBc*
   d. *ABC, aBC, AbC, abC, ABc, aBc, Abc,* and *abc*

6. Because the man can only produce one type of allele for each of his ten genes, he can only produce one type of sperm. The woman, on the other hand, can produce two types of alleles for each of her two heterozygous genes; she can produce 2×2 or 4 different kinds of eggs. As can be observed, as the number of heterozygous genes increases, more and more different types of gametes can be produced. For a population or species, this might be advantageous, as it would introduce more genetic variability into the population. Such variability might prove useful, in that the variant individuals might have better chances of surviving under a variety of environmental conditions.

7. The first-generation plants must all be double heterozygotes. When these plants are self-pollinated, $\frac{1}{4}$ (25%) of the second-generation plants will be doubly heterozygous.

8. The most direct way to accomplish this would be to allow a true-breeding mouse having yellow fur to mate with a true-breeding mouse having brown fur. Such true-breeding strains could be obtained by repeated inbreeding (mating of related individuals; for example, a male and a female of the same litter) of yellow and brown strains. In this way, it should be possible to obtain homozygous yellow and homozygous brown mice.

When true-breeding yellow and true-breeding brown mice are crossed, the progeny should all be heterozygous. If the progeny phenotype is either yellow or brown, then the dominance is simple or complete, and the phenotype reflects the dominant allele. If the phenotype is intermediate between yellow and brown, there is incomplete dominance. If the phenotype shows both yellow and brown, there is codominance.

9. a. The mother must be heterozygous ($I^A i$). The man having type B blood could have fathered the child if he were also heterozygous ($I^B i$).
   b. If the man is heterozygous, then he *could be* the father. However, because any other type B heterozygous male also could be the father, one cannot say that this particular man absolutely must be. Actually, any male who could contribute an O allele (*i*) could have fathered the child. This would include males with type O blood (*ii*) or type A blood who are heterozygous ($I^A i$).

10. a. The first-generation offspring will all be double heterozygotes and will be agouti.
    b. The second-generation offspring will be $\frac{9}{16}$ agouti (56.25%); $\frac{3}{16}$ black (18.75%); and $\frac{4}{16}$ albino (25%).

Chapter Eleven

1. a. Males inherit their X chromosome from their mothers.
   b. A male can produce two types of gametes with respect to an X-linked gene. One type will lack this gene and possess a Y chromosome. The other will have an X chromosome and the linked gene.
   c. A female homozygous for an X-linked gene will produce just one type of gamete containing an X chromosome with the gene.
   d. A female heterozygous for an X-linked gene will produce two types of gametes. One will contain an X chromsome with the dominant allele, and the other type will contain an X chromosome with the recessive allele.

2. a. Because this gene is only carried on Y chromosomes, females would not be expected to have hairy pinnae because they normally do not have Y chromosomes.
   b. Because sons always inherit a Y chromosome from their fathers and because daughters never do, a man having hairy pinnae will always transmit this trait to his sons and never to his daughters.

3. a. A 0% crossover frequency means that 50% of the gametes will be *AB* and 50% will be *ab*.
   b. Of the gametes, 10% will be recombinant (5% *Ab* and 5% *aB*), and 90% will be non-recombinant (45% *AB* and 45% *ab*).
   c. Of the gametes, 25% will be recombinant (12.5% *Ab* and 12.5% *aB*), and 75% will be non-recombinant (37.5% *AB* and 37.5% *ab*).

4. Ten map units means that 10% of the gametes produced by the double-heterozygote parent will be recombinant according to the following Punnett square:

	AB (45%)	ab (45%)	Ab (5%)	aB (5%)
ab	AaBb 45% of the progeny	aabb 45% of the progeny	Aabb 5% of the progeny	aaBb 5% of the progeny

5. The first-generation females must be heterozygous for both genes. The 42 red-eyed, vestigial-winged and the 30 purple-eyed, long-winged progeny represent recombinant gametes from these females. Because the first-generation females must have produced 600 gametes to give these 600 progeny, and because 42 + 30 of these were recombinant, the percentage of recombinant gametes is 72/600, or 12%, which implies that 12 map units separate the two genes.

6. The rare vestigial-winged flies could be explained by a deletion of the dominant allele from one of the chromosomes, due to the action of the x-rays.

7. If the longer-than-normal chromosome 14 represented the translocation of most of chromosome 21 to the end of a normal chromosome 14, then this individual would be afflicted with Down's syndrome due to the presence of this attached chromosome 21 as well as two normal chromosomes 21. The total chromosome number, however, would be 46.

8. The initial cells of the hybrid from a cross between *T. turgidum* and *T. tauschii* did have twenty-one chromosomes. These chromosomes were induced to double in the absence of cell division by application of colchicine; the result was the hexaploid, with forty-two chromosomes. Gametes from *T. aestivum* should have twenty-one chromosomes (ABD); when these combine with gametes from *T. turgidum* (fourteen chromosomes, AB), offspring with 21 + 14 = 35 chromosomes (AABBD) would arise. Because there is only one set of D chromosomes, normal meiotic pairing should not occur and these hybrids would be sterile.

Chapter Fifteen

1. The gene for hemophilia occurs on the X but not the Y chromosome. A male has only one X chromosome. Therefore, it would be impossible for a male simply to be a carrier; the allele associated with hemophilia would always be expressed. For each child produced by Victoria and Leopold, there would be a probability of $\frac{1}{2}$ (50%) that it would be a nonhemophilic son and $\frac{1}{2}$ (50%) that it would be a carrier daughter.

2. Assuming the mother is heterozygous (most individuals with Huntington's chorea are), the woman has a $\frac{1}{2}$ (50%) chance of being heterozygous and therefore of later developing the disorder. Also, if this woman married a normal male, they would have a 50% chance of having a child with the disorder. Thus the *total* probability of their having a child with Huntington's chorea is (0.5) (0.5) = 0.25, or $\frac{1}{4}$ (25%).

3. The first child can only be color blind if it is a boy. Why? The probability of this happening is 25%. Similarly, their second child also has a 25% chance of being color blind. The probability that both will be color blind is (0.25) (0.25) = 0.0625, or 6.25%.

4. This indicates that genetic information other than that necessary for sex determination must reside on the X chromosome. Such information is necessary for survival regardless of whether one is male or female. Obviously, this is not true for the Y chromosome, in that individuals (females) survive quite nicely in its absence. Perhaps one could simply imagine that the major function of the Y chromosome is to change what would have been a female individual into a male.

5. The only parent from whom this child could have received an X chromosome that bears a nonhemophilia allele is the mother. Therefore, nondisjunction must have occurred in the male.

6. A child with Klinefelter's syndrome could be produced if a Y-bearing sperm fertilized an egg having two X chromosomes (as a result of nondisjunction during egg development). Such a child could also be produced if a normal egg (with one X chromosome) were fertilized by a sperm having an X and Y chromosome (as a result of nondisjunction during sperm development).

7. The Punnett square for this situation would be as follows:

	X-bearing sperm	Y-bearing sperm
XX-bearing egg	trisomic XXX	Klinefelter's XXY
no X in egg	Turner's XO	dies before birth; has only Y

8. a. An unaffected male selected at random has 1 chance in 50 (2%) of being heterozygous.
   b. An unaffected female selected at random also has 1 chance in 50 (2%) of being heterozygous.
   c. If you selected an unaffected male and unaffected female at random, the probability that both will be heterozygous is (0.02) (0.02) = 0.0004, or 0.04%.
   d. The probability that a pair of unaffected individuals selected at random could have a child afflicted with PKU is given by (0.02) (0.02) (0.25) = 0.0001, or 0.01%. This is the same thing as 1/10,000, which suggests that about one birth in every 10,000 will be a child with PKU, assuming that only heterozygous individuals have such children (an assumption which is not completely true).

9. There would be 1 chance in 50 (2%) that a randomly selected mate would also be a PKU carrier. There would be a much greater chance that your first cousin would be a PKU carrier, because both of you would share a common ancestor and thus, possibly, a common source for the PKU allele. In fact, your first cousin would have 1 chance in 8 (12.5%) of also being a PKU carrier.

GLOSSARY

abortion Prevention of embryonic development in the uterus after implantation has occurred.

abscission (ab-SIH-zhun) Leaf (or fruit or flower) drop after hormonal action causes a corky cell layer to form where a leaf stalk joins a stem; nutrient and water flow is thereby shut off.

acid A substance that releases hydrogen ions (H^+) in a water solution, where it has a pH of less than 7.

acoelomate Type of animal that has no fluid-filled cavity between the gut and body wall.

actin A protein that functions in contraction.

action potential Nerve impulse; a dramatic reversal in membrane polarity of a neuron at rest. The action potential is all-or-none; once triggered, its strength does not change even if the stimulus strength changes.

active site Three-dimensional groove or pocket in an enzyme to which a specific set of substrates becomes temporarily bound and thereby is made more reactive.

active transport Movement of ions and molecules across a cell membrane, against a concentration gradient, by ATP expenditure. The ion or molecule is moved in a direction other than the one in which simple diffusion would take it.

adaptation An existing structural, physiological, or behavioral trait of an individual that promotes survival and reproduction under prevailing conditions.

adaptive radiation A branching of one lineage, two or more times, into evolutionary lines that radiate away from one another through partitioning of the existing environment or invasion of new ones.

adaptive zone For any lineage, a potential mode of life which it has not yet exploited but which is (or becomes) available in the same (or new) environments.

adenine (AH-de-neen) A purine; a nitrogen-containing base found in nucleotides.

adenosine diphosphate (ah-DEN-uh-seen die-FOSS-fate) ADP, a molecule involved in cellular energy transfers; formed by hydrolysis of ATP.

adenosine triphosphate ATP, a molecule that is a major carrier of energy from one reaction site to another in all living cells.

adhering junction In animal tissues, a cell-to-cell spot weld. Such junctions hold adjacent cells in place and permit them to function as a structural unit.

aerobic respiration Pathway of carbohydrate metabolism, including glycolysis, the Krebs cycle, and electron transport phosphorylation. The "spent" electrons are transferred finally to oxy-gen. Much greater net energy yield than anaerobic pathways.

allele (uh-LEEL) One of two or more alternative forms of a gene at a given gene locus.

allele frequency The relative abundance of different alleles carried by the individuals of a population. Also called gene frequency, which is something of a non sequitur.

allopatric speciation Speciation that occurs when geographic separation prevents gene flow and has assured reproductive isolation of demes (local breeding units of a population) or of populations of the same species.

alternation of generations In many plant life cycles, the alternation of diploid multicelled bodies with haploid multicelled bodies.

alveolus, plural **alveoli** (ahl-VEE-uh-luss) One of many small, thin-walled pouches in the lungs; sites of gas exchange between air in the lungs and the bloodstream.

amino acid (uh-MEE-no) A molecule having an amino group (NH_2) and an acid group ($-COOH$); a subunit for protein synthesis.

ammonification Decomposition of nitrogenous wastes and remains of plants and animals by some bacterial and fungal species.

amnion (AM-nee-on) In reptiles, birds, and mammals, a membrane that arises from the inner cell mass of a blastocyst; becomes a fluid-filled sac in which the embryo develops freely.

amyloplast A plastid having no pigments; functions in starch storage.

anaerobic pathway Any metabolic pathway that does not depend on oxygen as the final electron acceptor.

anaerobic respiration Pathway of carbohydrate metabolism that begins with glycolysis and ends with the transfer of "spent" electrons to inorganic compounds in the environment.

anaphase In mitosis, the stage when the two sister chromatids of each chromosome are separated and moved to opposite poles of the cell.

angiosperm (AN-gee-oh-sperm) Flowering plant.

animal Multicelled heterotroph; except for a few parasites, most ingest food, which is then digested and absorbed.

annual plant Vascular plant that completes its life cycle in one growing season.

anther In flowering plants, the pollen-bearing part of the male reproductive organ (stamen).

antheridium Sperm-producing cells or organ in a male gametophyte.

antibody Type of protein molecule, carried by the bloodstream, that binds to specific agents invading the body (antigens) and thereby marks them for disposal by other defense forces.

antigen Foreign cell or substance that has penetrated the body or some tissue and that triggers antibody production.

anus In some invertebrates and all vertebrates, the terminal opening of the gut through which solid residues of digestion are eliminated.

aorta (ay-OR-tah) Main artery of systemic circulation; carries oxygenated blood away from the heart to all regions except the lungs.

apical meristem In vascular plants, embryonic tissue zones where cells are produced by mitotic divisions; these cells then enlarge and differentiate into all other plant tissues.

archegonium Egg-producing cells or organ in a female gametophyte.

asexual reproduction Production of new individuals by any process that does not involve gametes.

assay Chemical testing to determine the presence and amount of the components of a system.

atom Smallest unit of an element that still retains the characteristics of that element.

atomic number A relative number assigned to each kind of element based on the number of protons in one of its atoms.

atomic weight The weight of an atom of any element relative to the weight of the most abundant isotope of carbon (which is set at 12).

australopithecine (ohss-trah-low-PITH-uh-seen) Humanlike hominoids that lived from about 3.8 to 1 million years ago.

autonomic nervous system (auto-NOM-ik) Those aspects of the vertebrate central and peripheral nervous system that regulate cardiac cells, muscle cells, smooth muscle cells (such as those of the stomach), and glands; generally not under conscious control.

autosome One of those chromosomes that are of the same number and kind in both males and females of the species.

autotroph "Self-feeder"; an organism able to build all the complex organic molecules it requires as its own food source, using only simple inorganic compounds. Compare *heterotrophs*.

axon Nerve cell process serving as a through-conducting pathway for messages that must travel rapidly, without alteration, from one body region to another.

bacillus, plural **bacilli** (bah-SILL-us, bah-SILL-eye) Rodlike form of bacterium.

bacteriophage (bak-TEER-ee-oh-fahj) Category of viruses that infect and destroy certain bacterial cells.

basal body A centriole that has given rise to the microtubular system of a cilium or flagellum and that remains attached at the base of the motile structure.

base Any substance that combines with hydrogen ions in a water solution, where it has a pH above 7.

behavior Any coordinated neuromotor response to changes in the external and internal states; a product of the integration of sensory, genetic, neural, and endocrine factors, and may be modified by learning.

biennial Flowering plant that lives two growing seasons.

bilateral symmetry Body plan whereby the right half is approximately equivalent to the left half.

binary fission Asexual reproduction by division of a body (or cell) into two equivalent parts.

biogeographic realm In one scheme, one of six major regions having a characteristic array of species that are generally isolated from the other realms by physical barriers that restrict dispersal.

biological clock Internal timing mechanisms that allow organisms to anticipate and adjust to environmental change. In plants, phytochromes may figure in the timing mechanism; in some vertebrates, the pineal gland seems to.

biological concentration Increasing concentration of a relatively nondegradable substance in body tissues, beginning at low trophic levels and moving up through those organisms that are diners, then are dined upon in food webs.

biomass Organic matter that accumulates over time; typically expressed as grams (dry weight) of organic matter per unit area.

biome A broad, vegetational subdivision of some biogeographic realm, shaped by climate and topography.

biosphere Narrow zone that harbors life, limited to the waters of the earth, a fraction of its crust, and the lower region of the surrounding air.

biosynthesis Assembly of the lipids, carbohydrates, proteins, and nucleic acids that make up a cell.

blastocyst In mammalian development, a modified blastula stage consisting of a hollow ball of surface cells (trophoblast) having inner cells massed at one end.

blastula In many animal species, an embryonic stage consisting of a hollow, fluid-filled ball of cells one layer thick.

blood pressure Fluid pressure, generated by heart contractions, that keeps blood circulating. Generally measured at large arteries of systemic circulation.

bronchus, plural **bronchi** (BRONG-cuss, BRONG-kee) Tubelike branchings of the trachea (windpipe) that lead to the lungs.

budding Asexual reproduction in which some cells differentiate and grow outward from the parent body, then the bud breaks away to form a new individual.

buffer In living cells, a substance that combines with and/or releases hydrogen ions as a function of pH.

bulk flow In response to a pressure gradient, a movement of more than one kind of molecule in the same direction in the same medium (gas or liquid).

calorie The amount of heat needed to raise the temperature of one gram of water by $1°C$.

Calvin-Benson cycle Stage of light-independent reactions of photosynthesis in which carbon-containing compounds are used to form carbohydrates (such as glucose) and to regenerate a sugar phosphate (RuBP) required in carbon dioxide fixation. The first product is a three-carbon compound (PGA).

cambium, plural **cambia** (KAM-bee-um) In vascular plants, embryonic tissue zones (meristems) that run parallel with the sides of roots and stems.

camouflage Adaptation in form, coloration, and/or behavior that enables an organism to blend with its background, the advantage being to escape detection. Also known as crypsis.

cancer Malignant tumor; a mass resulting from uncontrollable cell division.

capillary Small blood vessel whose thin walls are permeable to many materials; exchange point between blood and surrounding tissues.

carbohydrate Organic compound of carbon, hydrogen, and oxygen; sugar is an example.

carbohydrate metabolism The release of chemical bond energy from carbohydrates by means of phosphorylation and oxidation-reduction reactions.

carbon dioxide fixation First stage of light-independent reactions of photosynthesis; carbon dioxide from the air is combined with organic molecules.

carcinogen (CAR-sin-oh-jen) Any agent capable of promoting cancer.

cardiac cycle Sequence of heart muscle contractions and relaxation.

cardiovascular system Collectively, the blood, heart, and blood vessels.

carnivore Heterotroph that ingests other animals for food.

carpel In flowers, the central whorl of modified leaves that represents the female reproductive structure. Typically consists of a stigma, style, and ovary. May be more than one carpel per flower.

carrying capacity Environmental resistance to the growth of a given population; the maximum population density that can be sustained under a given set of conditions.

cell The basic *living* unit. There are large, complex organic molecules below this level of organization, but such molecules by themselves are non-living.

cell plate In plant cell division, a partition that forms from vesicles at the equator of the mitotic spindle, between the two newly forming cells.

cell wall Extracellular layer of material that surrounds the plasma membrane.

central nervous system Brain and spinal cord.

centriole One of a pair of short, barrel-shaped structures that gives rise to the microtubule system of a cilium or flagellum.

centromere (SEN-troh-meer) Localized, differentiated region of a chromosome where two sister chromatids are attached after DNA replication and before mitotic division.

cephalization Differentiation of one end of the animal body into a head in which nervous tissue and sensory organs are especially concentrated.

cerebellum Hindbrain region, overlying medulla, that integrates messages from receptors concerned with body position and motion, and from visual and auditory centers.

cerebrum In vertebrate forebrain, paired masses of gray matter; cerebral hemispheres overlying thalamus, hypothalamus, and pituitary. Includes primary receiving centers for receptors at body periphery, association centers for coordinating and processing sensory input, and motor centers for coordinating motor responses.

chemical bond Energy relationship in which the electron structure of one atom becomes linked with the electron structure of another atom (or atoms).

chemiosmotic theory Concept that an electrochemical gradient across a cell membrane drives ATP synthesis. Operation of electron transport systems builds up the hydrogen ion concentration on one side of the membrane. Then the electrical and chemical force of the H^+ flow down the gradient is linked to enzyme machinery that combines ADP with inorganic phosphate.

chemoreceptor Sensory cell or cell part that directly or indirectly transforms chemical stimuli into nerve signals.

chemosynthetic autotrophs A few kinds of bacteria that obtain energy from oxidizing inorganic substances (such as sulfur and ammonium) then use the energy in forming complex organic molecules from carbon dioxide and other simple substances.

chiasma, plural **chiasmata** (kai-AZ-mah, kai-az-MAH-tah) During meiosis, the region of contact between sister chromatids that have undergone synapsis; it indicates that the chromatids have exchanged corresponding segments.

chlorophyll Steroid-containing, light-trapping pigment molecule that acts as an electron donor in photosynthesis.

chloroplast Eukaryotic organelle that houses membranes, pigments, and enzymes of photosynthesis.

chorion (CORE-ee-on) In reptiles, birds, and mammals, outermost membrane around embryo. Its vascularized villi form a nutritional link with the mother; its hormonal secretion (chorionic gonadotropin) helps maintain the corpus luteum (hence the uterine lining) following implantation.

chromatid (CROW-mah-tid) One of two nucleoproteins making up a chromosome following DNA replication. Two sister chromatids joined at the centromere represent duplicate sets of hereditary information.

chromoplast A plastid having pigments that do not function in photosynthesis.

chromosomal mutation A change in the number or sequence of genes in a chromosome, or a change in the number of whole chromosomes or chromosome sets (due to abnormal distribution during meiotic cell division).

chromosome In eukaryotes, the vehicle by which hereditary information is physically transmitted from one generation to the next. Consists of a single DNA molecule and associated proteins (before replication) or of two identical DNA molecules and associated proteins (after replication).

cilium, plural **cilia** (SILL-ee-um) Short, hairlike structure containing a regular array of microtubules.

circulatory system In most multicelled animals, blood-containing conduits that transport materials to and from cells; also concerned with pH and temperature stabilization.

cleavage Rapid, successive divisions in an animal zygote that lead to increase in cell number but not in cell size.

coccus, plural **cocci** (COCK-us, COCK-eye) Spherical form of bacterium.

codominance Expression of both alleles of a gene locus, such that characteristics of both phenotypes appear; neither allele is completely able to mask expression of the other.

coelomate (SEE-la-mate) Type of animal that has a coelom (fluid-filled cavity surrounding the gut).

coenzyme Nonprotein organic molecule that serves as a carrier of atoms or functional groups during a reaction; needed for proper functioning of many enzymes.

cohesion Condition in which molecular bonds resist rupturing when under tension.

commensalism Symbiotic interaction in which benefits are positive for one species and neutral for the other.

community All those populations of different species that occupy a given area at a given time.

competition, interspecific Symbiotic interaction that can have negative effects on both species. Occurs when different species in a community have some requirement or activity in common.

competition, intraspecific Contest for limited resources between individuals of a population.

competitive exclusion Hypothesis based on experiments indicating that when two species compete intensely in the same resource category, one will be excluded from it because of the more effective competitive ability of the other.

complement About fifteen different proteins, circulating in blood, that amplify a local inflammatory response.

concentration gradient For a given substance, a greater concentration of its molecules in one region of a system than in another. A concentration difference between extracellular fluid and cytoplasm is an example.

condensation Covalent linkage of small molecules in an enzyme-mediated reaction that can also involve formation of water.

conditioning Form of learning in which a behavioral response becomes associated (by means of a reinforcing stimulus) with a new stimulus that was not previously associated with the response.

conjugation In some bacteria, transfer of DNA between two different mating strains that have made cell-to-cell contact, the outcome being genetic recombination.

consumers Mostly animals and predatory protistans; both heterotrophs (cannot build complex organic molecules from inorganic matter and obtain them by ingesting other organisms).

continuous variation Small degrees of phenotypic variation that occur over a more or less continuous range in a population.

contractile vacuole In some protistans, a membranous chamber that takes up excess water in the cell body, then contracts, expelling the water through a pore to the outside.

contraction In muscle cells and others, a shortening that alternates with relaxation of certain filaments.

control element Region of DNA whose function appears to be one of governing transcription of structural genes.

convergent evolution Evolution whereby morphologically distinct lineages that were only distantly related end up resembling each other. Usually indicates that they have adapted to the same kind of environment and have similar modes of living.

corpus luteum (CORE-pus LOO-tee-um) An endocrine structure that develops from a ruptured follicle in the ovary. Its progesterone and estrogen secretions help prepare the uterus for implantation.

cortex In general, a rindlike layer; the kidney cortex is an example. In vascular plants, ground tissue that makes up most of the primary plant body; supports plant parts and stores food.

cotyledon (cot-ill-EE-don) "Seed leaf"; often contains stored nutrients that are used in early growth when a seed germinates.

covalent bond A sharing of one or more electrons between atoms or groups of atoms. When electrons are shared equally, it is a nonpolar covalent bond. When they are shared unequally, it is a polar covalent bond.

creatine phosphate Compound that readily gives up phosphate to ADP; important storage form of phosphate that is used in regenerating ATP for muscle contraction.

crista In mitochondria, the inner, deeply folded membrane containing the electron transport chains involved in ATP formation.

crossing over In meiosis, the exchange of corresponding chromatid segments between homologous chromosomes.

cyclic adenosine monophosphate (cyclic AMP) A nucleotide involved in hormone-induced changes in cellular activity.

cyclic photophosphorylation Photosynthetic pathway in which electrons excited by sunlight energy move from a photosystem to a transport chain, then back to the photosystem. Energy released in the transport chain is coupled to ATP formation.

cytochrome (SIGH-toe-krome) Iron-containing protein molecule that acts as an electron carrier in transport chains of photosynthesis and aerobic respiration.

cytokinesis Cytoplasmic division accompanying or following nuclear division.

cytoplasm In a cell, everything but the plasma membrane and the nucleus (or, in bacteria, the nucleoid). Includes internal membranes and other structures that function in metabolism, biosynthesis, and cell movements. The structures are bathed in cytosol, a semifluid substance.

cytoplasmic lattice Intricately organized networks of microtubules and microfilaments by which cells anchor, rearrange, and move internal cell structures.

cytoplasmic streaming In plant cells especially, a constant directional motion of organelles.

cytosine (SIGH-toe-seen) A pyrimidine; one of the nitrogen-containing bases in nucleotides.

cytosol The continuous aqueous phase of cytoplasm, with its dissolved solutes.

DDT Dichlorodiphenyltrichloroethane; a chlorinated hydrocarbon developed as a pesticide but subject to biological concentration in food webs.

decomposers Mostly heterotrophic bacteria and fungi that obtain energy by breaking down organic remains or products of other organisms; their activities help cycle simple compounds back to autotrophs.

deme Local breeding unit of a population.

denaturation Disruption of bonds holding a protein in its three-dimensional form, such that its polypeptide chain(s) undergo partial or complete unfolding.

dendrite Relatively short, often branched, sometimes spiny cell processes where a neuron receives most incoming signals.

denitrification Reduction of nitrate or nitrite to gaseous nitrogen (N_2) and a small amount of nitrous oxide (N_2O) by bacteria that can use anaerobic pathways in poorly aerated soil.

deoxyribonucleic acid (dee-ox-ee-rye-bow-new-CLAY-ik) DNA; double-stranded helically coiled nucleic acid, in which the hydrogen bonds between strands can be unzipped and DNA's chemical messages exposed to agents of protein synthesis or DNA replication. Overall, a stable molecule in which genetic information is stored, yet which is subject to change in some of its structural details.

deuterostomes One of two main evolutionary lines of bilateral animals, as determined by patterns of embryonic development. Includes echinoderms and chordates.

diaphragm (DIE-uh-fram) Sheet of muscle tissue between the thoracic and abdominal cavities that functions in breathing movements. Also, a contraceptive device used to temporarily close off and thus prevent sperm from entering the uterus during sexual intercourse.

dicot (DIE-kot) Short for dicotyledon; class of flowering plants characterized primarily by seeds having embryos with two cotyledons (seed leaves), generally parallel-veined leaves, and floral parts generally arranged in threes or multiples of threes.

differential reproduction In a population, the reproduction of some genotypes more than others in a given time span; indirect outcome of primarily selection pressures, also of mutation, gene flow, and genetic drift.

differentiation Processes by which eukaryotic cells of identical genetic makeup become structurally and functionally different from one another, according to the genetically controlled developmental program of the species.

diffusion Tendency of like molecules to move from their region of greater concentration to a region where they are less concentrated; occurs through random energetic movements of individual molecules, which tend to become dispersed uniformly in a given system.

digestive system In multicelled animals, system for ingesting and preparing food molecules for absorption, and for eliminating residues.

diploid (DIP-loyd) State in which a cell contains two sets of morphologically equivalent chromosomes. Compare *haploid*.

directional selection Mode of natural selection that moves the frequency distribution of alleles in a steady, consistent direction, such that the phenotypic character of a population shifts as a whole.

disaccharide A carbohydrate; two monosaccharides covalently bonded.

disruptive selection Mode of natural selection that increases the frequency of two or more alleles that give rise to extreme forms of a trait, such that intermediate forms are selected against.

divergence A buildup of differences in allele frequencies (genetic differentiation) between reproductively isolated demes or populations of the same species.

diversity, organismic Sum total of variations in form, functioning, and behavior that have accumulated in different lineages. These variations generally are adaptive to prevailing conditions or were once adaptive to conditions that existed in the past.

dominance hierarchy Social ranking of members of a group.

dominant allele In a diploid cell, an allele whose expression masks the expression of its allelic partner at the same gene locus.

dormancy Cessation of growth under physical conditions that could be quite suitable for growth.

ecology Study of the interactions of organisms with one another and with the physical environment.

ecosystem A region of the physical environment, together with all of its organisms that secure, use, and transfer energy and material resources among themselves.

ectoderm In an animal embryo, an outermost cell layer that gives rise to the nervous system and the outer layer of skin.

effector A muscle (or gland) that responds to nerve signals by producing movement (or chemical change) that helps adjust the body to changes in internal and/or external conditions.

electric charge A property of matter that enables ions, atoms, and molecules to attract or repel one another.

electron Negatively charged unit of energy that orbits the nucleus of an atom.

electronegativity In a polar covalent bond, a characteristic of the atom that exerts the greater pull on the shared electrons; it behaves *as if* it carries a slight negative charge.

electron transport system In a cell membrane, several electron carriers and enzymes positioned in an organized array that enhances oxidation-reduction reactions. Such systems function in the release of energy that is used in ATP formation and other reactions.

element Substance composed of a single kind of atom.

embryonic development Those processes by which cells of an embryo become different in position, developmental potential, appearance, composition, and function.

endergonic reaction (en-dur-GONE-ik) Reaction to which energy from an outside source must be added before it proceeds.

endocrine element Cell or gland that produces and/or secretes hormones.

endocrine system System of cells, tissues, and organs functionally linked to the nervous system and whose chemical secretions help control body functioning.

endocytosis Engulfment of large particles or cells through formation of vesicles derived from the plasma membrane.

endoderm In an animal embryo, the innermost cell layer, which differentiates into tissues lining the gut and tissues of digestive glands.

endomembrane system In eukaryotic cells, a membrane system that functions in protein synthesis, modification, and transport. Includes the nuclear envelope, plasma membrane, endoplasmic reticulum, Golgi bodies, lysosomes, and microbodies.

endometrium (en-doh-MEET-ree-um) Mucous membrane of the uterus, consisting of epithelium and uterine glands.

endoplasmic reticulum, rough Membrane system, studded with ribosomes, that functions in the synthesis and transport of proteins.

endoplasmic reticulum, smooth Membrane system having varied functions. Some accept, modify, and transport proteins from rough ER. Some break down glycogen or fats; others take part in lipid production.

endoskeleton In chordates, the internal framework of bone, cartilage, or both.

endosperm Mass of tissue that surrounds embryo in a seed; in monocots, storage site for nutrients needed after seed germination.

endospore In some eubacteria, a resistant structure that surrounds the DNA when nutrient concentrations drop or temperatures become too high. The rest of the cell disintegrates after endospore formation.

energy Capacity to do work.

entropy A measure of how much energy in a system has become so dispersed (usually as evenly distributed, low-quality heat) that it is no longer available to do work.

enzyme A kind of protein that speeds up the rate of a metabolic reaction by lowering the activation energy required for that reaction.

epidermis Outermost tissue layer of a multicelled animal or plant.

episome Small circle of double-stranded DNA present in the cytoplasm of a bacterial cell, in addition to the main circular DNA molecule.

epistasis Interaction whereby one gene pair masks the effect of one or more other pairs.

epithelium Sheet of cells, one or more layers thick, lining internal or external surfaces of the multicelled animal body.

equilibrium, chemical The point at which a chemical reaction runs forward as fast as it runs in reverse, so that there is no further net change in the concentrations of products or reactants.

erythrocyte (eh-RITH-row-site) Red blood cell.

estrus (ESS-truss) Among mammals, the cyclic period of a female's sexual receptivity to the male.

estuary (ESS-chew-airy) A region where fresh water from a river or stream mixes with salt water from the sea.

eukaryote (yoo-CARRY-oht) A cell that has membranous organelles, most notably the nucleus.

evagination In membranes, an outfolding such as a fish gill.

evaporation Behavior of water molecules at the surface of a body of water heated beyond its boiling point; hydrogen bonds between molecules break, energy is released, and some molecules escape into the surrounding air.

evolution Successive changes in allele frequencies in a population, as brought about by such occurrences as mutation, genetic drift, gene flow, and selection pressure.

exergonic reaction (EX-ur-GONE-ik) Chemical reaction in which energy is released from the reactants, so that the products contain less chemical potential energy than the reactants.

exocrine gland Secretory structure whose products travel through ducts that empty at an epithelial surface.

exocytosis Expulsion of material enclosed in a membranous vesicle that fuses with the plasma membrane.

exoskeleton An external skeleton, as in arthropods.

exponential growth (EX-poe-NEN-shul) Increasingly accelerated rate of population growth due to an increasing number of individuals being added to the reproductive base. In the absence of control factors, all populations show exponential growth.

extinction Disappearance of an entire taxon; a major trend in evolution.

extracellular fluid In animals generally, the medium through which substances are continuously exchanged between cells and between body regions. In vertebrates most is interstitial fluid; the rest is blood plasma.

facilitated diffusion Molecular transport process driven by concentration gradients but dependent on proteins that act as channels across the plasma membrane.

fat A molecule composed of glycerol and three fatty acid molecules.

fatty acid Component of fats and waxes; long-chain hydrocarbon with an acid group (—COOH) attached.

feedback inhibition Control mechanism whereby an increase in some substance or activity inhibits the very process leading to (or allowing) the increase.

fermentation Pathway of carbohydrate metabolism that begins with glycolysis and ends with the "spent" electrons being transferred back to one of the carbohydrate breakdown products or intermediates.

fertilization Fusion of sperm nucleus with egg nucleus. In flowering plants, an additional sperm nucleus fuses with two other nuclei present in the ovule, forming a single triploid nucleus that will divide and give rise to endosperm; such fusions are called *double fertilization*.

first law of thermodynamics The total amount of energy in the universe remains constant; more energy cannot be created and existing energy cannot be destroyed. What already exists can only undergo conversion from one form to another.

flagellum, plural **flagella** (fluh-JELL-um) Structure involved in rapid cell movement through the environment. Longer and less numerous than cilia; contains system of microtubules.

fluid mosaic membrane structure Current model of membrane structure, in which diverse proteins and other molecules are suspended in a fluid lipid bilayer. Lipids with short or kinky tails disrupt the straight hydrocarbon-chain packing typical of much of the bilayer, making it somewhat fluid; lipids and proteins together constitute the "mosaic."

follicle In a mammalian ovary, one of the spherical chambers containing an oocyte on the way to becoming a mature egg.

food chain Linear sequence of who eats whom in an ecosystem.

food web Network of crossing, interlinked food chains in an ecosystem, encompassing primary producers, consumers, and decomposers.

fruit In flowering plants, the ripened ovary of one or more carpels, sometimes with accessory structures incorporated.

functional groups Atoms or groups of atoms that can bond covalently to the carbon backbone of organic molecules.

fungus Multicelled organism of a type that generally secretes enzymes that break down organic material in the outside environment; the resulting small molecules are then absorbed by individual cells.

gamete (GAM-eet) Mature haploid cell that functions as a sexual reproductive cell.

gametogenesis (gam-EET-oh-JEN-ih-sis) Formation of gametes.

gametophyte (gam-EET-oh-fight) Haploid, multicelled, gamete-producing phase in a plant life cycle.

ganglion Organized knot of neurons forming an integrative center. Ranges from tiny swellings in multiple body segments of earthworms to the mass called the human brain.

gap junction In animals, a small, open channel that directly links the cytoplasm of adjacent cells and that functions in extremely rapid communication between them.

gastrula Among some animals, the embryonic stage following blastulation; a two- or three-layered structure enclosing a central cavity that has an opening to the outside.

gene A unit of inheritance; a specific DNA region coding either for an RNA molecule or for the translation product of an RNA molecule (a polypeptide). Actual expression of a gene may be influenced by interactions with other genes and by conditions in the internal and external environments.

gene flow Change in allele frequencies due to immigration (new individuals join the population) or emigration (some individuals leave).

gene frequency More precisely, allele frequency: the relative abundance of different alleles carried by the individuals of a population.

gene locus Particular location on a chromosome for a given gene.

gene pair In diploid cells, the two alleles at a given gene locus.

gene pool Sum total of all genotypes in a given population. More accurately, allele pool.

genetic code Basic language of protein synthesis, by which nucleotide triplets in the DNA molecule call for specific amino acids used in protein synthesis.

genetic drift Random fluctuation in allele frequencies over time, due to chance occurrence alone.

genetic engineering Bypassing normal sexual or asexual processes that restrict the transfer of genes between entirely different species.

genetic equilibrium Theoretical baseline for measuring change in allele frequency in a population; the assumption is that stable allele ratios occur if mating is random, and if all individuals

have equal probability of surviving and reproducing.

genetic recombination Presence of new combinations of alleles in a DNA molecule. Can occur through crossing over at meiosis, chromosomal mutation, and gene mutation.

genotype (JEEN-oh-type) Genetic constitution of an individual. Can mean a single gene pair or the sum total of the individual's genes. Compare *phenotype*.

genus, plural **genera** (JEEN-us, JEN-er-uh) A broad category into which similar yet distinct species may be grouped, based on implied descent from a fairly recent common ancestor.

geotropism (GEE-oh-TROPE-izm) Plant response to the earth's gravitational force; also called gravitropism.

germ cells Animal cells that may develop into gametes. Compare *somatic cells*.

gill An outward extension (evagination) of the body surface that greatly increases the area available for oxygen uptake.

glomerulus (glow-MARE-yoo-luss) Cluster of capillaries in Bowman's capsule of the kidney.

glucagon Animal hormone secreted by pancreatic cells and essential in breakdown of glycogen (a polysaccharide) to glucose subunits.

glycerol (GLISS-er-ohl) Three-carbon molecule with three hydroxyl groups attached; combines with fatty acids to form fat or oil.

glycogen In animals, a starch that is a main food reserve; can be readily broken down into glucose subunits.

glycolysis (gly-CALL-ih-sis) In carbohydrate metabolism, the initial breaking apart of sugar molecules such as glucose, with the release of energy. Glycolysis may proceed under aerobic as well as anaerobic conditions; but it does not require oxygen to do so.

Golgi body (GOAL-jee) Stacked membrane system in which proteins exported from the ER become modified and enclosed in secretory or lysosomal vesicles pinched off from the Golgi membranes.

gonad (GO-nad) Reproductive organ in which gametes are produced.

graded potential Change in the membrane potential of a neuron by means of a small, local current flow across the membrane in response to incoming signals. Acting together, many graded potentials can cause a dramatic reversal in the polarity of charge (an action potential).

granum, plural **grana** In chloroplasts, stacked membrane system where sunlight energy is actually trapped and where ATP is formed.

green revolution Term for attempts to improve crop production in developing countries by creating high-yield crop varieties, and by encouraging use of modern agricultural practices, fertilizers, and equipment.

ground meristem Embryonic tissue zone, formed from apical meristem, that produces most of the plant body (excluding surface tissue layers and vascular tissues).

gymnosperm Plant in which seeds are carried on reproductive structures, without protective tissue layers. Conifers such as pines are examples.

habitat Place where an individual or population lives; its "address." Not a geographic range but a "place" character, such as a vegetation zone.

haploid (HAP-loyd) State in which a nucleus contains half the number of chromosomes characteristic of its species. For instance, meiosis reduces a diploid nucleus (with two chromosome sets) to the haploid state (one chromosome set).

Hardy-Weinberg rule If all individuals in a population have an equal chance of surviving and reproducing, then the frequency of each allele in the population should remain constant from generation to generation.

heart Muscular organ that pumps circulating blood through the animal body.

hemoglobin (HEEM-oh-glow-bin) Iron-containing protein that gives red blood cells their color; functions in oxygen transport.

hemorrhage Bulk flow of blood from damaged vessels.

herbivore Plant-eating animal.

heterospory In plants, production of spores of different types, which give rise to male or female gametophytes.

heterotrophs (HET-er-oh-trofes) Organisms that obtain carbon and all metabolic energy from organic molecules that have already been assembled by autotrophs. Include animals, fungi, many protistans, and most bacteria.

heterozygote Individual having nonidentical alleles at a given gene locus.

histone One of a class of structural proteins complexed with DNA in the eukaryotic chromosome.

homeostasis (HOE-me-oh-STAY-sis) For cells and multicelled organisms, maintaining internal conditions within some tolerable range throughout the life cycle even when conditions change.

homeostasis, dynamic Adjustments in the living state that shift the organism's form and behavior over time, as a function of the genetically prescribed developmental program of the species.

home range Area occupied over long periods by one group or individual animal but not aggressively defended against others of the species. Compare *territory*.

homing behavior An ability to return to part of the environment that serves as a home base after moving (or being moved) some distance away from it.

hominid Any primate in the human family. *Homo sapiens* is the only living representative.

hominoid Ape or human.

homologous chromosome In a eukaryotic nucleus, one of a pair of morphologically equivalent chromosomes. Sex chromosomes, which differ morphologically in males and females, also function as homologues. (Typically the two chromosomes of a homologous pair are derived from two different parents, but exceptions do occur, as in the case of self-fertilizing plants.)

homologous structure Resemblance in some body part between different lineages that can be traced to the same evolutionary beginning from a common ancestor.

homospory In some plants, production of only one type of spore rather than differentiated types. Compare *heterospory*.

homozygote Individual having two identical alleles at a given gene locus.

hormone Endocrine cell product, transported by body fluids, that triggers a specific cellular reaction in target tissues and organs some distance away.

hydrogen bond Type of chemical bond in which an electronegative atom weakly attracts a hydrogen atom that is covalently bonded to a different atom.

hydrolysis (high-DRAWL-ih-sis) Enzyme-mediated cleavage of a molecule into two or more parts by reaction with water.

hydrophilic Having an attraction for (able to hydrogen-bond with) water molecules; refers to a polar substance that readily dissolves in water.

hydrophobic Repelled by water molecules; refers to a nonpolar substance that does not readily dissolve in water.

hypha, plural **hyphae** Branched, tubelike filament; structural component of the meshlike, vegetative body of true fungi.

hypothalamus In vertebrates, forebrain region that, together with the pituitary gland, serves as the neuroendocrine control center.

immune system, vertebrate Phagocytic white blood cells, lymphocytes, and plasma cells and their products that take part in the body's defense against foreign configurations (for example, bacteria, viruses, or body cells that are mutant, damaged, or cancerous).

independent assortment Mendelian principle (later modified) that segregation of alleles for a given trait into gametes is independent of segregation of alleles for other traits. Independent assortment can occur from random alignment of homologous pairs of chromosomes at the spindle equator during meiosis. (But linkage groups on a given chromosome, and crossing over, may also influence allele segregation.)

inflammation Nonspecific defense response involving mobilization of phagocytic cells and complement; a series of homeostatic events that restore damaged tissues and intercellular conditions.

innate behavior Instinctive, or unlearned, response to an environmental stimulus.

innate releasing mechanisms Units of neurons that trigger unlearned responses to environmental stimuli.

integration, neural Moment-by-moment summation of all excitatory and inhibitory synapses acting on a neuron; occurs at each level of synapsing in a nervous system.

interneuron Main component of integrating centers such as the brain and spinal cord; integrates incoming information and influences other neurons in turn.

interphase Time interval (variable among species) in which a cell grows and maintains itself but does not divide. DNA is replicated at some point during interphase, prior to nuclear division.

interstitial fluid In vertebrates, that portion of the extracellular fluid that occupies spaces between cells and tissues. (The remaining portion is blood plasma.)

ion, negatively charged An atom (or group of atoms) that has gained one or more electrons and thereby has a net negative charge.

ion, positively charged An atom (or group of atoms) that has lost one or more electrons and thereby has a net positive charge.

ionic bond Mutual attraction between ions of opposite charge.

isogamy (EYE-soh-gam-ee) In some sexual reproductive modes, gametes that are all indentical (no differentiation into sperm and eggs).

isolating mechanism Some aspect of structure, functioning, or behavior that may prevent interbreeding between populations that are undergoing or have undergone speciation.

isotope Individual atom that contains the same number of protons as other atoms of a given element, but that has a different number of neutrons; hence isotopes of that element have different mass numbers.

key character Particular trait that forms the basis of major evolutionary developments in form, behavior, or both. An example is the feather, which developed in at least one dinosaur lineage and which led to bird flight.

kidney Organ of salt and water regulation; its nephron/capillary units are concerned with filtration of water and other noncellular components of blood, selective reabsorption of solutes and most of the water, and tubular secretion (through active transport) of certain substances from the capillaries.

kinetic energy Energy associated with motion.

Krebs cycle Stage of aerobic respiration in which pyruvate fragments are completely broken down into carbon dioxide; molecules reduced in the process can be used in forming energy carriers.

larva, plural **larvae** Immature form of an animal that undergoes metamorphosis to the adult form.

larynx Tube that leads to the lungs. Contains vocal cords, the production site of sound waves used in speech.

learning Modification of behavior, arising from specific experiences during the lifetime of an animal.

leucoplast In some plant cells, colorless plastid in which starch grains and other substances may be stored.

life cycle For any species, the genetically programmed sequence of events by which individuals are produced, grow, develop, and themselves reproduce.

light-dependent reactions First stage of photosynthesis, concerned with harnessing sunlight and using it as an energy source of ATP and/or NADPH synthesis.

light-independent reactions A two-stage photosynthetic process. First, carbon dioxide is combined with a sugar phosphate (RuBP), then the carbon atoms are locked into intermediate compounds. Second, ATP and NADPH are used in converting those compounds to food molecules, and the RuBP is replaced.

lineage Single line of descent.

linkage The group of genes physically located on the same chromosome. "Linkage mapping" means determining the positions of genes relative to one another on a given chromosome.

lipid Hydrophobic organic molecule to which at least some hydrophilic groups are attached; a lipid thus has both water-insoluble and water-soluble parts. Examples are fats, oils, waxes, and phospholipids.

liposome Microscopic, closed bag of water formed under experimental conditions from simple lipids.

lymphocyte Phagocytic white blood cell that carries out specific immune responses by recognizing and disposing of foreign agents or substances in a highly discriminatory way.

lymphoid organs Those organs (and some tissue regions) that function as cell production centers and as sites for some defense responses; bone marrow, thymus, lymph nodes, spleen, appendix, tonsils, adenoids, and patches of small intestine.

lymph vascular system Network of vessels that supplements the blood circulation system; reclaims water that has entered interstitial regions from the bloodstream; also transports fats from small intestine to bloodstream. Fluid in its vessels is called *lymph*.

lysosome Membrane-bound organelle containing hydrolytic enzymes that can dispose of malfunctioning or worn-out cell parts and foreign particles.

macroevolution Large-scale rates, trends, and patterns of change above the species level.

mantle In mollusks, a body wall surrounding internal parts; secretes substances that form the molluscan shell.

mass number Total number of protons and neutrons in the nucleus of atoms of a given element.

maternal messages Messenger RNA that becomes regionally positioned in the cytoplasm of maturing eggs and that becomes activated upon fertilization; their messages direct the primary events of embryonic development.

mechanoreceptor Sensory cell or cell part that detects mechanical energy associated with changes in pressure, position, or acceleration.

medusa (meh-DOO-sah) Free-swimming, bell-shaped stage in cnidarian life cycles.

megaspore In seed plants, a spore that develops into a female gametophyte.

meiosis (my-OH-sis) Two-stage nuclear division process in which the number of chromosome sets in each daughter nucleus is haploid (half of what it was in the parent nucleus). Basis of gamete and meiospore formation. Compare *mitosis.*

meiospore Haploid cell that divides by mitosis

and differentiates into multicelled haploid body (gametophyte).

menopause End of the period of a human female's reproductive potential.

menstrual cycle The cyclic reproductive capacity of female humans and other primates.

menstruation Periodic sloughing of the blood-enriched lining of the uterus when pregnancy does not occur.

meristems Embryonic tissue zones giving rise to cells that then divide, enlarge, and differentiate into all other tissues of land plants.

mesoderm In some animal embryos, a tissue layer between ectoderm and endoderm; gives rise to tissues of muscles, skeleton, circulatory system, inner layer of skin, kidney, and reproductive tract.

mesosome In some bacteria, infoldings of the plasma membrane around replicated DNA prior to cell division.

metabolic pathway In a cell, breakdown or synthesis reactions that occur in sequential, stepwise fashion.

metabolic reaction Some form of internal energy change in a cell.

metabolism All activities by which organisms extract and transform energy from their environment, and use it in manipulating materials in ways that assure maintenance, growth, and reproduction.

metamorphosis (met-uh-more-FOE-sis) In the development of eukaryotes, genetically programmed change in form of an organ or structure; also, drastic changes of a larval stage of an animal into the adult form.

metaphase In mitosis, stage when microtubules increase in number and become organized into mitotic spindle, which is responsible for separating sister chromatids from each other.

metazoan Multicelled animal.

microfilament Extremely fine cell structure composed of actin and myosin; involved in cell shape, motion, and growth.

microspore In seed plants, a spore that develops into a male gametophyte.

microtubular spindle A parallel array of microtubules that helps establish polarity in a dividing nucleus; in many species, also helps move sister chromatids to opposite poles.

microtubule Hollow cylinder of (mostly) tubulin subunits; involved in cell shape, motion, and growth; functional unit of cilia and flagella.

microvillus A slender, cylindrical extension of the animal cell surface that functions in absorption or secretion.

migration A cyclic movement between two distant regions at times of year corresponding to seasonal change.

mimicry Situation in which one species (the mimic) bears deceptive resemblance in color, form, and/or behavior to another species (the model) that enjoys some survival advantage.

mitochondrion, plural mitochondria (MY-toe-KON-dree-on) Eukaryotic organelle in which the main energy-extracting pathways of aerobic respiration occur.

mitosis (my-TOE-sis) Nuclear division in which the number of chromosome sets is maintained from one cell generation to the next. Basis of reproduction of single-celled eukaryotes; basis of physical growth (through cell divisions) in multicelled eukaryotes.

molecule Two or more identical or different kinds of atoms linked by chemical bonds.

monoclonal antibodies Clones of hybrid B-cells used to produce large amounts of pure antibodies, which are used in passive immunization and medical research.

monocot Short for monocotyledon; a flowering plant in which seeds have only one cotyledon, whose floral parts generally occur in threes (or multiples of threes), and whose leaves typically are parallel-veined. Compare *dicot.*

monosaccharide A simple sugar molecule that typically has a skeleton of five, six, or seven carbon atoms.

morphogenesis (MORE-foe-GEN-ih-sis) Process by which groups of similar cells become spatially coordinated, producing structures of genetically programmed shapes and patterns.

motor neuron Type of neuron that carries action potentials to branched axonal endings that synapse with cells of muscles or glands; leads out from the central nervous system.

motor unit A motor neuron and all the muscle fibers under its control.

multiple allele system In a given population, all the possible alternatives for a given gene locus.

muscle fiber Contractile cell of skeletal, smooth, or cardiac muscle tissue.

mutation A heritable change in the kind, structure, sequence, or number of the component parts of a DNA molecule.

mutualism Type of symbiotic relationship in which positive benefits exist and are important to the survival of both species; obligatory interaction.

mycelium, plural mycelia (my-SEE-lee-um) In true fungi, a matlike, often underground structure formed from hyphae.

mycoplasma (MY-coe-PLAZ-mah) One of the smallest bacteria known; typically a disease agent lacking a cell wall and living in the moist tissues of animals.

myofibril Fine, threadlike structure composed of actin and myosin filaments; the component of muscle fibers.

NAD+ Nicotinamide adenine dinucleotide, oxidized form.

NADH Nicotinamide adenine dinucleotide, reduced form.

NADP+ Nicotinamide adenine dinucleotide phosphate, oxidized form.

NADPH Nicotinamide adenine dinucleotide phosphate, reduced form.

natural selection Differential reproduction; result of selective agents in environment acting on phenotypes in ways that lead to differential survival and reproduction of genotypes. Traits that are most adaptive in a given environment become increasingly represented among individuals in a population, for their bearers (which in some way have a better chance of surviving and reproducing) contribute proportionally more offspring to the next generation.

negative feedback mechanism Homeostatic control whereby an increase in some substance or activity sooner or later inhibits the very processes leading to (or allowing) the increase.

nematocyst Stinging structure of a specialized cell type (cnidocyte) that occurs in cnidarian epidermis.

nephridium, plural **nephridia** (neh-FRID-ee-um) In invertebrates such as earthworms, organ for excreting fluids and metabolic wastes.

nephron In the kidney, one of numerous functional units involved in filtration of water and other noncellular components of blood; in selective reabsorption; and in tubular secretion.

nerve In peripheral nervous system, a bundle of axons held together by connective tissue. Such nerves and their branchings transmit signals to and from distinct body regions.

nerve impulse Action potential.

nerve net In some invertebrates, neurons dispersed through epithelium yet functionally linked to sensory cells, each other, and muscle tissue. Permits diffuse response to stimuli; unlike nervous system, has little orientation to information flow (the neurons can carry signals in either direction).

nervous system Constellations of neurons oriented relative to one another in precise message-conducting and information-processing pathways.

neuroglia (NUR-oh-GLEE-uh) Cells intimately associated with neurons; in vertebrates they represent at least half of the volume of the nervous system.

neuromuscular junction Zone where axons of motor neurons branch into terminal endings that lie next to a muscle cell membrane. Transmitter substances released from the neurons can bring the muscle cell membrane to threshold, the outcome being action potentials that trigger contraction.

neuron In most animals, a cell that responds to specific chemical, electrical, or mechanical stimuli in three ways: it can *integrate* different incoming signals, *propagate* excitation as a pulse of information along its plasma membrane, and *transmit* information about change to other neurons, muscles, or glands.

neurosecretory hormone Secretory product of certain nerve cells whose messages travel, by way of interstitial fluid or the bloodstream, to nonadjacent cells.

neutron Subatomic particle of about the same size and mass as a proton but having no electric charge.

niche, fundamental (nitch) The *full* range of abiotic and biotic conditions under which a species can live and reproduce.

niche, realized The *actual* range of conditions under which a species exists, determined in large part by interactions with other species.

nicotinamide adenine dinucleotide Nucleotide that functions as an electron acceptor and transporter in oxidation-reduction reactions.

nicotinamide adenine dinucleotide phosphate Nucleotide that functions as an electron acceptor and transporter in several metabolic pathways, most notably photosynthesis.

nitrification Process by which certain soil bacteria strip ammonia or ammonium of electrons, and nitrite (NO_2^-) is released as a reaction product. Other soil bacteria then use nitrate for energy metabolism, yielding nitrate (NO_3^-).

nitrogen fixation Among some bacteria, assimilation of gaseous nitrogen (N_2) from the air; through reduction reactions, electrons (and associated H^+) become attached to the nitrogen, thereby forming ammonia (NH_3) or ammonium (NH_4^+).

noncyclic photophosphorylation Photosynthetic pathway in which new electrons derived from water molecules flow through two photosystems and two transport chains, the result being formation of ATP and NADPH.

nonidentical twins Individuals resulting from fertilization of two different eggs by two different sperm.

notochord Somewhat flexible rod of cartilage; probable forerunner to the chordate endoskeleton. During embryonic development of complex vertebrates, it is replaced by a vertebral column.

nuclear envelope Double membrane at the surface of a eukaryotic nucleus.

nucleic acid (new-CLAY-ik) Long-chain, single- or double-stranded nucleotide; DNA and RNA are examples.

nucleoid In bacterial cells, the irregularly shaped region in which DNA is concentrated.

nucleolus Within the nucleus of a nondividing cell, a mass of proteins, RNA, and other material used in ribosome synthesis.

nucleoplasm Semifluid substance enclosed by the nuclear envelope.

nucleoprotein A compound of nucleic acids and proteins. Eukaryotic chromosomes are one example.

nucleotide (NEW-klee-oh-tide) Molecule containing at least a five-carbon sugar (ribose), a nitrogen-containing base (either purine or pyrimidine), and a phosphate group. Structural unit of adenosine phosphates, nucleotide coenzymes, and nucleic acids.

nucleus In atoms, the central core of one or more positively charged protons and (in all but hydrogen) electrically neutral neutrons. In eukaryotic cells, the membranous organelle that houses the DNA.

omnivore A species able to feed on organisms at different trophic levels.

oogamy (OO-OH-gam-ee) In some sexual reproductive modes, gametes that differ in size and

motility. One gamete typically is small and motile (a sperm, for example); the other is larger and nonmotile (the egg).

oogenesis (OO-oh-JEN-uh-sis) Formation of female gamete, from a diploid reproductive cell (oogonium) to a mature haploid ovum.

operon A set of control elements and structural genes operating as a unit.

organ Body unit composed of one or more types of tissues interacting as a structural, functional unit.

organelle In cytoplasm, a structure whose molecular organization enhances specific cell activities. Typically membrane-bound, as in chloroplasts and mitochondria.

osmosis (OSS-MOE-sis) Movement of water molecules across a differentially permeable membrane in response to a concentration and/or pressure gradient.

ovary The primary female reproductive organ in which oogenesis occurs.

oviduct Passageway through which ova travel from the ovary to the uterus.

ovule In seed-bearing plants, the structure destined to become the seed; includes the female gametophyte (with egg cell) and tissue-layer covering.

oxidation The loss of one or more electrons from an atom or molecule.

oxidation-reduction reaction An electron transfer from one atom or molecule to another. Often hydrogen is also transferred along with the electron or electrons.

oxidative phosphorylation Use of electron energy being released during oxidation reactions to phosphorylate (tack a phosphate group onto) a molecule such as ADP (which yields energy-rich ATP).

parallel evolution Evolution, in similar ways and at about the same rate, of independent lineages that resemble each other; the outcome is that the resemblance persists.

parasite Belonging to a species that obtains nourishment from living organisms but typically does not kill the host outright.

parasitism Extreme form of symbiosis in which the interaction is positive for one species and negative for the other; often viewed as a weak form of predation.

parasitoid Insect larva that kills its host by completely consuming the hosts's soft tissue before the insect metamorphoses into an adult.

parasympathetic nerves Nerves that operate antagonistically with sympathetic nerves; generally dominate internal events when environmental conditions permit normal body functioning.

passive transport Movement of a substance across a cell membrane without any direct energy outlay by the cell. Diffusion is an example.

pathogen (PATH-oh-jen) Disease-causing organism.

penis Male accessory reproductive organ from which sperm are expelled into the female reproductive tract during sexual intercourse.

peptidoglycan Repeating structure of sugars and amino acids found only in cell walls of eubacteria.

perennial A plant that lives year after year.

pericyle In roots of gymnosperms and flowering plants, ground tissue (between phloem and endodermis) that shows meristematic activity during secondary growth. Its cells become aligned with the vascular cambium and help form a continuous ring of active cambium.

periderm In stems and roots of gymnosperms and flowering plants, a protective covering that replaces epidermis during secondary growth.

peripheral nervous system (per-IF-ur-uhl) Various nerve processes that connect the spinal cord and brain with receptors, muscles, and glands.

peristalsis (pare-ih-STALL-sis) An alternating progression of contracting and relaxing muscle movements along the length of a tubelike organ (such as the esophagus).

pH Whole number referring to the number of hydrogen ions present in a liter of a given fluid.

phagocytosis "Cell-eating"; the engulfment of solid particles or cells as by amoebas and certain white blood cells.

pharynx Muscular tube that is the gateway to the digestive tract and to the windpipe (trachea).

phenotype (FEE-no-type) Observable trait or traits of an individual; arises from interactions between genes, and between genes and the environment.

pheromone (FARE-oh-moan) A chemical, secreted by exocrine glands, whose target receptor cells reside in other organisms of the same species. Pheromones may trigger behavioral changes; some are sex attractants; trail markers, or alarm signals.

phloem (FLOW-um) In vascular plants, a tissue that transports food through the plant body; some of its components also function in storage and structural support.

phospholipid Lipid molecule composed of glycerol, fatty acids, a phosphorus-containing compound, and (usually) a nitrogen-containing base.

phosphorylation (FOSS-for-ih-LAY-shun) Addition of one or more phosphate groups to a molecule.

photolysis First step in noncyclic photophosphorylation, when water is split into oxygen, hydrogen ions, and their associated electrons; photon energy indirectly drives the reaction.

photoreceptor Light-sensitive sensory cell.

photosynthesis The trapping of solar energy and its conversion to chemical energy, which is used in manufacturing food molecules from carbon dioxide and water.

photosynthetic autotrophs All plants, some protistans, and a few bacteria able to obtain energy from sunlight. They use the energy in building complex organic molecules from environmentally derived carbon dioxide and other simple inorganic substances.

photosystem Functional light-trapping unit in photosynthetic membranes; contains pigment molecules and enzymes.

phototropism Movement or growth curvature toward light.

phyletic evolution Change *within* an established lineage.

phytochrome Light-sensitive pigment molecule whose activation and inactivation trigger hormone activities governing leaf expansion, stem branching, stem length, and, in many plants, seed germination and flowering.

phytoplankton Community of photosynthetic microorganisms in freshwater or saltwater environments.

pinocytosis (PIN-oh-sigh-TOE-sis) "Cell-drinking"; engulfment of liquid droplets.

placenta (play-SEN-tuh) In the uterus, an organ made of extensions of the chorion and the endometrium. Through this composite of embryonic and maternal tissues and vessels, nutrients reach the embryo and wastes are carried away.

plant Generally, multicelled organism able to build its own food molecules through photosynthesis.

plasma Liquid component of blood.

plasma membrane Outermost membrane of a cell. Its surface has molecular regions that detect changes in external conditions. Spanning the membrane are passageways through which substances move inward and outward in controlled ways.

plasmid In some bacteria, a small circle of DNA in addition to the main DNA molecule.

plasmodesma In a multicelled plant, a junction between the linked walls of adjacent cells through which nutrients and other substances are transported.

plastid In some plant cells, a storage organelle; some plastids also function in photosynthesis.

platelet Component of blood that functions in clotting.

pleiotropism Multiple phenotypic effect of a single gene; the action of the gene affects many developmental or maintenance activities.

pollen grain In gymnosperms and flowering plants, the immature male gametophyte (gamete-producing body).

pollination The transfer of pollen grains to the female gametophyte of a plant.

pollutant Any substance with which an ecosystem has had no prior evolutionary experience, in terms of kinds or amounts, and that can accumulate to disruptive or harmful levels. Can be naturally occurring or synthetic.

polymer A molecule composed of from three to millions of subunits of relatively low molecular weight that may or may not be identical.

polymorphism In a population, the persistence of two or more forms of a trait, at a frequency that is greater than can be accounted for by newly arising mutations alone.

polyp (POH-lip) Vase-shaped, sedentary stage of cnidarian life cycles.

polypeptide Chain of amino acids linked by condensation reactions.

polyploid Having three or more sets of chromosomes in a cell.

polyribosome During protein synthesis, a clustering of ribosomes engaged in translation of a messenger RNA molecule.

polysaccharide Three or more simple sugar molecules bonded together covalently.

population Group of individuals of the same species occupying a given area at a given time.

population growth The difference between the birth rate and death rate, plus any new members added through immigration or lost through emigration.

potential energy Energy in a potentially usable form that is not, for the moment, being used.

predator Free-living organism that captures and ingests other living organisms as a means of obtaining nutrients.

primary growth Following seed germination, the cell divisions, elongation, and differentiation that produce the primary plant body.

primary production, gross For a given ecosystem, the total amount of solar energy converted to organic compounds during photosynthesis.

primary production, net For a given ecosystem, the energy remaining after aerobic respiration by autotrophs and stored over time as organic matter (biomass).

primary productivity The rate at which energy becomes stored in organic compounds through photosynthesis.

procambium In vascular plants, embryonic tissue (meristem) that gives rise to vascular tissue.

producer An autotrophic organism; able to build its own complex organic molecules from simple inorganic substances in the environment.

prokaryote (pro-CARRY-oht) Single-celled organism that has no membrane-bound nucleus or other internal organelles; all bacteria are prokaryotes.

prokaryotic fission Form of bacterial cell reproduction; membrane growth divides the replicated DNA and the cytoplasm into daughter cells.

prophase In mitosis, the stage when chromatin coils into compact chromosome bodies.

protein Molecule composed of one or more chains of amino acids (polypeptide chains).

protein primary structure The sequence of amino acids that forms a polypeptide chain.

protistan Single-celled eukaryote.

protocooperation Symbiotic relationship in which two species benefit, although the interaction is not essential (nonobligatory).

proton Positively charged unit of energy that is found in the atomic nucleus.

protostomes One of two main evolutionary lines of bilateral animals, as determined by patterns of embryonic development. Includes mollusks, annelids, and arthropods.

pseudocoelomate Type of animal that has a body cavity in which internal organs are freely suspended.

pseudopod (soo-doe-pod) "False foot"; a nonpermanent cytoplasmic extension of the cell body.

pulmonary circulation Pathways of blood flow leading to and from the lungs.

purine Nucleotide base having a double ring structure. Examples are adenine and guanine.

pyrimidine (pih-RIM-ih-deen) Nucleotide base having a single ring structure. Cytosine and thymine are examples.

pyruvate (PIE-roo-vate) Three-carbon compound produced during glycolysis.

quantum evolution Idea that most higher taxa originate by the rapid crossing of adaptive thresholds, not by gradual change within an established lineage.

radial symmetry General arrangement of body parts in a regular pattern about a central axis, much like spokes of a bike wheel.

radicle In plant seeds, the embryonic root; typically, longitudinal growth of its cells gives rise to a slender primary root.

ray system Primarily parenchyma cells that act as conduits and food storage centers in wood.

receptor Sensory cell or cell part that may be activated by a specific stimulus in the internal or external environment.

recessive allele In the heterozygous state, an allele whose expression is fully or partially masked by expression of its partner; recessive alleles can be fully expressed in the homozygous state.

recombinant DNA Whole molecules or fragments that incorporate parts of different parent DNA molecules.

reduction The gaining of one or more electrons by an atom or molecule.

reflex arc A nerve pathway that coordinates a fixed (stereotyped) sequence of stimulus-induced events, including the response to the stimulus.

releaser A specific environmental stimulus that triggers an innate releasing mechanism, which leads to an instinctive (unlearned) response.

reproduction, asexual Production of new individuals by any process that does not involve gametes.

reproduction, sexual Process of reproduction that begins with meiosis, proceeds through gamete formation, and ends at fertilization.

reproductive isolating mechanism Any aspect of structure, functioning, or behavior that prevents interbreeding.

respiration In most animals, the overall exchange of oxygen from the environment and carbon dioxide wastes from cells by way of circulating blood. Compare *aerobic respiration.*

resting membrane potential Steady voltage difference that exists across the plasma membrane of a neuron at rest (one not being stimulated).

rhizoid Long, single cell or filament that anchors a gametophyte to the ground.

ribonucleic acid (RYE-bow-new-CLAY-ik) RNA; a category of nucleotides used in translating the genetic message of DNA into actual protein structure.

ribosome In both prokaryotic and eukaryotic cells, a structure made of RNA and proteins and the site of protein synthesis.

salt Compound that forms by the reaction between an acid and a base; usually dissociates into positive and negative ions in water.

saprobe Heterotroph that obtains nutrients from nonliving organic matter.

sarcolemma The plasma membrane surrounding a muscle fiber.

sarcomere Fundamental unit of contraction in skeletal muscle; repeating bands of actin and myosin that appear between two Z-lines.

sarcoplasmic reticulum A continuous system of membrane-bound chambers that surrounds myofibrils within a muscle fiber and that stores calcium ions necessary for the mechanism of muscle contraction.

second law of thermodynamics When left to itself, any system along with its surroundings undergoes energy conversions, spontaneously, to less organized forms. When that happens, some energy gets randomly dispersed in a form (often evenly distributed, low-grade heat) that is not as readily available to do work.

secondary growth In vascular plants, an increase in stem and root diameter, made possible by cambial activity that gives rise to secondary xylem and phloem.

seed In gymnosperms and flowering plants, a fully mature ovule (contains the plant embryo) with tissue layers (integuments) forming the seed coat.

segmentation In some animals such as earthworms, repeats of similar body units.

segregation, allelic Mendelian principle that two units of heredity (alleles) exist for a trait, and that during gamete formation, the two units of each pair are separated from each other and end up in different gametes.

semen Sperm-bearing fluid expelled from the penis during male orgasm.

semiconservative replication Manner in which a DNA molecule is reproduced; formation of a complementary strand on each of the unzipping strands of a DNA double helix, the outcome being two "half-old, half-new" molecules.

senescence Sum total of processes leading to death of a plant or any of its organs; cause appears to be built into the life cycle of the species.

sensory neuron Type of neuron that carries signals about changing conditions into integrating centers (such as the central nervous system).

sex chromosomes In most animals and some plants, chromosomes that differ in number or kind between males and females. All other chromosomes are called autosomes.

sex-linked gene One located only on a female X chromosome; has no allelic partner on the male Y chromosome.

sieve element Food-conducting cell in phloem.

sodium-potassium pump Cotransport mechanism built into nerve cell membrane. Actively pumps sodium and potassium ions across the plasma membrane, thereby helping to maintain the ion distributions and voltage difference characteristic of the resting membrane.

solute (SOL-yoot) A substance dissolved in some solution. (A dissolved substance is one that has dissociated into charged parts, and that has spheres of hydration around those parts which keep them from interacting.)

solvent Fluid in which one or more substances is dissolved.

somatic cells Cells that make up body tissues.

somatic nervous system Motor neurons that convey signals from the brain and spinal cord to skeletal muscles. Some of its communication lines are under conscious control in complex vertebrates.

species One or more populations whose members interbreed under natural conditions and produce fertile offspring, and who are reproductively isolated from other such groups.

sperm Mature male gamete.

spermatogenesis (sperm-AT-oh-JEN-ih-sis) Formation of a mature sperm from a diploid reproductive cell (spermatogonium).

sphere of hydration Through positive or negative interactions, a clustering of water molecules around a substance that has dissociated into charged parts in solution.

sphincter Ring of muscle that serves as a gate in some tubelike system (such as the one between stomach and small intestine).

sporangium, plural **sporangia** (spore-AN-gee-um) In plants, hollow single-celled or multicelled structure in which spores are produced.

spore In plants, a reproductive cell that develops into a haploid gametophyte. In fungi, a reproductive cell that develops into a haploid mycelium.

sporophyte Diploid, spore-producing stage of plant life cycles.

sporozoite Infective, sporelike stage of sporozoan life cycles.

stabilizing selection Mode of natural selection that decreases the frequency of alleles that give rise to extreme forms of a trait, such that intermediate forms already well adapted to prevailing conditions are favored.

stamen In flowering plants, the male reproductive organ; commonly consists of pollen-bearing structures (anthers) positioned on single stalks (filaments).

steroid Lipid consisting of multiple carbon ring structure to which different atoms may be attached.

stimulus Any detected change in an organism's external environment or within its body. Every stimulus is some form of energy change (for example, a change in heat, sound wave, chemical, or light energy).

stoma, plural **stomata** Paired guard cell that serves as a gate across leaf epidermis; controls movement of carbon dioxide into the leaf.

stretch reflex Automatic contraction of a muscle whenever conditions cause an increase in its length.

stroma In chloroplasts, the semifluid matrix, surrounding the grana, where complex organic molecules are assembled.

structural gene Gene that codes for the structure of a protein.

substrate Molecule or molecules of a reactant on which an enzyme acts.

succession, primary Gradual, sequential replacement of communities, beginning with pioneer species, until a stable climax stage is reached (then, the array of species is locked in materials and energy use in ways that allow it to remain relatively stable and self-perpetuating).

succession, secondary Reestablishment of a climax community that has been disrupted in whole or in part.

surface-to-volume ratio In cells, a physical constraint on increased size: as the cell's linear dimensions grow, its surface area does not increase at the same rate as its volume (hence each unit of plasma membrane would be called upon to serve increasing amounts of cytoplasm).

symbiosis Between two (or more) species, recurring interaction that can be positive, negative, or neutral for one or both participants. Protocooperation, mutualism, commensalism, predation, parasitism, and interspecific competition are forms of symbiosis.

sympathetic nerves Nerves that usually operate antagonistically with parasympathetic nerves; in times of stress, danger, excitement, and heightened awareness, they dominate internal events and mobilize the whole body for rapid response to change.

sympatric speciation Outcome when two or more populations occupying the same distribution range have undergone reproductive isolation before genetic differentiation has transformed them into separate species.

synapse Specialized junction where an axon (or some other part) of one neuron terminates next to another neuron. At an *excitatory* synapse, a transmitter substance released from the first neuron produces changes in the receiving cell that bring its membrane closer to threshold. At an *inhibitory* synapse, a transmitter substance released from the first neuron produces changes in the receiving cell that drive membrane potential away from threshold.

synapsis In meiosis, the point-by-point alignment of the two sister chromatids of one chromosome with the two sister chromatids of its homologue.

systemic circulation Pathways of blood flow leading to and from all body parts except the lungs.

telophase Final stage of mitosis, during which the separated chromosomes uncoil and become enclosed within newly forming daughter nuclei.

territory Among animal species, an area defined not by any particular behavior (such as defense) but by the degree to which it is used exclusively by the occupants.

testis, plural **testes** Male gonad; reproductive organ in which male gametes and sex hormones are produced.

threshold value In neurons, the minimum change in membrane potential necessary to produce an action potential.

thymine Nitrogen-containing base found in some nucleotides.

tight junction In epithelium, a type of cell-to-cell junction that bars the free passage of molecules across the tissue layer.

tissue One or more types of cells interacting as a structural, functional unit.

trachea, plural **tracheae** A tube for breathing; in land vertebrates, the windpipe that carries air between the larynx and bronchi.

tracheid Typically elongated cell, dead at maturity, that passively conducts water and solutes in xylem.

transcription Synthesis of a messenger RNA molecule having a nucleotide sequence that is complementary to the DNA region on which it is assembled.

transduction Following a bacteriophage attack, the transfer of DNA fragments between bacteria. The fragments become packaged in a viral coat, and may undergo recombination with the DNA molecule of the new bacterial host.

transformation Transfer of DNA fragments from experimentally ruptured cells to a bacterial cell, where they may undergo random recombination with the bacterial DNA.

translation Assembly of amino acid subunits into a specific polypeptide chain, directed by a specific sequence of information contained in a messenger RNA molecule.

translocation In vascular plants, the transport of soluble food molecules (mostly sucrose) from one plant organ to another; occurs in sieve tubes of phloem tissue.

transmitter substance Neuron secretion, released in tiny amounts, that triggers change in the membrane potential of an adjacent cell.

transpiration Evaporative water loss from stems and leaves.

trophic level In an ecosystem, all those species that obtain energy primarily from a common source. An example is all the photosynthetic organisms in an estuary; they all obtain energy from the sun.

turgor pressure In general, osmotically induced internal pressure. In plant cells, the pressure applied to cell walls as water is absorbed.

urinary system In mammals, a tubular network of organs concerned with regulating water and solute levels in the body; consists of paired kidneys, paired ureters, a bladder, and a urethra.

urkaryote Proposed bacterial ancestor of eukaryotes, long since vanished.

uterus A chamber in which the developing embryo is contained and nurtured during pregnancy.

vacuole, central In plant cells, a membrane-bound, fluid-filled sac that may take up most of the cell interior; main function is to increase cell size and surface area, thereby enhancing absorption of nutrients from a relatively dilute external environment. In animals, vacuoles serve as storage organelles.

vagina Female accessory reproductive organ that receives sperm from the male penis; forms part of the birth canal, and acts as a channel to the exterior for menstrual flow.

vascular cambium In vascular plants, a lateral meristem that increases stem or root diameter.

vascular tissue In multicelled organisms of many species, internal conducting tissue for fluids and nutrients.

vein Vessel that carries blood back to the heart.

vernalization Cold-temperature stimulation of the flowering process.

vertebra, plural **vertebrae** One of a series of hard bones that form the backbone in most chordates.

vertebrate Animal having a backbone made of bony segments called vertebrae.

vesicle In cytoplasm, a small, membrane-bound sac in which various substances may be transported or stored.

vessel element Typically elongated cell, dead at maturity, that passively conducts water and solutes in xylem.

vestigial structure Body part that no longer has any apparent role in the functioning of an organism.

viroid Infectious nucleic acids that have no protein coat; tiny rods or closed circles of single-stranded RNA.

virus Obligate, intracellular parasite consisting of nucleic acid encased in protein; incapable of metabolism or reproduction without a host cell, hence is often not considered alive.

vision Precise light focusing onto a layer of photoreceptive cells that is dense enough to sample details concerning a given light stimulus, followed by image formation in the brain.

white matter Myelin sheaths that surround axons of neurons in the spinal cord.

wild-type allele In natural populations, the most common allele of a multiple allele system.

xylem (ZEYE-lem) In vascular plants, a tissue that transports water and solutes through the plant body.

zygote (ZEYE-goat) In most multicelled eukaryotes, the first diploid cell formed after fertilization (fusion of nuclei from a male and female gamete).

INDEX

Italicized numbers refer to illustrations and tables.

A band, *369*
Abdominal cavity, *316, 401*
Abiotic assembly of organic compounds, 502, *502, 506*
ABO blood group, 168–169, *169,* 177
Abortion, 242, 244, 474, 476
Abscisic acid, 272, 291, 292, *292,* 297, 298, 301
Abscission, 292
Absorption
  by animal, 410
  by digestive system, 415–417, 431
  by fungus, 539, 545
  by mycorrhiza, 267–268
  by photoreceptor, 360
  by pigment (*see* Pigment, plant; Pigment, animal)
  by plant, 256, 264–268, 272
Absorption spectrum, *114*
Absorptive state, 424
Acceleration, sense of, 357–359
Accessory reproductive organ, 459
Acclimation, 430
Accommodation, visual, 363, *364*
Acellular slime mold, 545
Acetabularia, 233, *233*
Acetaldehyde, 126
Acetylcholine, 325, 326, *327,* 370–371, 524
Acetyl-CoA (coenzyme A), 128, *130, 132*
Acid, 45–47, *46*
Acid deposition, 672–674, *674*
Acid rain, 673
Acid snow, 673
Acoelomate, 562, *562*
Acorn, 302
Acrosome, 461
ACTH (adrenocorticotrophic hormone), 346, 350, *350, 426*
Actin, 77, 148, 366, 369–372, *369, 371, 372*
Action potential
  basis of, 322, 325, 356
  defined, 322, 325
  duration, 322
  frequency, 337–338, *337,* 340, 341
  in muscle contraction, 370–371, 372
  propagation, 323–324, *324,* 325
  recording, *323*
  role in nervous system, 330

Activation energy, 102, *102,* 103
Active site, 103, 104
Active transport
  in absorption, 415–416
  and ATP, 107–108
  defined, 92
  in kidney function, 434
  and neural function, 321–322, *321*
  in plant cells, *257, 272,* 274
  types of, 92, *92,* 94–95
Adaptive, defined, 3, 32, 484
Adaptive radiation, *494,* 495, 496, *496,* 498, 512, 513, 514
Adaptive zone, 496, *496,* 497, 498, 506, 512
Adenine, 195–199, 227
Adenosine
  diphosphate (*see* ADP)
  monophosphate (*see* AMP)
  phosphate, 56
  triphosphate (*see* ATP)
Adenovirus, *526*
Adenyl cyclase, 345
ADH (antidiuretic hormone; *see also* Vasopressin), *348,* 349, *350,* 436, *436, 438*
Adhering junction, 82, *306, 307*
Adipose tissue, *310,* 311
Adjustment, lens, 363
Adolescence, 350
ADP (adenosine diphosphate), 56, 106, 107, 108
Adrenal gland, 346
  cortex, *350, 351,* 352
  location, *346,* 352
  medulla, *351,* 352, 430
  neural control of, 352
Adrenalin (*see* Epinephrine)
Adrenocorticotrophic hormone (*see* ACTH)
Adventitious root, 256, *289*
Adventitious stem, 256
Aegilops, 189
Aegyptopithecus, 592, 593
Aerobic respiration, 6
  in ecosystem, 633, *633,* 638
  electron transfer in, *123,* 506
  and evolution of life, 133, 506
  link with photosynthesis, 110–111, *110, 117, 123,* 133
  in muscle tissue, 370
  net energy yield, 124, *125,* 131–132, *131, 132*
  origin of, 506
  overview of, 124
  reactions, 126*ff.*

African sleeping sickness, 533
African swallowtail butterfly, 488, *488*
Age structure, population, 611, *611, 613*
Agglutination, 169–170, *169*
Aggression, 332, 461
Aggressive mimicry, *622,* 685
Aging, 174–175, 456–458
Agnathus, 585
Agriculture
  and genetic engineering, 189
  and green revolution, 641
  land available for, 642
  monocrop, 541
  and population size, 640–642
  slash-and-burn, 664–665
  and synthetic fertilizer, 639
  in tropical rain forest, 664–665
AIDS (acquired immune deficiency syndrome), 528
Air
  in alveoli, 404
  currents, 649–650, *650*
  temperature, 428
Air pollution, 486–488, *487,* 672–674, *674*
Air sac, 586
Albatross, 684, 686–688, *687*
Albinism, 171, 172, 242
Albumin, 55, 376
Alcohol, 44, *44*
Alcoholic fermentation, *125,* 126
Aldehyde, 44, 48
Alder, 644, 662
Aldosterone, 436
Alfalfa root, *258*
Alga
  blue-green (*see* Cyanobacteria)
  brown, 548, *548,* 549–550, *550*
  classification, 548, *548*
  defined, 548
  golden, 530, *548*
  green, 10, 119, 508, 537, 544, 548, *548,* 550, *550*
  of lichen, 544, *544*
  nitrogen-fixing, *521,* 523
  red, *10, 61,* 508, 548–549, *548, 550*
Alkaptonuria, 212
Allantois, *466,* 469, *587*
Allele
  defined, 153, 163, 481
  frequency, 481*ff.*
  pool, 481
  segregation during meiosis, 153
Allergy, 376, 394–395

Alligator, *445*
Allison, A., 490
Allopatric speciation, 492–493
All-or-nothing event, 322, 337
Allosteric enzyme, 105, *105*
Alpha cell, 424–425, *425, 426*
Alpha globulin, 377, 385
Alpha pattern, protein, *54*
Alpha rhythm (EEG), 340, 341
Alternation of generations, 156, 158
Altruism, 686*ff.*
Alvarez, L., 515
Alvarez, W., 515
Alveolar duct, 400
Alveolus, 399–400, *401,* 404
Amanita, 542
American bittern, *625*
Amine, *44,* 345, 347
Amino acid(s)
  abiotic synthesis, 502
  assembly, 132
  components of, *44,* 53
  digestion of, 415, *418*
  essential, 419
  genetic code for, 214–215, *215*
  metabolism, *132,* 424
  peptide bonding between, 53, *53*
  and protein synthesis, 53–55, *53*
  structure, 53–55, *53*
Amino group, 44
Aminopeptidase, *418*
Ammonia, 121, *424,* 638
Ammonification, 638, *639*
Ammonium, 121, 638
Amnesia, retrograde, 340
Amniocentesis, 243–244, *244*
Amnion, 243, 468, *470, 587*
Amniotic cavity, *466*
Amniotic fluid, 468
Amoeba
  characteristics, 533
  light sensitivity, 360
  phagocytosis by, 95, *96*
  slime mold, 231–232, *232*
Amoeba, 96, 143, 533
Amoebic dysentery, 533
Amoebocyte, 566, *566*
Amoeboid protozoan (Rhizopoda), *531, 532,* 533–534
AMP, 107 (*see also* Cyclic AMP)
Amphetamine, *342, 343*
Amphibian (Amphibia)
  characteristics, 586
  classification, 582, *586*
  egg, 74, 448–449, *448*
  evolution, *510,* 513, 514, *583,* 585

Amphioxus, 584, *585*
Amplexus, *440*
Amplification, stimulus, 355
Amplitude (sound), 357
Amylase, *418*
Amyloplast, 74, 75, *83*
Amylose, 49, *49*
Anabaena, 61, *521*, *522*
Anaerobic respiration, 126, 370, 638–639
  in bacteria, 521
  electron transfer in, *123*, 124, 126, 506
Analgesic, 341, *342*, 348, 353
Analogous structure, 497
Anaphase
  of meiosis, *150*, 151, 153, *155*
  of mitosis, 144, *144*, 145, 147, *155*
Anastral spindle, 145
Androgen, 8, *351*, 352
Aneuploidy, 187, *208*
Angiosperm, 249, 277
Angler fish, 685, *685*
Angiotensin, *351*, 352, 436
Angstrom, *60*
Animal (Animalia)
  aquatic, 398–399
  basic functions, 315, *315*
  body plans, 562–563, *562*
  characteristics, 449, 562–563
  classification, *34*, 35–36, *35*, 563
  defined, *34*, 562
  development (*see* Development)
  evolution, 508*ff.*, *510*, 561*ff.*, *563*
  life cycle, 156, *156*
  reproduction, 441*ff.*, 562
  society, 690*ff.*
Animal cell
  characteristics, 306–307
  examples of, *67*
  generalized, *65*
Animal pole, *447*, 448
Annelid (Annelida)
  body plan, *562*, *563*, 577
  characteristics, *564*, 576
  classification, 563, *564*, *572*
  digestive system, 410
  evolution, 577
  growth, reproduction, 344
  motor system, 367, 577
Annual (plant), 277, 297
Annual growth layer, 262
Anopheles, *535*
Antagonism
  muscle, 367–368
  parasympathetic and sympathetic nerves, 413
Antagonistic muscle system, *366*, 367
Anterior (of transverse plane), *560*
Anther, 278
Antheridium, 551
Anthophyta, *554*, 558–559, *559*
Anthropoid, 590, *593*
Antibiotic-resistant bacteria, 525
Antibody, 38, 169, 376, 390–392, *391*, *394*, 471

Anticoagulation, 386
Anticodon, 218, 221
Antidepressant, *342*
Antidiuretic hormone (*see* ADH)
Antigen, 169, *391*, 392
Anus, 411, *411*, 417, 562, 572
Aorta, 378, *379*, 382
Ape, 190, 590, 592
Aphid, 273–274, *273*
Apical meristem, 249, *249*, 250, 260
Aposematic marking, *622*
Appeasement behavior, 692, *692*, *693*
Appendicitis, 418, *420*
Appendicular portion, endoskeleton, 367–368
Appendix, *411*, 418
Apple, 188, *285*
Aquatic ecosystem
  estuarine, 655, *657*, 658
  freshwater, 655
  hydrothermal, *656*
  lake, 655–656, *655*
  lentic, 655
  lotic, 655
  marine, 655, 656
  open ocean, 656–658, *656*, *657*
Aqueous humor, *363*
Archaebacteria, *34*, *34*, 35, 506, 522–523, *522*
Archaeopteryx, 498, *499*
Archegonium, 551
Archenteron, 446, *447*, 449
Arctic fox, 587
Arctic tundra, 636–638, *637*, 659
Arctotis acaulis, *283*
Arenavirus, *526*
Argentine fire ant, *646*
Aristotle, 26, *26*
Arteriole, 377, 381, 382, 467
Arteriosclerosis, 386
Artery, 374, 377, 378, *379*, 381, *382*, 433, *435*
Arthrobotrys, *545*
Arthropod (Arthropoda)
  adaptations, 578–580
  body plan, *562*, 563
  characteristics, *564*
  classification, 563, *564*, *572*, 578
  digestive system, 367
  as disease vector, 524
  evolution, 578
  motor system, 578
  segmentation, 578, *579*
Artifact, in microscopy, *62–63*
Artificial kidney, 437
Artificial selection, 31, 682–683, *683*
Ascaris, 143, *143*
Ascoscarp, 541, *541*
Ascus, 541, *541*
Asexual reproduction (*see* Reproduction, asexual)
Assay, 193
Association cortex, *336*, 337, 340, *365*
Asthma, 394
Astral spindle, 144

Atherosclerosis, 386–387
Athlete's foot, 542
Atmosphere
  defined, 649
  early, 501, 506
  and evolution of life, 117, 506
  properties of, *405*, 649
Atom, *6*, 38*ff.*
Atomic number, *38*, 39
ATP (adenosine triphosphate)
  abiotic synthesis of, 502
  and active transport, 94, *95*, 272
  cell cycling of, 108
  energy of, 106, 122
  in evolution of metabolism, 505–506
  function, *6*, 56
  hydrolysis, 106
  in movement, *81*
  in muscle contraction, 370, 372
  and plant function, 272, 274
  structure, 106, *106*
  yield from glucose metabolism, 123
  yield from oxidative phosphorylation, 123
ATP formation, 74, 106, 108, 122
  in aerobic respiration, *123*, 124, 125, 126*ff.*
  in anaerobic respiration, *123*, 126
  chemiosmotic theory of, 117
  control of, 132–133
  in fermentation, *123*, 126
  in glycolysis, 124, 126–128, *127*
  in photosynthesis, 111*ff.*, *115*, *116*
Atrioventricular node, 380, *380*
Atrioventricular valve, 378, *379*, *379*
Atrium, heart, 378*ff.*, *379*
Atrium, sponge, 566, *566*
Auditory cortex, *336*, 336
Auditory nerve, 358
Aurelia, 360, *360*
Australopithecine, 593, *593*, 594
Autoclave, 523
Autoimmune disease, 395
Autonomic nervous system, *331*, 332, 333, *334*, *348*, 380, 381, 413
Autophagic vacuole, 72
Autosomal recessive inheritance, 238
Autosome, 179, 182
Autotroph
  bacterial, 521
  chemosynthetic, 111, 121, *656*
  defined, *34*, 111
  origins, 506
  photosynthetic, 111
  use of glucose, 119
Auxin, 291–293, *292*, 295*ff.*
Avery, O., 193, 204
Aves (*see* Bird)
Axial portion, endoskeleton, 367
Axillary bud, 259
Axon, 319, 320, *320*, 323*ff.*
Ayala, F., 492

Baboon, 690–691
Bacillus, 523
Backcross, 181, *182*
Bacteriophage, 194, *195*, *196*
Bacteriorhodopsin, 522
Bacterium (Bacteria, Prokaryote)
  aerobic, 124, 521
  anaerobic, 126, 521, 522, 523–524
  autotrophic, 521
  and bacteriophage, 194, *195*, *196*
  behavior, 521
  body plan, 64, 520
  cell wall, 4, *5*, 79, 521
  chemosynthetic, 111, 121, 656
  classification, 34, *34*, 521, 523
  conjugation, 204, *205*
  as decomposer, 521
  denitrifying, 126, 638
  DNA, *202*
  evolution, 505–506, *510*, 521
  flagellum, 80, *80*, 522
  in gastrointestinal tract (enteric), 417, 525
  genetic recombination in, 204, 205
  Gram-positive and Gram-negative, 521, *522*
  heterotrophic, 521
  of hydrothermal vent, 656
  metabolism, 505–506, 521
  methane-producing, 126, 522
  movement by, 80, 522
  nitrifying, 121, 638
  nitrogen-fixing, 638
  parasitic, 521, 524
  pathogenic, 521, 527
  photosynthetic, 115–116, 521, *522*, 537
  plasmid of, 205–206
  receptors, 494, 522
  representative, 522–524
  reproduction, 140, *140*, *141*
  roles in biosphere, 521, 523, 524–525
  sulfur-oxidizing, 121, 522–523
  symbiotic, *267*, 410, 507, *507*, 521
  transduction, 204
  transformation, 204
  vitamin synthesis by, 525
Balance, sense of, 357–359
Balanced polymorphism, 489–490
Bald cypress, *3*
Bark, 256
Baroreceptor, 436
Barr, M., 230
Barr body, 230, *230*
Basal body, *80*, 81
Base, 45–47, *46*
Base (nitrogen-containing), 56, 194
Base pairing, DNA, 198–199
Basidiocarp, 542
Basidium, 542, *543*
Basilar membrane, ear, *358*
Basophil, 376, *376*
Bat, *27*, 354–355, *354*, 685
Bates, H., *622*
Batesian mimicry, 622–623

Bateson, W., 171
Bathypelagic zone, 656
Batten, R., 513
Bazazz, F., 619–620
B-cell, 376, 390–392, *391*
Bdellovibrio, 507
Beadle, G., 212–213
Beagle, H.M.S., 30, *30*
Bean, 248, 280, 290, 295, 299 (*see also* Soybean)
Bear, 409, *409*
Bee, 282, *283*, 395, 399, 429 (*see also* Honeybee)
de Beer, G., 498
Beeswax, 52
Beet, E., 213
Beetle, 17, *18*, 282, 429, 624, *626*
Behavior
  adaptive aspects of, 686*ff*.
  aggressive, 461, 488, 618–619, 680, 686, 687
  altruistic, 686
  appeasement, 692, *692*, *693*
  associative learning, 680
  of bacteria, 522
  and body temperature, *428*, *429*
  camouflaging, *11*, 624, *625*
  characteristics, 520–522
  chemotaxis, 232, 450
  competitive, 619, 688
  conditioned, 680
  cooperative, 689, 691
  courtship, 492, 686–688, *687*
  defense, 624, *626*
  defined, 679
  ecological aspects of, 683–687
  and environment, 680–681
  escape-swimming, 574, 679
  evolution of, 679, 682–683
  extinction of, 680
  feeding, 680, 684, 685, *685*
  genetic basis of, 680–681, 682
  homing, 684
  human, 595–596, 696–697
  and hypothalamus, 332
  imprinting, 681–682, *681*
  innate, 680
  insight learning, 622, 680
  latent learning, 680
  mate-guarding, 689
  mate-stealing, 689
  maze-running, 680, 682, *683*
  migratory, 684–685
  and natural selection, 683
  neural control in, 332, 348, 679
  neuromotor basis of, 373
  in overcrowded populations, 609
  pair bonding, 596
  parental, 689, 690
  phototaxis, 360, 521
  predator-prey, 615, 622–628, 622, 625, 685, *685*
  as reproductive isolating mechanism, 492
  schooling, 690, *691*

and selection theory, 686*ff*.
  selfish, 689*ff*.
  sexual, 461, 680, *681*, 682, 689
  social, 608, 689*ff*.
  territorial, 489, 608, 620, *679*, 688
  water-seeking, 436
Behavioral isolation, 492, *493*
Benson, A., 118
Benzopyrene, 675
Bernal, J., 503
Bernard, C., 316
Beta cells, 424–425, *425*, 426
Beta globulin, 377
Beta pattern, protein, *54*
Bicarbonate, 46, 47, 101, 375, 405, 413, 414, 417
Biceps, *367*, 368, *368*
Biennial (plant), 297
Bilateral symmetry, 329–330, *561*, 562
Bile, 417
Bile salts, *413*, 417
Binary fission, 140, *141*
Binomial system of nomenclature, 26–27, *27*
Biogeochemical cycles, 652–654
Biogeographic realm, 658, *658*
Biological clock, 301, 683–684
Biological concentration, 631–632
Biological organization
  and "Chain of Being," 26
  and energy flow, 135
  and evolutionary principle, 20
  levels of, 5, *6*
Biological rhythm, 651
Bioluminescence, *106*, 531
Biomass, 632
Biome
  defined, 658
  map, 659
  types, 658*ff*.
Biosphere
  components of, 649
  defined, *6*, 600, 649
  human impact on, 669*ff*., 677–678
  interdependency in, 17, 648–649
Biosynthesis, 107, 132–133
Biotic potential, 602
Biotin, 212
Bipolar cell, retina, *364*
Bird (Aves)
  beak, 30, *31*, 315, 496, *586*
  blood circulation, 374, 377, *377*
  body temperature, 429, 430
  bone, *368*, *586*
  camouflage by, *625*
  characteristics, *586*
  classification, 582, *586*
  digestive system, 410, *410*
  evolution, 498, *499*, 511, 515, 583, 585
  eye, *363*
  feather, *8*, *169*, *314*
  feather fluffing, *8*
  homing by, 684

  imprinting among, 681–682, *681*
  migration, 684–685
  as pollinator, *277*, *282*, *283*
  skeleton, 368, *368*
Bird-of-paradise (*Strelitzia*), *283*
Bird's nest fungus, 442, *543*
Birth control, human, 474–476
Biston betularia, 9, 486–488, *487*
Bivalve (Bivalvia), 573, 574–575, *574*
Bladder
  gall, *411*, *413*, 417
  human, 432, 433, *434*, 467
  neural control of, 334
Blade, 261, 550
Blastocoel, *447*, 449, 562
Blastocyst, 443, 449, 466, 468, *468*
Blastodisk, 443
Blastopore, 447
Blastula, 443, 447, 449
Blending theory of inheritance, 160, 166, 175
Blind sac, animal, 562
Blood, vertebrate
  cell (*see* Red blood cell; White blood cell)
  cellular components of, 375, 376–377, *376*
  circulation, 352, 374–375, 381*ff*.
  composition, 375
  defined, 374
  distribution, 316
  filtration, 382, *383*
  formation, 311–312
  functions, *310*, 313, 316, 374
  plasma, 375, 377
  pressure, 378, 381, 383–384, 436
  in spleen, 389
  transfusion, 169–170
  type (human), 169–170, *169*
  volume, 352, 375, 383, 435
Blood clotting, 89, 238, 376, 377, 385–386, *385*
Blood flow
  chemical control, 381
  distribution, 381, 383–384
  neural control, 381
Blood fluke, 570, *570*
Blood vessel, 374, 377, 466
  in bone, 312, *312*
  structure, 382
  types of, 381–383, *382*
Blowfly, *609*
Blue Andalusian chicken, 168, *169*
Blue-gray gnatcatcher, 616, *617*
Blue-green alga (*see* Cyanobacteria)
Blue lobster, *579*
Blue whale, 626, *631*
Blue wrasse, *11*
Boa constrictor, 429
Body cavity, 316, *316*
Body size
  and morphogenesis, 450
  and surface-to-volume ratio, 61, *61*
  and trophic level, 635

Bolus, 414
Bombardier beetle, 624, *626*
Bombykol, 356
Bombyx mori, 356
Bond (chemical), 42*ff*.
  covalent, 43–44
  defined, 42
  double, 43
  "high-energy," 106
  hydrogen, 44–45
  hydrophobic (*see* Hydrophobic interaction)
  ionic, 42, *42*
  peptide, 53
  and photosensitivity, *114*
  single, 43
  triple, 43
Bond energy
  of ATP hydrolysis, 106
  of covalent bonds, 45
  of hydrogen bonds, 45
  of ionic bonds, 45
Bone
  bird, *368*, *586*
  calcium in, 311, 312–313
  cell, 312–313
  of endoskeleton, 367
  function, *310*, 311
  marrow, 311–312, *312*, 352, 376, *388*
  structure, *310*, 311–313, *312*
Bony fish, 513, 582, *583*, *586*
Book lung, 579, *579*
Boreal forest, *659*, 666, *666*
Boron, *264*, *266*
Bottleneck, 483
Botulism, 395, 524
Bowman's capsule, 433–434, *435*
Brain (*see also specific brain regions*)
  amphibian, 588
  analgesic, 341–342
  anthropoid, 593
  cat, *333*
  chimpanzee, *333*
  evolution, 330, 332, 588, *589*
  frog, 331, *333*
  function, 317
  human, *331*, 335*ff*., *335*, *336*, 593–594
  information processing in, 337–338, *338*
  invertebrate, 330
  opossum, *333*
  pigeon, *333*
  rabbit, *333*
  reptile, 588
  shark, *333*
  stroke, 386
  triune, *589*
  vertebrate, 330, 331–335, *333*
  visual perception in, *338*
Bread mold, 541
Breathing, 402–403, 414
Breed, 31
Breeder reactor, 676

Brenner, S., 214–215, *215*
Bridges, C., 182
Bridging cross, *189–190*
Brittle star, 581, *582*
Broca's area, *336*
Bromeliad, *662*, 663
Bronchial tree, 400
Bronchiole, 400, *401*
Bronchitis, 407
Bronchus, *334*, 400, *401*
Brown, R., 59
Brown alga (Phaeophyta), 548, *548*, 549–550, *550*
Brown recluse spider, *579*
Bryophyte (Bryophyta), *548*, 551–552, *551*
Bubonic plague, 524, *610*
Bud, vascular plant, *248*, 259, *259*, 300–301
Budding
  in animals, 441
  cnidarian, 568
  fungal, 540
  Obelia, *567*
  sponge, 441, 566
Buffer, 47
de Buffon, G., 28
Bulb, *287*
Bulbourethral gland, *459, 460*, 461
Bulk, in diet, *420*
Bulk flow, 93, 385
Bundle sheath cell, 120
Burgess shale fossils, *512*
Buttercup (*Ranunculus*), 172, *174*, *257, 294*, 624
Butterfly, 488, *488, 623, 652*

C3 plant, 120
C4 plant, 120
Cabell, J., 598
Cactus, 28, *283*, 293–294
Caffeine, 414
Cairns, J., 200
Cairns-Smith, G., 503
Calcitonin, *351*, 352
Calcium, *38*
  abundance in human body, *38*
  in blood clotting, 385
  in bone, 311, 312–313, 538
  carbonate, 311, 573
  endocrine control of, *351*, 352
  in human nutrition, 423
  in muscle function, 71, 371, *371*, 372
  in neural synapse, 325
  in plaque formation, 386–387
  phosphate, 311
  in plants, *264, 266*
  pump, 94–95
Calico cat, 230, *231*
Caloric needs, human, 418
Calvin, M., 118
Calvin-Benson cycle, 118–119, *119*, 120
Cambium (Cambia)

cork, 250, 256
  vascular, *249*, 250, 258, *258*, 261, 303, 304
Cambrian, *495*, 508, *509, 510, 512, 563*
Camouflage, *11*, 624, *624, 625*, 626
Campbell, B., 595
Canadian lynx, *620*, 621–622
Cancer
  causes of, 236, 392, *526, 529*, 676
  cell, 235, *393*
  characteristics of, 235
  and cigarette smoke, 407, *408*
  of colon, *420*
  defined, 235
  and immune system, *391*, 392–394
  lung, 407, *408*, 672
Candida, 525
Cannon, W., 316
Cape buffalo, 12, *14*
Capillary, air (insect), 399
Capillary, blood, 374
  and alveolus, 401, *401*, 404–405
  defined, 382
  function, 382–383, *383*
  in inflammatory response, 389
  peritubular, 433–434, *438*
  structure, 382, *382*
  uterine, 467
Capillary, lymph, 388
Capillary bed
  of fish gill, 377, *377*, 398–399, *398*
  of hypothalamus-pituitary, 349, *349*
  of intestine, *378*
  of kidney, 433
  of lung, *378*
  systemic, *378*
Capsella, embryonic development, 284, *284*
Carapace, 580
Carbaminohemoglobin, 375, 405
Carbohydrate
  abiotic synthesis of, 502
  assembly sites, 119
  defined, 48
  digestion, 416, *418*
  and human nutrition, 419
Carbohydrate metabolism, 122ff.
  activities in, 122
  categories of, 124
  defined, 122
  and nutrition, 424–426, *424*
  overview, 122–126, *125*
Carbon, *38*, 39
  abundance in human body, *38*
  bonding, 43–44
  cycle, 133, *134*, 653–654, *654*
  in plant function, *265*
Carbon dioxide
  acquisition by plants, 264, 265, 270
  atmospheric concentration, 264, 654

in blood, 375, 381, 405–406
  elimination from animal, 399, 400, 404–406
  fixation, 118–119, *119*, 120, 653
  in Krebs cycle, 126, 127, *130*
  in leaf, 120
  partial pressure, 404, *404*
  and photorespiration, 120
  in photosynthesis, 111, 118–119, *119, 120*
  in respiratory system, 404–406
  stomatal control of, 270–272
Carbonic acid, 46, 47, 101, 405–406
Carbonic anhydrase, 405
Carboniferous, *495*, 508, *510*, 513–514, 552
Carbonyl group, *44*
Carboxyl group, *44*, 51
Carboxypeptidase, *418*
Cardiac conduction system, 380–381, *380*
Cardiac cycle, 378–379
Cardiac muscle (heart muscle), 313, *313*, 332, 368–369, 379–380, *381*
Cardiac pacemaker, 380
Cardiovascular disorders, 386–387
Carnation, leaf surface, *52*
Carnivore, *630*, 632–633, *633, 634*
Carotenoid, 52, 114, *114*, 295, 522, 537
Carp, *644*
Carpal, 367
Carpel, *161*, 278, *278, 286*
Carrot, 256, 286–287, 297
Carrying capacity, 605, *605*, 606–607, *606*
Cartilage, *310*, 311
Casparian strip, 257, *257*, 268
Caspian tern, *689*, 690
Cat, 172, *173*, 230, *231, 333, 338*
CAT box, chromosome, 230
Catastrophism, 28
Caterpillar, *7, 625*, 685, *685*
Cattail, *283*
Cecropia moth, *455*
Cecum, *411, 418*
Cedar, *262*
Cell
  aging and death, 453, 456–458
  defined, 5, *6*
  differentiation, 231, 450, 454–456
  enlargement, 289–290, 450
  excitability, 319
  eukaryotic, nature of, 64–65
  functional zones, 59
  gene control in, 223
  interactions, 289, 450
  junctions, 81–82, 306–308, *306, 307*, 380
  membrane (*see* Membrane, cell)
  migration, *448, 449*, 450, 469
  movement, 76ff., *447–448*
  oldest known, 504, *505*
  origins of, *503 , 504*
  percent water in, 85

prokaryotic, nature of, 64
  reproduction, 138ff.
  role of DNA in, 139–140; *139, 140*
  shape, 76, 78, 79
  size, 60–61
  structural organization, 59, 76, 77, 89, 133–134
  structure-function, summary of, 82, *83*
  surface markers, 95–97, 235, 345, 392, 395–396, 450
  tolerance ranges of, 83
  "typical," 65, *65*
  water in functioning of, 85ff.
Cell count, blood, 375
Cell cycle, 138, 144, *144*
Cell division, 138ff., 159
Cell environment, 85
Cell junctions, 81–82, *82*
Cell theory, 58–59
Cellular slime mold, 231–232, *232*
Cellulose
  in cell walls, 79, *79*, 251, 257, 291, 303
  digestion, 410, 525
  structure, 49, *50*
Cell wall
  bacterial, 4, *5*, 64, *64*, 521
  components, 79
  function, 78, *83*
  fungal, 65
  plant, *5*, 64, *64, 65*, 79, *79*, 148, *149*, 251, 291
  primary, 79, *79*, 251
  protistan, 65
  secondary, 79, *79*, 252, *252, 253, 253*
  structure, 78–79
Cenozoic, *495, 495*, 511, 516, *516*, 590
Centipede, 578, *579*, 580–581
Central nervous system, 330, 331–332, *331*, 346
Central vacuole, 64, *66*, 75–76, *83*, 264
Centrifuge, 201
Centriole, 80–81, *81, 83*, 144–146, *148*
Centromere, 142, *142, 146*, 147, 149, 227
Cephalization, 328, 329, 563
Cephalochordata, 582
Cephalopod (Cephalopoda), 361–362, *512*, 573, 574, *574*
Cercaria, *570*
Cerebellum, 332
Cerebral cortex, 335–338, *336*, 682
Cerebral hemisphere, 332, 335, *335*, 339–340, *339*
Cerebrum, 332
Cervical nerve, *331*
Cervix, 462, *462, 463*, 466
Cestode, *570*
"Chain of Being," 26, 27
Chambered nautilus, *10*

Chancre, 527
Chaparral, 659, 661, 661
Chargaff, E., 194, 197
Chase, M., 194, 196
Cheetah, 12
Chelicerate (Chelicerata), 578, 580
Chemical bond (see Bond, chemical)
Chemical defense, 624
Chemical reaction
  control over, 105, 132, 134
  energy change in, 100–101
  reversible, 46
Chemiosmotic theory of ATP
    formation, 117, 129
Chemoreceptor, 355, 356, 404, 413,
    522
Chemosynthesis, 121
Chemosynthetic autotroph, 111
Chemotaxis, 232, 450, 521
Chemotherapy, 393
Cherry, 278, 286, 286, 301
Chestnut blight, 646
Chiasma, 152, 152
Chick(en), 168, 169, 170, 171, 443,
    449, 451
Childbirth, 468, 473
Chimaera, 586
Chimpanzee, 143, 186, 190, 590, 596
Chipmunk, 614–615, 616
Chitin, 49, 367, 399, 578
Chlamydia, 522, 528
Chlamydial infection, 527, 528
Chlamydomonas, 537, 548, 550
Chloride ion, 39
Chlorine, 38, 38, 39, 264, 266
Chlorophyll
  absorption spectrum for, 114
  in algae, 549, 549, 550
  as chloroplast pigment, 75,
    113–115, 114, 295
  in cyanobacteria, 523
  structure, 52, 112–113, 112
Chloroplast
  assembly of lipids and amino
    acids, 119–120
  ATP formation in, 117
  function, 74, 83, 112–113, 112,
    117
  movement, 76, 78
  origin of, 507
  photosynthesis in, 112ff., 112
  pigments, 113–115, 114
  size, 74
  storage in, 119
  structure, 74–75, 75
Cholecystokinin, 351, 352, 413, 413
Cholesterol, 52, 91, 377, 386–387
Chondrichthyes, 586
Chordate (Chordata)
  body plan, 562, 563
  characteristics, 564, 582ff.
  classification, 564, 564, 572, 582
  evolution, 572, 582ff.
  family tree, 583
  representatives, 586–587

Chorion, 466, 468, 470
Chorionic, 466, 468, 470
Chorionic gonadotrophin, 464, 468
Choroid, 363, 363
Chromatid
  in meiosis, 152–153
  in mitosis, 147–148, 147, 148
  sister, formation of, 142
  structure, 142, 142
Chromatin, 68–69, 68, 228
Chromoplast, 74, 75, 83
Chromosomal mutation, 179, 208,
    240ff., 479
Chromosomal theory of inheritance,
    179
Chromosome
  abnormalities, 185ff.
  appearance, 142, 142, 143
  assortment, 166, 176, 179
  autosome, 179
  banding pattern, 184, 185, 185,
    233, 234
  versus chromatin, 68–69
  crossing over, 152–153, 154, 179,
    183
  defined, 179
  Drosophila, 178, 180–181, 180
  duplicated, 142, 142, 149
  evolution, 187
  fission, 188, 208
  function, 83
  fusion, 188, 208
  gene sequence in, 227
  homologous, 149ff., 159, 179
  human, 142, 142, 180, 223
  inactivation, 230
  karyotype, 184, 185
  lampbrush, 234, 235
  mapping, 183, 184
  in meiosis, 141ff.
  in mitosis, 141ff.
  number, 141, 142–143, 143, 179,
    188, 240ff.
  polytene, 178, 184
  puffing, 233, 234
  random activation, 230
  set, eukaryotic, 141, 159, 179
  sex, 149, 179–180, 179, 180
  structure, 142, 142, 144, 185, 223,
    229–230, 229
Chrysaora, 586
Chrysophyte, 530, 531
Chymotrypsin, 414, 418
Cicada, 492
Cigarette smoking, 406, 407, 408,
    473
Ciliate protozoan (Ciliophora), 531,
    532, 534–537, 536
Cilium (Cilia)
  in bronchitis, 407
  of epithelium, 80, 406
  of flame cell, 569, 569
  function, 81
  in gill slit, 584
  movement mechanism, 81
  of Paramecium, 63, 535, 536

structure, 80–81, 80, 81
Circadian rhythm, 302, 683
Circulation, blood
  function, 374
  pulmonary, 377, 378
  rate of, 374
  systemic, 377, 378
Circulatory shock, 395
Circulatory system
  amphibian, 588, 589
  annelid, 577
  bird, 588, 589
  closed, 374–375
  fish, 588, 589
  human, 374
  insect, 374
  invertebrate, 374–375
  and lymph vascular system, 375,
    386
  open, 374
  reptile, 588, 589
  and thermal regulation, 374, 430
  vertebrate, 374–375, 588, 589
Citrate, 130
City as ecosystem, 667–668, 668
Cladonia, 544
Clam, 573, 574–575
Class (taxon), 27, 493
Classification scheme
  five-kingdom, 34–36, 34, 35
  Linnean, 26–27, 27
  phylogenetic, 34, 493
Clavicle, 367
Claw, 315
Clear-cutting, 666
Cleavage, 443, 443, 448–449, 468,
    468, 572
Cleavage furrow, 148, 149
Climate, 649–652, 659
Climax community, 643, 658
Clitoris, 463, 467
Clock, internal (see Biological clock)
Clone
  animal, 441
  B–cell, 390–392, 391
  carrot, 285–286
  crop, 287
  defined, 206
  in monoclonal antibody
    production, 394
  in recombinant DNA research,
    206
  T–cell, 390–392, 391
Closed circulation system, 374–375
Clostridium, 522, 523–524, 525
Clot, blood, 385–386, 385
Clownfish, 10
Club fungus (Basidiomycota), 540,
    542, 542, 543
Club moss (see Lycopod)
Cnidarian (Cnidaria)
  body plan, 562
  characteristics, 374, 564
  classification, 563, 564
  evolution, 508

growth, reproduction, 344
  nervous system, 328–329, 329
Cnidocyte, 568
Coagulation, 385
Coal deposits, 514, 675
Coast live oak, 302–304, 303
Coat color, 172, 177, 230, 231
Coccygeal nerves, 331
Cochlea, 358
Cocklebur, 298
Coco-de-mer, 285
Coconut, 285
Codominance, 168, 169
Codon, 216, 216, 218ff.
Coelenterate (see Cnidarian)
Coelom, 448, 572–573
Coelomate, 562–563, 562
Coenzyme, 56, 104, 123, 130, 503
Coenzyme CoA (acetyl-CoA), 128,
    130
Coevolution, 614
  defined, 622
  in ecosystem, 669
  mimicry as outcome, 622, 622
  mutualistic, 626–627, 627
  of parasite and host, 627
  of parasitoid and host, 628
  of plant and pollinator, 277,
    280–282, 282–283
  reciprocal selection pressure in,
    622
Cofactor, 104, 266
Cohesion, 86–87
Cohesion theory of water transport,
    269, 270
Coitus, 467
Colchicine, 188, 189
Coleoptile, 285, 289, 292–293, 293
Coleus, 259
Collagen, 54–55, 56, 227, 310, 311,
    311, 385
Collar cell, 306, 566, 566
Collecting duct, 433, 434, 435, 436,
    438
Collenchyma, 251, 251
Colloidal particle, 88
Colon (see Intestine, large)
Colonial animals, 12
Color blindness, 240, 240
Color perception, 364
Columnar epithelium, 308, 309, 309
Colwell, R., 483
Coma, EEG pattern, 341
Comb shape, in poultry, 170, 171
Commensalism, 617–618, 617
Common egret, 3
Common field mushroom, 542, 543
Communication
  between cells, 82, 307, 380
  chemical (see Chemoreceptor)
  neural, 319, 325, 326, 331
  social, 355
  sound, 355, 357
Community
  climax, 643, 658

Community (continued)
cyclic replacement in, 643–644
defined, 6, 600, 614
interactions, 614, 617, 617
succession, 643–644, 644
Compass sense, 684
Competition, interspecific
and coexistence, 619–620
defined, 618
effect of, 617, 618
exploitative, 618
interference, 618–619
Competition, intraspecific, 608, 609, 618, 688
Competitive exclusion, 618–619
Complement, 389, 396
Composite (flower), 283
Compound, chemical, 38
Compound eye, 362, 363
Computer simulation, neural plate development, 452
Concentration gradient, 92
Conch, 361
Condensation reaction, 47–48, 48
Conditioned reflex, 680
Condom, 475, 527
Conduction, 427
Cone, photoreceptor cell, 364–365, 364, 365
Cone, seed plant, 556, 557, 557, 558, 558
Conifer (Coniferophyta), 554, 556, 557–558, 558, 559
Coniferous forest, 636, 663, 666
Conjugation, 204, 205
Connective tissue, 308, 310–313, 310, 311, 374
Conscious experience, 339–341
Consumer, 19, 600, 633
Contest competition, 608
Continental drift, 509
Continuous feeding, 410
Continuous variation, 175, 176, 479, 479
Contractile cell, Hydra, 329
Contractile vacuole, 535, 536
Contraction, intracellular, 77
Contraction, muscle
in antagonistic muscle system, 366, 366, 368, 368
ATP used in, 370, 372
calcium ions in, 71, 371, 371, 372
cardiac, 313, 313, 368, 378, 379–380, 381
in childbirth, 317
control of, 370–371, 372, 413
defined, 77, 313
of eye muscles, 362
and heat production, 429, 430
mechanism, 370, 372
of molluscan mantle, 575
neural basis of, 326–327, 327, 370–371, 372
and shivering response, 430
skeletal, 313, 313, 368

smooth, 313, 313, 368
tetanic, 372, 373
in Tritonia, 679
twitch, 372, 373
of urinary bladder, 433
of uterus, 461
in ventilation, 402–404
in water-vascular system, 581
Control group, 23–24, 193
Controlled cell death, 453, 456–458
Controlled variable, 23
Convection, 429
Convergence, visual, 363
Convergent evolution, 494, 495, 496, 497
Copepod, 567, 578, 580, 580, 656
Copernicus, N., 25
Copper, 264, 265
Copperhead, 445
Coral, 9ff., 10, 12, 508, 567
Coral fungus, 543
Coral reef, tropical, 9–12, 10–11, 512
Core temperature, 430, 432
Corepression, 225
Cork, 256
Cork cambium, 250, 256, 258, 258
Corliss, J., 656
Corm, 287
Corn
chromosome number, 143, 143
development, 265, 289ff., 289
epidermis, 254
height, 264, 293, 293
photosynthesis in, 120
pollination, 280
response to sunlight, 295
root, 267, 289, 296
seed, 285, 285
stem, 254, 289
Cornea, 361, 361, 363, 363
Cornhill, F., 387
Coronary circulation, 382
Coronary occlusion, 387
Coronavirus, 526
Corpus callosum, 335, 339–340, 339
Corpus luteum, 463, 464, 464, 465
Correns, C., 178
Cortex, egg, 448
Cortex, kidney, 434, 435, 438
Cortex, plant
embryonic source, 249–250
function, 249
root, 256, 257, 258, 258
stem, 250, 250, 260
Cotransport mechanisms, 94–95, 321, 416
Cotyledon (seed leaf), 249, 285, 285, 290
Countercurrent exchange, 438
Countercurrent flow, 390, 588
Countercurrent multiplication, 438, 439

Courtship behavior, 442, 686–688, 687
Covalent bond
of amino acids, 53
of carbon, 43–44
in condensation, 47–48
defined, 43
double, 43
nonpolar, 43
polar, 43
triple, 43
Cowbird, 627–628
Crab, 11, 357, 578, 580, 580
Crab spider, 625
Cranial cavity, 316
Cranium, 367
Crater Lake, 516
Creatine, 434
Creatine phosphate, 370
Creosote bush, 294
Cretaceous, 495, 511, 515, 516
Crick, F., 192, 198–199, 214–215
Crinoid, 581, 582
Crista, mitochondrial, 74, 74
Crop, bird, 410
Crop, earthworm, 410
Crop, food
and air pollution, 672, 674
and dormancy, 301
fungal attack on, 189, 540–541, 542
monocrop, 541
production, 189–190, 207, 641–642
in tropical rain forest, 663–664
Cross-fertilization, 161
Crossing over, chromosomal
at cytological level, 152–153, 154, 159, 179, 183, 207, 208
at molecular level, 203–204, 204
summary, 208
Crown-of-thorns, 10
Crustacean (Crustacea), 508, 578, 580, 580
Crypsis (see Camouflage)
Cuboidal epithelium, 308, 309, 309
Cultural evolution (see Evolution, cultural)
Cupula, 359
Cuspid, 414
Cuticle, animal, 361, 367, 454, 569, 572, 578
Cuticle, plant, 255, 260–261, 270, 551
Cutin, 51–52, 79, 255
Cuttlefish, 361–362, 573, 575, 575
Cuvier, G., 28, 29
Cyanobacteria
characteristics, 523
classification of, 34, 64, 506
nitrogen fixation by, 521, 523
and oldest known fossils, 505
and putrification of lakes, 671
symbiotic, 544
Cycad (Cycadophyta), 554, 556, 557

Cycle, resource
through biosphere, 17, 19
carbon, 133, 134, 653–654, 654
gaseous, 653–654
hydrologic, 652–653, 653
nitrogen, 638–639, 639, 653
phosphorus, 654
sedimentary, 654
Cyclic AMP (cyclic adenosine monophosphate), 56, 232, 345
Cyclic photophosphorylation, 115, 115, 118
Cyclic replacement, community, 643–644
Cysteine, 419
Cytochrome, 55, 108, 109
Cytogenetics, 184
Cytokinesis, 140, 141, 148, 149
Cytokinin, 291–292, 292, 299, 299
Cytology, 178
Cytoplasm
defined, 59
egg, localized differences in, 139–140, 289, 443, 444–448
function, 59
molecular organization of, 76–77, 88–89
Cytoplasmic lattice, 64–65, 76–77, 76, 83, 448
Cytoplasmic streaming, 77–78, 78
Cytosine, 197–199
Cytosol, 59

Damselfly, black–winged, 688, 689
Dark reactions (see Light-independent reactions)
Darwin, C., 18, 29
and blending theory of inheritance, 160
development of evolutionary theory by, 29, 31–33, 484
plant growth studies by, 295
Darwin's finches, 30, 31
Day-neutral plant, 298, 298
DDT, 23, 631–632
Deamer, D., 504
Death
aging and, 456–458
at cellular level, 453, 456–458
commentary on, 457–458
rigor mortis following, 370
and senescence, 299
Deciduous forest, 659, 663, 665–666, 665
Deciduous plant, 261, 299, 300
Decomposer, 600, 630, 632–633, 633, 634
Deductive reasoning, 21
Defense responses
nonspecific, 389
specific, 390ff.
Defense system, 315
Dehydration synthesis (see Condensation reaction)
Delbrück, M., 194

Deletion, chromosomal, 179, 185, *208*
Deltoid, *367*
Deme, 490
Denaturation, 55, 105, 428
Dendrite, *319*, 320, *320*
Denitrification, 638–639, *639*
Denitrifying bacteria, 126
Dense connective tissue, *310*, 311, *311*
Density-dependent mechanism, 608
Density-gradient centrifugation, *201*
Density-independent mechanism, 608
Dentine, 413
Deoxyribonucleic acid (*see* DNA)
Deoxyribose, 49
Dependent variable, 23
Dermis, *314*, 315
Desalinization, 642
Desert, *659*, 660–661, *660*
Desulfovibrio, 506, *522*
Detrital food web, 633, *633*, 658, 661
Detritus, 632, *633*, 635, *636*
Detritus feeders, 633
Deuterostome (Deuterostomia), 572–573
Development
    defined, 7, 230
    eukaryotic, 230
    genetic basis of, 230, 288–289, 444–445, 456
    pattern formation in, 451–453
    principles of, 456
Development, animal
    Amphioxis, *448*, 449
    bird, 454
    chick, *443*, 449, *451*
    deuterostome, 572–573
    direct, 454
    and environment, 172–173, 174, 450
    of finger, 172–174
    of foot, 456–458
    frog, 440–441, *443*, 444, *446–447*
    gastropod, 573–574
    of hand, 456–458
    hormones and, 345, *351*, 352, 450
    human, 312, *443*, 459, 467*ff.*, *466ff.*
    indirect, 454
    mammal, 444, 454
    mosaic, 454, 456
    moth, 7, *7*
    protostome, 572–573
    regulative, 454–455, 456
    reptile, 454
    sea urchin, *443*
    stages of, 443–444, *443*, 562
    of toe, 172–173, *174*
    and X–chromosome inactivation, 230
Development, vascular plant
    dicot, 256, 284, *284*, 288*ff.*, *290*
    flowering plant, 284–286, 288*ff.*
    hormones and, 292*ff.*

leaf, 249–250
monocot, 285, *285*, 288*ff.*, *288*
oak as case study, 302–304, *303*
open growth property of, 249
root, 249–250
shoot, 249–250
stem, 250, *250*
Devonian, 495, 508, *510*, 513
De Vries, H., 178
Diabetes, 207, 242, 395
Dialysis, kidney, 437
Diaphragm
    of body, 400, *401*, 402
    contraceptive, 475, *475*
Diarrhea, *420*
Diastole, 378, *379*
Diatom, 530, *530*, *531*, 631
Dicot
    characteristics, 249
    classification, *554*, 559
    floral structure, *554*, 559
    growth and development, 284, *284*, 289*ff.*
    leaf, *271*
    root, 256, 267–268
    seed, 284, *284*
    stem, 250, *250*
Dictyosome, 71
Dictyostelium discoideum, 231–232, *232*, 545
Didinium, 536, 537
Diet, human, 419, *420*, 435
    and embryonic development, 450
    during pregnancy, 470
    and protein utilization, 640
    in treating genetic disorders, 242, *243*
Differential growth, 450
Differential reproduction, 32, 484
Differentiation (*see also* Development)
    Acetabularia, 233, *233*
    in animal embryo, 451
    cell, 231, 233, 450, 454–456
    defined, 231
    in *Dictyostelium discoideum*, 231–232, *232*
    and environment, 232–233
    and gene expression, 231
    human embryo, 469
    in plant, 288–289, *291*
    and variable gene activity, 230*ff.*
Diffusion
    and cell size, 60
    defined, 92
    facilitated, *92*, 93, *93*
    gas, 398–399
    in gill, 398–399, *398*
    in human respiratory system, 404–406
    in intestine, 416
    across neural membrane, 321, 322
    rate of, 92
    simple, 92–93, *92*
    and surface-to-volume ratio, 60
Digestion

carbohydrate, *418*
defined, 410
enzymes of, summary, *418*
fat, *418*
hormonal control in, *351*, 352, 413, *413*
by insect-eating plant, *255*
lysosomal, 72
neural control in, 412–413
nucleic acid, *418*
protein, *418*
Digestive system (*see also* Gastrointestinal tract)
    annelid, 410
    arthropod, 410
    bird, 410, *410*
    complete, 410, *410*
    defined, 409
    earthworm, *410*
    echinoderm, 410
    flatworm, 409
    function, 315, 410
    human, 308, 411*ff.*, *411*
    incomplete, 409–410, *410*
    links with circulatory system, 409, *410*
    links with respiratory system, 409, *410*
    mollusk, 410
    movement in, 368
    planarian, 409, *410*
    ruminant, 410, 525
Diglyceride, 51
Dihybrid cross
    Drosophila, 182
    pea plant, 162, 166, *167*, 176
Dihydroxyacetone phosphate (DHAP), *127*, 128
Dikaryotic hypha, 542, *542*
Dilution effect, 690
Dimorphism, 485, 488, 489
Dinoflagellate, 531, *532*
Dinoflagellate blooms, and fish kill, 531, *532*
Dinosaur, 498, 514–516, *515*, 591
Dioecious, 564–565
Dipeptide, 53, 219, *220*
Diplococcus pneumoniae, 193, *193*
Diploid state
    in animal life cycle, 156–157, *156*
    defined, 141, 179
    in plant life cycle, 157–158, *158*, 539, 546–547, *546*, *547*
Direct development, 454
Directional selection, 485, *485*, 486–488, *487*
Disaccharidase, *418*
Disaccharide, 49, *49*
Discontinuous feeding, 410, *411*
Discontinuous variation, 175, 479
Dismorphia, 623
Disruptive selection, 485, *485*, 488, *488*
Dissociation (molecular), 45–46, 47, 88
Dissolved substance, 45, 88

Distal tubule, 433, 434, *435*, 436, *438*
Disulfide, *53*
Divergence, 491, *494*, 495–496, 497
Diversity of life
    defined, 13
    and evolutionary theory, 19, 33
    examples of, 9*ff.*
    molecular basis of, 199, 209
    origins of, 13
    perspective on, 517–518
    relation to unity, 18–19, 209
    sources of, 179, 209
Division (taxon), *27*, 493, 540
Dixon, H., 270
DNA (deoxyribonucleic acid)
    bacterial, 200, *202*
    base pairing, 198–199
    characteristics of, 8–9, 198–199, 203, 205, 211
    characterization of, 192*ff.*
    discovery of, 192
    eukaryotic versus prokaryotic, 227
    exon, 227, 228, *228*
    function, 57, *83*
    intron, 227–228, *228*
    mutation, 8, 207–208, *208*
    of nucleosome, 229, *229*
    plasmid, 205, *206*
    potential for structural diversity, 198–199, 209
    prokaryotic, 140, 200, *202*, 227
    and protein synthesis, 211*ff.*
    recombinant, 203–207, *204*, *206*
    repetitive, 227
    replication fork, 200–201, 203
    role in cell reproduction, 134, 139–140, *139*, 158
    sequence organization in eukaryotes, 227
    single–copy, 227
    structure, 56–57, 139, 194–199, *197*, *198*, 200
    transcription, 211, 216–217, *217*
    transcriptional controls over, 223, 225, 227–229
    viral, 194, *195*, *196*, 205
    Z-form versus ß-form, *200*
DNA ligase, 203, 206
DNA replication
    enzymes in, 202–203, 207
    origin and direction of, 200, *202*, 203
    prokaryotic, 200–202, *202*
    role in inheritance, 139–140, *139*, *140*, 203
    semiconservative nature of, 199, *199*, 203
    strand assembly, 200–203, *202*, 203
    summary of, 203
    time of, 144, *144*, 203
DNA polymerase, 202, 204
DNA virus, 526, *526*
Dog, *27*, 680
Dogwood, *259*, 662

Dominance, genetic
  defined, 163
  incomplete, 168, *169*
  limitations of concept, 176
  in Mendel's dihybrid cross, 166, 167
  in Mendel's monohybrid cross, *161*, 162
  in multiple allele system, 168
  versus recessiveness, 162
Dominance hierarchy, 691–692
Donahue, J., 198
Dopamine, 325, 341, 342, *342*
Dormancy, plant, 300–301, *300*
Dorsal, defined, *560*
Dorsal lip, *446*, 453, *453*
Double fertilization, plant, 280, *281*, 285
Doubling time, population, 602–603
Douglas fir, *300*
Down's syndrome, 191, 240, *241*
Downy mildew, 540
Dreaming, 340, 341
Drone, *694*, 696
Drosophila (fruit fly)
  autosome, *180*
  behavioral isolation, 492, *493*
  biotic potential, 602
  chromosome number, *143*, *180*, 188
  chromosome puffing, 233, *234*
  eye color, 180–181, *180*, *181*
  and gene function studies, 179ff.
  genetic map for, *184*
  genome, 227
  polytene chromosome, *178*, 233
  sex chromosome, *180*
  studies of mutations in, 179ff.
  suitability for experiments, 179
Drug
  abuse, 343
  intake during pregnancy, 471–474
  and nervous system, 342–343, *342*
Dry acid deposition, 672–673
Dryas, 644
Dryopithecine, 592–593, *593*
Dutch elm disease, 542, *644*
Dwarfism, 350
Dynein, *81*

Ear, 311, 332, 357–359, *358*, *359*
Ear canal, *358*
Eardrum, *358*
Earlobe, 177
Ear stones, 359
Earth, *648*
  formation, *500*, 501

history, 500ff.
  tectonic plates, 508, *509*
Earthworm, *143*, 410, *410*, 330 (see also Annelid)
  digestive system, 410, *410*, 577
  feeding behavior, 576, 633
  hydrostatic skeleton, 367
  learning by, 680
  nephridium, *557*
  nervous system, *330*
  reproduction, 441
East, E., 175
East African Rift Valley, 12, *13*, 593
Ecdysone, 234
Echinoderm (Echinodermata)
  body plan, *562*
  characteristics, 5, *564*, 581, *582*
  classification, 563, *564*, 572
  defined, 581
  digestive system, 410
  evolution, 508, 572, 581
  movement, 581, *581*
Echolocation, 355, 685
Ecological density, 600
Ecological interactions and evolution, 599–600
Ecology, 17, 517, 599
Ecosystem
  abiotic components, 600
  aquatic, 632, 635, 655–658, *656*, *657*, *658*
  arctic tundra, 636–638, *636*, 637
  and biosphere, 649
  biotic components, 600
  city as, 667–668, *668*
  coevolution in, 669
  defined, *6*, 600, 630
  distribution, 649, 650, *650*
  energy fixation base, 629, 630
  energy flow through, 632–635, *633*, *634*
  food webs in, 630
  forest, 635
  human impact in, 669
  hydrothermal, *656*
  nutrient concentration base, 629, 630
  nutrient flow through, 635, *636*
  terrestrial, 658ff.
  trophic levels, 630, *630*
  of tropical reef, *9ff.*
Ecosystem analysis, *634*, 635
Ectoderm, 307, *447*, 449
Ectotherm, 429–430
EEG pattern, 340–341, *341*
Effector, 320
Egg (ovum)
  alligator, *445*
  amphibian, 448–449, *448*, *586*
  bird, 442, *445*, 449, *586*
  boa constrictor, 429
  chick, *443*
  cleavage, *443*, *443*, 448–449, *468*, *468*, 572
  duckbilled platypus, *445*
  fertilization, 150, *443*

fish, 449
  frog, 440, *440*, *443*
  gene controls in, 444
  honeybee, *695*
  human, 442, *443*, 449, *467*
  mammal, 449
  maternal messages of, 445, 457
  in oogenesis, 157, *157*
  parthenogenesis, 441
  plant, 280, 546–547
  pine, 558, *558*
  reptile, 449, 514, *587*
  sea urchin, 442, *443*
  snake, 429, 444, *445*
  yolk, 442, 444, 445, 448–449
Egg fungus (Oomycota), 540–541
Eggshell, in evolution, 514
Egret, *3*, 686, 697
Ejaculation, 467
Ejaculatory duct, 460, 461
Elastin, 310, *310*
Electric charge, 39, 320, 321, 322
Electric eel, 355
Electric gradient, 92, 107, 117, 320
Electroencephalogram (EEG), 340–341, *341*
Electromagnetic spectrum, *114*
Electron, 5
  acceptor, 108–109, *108*
  carrier, 106, 108–109, *108*
  in chemical bonding, 42
  defined, 39
  donor, 108–109, *108*
  energy levels for, 40, *40*
  excitation, 41–42
  in microscopy, 62–63
  in oxidation-reduction reactions, 108–109
  representation of, 40, *41*
  transfer, 108–109, 123, *123*, 506
Electron transport phosphorylation, *125*, 126, 129, *129*, 131–132, *131*, *132*
Electron transport system
  in aerobic respiration, 124, 129
  defined, 109
  function, 109
  in photosynthesis, *113*, 115–117, *115*, *116*, 118
Electronegativity, 43, 44
Electrophoresis, 213, *214*, 483
Electroreceptor, 355
Element, chemical
  atomic structure, 39
  common in organisms, 38
  defined, 38
  essential in plant nutrition, *265*, 266–267, *266*
  properties of, 38ff., *38*
Elephant, 17, *18*
Elephant seal, 483, 688
Elk, 688
El Niño, 658
Embryo
  animal, 306

Capsella, 284, *284*
  chick, *443*, 449, *451*
  flowering plant, 284–286, 288–289
  frog, 440, *443*
  human, *443*, *446*, 468ff.
  newt, 450, *452*
  rabbit, 454–455
  salamander, 452–453, *453*
Embryonic development (see Development)
Embryonic disk, *466*, 468, 469
Embryonic induction, 452–453, *453*
Embryonic membrane, 449, 468–469
Embryo sac, 280, *281*
Emerson, R., 175
Emotional states, 342, 415
Emperor penguin, 608
Emphysema, *406*, 407
Emulsion, 417
Endergonic reaction, 101
Endocardium, 378
Endocrine gland, 309, 345
Endocrine system
  cells of, 345
  components, 346, *346*
  evolution, 347
  function, 315, 347
  links with nervous system, 347–350
Endocytosis, 92, 95, *96*
Endocytotic vesicle, 72
Endoderm, 307, *447*, 449
Endodermis, 256–257, *256*, *257*, 258
Endogenous rhythm, 302
Endomembrane system, 69, 72
Endometrium, *463*, 464, 466, 467
Endonuclease, 204, 205–206
Endoplasmic reticulum, 64, 68–71, *70*, *83*, 417
Endorphin, 341, *342*, 348
Endoskeleton, *366*, 367–368, *586*, *587*
Endosperm, 280, *281*, 285, *285*
Endospore, 523, *523*
Endospore-forming bacteria, 523–524, *523*
Endothelium, 382
Endotherm, 429
Energy
  activation, 102, *102*, 103
  active transport, 94
  carrier molecules, 106ff.
  consumption, human population, 674ff.
  defined, 5
  food, 418–419
  heat, 429
  hill diagram, *102*
  kinetic, 99
  levels, electron, 40–42, *41*, 123
  light, perception, 359–360
  light, in photosynthesis, 111, 113–115, *114*
  mechanical, 355
  in muscle contraction, 370, 372
  nuclear, 675–677

Energy (continued)
photon, 100, 113, *114*
potential, 99
of pyrophosphate bond, 106
quality of, 99, 100
quantity available, 98–99
solar, 629, 633, *633, 634,* 677
stimulus, 317, 355
transfer, 6, 38, 98, 106*ff.*
wind, 677
Energy budget, 635
Energy conversion (transformation)
in carbohydrate metabolism, 124*ff.*
in food web, 633, 640
and metabolism, 6
and second law of thermodynamics, 100
Energy flow
through biosphere, 16–17, *19,* 100, 135
through ecosystem, 632–635, *633, 634,* 635
Enkephalin, 341, *342*
Entovirus, *526*
Entropy, 100
Environment
adaptation to, 3, 8, 517
and animal development, 450
and behavior, 680–681
cellular, 85
and differentiation, 231*ff.*
and DNA, 8–9, 209
and evolution, 500*ff.*
and gene expression, 172–175, 176, 233, 234
and homeostasis, 8
and human evolution, 592, 595–596
internal, of animal, 316
and plant development, 293*ff.*
pollution of, 669–675
and population growth, 604–605
Environmental resistance, 604
Enzyme
and activation energy, 102–104, *102*
allosteric, 105
in biosynthesis, 132–133
in carbohydrate metabolism, 122, 132
in chemical bonding, 48
and chemical control, 105, 132–133
defined, 52, 102
digestive, 418
DNA replication and repair, 202–203
of electron transport system, 109, 123
function, 103–104
heat-sensitive, 172, *173*
in implantation, 468
inactive precursor, 105

of insect-eating plant, 255
lysosomal, 72
mode of action, 103–104, *103, 104*
in muscle contraction, 370
and origin of life, 503
in recombinant DNA studies, 204–206
in RNA transcript processing, 227–228
structure, 103–104
Enzyme activity
and cofactor, 104
control of, 105, 223–224, *224*
and gene function studies, 212–213
and hormone action, 345–346
and pH, 104
role in cell reproduction, 139–140, *139*
temperature and, 105, 428
Eocene, *495,* 517
Eosinophil, 376, *376*
Ephedra, *554,* 557
Epidermal hair, leaf, *255*
Epidermis, animal, 314–315, *314*
Epidermis, vascular plant, 249, 250, *250,* 255–256, *255,* 260–261, *261*
Epididymis, *459, 460,* 461
Epiglottis, 400, *401,* 411
Epilepsy, 339
Epinephrine, 325, 335, *342, 351,* 352, 430
Epipelagic zone, 656
Episome, 204, 205, *205*
Epistasis, 171–172, *171,* 177
Epithelium
alveolar, 400–401
cell junction in, 81–82, 306–307, *307*
structure and function, 308
types of, 308–309, *308*
Equilibrium
chemical, 101–102
genetic, 481
organ of, 357–359, *360*
Equisetum, 143, 553, *553, 554*
Equus, 143
Erythrocyte (*see* Red blood cell)
Erythropoeitin, *351,* 352, 375–376
Escherichia coli
attack by bacteriophage, 194, *195*
binary fission, *141*
body plan, *64*
classification, *522*
conjugation, 204, *205*
DNA, 200, *202*
in intestine, 525
lactose operon in, 224–225
metabolism, 126
movement, 522
Esophagus, 411, *411,* 414
Essential amino acids, 419
Estrogen, 8, *348, 350, 351,* 352, 464–467, *464, 465*
Estrous cycle, 462

Estuary, 655, 658
Ethanol, *125, 126,* 542
Ethylene, 291, 292, *292,* 299
Eubacteria, 34, *34, 35,* 506, *522,* 523–524
Euglena (Euglenophyta), 529, 530, *530*
Euglenid, 530, *531*
Eukaryote
defined, *34,* 64
development, 224, 230
DNA, 227
fossil, *505*
gene regulation, 224, 227*ff.*
genome, 227
life span, 456
organelles of, 64, 82, *83*
origin and evolution, 506–508
versus prokaryote, 64–65, 224, 227, 230
Euterpe, 603
Eutheria, 587
Eutrophic lake, 656
Evagination, 400
Evaporation, 86, 268–270, *269,* 429, 431, 432, 578, 653
Evening primrose, 492
Evergreen plant, 261
Evolution, biological
and adaptive radiation, *494,* 495–496, *496*
of animals, 508*ff., 510,* 561*ff., 563*
of cell, *503, 504*
of chromosome, 187
conservative nature of, 498
convergent, *494, 495, 496*
correlated with earth history, 500*ff., 510–511*
defined, 20, 481
and divergence, *494,* 495–496
of eukaryotes, 506–508
and extinction, 498–499, 512, 513, 514, 515
through gene flow, 481
gradualistic model of, 497, *497*
human, 186, 190, 590*ff.*
key characters in, 498, 506, 512, 561, 582, 585, *587,* 591, 592
of metabolic pathways, 115–117, 505–506
mosaic, 498
of multicellular forms, 537–538
through mutation, 481–482
through natural selection, 18–19, 32–33, 481
parallel, *494, 495, 496,* 575
perspective on, 36, 517–518
phyletic, 497, *497*
of plants, 115–116, 508, 546–547, 560
primate, 590*ff.*
principle of, 18–19, 20, 36

of prokaryotes, 504–506, *505*
punctuational model of, 497–498, *497*
quantum, 497–498, *497*
sources of, 481*ff.*
of species, 490–493, *491*
symbiosis in, 506–507, *506*
time scale for, 494–495, *495*
Evolution, chemical, 501–503
Evolution, cultural, 594, *595–596*
Evolutionary theory, history of, 25*ff.*
Evolutionary tree
construction of, 495
Haeckel's, 33
Evolutionary trends, 497–499
Excitability, cell, 313, 319, 352, 380
Excitatory synapse, 325, 326
Excretory system, 315
Exercise
and blood circulation, 389
breathing during, 402
and lactate buildup, 370, 425
Exergonic reaction, 101
Exhalation, 402–404, *403*
Exocrine gland, 309, *310, 350,* 356, 389, 414
Exocytosis, 92, 95, *96,* 325
Exon, 227–228, *228*
Exoskeleton, *366, 367,* 578
Experiment, nature of scientific, 22–24
Experimental group, 23, 193
Experiments, examples of
artificial selection, 682–683, *683*
associative learning, 680
backcross, 181, *182*
bacterial transformation, 193
bridging cross, *189*
cell death, 456
deciphering genetic code, 214–215, *215*
dihybrid cross, 166, *167*
DNA replication, *201*
dormancy, plant, 300–301, *300*
effects of DDT, 23–24
enzyme control, *E. coli,* 224–225
flowering, 298, *298*
gene function, *Neurospora,* 212, 213, *213*
gene location, *Drosophila,* 181–183, *181, 182*
gene replacement, 244–246
genetic engineering, *189–190*
grafting, *Acetabularia,* 233, *233*
gravitropism, 296–297, *296*
interspecific competition, 618, *619*
mark-release-recapture, 487, *487*
monohybrid cross, 161, *162*
nuclear transplant, 233, *233*
into origin of life, 502, *502,* 504, *504*
overcrowding, 609
perception, conscious, 339–340

Experiments, examples of
(continued)
perception, visual, 338
phototropism, 295–296, 295
plant breeding, 189–190
plant growth, 293, 293, 295ff.
plant wilting, 267
senescence, 299, 299
sieve-tube pressure, 273–274, 273
split-brain, 339–340, 339
stimulus deprivation, 340
stomatal closure, 271
testcross, 163, 165
thigmomorphogenesis, 297
tissue formation, 306, 452
translocation, 274
transplant, embryonic, 395, 452–453, 452, 453, 454–456
transplant, nuclear, 233, 233
x–ray diffraction, 197
Exploitative competition, 618
Exponential growth, 602, 603, 605–606, 607, 612
External fertilization, 442
External oblique muscle, 367
Extinction, behavioral, 680
Extinction, species, 498–499, 512, 513, 514, 515, 669
Extracellular fluid, 316, 431ff. (see also Interstitial fluid)
Extrinsic clotting mechanism, 386
Extrinsic factor, 608
Eye
abalone, 361
bird, 363
cephalopod, 361–362, 512
compound, 362, 363
conch, 361
defined, 361
frog, 452
human, 363, 363, 364–365
insect, 362, 363
land snail, 361
mollusk, 361–362, 361
octopus, 361–362, 361
primate, 591, 592
vertebrate, 363
Eyelid formation, 453
Eyespot, 360–361, 361, 530

Facial bones, 367
Facilitated diffusion, 92, 92, 93, 93
Facultative anaerobe, 521
FAD (flavin adenine dinucleotide, oxidized), 104, 130
FADH$_2$ (flavin adenine dinucleotide, reduced), 104, 129, 130
Fall overturn, lake, 655
Fallopian tube (see Oviduct)
Family (taxon), 27, 34, 493
Farsightedness, 364
Fat
assembly sites, 71, 119, 139

and atherosclerosis, 386
in blood plasma, 376
components of, 44
digestion, 415–417, 418
metabolism, 132, 133, 424–426, 424
storage in animals, 310, 311, 351
storage in plants, 273
structure, 50–51, 51
transport in lymph vessel, 388
transport in plants, 273
Fatty acid, 50–51, 51, 351, 415–417, 418
Feather, 8, 169, 314, 315
Feces, 417, 420, 432
Feedback
in animal development, 450
in blood cell count, 375–376
in body temperature, 317, 430, 431
in epilepsy, 339
in gonadal function, 462, 464, 465
and homeostasis, 317
hormonal, 346, 450, 462
in human activities, 677–678
inhibition, 105, 224
negative, 225, 317, 414, 450, 462, 465
in neuroendocrine control center, 348
between neurons, 338
in organ systems, 317
in plant growth, 272, 272, 304
in population size and rate of increase, 605–606
positive, 317, 322, 325, 415, 465
in reproductive cycle, 464
in stomach secretions, 414
and water balance, 436
Feedforward control, 317, 678
Feeding behavior, 410, 411, 680, 684, 685, 685
Feeding relationships (who eats whom), 10–11, 12–13, 630
Female gametophyte, 280, 281
Femur, 367
Fermentation, 123, 124, 125, 126, 506, 525
Fern (Pterophyta), 553, 553, 554, 556, 556
Fertility control, 473–474
Fertility rate, population, 611–612
Fertilization, animal
amphibian, 448
bird, 442
defined, 150, 443
and egg cytoplasmic activity, 443
external, 442
frog, 440
of hermaphrodite, 441
human, 464, 467
internal, 442
mammal, 442
between proglottids, 571
reptile, 442

self, 441, 571
in vitro, 472
Fertilization, plant
defined, 150, 277
double, flowering plant, 280, 281
and free water, 546–547
Fetus, 469, 470, 471
Fiber, sclerenchyma, 252, 253, 254
Fibrin net, 385, 385
Fibrinogen, 377, 385
Fibroblast, 310, 310
Fibroma, 526
Fibrous root system, 256, 267
Fibula, 367
Fight-flight response, 333–335
Filter feeder, 574, 584
Filtration
in capillary bed, 382, 383
in glomerulus, 434
Finch
Darwin's, 30, 31
tool–using, 684, 685
Finger, formation of, 172–174
Fire, in succession, 643, 662
Fire ant, 646
Fire blight, 524
First law of thermodynamics, 98
Fish
blood circulation, 377, 377
body temperature, 428, 429
bony, 513, 582, 583, 586
brain, 332
camouflage among, 11, 685
egg, 449
evolution, 510, 511, 513
eye, 363
farming, 641
gill, 377
harvesting, 641
heart, 377, 377
jawed, 512–513, 582, 585
jawless, 513, 582, 583, 585
lobe-finned, 513, 513
ray-finned, 586
scale, 513
schooling, 690, 691
swim bladder, 585–588, 588
teleost, 586
of tropical reef, 11, 12
Fissure of Rolando, 336
Fitness, 600, 606
Flagellate protozoan (Mastigophora), 531, 532–533, 533
Flagellin, 80
Flagellum
of bacterium, 80, 80, 520, 522
of collar cell, 566, 566
of eukaryotic cell, 80–81, 80, 81
of protistan, 532, 535
Flame cell, 569, 569
Flatworm
body plan, 374, 562, 562
characteristics, 569–571

digestive system, 410, 410
growth, reproduction, 344
nervous system, 330
origins, 571
transverse fission, 441
Flavin adenine dinucleotide (see FAD)
Flavin mononucleotide (see FMN)
Flavoprotein, 296
Flemming, W., 178
Flesh fly, 623
Float, kelp, 550
Florigen, 292, 298
Flower
coevolution with pollinators, 277, 280–282, 282–283
defined, 249, 277
of dicot, 554, 559
examples of, 259, 277, 278, 282–283
imperfect versus perfect, 278
of monocot, 554, 559
structure, 277–278, 278
Flowering, 292, 294, 297–298, 298
Flowering plant (see Plant, flowering)
Fluid mosaic model of membrane, 89–91, 91, 93
Fluke, 569, 570, 570
FMN, 108, 109
Focusing
in microscopy, 62–63
visual, 363, 364
Follicle
of hair, 315
of oocyte, 463
Follicle-stimulating hormone (see FSH)
Food chain, 630
Food energy, 418–419
Food web, 630, 631, 632–633, 633, 658
Foot, molluscan, 573, 573, 574
Foraminiferan, 531, 533–534, 534
Ford, E., 486
Forebrain, 332, 333
Forest
boreal (taiga), 659, 666, 666
coniferous, 636, 663, 666
deciduous, 659, 663, 665–666, 665
montane coniferous, 659, 666, 667
rain, 659, 662, 663–665
sequoia, fire prevention in, 443
temperate, 659, 665, 666
tropical, 659, 663
water retention by, 653
Fossil fuel, 653, 653, 675
Fossils
hominid, 594, 595
interpretations of, 8, 491, 497, 593, 594, 595
oldest known, 505
record, 502, 508, 512
Founder effect, 483
Fovea, 363, 364

Fox, S., 504
Franklin, R., 197
Freeze-etching, 89, *90*
Freeze-fracturing, 89, *90*
Frog
  adult form, 4
  amplexus, *440*
  chromosome number, *143*
  egg, 440, *440*
  embryonic development,
    440–441, *446–447*
  eye development, *452*
  fertilization, 440
  reproduction, 440–441
  tadpole, 440
  zygote, 440
Frontal lobe, *335*
Frontal plane, *560*
Fructose, *48, 49*
Fruit, 252, 277, *278*, 285–286, *285*,
  286, 626
Fruit fly (*see Drosophila*)
Fruiting body, 542, *542*, *543*, 545,
  545 (*see also* Sporocarp)
FSH (follicle-stimulating hormone),
  350, *350*, 461–462, *462*,
  464–465, *464, 465*
Fucus, *548*
Fumarate, *130*
Functional groups, 44, *44*
Fundamental niche, 615–616, 618
Fungus (Fungi)
  cell wall, 79
  characteristics, 539
  classification, *34*, 35–36, *35*
  crop damage by, *189*, 540–541,
    542
  cross-wall, 540, *542*
  as decomposer, 539
  defined, *34*
  divisions, 540
  evolution of, 508, *510*
  examples of, *539, 540, 541, 542*
  life cycle, 540, *540, 542*
  mycorrhizal, 268, *268*
  parasitic, *189*, 539, 540
  saprobic, 539, 540
  symbiotic, 544
Fungus imperfecti, *143*, 545, *545*
Fur, 430–431
Fusiform initial, 261
Fusion power, 677

Galactose, 49
Galactosemia, 238, *238*, 242
Galápagos Islands, 30, *30*
Galápagos tortoise, *20*, 618
Galileo, 25, 58
Gallbladder, *411, 413*, 417, 475
Gamete, defined, 150 (*see also* Egg;
  Sperm)
Gametogenesis
  animal, 156, 443, *443*
  defined, 156, 443
  gene activity during, *443*

plant, 157
Gametophyte
  defined, 157, 546
  flowering plant, 276, 277
  green alga, 550
  horsetail, 553
  in life cycle, 157–158, *158*
  lycopod, 552
  moss, 552
  pine, 158, 557–558
Gamma globulin, 55, 377
Ganglia, 329, 332
Ganglion cell, retina, *364*
Gap junction, 82, 307, 380
Garrod, A., 212
Gaseous cycles, 653–654
Gas exchange and transport
  alveolus and capillary, 399–401
  arthropod, *399, 565*
  carbon dioxide diffusion in, 399,
    404
  chordate, *565*
  cnidarian, 398, *565*
  and early land invasions, 513
  echinoderm, *565*
  and emphysema, 407
  fish, 398–399, *398*
  flatworm, *565*
  in gill, 398–399, *398*
  human, 400 *ff.*
  human embryo, 469
  insect, 399, *399*
  land vertebrate, 399–400
  and lung, 399–400
  mechanisms, 400, 404–406
  mollusk, *565*
  oxygen diffusion in, 398–399, 404
  in respiratory system, 400,
    404–406
  and sickle-cell anemia, 172, *173*
  sponge, 398, *565*
  and trachea, 399, *399*
Gas transfer, leaf, 264, 272
Gastric fluid, 47, 414
Gastric inhibitory peptide (GIP),
  413, *413*, 415
Gastrin, 345, *351, 352*, 413, *413*, 414
Gastrointestinal tract, human
  control of, 346, *351, 352*, 412–413
  defined, 411
  disorders, 420
  motility, 412, *412*
  organs of, 413*ff.*, *413*
  structure, 412, *412*
Gastropod (Gastropoda), 573–574,
  574
Gastrovascular cavity, 568, 569
Gastrula, *443, 449*
Gastrulation, 443, *443, 448, 449*, 469
Gause, G., 618
G-banding, chromosome, 184, *185*
Gel state, 89, 385
Gemmule, 441, 566
Gene (*see also* Allele; DNA,
  eukaryotic)

activity in development, 230*ff.*,
  443, 444, 448, 449, 456
allelic states of, 153, 163
complementation, 482
defined, 139, 179
epistatic, 171–172, *171*
linkage, 166, 182
locus, 163
mapping, 152, 183, *184*
modifier, 171–172
mutation within, 207–208, *208*,
  214–215, *215*, 479
pair, 163
pleiotropic, 172, *173*
pool, 481 (*see also* Allele, pool)
recombination (*see*
  Recombination, genetic)
regulator, 225, *226*
replacement, 243, 244
role in cell reproduction, 139
sex-linked, 181, 182
structural, 225
transcription (*see* DNA,
  transcription)
Gene expression
  control of, 223*ff.*, 230*ff.*
  and differentiation, 231*ff.*, 289
  effect of gene interactions on,
    170–172, 498, 682
  and environment, 172–173, 233,
    234, 680–681
  variable, 170*ff.*
Gene flow, 481, 483–484
Genetic code, 214–216, *216*, 222
Genetic counseling, 243–244, *243*
Genetic disorders, human, 170, 207,
  212, 228, 237*ff.*
Genetic drift, 481, 482–483, *483*
Genetic engineering, *189–190*, 206,
  207, 524
Genetic equilibrium, 481
Genetic recombination (*see*
  Recombination, genetic)
Genetic screening, 242, *243*
Genetic variation
  continuous, in polygenic
    inheritance, 175
  and independent assortment, 166
  sources of, 179, 209
Genital herpes, 528
Genome, 227
Genotype (hereditary material), 163,
  165, 209
Genotypic cure, 237–238
Genus, 26–27, *27*, 34, 493
Geoduck, 574–575
Geologic time scale, 495, *495*
Geotropism (*see* Gravitropism)
German measles, 471
Germ cell, 306
Germ layer, 443, *443*
Germination, 73, 277, *278*
Giant moth, *7*
Gibberellic acid, 292
Gibberellin, 291–293, *292, 293*, 301

Gibbon, 190, *591*
Giemsa stain, 184
Gigantism, 350
Gila woodpecker, *283*
Gill
  amphibian, 586
  arch, *398, 469*, 512
  capillary, 377, *377*
  chordate, 585
  fish, 377, 398–399, *398, 586*
  fungal, 542, *543*
  mollusk, 573, *573*
Gill slit, 584, *584, 586*
Ginkgo (Ginkgophyta), 554, 556,
  557
Ginkgo biloba, 497
Giraffe, 12, *14*
Gizzard, 410
Glaciation, 514
Glacier Bay, *644*
Gland
  animal, 309, *310*
  as effector, 320
  endocrine, 309, 345
  exocrine, 309, *310*, 389
  nerve signal to, 333
  plant, 255, *255*
  sweat, 431
Glandular epithelium, 309, 346, *346*,
  351, 352
Glandular organ, 411
Glans penis, 467
Globin, 228
Globulin, 377
Glomerular filtration, *434*
Glomerulus, 433, 434, *435*
Glorybower, *283*
Glottis, 400
Glucagon, *351, 352*, 424–425, *425*,
  426
Glucocorticoid, *351, 352*, 426
Glucose
  in blood, 377
  as digestion product, 415
  formation in photosynthesis, 111,
    118–119, *119*
  metabolism, 123, 124*ff.*, *125*,
    424–426
  structure, *48, 49*
Glutamate (glutamic acid, ionized
  form), *53*, 172, 213, *215*
Glycerol, 50, *51*
Glycine, *53*
Glycogen, 49, *50*, 316, 413, 414
Glycolipid, 52
Glycolysis
  defined, 124
  links with photosynthesis,
    110–111, *110*
  net yield of, 124
  overview of, *125*, 126
  reactions of, 124, *125*, 126–128,
    127
Glycoprotein, 55, 352, 414, 428
Glyoxysome, 73, *73*

Gnetophyte (Gnetophyta), *554*, *557*, *557*
Gnetum, *554*, *557*
Goatfish, *10*
Goblet cell, 309
Golgi bodies, 64, 69, 70, 71–72, *72*, *83*, 148
Gonad, 346, *346*, 352, 459
Gondwana, 508, *510*, 511, 512
Gonium, 537, *537*
Gonorrhea, 527
Gonyaulax, 531
Gorilla, *123*, *143*
Graded potential, 322, 325, 326, 330, *364*
Gradients, types of, 92
Gradualistic model of evolution, 497, *497*
Graft, animal, 391
Graft, plant, 251
Gram, H., 521
Granulocyte, 390
Granum, 75, *75*, 112, *112–113*
Grapes, *123*
Grass, 120
Grasshopper, 152, 179, *330*
Grasshopper mouse, 624, *626*
Grassland, 12, 516, 658, *659*, 662–663
Gravitropism, 296–297, *296*
Gray crescent, *446*, 448, *448*
Gray matter, 331, *332*, 335
Grazing food web, 632–633, *633*, *637*
Great egret, 686, 697
Green alga (Chlorophyta), *10*, 508, 537, 544, 548, *548*, 550, *550*
Green color blindness, 240, *240*
Green revolution, 641
Green tube coral, *12*
Griffith, F., 166, *166*, 204
Gross primary production, 632, 651, 657
Ground meristem, 249–250, *249*, *250*
Grouse, 489, *489*
Growth
  in animal, 205, 345, 350, *350*, 443, *443*, 450
  exponential, 602–603, *604*
  logistic, 605–606, *605*
  membrane, in prokaryotic fission, 140
  mitotic basis of, *140*, 141
  patterns, 450–451, *451*
  plant, 249–250, 289–291, *291*
  population (*see* Population, growth)
Growth hormone, 207, 345, 350, *350*, 450
Guanine, 195–199
Guanosine triphosphate, 219
Guard cell, *254*, 255, 270–271, *271*, 291
Gymnosperm, 249, 255, 256, *510*,

514, 556–558
Gyre, 650

Habitat, 600, 614–615, 616, *616*
Haeckel, E., 33
Haemanthus, *145*
Hair cell, 357, *358*, 359, *359*
Hair follicle, 315
Half-life, radioactive element, *494*
Halobacterium, 522, *522*
Haploid state
  in animal life cycle, 156–157, *156*
  defined, 141
  in fungal life cycle, 539, *540*
  and meiosis, 151
  in plant life cycle, 157–158, *158*, 546–547, *546*, *547*
Hardy, G., 481
Hardy–Weinberg rule, *480*, 481
Harelip, 242
Hargreaves, W., 504
Haversian canal system, 312, *312*
Hawaiian honeycreeper, *496*
Hawkweed, 166
Hay fever, 394
Hayflick, L., 456
Heart
  amphibian, 588
  annelid, 577
  atrium, 378–379, *379*
  beat, 378, 380
  bird, 377, *377*, 588
  contraction (*see* Contraction, cardiac)
  defined, 374, 378
  earthworm, 577
  fish, 377, *377*, 588
  human, 378–381, *379*, 400
  mammal, 377, *377*, 378
  neural control of, *334*
  reptile, 588
  structure, 378, *379*
  valve, 378, *379*
  ventricle, 378–379, *379*
  vertebrate, 313
Heart attack, 387
Heat
  balance, 429
  body, 311, 429
  of fusion, 86
  loss, 429
  production, 429, 430
  of vaporization, 86
HeLa cell, 235
Helianthus, 112, 251
Heliozoan, 534, *534*
Heme group, 54, *54*, *55*, 375
Hemodialysis, 437
Hemoglobin, 52
  as oxygen carrier, *55*, 404–406
  in sickle-cell anemia, 172, 213, *215*
  structure, 54, *54*, *55*, *55*, 215
Hemophilia, 238–240, *239*
Hemorrhage, 385, 389

Hemostasis, 384–385
Henslow, J., 30
Hepatic portal vein, *378*
Herbivore, 630, 632–633, *633*, 644
Hermaphrodite, 441, *564*
Heron, *684*, 685
Herpesvirus, 526, 528–529, *529*
Hershey, A., 194, *196*
Heterospory, *546*, 547
Heterotherm, 429
Heterotroph, *34*, 111, 505, 562
Heterozygote, 163
High-density lipoprotein (HDL), 387
Hindbrain, 332, *333*, *589*
Histamine, 394, 414
Histone, 229, *229*
Holdfast, 550
Holliday, R., 204
Home base, 596
Homeostasis
  cellular, 102
  and circulation system, 375
  defined, 8
  dynamic, 8
  and lymph vascular system, 375
Homeostatic control
  of body fluids, 428, 435–436, *436*
  of body temperature, 428–431, *431*
  and fight-or-flight response, 335
  of glucose metabolism, 424
  and inflammatory response, 389
  of internal environment, 316
  nature of, 8, 316–317
  in population growth, 608
  and systems integration, 317–318
Homing behavior, 684
Hominid, 593–594, *594*
Hominoid, 590, 592–593, 595–596
Homo erectus, 593–594, *593*
Homologous chromosomes
  and crossing over, 152
  defined, 149, 159
  and genetic recombination, 153
  in meiosis, 149ff., 166
Homologous structure, 27, *27*, 497
Homo sapiens, *143*, 593, 594
Homospory, *546*, 547
Homozygote, 163
Honeybee, 680–681, 682, 694–695, 696 (*see also* Bee)
Hooke, R., 58
Hormone, animal (*see also* specific types)
  activation rate, 346
  categories, 345–346
  and childbirth, 317
  concentration, blood, 346
  defined, 309, 345
  in development, 450
  in digestion, 413, *413*, 415
  function, 344–345
  and gonadal function, 461–462, *462*

  in growth and reproduction, 345
  in kidney function, 435–436, *436*, *438*
  invertebrate, 347
  mechanisms, 345–346, *344*, *346*
  in metabolism, *351*, 352
  neural control of, 346
  in neuroendocrine feedback, *348*
  neurosecretory, 344
  ovarian, *351*, 352, 464, *464*
  and red blood cell production, 375–376
  removal from bloodstream, 346
  in reproductive cycle, 442
  in salt and water balance, *351*, 352, 436, *436*, *438*
  secretion control, 348, *348*
  secretion rate, 345
Hormone, plant (*see also* specific types)
  categories, 291, *292*
  defined, 289
  in growth and development, 289, 291ff.
  known and suspected effects of, 292, *292*
  in parthenogenesis, 287
  response to environmental change, 293ff.
  in senescence, 299
Hornwort, 548, 551
Horse, 27, *143*
Horseshoe crab, 486, *486*, 578, 580
Horsetail, *143*, 553, *553*, *554*, 556
House sparrow, *644*
Hubel, D., *338*
Human
  behavior, 696–697
  biotic potential, 602
  birth weight, 485, *485*
  blood type, 168–169
  body cavities, 316, *316*
  body composition, *38*
  body proportions, *451*
  body temperature, 430, 432
  brain, *331*, 335ff., *335*, *336*
  circulation system, 374, 377ff., *378*
  culture, 594, 595
  death, 457–458
  development (*see* Development, animal)
  digestive system, 411ff., *411*
  disease (disorder), 244–245, 386–387, 420, 524, 526–529, *526*, 532, 533, 534, *535*
  ear, 357–359, *358*, *359*
  evolution, 516, 590ff.
  eye, 363, *364–365*
  genetics, 237ff.
  genome, 227
  heart, 378, *379*, 381
  impact on biosphere, 669ff., 677–678
  motor system, 367–368, *367*

Human (continued)
  nervous system, 331, 334
  nutrition, 418–421
  origins, 590ff.
  population doubling time, 610
  population growth, 609ff., 610
  reproductive system, 459–462
    460, 463
  resource utilization by, 640–642,
    669ff.
  respiratory system, 400–401, 401
  skin color, 175
  urinary system, 432–433, 435
  water balance in, 432
Human chromosome
  abnormalities, 240–241
  evolution, 186, 190
  karyotype for, 184, 185
  number, 142, 143
  sex, 180
  structure, 142, 142, 180, 223
Humerus, 367, 368
Hummingbird, 277, 283
Humphreys, T., 306
Hunger, 332
Huntington's chorea, 170–171, 246
Huxley, T., 33
Hybrid, 162, 493
Hybrid infertility, 492
Hybridization, 188, 188, 189, 493
Hydra, 328, 329, 567, 567
Hydrocarbon, 43
Hydrochloric acid, 38, 413
Hydrogen, 38, 40, 40, 41, 264, 265
Hydrogen bonding
  defined, 44
  in DNA double helix, 198, 199
  in liquid water, 44–45, 44, 86–87
  in proteins, 54, 54
  and water transport, plant, 87,
    269, 270
Hydrogen ion (H⁺), 45
  in blood, 296
  in carbohydrate metabolism, 123
  in digestion, 414
  in energy transfers, 108–109
  in evolution of metabolism, 506
  and pH, 45–47, 46
  in photosynthesis, 111, 113, 117,
    118
  in respiration, 405, 406
Hydrologic cycle, 652–653, 653
Hydrolysis, 47–48, 48
  of ATP, 106
  defined, 47–48
  in lysosome, 72
Hydrophilic interaction, 45
Hydrophobic interaction, 45
Hydrosphere, 649
Hydrostatic pressure, blood, 382,
  383, 386, 389, 434
Hydrothermal vent ecosystem, 656
Hydroxide ion (OH⁻), 46
Hydroxyl group, 44, 44, 51
Hyena, 12, 16
Hypertension, 386

Hypertonic solution, 94
Hypha, 540, 541, 542, 542, 543, 543
Hypocotyl, 290
Hypothalamus
  and behavior, 332
  and body temperature, 430, 431
  function, 332
  and gonadal function, 462, 462,
    464, 465, 465
  link with pituitary, 347–350, 347,
    348, 349
  location, 332, 335
  and neuroendocrine feedback
    loops, 348, 348
  secretions, 347–350, 348, 350
  and solute levels, 435–436, 436
Hypothermia, 432
Hypothesis, defined, 21, 22
Hypotonic solution, 94
Hypoxia, 405

IAA (indoleacetic acid), 292, 293
I band, 369
Ice, 86, 87
Identical twin, 174, 396, 456
IgE, 394
IgG, 395
Ilium, 415
Immune response, 376, 390–392,
  391, 395, 396–397, 528, 570
Immune surveillance, 351, 353, 390,
  392
Immune system, 390ff.
Immune therapy, 393–394
Immunity, passive, 394, 395
Immunization, 392
Immunofluorescence, indirect, 77
Impala, 12, 14
Implantation, 464, 466, 466, 468
Imprinting, 681–682, 681
Inborn errors of metabolism, 212
Incisor, 414
Incomplete digestive system,
  409–410, 410
Incomplete dominance, 168, 168,
  176
Independent assortment, 166, 176,
  182
Independent variable, 23
Indigo bunting, 684
Indolacetic acid (IAA), 292
Induced-fit model, enzymes,
  103–104, 104
Induction, lactose operon, 225, 226
Inductive reasoning, 21
Industrial smog, 674
Infectious cycle, bacteriophage, 194,
  195
Infectious mononucleosis, 526,
  529
Inflammation, 389, 391, 396–397
Inflammatory response, 389, 394
Influenzavirus, 526–528, 526, 529
Infrared radiation, 114, 429
Ingram, V., 213, 214

Inhalation, 402–404, 403
Inheritance, defined, 8
Inhibition, feedback, 105, 224
Inhibitory synapse, 325–326
Innate behavior, 680
Innate releasing mechanism, 680
Inner cell mass, 449, 466, 469
Inner ear, 258
Inorganic compound, 43, 47
Insect (see also specific kinds)
  blood circulation, 374
  body temperature, 429
  characteristics, 578–579, 580–581
  classification, 578
  compound eye, 362, 363
  development, 7, 7
  evolution, 514, 578, 580–581
  olfactory receptor, 357
  pollinator, 282, 283
  society, 693–696
Insect-eating plant, 255, 255
Insecticide, 523, 523, 524, 631
Insight learning, 680
Instrumental conditioning, 680
Insulin, 53, 424, 450
  and diabetes, 207, 242, 395
  in organic metabolism, 424–425,
    425, 426
  production and secretion, 351,
    352, 424
Integration, neural, 319, 326, 332,
  365
Integument, seed, 280, 281, 285
Integumentary system, 315
Interferon, 394
Intercalated disk, 379, 379
Intercostal muscle, 402, 403, 404
Intercostal nerve, 403
Interference competition, 618
Interferon, 394
Interkinesis, 151–152
Internal fertilization, 442
Interneuron, 320, 330
Internode, stem, 248, 259
Interphase, 144, 144, 146, 146
Interstitial cell, 459, 460, 462, 462
Interstitial cell stimulating hormone
  (see LH)
Interstitial fluid, 317
Intervertebral disk, 311, 332
Intestine, large (colon), 411, 411,
  413, 417
Intestine, small, 388, 411, 411, 413,
  415–416
Intrinsic clotting mechanism, 385,
  385
Intrinsic factor, 608, 609
Intron, 227–228, 228
Invagination, 400
Inversion, chromosomal, 179, 186,
  208
Invertebrate (see also specific types)
  blood circulation, 374–375
  evolution, 510, 513
  nervous system, 330
  photoreception, 360

sensory organs, 360ff., 360
In vitro fertilization, 472
Iodine, 38
Ion
  in blood plasma, 377
  defined, 39
  formation in water, 47
  roles in cell, 47
  and spheres of hydration, 88
Ionic bonding, 42
Ionic crystal, 42
Iris, eye, 361, 362, 363, 363
Iron, 38, 104, 121, 264, 266
Irritable colon syndrome, 420
Islets of Langerhans, 416 (see also
  Pancreatic islets)
Isogamy, 546, 546
Isoleucine, 419
Isomer, 49
Isotonic solution, 94
Isotope, 39, 194, 196, 201
IUD (intrauterine device), 475, 476

Jacob, F., 224–225
Jade plant, 286, 287
Janssens, F., 183
Japanese beetle, 644
Jaw, evolution of, 512, 585, 585
Jawed fish, 512–513, 582, 585
Jawless fish, 512, 582, 583, 585
Jejunum, 415
Jellyfish, 328, 360, 562, 567 (see also
  Cnidarian)
Johansen, D., 593
Joint, 368, 368
J–shaped curve, 603, 610, 669
Jumping genes, 187
Jumping spider, 366, 367
Jurassic, 495, 511, 514

K (See carrying capacity)
Kalahari Desert, 648
Kangaroo, 445
Kangaroo rat, 431, 433
Karyotype, 184, 185
Katydid, 625
Kelp, 548, 549, 550
Keratin, 314
Kerogen, 675
Ketone, 44, 48
Kettlewell, H., 487
Key character, 498, 506, 512, 561,
  582, 585, 587, 591, 592
Kidney
  artificial, 437
  dialysis, 437
  function, 352, 433–434, 438
  in hormone function, 352,
    375–376
  hormones acting on, 350, 351,
    436, 438
  structure, 432–433, 435
  transplant, 437
Kidney stone, 437

Killer whale, 626, *631*
Kilocalorie, defined, 45
Kinetic energy, 99
Kinetochore, 147
Kingdom (taxon), 27, 34
Kirtland warbler, 627
Klinefelter's syndrome (*see* Trisomy XXY)
Kohler, G., 394
Krakatoa, 248
Krebs cycle, *125*, 126, 128*ff.*, *129*, *130*, *131*, *132*
Krill, 626, *631*, 656
K–selection, 606–607, *606*, 643

Labium (genital), *463*
Labyrinthodont, 513
Lactate, 126, 370, 425
Lactate fermentation, *125*, 126
Lactobacillus, 522, *525*
Lactose, 49, 224, 238
Lactose operon, 225, *226*
Lacunae (uterus), 469
Lake
  acid deposition in, 673
  ecosystem, 655–656, *656*
  succession of, 528
Lamarck, J., 29
Lamarckian theory, 29
Lamella
  bone, 312, *312*
  gill, *398*
  middle, in plant cell, *79*
Lampbrush chromosome, 234, *235*
Lamprey, 582, 644
Lancelet, 582, 584–585, *585*
Language, 340, 343, 682
Laparoscope, 470
Large intestine (colon), 411, *411*, *413*, 417
Larrea, 294
Larva
  bee, *695*
  beetle, 17, *18*, 633
  defined, 454
  fluke, *570*
  grasshopper, 454, *455*
  moth, 7, *7*, 454, *455*
  nematode, *572*
  sawfly, 628
  sea urchin, *443*
  tadpole, 440, *443*
  tunicate, 584, *584*
  yucca moth, *627*
Larynx, 400, *401*, 462
Late blight, 540–541
Latent learning, 680
van Lawick-Goodall, J., 586
Law of the minimum, 604–605
Law of tolerance, 605
Lawless, J., 503
Laurasia, 513
Laurentia, 508, *510*, 512
Leaf
  abscission, 292
  compound, 261

development, 172, 260–261, 290, 292, *292*, 294, *295*
  dicot, *290*, 554
  epidermal specializations, 255, *255*, 261
  function, 261, 264, 272
  gas transfer in, 264, 272
  hormones in, 293
  monocot, 554
  movement, *300*, 301
  primary, *289*, 290
  primordia, *259*, 260
  simple, 261
  structure, 260–261, *261*
  tissue, *249*
  trifoliate, *290*
  vein, 260, *260*
  water movement from, 270–271
Learning, 680, 682
Leech, 576
van Leeuwenhoek, A., 59
Leibig, J., 604
Lemming, *637*, 638, 686
Lens
  in eye, 360, 361, *361*, *362*, 363
  in microscopy, *62*
Leonard, W., 22
Leopard, 615
Leopard seal, *631*
Leucine, 419
Leukemia, 235, *526*
Leukocyte (*see* White blood cell)
Levels of biological organization, 5, *6*, 135
Leyhausen, P., 620
LH (luteinizing hormone), 350, *350*, 461–462, *462*, 464–465, *464*, *465*
Lichen, 544, *544*
Life
  diversity (*see* Diversity of life)
  evolutionary history, 500*ff.*
  molecular basis of, 38
  organization of, 4–5, *6*, 133–135
  origins of, 5, 501–504, *503*
  problems in defining, 2–3
  unity (*see* Unity of life)
Life cycle
  alternation of generations in, 156
  amoeboid protozoan, 533
  animal, 156–157, *156*
  asexual reproduction in, 156, *156*, 534
  defined, 138
  Drosophila, 234
  fern, *556*
  field mushroom, 542, *542*
  flowering plant, 276–277, *278*
  fungal, 540, *540*, 542
  green alga, *551*
  insect, 7, *7*, 234
  moss, *552*
  moth, 7, *7*
  Obelia, 567
  pine, 557–558, *558*
  plant, 157–158, *158*, 547
  Plasmodium, 535

sea lettuce, *551*
  sexual reproduction in, 156, *156*
  slime mold, 231–232
  yucca moth, *267*
Life expectancy, 601, *602*
Life table, 601, *602*
Ligament, *310*, 311, 368
Light
  biological sensitivity to, *114*
  and flowering process, 298, *298*
  focusing, *62*, 360, 363, 364
  and photoperiodism, 353
  and photoreception, 359*ff.*
  and photorespiration, 120
  and photosynthesis, 113–115, *114*, 118
  and phototaxis, 360, 521
  and phototropism, 295–296, *295*
  rays, *114*
  refraction, *62*, 363
  spectrum, *114*
Light-dependent reactions, 111, 113*ff.*, 118
Light-independent reactions, 111, 118–119, *119*
Light microscope, *62*
Lignin, 79, 303
Lilac, *300*, 301
Liliopsida, 249
Lilium, 143
Lily, 143
Limbic system, 341, *589*
Limnetic zone, 655
Limpet, 361
Limulus polyphemus, 486
Lineage, 495
Linkage, gene, 182
Linkage group, 182
Linkage mapping, 183, *184*
Linnaeus, C. (von Linné), 26, 479
Linnean system of classification, 27, *27*
Lion, 12, *16*
Lion fish, *11*
Lion-tiger hybridization, 491
Lipase, pancreatic, 417, *418*
Lipid
  abiotic synthesis of, 502
  assembly in chloroplast, 119
  bilayer, 89, *90*, 91, *91*
  of cell membrane, 89–91
  defined, 50
  metabolism, 132–133, *131*, 351, 352
  structure, 50
  transport in blood, 386–387
Lipoprotein, 56, 377, 387
Liposome, 504, *504*
Lithops, 624, *624*
Lithosphere, 649
Littoral, 655
Liver
  defined, 417
  in digestion, 411, 417, *417*
  functions, 317, 421, 424

and hormones, 340
  human, 411, *411*, 417, *417*, 421, 424
  in organic metabolism, 421, 424, *424*, 425
Liverwort, 548, 551–552, *551*
Lobaria, 544
Lobe-finned fish, 513, *513*
Lobster, 360, 578, *579*, 580
Local breeding unit, 490
Logistic growth, 605–606
Loligo, 323
Long-day plant, 298, *298*
Loop of Henle, 433, 434, *435*, 438
Loose connective tissue, 310–311, *310*, *311*
Lorenz, K., *681*, 682
Lotka, A., 620
Lovejoy, C. O., 595–596
Low-density lipoprotein (LDL), 387
LSD, *342*, 343
Luciferase, *106*
Lucilia, 609
Lucy, 593, *594*, 595
Lumbar nerves, 331
Lumbricus, 143
Lumen, 383
Lung
  artificial, 403
  blood flow, 377, *377*, 378, *378*
  cancer, 407, 672
  capillaries, 377
  in emphysema, *406*, 407
  evolution, 513
  human, 400, 401*ff.*, *401*
  tissue, 400–401
  vertebrate, 399, 585–588, *588*
Lungfish, 513
Luria, S., 194
Luteinizing hormone (*see* LH)
Lwoff, A., 224
Lycopod (Lycophyta), 552, 553, *554*, 556
Lycopodium, 552, *553*
Lyell, C., 30
Lymph, 386
Lymphatic duct, 388
Lymphatic system, 386, *388*, 390
Lymph capillary, 388
Lymph duct, 388
Lymph node, 388, *389*, 390
Lymphocyte
  function, 376, 390
  in lymphoid organs, 388–389
  memory, *391*, 392
  structure, 376
  and thymus, *351*, 353
Lymphoid organ, 386, 388, *388*
Lymphokine, 392
Lymph vascular system, 375, 388, *388*
Lymph vessel, 388, 415, *415*
Lyon, M., 230
Lyonization, 230

Lysine, *53*, 419
Lysis, 194
Lysosome, 64, 72, *73*, *83*, *96*
Lytic pathway, *195*

MacLean, P., *589*
Macroevolution
  defined, 493
  patterns, *494*, 495–497
  time scale for, 494–495, *495*
Macromolecule, 47, 503
Macronutrient, 265, *265*
Macrophage, 388, 390, *391*, 392, *393*
Magnesium, *38*, 264, 266
Magnetic sense, 522, 684–685
Magnoliopsida, 249
Major histocompatibility complex
  (MHC), 395–396
Malaria, 489, 631
Malate, *130*
Malignant cell, 235, 392
Mallard duck, 479, *489*
Malthus, T., 32
Maltose, 49
Mammal (Mammalia)
  body temperature, 429, 430–431
  bone, 311, 312
  characteristics, *587*
  classification, 582, *587*
  estrus in, 462
  evolution, *511*, 514, 516, *517*, *583*, 585, 590–591
  eye, 363
  reproductive strategies, 595–596
Mammary gland, *350*
Manganese, *264*, 266
Mangold, H., 453, *453*
Mantle, 573, *573*, 575
Mantle cavity, 573, *573*, 574, 575
Map sense, 684
Marabou stork, 12, *16*
Margulis, L., 506–507
Marine worm, 576
Marrow, bone, 312–313, 375, 376, *388*
Marsupial, 28
Mass number, *38*, 39
Maternal message, 445, 451
McClintock, B., 187
Mechanoreceptor, 355, 356–359, *358*, 415, 467
Meditation, 340
Mediterranean shrubland, *659*, 661–662
Medulla, kidney, 433, *435*, 438
Medulla oblongata, 332
Medusa, *567*
Megakaryocyte, 377
Megaspore, 277, *278*, 279–280, *281*, 547
Meiosis
  abnormalities during, 185–187, 493
  chromosome rearrangements during, 153, 179

crossing over during, 153, 179, 183, *183*, 203
defined, 141, 158
discovery of, 178
and DNA sequence
  organization, 227
in flowering plant, 277, *278*, 280, *281*
and gametogenesis, 156
independent assortment during, 165, 179
in menstrual cycle, 465
versus mitosis, *140*, 141, 158–159
stages of, 149–153, *150*
summary of, *154*, 158
Meiospore, *156*, 157, 278
Melanin, *171*, 172, 175, 348
Melatonin, 683
Meltdown, 676
Membrane
  cell, 59, 89ff.
  and cell evolution, 133–134, 504
  components, 55
  differential permeability, 91, 320
  diffusion across, 92–93, *92*, 321, 399
  embryonic, 449, 468–469
  excitability, 313, 319
  fluid mosaic model, 89–91, *91*
  function, summary of, 91, 97
  gate, 322, 323
  lipid bilayer of, 89–91
  mitochondrial, 74, *74*, 129, *129*
  nuclear, 68, *69*
  origin of, 504
  plasma, 4, *5*, 59, *83*, 504
  protein, 90, *90*, 91, 95, 117, 322
  pump, 94–95, 321–322, *321*
  shuttle, 131, *131*
  structure, summary of, 91
  thylakoid, 113, 117, 118
Membrane surface receptors
  and cancer, 235, 392
  defined, 95
  function, 95–97
  in hormone action, 345
Membrane transport, 91ff., 257, 320–321, *321*
Memory, 340
Memory lymphocyte, *391*, 392, 396
Memory trace, 340
Mendel, G., 160ff., *160*, 168, 170, 175–176, 178
Mendelian principle of independent
  assortment, 166, 176
Mendelian principle of segregation, 163, 176, 181
Menopause, 462–464
Menstrual cycle, 8, 462–467, *464*, *465*
Meristem, 249–250, *249*, *250*, 290, *291*, 302
Meselson, M., 199, *201*
Mesoderm, 307, *447*, 449, 562–563
Mesoglea, 568

Mesopelagic zone, 656
Mesophyll, 120, *249*, 251, *251*, 260, *261*
Mesosome, 508, *508*
Mesozoic, 495, *495*, *511*, 514
Messenger RNA (*see* RNA, messenger)
Metabolic reaction, 100, 102
Metabolism
  carbohydrate, 122ff., *351*, 352
  defined, *6*
  energy transfers in, 41
  fat, 132–133, *131*
  glucose, 123ff.
  intermediates in, 101
  ion release during, 377
  lipid (fat), *131*, 132–133, *351*, 352
  organic, 421, 424–426
  origin and development of, 505–506, *507*
  pathways of, 101, 505–506
  product of, 100
  protein, 132, *132*, *351*, 352
  rate of, 352, 429
  reactant in, 100
  temperature range for, 429
Metacarpal, *367*
Metamorphosis, 454, *455*, 582
Metaphase
  meiosis, *150–151*, 152, 153, *154*
  mitosis, 144, *144*, *145*, 146–147, *146*, *154*
Metastasis, malignant cell, 235
Metatarsal, *367*
Metatheria, *587*
Metazoan, 508, *509*, 562
Methane, 43, 502
Methanobacteria, 522, *522*, 525
Methanogen (methane-producing
  bacterium), 126, 521, 522, *522*
Methionine, 216, *216*, 222, 419
Methyl mercury, 673
MHC (major histocompatibility
  complex), 395–396
Micelle, 417
Microbody, 64, 73, *73*, *83*
Microfilament
  in animal embryo, 450
  in cytokinesis, 148
  in cytoplasmic lattice, 76, 77, *77*
  and cytoplasmic streaming, *78*
  defined, 77
  roles of, 77–78, *83*
  structure, 77
Micronutrient, 265–266, *265*
Micropyle, 280, *281*
Microscopy, 58–59, 61, *62–63*, 178
Microsphere, 4, *4*, 504, *504*
Microspore, 277, *278*–279, *278*, *279*, 302, 547
Microtubular spindle
  in meiosis, 153
  in mitosis, 144–145, *146*, 148
  role of, 143
  structure, *143*, *144*

Microtubule
  in animal embryo, 450
  of cilium, 80
  in cytoplasmic lattice, 76, *76*, *77*, 78
  of flagellum, 80, *81*
  and plant cell wall formation, 78
  in plant embryo, 289
  of pseudopod, 385
  roles of, 78, *83*
  structure, 78, *78*
Microtubule organizing center
  (MTOC), 78, *83*, 145
Microvillus
  fine structure, 79, *79*
  intestinal, 415, *416*
  of photoreceptor, 361, *362*, 363
  sponge, 566, *566*
Midbrain, 332, *333*, *589*
Middle earbones, *358*
Miescher, J., 192
Migration
  animal, 651, 684–685
  bird, 684–685
  cell, *448*, 449, 450
  defined, 684
  monarch butterfly, *652*
Miller, S., 502, *502*
Milliosmole, *438*
Millipede, 578, 580–581
Millivolt, 321
Milstein, C., 394
Mimicry
  aggressive, *622*, 685
  Batesian, *622–623*
  defined, 488, 624
  Müllerian, *622–623*
  speed, *622–623*
Mineral
  in bone, *310*, 311
  in human nutrition, 421, 423
  in plant function, 266–267, *266*
  intake during pregnancy, 470
Mineralocorticoid, *351*, 352
Miocene, *495*, 592, 595
Miracidia, *570*
Mitochondrial code, 222
Mitochondrion
  ATP formation in, 74, 117, 124, *125*, 128ff.
  function, 64, *83*
  membrane, 74, *74*, 129, *129*, 131, *131*
  number in cells, 74
  origin, 222
  size, 74
  structure, 74, *129*
Mitosis
  and cell cycle, 144, *144*
  defined, 141, 144
  discovery of, 178
  length of, 144, *144*
  and life cycle, 156, *156*
  versus meiosis, 141, 149, *154*, 158

Mitosis (continued)
  and number of chromosome sets, 141
  origin of term, 144
  stages of, 144ff.
  summary of, 158
Modifier gene, 171–172
Molar, 413, 592, 593
Mold, 212
Mole (unit of measure), 45
Molecule, 6, 39
Molecular basis of life, 38, 340
Molecular motion, 88, 92, 99
Mollusk (Mollusca)
  body plan, 562, 573, 573
  characteristics, 564, 573–575
  classification, 563, 564, 572
  digestive system, 410
  evolution, 508, 512, 572
  eye, 361–362, 361
Molting, 454, 455
Molybdenum, 264, 266
Monarch butterfly, 652
Monera (Moneran) (see also Bacterium), 34, 34
Monkey, 590, 592
Monoclonal antibody, 394
Monocot
  characteristics, 249
  classification, 554, 559
  floral structure, 554, 559
  growth and development, 257, 285, 285, 290ff.
  root, 257, 267
  seed, 285, 285
  stem, 250
Monocrop agriculture, 541
Monocyte, 376, 376, 390
Monod, J., 224–225
Monoecious, 564–565
Monoglyceride, 51, 415, 416
Monohybrid cross, 161, 162–165, 176
Monosaccharide, 48–49, 49, 415, 416, 418
Monosomy, 187
Monotreme, 445
Monsoon grassland, 622–623
Moorhead, P., 456
Moray eel, 11
Morel, 542, 543
Morgan, T., 179ff.
Morphogenesis, 450–453
Morula, 443, 449, 468
Mosaic evolution, 498
Mosaic theory, image formation, 363
Moscona, A., 306
Mosquito, 143, 357, 534, 535
Moss, 548, 551–552, 551, 552
Moth, 7, 7, 356, 429, 486–488, 487, 685
Motor cortex, 336, 336
Motor end plate, 369
Motor neuron

axon, 326, 327
  defined, 320
  and muscle contraction, 326–327, 327, 369, 370–371, 372
  in reflex arc, 327–328, 328
  structure, 320
Motor score, 680
Motor system
  annelid, 367
  arthropod, 366, 578–579
  basis of, 366
  bird, 366, 368
  categories, 366
  of cells, 366
  cephalopod, 574
  earthworm, 366, 367
  echinoderm, 581, 581
  human, 367–368, 367
  sea anemone, 366–367, 366
  sea star, 366
  spider, 366, 367
  vertebrate, 311, 367
Motor unit, 369
Moufet, T., 26
Mountain avens, 644
Mount Saint Helens, 248
Mouth (oral cavity), 413–414, 413
Movement
  cellular, 76ff.
  of cilia, 80–81, 81
  of flagella, 80–81, 81
  lever system of, 311
  neural control of, 332, 336, 336
  peristaltic, 412, 412
  segmentation, 412, 412
  systems of (see Motor system)
Mucin, 414
Mucosa, 412, 412, 413, 414–415
Mucus, 413, 466
Mule, 492
Muller, F., 622
Mullerian mimicry, 622–623
Multicellularity
  defined, 6
  evolution of, 537–538
  nature of, 61, 61
Muscle
  antagonistic movement, 368, 368
  attachment to bone, 311, 367–368, 369
  cardiac, 313, 313, 368, 379–380, 380, 381
  contraction (see Contraction, muscle)
  cramping, 425
  as effector, 320
  eye, 362, 363, 364
  fiber, 313, 368, 369, 369, 370, 372, 379, 380
  and heat production, 313
  joint, 368, 368
  lactate build–up in, 370
  and motor cortex, 336
  rigor, 370

skeletal, 313, 313, 368–369, 370, 374
smooth, 313, 313, 368
spasm, in hemorrhage, 385
sphincter, 383, 412
spindle, 328, 328
striated, 313 (see also Muscle, skeletal)
summary of, 372
system, 315 (see also Motor system)
tissue, 308, 310, 313
tone, 373
twitch, 372, 373
in ventilation, 402–404, 403
Mushroom, 542, 542, 543
Musk oxen, 690, 691
Mutation
  and allele frequency, 481
  base-pair substitution, 207, 208, 213, 215
  chromosomal, 179, 185ff., 207, 208
  defined, 8–9, 481
  and diversity, 209, 479
  and environment, 208, 482
  and evolution, 208–209
  frameshift, 207, 208, 215
  gene, 207, 208, 214–215, 215
  harmful, 482
  induced, 212
  inevitability of, 207, 482
  load, 482
  molecular, 207, 208, 208
  nutritional, 212–213, 213
  sex-linked, 239–240
  and sexual reproduction, 482
  summary of, 208
Mutualism, 617, 617, 626–627, 627
Mycelium, 539–540, 542, 542
Mycena, 106
Mycoplasma, 522, 524, 525
Mycorrhiza (fungus-root), 268, 268, 544, 626, 664
Myelinated axon, 324, 331
Myelin sheath, 324, 324
Myers, C., 609
Myocardium, 378, 379, 380, 381, 382
Myofibril, 369–370, 369
Myosin, 77, 148, 366, 369, 370–372, 371, 372

NAD$^+$ (nicotinamide adenine dinucleotide, oxidized), 104, 108, 108, 123, 124
NADH (nicotinamide adenine dinucleotide, reduced)
  formation in carbohydrate metabolism, 123, 124ff., 130
  function, 108, 108, 123
  use in aerobic respiration, 129ff.
NADP$^+$ (nicotinamide adenine dinucleotide phosphate, oxidized), 108, 108, 111, 118

NADPH (nicotinamide adenine dinucleotide phosphate, reduced)
  formation in photosynthesis, 111–112, 116–117, 116
  function, 108–109, 108
  and photosensitivity, 114
  use in light-independent pathway, 118–119
Nanometer, defined, 60, 60
Nasal cavity, 400, 401
Natural selection (see also Selection, natural)
  and allele frequencies, 481
  and behavior, 686ff.
  defined, 13, 481
  and dimorphism, 485
  and evolution, 32–33, 481
  examples of, 484–490
  modes of, 484–485, 485, 488
  and polymorphism, 485, 489
  theory of, 32, 484
Nautilus, 10, 512, 573, 575
Neanderthaler, 594
Nearsightedness, 364
Nectaries, 255
Neel, J., 213
Negative feedback, 225, 317, 414, 450, 462, 465
Neisseria, 522, 527
Nematocyst, 568, 568
Nematode (Nematoda)
  characteristics, 47, 86, 564, 571–572
  classification, 563, 564
  parasitic, 571, 572
  as prey, 545
Neocortex, 589
Nephridium, 573, 577, 577
Nephron, 433–434, 435
Nerem, R., 387
Nerve
  auditory, 358
  defined, 338
  human, 331
  intercostal, 403
  invertebrate, 330
  optic, 339–340, 339
  parasympathetic, 333, 334, 413
  phrenic, 403
  sympathetic, 333, 334, 413
Nerve cell (see Neuron)
Nerve cord, 330, 330, 588
Nerve impulse (see Action potential)
Nerve message
  basis of, 320–324, 325
  information content, 337–338
Nerve net, 328–329
Nerve tissue, 308, 310
Nervous system
  annelid, 330
  arthropod, 330
  autonomic, 331, 332, 333, 334, 380
  bilaterally symmetrical, 329–330
  central, 330, 331–332, 331

Nervous system (continued)
  components, 320
  cnidarian, 328–329, *329*
  drug effects on, 342–343, *342*
  earthworm, *330*
  evolution, 328–330, 347
  flatworm, *330*
  function, 315, 319–320, 330
  grasshopper, *330*
  human, *331*, *334*
  integration in, 326
  invertebrate, *330*
  links with endocrine system,
    347–348, *348*
  operating principles of, 330
  organization, 319–320, 326
  peripheral, 330, *331*, 332–333
  radially symmetrical, 328, *329*
  shrimp, *330*
  snail, *330*
  somatic, *331*, 332, 333
  vertebrate, 330–335, *331*
Net primary production, 632
Net protein utilization, 419, *419*
Neural control
  of behavior, 332, 348, 679, 682
  of blood distribution, 381
  of body temperature, 430, *431*
  of breathing, 403–404
  of gastrointestinal tract, 412–413
  of hormones, 346
  of organic metabolism, 424
Neural fold, *447*
Neural plate, *447*, 450, 452
Neuroendocrine control center,
  347–348, *348*
Neuroglia, 320, 324
Neuromotor response, 373, 679
Neuromuscular junction, 326–327,
  327, 369
Neuron
  classes of, 319–320
  defined, 312, 319
  embryonic precursor, 450
  function, 319
  information-processing zones,
    320, *320*
  life span, 340
  message conduction, 320–324,
    325
  modifications to, 340
  myelinated, 323–324, *324*
  structure, *319*, 320, *320*
  synapsing, 319, 325–327, *338*
Neurosecretory hormone, 344–345,
  347
Neurospora crassa, 212, *213*, 541–542
Neurotoxin, 524, 531
Neurotransmitter (*see* Transmitter
  substance)
Neutron, 5, 39
Neutrophil, 376, *376*
Newt, 450, *452*
Niche, 615–616, *617*, 618
Nicholson, A., *609*
Nicolson, G., 89

Nicotinamide adenine dinucleotide
  (*see* NAD$^+$ and NADH)
Nicotinamide adenine dinucleotide
  phosphate (*see* NADP$^+$ and
  NADPH)
Nilsson-Ehle, H., 175
Nitrate, 121, 126
Nitrification, 638, *639*
Nitrifying bacteria, 121, 638
Nitrite, 121
Nitrogen, *38*
  abundance in human body, *38*
  in agriculture, 639
  in atmosphere, 638
  fixation, *267*, 638, *639*
  gaseous, 267, *267*, 638
  oxides of, 672–674
  in peat, 637, *644*
  in plant function, *264*, *266*, 267,
    267
Nitrogen cycle, 638–639, *639*, 653
Nitrous oxide, 638
Nocireceptor, 355
Node, stem, 248, 259, 261, 286, *287*,
  289, *290*
Node of Ranvier, 324, *324*
Nodule, legume root, 267, *267*
Noncyclic photophosphorylation,
  116–117, *116*, *118*
Nondisjunction, 187, 240, 241, 246
Norepinephrine, 325, 335, 341, *342*,
  351, 352
North American grouse, 489, *489*
Northern sea lion, 488–489, *489*
Nose, 311, 356, 400, *401*
Notochord, *447*, 582, 583, 584, *584*
Nuclear energy, 675–677
Nuclear envelope, 68, *68*, *69*, 508
Nuclear pore, 68, *69*
Nuclear wastes, 676–677
Nucleic acid, 56–57, 417
Nucleoid, 59, 64, *64*, *83*
Nucleolus, *68*, *69*, *83*, 146, *146*, 227
Nucleoplasm, 68, *68*
Nucleoprotein, 56, 142, 229
Nucleosome, *228*, 229–230, *229*
Nucleotide
  abiotic synthesis of, 502
  categories of, 56–57
  defined, 194
  DNA, 56, 139, 194*ff.*
  RNA, 211
  structure, *44*, 56, 194–195
  triplet, genetic code, 214–215,
    215, *216*
Nucleotide coenzyme, 56
Nucleus, atomic, 39
Nucleus, cell
  defined, 59
  division of, *140*, 141*ff.*
  function, 59, 68, *83*
  micrographs of, *68*, *69*
  origin, 508
  of red blood cell, 375
  structure, 68–69, *69*
Nudibranch, 573, 574, *574*, 679

Nutria, *644*
Nutrient cycling, 635–639
Nutrient flow, model of, 635, *636*
Nutrient recovery hypothesis, 638
Nutrition
  animal, 409
  defined, 409
  E. coli, 224
  fungi, 212
  human, 418–421
  human embryo, 468–469, 470
  plant, 265–267, *265–267*
Nutritional mutant, 212, *213*
Nymph, 454

Oak, 280, 302–304, *303*
Oat, 262, 293, 295
Obelia, 567
Obligate anaerobe, 521
Occipital lobe, 336, *336*, 339
Ocean (sea)
  characteristics of, 428
  currents, 649, 650–651, *651*
  ecosystems, 656–658
  origin and evolution, 502*ff.*,
    510
  zones, 656
Oceanic ridge, *509*
Ocelli (eyespots), 360–361, *361*,
  530
Octopus, 330, 361–362, *361*, 512,
  573, 575
Oil, 45, 675
Oil shale, 675
Okazaki, R., 201
Olfaction, 356
Olfactory receptor, 356, *357*
Oligocene, *495*
Oligotropic lake, 656
Ommatidium, *362*, 363
Omnivore, *630*
Onchyophora, 581, *581*
One gene, one enzyme, 213
One gene, one polypeptide, 214
Oocyte, 157, *157*, 230, 444–447, 451,
  463
Oogamy, 546, *546*
Oogenesis, 157, *157*
Oogonium, 157, *157*
Ooplasmic localization, 451
Open circulation system, 374
Operator (DNA site), 225, *226*
Operculum, 398, 568, 586
Operon, 224–225, *226*
Ophioglossum, 143
Opossum, *445*
Optic chiasma, 335
Optic lobe, 332
Optic nerve, 339, *339*, 363, 364–365
Orangutan, *143*
Orbital, electron, 40, *40*, 43, 54
Orchid, 277, 282, 283, 285, 286
Ordovician, *495*, 508, *510*, 512
Organ, 6, 307, 314, *315*

Organelle, 6, 64
Organ of Corti, 358, *359*
Organ of equilibrium, 357–358
Organ formation, *442*, 443, *443*, *451*,
  469
Organic compound, 43, 502
Organic metabolism, 421, 424–426
Organic soup, 502
Organogenesis, 443, *443*
Organ system, *6*, 308, 314, 315, *315*
Orgasm, 467
Origin of life, 5, 501–504, *503*
Osculum, 566, *566*
Osmoregulation (*see* Solute
  regulation; Water, regulation)
Osmosis, 92, *92*, 93–95, *95*
Osmotic pressure gradient
  in capillary bed, 382, *383*, 386, 389
  in kidney, 434
  in phloem, 274
  in plant cell, 267, 272
  in xylem, 269, 274
Osmotic shocking, 196
Osseous tissue (*see* Bone)
Ossification, 312
Osteichthyes, 586
Osteoblast, 310, 312–313
Osteoclast, 310, 312–313
Otolith, 359
Oval window, 358
Ovarian function, 464–465
Ovary, animal
  defined, 442, 462
  and hormones, *350*, 351
  human, 462–465, *462*, *463*, *465*
Ovary, plant, 278, *278*, *279*–280,
  280, 281
Overcrowding, studies of, 609
Oviduct, 462, *462*, 463
Oviparity, 444, *445*
Ovoviparity, 444, *445*
Ovulation, 463, 464, 465, 466
Ovule, 279–280, *281*, 285, 558
Ovum (*see* Egg)
Owl, 586, 626
Oxaloacetate, 120, *130*
Oxidation, 108, 501
Oxidation-reduction reaction
  in carbohydrate metabolism,
    122–123, 126
  nature of, 108–109
  in photosynthesis, 116
Oxidative phosphorylation (*see*
  Electron transport
  phosphorylation)
Oxygen, *38*
  abundance in human body, *38*
  acquisition, by animals, 398–399
  and aerobic respiration, 117, 124,
    129, 133, 506
  atmospheric, 133, *405*, 506
  in blood, *55*, 375, 382, *383*
  by-product of photosynthesis,
    111, 133
  diffusion in water, 398
  as electron acceptor, *108*, 109, 124

Oxygen (*continued*)
free, effect on biological molecules, 501
partial pressure, 404–405, *404, 405*
and plant function, *264,* 265
in respiratory system, 398ff.
Oxyhemoglobin, 375, 404–405
Oxytocin, 317, *348, 349, 350*
Ozone layer, atmosphere, 649

Pacemaker, 380
Pain, 332, 336, 337, 341, *342,* 355, 389
Pair bonding, 596, 687
Paleocene, *495*
Paleoecology, 517
Paleozoic, 495, *495,* 508, *510*
Palisade mesophyll, 260, *261*
Palm, *603*
Pancreas, 411, *411, 413,* 416–417, *417*
Pancreatic islets, 346, *346, 351,* 352, 395, 416
Pandemic disease, 526
Pandorina, 537, 537
Pangea, *511,* 514
PANS (peroxyacylnitrates), 674
Papilio dardanus, 488, 488
Papovavirus, *526*
Parallel evolution, *494, 495,* 496, 575
Paramecium, 63, 535, *536,* 618, *619*
Paramyxovirus, *526*
Paranoid schizophrenia, 342
Parapatric speciation, 493
Parapodium, 577, 578
Parasite
bacterial, 521
characteristics, 627–628
cowbird, 627–628
flatworm, 569, 570
fluke, 627
fungal, 539, 540–541, 542
nematode, 571, *572*
Plasmodium, 534
protozoan, 532, 533, 534
social, 627–628
Trichenella, 572
Parasitism, 521, *617,* 618, 627–628
Parasitoid, 627–628
Parasympathetic nerve, *331, 333, 334, 335,* 413
Parathyroid, 346, *346, 351,* 352
Parathyroid hormone, *351, 352*
Parazoa (*see* Sponge)
Parenchyma, 251, *251,* 286
Parietal lobe, *335*
Parthenogenesis, 286, *286*
Partial pressure (respiratory system)
carbon dioxide, 404–405, *404*
oxygen, 404–405, *404*
Parvovirus, *526*
Passion flower (*Passiflora*), 283
Passive immunity, 394, 395
Passive transport, 92, *92*
Patella, *367*

Pattern formation, embryo, 450
Pauling, L., 197–198, 213
Pavlov, I., 680
Pea (*Pisum sativum*), 161ff., *161, 280, 287, 295*
Peacock, *314*
Peat, 637, *644,* 653
Pectin, 149, 251
Pectoralis major, *367*
Pedigree diagram
examples of, *174, 239*
symbols used in, *174*
tracking traits with, 237
Pellicle, 530, *530*
Pelvic girdle, 28, *28, 367,* 368
Pelvic inflammatory disease, 528
Penetrance, 170–171
Penguin, 608, 631
Penicillin, 434, 545
Penicillium, 47, 143, 545
Penis, 433, 442, *459, 460,* 461, 467, 569
PEP (phosphoenol pyruvate), 120, *127*
Peppered moth, 486–488, *487*
Pepsin, 414
Pepsinogen, *413,* 414
Peptic ulcer, 414–415
Peptidase, 414
Peptide bond, 53, *53,* 414
Peptidoglycan, 521, 522
Pepys, S., 244
Perception, stimulus
color, 336, *364–365*
of environmental change, 288, 294, 297–302, 651, 683–685
information coding in, 337–338
odor, 356
pain, 336, 337
pressure, 337, 356–359
sound, 337, 357, *358*
visual, 337, *338*
Perennial, 277, 297
Perforation plate, 253, *253*
Pericycle, *256, 257, 257, 258, 258,* 302
Periderm, 256, 258, *258*
Peripatus, 581
Peripheral nervous system, 330, *331,* 332–333
Peristalsis, 412, *412,* 414, 461
Peritoneum, 562–563
Peritubular capillary, 433–434, *438*
Permafrost, 637, *637*
Permian, *495,* 508, *511,* 514
Peroxisome, 73
Pesticide resistance, 487–488
Petal, 277, *278*
Petral, *631*
Pfr (phytochrome), 294–295, 298, *300,* 301
PGA (phosphoglyceric acid), 118–119, *119,* 120, *120*
PGAL (phosphoglyceraldehyde), 118, 119, *119,* 120, *127,* 128

pH
and cell functioning, 46–47
and enzyme activity, 104–105, 224
in gastrointestinal tract, 414
of human semen, 461
and oxygen transport, 405, 406
scale, 46–47, *46*
of soil, 121
Phaeophyta, 428, *428–429, 429, 432,* 567
Phagocytosis, 95, *96,* 376, 389, 390, *391, 396,* 406
Phalange, *367*
Pharynx, 400, *401,* 410, 414, 513, 569, 576
Phaseolus, 248
Phenothiazine, *342*
Phenotype
defined, 163
environmental effects on, 172–173, 176
factors governing, 171
and penetrance, 170–171
Phenotypic "cure," (treatment), 237, 242ff.
Phenylalanine, *53,* 419
Phenylketonuria (PKU), 212, 242–243, 246
Pheromone, 356, *624*
Phloem, *249,* 254, *254,* 273–274
Phosphate group, 44, 106
Phosphate, inorganic, 106
Phosphoenol pyruvate (*see* PEP)
Phosphofructokinase, 132
Phosphoglyceraldehyde (*see* PGAL)
Phosphoglyceric acid (*see* PGA)
Phospholipid, 44, 52, 89, *91,* 377
Phosphorus, *38*
abundance in human body, *38*
in human nutrition, 421, *423*
in plant function, *264, 266*
Phosphorus cycle, 654
Phosphorylation
and ATP, 107, 115
in carbohydrate metabolism, 122–123
defined, 107
oxidative (*see* Electron transport phosphorylation)
and protein function, 223
Photochemical oxidant, 674
Photochemical smog, 674
Photolysis, *116,* 117, 118
Photon, 113, *114,* 355, 359
Photoperiodism, 353
Photophosphorylation
cyclic, 115, *115,* 118
noncyclic, 116–117, *116,* 118
simplest known system, 522
Photoreception, 359–363, *364*
Photoreceptor, 355, 360, *361, 362*
Photorespiration, 120
Photosensitivity, *114*
Photosynthesis, 6
and carbon cycle, 653, *654*

chemical equations for, 111
defined, 111
in ecosystem, 629, 632–633, *633, 634,* 656
electron excitation in, 40, 41
and evolution of life, 115–117, 133
light–dependent reactions, 111, *112,* 113ff.
light–independent reactions, 111, 118–119
links with respiration, 110–111, *110*
origin of, 506
overview of, 111–112
rate of, 120–121
and stomatal action, 270–272
summary of, 118, 119, *120*
use of products from, 119–120
Photosynthetic autotroph, 111
Photosynthetic bacterium, 115–116, 521, *522*
Photosystem, *113,* 114ff., *115, 116*
Phototaxis, 360, 521
Phototropism, 295–296, *295*
Phrenic nerve, 403
Phycobilin, 523, 548
Phycocyanin, *114*
Phycoerythrin, *114*
Phyletic evolution, 497, *497*
Phylogenetic system of classification, 34
Phylum, 27, 34, 493
Phytochrome, 294–295, 298, *300,* 301, 303
Phytophthora, 540–541
Phytoplankton, 516, 530
Pigeons, 31, *32,* 614
Pigment, animal
bile, 417
light-absorbing, 360, *362, 363, 364–365*
melanin, *171,* 172
oxygen-carrying, 52, *55*
Pigment, plant
photosynthetic, 52, 75, *83,* 113–115, *114,* 118, 522, *549*
phototropic, 296
phytochrome, 294–295, 298, 301
Pigmy chimpanzee, *590*
The Pill, 475, *475*
Pillar coral, 12
Pilus, 205
Pine (*Pinus*), *143, 263,* 268, *268,* 554, 557–558, *558, 559*
Pineal gland, 346, 353, 683
Pinnae, 191, *358*
Pinocytosis, 95, *96*
Pioneer species, 643, *644*
Pisum sativum, 143, 161
Pit, in secondary walls, 252, 253, *253*
Pitelka, F., 638
Pith, 250, *250, 257, 258*
Pituitary, 346
and gonadal function, 462, *462,*

Pituitary (*continued*)
464, 465, *465*
link with hypothalamus, 347–350, *348, 349,* 430
location, *335, 346*
secretions, 348–350, *350*
structure, 347–348, *348*
Placenta, 469, *470*
Placoderm, *583,* 585
Planarian, 410, *411*
Plant (Plantae) (*see also specific divisions*)
annual, 297
aquatic, 249
biennial, 297
breeding, *189–190*
characteristics, overview, 248–249
classification, *34,* 35–36, *35*
defined, *34*
development, 249–250, 284–286, 288*ff.*
diseases, *80, 189,* 524, 540–541
divisions, 548, *548, 554*
dry weight, 265
energy demands, 115
evolution, 116, 508*ff., 510,* 546–547, 560
flowering, 249*ff.,* 288*ff., 515, 544,* 558–559, *559,* 624–626
growth, nature of, 249–250, 256–262, 288–291, *291*
hormonal responses, 289, 291*ff.*
insect-eating, 255, *255*
invasion of land, 513, *514*
life cycle (*see* Life cycle)
monocot versus dicot, 249, 250, 257, 259, *260*
nonvascular, 249, 546, *548*
nutrition (*see also* Photosynthesis), 265–267, *266*
perennial, 278, 297
pollinators, 280–282, *283–284, 491, 492, 547,* 626
polypoid, 187–188
reproduction (*see* Reproduction, plant)
reproductive trends, 546–547, *546*
responses to environment, 259, 293*ff.*
role in biosphere, 560
tissues, 249*ff.*
toxins, *621,* 622
types of, 248–249
"typical," 248–249, *248*
vascular, 248*ff.,* 552*ff.*
Plant cell
chromosomes, 179
examples of, *4, 66*
generalized, *65*
types of, 251–254
wall, 65, *65, 66, 79, 79*
water movement in, *94*
Plant physiology, 265
Planula, 329, *567,* 568
Plaque, 386–387, *387*
Plasma, blood, 317, 375, 377

Plasma cell, 376, 388, 390, *391*
Plasma membrane (*see* Membrane, plasma)
Plasma protein, 375, 377, 389
Plasmid, 205–206, *206*
Plasmodesmata, 82, *82*
Plasmodium, 489, 534, *535*
Plastid, 64, *83*
Platelet, 376–377, *376, 384,* 385
Plate tectonic processes, 508, *509*
Platyhelminthes, 563, *564*
Pleiotropism, 172, *173*
Pleistocene, *495,* 592
Plesiosaur, *515*
Pleural sac, 401–402, *402*
Pliocene, *495,* 517
Pneumonia, 193, 524
Polar body, 157, *157*
Polarity
in animal zygote, 445–448
of charge, neural membrane, 320–321, 322
in covalent bond, 43
in dividing nucleus, 143
in oocyte and egg, 445–448
in plant zygote, 284, *284,* 289
in water molecule, 43, 133
Polio vaccine, 392
Poliovirus, 392, 403
Pollen grain, 158, 277, 278, 279, *279,* 547, 557–558
Pollen tube, 277, 279, *279,* 558, *558*
Pollination, 277, *278, 279,* 280
Pollinator, 280–282, *283–284,* 491, *492, 547,* 626
Pollutant, defined, 669
Pollution
air, 486–487, 672–674, *674*
solid-waste, 670
water, 670–672, *673*
Poly–A tail, 227, *228*
Polychaete, 575, *575*
Polydactyly, 172–174, *174*
Polygene, 175
Polygenic inheritance, 175
Polymer, 47
Polymorphism, 485, 489–490
Polyp, 329, *567*
Polypeptide, 53, *53, 54, 55,* 70, 214, 215
Polypeptide hormone, 345–346, *345*
Polyploidy, 141, 187–188, *208,* 493
Polysaccharide
digestion, 413, *418*
in plant cell wall, 291
structure, 49
Polysome (Polyribosome), 219
Polytene chromosome, *178,* 184
Pons, *335,* 341
Population
carrying capacity, 605, *605, 606–607, 606*
defined, *6,* 479, 600
density, 600–601
distribution, 600–601
doubling time, 602

growth, 601, 602*ff.,* 620
human, 609*ff.*
rate of increase, 602
size, 601, *619*
variation in, 31–32, 479*ff.*
Porifera (*see* Sponge)
Porpoise, *691*
Portal vessels, hypothalamic, 349, *349*
Porter, K., 76
Positive feedback, 317, 322, 325, 339, 415
Post-absorptive state, 424
Posterior (of transverse plane), *560*
Potassium, *38*
abundance in human body, *38*
gated channel, 322, 325
in human nutrition, *423*
in nerve function, 320–323, *321*
in plants, *264, 266,* 267
and stomatal action, 271, *271*
Potato, 119, *143,* 188, 540–541
Potential energy, 99
Powdery mildew, 542
Poxvirus, *526*
Prairie, *661,* 662
Precambrian, *495,* 508, 572, 581
Precapillary sphincter, 383
Predation, 614, 620, 625
camouflage in, 624, *625*
coevolution in, 622
and dilution effect, 690
energy outlay for, 626
mimicry in, 622, *622–623*
models of, 620–621
parasitism as, 618
and population growth, 608–609
and seed dispersal, 624–626
as symbiotic interaction, *617,* 618
Predator
animal, *564,* 600
fungal, 545, *545*
protistan, 534–537, *536,* 600
Pregnancy, human
defined, 467
and Down's syndrome, 240, *241,* 243
and drugs, 471–473
infection during, 471
nutrition during, 470
and smoking, 473
stages of, 469
and syphilis, 528
weight gain during, 470
Premature birth, human, 469–470
Premotor cortex, *336*
Prenatal diagnosis, 243–244, *244*
Pressure flow theory, 274
Pressure gradient, 92
Prey capture
Amoeba-ciliate, *96*
Didinium-Paramecium, 536
leopard-baboon, *615,* 620
lion-zebra, *16*
lynx-hare, *620*

mouse-beetle, *626*
spider-fly, *625*
Price, P., 628
Primary endosperm cell, 280
Primary immune response, 390–392, *391,* 396–397
Primary productivity, 632
Primary root, 290
Primary structure, protein, 53, 54
Primary succession, 643, *644*
Primary treatment, waste water, 671
Primary wall, plant cell, 79, *79, 251*
Primate (Primates)
characteristics, 592
evolution, 186, 190, 590*ff.*
origins, 590–591
Primordial follicle, *463,* 464
Principle, biological, 20, 24
Probability, 163–165
Proboscis, 7, 576
Procambium, 249–250, *249, 250*
Process, nerve, 320
Prochloron, 537
Producer, *19,* 600
Profundal zone, *655*
Progesterone, *351,* 464–466, *464, 465*
Proglottid, 570–571, *571*
Prokaryote
defined, *34,* 64
versus eukaryote, 64–65, 224, 227
gene regulation, 224*ff.*
genome, 227
organelles, 64, *83*
origins, 504–505
reproduction (*see* Reproduction, prokaryotic)
Prokaryotic fission, 140, *140, 141*
Prolactin, 350, *350*
Proline, *54, 56,* 216, *216*
Promoter (DNA site), 217, 225, *226*
Prophase
meiosis, *150,* 152–153, *154*
mitosis, 144–146, *144, 145, 146*
Prosimian, 590
Prostaglandin, 353, 394, 461
Prostate gland, *457, 460,* 461, 467
Protein
agricultural source of, 640–641
assembly sites, 64, 70, 119, 139
in cell reproduction, 139, *139*
in clot formation, 385–386
denaturation, 55
digestion, 414, 415, *418*
diverse roles of, 52–53, 55
gate, 322, 323
membrane, 90, *90,* 91, 95, 117, 322
metabolism, 132, *132, 351, 352,* 421, 424
plasma, 375, 377, 389
repressor, 225, *226*
structure, 53*ff.*
transport, in plants, 273
utilization, human, 640–641

Protein kinase, 345–346
Protein synthesis
  control of, 223ff.
  and endoplasmic reticulum, 70
  origin of, 502–503
  stages of, 216–220, *220*
  summary, 211, *211*, 220–221
Proteus, 522, 525
Prothrombin, 385
Protistan (Protista)
  characteristics, 529–530
  classification, *34, 35, 35*
  defined, *34*
  evolution, 532
  heterotrophic, 531, 532, 533, 534
  parasitic, 532, 533, 534
  pathogenic, 532
  photosynthetic, 530, 531
  summary of groups, 531
Protocooperation, 617, *617*
Protoderm, 249, *249, 250*
Proton, 5, 39
Protostome (Protostomia), 572–573
Prototheria, *556*
Protozoa, *531,* 532–537
Prunus, 278
Pseudocoelomate, 562, *562*
Pseudomonas, 80, 522
Pseudopod, 385, *385,* 450
Pterophyta, 553–556, *554*
Pterosaur, *515*
Puberty, 8, 459
Pulmonary artery, 378, *379*
Pulmonary circulation, 377, *378,*
  386, 588
Pulmonary vein, *379*
Pulse pressure, 384, 386
Punctuational model of evolution,
  497, *498*
Punnett square method, 164–165,
  164, 165, 238, *480*
Pupa, *7, 7*
Pupil, 362
Purine, 56, 195–196, 198
Pyloric sphincter, *411,* 412, 415
Pyramid of biomass, 635
Pyramid of numbers, 635
Pyrimidine, 56, 195–196, 198
Pyrophosphate bond, 106
Pyrrophyta, 548
Pyruvate, 104, 124, *125,* 126, *127,*
  128, *130, 131*
Pyruvic acid (*see* Pyruvate)
Python, *587*

Quadriceps, *367*
Quantitative inheritance, 175
Quantum evolution, 497–498, *497*
Quaternary, *495*
Quaternary structure, protein,
  54–55, *55*
Queen Victoria, hemophilic
  descendants of, 239–240, *239*

Quercus agrifolia, 302, 303
r-Selection, 606–607, *606, 643*
Rabbit, 454–456, *456*
Radial symmetry, 328, *329,* 562
Radiation
  infrared, *114,* 429
  ultraviolet, *114,* 207
  x–ray, *114,* 197
Radicle, *288, 289, 289*
Radioactive dating, *494, 495*
Radioactive element, *494*
Radiolarian, *531,* 534, *534*
Radius, *367*
Radula, 573, *573*
Ragweed pollen, *279*
Rainfall, 650, *650*
Rain forest, *659,* 663–665, *662*
Rain shadow, 652
Rana pipiens, 143, 440
Randomization, 24
Ranunculus, 172, 174, 257, 294, 624
RAS (reticular activating system),
  341
Rattlesnake, *171*
Ray, 582, *586*
Ray-finned fish, *586*
Ray initial, 261
Ray system, 261
Reabsorption, in kidney, 434, 436,
  438
Realized niche, 615–616, *617*
Receptacle, floral, 277, *278*
Receptive field, 337, *364*
Receptor
  for analgesics, 341
  of blood pressure, 436
  of blood solute levels, 404
  chemoreceptor, 355, 404, 522
  defined, 317, 355
  distribution in body, 337, 355
  electroreceptor, 355
  function, 317
  links with cerebral cortex,
    337–338
  mechanoreceptor, 355, 356–359,
    467
  nocireceptor (pain), 337, 355,
    389
  photoreceptor (light), 355
  stretch (muscle spindle), 328, *328,*
    356, 433
  thermoreceptor, 355, 430, *431*
  in vertebrate evolution, 585
Recessiveness
  defined, 163
  versus dominance, 162, 163
  in Mendel's dihybrid cross, 166,
    167
  in Mendel's monohybrid cross,
    161, 162
  in multiple allele system, 168–169
Reciprocal innervation, 368
Recombinant DNA, 203–207, *204,*
  206, 227, 244
Recombination, genetic

and crossing over, 152–153, 159,
  183, *183,* 203–204, *204,* 481
and evolution, 481
and independent assortment,
  166, 481
and linkage mapping, 183
and phenotypic variation, 479
Rectum, 411, *411,* 417
Rectus abdominus, *367*
Rectus femoris, *367*
Red alga (Rhodophyta), *10,* 12, 61,
  508, 548–549, *548, 550*
Red blood cell (erythrocyte)
  in carbon dioxide transport, 375,
    405
  in fibrin net, 385
  freeze–fractured and etched, *90*
  function, 375
  gene expression in, 231
  life span, 375–376
  membrane, *90, 91*
  number in adult human, 375
  in oxygen transport, 375, 404–405
  pinocytosis by, *96*
  production, 311–312, *351,* 352,
    375, 388–389
  sickled, 172, *173*
  size, 61
  in solutions, 8, 94, *94*
  structure, 375, *375*
Red marrow, 311, *312,* 375
Red tide, 531
Reduction reaction, 108
Redwood, 265
Reef (organic), 9–12, *10–11,* 512
Reflex arc, 327–328, *328*
Reflex response
  in blood vessel damage, 384
  conditioned, 680
  in pharynx, 414
  reciprocal, 368
  stretch, 327–328, *328,* 373
  in urinary discharge, 433
  vertebrate, 331
Refraction, *62,* 363
Refractory period, 323
Regeneration, 251, 454
Regulation (animal development),
  454–456
Regulator gene, 225, *226*
Reindeer, *607*
Reindeer moss, *544*
Releaser, behavioral, 680
REM sleep, 341
Renal pelvis, 433, *435*
Renin, *348,* 436
Reovirus, *526*
Repression, lactose operon, 225, *226*
Reproduction (*see also* Life cycle)
  animal, 344, 441–442, 562
  arthropod, 441
  asexual, 156, *156,* 277, 286, *286,*
    441, 540
  bacterial, 140, *140, 141*
  brown alga, *549,* 550
  bryophyte, *549,* 552

by budding, 441, 540
and carrying capacity, 606–607
cell, 138ff., 158
of chloroplast, 507
chordate, *565*
by cloning, 441
cnidarian, 441, *565*
conifer, *555,* 557–558, *558*
cycad, *555*
defined, 138
delayed, human, 612
differential, and natural selection,
  32, 484
earthworm (annelid), 441, *565*
echinoderm, *565*
eukaryotic, 140–141
fern, *555,* 556
by fission, 140, *141,* 441, 540
flatworm, *565,* 569, 571
flowering plant, 277ff., *555*
frog, 440–441
fungi, 540, *540*
and genetic recombination, 153
ginkgo, *555*
gnetophyte, *555*
green alga, *549,* 550
hermaphroditic, 441
and hormones, 344
horsetail, 553, *555*
human, 459ff.
Hydra, 441
isogamous, 546, *549*
lycopod, 552, *555*
and meiosis, 140, 141
and mitosis, 140, 141
molecular aspects of, 139–140,
  139, 140
mollusk, *565*
nature of, 6–7, 441
nematode, *565*
oogamous, 546, *549*
parthenogenic, 286, *286,* 441
plant, 249, 277ff., *549, 555*
prokaryotic, 140, *140, 141*
red alga, 548–549, *549*
by regeneration, 251, 454
sexual, 150, 156, *156,* 276, 441,
  482, 540
sponge, 441, *565*
tapeworm, 441
timing of, 442, 492
vegetative, 286, *287*
viral, 194, 526
Reproductive cycle, animal, 442
Reproductive isolating mechanism,
  491–493
Reproductive system, 315
Reptile (Reptilia)
  blood circulation, 588
  body temperature, 429
  brain, 332
  characteristics, *587*
  classification, 567–582, *587*
  evolution, 498, *499, 510,* 514, *583*
Research tools, examples of
  aphid as, 273–274, *273*

Research tools (continued)
  bacteriophage infectious
    cycle, 194, 196
  colchicine, 188, 189
  compound light microscope, 62
  computer simulations, 452
  density-gradient centrifugation,
    201
  Drosophila as, 179
  ecdysone, 234
  electrode, 323
  electrophoresis, 213, 214
  freeze-etching, 89, 90
  freeze-fracturing, 89, 90
  giant axon, squid, 323
  Hardy-Weinberg rule, 480, 481
  immunofluorescence, indirect, 77
  laparoscope, 472
  monoclonal antibody, 394
  Neurospora, 212
  oscilloscope, 323
  radioactive dating, 494, 495
  radioactive isotope labeling, 194,
    196, 201, 214
  restriction enzyme, 205–206
  scanning electron microscope, 63
  transmission electron microscope,
    62
  x-ray diffraction, 197
Resource category (niche
    dimension)
  and coexistence, 619–620, 619
  and competition, 618
  graph of, 615–616, 617
Resource cycle (see Cycle, resource)
Resource partitioning, 619–620, 619
Resource recovery system, 671
Respiration, aerobic (see Aerobic
    respiration)
Respiration (breathing), 400 ff.
Respiratory center, 404
Respiratory system, vertebrate
  cilia in, 406, 406, 407
  evolution of, 585–588, 588
  functions, 400
  gas exchange in, 400, 404
  gas transport in, 400, 404–406
  human, 400–401, 401
  overview of, 400
  ventilation in, 400
Resting membrane potential, 321,
    322, 323, 325
Restriction endonuclease, 205–206
Rete mirable, 588
Reticular activating system (RAS),
    341
Reticular formation, 341
Retina, 361, 361, 452, 452
Retrograde amnesia, 340
R group, protein, 53, 53
Rhabdovirus, 526
Rhinoceros, 12, 14
Rhinovirus, 526
Rhizobium, 521, 522
Rhizoid, 233, 233, 548, 552

Rhizome, 287, 513, 513, 553
Rhizopus, 541
Rhodophyta (see Alga, red)
Rhodospirillum, 522
Rhynia, 513, 513
Rib cage, 367, 384, 388, 402, 403
Riboflavin, 104, 296
Ribonucleic acid (see RNA)
Ribose, 49, 195
Ribosome
  assembly, 69, 219, 221
  and endoplasmic reticulum, 70,
    70, 76
  function, 64, 83, 218–219
  and nuclear envelope, 68
  and nucleolus, 69
  structure, 218, 218
Ribulose bisphosphate (RuBP), 118,
    119, 120, 120
Rickettsiae, 522, 524
Right lymphatic duct, 388
Rigor mortis, 370
RNA
  complementarity to DNA, 211
  function, 57, 83
  messenger (mRNA), 211, 216ff.
  processing, 227–228, 228
  ribosomal (rRNA), 211, 217ff.
  role in cell reproduction, 139–140,
    139
  structure, 57, 218
  synthesis, 216–217
  transcript, 217, 223, 227–229, 228,
    445
  transfer (tRNA), 211, 217ff.
  viral, 194
RNA polymerase, 217, 225, 226,
    226, 234
RNA virus, 526, 526
Rock dove, 31, 32
Rocky Mountain spotted fever, 524
Rod cell (photoreceptor), 364–365
Rooster, 681
Root
  acquisition of resources, 256, 264,
    267–268, 272, 272
  adventitious, 256
  cap, 256, 256, 296, 297
  development, 256–258, 258
  endodermis, 256–257, 257
  fibrous, 256, 267
  function, 256, 272, 272
  hair, 255, 256, 256, 267–268, 288
  nodule, 267, 267
  pericycle, 256, 257, 257, 302
  periderm, 256, 258, 258
  primary, 289, 290, 290
  primary growth, 256–257, 258
  secondary growth, 258, 258
  system, 248, 249, 256, 290
  taproot, 256, 267
  tip, 256
  water movement into, 256–257,
    257, 267
Root, R., 617
Rotation, sense of, 359

Rothenbuhler, R., 682
Rough endoplasmic reticulum, 70,
    70
Round window, 358
Roundworm, 562, 562, 564, 571–572
Roux, W., 178
RuBP-carboxylase, 118
Rumen, 525
Ruminant, 410
Runner, plant, 286, 287
Rust, fungal, 189

Sabin polio vaccine, 392
Sac fungus (Ascomycota), 540,
    541–542, 541
Sacral nerves, 331
Sage, 491, 492
Sagittal plane, 560
Saguaro cactus, 283
Salamander, 452–453, 453, 586
Saliva, 414
Salivary amylase, 413, 414, 418
Salivary gland, 334, 411, 411, 413,
    414
Salt, 47 (see also Solute)
Salt, table, 42
Saltatory conduction, 324
Salt balance (see Solute regulation)
Saltbush, 255
Salt marsh, 657, 658
Salvia, 492
Sampling error, 24
Sanger, F., 53
Saprobe, 539, 540, 542, 559
Sarcolemma, 370–371, 371, 380
Sarcomere, 369, 369, 370, 379
Sarcoplasmic reticulum, 71, 370,
    371, 372
Sargassum, 548, 549
Sartorius, 367
Saturated fat, 51, 51
Saunders, J., 456
Savanna, 12, 13, 592, 595, 629,
    662–663, 690
Sawfly, 628, 628
Scala Naturae, 26
Scales, 315, 586, 587
Scallop, 573, 574
Scanning electron microscope, 63
Scapula, 367
Scarlet cup fungus, 541
Scavenger, 12, 16, 569, 576
Scent-fanning, 695
Scent-marking, 620
Schistosoma, 570, 570
Schistosomiasis, 570, 627
Schizophrenia, 342
Schleiden, M., 59
Schooling behavior, 690, 691
Schulman, J., 472
Schulz, A., 638
Schwann, T., 59
Schwann cell, 320, 323–324
Science
  methods of, 21–25, 162, 620
  and society, 25

  and subjectivity, 25
  testing in, 21–23
Sclater, W., 658
Sclera, 363, 363
Sclereid, 252, 252
Sclerenchyma, 252, 252
Scolex, 570, 571
Scorpion, 578, 580
Scorpion fish, 11
Scotch broom, 283
Scramble competition, 608, 609
Scrotum, 450, 459
Scrubjay, 691–692
Sea anemone, 10, 12, 328, 567
Sea cucumber, 581, 582
Sea lettuce, 548, 550, 550, 551
Sea lion, 488–489, 489, 657
Sea nettle, 568
Sears, E., 189–190
Sea slug, 374
Sea squirt (see Tunicate)
Sea star, 10, 12, 454, 562, 581, 582
Sea urchin, 442, 443, 581, 582
Sebaceous gland, 314, 315
Secondary growth, plant, 250,
    258–259, 258, 261–262, 263
Secondary immune rsponse, 391,
    392, 395, 396–397
Secondary sexual traits, 459,
    461–462
Secondary structure, protein, 54
Secondary succession, 643
Secondary treatment, waste water,
    671
Secondary wall, plant cell, 79, 79
Second law of thermodynamics, 99,
    100
Second messenger, hormone action,
    345, 345
Secretin, 351, 352
Secretion
  hormonal, 345, 348, 348
  in kidney, 434
Secretory cell, 71, 214
Sedimentary cycles, 654
Seed
  Capsella, 284, 284
  coat, 284, 301
  corn, 285
  cycad, 556
  defined, 285
  development, 277, 279
  dicot, 284, 284
  dispersal, 277, 286, 624–626
  dormancy, 301
  endosperm, 285
  flowering plant (angiosperm),
    277, 278, 285, 285
  germination, 273, 289–290, 294,
    302, 303, 643, 662
  leaf (see Cotyledon)
  in Mediterranean shrubland,
    662
  monocot, 285, 285
  oak, 302
  pine, 558

Seed (continued)
  in plant evolution, 547–548
  sequoia, 643
Seedling, 278, 289, 290, 295, 296
Segmentation, 563, 577, 578, 579
Segmentation movements, 412, 412, 415
Segregation gene, 166, 176
Selection
  artificial, 31, 682–683, 683
  directional, 485, 485, 486–488, 487
  disruptive, 485, 485, 488, 488
  natural, 13, 32, 481, 484–490
  sexual, 488
  stabilizing, 485–486, 485, 486
Self-replication
  DNA, 199
  origin of, 502–503, 503
Semen, 461
Semicircular canals, 358, 359
Semiconservative replication, DNA, 199, 199
Semilunar valve, heart, 378–379, 379
Seminal vesicle, 459, 460, 461, 467
Seminiferous tubule, 459, 460, 460
Senescence, 299, 299
Sensitive period, 681
Sensory cortex (see Somatosensory cortex)
Sensory neuron, 320
Sensory organ, 355, 356, 361
Sepal, 277, 278, 285, 285
Sepia, 575
Septum, heart, 379
Sequoia, 643
Serosa, 412, 412
Serotonin, 341, 342, 342, 385, 394
Sertoli cell, 462
Sessile, defined, 563
Seta, 367, 577
Sex
  attractant, 356
  chromosome, 149
  determination, 180, 180, 182
  differences, male and female, 182
  hormone, 351, 352, 459
  hypothalamic influence over, 332
Sex chromosome abnormality, 241–242
Sex-linked gene, 181, 182
Sex-linked recessive inheritance, 239–240
Sexual arousal, 317, 461, 467
Sexual dimorphism, 488–489, 489
Sexual reproduction (see Reproduction, sexual)
Sexual selection, 488
Sexually transmitted disease, 524, 527–528, 533
Shark, 582, 586
Sheep tapeworm, 571
Shelf fungus, 593
Shelford, V., 605
Shepherd's purse embryo, 284, 284, 285

Shipworm, 575
Shivering response, 430, 431
Shoot apical meristem, 259, 259
Shoot system, vascular plant, 248, 249, 258
Short-day plant, 298, 298
Shortgrass prairie, 633, 661, 662
Shrew, 590, 591
Shrimp, 330, 357
Shrubland, 658, 661–662
Siamese cat, 172, 174
Sickle-cell anemia, 172, 173, 213, 215, 215, 243
Sickle–cell polymorphism, 488–489
Sieve element, 254, 274
Sieve plate, 254, 254
Sieve-tube member, 254, 254, 274
Silk moth, 356
Silurian, 495, 508, 510, 512–513
Silver Springs ecosystem, 634
Simple epithelium, 308, 309
Simpson, G., 497
Singer, S., 89
Sinoatrial node, 380, 380
Siphon, 574
Sitka spruce, 644
Sivapithecus, 592
Skate, 586
Skeletal muscle
  basis of contraction, 333, 370, 372
  function, 313
  motor unit, 369
  structure, 313, 369–370, 369
  tissue, 368–369
Skeletal muscular system, 311
Skeleton
  bird, 368, 368
  bony, 311
  embryonic, 311
  endoskeleton, 366, 367–368, 582, 586, 587
  evolution of, 538
  exoskeleton, 366, 367
  in fossil record, 508, 512, 513
  human, 367–368, 367
  hydraulic, 366, 367
  hydrostatic, 366, 367, 564, 572, 577
  vertebrate, 367, 582
Skin, 175, 314–315, 314, 317, 389
Skua, 631
Skull, 331, 585
Slash-and-burn agriculture, 664–665
Sleep center, 341, 350
Sleeping, 340–341, 341
Sleep position, leaf, 302
Sliding filament model, muscle contraction, 370
Slime mold, 231–232, 232, 545, 545
Slow-wave sleep, 341
Small intestine, 334
Smog, 674
Smooth endoplasmic reticulum, 70–71, 70

Smooth muscle, 313, 313, 333, 368
Snail, 330, 445, 573–574, 573
Snake, 27, 171, 444, 445, 587
Snake caterpillar, 685, 685
Snapdragon, incomplete dominance in, 168, 168
Snow buttercup, 294
Snow goose, 479
Snowshoe hare, 620, 621–622, 621, 669
Social behavior, 690ff.
Social parasitism, 627–628
Social subordinate, 692–693
Society
  bee, 694–695, 696
  bird, 690
  insect, 693–696
  mammal, 690
  and science, 25
Sodium, 38
  abundance in human body, 38
  atom, 39, 41
  gated channel, 322, 323, 325
  in human nutrition, 423
  in nerve function, 320–323, 321
Sodium chloride, 42, 42, 47, 438
Sodium hydroxide, 47
Sodium-potassium pump, 94, 321, 321, 322, 324, 436
Soft–rot disease, 80, 524
Soil
  aeration by earthworm, 576
  components of, 658
  and ecosystem distribution, 658, 659
Solar energy, 677
Soldier fish, 586
Solid-waste pollution, 670, 671
Sol state, 89
Solute, 88
Solute (salt) regulation
  in animal, 431–432, 565, 577
  in earthworm, 557
  in human, 435–436, 438
  in land plant, 272, 274
  mechanisms of, 432ff.
Solvent, 88
Somatic cell, 306, 308
Somatic nervous system, 331, 332, 333
Somatosensory cortex, 336, 336
Sorex, 591
Sorus (Sori), 556
Sound perception, 357, 358, 359
Sound production, 400, 401
Soybean, 289ff., 290
Spanish moss, 3
Spartina, 657, 658
Speciation
  allopatric, 492–493
  divergence leading to, 491, 491
  nature of, 490–491
  parapatric, 493
  through polyploidy and

hybridization, 493
  sympatric, 493
Species
  defined, 26, 490, 491
  epithet, 27
  equilibrium, 643
  evolution of, 32–33, 490–493, 491
  introductions, 646–647, 646
  in Linnean scheme, 27, 27
  opportunistic, 643
  pioneer, 643, 644
  problem in defining, 26, 36, 491, 497
Specific heat, 86
Speech, 401, 682
Spemann, H., 452–453
Sperm
  defined, 157
  formation, 157, 157
  human, 460–461, 461, 467, 474
  penetration of egg, 447, 448
  sponge, 567, 567
  and in vitro fertilization, 472
  water medium for, 442, 546–547
Spermatid, 157, 157, 460, 461
Spermatocyte, 157, 157, 460, 460
Spermatogenesis
  generalized view of, 157, 157
  human, 460–462, 460
Spermatogonium, 460, 460
Sperry, R., 339
Sphagnum moss, 47
Sphenopsid (Sphenophyta), 553, 554
Sphere of hydration, 88
Spicule, 563, 566
Sphincter, 383, 412
Spider
  camouflage by, 625
  classification, 578
  gas exchange, 399, 579
  motor system, 366, 367
  segmentation, 579
  sound perception, 357
Spinal cavity, 316
Spinal cord
  function, 331, 373
  structure, 330, 331–332, 331, 332
Spirochete, 522, 527
Spleen, 388–389, 388
Split-brain studies, 339–340, 339
Sponge (Porifera), 10, 566
  body plan, 374, 562, 563–566, 566
  characteristics, 328, 563–567, 564
  classification, 563, 564
  reproduction, 441, 566–567
  tissue properties, 306
Spongy bone tissue, 311–312
Spongy mesophyll, 260, 261
Spontaneous assembly of organic compounds, 502, 506
Sporangium, 551
Spore
  fungal, 540, 541, 541, 542, 545
  plant, 157, 276, 277, 278, 280,

Spore (continued)
  546–547, *546*
  slime mold, 231, *232*
Sporocarp, 231, *232*
Sporophyte
  compared to gametophyte, 157–158
  defined, 157
  flowering plant, 277
  horsetail, 553, *553*
  lycopod, 552, *553*
  moss, 552
  pine, 158, 558
  in plant evolution, 547
Sporozoan, *531*, 532, 534, *535*
Sporozoite, 490, *535*
Spring overturn, lake, 655
Squamous epithelium, *308, 309, 309*
Squid
  axon, *323*
  characteristics, 573, 575
  evolution, 512, 575
  eye, 361–362, 512
  mantle, *323*
  nervous system, *330*
S–shaped (sigmoid) curve, 605, *605*
Stabilizing selection, 485–486, *485, 486*
Stahl, F., 199, *201*
Staining, in microscopy, 62
Stamen, *161*, 278, *278*, 285, *285*, 492
Staphylococcus, 522, *525*
Starch
  digestion, *413*, 414
  grain, 75
  in plant, 75, 119, 273
  structure, 49, *49*
Starling, *644*, 684
Starvation, 640
Statocyst, 329, *360*
Statolith, *360*
Stem
  development, 250, *250*
  dicot, 250, *250*, 259, 260
  elongation, 292–293, *292, 294*
  function, 258, 272, *272*
  growth of, 250, *250, 259ff.*
  hormones influencing, 292, *292*, 293
  monocot, 250, 259, 260
  nodes and internodes, *248, 259, 261*
  runner, 286, *287*
  structure, 250, *250*, 259, 260
  transport in, 250, 258
Stem cell, 376, 454
Stephanotis, *283*
Stereoisomer, 503
Sternum, *367*
Steroid, 50, 52
Steroid hormone, *344*, 345
Steward, F., 286
Stigma, *278, 278, 279*, 491, *492*
Stimulus
  amplification, 355

defined, 317, 355
energy, 317, 355
perception of, 337–338, *338*, 355
types of, 355
visual, *338*, 360
Stipe, *548*, 550
Stoma (stomata)
  defined, 255, 551
  function, 270–272, *271, 272*
  location, *254*, 255, 260, *261*
  and photorespiration, 120
  and photosynthesis, 270–271
Stomach
  emptying, 416
  function, 412, *413*
  human, 411, *411*
  neural control of, *334*, 415
  ruminant, 410
  secretions, *413*, 414
Stone cell, 252, *252*
Stratified epithelium, *308, 309*
Strawberry, 286, *286*, 287
Streptococcus, 522, *525*
Stretch receptor, 327–328, *328*, 356, 433
Stretch reflex, 327–328, *328*, 373
Stress, response to, 341, *351*
Striated muscle, *313* (*see also* Skeletal muscle)
Strip mining, 675
Strobilus (Strobili), 552, 553, *553*
Stroke, 386
Stroma, 75, *75, 112–113*, 113, 117
Stromatolitic rock, *505*
Strombus, *361*
Structural formula, 43
Structural gene, 225
Structural isomer, 49
Sturtevant, A., 183
Style (of carpel), 278, *278*
Stylet, aphid, 273, *273*
Subcutaneous layer, skin, *314*, 315
Suberin, 52, 256, 257, *257*
Submucosa, 412, *412*
Substrate of enzyme, 103, *103*
Succession, 643–644, *644*
Successional shrubland, 662
Successional species, 622
Succinate, *130*
Succulent, 260
Sucrose, 49, 119, 272, 273–274
Sugar, 44, 48–49, 254
Sulfate, *123*, 506
Sulfobolus, 522, *522*
Sulfur, *38*, 120, *264, 266*
Sulfuric acid, 121, 574, 673, 674
Sulfur oxides, 672–674
Sulfur-oxidizing bacteria, 121, 522
Sunflower, *112*, 251, *296*
Sunlight (*see* Energy, light)
Surface tension, water, 87, *87*
Surface-to-volume ratio, 60, *60, 61*
Survivorship curve, 601, *603*, 606
Suspension, 88
Suspensor, 284, *284*

Swallowing, 400
Swallowtail butterfly, 488, *488*
Sweat gland, *314*, 315
Sweating, 429, 431, 432
Swim bladder, 585–588, *588*
Symbiosis
  defined, 507, 617
  examples of, *267, 268, 507*, 521, *544, 644*
  types of, 617–618, *617*
Symbiotic origin of chloroplast, 507
Symbiotic origin of mitochondrion, 222, 507, *507*
Sympathetic nerve, *331*, 333, *334*, 335, 381, 413, 436
Sympatric speciation, 493
Synapse, neural
  changes in, 340
  defined, 319, 325
  and direction of nerve message, 319, *326*
  excitatory, 325, 326
  inhibitory, 325–326
  modifications to, 340
  at neuromuscular junction, 326–327, *327*
  organization in brain, *338*
Synapsis, chromosomal, 152, 159
Synaptic cleft, 325, 326, *326, 327*
Synaptic transmission, 325–327, *326*
Syndrome, defined, 240
Syphilis, 527
System, defined, 98
Systemic circulation, 377, *378*, 386, 588
Systems integration, 317–318
Systole, 378, *379*

T2 (bacteriophage), *195*
T4 (bacteriophage), *195*
Tactile receptor, 356
Tadpole, 440
Taiga, *659*, 666, *666*
Tallgrass prairie, *661*, 662
Tamarisk, 255
Tapeworm, 569, 570–571, *571*
Taproot system, 256
Target cell (hormone), 289
Targeted drug therapy, 394
Tarsal, *367*
Tarsier, 590, *591*
Taste bud, 356, *357*
Taste receptor, 356
TATA box, chromosome, 230
Tatum, E., 212–213
Taxon (taxa), 493
T-cell, 376, 390–392, *391*
Tectorial membrane, *358*
Teleost, *586*
Telophase
  meiosis, *150*, 152, *153, 155*
  mitosis, 144, *144, 145, 147*, 148, *155*
Temperate forest, *659*
Temperate grassland, *659*

Temperature
  air, 428–429
  body, controls over, 317
  core, 430, 432
  defined, 86
  and dormancy, 300–301
  effect on plant growth, 293–294, 300–301, *300*
  environmental, 429, *429*
  and enzyme activity, 105, 428
  and hypothalamus, 430, *431*
  range for metabolism, 428–429, *429*
  stabilization in water, 86
Temperature gradient, 92
Temporal lobe, *339*
Tendon, *310*, 311, 368
Tentacle, *329*, 568, 575
Tern, *689*, 690
Terpene, 52
Territorial behavior, 489, 608, 620, *679*, 688
Territory, 489, 608, 620
Tertiary, *495*
Tertiary structure, protein, 54
Tertiary treatment, waste water, 672
Testcross, 163, *165*
Testis, 182, *350*, 442, 450, 459, *459*, 460
Testosterone, 346, *348, 350, 351*, 459, 461–462, *462*
Tetanic contraction, 372, 373
Tetanus
  disease, 392, 395, 524
  of muscle, 373
Tethys Sea, *511*, 512
Tetrad, chromosome, 152
Tetraploidy, 187, *189–190*
Thalamus, 332, 335, 341, 365
β–Thalassemia, 228
Thalidomide, 471
Thallus, 550
Thecodont, *515*
Theory, defined, 24
Thermal inversion, 674
Thermacidophiles, 522–523, *522*
Thermocline, 655, 656, 657
Thermoreceptor, 355, 430, *431*
Thigmomorphogenesis, 297, *297*
Thigmotropism, 297
Thirst mechanism, 432, 435, 436
Thomas, L., 457
Thoracic cavity, *316*, 400, *401, 402*
Thoracic duct, 388
Thoracic nerves, *331*
Thorn forest, *659*
Threonine, 419
Threshold value, 322, *323*
Thrombin, 385
Thrombocyte (*see* Platelet)
Thromboplastin, 385
Thylakoid, 112–113, *113*, 114, 117, 118
Thymine, 195, 198

Thymosin, *351*, 353
Thymus, 346, *346*, *351*, 353, 388, *388*, 389, 395–396
Thyroid, 346, *346*, *350*, *351*, 352, 430, 450
Thyroid-stimulating hormone (TSH), *348*, 350, *350*
Thyroxin, *351*, 352, 430
Tibia, *367*
Tibialis anterior, *367*
Tight junction, 81, 307, *307*, 308
Tipton, V., 244
Tissue, *6*, 306
 animal, 306*ff.*, 450
 formation, 97, 306
 plant, 249*ff.*
Tissue culture propagation, 286–287, *287*
Titanic, 432
Tobacco mosaic virus, 526, *526*
Toe formation, 172–173, *174*
Tolerance curve, 605, *605*
Tomato, 297, *297*
Tongue, 400, *401*
Tongue rolling, 177
Tonsil, 388
Toon, B., 576
Tooth, 413–414
Torsion, 573–574
Trace element, 421
Trachea, 399, *399*, 579, *579*
Tracheid, 252
Tranquilizer, 342, *342*, 471
Transcription
 controls over, 223*ff.*
 defined, 211
 in development, 234, 289, 445, 449
 process, 216–217, *217*, 220–221
Transduction, genetic, 204
Transformation, genetic, 193, 204–205
Translation
 controls over, 223*ff.*
 defined, 211
 in development, 289, 445, 449
 process, 217–221, *220*
Translocation, chromosomal, 179, 186–187
Translocation, in plants, 273–274
Transmission electron microscope, *62–63*
Transmitter substance, 325, 326, 342, 344
Transpiration, 268–270, *269*, 271
Transplant
 Acetabularia cap, 233, *233*
 frog nucleus, 234
 kidney, 437
 and major histocompatibility complex, 395–396
 organ, 396
 rabbit cell, 454–456, *456*
 rejection, 396, 437
 salamander, 452–453, *453*
 tissue, 395–396

Transport mechanism (*see* Membrane transport)
Transposition, 186–187
Transverse tubule system, 370, *371*
Tree farming, 666–667
Tree rings, 262
Trematode, 569
Treponema, *522*, 527
Triassic, *495*
Triceps, *367*, 368, *368*
Trichinella, *572*
Trichinosis, *572*
Trichomonas, *533*
Trichophyton, *542*
Trichoplax, 537–538, *538*, 562
Trichosome, 533
Triglyceride, 51, *51*, 71, 417, *418*
Trilobite (Trilobita), 508, *509*, 514, 578
Triplet, nucleotide, 216
Triploid nucleus, 280
Triploidy, 187
Trisomy, 187, 240
Trisomy XXY and XYY, 241, 246
Triticum, *188*, *189–190*
Tritonia, 679
tRNA (*see* RNA, transfer)
Trophic level, 630, *630*, 631, 635
Trophoblast, 468, 469
Tropical deciduous forest, *659*, 666
Tropical evergreen forest, *659*
Tropical rain forest, *659*, *662*, 663–665
Tropical reef, *9ff.*
Tropical savanna, *659*, 662
Tropical scrub forest, *659*
Tropism, plant, 295–297
Tropomyosin, 371, *371*, 372
Troponin, 371, *371*, 372
True-breeding strain, 162, 180
Tryon, R., 682, *683*
Trypanosome, *533*
Trypsin, 414, *418*
Tryptophan, 216, *216*, 222, 225, 419
Tschermak, E. Von, 178
Tubal ligation, 475, *475*
Tube foot, 581, *581*
Tuber, 287
Tubular secretion, 434
Tubulin, 77, 78, *78*
Tulip tree leaf, *260*
Tumor, 235, 393, *526*
Tuna, 429
Tundra, 636–638, *637*, 659
Tunicate, 582, 583–584, *584*
Turbellarian, 569, *569*
Turgor pressure, 267, *267*, 270–271, 291
Turner's syndrome, 240–241
Twins, 174, 456
Twitch contraction, 373
Tympanic membrane, *358*
Type A personality, 387
Type B personality, 387
Typhus, 524

Typological approach, classification, 479
Tyrosinase, *171*, 172
Tyrosine, *171*, 172, 419

Ulcer, 414–415, *420*
Ulna, *367*
Ultraviolet light, *114*, 207, 649
Ulva, *548*, 550, *550*, *551*
Umbilical cord, 469
Unger, F., 161
Ungulate, 12
Uniformitarianism, 30
Uniramia, 578
Unity of life
 in cell architecture, 59, 82
 in ecological interdependency, 17
 energetic basis of, 5
 and evolutionary theory, 19, 209
 and genetic code, 216
 in metabolic activity, 6, 9
 molecular basis of, 5, 9, 199, 209, 216
 in origins, 9
 perspective on, 18, 517–518
 relation to diversity, 9, 209
 and reproduction, 138
Unsaturated fat, 51, *51*
Upwelling, 650, 657–658
Uracil, 211
Urea, 424, *424*, 431, 432, 433
Ureter, 432, 433, 434
Urethra, 432, 433, 434, 459, 467
Urey, H., 502
Uric acid, 434
Urinary bladder, 432, 433, 434
Urinary system
 function, 432
 human, 432–433, 434–435
 mechanisms, 433–436, *436*
 urine concentration in, *438*
Urine, 433, 434, 436, *438*
Urkaryote, 34, *35*, 506, 507
Urochordata, 582
Usnea, 444
Uterine function, 466–467
Uterus, *350*, *351*, 462, *462*, 463

Vaccine, 392–395, 524
Vacuole
 autophagic, 72
 central, 64, *66*, 284, *284*, 303
 contractile, 535, 536
Vagina, 442, 462, *462*, *463*, 467
Valine, 172, 213, *215*
Variable (test), 21, 22–23
Variable expressivity, gene, 170*ff.*
Variation
 continuous, 175, 479, *479*
 discontinuous, 175, 479
 in DNA structure, 198–199, *200*
 environmental, 8–9
 and evolution, 479–481
 genetic (*see* Genetic variation)
 and natural selection, 32

phenotypic, 175, 479
 sources of, 179, 209, 479*ff.*
Vascular bundle, 250, *250*, 258, 260
Vascular cambium (*see* Cambium, vascular)
Vascular column, root, 256–257, *257*
Vascular plant (*see* Plant, vascular)
Vascular tissue, 249–250, *249*, *250*, 546
Vas deferens, *459*, *460*, 461
Vasectomy, 475, *475*
Vasoconstriction, 381, 385, 430, 436
Vasodilation, 381, 389, 415
Vasopressin (*see also* ADH), 349, *350*
Vegetal pole, 447, *448*
Vein
 blood, 374, 377, *382*, 383
 leaf, 260, *260*
Vena cava, 379
Venous valve, *382*, 383, *384*
Ventilation, 400, 402–404
Ventral, defined, *560*
Ventricle, heart, 378*ff.*, *379*
Venule, 377, *382*, 383
Venus flytrap, 255
Vernalization, 297
Verongia, *566*
Vertebra, 585
Vertebral column, 331, *367*, 582
Vertebrate (Vertebrata)
 blood, *376*
 brain, 331–332, *333*, 335
 characteristics, 585–589
 circulation system, 374–375, 377, *377*
 classification, 582
 endocrine elements, 347
 evolution, 332, 390, 512–513, 585–588, *585*, *588*, *589*
 eye, 363, *364–365*
 heart, 588, *589*
 immune system, 390
 jaw, 512, 585, *585*
 lung, 585–588, *588*
 nervous system, 330–335, *331*, *588*, *589*
 sensory receptor, *355*
 skeleton, 367
 stimulus perception, 356, 357–358
 swim bladder, 585, 588, *588*
Vertical system, stem, 261
Vespula, *623*
Vessel, blood (*see* Artery; Capillary; Vein)
Vessel, xylem, 253, *253*
Vestigial structure, 28, *28*
Vibration, 356, *358*
Villus, 415–416, *415*, *416*, 468
Viral capsid, 526
Virchow, R., 59
Viroid, 529
Virus
 bacteriophage, 194, *195*, *196*
 and cancer, 236
 classification, *526*

Virus *(continued)*
  defined, 526
  dependency on host, 526
  as disease agent, 526–529
  DNA, 526, *526*
  living versus nonliving, 526
  origin of, 526
  RNA, 194, 526, *526*
  structure, 4, *4*
Visceral mass, 573, *573, 575*
Vision, 360
Visual acuity, *364*
Visual cortex, 336, *364*
Visual field, 339, *339*
Visual perception, 337, *338, 360*
Visual system, 360
Vitamin
  baterial manufacture of, 525
  coenzymes, 104
  fat-soluble, 377, 422
  in human nutrition, 421
  intake during pregnancy, 470
  water-soluble, 422
Vitreous body, 361, *363*
Viviparity, 444, *445*
Vocal cords, 400, *401*
Voltage difference, 321
Volterra, V., 620
Volvox, 99, 537, 537
Vorticella, 536, *537*
Vulture, 12, *16*
Vulva, 462

Wallace, A., 22, 33, *33,* 160, 484,
  658
Warbler, 627, 683–684
Warning coloration, 488, 622, 624
Wart, *526*
Wasp, *395, 623*
Waste-water treatment, 524–525
Water

absorption, 416, 431
amount in cell, 85
availability for humans, 671–672
and cell function, 85*ff.*
and condensation reaction, 47
in early atmosphere, 501
and filtration, 382, *383*
formation in respiration, 124, 129
global cycling of, 653
hydrogen bonds in, 43, *44*
and hydrophilic substance, 45
and hydrophobic substance, 45
molecule, 43, 45
osmotic movement of, 92, *92,*
  93–95, 95, 264–265, 267, 269,
  272, 274, 302, 546
pH of, 46, *46*
in photosynthesis, 111–112, 270,
  506
properties of, 45, 86–88
regulation, in animal, 431*ff.*
and turgor pressure, 267, *267*
Water bear, *85,* 86
Water buttercup, 172, *174*
Water canal system, 566
Water hyacinth, 646–647, *646*
Water mold, 540
Water pollution, 670–672, 673
Water propulsion (cephalopod), 574
Water scorpion, 580
Water and solute balance
  control of, 435–436, *438*
  nature of, 431–432
  in urinary system, 432*ff.*
Water strider, *87*
Water-vascular system, 581, *581*
Watson, J., *192,* 198–199
Wavelength, light
  absorption in chloroplast,
    113–115
  absorption by plant pigments,

    113–115, *114*
  versus electron wavelength, *62*
  energies, *62, 114*
  penetration of atmosphere, 649
  and range of photosensitivity, *114*
  visual perception of, *364*
Wax, 50, 51, *52,* 255
Weddell seal, 631
Weinberg, W., 481
Weintraub, H., 230
Weismann, A., 178
Welwitschia, 554, 557, *557*
Went, F., 295, 296
Wet acid deposition, 673
Weyland, N., 619–620
Whale, *61*
Wheat, 188, *188, 189–190*
Wheat rust, 542
White blood cell
  count, 376
  in defense responses, 376
  types of, 376, *376*
White matter, 331, *332,* 335
Whittaker, R., 34
Who eats whom (*see* Feeding
  relationships)
Wiebe, H., 270
Wiesel, T., *338*
Wild boar, *644*
Wild-type allele, defined, 180
Wilkins, M., 197
Williams, G., 686
Willows, D., 679
Wilson's disease, 242
Wilting, plant, 267, *267*
Wind currents, 649
Wind energy, 677
Wobble effect, 218
Wolf, 691, *693*
Wood, 258, 261–262, *262*
Woodpecker, *283*

Woodpecker finch, *684*

Xanthophyll, 549, *549, 550*
X chromosome, 179–181, *180, 182*
X chromosome inactivation, 230
X-ray diffraction, 197
Xylem
  function, *249,* 252–253
  structure, 252–253, *253*
  water transport in, 253, 256–257,
    268–270, *269*

Y chromosome, 179–180, *180*
Yeast, *123,* 126, 542
Yellow marrow, 312, *312*
Yellowjacket, *623*
Yolk, 442, 444, *445,* 448–449
Yolk plug, *446*
Yolk sac, *466,* 468
Yucca moth, 626–627, *627*
Yucca plant, 626–627, *627*

Zamia, 554
Zea mays, 143, 285, 289, 292
Zebra, 12, *14*
Zero population growth, 601, 612
Zinc, *264, 266*
Z line, *369, 370*
Zooplankton, 656
Zygospore-forming fungus
  (Zygomycota), 540, 541–542
Zygote
  animal, 306
  defined, 157
  frog, 440
  fungus, 540
  plant, 284, *284, 289,* 302, 546